AF650553

About Pearson

Pearson is the world's learning company, with presence across 70 countries worldwide. Our unique insights and world-class expertise comes from a long history of working closely with renowned teachers, authors and thought leaders, as a result of which, we have emerged as the preferred choice for millions of teachers and learners across the world.

We believe learning opens up opportunities, creates fulfilling careers and hence better lives. We hence collaborate with the best of minds to deliver you class-leading products, spread across the Higher Education and K12 spectrum.

Superior learning experience and improved outcomes are at the heart of everything we do. This product is the result of one such effort.

Your feedback plays a critical role in the evolution of our products and you can contact us - reachus@pearson.com. *We look forward to it.*

Electrical Machines, Drives, and Power Systems

Updated Sixth Edition

Theodore Wildi
Professor Emeritus, Laval University

Contributions by

Arun Ingole
Ex-General Manager
Siemens Ltd.

Pearson

Authorized adaptation from the United States edition, entitled *Electrical Machines, Drives, and Power Systems, Sixth Edition*, ISBN 9780131776913, by Wildi, Theodore, published by Pearson Education Inc.© 2006.

Indian Subcontinent Adaptation

ISBN 978-93-570-5329-7

First Impression

Published by Pearson India Education Services Pvt. Ltd, CIN: U72200TN2005PTC057128.

Head Office: 1st Floor, Berger Tower, Plot No. C-001A/2, Sector 16B, Noida - 201 301, Uttar Pradesh, India.
Registered Office: Featherlite, 'The Address' 5th Floor, Survey No 203/10B, 200 Ft MMRD Road, Zamin Pallavaram, Chennai - 600044, Tamilnadu, India.
Website: in.pearson.com, Email: companysecretary.india@pearson.com

Printer: Saurabh Printers Pvt. Ltd.

PREFACE

In preparing the sixth edition of this book, I wanted to introduce several new topics that are having an important impact in the field of electric power. Consequently, in the next few paragraphs I wish to bring these five new topics to your attention.

1. In Chapter 13, Sections 13.23 to 13.26, I explain the properties and behavior of the doubly-fed induction machine. The speed is varied by applying a fixed frequency to the stator and a variable frequency to the rotor, hence the name "doubly-fed." Such machines have traditionally been used as variable-speed motors to drive large pumps. However, they have found a new application in the form of doubly-fed wind turbine generators to produce electricity. Owing to the importance of wind turbines, I thought it necessary to devote some space and time to this special machine.
2. In Chapter 21, Sections 21.45 to 21.51, I made some important modifications to the treatment of pulse-width modulation (PWM). New text and figures have been added to better illustrate this technology.
3. Chapter 23 covers several methods of electronically controlling the speed of electric motors. In Sections 23.31 to 23.40 I have added another important method named Direct Torque Control (DTC). Instead of using constant frequency pulse-width modulation and vector control, DTC employs a special bang-bang (hysteresis) technique. Thus, DTC requires a new viewpoint regarding speed and torque control. The explanation is straightforward, based on induction motor principles.
4. In Chapter 24, Sections 24.28 to 24.35, I discuss wind power and the use of turbines to extract energy from the wind. Several methods of generating electric power are explained, each with its own particular merits.
5. Chapter 28, Sections 28.20 to 28.24 introduces the HVDC Light™ method of transmitting electric power. An important new way of carrying power to remote locations, it has been rendered possible on account of the ever-increasing power-handling capacity of IGBTs. Their high switching frequencies permit use of the PWM techniques using converters in the tens of megawatt range. As a result, the size of harmonic filters is greatly reduced and, more importantly, the converters can absorb or deliver reactive power as required.

As an added feature, the Instructor's Manual for this sixth edition has been completely transformed. Instead of the handwritten Solution to Problems, the entire manual is now typeset, making it much easier to read. Also, as an independent source of information, industrial problems (and solutions) are regularly displayed on the Theodore Wildi Web site: http://www.wildi-theo.com.

The new material presented in the sixth edition amounts to about 50 pages. However, it is important to recognize that these extra pages rest upon hundreds of pages that are already in the book. For example, if a book were written about wind generators alone, it would require at least 200 pages to describe the principle of induction machines, power electronics, speed control, and so on. The broad coverage of my book permits the introduction of such important new topics without having to re-explain the underlying principles. They are already there. Also, it offers the reader the special advantage of seeing how all these technical subjects hang together.

An overview of evolving technologies

The previous edition of my book was prompted in part by the great increase of computers in industrial controls and automation. Computer programs can simulate relays and relay contacts. These on/off computerized controls have eliminated the wiring and installation of hardware components in favor of virtual relays and contacts that can be programmed on a keyboard. With the help of Internet communications, these programmable logic controllers (PLCs) are often integrated with the overall manufacturing process, leading seamlessly to integration with management, sales, procurement, and consumer satisfaction.

Similar upheavals have occurred in power technology. It is simply amazing to witness the entrance of power electronics into every facet of industrial drives. Thus, it is no longer pertinent to discuss dc and ac machines in isolation because wherever they are being installed, an electronic control forms part of the package. Consequently, the term *drive* now involves not the motor alone but the entire unit that directs the torque and speed of the machine. This directly influences the way that courses on electric power are being taught.

How has this dramatic change come about? It is mainly due to the development of high-power solid state switching devices, such as insulated gate bipolar transistors (IGBTs), that can operate at frequencies of up to 20 kHz. The change has also been driven by thyristors and gate turn-off thyristors (GTOs) that can handle current of several thousand amperes at voltages of up to 5 kV. Another key element is the computing power of microprocessors that can process signal data in real time with incredible speed.

The high switching frequencies of IGBTs permit the use of pulse-width-modulation techniques in power converters. This, in turn, enables torque and speed control of induction motors down to zero speed.

Most industrial drives are in the fractional horsepower to the 500 hp range. That is precisely the range now available for control by IGBTs. The result has been an explosion in the retrofitting of outmoded drives. Lower maintenance costs, higher efficiency, and greater productivity have made such changeovers economically attractive. Thus, dc drives are being replaced by induction motor drives which require less maintenance, while offering equal and often superior dynamic performance.

Every sector of industrial and commercial activity has therefore been affected by this revolutionary converter technology. Electric elevators; electric locomotives; electric transit vehicles; servomechanisms; heating, ventilating, and air conditioning systems; fans; compressors; and innumerable industrial production lines are being modified to utilize this new technology.

The change is also affecting the transmission and distribution of electric power—an industry that has been relatively stable for over 50 years. Here, we are seeing large rotating machines, such as synchronous condensers and frequency changers, being replaced by solid-state converters that have no moving parts at all.

Important development work has also resulted in the creation of high-power static switches, thyristor-controlled series capacitors, and converters that can fill the role of phase-shift transformers. These new methods of power flow control, known by the acronym FACTS (Flexible AC Transmission Systems), will permit existing transmission and distribution lines to carry more power to meet the ever-increasing demand for electricity. On account of their extremely fast response, the converters can also stabilize a network that may suddenly be menaced by an unexpected disturbance.

It is a remarkable fact that these innovations all rest on a common base. In other words, the converter technology used in electric motor drives is similar to that employed to control the flow of power in electric utilities. As a result, everything falls neatly and coherently into place. The teaching and learning of electric machines, drives, and power systems is thereby made much easier.

A brief look at some key chapters

The writing of circuit equations is included in Chapter 2. Most students know how to solve such equations but many experience difficulty in *formulating* them. I disclose an ac/dc circuit-solving methodology that is particularly easy to follow. Readers will be glad to refer to this section as a convenient reminder of the circuit-solving procedure.

Chapter 11 on *Special Transformers* includes higher frequency transformers. The reader is guided through the reasoning behind the design of such transformers, and why they become smaller as the frequency is increased. High-frequency transformers are directly related to the higher frequencies encountered in switching converters.

Chapter 16 on *Synchronous Generators* shows why an increase in size inevitably leads to higher efficiencies and greater outputs per kilogram. This fundamental aspect of machine design will interest many readers.

Chapter 18 develops the equivalent circuit diagram of a single-phase induction motor. It presents a rigorous, yet simple approach, based on the 3-phase induction motor.

Chapter 21 on the *Fundamental Elements of Power Electronics* discusses switching converters and pulse-width-modulation (PWM) techniques. It illustrates the extraordinary versatility of IGBT converters and how they can be made to generate almost any waveshape and frequency.

Chapter 23 on *Electronic Control of Alternating-Current Motors* covers the properties of induction motors operating at variable speeds. A special section explains the basics of PWM drives and flux vector control.

Chapter 29, titled *Transmission and Distribution Solid-State Controllers,* explains the technologies that are being developed to electronically control the flow of electric power. It also discusses the quality of electric power as regards sags, swells, harmonics, and brownouts. As deregulation of electric power becomes a reality, these electronic methods of controlling the quality of electricity will become increasingly important.

Chapter 30 on *Harmonics* reveals how they are generated and how they affect the behavior of capacitors, inductors, cables, transformers, and the quality of electric power. Harmonics are often viewed with awe and trepidation. This chapter explains in simple language where they come from and how they can be minimized and controlled.

To whom is this book addressed?

The subject matter covered in this book requires only a background in basic circuit theory, algebra, and some trigonometry.

Owing to its user-friendly treatment of even complex topics, this book will meet the needs of a broad range of readers. First, it is appropriate for students following a 2-year electrical program in community colleges, technical institutes, and universities. Owing to its very broad coverage, the text can also be incorporated in a 4-year technology program. Many universities have adopted the book for their electric power service courses.

Instructors responsible for *industrial training* will find that this book contains a wealth of practical information that can be directly applied to that greatest laboratory of all—the electrical industry itself.

Finally, at a time when much effort is being devoted to continuing education, this book, with its many worked-out problems, is particularly well adapted for self-study.

The exercises at the end of each chapter are divided into three levels of learning—practical, intermediate, and advanced. Furthermore, to encourage the reader to solve the problems, answers are given at the end of the book.

For further information, the reader is invited to consult the list of books, technical articles, and Web sites in the References section toward the end of the book.

A quick glance through the book shows the importance given to photographs. All equipment and systems are illustrated by diagrams and pictures, showing them in various stages of construction or in actual use. Some students may never have visited an industrial plant or seen up close the equipment used in the transmission and distribution of electrical energy. The photographs help convey the magnificent size of these devices and machines.

Throughout the 31 chapters, a conscious effort was made to establish coherence, so that the reader can see how the various concepts fit together. For example, the terminology and power equations for synchronous machines are similar to those found in transmission lines. Transmission lines, in turn, bring up the question of reactive power. And reactive power is an important aspect in electronic converters. Therefore, knowledge gained in one sector is strengthened and broadened by discovering that it can be used in another sector. As a result, learning about electrical machines, drives, and power systems becomes a challenging, thought-provoking experience.

In order to convey the real-world aspects of machinery and power systems, particular attention has been paid to the inertia of revolving masses, the physical limitations of materials, and the problems created by heat. This approach falls in line with the multidisciplinary programs of many colleges and technical institutes.

In summary, this book employs a theoretical, practical, multidisciplinary approach to give a broad understanding of electric power technology. Clearly, it is no longer the staid subject it was considered to be some years ago. There is good reason to believe that this dynamic, expanding field will open career opportunities for many people.

I would like to make a final remark concerning the use of my book. As mentioned previously, power technology has made a quantum jump in the past 10 years, mainly on account of the availability of fast-acting semiconductors. In the field of electrical machines, drives, and power systems, there will now ensue a long period of consolidation during which existing machines and devices will be replaced by newer models. But the basic technology covered in this book will not change significantly in the foreseeable future. Consequently, the reader will find that this edition can also be used as a valuable long-term reference book.

Acknowledgments

In preparing this sixth edition and previous editions, I would like to acknowledge the important contribution of the following persons.

Professors and reviewers: Robert T. H. Alden, Professor Emeritus, McMaster University; Ramon E. Ariza, Delgado Community College; Fred E. Eberlin, Educational Consultant; David Krispinsky, Rochester Institute of Technology; Athula Kulatunga, Southeast Missouri State University; Rick Miller, Ferris State University; M. H. Nehir, Montana State University; Martin M. Peros, Seneca College; James E. Roach, Bob Jones University; Chandra Sekhar, Purdue University; Gerald Sevigny, Southern Maine Technical College; Philippe Viarouge and Hoang Le-Huy, Laval University; Stacy Wilson, Western Kentucky University; and Thomas Young, Rochester Institute of Technology.

I extend a special note of thanks to Scott Norr, University of Minnesota–Duluth, and Andrzej Trzynadlowski, University of Nebraska–Reno, for their valuable feedback.

Commercial, industrial, and institutional contributors: Gilbert Sybille of Hydro-Quebec Power System Simulation Laboratory (IREQ), André Dupont, Raj Kapila, G. Linhofer, and Katherine Sahapoglu of ABB; Roger Bullock, Gerry Goyette, Jim McCormick, James Nanney, Darryl J. Van Son, and Roddy Yates of Baldor Electric Company; Jacques Bédard, Guy Goupil, and Michel Lessard of Lab-Volt Ltd.; Richard B. Dubé of General Electric Company; Abdel-Aty Edric and Ashock Sundaram of Electric Power Research Institute; Neil H. Woodley of Westinghouse Electric Corporation; Maurice Larabie, Jean-Louis Marin, and Bernard Oegema of Schneider Canada; Carl Tobie of Edison Electric Institute; Damiano Esposito and Vance E. Gulliksen of Carnival Cruise Lines; Scott Lindsay of Daiya Control Systems; Louis Bélisle and Jean Lamontagne of Lumen; Benoit Arsenault and Les Halmos of Allen Bradley.

I also want to express my appreciation to Charles E. Stewart, Jr, Publisher; to Mayda Bosco, Associate Editor; and to Alexandrina B. Wolf, Senior Production Editor, of Prentice Hall, for planning, coordinating, and administering this text.

My son, Karl, continued to provide his valuable help in preparing the word-processing of this latest edition.

My thanks also go to my wife, Rachel, for having supported me in my continuing vocation as author, consultant, and teacher.

I also wish to voice my gratitude for the instructors and students, practicing engineers, and technicians who asked questions and made suggestions by e-mailing their messages to **wildi@wildi-theo.com**. You are cordially invited to do the same.

Theodore Wildi

We would like to thank Mr Arun Ingole, Ex-General Manager, Siemens Ltd., for his contributions towards the adaptation and making this book more suitable for the Indian readers.

BRIEF CONTENTS

CONTENTS

To Rachel

PART ONE

Fundamentals

CHAPTER 1
Units

1.0 Introduction

Units play an important role in our daily lives. In effect, everything we see and feel and everything we buy and sell is measured and compared by means of units. Some of these units have become so familiar that we often take them for granted, seldom stopping to think how they started, or why they were given the sizes they have.

Centuries ago the foot was defined as the length of 36 barleycorns strung end to end, and the yard was the distance from the tip of King Edgar's nose to the end of his outstretched hand.

Since then we have come a long way in defining our units of measure more precisely. Most units are now based upon the physical laws of nature, which are both invariable and reproducible. Thus the meter and yard are measured in terms of the speed of light, and time by the duration of atomic vibrations. This improvement in our standards of measure has gone hand in hand with the advances in technology, and the one could not have been achieved without the other.

Although the basic standards of reference are recognized by all countries of the world, the units of everyday measure are far from being universal. For example, in measuring length some people use the inch and yard, while others use the millimeter and meter. Astronomers employ the parsec, physicists use the ångström, and some surveyors still have to deal with the rod and chain. But these units of length can be compared with great accuracy because the standard of length is based upon the speed of light.

Such standards of reference make it possible to compare the units of measure in one country, or in one specialty, with the units of measure in any other. Standard units of length, mass, and time are the anchors that tie together the units used in the world today.

1.1 Systems of units

Over the years systems of units have been devised to meet the needs of commerce, industry, and science. A system of units may be described as one in which the units bear a direct numerical relationship to each other, usually expressed as a whole number. Thus in the English system of units, the inch, foot, and yard are related to each other by the numbers 12, 3, and 36.

The same correlation exists in metric systems, except that the units are related to each other by multiples of ten. Thus the centimeter, meter, and kilometer are related by the numbers 100, 1000, and 100 000. It is therefore easier to convert meters into centimeters than to convert yards into feet, and this decimal approach is one of the advantages of the metric system of units.*

Today the officially recognized metric system is the International System of Units, for which the universal abbreviation is *SI.* The SI was formally introduced in 1960, at the Eleventh General Conference of Weights and Measures, under the official title "Système international d'unités."

1.2 Getting used to SI

The official introduction of the International System of Units, and its adoption by most countries of the world, did not, however, eliminate the systems that were previously employed. Just like well-established habits, units become a part of ourselves, which we cannot readily let go. It is not easy to switch overnight from yards to meters and from ounces to grams. And this is quite natural, because long familiarity with a unit gives us an idea of its magnitude and how it relates to the physical world.

Nevertheless, the growing importance of SI (particularly in the electrical and mechanical fields) makes it necessary to know the essentials of this measurement system. Consequently, one must be able to convert from one system to another in a simple, unambiguous way. In this regard the reader will discover that the conversion charts listed in the Appendix are particularly helpful.

The SI possesses a number of remarkable features shared by no other system of units:

1. It is a decimal system.
2. It employs many units commonly used in industry and commerce; for example, volt, ampere, kilogram, and watt.
3. It is a coherent system that expresses with startling simplicity some of the most basic relationships in electricity, mechanics, and heat.
4. It can be used by the research scientist, the technician, the practicing engineer, and by the layman, thereby blending the theoretical and the practical worlds.

Despite these advantages the SI is not the answer to everything. In specialized areas of atomic physics, and even in day-to-day work, other units may be more convenient. Thus we will continue to measure plane angles in degrees, even though the SI unit is the radian. Furthermore, *day* and *hour* will still be used, despite the fact that the SI unit of time is the second.

1.3 Base and derived units of the SI

The foundation of the International System of Units rests upon the seven base units listed in Table 1A.

TABLE 1A BASE UNITS

Quantity	Unit	Symbol
Length	meter	m
Mass	kilogram	kg
Time	second	s
Electric current	ampere	A
Temperature	kelvin	K
Luminous intensity	candela	cd
Amount of substance	mole	mol

From these base units we derive other units to express quantities such as area, power, force, magnetic flux, and so on. There is really no limit to the number of units we can derive, but some occur so frequently that they have been given special names. Thus, instead of saying that the unit of pressure is the newton per square meter, we use a less cumbersome name, the *pascal.* Some of the derived units that have special names are listed in Table 1B.

TABLE 1B DERIVED UNITS

Quantity	Unit	Symbol
Electric capacitance	farad	F
Electric charge	coulomb	C
Electric conductance	siemens	S

* The metric unit of length is spelled either *meter* or *metre.* In Canada the official spelling is *metre.*

TABLE 1B *(continued)*

Quantity	Unit	Symbol
Electric potential	volt	V
Electric resistance	ohm	Ω
Energy	joule	J
Force	newton	N
Frequency	hertz	Hz
Illumination	lux	lx
Inductance	henry	H
Luminous flux	lumen	lm
Magnetic flux	weber	Wb
Magnetic flux density	tesla	T
Plane angle	radian	rad
Power	watt	W
Pressure	pascal	Pa
Solid angle	steradian	sr

1.4 Definitions of base units

The following official definitions of the SI base units illustrate the extraordinary precision associated with this modern system of units. The text in italics is explanatory and does not form part of the definition:

The **meter** (m) is the length of the path travelled by light in vacuum during a time interval of 1/299 792 458 of a second.

In 1983 the speed of light was defined to be 299 792 458 m/s exactly.

The **kilogram** (kg) is the unit of mass; it is equal to the mass of the international prototype of the kilogram.

The international prototype of the kilogram is a particular cylinder of platinum-iridium alloy that is preserved in a vault at Sèvres, France, by the International Bureau of Weights and Measures. Duplicates of the prototype exist in all important standards laboratories in the world. The platinum-iridium cylinder (90 percent platinum, 10 percent iridium) is about 4 cm high and 4 cm in diameter.

The **second** (s) is the duration of 9 192 631 770 periods of the radiation corresponding to the transition between the two hyperfine levels of the ground state of the cesium-133 atom.

A quartz oscillator, tuned to the resonant frequency of cesium atoms, produces a highly accurate and stable frequency.

The **ampere** (A) is that constant current which, if maintained in two straight parallel conductors of infinite length, of negligible circular cross-section, and placed 1 meter apart in vacuum, would produce between these conductors a force equal to 2×10^{-7} newton per meter of length.

The **kelvin** (K), unit of thermodynamic temperature, is the fraction 1/273.16 of the thermodynamic temperature of the triple point of water.

Pure water in an evacuated cell is cooled until ice begins to form. The resulting temperature where ice, water, and water vapor coexist is called the triple point of water and is equal to 273.16 kelvins, by definition. The triple point is equal to 0.01 degree Celsius (°C). A temperature of 0°C is therefore equal to 273.15 kelvins, exactly.

The **candela** (cd) is the luminous intensity, in a given direction, of a source that emits monochromatic radiation of frequency 540×10^{12} hertz and that has a radiant intensity in that direction of 1/683 watt per steradian.

The **mole** (mol) is the amount of substance of a system that contains as many elementary entities as there are atoms in 0.012 kilogram of carbon 12.

Note: When the mole is used, the elementary entities must be specified and may be atoms, molecules, ions, electrons, other particles, or specified groups of such particles.

1.5 Definitions of derived units

Some of the more important derived units are defined as follows:

The **coulomb** (C) is the quantity of electricity transported in 1 second by a current of 1 ampere. (*Hence 1 coulomb = 1 ampere second.*)

The **degree Celsius** (°C) is equal to the kelvin and is used in place of the kelvin for expressing Celsius temperature (symbol t) defined by the equation $t = T - T_o$ where T is the thermodynamic temperature and $T_o = 273.15$ K, by definition.

The **farad** (F) is the capacitance of a capacitor between the plates of which there appears a difference of potential of 1 volt when it is charged by a quantity of electricity equal to 1 coulomb. (*1 farad = 1 coulomb per volt*)

The **henry** (H) is the inductance of a closed circuit in which an electromotive force of 1 volt is produced when the electric current in the circuit varies uniformly at a rate of 1 ampere per second. (*Hence 1 henry = 1 volt second per ampere.*)

The **hertz** (Hz) is the frequency of a periodic phenomenon of which the period is 1 second.

The **joule** (J) is the work done when the point of application of 1 newton is displaced a distance of 1 meter in the direction of the force. (*Hence 1 joule = 1 newton meter.*)

The **newton** (N) is that force which gives to a mass of 1 kilogram an acceleration of 1 meter per second per second. (*Hence 1 newton = 1 kilogram meter per second squared.*)

Although the newton is defined in terms of a mass and an acceleration, it also applies to stationary objects and to every application where a force is involved.

The **ohm** (Ω) is the electric resistance between two points of a conductor when a constant difference of potential of 1 volt, applied between these two points, produces in this conductor a current of 1 ampere, this conductor not being the source of any electromotive force. (*Hence 1 ohm = 1 volt per ampere.*)

The **pascal** (Pa) is the unit of pressure or stress equal to one newton per square meter.

The **radian** (rad) is the unit of measure of a plane angle with its vertex at the center of a circle and subtended by an arc equal in length to the radius.

The **siemens** (S) is the unit of electric conductance equal to one reciprocal ohm. (*The siemens was formerly named the mho.*)

The **steradian** (sr) is the unit of measure of a solid angle with its vertex at the center of a sphere and enclosing an area of the spherical surface equal to that of a square with sides equal in length to the radius.

The **tesla** (T) is the unit of magnetic flux density equal to one weber per square meter.

TABLE 1C PREFIXES TO CREATE MULTIPLES AND SUBMULTIPLES OF SI UNITS

Multiplier	Exponent form	Prefix	SI symbol
1 000 000 000 000 000 000 000 000	10^{24}	yotta	Y
1 000 000 000 000 000 000 000	10^{21}	zetta	Z
1 000 000 000 000 000 000	10^{18}	exa	E
1 000 000 000 000 000	10^{15}	peta	P
1 000 000 000 000	10^{12}	tera	T
1 000 000 000	10^{9}	giga	G
1 000 000	10^{6}	mega	M
1 000	10^{3}	kilo	k
100	10^{2}	hecto	h
10	10^{1}	deca	da
0.1	10^{-1}	deci	d
0.01	10^{-2}	centi	c
0.001	10^{-3}	milli	m
0.000 001	10^{-6}	micro	μ
0.000 000 001	10^{-9}	nano	n
0.000 000 000 001	10^{-12}	pico	p
0.000 000 000 000 001	10^{-15}	femto	f
0.000 000 000 000 000 001	10^{-18}	atto	a
0.000 000 000 000 000 000 001	10^{-21}	zepto	z
0.000 000 000 000 000 000 000 001	10^{-24}	yocto	y

The **volt** (V) is the difference of electric potential between two points of a conducting wire carrying a constant current of 1 ampere, when the power dissipated between these points is equal to 1 watt. (*Hence 1 volt = 1 watt per ampere.*)

The **watt** (W) is the power that gives rise to the production of energy at the rate of 1 joule per second. (*Hence 1 watt = 1 joule per second.*)

The **weber** (Wb) is the magnetic flux that, linking a circuit of one turn, produces in it an electromotive force of 1 volt as it is reduced to zero at a uniform rate in 1 second. (*Hence 1 weber = 1 volt second.*)

1.6 Multiples and submultiples of SI units

Multiples and submultiples of SI units are generated by adding appropriate prefixes to the units. Thus prefixes such as *kilo, mega, nano,* and *centi* multiply the value of the unit by *factors* listed in Table 1C. For example,

1 *kilo*ampere = 1000 amperes,

1 *nano*second = 10^{-9} seconds,

1 *mega*watt = 10^6 watts.

1.7 Commonly used units

Tables 1D, 1E, and 1F list some common units encountered in mechanics, thermodynamics, and electricity. They contain notes particularly useful to the reader who is not yet familiar with the SI.

TABLE 1D COMMON UNITS IN MECHANICS

Quantity	SI unit	Symbol	Note
Angle	radian	rad	1
Area	square meter	m^2	2
Energy (or work)	joule	J	
Force	newton	N	3
Length	meter	m	
Mass	kilogram	kg	
Power	watt	W	
Pressure	pascal	Pa	4
Speed	meter per second	m/s	
Speed of rotation	radian per second	rad/s	5
Torque	newton meter	N·m	
Volume	cubic meter	m^3	
Volume	liter	L	6

1. Although the radian is the SI unit of angular measure, we use the degree almost exclusively in this book (1 rad ≈ 57.3°).
2. Most countries, including Canada (as well as some organizations in the United States), use the spelling *metre* instead of *meter.*
3. The newton is a very small force, roughly equal to the force needed to press a doorbell.
4. The pascal is a very small pressure equal to 1 N/m^2.
5. In this book we use the revolution per minute (r/min) to designate rotational speed (1 rad/s = 9.55 r/min).
6. This unit of volume is mainly used for liquids and gases. It is spelled *liter* or *litre*. The official spelling in Canada is *litre*.

TABLE 1E COMMON UNITS IN THERMODYNAMICS

Quantity	SI unit	Symbol	Note
Heat	joule	J	
Thermal power	watt	W	
Specific heat	joule per (kilogram kelvin)	J/kg·K or J/kg·°C	1
Temperature	kelvin	K	2
Temperature difference	kelvin or degree Celsius	K or °C	1
Thermal conductivity	watt per (meter-kelvin)	W/m·K or W/m·°C	1

1. A temperature difference of 1 K is exactly equal to a temperature difference of 1°C. The °C is a recognized SI unit and, in practical calculations, it is often used instead of the kelvin.
2. Thermodynamic, or absolute, temperature is expressed in kelvins. On the other hand, the temperature of objects is usually expressed in °C. The absolute temperature T is related to the Celsius temperature t by the equation $T = t + 273.15$.

TABLE 1F COMMON UNITS IN ELECTRICITY AND MAGNETISM

Quantity	SI unit	Symbol	Note
Capacitance	farad	F	
Conductance	siemens	S	1
Electric charge	coulomb	C	
Electric current	ampere	A	
Energy	joule	J	
Frequency	hertz	Hz	2
Inductance	henry	H	
Potential difference	volt	V	
Power	watt	W	
Resistance	ohm	Ω	
Resistivity	ohm meter	Ω·m	
Magnetic field strength	ampere per meter	A/m	3
Magnetic flux	weber	Wb	
Magnetic flux density	tesla	T	4
Magnetomotive force	ampere	A	5

1. Formerly called *mho*.
2. 1 Hz = 1 cycle per second.
3. 1 A/m = 1 ampere turn per meter.
4. 1 T = 1 Wb/m^2.
5. What was formerly called an *ampere turn* is now simply called *ampere:* 1 A = 1 ampere turn.

1.8 Conversion charts and their use

Unfamiliar units can be converted to units we know well by using standard conversion tables. But this is strictly an arithmetic process that often leaves us wondering if our calculations are correct.

The conversion charts in the Appendix eliminate this problem because they show the relative size of a unit by the position it occupies on the page. The largest unit is at the top, the smallest at the bottom, and intermediate units are ranked in between.

The units are connected by arrows, each of which bears a number. The number is the ratio of the larger to the smaller of the units that are connected and, hence, its value is always greater than unity. The arrow always points toward the smaller unit.

In Fig. 1.1, for example, five units of length—the mile, meter, yard, inch, and millimeter—are

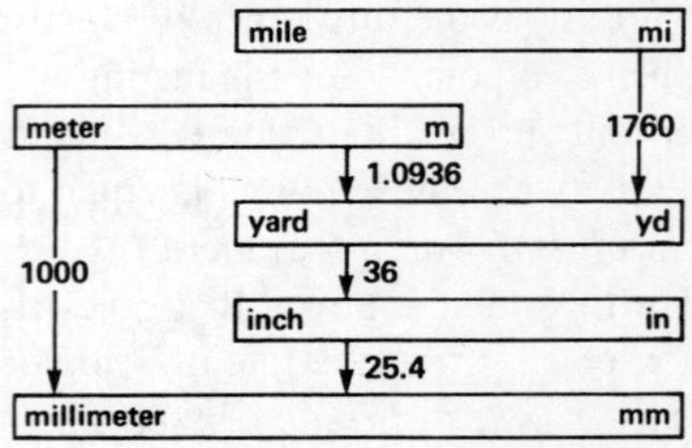

Figure 1.1
Conversion chart for units of length.
Conversion chart adapted and reproduced with permission. (Copyright © 1991,1995 by Sperika Enterprises Ltd. All rights reserved. Drawn from "Metric Units and Conversion Charts" by Theodore Wildi. IEEE Press, Piscataway, NJ, 08855-1331.)

listed in descending order of size, and the lines joining them bear an arrow that always points toward the smaller unit. The numbers show the relative size of the connected units: the yard is 36 times larger than the inch, the inch is 25.4 times larger than the millimeter, and so on. With this arrangement we can convert from one unit to any other by the following simple method.

Suppose we wish to convert from yards to millimeters. Starting from *yard* in Fig. 1.1, we have to move downward in the direction of the two arrows (36 and 25.4) until we reach *millimeter.*

Conversely, if we want to convert from millimeters to yards, we start at *millimeter* and move upward against the direction of the arrows until we reach *yard.* In making such conversions we apply the following rules:

1. If, in traveling from one unit to another, we move in the direction of the arrow, we ***multiply*** by the associated number.
2. Conversely, if we move against the arrow, we ***divide.***

Because the arrows point downward, this means that when moving down the chart we multiply, and when moving up, we divide. Note that in moving from one unit to another, we can follow any path we please; the conversion result is always the same.

The rectangles bearing SI units extend slightly toward the left of the chart to distinguish them from other units. Each rectangle bears the symbol for the unit as well as the name of the unit written out in full.

Example 1-1

Convert 2.5 yards to millimeters.

Solution

Starting from *yard* and moving toward *millimeter* (Fig. 1.1), we move downward in the direction of the arrows. We must therefore multiply the numbers associated with each arrow:

$$2.5 \text{ yd} = 2.5\,(\times\ 36)\,(\times\ 25.4) \text{ millimeters}$$
$$= 2286 \text{ mm}$$

Example 1-2

Convert 2000 meters into miles.

Solution

Starting from *meter* and moving toward *mile,* we move first with, and then against, the direction of the arrows. Consequently, we obtain

$$2000 \text{ meters} = 2000\,(\times 1.0936)\,(\div 1760) \text{ miles}$$
$$= \frac{2000 \times 1.0936}{1760}$$
$$= 1.24 \text{ mi}$$

Example 1-3

Convert 777 calories to kilowatt-hours.

Solution

Referring to the chart on ENERGY (Fig. 1.2) and moving from *calorie* to *kilowatt-hour,* we first travel downward (with the arrow 4.184) and then upward (against the arrows 1000, 1000, and 3.6). Applying the conversion rule, we find

$$777 \text{ calories}$$
$$= 777\,(\times\ 4.184)\,(\div\ 1000)\,(\div\ 1000)\,(\div\ 3.6)$$
$$= 9.03 \times 10^{-4} \text{ kW} \cdot \text{h}$$

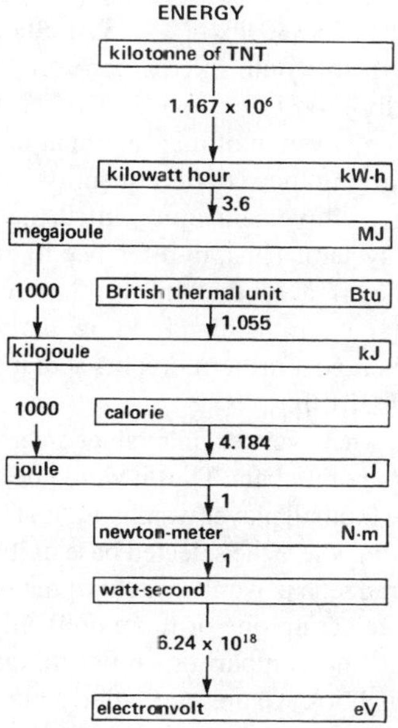

Figure 1.2
See Example 1-3.
(Conversion chart adapted and reproduced with permission. Copyright © 1991,1995 by Sperika Enterprises Ltd. All rights reserved. Drawn from "Metric Units and Conversion Charts" by Theodore Wildi. IEEE Press, Piscataway, NJ, 08855-1331.)

1.9 The per-unit system of measurement

The SI units just described enable us to specify the magnitude of any quantity. Thus mass is expressed in kilograms, power in watts, and electric potential in volts. However, we can often get a better idea of the size of something by comparing it to the size of something similar. In effect, we can create our own unit and specify the size of similar quantities compared to this arbitrary unit. This concept gives rise to the *per-unit* method of expressing the magnitude of a quantity.

For example, suppose the average weight of adults in New York is 130 lb. Using this arbitrary weight as a base, we can compare the weight of any individual in terms of this base weight. Thus a person weighing 160 lb would have a per-unit weight of 160 lb/130 lb = 1.23. Another person weighing 115 lb would have a per-unit weight of 115 lb/130 lb = 0.88.

The per-unit system of measurement has the advantage of giving the size of a quantity in terms of a particularly convenient unit, called the *per-unit* base of the system. Thus, in reference to our previous example, if a football player has a per-unit weight of 1.7 we immediately know his weight is far above average. Furthermore, his actual weight is $1.7 \times 130 = 221$ lb.

Note that whenever per-unit values are given, they are always pure numbers. Thus it would be absurd to state that the football player weighs 1.7 lb. His weight is 1.7 *per-unit,* where the selected base unit is 130 lb.

To generalize, a per-unit system of measurement consists of selecting one or more convenient measuring sticks and comparing similar things against them. In this book we are particularly interested in selecting convenient measuring sticks for voltage, current, power, torque, and impedance.

1.10 Per-unit system with one base

If we select the size of only one quantity as our measuring stick, the per-unit system is said to have a single base. The base may be a power, a voltage, a current, or a velocity. For example, suppose that three motors have power ratings of 25 hp, 40 hp, and 150 hp. Let us select an arbitrary base power P_B of 50 hp. The corresponding per-unit ratings are then 25 hp/50 hp = 0.5, 40 hp/50 hp = 0.8, and 150 hp/50 hp = 3. Thus, in this per-unit world where the base is 50 hp, the three motors have power ratings of 0.5, 0.8, and 3 pu, respectively.

We could equally well have selected a base power of 15 hp. In this case the respective per-unit rating would be 25 hp/15 hp = 1.67, 40 hp/15 hp = 2.67, and 150 hp/15 hp = 10.

It is therefore important to know the magnitude of the base of the per-unit system. If we do not know its value, the actual values of the quantities we are dealing with cannot be calculated.

The per-unit method can also be applied to impedances. Consider, for example, the circuit in

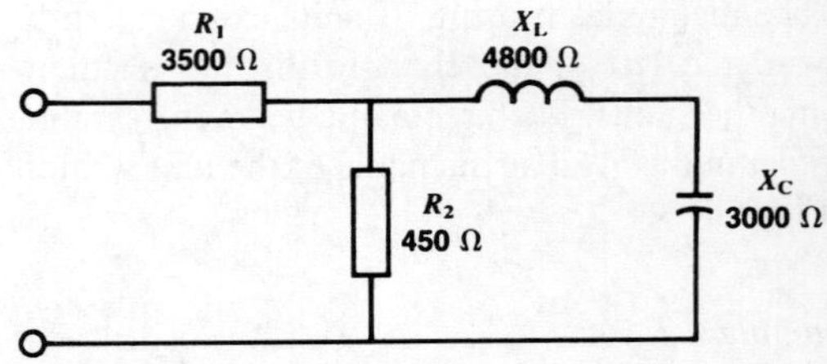

Figure 1.3
Conventional circuit.

Fig. 1.3, composed of several resistors, capacitors, and inductors having the impedances shown. If we decide to use an impedance of 1500 ohms as the base, the per-unit impedances are as follows:

$$R_1(\text{pu}) = \frac{3500\ \Omega}{1500\ \Omega} = 2.33$$

$$R_2(\text{pu}) = \frac{450\ \Omega}{1500\ \Omega} = 0.30$$

$$X_L(\text{pu}) = \frac{4800\ \Omega}{1500\ \Omega} = 3.2$$

$$X_C(\text{pu}) = \frac{3000\ \Omega}{1500\ \Omega} = 2$$

The per-unit circuit (Fig. 1.4) contains the same elements as the real circuit, but the impedances are now expressed in per-unit values. We can solve this circuit as we would any other circuit. For example, if vector notation is used, the per-unit circuit is that shown in Fig. 1.5.

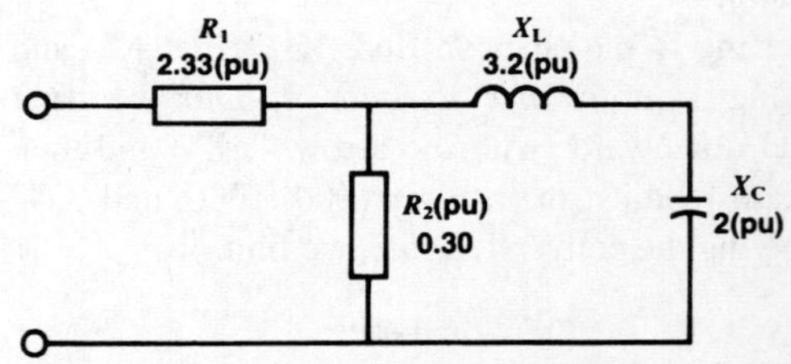

Figure 1.4
Per-unit circuit.

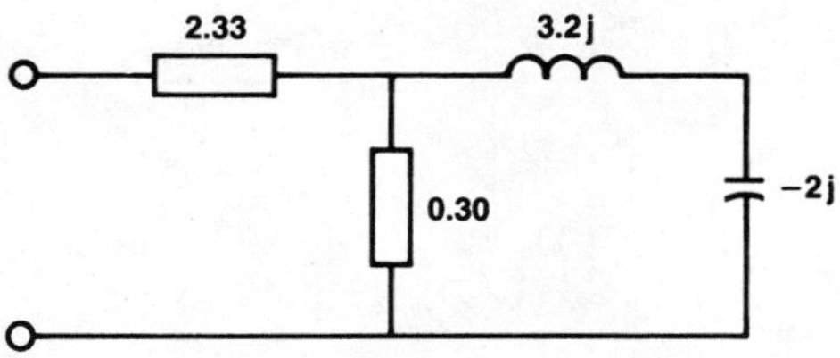

Figure 1.5
Per-unit circuit with j notation.

1.11 Per-unit system with two bases

In electrotechnology the per-unit system becomes particularly useful when two bases are used. The bases are usually a base voltage E_B and a base power P_B. Thus the selected base voltage may be 4 kV and the selected base power 500 kW.

The two base values can be selected quite independently of each other.

One interesting feature of the voltage/power per-unit system is that it automatically establishes a corresponding base current and base impedance. Thus the base current I_B is

$$I_B = \frac{\text{base power}}{\text{base voltage}} = \frac{P_B}{E_B}$$

and the base impedance Z_B is

$$Z_B = \frac{\text{base voltage}}{\text{base current}} = \frac{E_B}{I_B}$$

For example, if the base voltage is 4 kV and the base power is 500 kW, the base current is

$$I_B = P_B/E_B = 500\,000/4000 = 125 \text{ A}$$

The base impedance is

$$Z_B = E_B/E_B = 4000 \text{ V}/125 \text{ A} = 32$$

In effect, by selecting the voltage/power per-unit system we also get a base current and a base impedance. Consequently, the so-called 2-base per-unit system really gives us a 4-base per-unit system.

In order to understand the significance of this result, the reader should study the two following examples. The bases are the same as before, namely

$$E_B = 4 \text{ kV} \qquad I_B = 125 \text{ A}$$
$$P_B = 500 \text{ kW} \qquad Z_B = 32\ \Omega$$

Example 1-4

A 400 Ω resistor carries a current of 60 A. Using the above base values, calculate:

a. The per-unit resistance
b. The per-unit current
c. The per-unit voltage across the resistor
d. The per-unit power dissipated in the resistor
e. The actual E and P of the resistor

Solution

a. The per-unit resistance is

$$R(\text{pu}) = 400\ \Omega/32\ \Omega = 12.5$$

b. The per-unit current is

$$I(\text{pu}) = 60 \text{ A}/125 \text{ A} = 0.48$$

c. The per-unit voltage across the resistor is

$$\begin{aligned} E(\text{pu}) &= I(\text{pu}) \times R(\text{pu}) \\ &= 0.48 \times 12.5 \\ &= 6 \end{aligned}$$

d. The per-unit power is

$$\begin{aligned} P(\text{pu}) &= E(\text{pu}) \times I(\text{pu}) \\ &= 6 \times 0.48 \\ &= 2.88 \end{aligned}$$

e. The actual voltage across the resistor is

$$\begin{aligned} E &= E_B \times E(\text{pu}) \\ &= 4 \text{ kV} \times 6 \\ &= 24 \text{ kV} \end{aligned}$$

The actual power dissipated in the resistor is

$$\begin{aligned} P &= P_B \times P(\text{pu}) \\ &= 500 \text{ kW} \times 2.88 \\ &= 1440 \text{ kW} \end{aligned}$$

Example 1-5

A 7.2 kV source delivers power to a 24 Ω resistor and a 400 kW electric boiler (Fig. 1.6). Draw the equivalent per-unit circuit diagram. Use the same base values as in Example 1-4.

Calculate

a. The per-unit E(pu), R(pu), P(pu)
b. The per-unit current I_2(pu)
c. The per-unit line current I_L(pu)
d. The per-unit power absorbed by the resistor
e. The actual power absorbed by the resistor
f. The actual line current

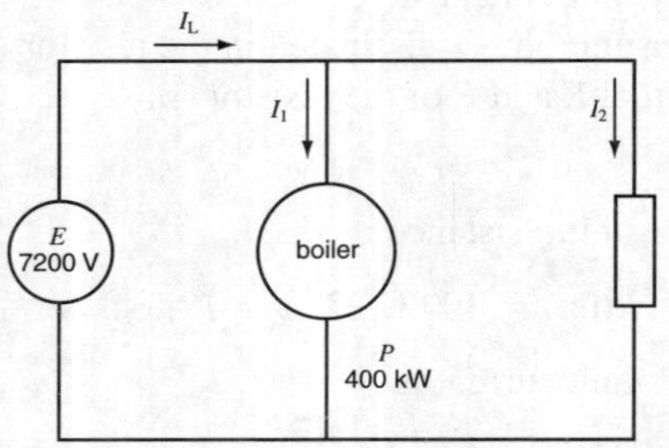

Figure 1.6
See Example 1-5.

Solution

a. The per-unit line voltage is

$$E_1(\text{pu}) = 7.2\text{ kV}/4\text{ kV} = 1.8$$

The per-unit resistance is

$$R(\text{pu}) = 24/32\ \Omega = 0.75$$

The per-unit power of the boiler is

$$P(\text{pu}) = 400\text{ kW}/500\text{ kW} = 0.8$$

We can now draw the per-unit circuit (Fig. 1.7).

b. The per-unit current I_2 is

$$I_2(\text{pu}) = E(\text{pu})/R(\text{pu}) = 1.8 \div 0.75 = 2.4$$

c. The per-unit current I_1 is

$$I_1(\text{pu}) = P(\text{pu})/E(\text{pu}) = 0.8/1.8 = 0.444$$

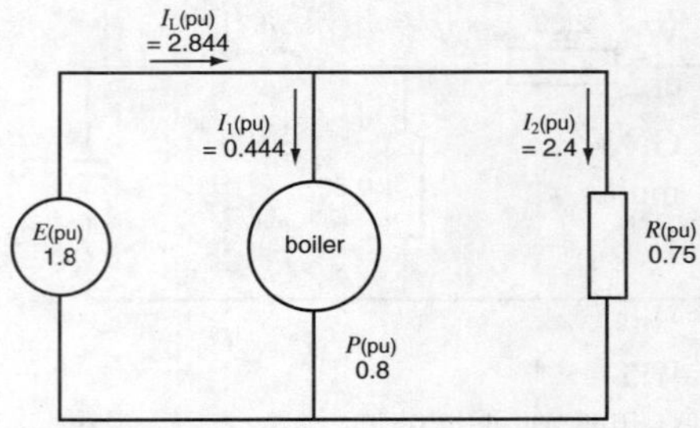

Figure 1.7
Per-unit version of Figure 1.6.

The per-unit line current I_L is

$$I_L(\text{pu}) = I_1(\text{pu}) + I_2(\text{pu}) = 0.444 + 2.4 = 2.844$$

d. The per-unit power in the resistor is

$$P(\text{pu}) = E(\text{pu}) \times I_2(\text{pu}) = 1.8 \times 2.4 = 4.32$$

e. The actual power in the resistor is

$$P_2 = P_B \times P(\text{pu}) = 500\text{ kW} \times 4.32 = 2160\text{ kW}$$

f. The actual line current is

$$I_2 = I_B \times I_L(\text{pu}) = 125 \times 2.844 = 355.5\text{ A}$$

Questions and Problems

1-1 Name the seven base units of the International System of Units.

1-2 Name five derived units of the SI.

1-3 Give the symbols of seven base units, paying particular attention to capitalization.

1-4 Why are some derived units given special names?

1-5 What are the SI units of force, pressure, energy, power, and frequency?

1-6 Give the appropriate prefix for the following multipliers: 100, 1000, 10^6, 1/10, 1/100, 1/1000, 10^{-6}, 10^{-9}, 10^{15}.

Express the following SI units in symbol form:

1-7 megawatt
1-8 terajoule
1-9 millipascal
1-10 kilohertz
1-11 gigajoule
1-12 milliampere
1-13 microweber
1-14 centimeter
1-15 liter
1-16 milligram
1-17 microsecond
1-18 millikelvin
1-19 milliradian
1-20 terawatthour
1-21 millitesla
1-22 millimeter
1-23 revolution
1-24 megohm
1-25 megapascal
1-26 millisecond
1-27 picofarad
1-28 kilovolt
1-29 megampere
1-30 kiloampere
1-31 kilometer
1-32 nanometer
1-33 milliliter

State the SI unit for the following quantities and write the symbol:

1-34 rate of flow
1-35 frequency
1-36 plane angle
1-37 magnetic flux
1-38 density
1-39 power
1-40 temperature
1-41 mass

Give the names of the SI units that correspond to the following units:

1-42 Btu
1-43 horsepower
1-44 line of flux
1-45 inch
1-46 ångström
1-47 cycle per second
1-48 gauss
1-49 line per square inch
1-50 °F
1-51 bar
1-52 pound-mass
1-53 pound-force
1-54 kilowatt-hour
1-55 gallon per minute
1-56 mho
1-57 pound-force per square inch
1-58 revolution
1-59 degree
1-60 oersted
1-61 ampere turn

Make the following conversions using the conversion charts:

1-62 10 square meters to square yards
1-63 250 MCM to square millimeters
1-64 1645 square millimeters to square inches
1-65 13 000 circular mils to square millimeters
1-66 640 acres to square kilometers
1-67 81 000 watts to Btu per second
1-68 33 000 foot pound-force per minute to kilowatts
1-69 250 cubic feet to cubic meters
1-70 10 foot pound-force to microjoules
1-71 10 pound-force to kilogram-force
1-72 60 000 lines per square inch to teslas
1-73 1.2 teslas to kilogauss
1-74 50 ounces to kilograms
1-75 76 oersteds to amperes per meter
1-76 5 000 meters to miles
1-77 80 ampere hours to coulombs
1-78 25 pound-force to newtons
1-79 25 pounds to kilograms
1-80 3 tonnes to pounds
1-81 100 000 lines of force to webers
1-82 0.3 pounds per cubic inch to kilograms per cubic meter
1-83 2 inches of mercury to millibars
1-84 200 pounds per square inch to pascals
1-85 70 pounds-force per square inch to newtons per square meter
1-86 15 revolutions per minute to radians per second
1-87 A temperature of 120°C to kelvins
1-88 A temperature of 200°F to kelvins
1-89 A temperature difference of 120° Celsius to kelvins

1-90 A resistance of 60 Ω is selected as the base resistance in a circuit. If the circuit contains three resistors having actual values of 100 Ω, 3000 Ω, and 20 Ω, calculate the per-unit value of each resistor.

1-91 A power of 25 kW and a voltage of 2400 V are selected as the base power and base voltage of a power system. Calculate the value of the base impedance and the base current.

1-92 A resistor has a per-unit value of 5.3. If the base power is 250 kW and the base voltage is 12 470 V, calculate the ohmic value of the resistor.

1-93 A length of 4 m is selected as a base unit.

Calculate

a. the per-unit length of 1 mile
b. the per-unit length of 1 foot
c. the magnitude of the base area (in m^2)
d. the magnitude of the base volume (in m^3)
e. the per-unit value of a volume of 6000 m^3
f. the per-unit value of an area of 2 square miles

Industrial application

1-94 A motor has an efficiency of 92.6%. What is the efficiency in per-unit?

1-95 A variable-speed motor having a nameplate rating of 15 hp, 890 r/min develops a torque of 25 newton meters at 1260 r/min. Calculate the per-unit values of the torque, speed, and power.

1-96 Three resistors have the following ratings:

resistor	resistance	power
A	100 Ω	24 W
B	50 Ω	75 W
C	300 Ω	40 W

Using resistor A as a base, determine the per-unit values of the resistance, power, and voltage rating of resistors B and C, respectively.

1-97 A 30 hp cage motor has the following current ratings:

FLA: full-load current 36 A

LRA: locked rotor current 218 A

NLA: no-load current 14 A.

Calculate the per-unit values of LRA and NLA.

CHAPTER 2

Fundamentals of Electricity, Magnetism, and Circuits

2.0 Introduction

This chapter briefly reviews some of the fundamentals of electricity, magnetism, and circuits. We assume the reader is already familiar with the basics, including the solution of electric circuits. However, a review is useful because it focuses on those items that are particularly important in power technology. Furthermore, it establishes the notation used throughout this book to designate voltages and currents. Some of the topics treated here will also provide the reader with a reference for subjects covered in later chapters.

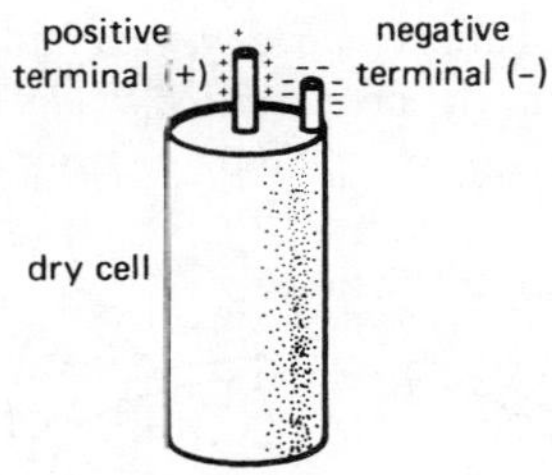

Figure 2.1
Dry cell.

2.1 Conventional and electron current flow

Consider the dry cell shown in Fig. 2.1, having one positive (+) and one negative (−) terminal. The difference of potential between them (measured in volts) is due to an excess of electrons at the negative terminal compared to the positive terminal.

If we connect a wire across the terminals, the potential difference causes an electric current to flow in the circuit. This current is composed of a steady stream of electrons that come out of the negative terminal, move along the wire, and reenter the cell by the positive terminal (Fig. 2.2).

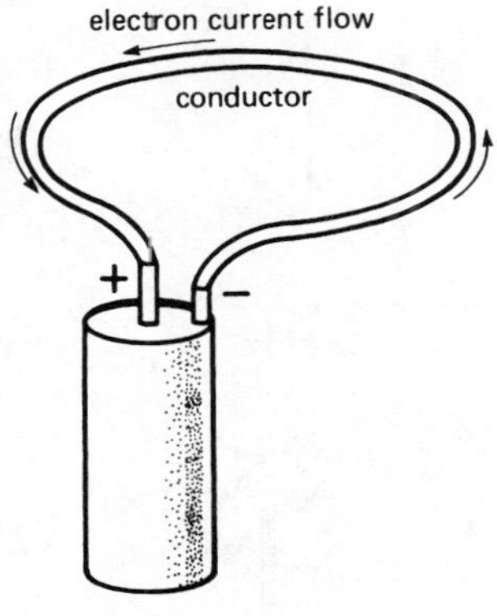

Figure 2.2
Electron flow.

Before the electron theory of current flow was fully understood, scientists of the 17th century arbitrarily decided that current in a conductor flows from the positive terminal to the negative terminal (Fig. 2.3). This so-called *conventional current flow* is still used today and is the accepted direction of current flow in electric power technology.

In this book we use the conventional current flow, but it is worth recalling that the actual electron flow is opposite to the conventional current flow.

2.2 Distinction between sources and loads

It is sometimes important to identify the sources and loads in an electric circuit. By definition, *a source delivers* electrical power whereas *a load absorbs* it. Every electrical device (motor, resistor, thermocouple, battery, capacity, generator, etc.) that carries a current can be classified as either a source or a load. How can we tell the one from the other?

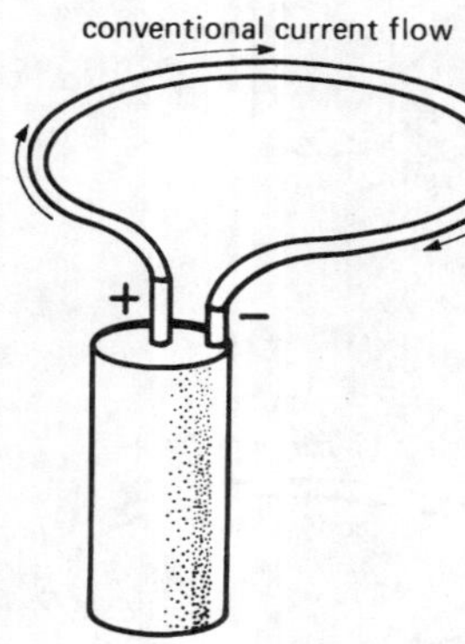

Figure 2.3
Conventional current flow.

In order to establish a general rule, consider two black boxes A and B that are connected by a pair of wires carrying a variable current *I* that is continually changing in direction (Fig. 2.4). The voltage drop along the wires is assumed to be zero. Each box contains unknown devices and components that are connected in some way to the external terminals A_1, A_2 and B_1, B_2. A variable voltage exists across the terminals, and its magnitude and polarity are also continually changing. Under such highly variable conditions, how can we tell whether A or B is a source or a load?

To answer the question, suppose we have appropriate instruments that enable us to determine the *instantaneous polarity* (+)(−) of the voltage across the terminals and the *instantaneous direction* of conventional current flow. The following rule then applies:

- A device is a source whenever current flows out of the positive terminal.
- A device is a load whenever current flows into a positive terminal.

If the instantaneous polarities and instantaneous current flow are as shown in Fig. 2.4, it follows from the rule that box A is a source and box B is a load. However, if the current should reverse while the polarity remains the same, box B would become the source and box A the load.

The above rule for establishing whether a device is a source or load is very simple, but it has important applications, particularly in alternating current circuits.

Some devices, such as resistors, can behave only as loads. Other devices, such as photocells, can act only as sources. However, many devices can behave either as sources or as loads. Thus when a battery

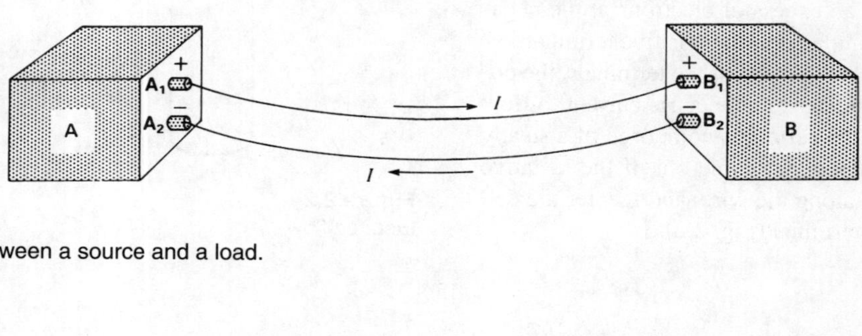

Figure 2.4
Distinction between a source and a load.

delivers electric power, it acts as a source (current flows out of the (+) terminal); when it is being recharged, it acts as a load (current flows into the (+) terminal). Similarly, electric motors usually act as loads on a system, but they can briefly behave like generators if the electromechanical conditions are appropriate. The same thing is true of capacitors. When a capacitor is discharging it acts as a source and current flows out of the (+) terminal. On the other hand, when the capacitor is charging up, it acts as a load and current flows into the (+) terminal.

2.3 Sign notation

In arithmetic we use the symbols (+) and (−) to describe addition and subtraction. In electricity and mechanics, we broaden the meaning to indicate the *direction* of an electric current, of a mechanical force, of a rotational speed, etc., compared to an arbitrarily chosen direction. For example, if the speed of a motor changes from +100 r/min to −400 r/min, it means that the direction of rotation has reversed. This interpretation of (+) and (−) signs is frequently met in the chapters that follow.

2.4 Double-subscript notation for voltages

We now describe a system of notation that enables us to indicate the polarity of voltages. Fig. 2.5 shows a source G having a positive terminal A and a negative terminal B. Terminal A is positive *with respect to* terminal B. Similarly, terminal B is negative *with respect to* terminal A. Note that terminal A is not positive by itself: it is only positive with respect to B.

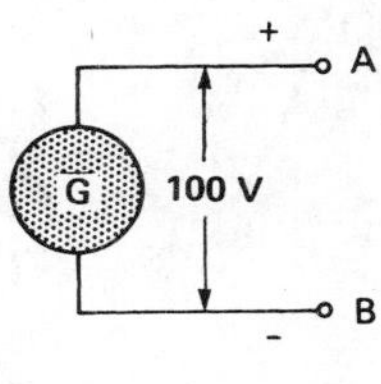

Figure 2.5
Double-subscript notation to designate a voltage.

The potential difference and the relative polarities of terminals A and B can be designated by the *double-subscript notation,* as follows:

- $E_{AB} = +100$ V, which reads, the voltage between A and B is 100 V, and A is positive with respect to B.
- $E_{BA} = -100$ V, which reads, the voltage between A and B is 100 V, and B is negative with respect to A.

As another example, if we know that the generator voltage in Fig. 2.6 has a value $E_{21} = -100$ V, we know that the voltage between the terminals is 100 V and that terminal 2 is negative with respect to terminal 1.

2.5 Sign notation for voltages

Although we can represent the value and the polarity of voltages by the double-subscript notation (E_{12}, E_{AB}, etc.), we often prefer to use the *sign notation.* It consists of designating the voltage by a symbol (E_1, E_2, V, etc.) and identifying one of the terminals by a positive (+) sign. For example, Fig. 2.7 shows a source E_1 in which one of the terminals is *arbitrarily* marked with a positive (+) sign. The other terminal

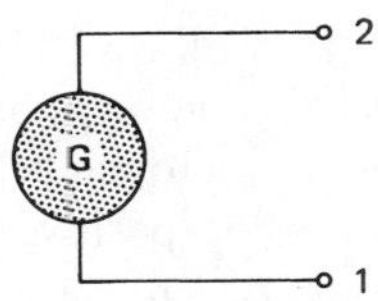

Figure 2.6
If $E_{21} = -100$ V, terminal 2 is negative with respect to terminal 1.

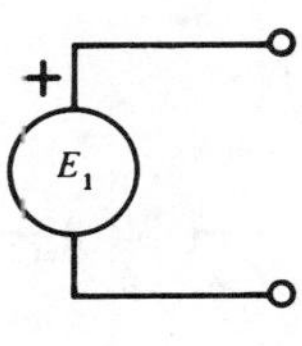

Figure 2.7
Sign notation to designate a voltage.

is unmarked, but is automatically assumed to be negative with respect to the (+) terminal.

With this notation the following rules apply:

- If we state that $E_1 = +10$ V, this means that the real polarity of the terminals corresponds to that indicated in the diagram. The terminal bearing the (+) sign is then actually positive and the other terminal is negative. Furthermore, the magnitude of the voltage across the terminals is 10 V.
- Conversely, if $E_1 = -10$ V, the real polarity of the terminals is the reverse of that shown on the diagram. The terminal bearing the (+) sign is actually negative, and the other terminal is positive. The magnitude of the voltage across the terminals is 10 V.

Example 2-1

The circuit of Fig. 2.8 consists of three sources—V_1, V_2, and V_3—each having a terminal marked with a positive (+) sign. The sources are connected in series to a resistor *R*, using jumper wires A, B, C, and D.

Determine the actual value and polarity of the voltage across each source, knowing that $V_1 = -4$ V, $V_2 = +10$ V, and $V_3 = -40$ V.

Solution

Using the rules just stated, we find that the true values and polarities are as shown in Fig. 2.9. However, in directing our attention to jumper A, it seems impossible that it can be both positive (+) and negative (−). However, we must remember that A is neither inherently positive nor inherently negative. It only has a polarity with respect to jumpers B and C, respectively. In effect, point A is *negative* with respect to point B and *positive* with respect to point C. That is why A carries both a positive and a negative sign.

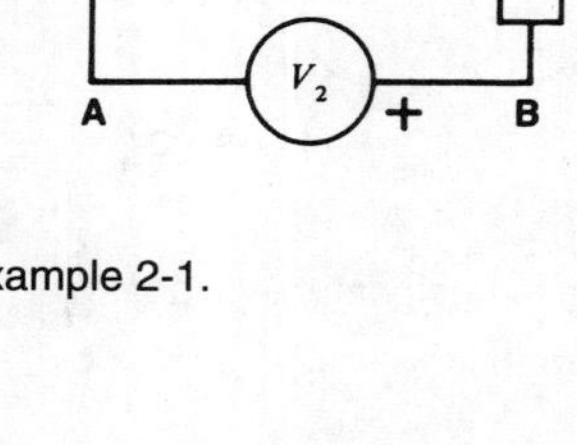

Figure 2.8
Circuit of Example 2-1.

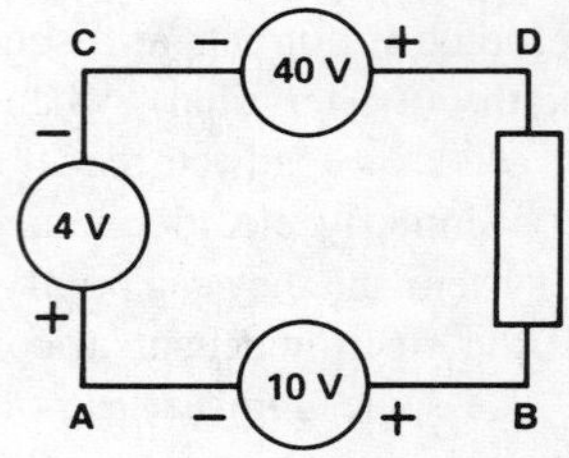

Figure 2.9
Solution of Example 2-1.

2.6 Graph of an alternating voltage

In the chapters that follow, we encounter sources whose voltages change polarity periodically. Such *alternating voltages* may be represented by means of a graph (Fig. 2.10). The vertical axis indicates the voltage at each instant, while the horizontal axis indicates the corresponding time. Voltages are positive when they are above the horizontal axis and negative when they are below. Fig. 2.10 shows the voltage E_{21} produced by the generator of Fig. 2.6.

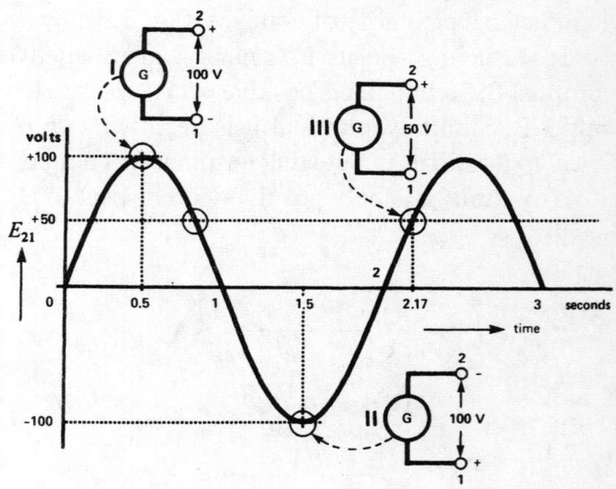

Figure 2.10
Graph of an alternating voltage having a peak of 100 V.

Starting from zero, E_{21} gradually increases, attaining $+100$ V after 0.5 second. It then gradually falls to zero at the end of one second. During this one-second interval, terminal 2 is positive with respect to terminal 1 because E_{21} is positive.

During the interval from 1 to 2 seconds, E_{21} is negative; therefore, terminal 2 is negative with respect to terminal 1. The instantaneous voltages and polarities of the generator at 0.5, 1.5, and 2.17 seconds are shown by insets I, II, and III of Fig. 2.10.

2.7 Positive and negative currents

We also make use of positive and negative signs to indicate the direction of current flow. The signs are allocated with respect to a reference direction given on the circuit diagram. For example, the current in a resistor (Fig. 2.11) may flow from X to Y or from Y to X. One of these two directions is considered to be positive (+) and the other negative (−).

Figure 2.11
Current may flow from X to Y or from Y to X.

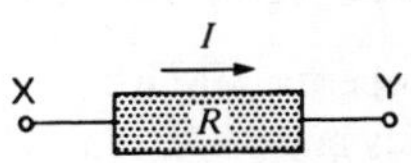

Figure 2.12
Circuit element showing positive direction of current flow.

The *positive* direction is shown *arbitrarily* by means of an arrow (Fig. 2.12). Thus, if a current of 2 A flows from X to Y, it flows in the positive direction and is designated by the symbol $+2$ A. Conversely, if current flows from Y to X (direction opposite to that of the arrow), it is designated by the symbol -2 A.

Example 2-2

The current in a resistor R varies according to the graph shown in Fig. 2.13. Interpret the meaning of this graph.

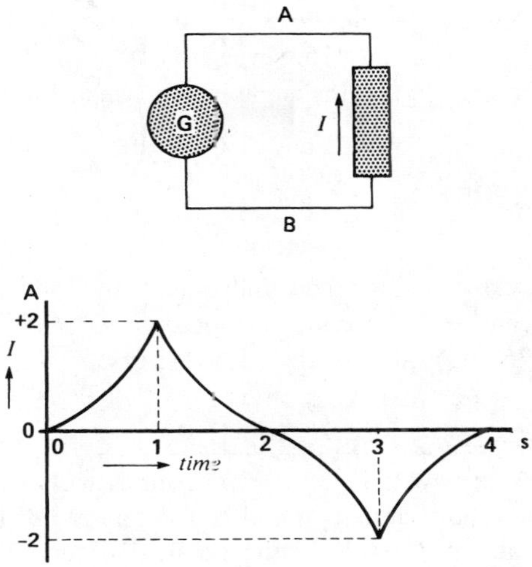

Figure 2.13
Electric circuit and the corresponding graph of current. The arrow indicates the positive direction of current flow.

Solution

According to the graph, the current increases from zero to $+2$ A during the interval from 0 to 1 second. Because it is positive, the current flows from B to A in the resistor (direction of the arrow). During the interval from 1 to 2 seconds, the current decreases from $+2$ A to zero, but it still circulates from B to A in the resistor. Between 2 and 3 seconds, the current increases from zero to -2 A and, because it is negative, it really flows in a direction opposite to that of the arrow; that is, from A to B in the resistor.

2.8 Sinusoidal voltage

The ac voltage generated by commercial alternators is very nearly a perfect sine wave. It may therefore be expressed by the equation

$$e = E_m \cos (2\pi ft + \theta) \qquad (2.1)$$

where

e = instantaneous voltage [V]

E_m = peak value of the sinusoidal voltage [V]

f = frequency [Hz]

t = time [s]

θ = a fixed angle [rad]

The expression $2\pi ft$ and θ are angles, expressed in radians. However, it is often more convenient to express the angle in degrees, as follows:

$$e = E_m \cos(360 ft + \theta) \qquad (2.2)$$

or

$$e = E_m \cos(\phi + \theta) \qquad (2.3)$$

In these equations the symbols have the same significance as before, and the time-dependent angle ϕ (= 360 ft) is also expressed in degrees.

Example 2-3

The sine wave in Fig. 2.14 represents the voltage E_{ab} across the terminals **a** and **b** of an ac motor that operates at 50 Hz. Knowing that $\theta = 30°$, and E_m = 100 V, calculate the voltage at $t = 0$ and at t = 27.144 s.

Solution

The voltage at $t = 0$ is

$$\begin{aligned} e_{ab} &= E_m \cos(360 ft + \theta) \\ &= 100 \cos(360 \times 50 \times 0 + 30°) \\ &= 100 \cos 30° \\ &= 86.6 \text{ V} \end{aligned}$$

At this moment the voltage is +86.6 V and terminal **a** is therefore positive with respect to terminal **b.**

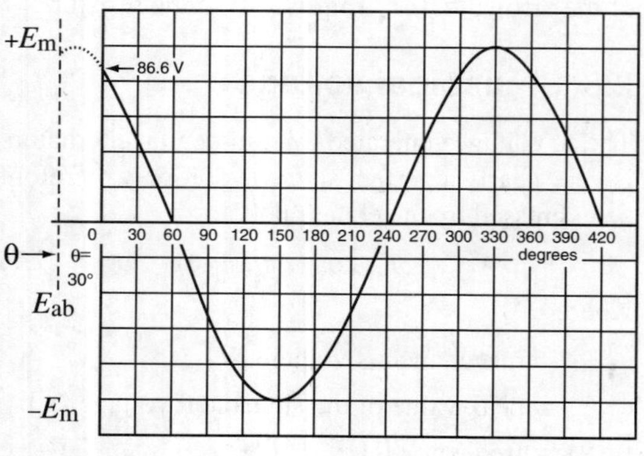

Figure 2.14
Sinusoidal voltage having a peak value of 100 V and expressed by $e_{ab} = E_m \cos(360 \text{ ft} + 30°)$.

The voltage at $t = 27.144$ s is

$$\begin{aligned} e_{ab} &= 100 \cos(360 \times 50 \times 27.144 + 30°) \\ &= 100 \cos 488\,622° \\ &= -20.8 \text{ V} \end{aligned}$$

Thus, at this moment the voltage is −20.8 V and terminal **a** is negative with respect to terminal **b.** Note that an angle of 488 622° corresponds to 488 622/360 = 1357 complete cycles plus 0.2833 cycle. The latter corresponds to 0.2833 × 360° = 102°, and 100 cos 102° = −20.8v.

2.9 Converting cosine functions into sine functions

We can convert a cosine function of voltage or current into a sine function by adding 90° to the angle θ. Thus,

$$E_m \cos(360 ft + \theta) = E_m \sin(360 ft + \theta + 90°) \qquad (2.4)$$

Similarly, we can convert a sine function into a cosine function by subtracting 90° from the angle. Thus,

$$I_m \sin(360 ft + \theta) = I_m \cos(360 ft + \theta - 90) \qquad (2.5)$$

2.10 Effective value of an ac voltage

Although the properties of an ac voltage are known when its frequency and peak value E_m are specified, it is much more common to use the effective value E_{eff}. For a voltage that varies sinusoidally, the relationship between E_{eff} and E_m is given by the expression

$$E_{eff} = E_m/\sqrt{2} \qquad (2.6)$$

The effective value of an ac voltage is sometimes called the RMS (root mean square) value of the voltage. It is a measure of the heating effect of the ac voltage as compared to that of an equivalent dc voltage. For example, an ac voltage having an effective value of 135 volts produces the same heating effect in a resistor as does a dc voltage of 135 V.

The same remarks apply to the effective value of an ac current. Thus a current that varies sinusoidally and whose peak value is I_m possesses an effective value I_{eff} given by

$$I_{eff} = I_m / \sqrt{2} \quad (2.7)$$

Most alternating current instruments are calibrated to show the *effective value* of voltage or current and not the *peak value* (Fig. 2.15). When the value of an alternating voltage or current is given it is understood that it is the effective value. Furthermore, the subscript in E_{eff} and I_{eff} is dropped and the effective values of voltage and current are simply represented by the symbols E and I.

Example 2-4

A 60 Hz source having an effective voltage of 240 V delivers an effective current of 10 A to a circuit. The current lags the voltage by 30°. Draw the waveshape for E and I.

Solution

a. The peak voltage is

$$E_m = E\sqrt{2} = 240\sqrt{2} = 339 \text{ V}$$

b. The peak current is

$$I_m = I\sqrt{2} = 10\sqrt{2} = 14.1 \text{ A}$$

c. Let us assume the voltage is given by

$$\begin{aligned} e &= E_m \sin 360\,ft \\ &= 339 \sin 360 \times 60\,t \\ &= 339 \sin 21\,600\,t \end{aligned}$$

d. Owing to the phase lag of 30°, the current is given by

$$\begin{aligned} i &= I_m \sin(360\,ft - 30) \\ &= 14.1 \sin(21\,600\,t - 30) \\ &= 14.1 \sin(\phi - 30) \end{aligned}$$

e. The waveshapes giving the instantaneous values of e and i are shown in Fig. 2.16.

2.11 Phasor representation

In most power studies the frequency is fixed, and so we simply take it for granted. Furthermore, we are not particularly concerned with the instantaneous voltages and currents but more with their RMS magnitudes and phase angles. And because the voltages are measured in terms of the effective values E

Figure 2.15
Commercial voltmeters and ammeters are graduated in effective values. This range of instruments has scales ranging up to 2500 A and 9000 V.
(Courtesy of General Electric)

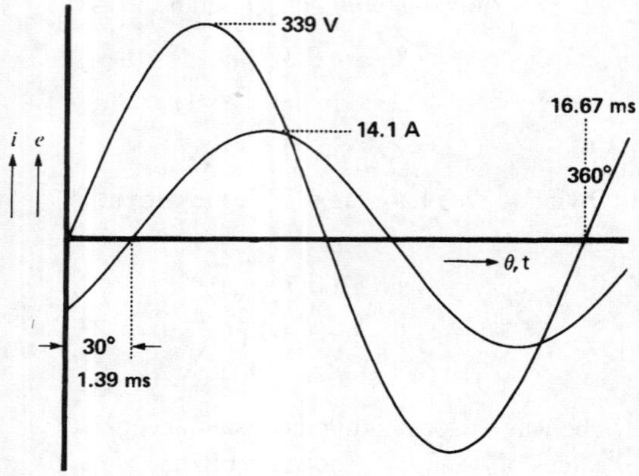

Figure 2.16
Graph showing the instantaneous values of voltage and current. The current lags 30° behind the voltage. The effective voltage is 240 V and the effective current is 10 A.

rather than the peak values E_m, we are really only interested in E and θ.

This line of reasoning has given rise to the *phasor* method of representing voltages and currents.

The basic purpose of phasor diagrams is to show the magnitudes and phase angles between voltages and currents. A phasor is similar to a vector in the sense that it bears an arrow, and its length is proportional to the effective value of the voltage or current it represents. The angle between two phasors is equal to the electrical phase angle between the quantities.

The following rules apply to phasors:

1. Two phasors are said to be in phase when they are parallel to each other and point in the same direction (Fig. 2.17). The phase angle between them is then zero.
2. Two phasors are said to be out of phase when they point in different directions. The phase angle between them is the angle through which one of the phasors has to be rotated to make it point in the same direction as the other. Thus, referring to Fig. 2.18, phasor I has to be rotated counterclockwise by an angle θ to make it point in the same direction as phasor E. Conversely, phasor E has to be rotated clockwise by an angle θ to make it point in the same direction as phasor I. Consequently, whether we rotate one phasor or the other, we have to sweep through the same angle to make them line up.
3. If a phasor E has to be rotated *clockwise* to make it point in the same direction as phasor I, then phasor E is said to **lead** phasor I. Conversely, a phasor I is said to **lag** behind phasor E if phasor I has to be rotated *counterclockwise* to make it point in the same direction. Thus, referring to Fig. 2.18, it is clear that phasor E leads phasor I by θ degrees. But we could equally well say that I lags behind E by θ degrees.
4. Referring now to Fig. 2.19 we *could* rotate phasor I clockwise by an angle β to make it

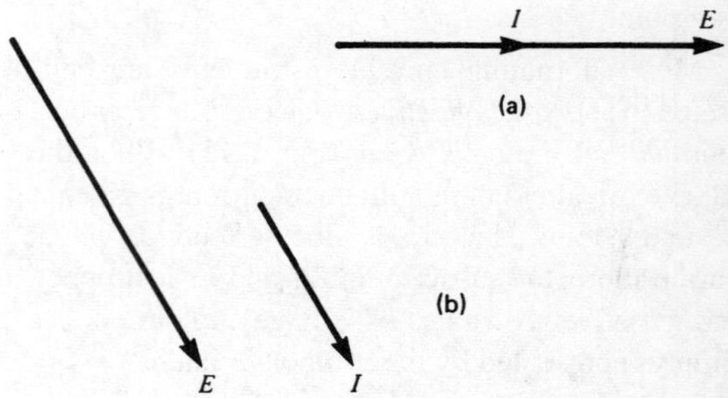

Figure 2.17
The current phasor I and voltage phasor E are in phase.

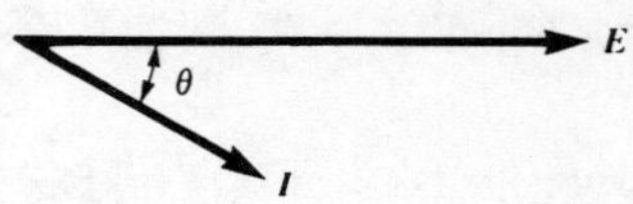

Figure 2.18
Phasor I lags behind phasor E by an angle of θ degrees.

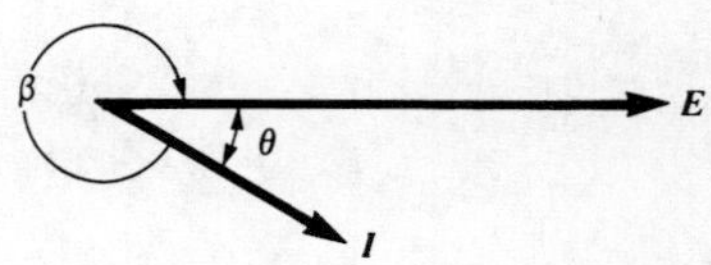

Figure 2.19
Phasor I leads E by β degrees. But phasor I also lags E by θ degrees.

point in the same direction as phasor E. We could then say that phasor I leads phasor E by β degrees. But this is the same as saying that phasor I lags phasor E by θ degrees. In practice, we always select the smaller phase angle between the two phasors to designate the lag or lead situation.

5. Phasors do not have to have a common origin but may be entirely separate from each other, as shown in Fig. 2.20. By applying rule 3, we can see that E_1 is in phase with I_1 because they point in the same direction. Furthermore, phasor I_2 leads phasor E_1 by 90°, and E_2 lags behind I_2 by 135°.

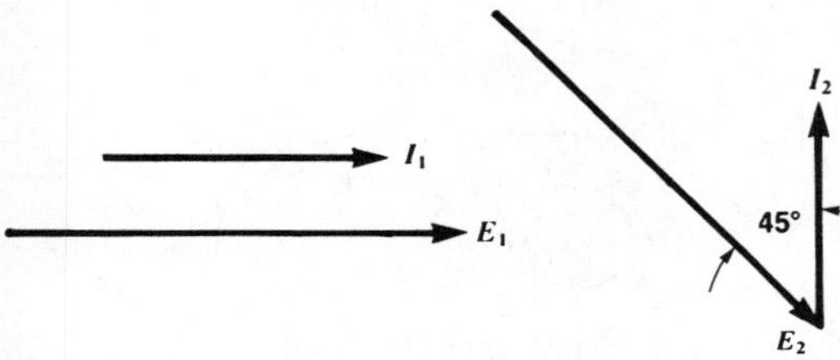

Figure 2.20
Phasors do not have to start from a common origin to show their magnitudes and phase relationships.

In the same way, the three phasors E_{ab}, E_{bc}, and E_{ca} in Fig. 2.21a can be rearranged as shown in Fig. 2.21b without affecting the phase relationship between them. Note that E_{ab} in Fig. 2.21b still points in the same direction as E_{ab} in Fig. 2.21a, and the same is true for the other phasors.

Fig. 2.21c shows still another arrangement of the three phasors that does not in any way alter their magnitude or phase relationship.

The angle between two phasors is a measure of the time that separates their peak positive values. Knowing the frequency, we can calculate the time.

Example 2-5

Draw the phasor diagram of the voltage and current in Fig. 2.16. Calculate the time interval between the positive peaks of E and I.

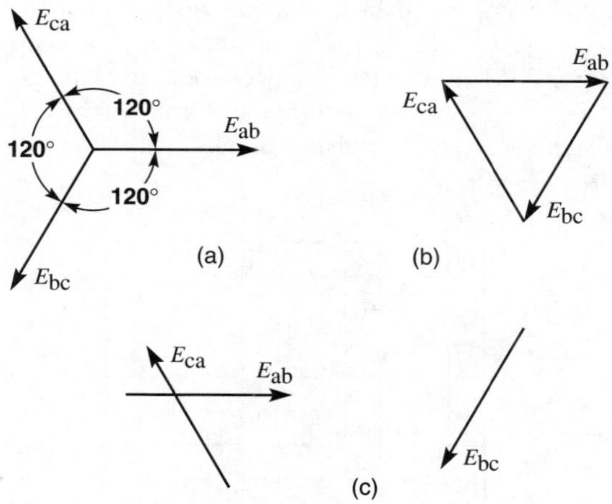

Figure 2.21
Different ways of showing the phase relationships between three voltages that are mutually displaced at 120°.

Solution

To draw the phasor diagram, we select *any* arbitrary direction for phasor E, making its length equivalent to 240 V. Phasor I is then drawn so that it lags 30° behind E with a length equivalent to 10 A (Fig. 2.22). Knowing that the frequency is 60 Hz, the time interval between the positive peaks is given by

$$\theta = 360\,ft$$

$$30 = 360 \times 60\,t$$

$$t = 1.39 \text{ ms}$$

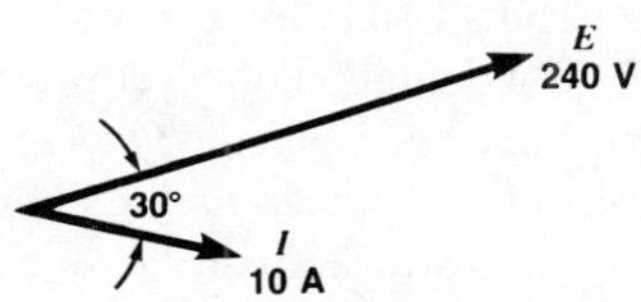

Figure 2.22
Phasor diagram of the voltage and current given in Fig. 2.16.

2.12 Harmonics

The voltages and currents in a power circuit are frequently not pure sine waves. The line voltages usually have a satisfactory waveshape but the currents are sometimes badly distorted, as shown in Fig. 2.23. This distortion can be produced by magnetic saturation in the cores of transformers or by the switching action of thyristors or IGBTs in electronic drives.

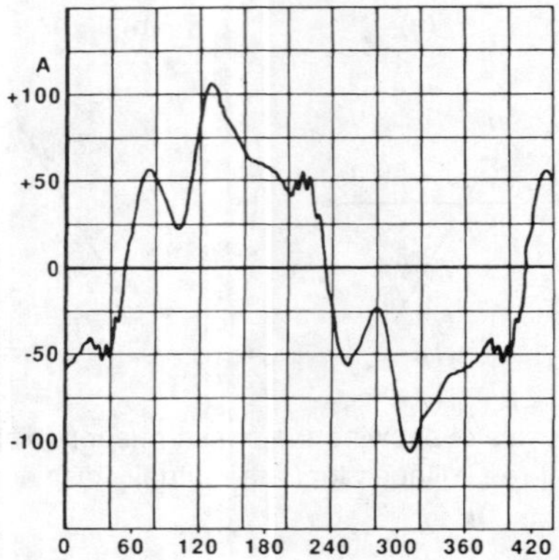

Figure 2.23
This severely distorted 60 Hz current obtained on an electronic drive contains the following harmonics: fundamental (60 Hz) = 59 A; fifth harmonic (300 Hz) = 15.6 A; seventh harmonic (420 Hz) = 10.3 A. Higher harmonics are also present, but their amplitudes are small.
(Courtesy of Electro-Mécanik.)

The distortion of a voltage or current can be traced to the harmonics it contains. A harmonic is any voltage or current whose frequency is an integral multiple of (2, 3, 4, etc., times) the line frequency.

Consider a set of sine waves in which the lowest frequency is *f*, and all other frequencies are integral multiples of *f*. By definition, the sine wave having the lowest frequency is called the *fundamental* and the other waves are called *harmonics*. For example, a set of sine waves whose frequencies are 20, 40, 100, and 380 Hz is said to possess the following components:

fundamental frequency: 20 Hz (the lowest frequency)

second harmonic: 40 Hz (2×20 Hz)

fifth harmonic: 100 Hz (5×20 Hz)

nineteenth harmonic: 380 Hz (19×20 Hz)

In order to understand the distorting effect of a harmonic, let us consider two sinusoidal sources e_1 and e_2 connected in series (Fig. 2.24a). Their frequencies are respectively 60 Hz and 180 Hz. The corresponding peak amplitudes are 100 V and 20 V. The fundamental (60 Hz) and the third harmonic (180 Hz) voltages are assumed to pass through zero at the same time, and both are perfect sine waves.

Because the sources are in series, the terminal voltage e_3 is equal to the sum of the instantaneous voltages produced by each source. The resulting terminal voltage is a flat-topped wave (Fig. 2.24b). Thus, the sum of a fundamental voltage and a harmonic voltage yields a nonsinusoidal waveform whose degree of distortion depends upon the magnitude of the harmonic (or harmonics) it contains.

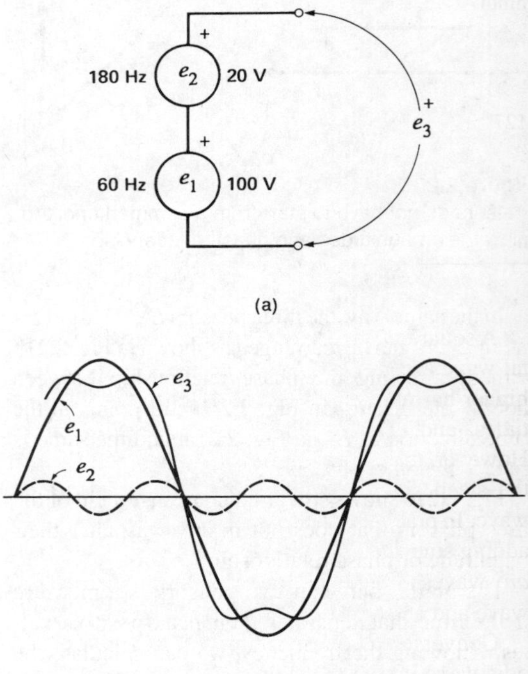

Figure 2.24

a. Two sinusoidal sources having different frequencies connected in series.
b. A fundamental and third harmonic voltage can together produce a flat-topped wave.

We can produce a periodic voltage or current of any conceivable shape. All we have to do is to add together a fundamental component and an arbitrary set of harmonic components. For example, we can generate a square wave having an amplitude of 100 V and a frequency of 50 Hz by connecting the following sine wave sources in series, as shown in Table 2A.

TABLE 2A 100 V SQUARE WAVE

Harmonic	Amplitude [V]	Freq. [Hz]	Relative amplitude
fundamental	127.3	50	1
third	42.44	150	1/3
fifth	25.46	250	1/5
seventh	18.46	350	1/7
ninth	14.15	450	1/9
.	.	.	.
.	.	.	.
.	.	.	.
127th	1.00	6350	1/127
.	.	.	.
.	.	.	.
.	.	.	.
n^{th}	127.3/n	50 n	1/n

A square wave is thus composed of a fundamental wave and an infinite number of harmonics. The higher harmonics have smaller and smaller amplitudes, and they are consequently less important. However, these high-frequency harmonics produce the steep sides and pointy corners of the square wave. In practice, square waves are not produced by adding sine waves, but the example does show that *any* waveshape can be built up from a fundamental wave and an appropriate number of harmonics.

Conversely, we can *decompose* a distorted periodic wave into its fundamental and harmonic components. The procedure for decomposing a distorted wave is given in Chapter 30.

Harmonic voltages and currents are usually undesirable, but in some ac circuits they are also unavoidable. Harmonics are created by nonlinear loads, such as electric arcs and saturated magnetic circuits. They are also produced whenever voltages and currents are periodically switched, such as in power electronic circuits. All these circuits produce distorted waveshapes that are rich in harmonics.

In ac circuits the fundamental current and fundamental voltage together produce fundamental power. This fundamental power is the useful power that causes a motor to rotate and an arc furnace to heat up. The product of a harmonic voltage times the corresponding harmonic current also produces a harmonic power. The latter is usually dissipated as heat in the ac circuit and, consequently, does no useful work. Harmonic currents and voltages should therefore be kept as small as possible.

It should be noted that the product of a fundamental voltage and a harmonic current yields zero net power.

Harmonics are covered in greater detail in Chapter 30.

2.13 Energy in an inductor

A coil stores energy in its magnetic field when it carries a current *I*. The energy is given by

$$W = \frac{1}{2}LI^2 \tag{2.8}$$

where

W = energy stored in the coil [J]

L = inductance of the coil [H]

I = current [A]

If the current varies, the stored energy rises and falls in step with the current. Thus, whenever the current increases, the coil absorbs energy and whenever the current falls, energy is released.

The properties of an inductor are more fully discussed in Section 2.31.

2.14 Energy in a capacitor

A capacitor stores energy in its electric field whenever a voltage *E* appears across its terminals. The energy is given by

$$W = \frac{1}{2}CE^2 \tag{2.9}$$

where

W = energy stored in the capacitor [J]
C = capacitance of the capacitor [F]
E = voltage [V]

Example 2-6

A coil having an inductance of 10 mH is connected in series with a 100 μF capacitor. The instantaneous current in the circuit is 40 A and the instantaneous voltage across the capacitor is 800 V. Calculate the energy stored in the electric and magnetic fields at this moment.

Solution

The energy stored in the coil is

$$W = 1/2\, LI^2 = 1/2 \times 10 \times 10^{-3} \times 40^2$$
$$= 8 \text{ J}$$

The energy stored in the capacitor is

$$W = 1/2\, CE^2 = 1/2 \times 100 \times 10^{-6} \times 800^2$$
$$= 32 \text{ J}$$

2.15 Some useful equations

We terminate this section with a list of useful equations (Table 2B) that are frequently required when solving ac circuits. The equations are given without proof on the assumption that the reader already possesses a knowledge of ac circuits in general.

TABLE 2B IMPEDANCE OF SOME COMMON AC CIRCUITS

Circuit diagram	Impedance	Equation
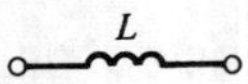	$X_L = 2\pi fL$	(2.10)
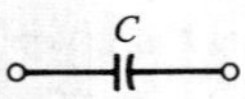	$X_C = \dfrac{1}{2\pi fC}$	(2.11)
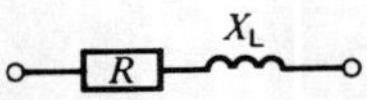	$Z = \sqrt{R^2 + X_L{}^2}$	(2.12)
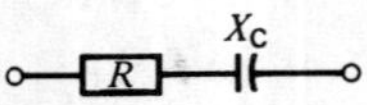	$Z = \sqrt{R^2 + X_C{}^2}$	(2.13)
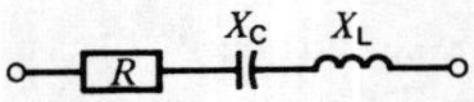	$Z = \sqrt{R^2 + (X_L - X_C)^2}$	(2.14)
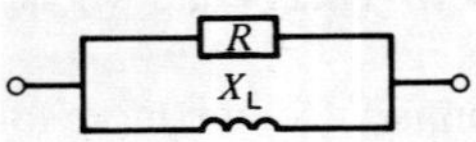	$Z = \dfrac{R\,X_L}{\sqrt{R^2 + X_L{}^2}}$	(2.15)
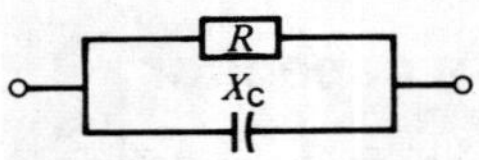	$Z = \dfrac{R\,X_C}{\sqrt{R^2 + X_C{}^2}}$	(2.16)
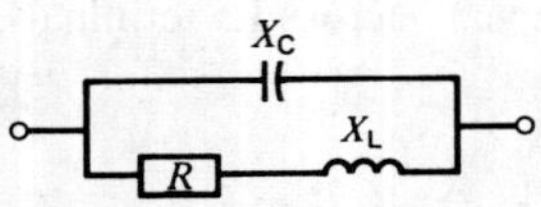	$Z = \dfrac{X_C\sqrt{R^2 + X_L{}^2}}{\sqrt{R^2 + (X_L - X_C)^2}}$	(2.17)

ELECTROMAGNETISM

2.16 Magnetic field strength *H* and magnetic flux density *B*

Whenever a magnetic flux ϕ exists in a body or component, it is due to the presence of a magnetic field strength *H*, given by

$$H = U/l \qquad (2.18)$$

where

H = magnetic field strength [A/m]
U = magnetomotive force acting on the component [A] (or ampere turn)
l = length of the component [m]

The resulting magnetic flux density is given by

$$B = \phi/A \qquad (2.19)$$

where

B = magnetic flux density [T]
ϕ = flux in the component [Wb]
A = cross section of the component [m^2]

There is a definite relationship between the magnetic flux density (*B*) and the magnetic field strength (*H*) of any material. This relationship is usually expressed graphically by the *B-H* curve of the material.

2.17 *B-H* curve of vacuum

In vacuum, the magnetic flux density *B* is directly proportional to the magnetic field strength *H*, and is expressed by the equation

$$B = \mu_o H \qquad (2.20)$$

where

B = magnetic flux density [T]
H = magnetic field strength [A/m]
μ_o = magnetic constant [$= 4\pi \times 10^{-7}$]*

* Also called the permeability of vacuum. The complete expression for μ_o is $4\pi \times 10^{-7}$ henry/meter.

In the SI, the magnetic constant is fixed, by definition. It has a numerical value of $4\pi \times 10^{-7}$ or approximately 1/800 000. This enables us to write Eq. 2.20 in the approximate form:

$$H = 800\,000\,B \qquad (2.21)$$

The *B-H* curve of vacuum is a straight line. A vacuum never saturates, no matter how great the flux density may be (Fig. 2.25). The curve shows that a magnetic field strength of 800 A/m produces a flux density of 1 millitesla.

Nonmagnetic materials such as copper, paper, rubber, and air have *B-H* curves almost identical to that of vacuum.

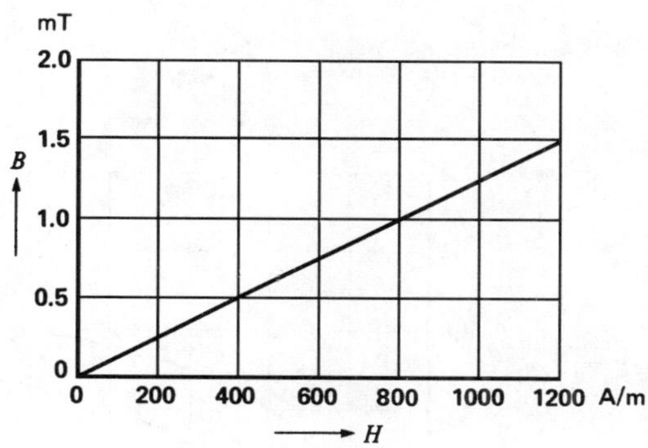

Figure 2.25
B-H curve of vacuum and of nonmagnetic materials.

2.18 *B-H* curve of a magnetic material

The flux density in a magnetic material also depends upon the magnetic field strength to which it is subjected. Its value is given by

$$B = \mu_o\, \mu_r H \qquad (2.22)$$

where *B*, μ_o, and *H* have the same significance as before, and μ_r is the relative permeability of the material.

The value of μ_r is not constant but varies with the flux density in the material. Consequently, the relationship between *B* and *H* is not linear, and this makes Eq. 2.22 rather impractical to use. We prefer to show the relationship by means of a *B-H* saturation curve. Thus, Fig. 2.26 shows typical saturation curves of three materials commonly used in electrical machines: silicon iron, cast iron, and cast steel. The curves show that a magnetic field strength of 2000 A/m produces a magnetic flux density of 1.4 T in cast steel but only 0.5 T in cast iron.

2.19 Determining the relative permeability

The *relative permeability* μ_r of a material is the ratio of the flux density in the material to the flux density that would be produced in vacuum, under the same magnetic field strength *H*.

Given the saturation curve of a magnetic material, it is easy to calculate the relative permeability using the approximate equation

$$\mu_r \approx 800\,000\, B/H \qquad (2.23)$$

where

B = flux density in the magnetic material [T]

H = corresponding magnetic field strength [A/m]

Example 2-7

Determine the permeability of silicon iron (1%) at a flux density of 1.4 T.

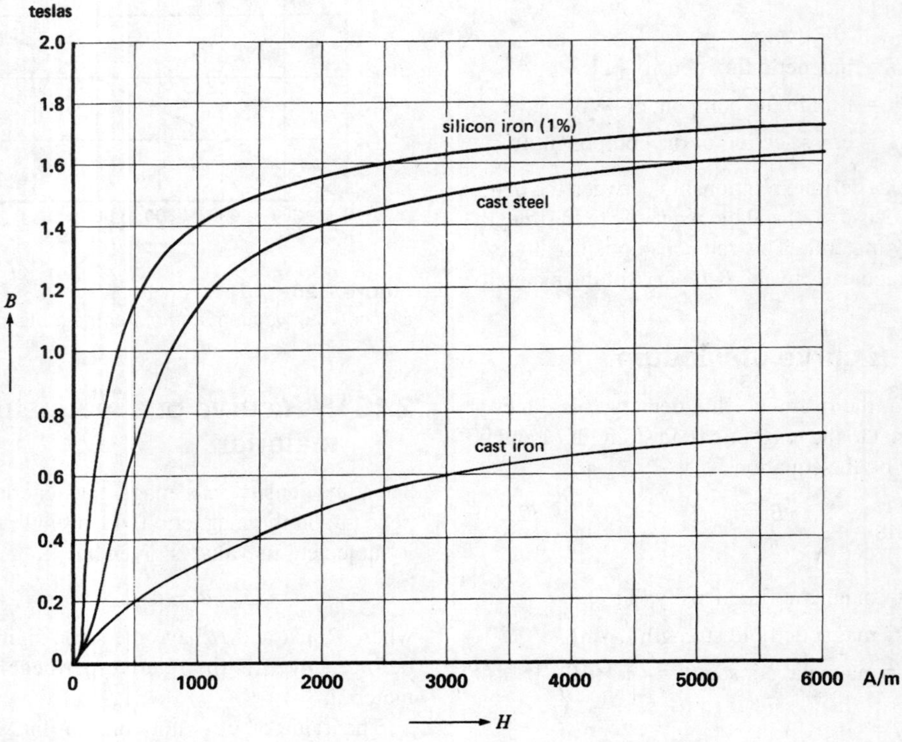

Figure 2.26
B-H saturation curves of three magnetic materials.

Solution
Referring to the saturation curve (Fig. 2.26), we see that a flux density of 1.4 T requires a magnetic field strength of 1000 A/m. Consequently,

$$\mu_r = 800\,000\, B/H$$
$$= 800\,000 \times 1.4/1000 = 1120$$

At this flux density, silicon iron is 1120 times more permeable than vacuum (or air).

Fig. 2.27 shows the saturation curves of a broad range of materials from vacuum to Permalloy®, one of the most permeable magnetic materials known. Note that as the magnetic field strength increases, the magnetic materials saturate more and more and eventually all the *B-H* curves follow the *B-H* curve of vacuum.

2.20 Faraday's law of electromagnetic induction

In 1831, while pursuing his experiments, Michael Faraday made one of the most important discoveries in electromagnetism. Now known as **Faraday's law of electromagnetic induction,** it revealed a fundamental relationship between the voltage and flux in a circuit. Faraday's law states:

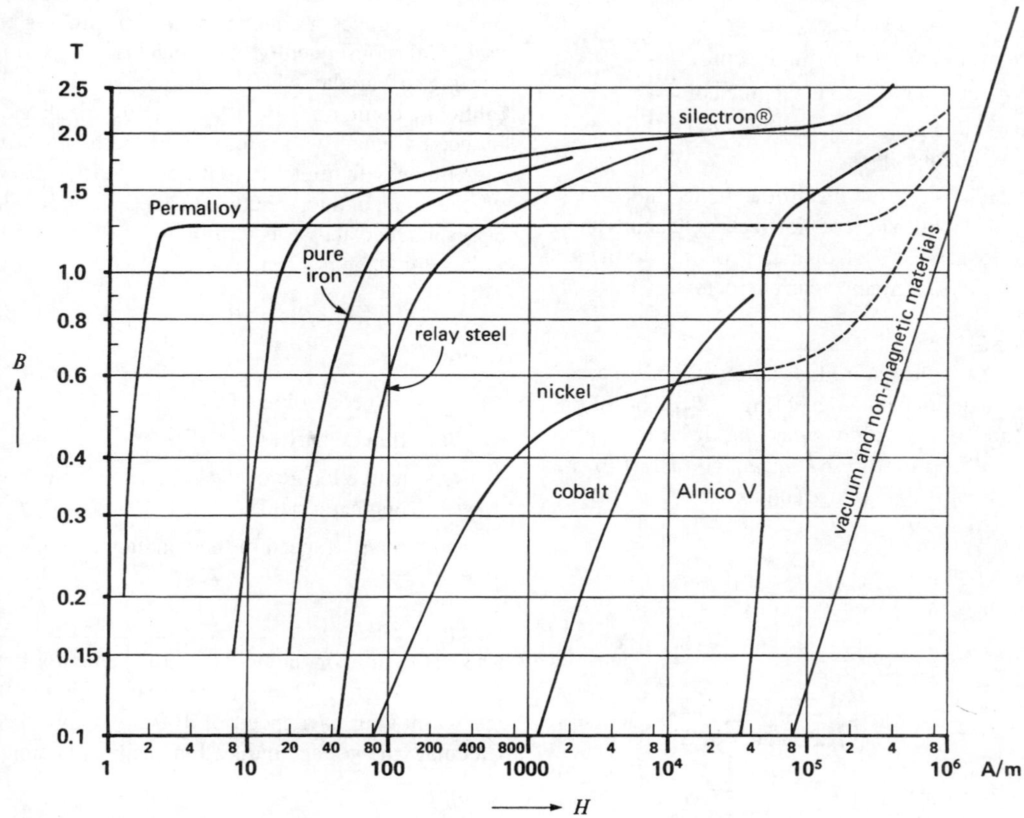

Figure 2.27
Saturation curves of magnetic and nonmagnetic materials. Note that all curves become asymptotic to the *B-H* curve of vacuum where *H* is high.

1. **If the flux linking a loop (or turn) varies as a function of time, a voltage is induced between its terminals.**
2. **The value of the induced voltage is proportional to the rate of change of flux.**

By definition, and according to the SI system of units, when the flux inside a loop varies at the rate of 1 weber per second, a voltage of 1 V is induced between its terminals. Consequently, if the flux varies inside a coil of N turns, the voltage induced is given by

$$E = N\frac{\Delta\Phi}{\Delta t} \qquad (2.24)$$

where

E = induced voltage [V]
N = number of turns in the coil
$\Delta\Phi$ = change of flux inside the coil [Wb]
Δt = time interval during which the flux changes [s]

Faraday's law of electromagnetic induction opened the door to a host of practical applications and established the basis of operation of transformers, generators, and alternating current motors.

Example 2-8

A coil of 2000 turns surrounds a flux of 5 mWb produced by a permanent magnet (Fig. 2.28). The magnet is suddenly withdrawn causing the flux inside the coil to drop uniformly to 2 mWb in 1/10 of a second. What is the voltage induced?

Solution

The flux change is

$$\Delta\Phi = (5 \text{ mWb} - 2 \text{ mWb}) = 3 \text{ mWb}$$

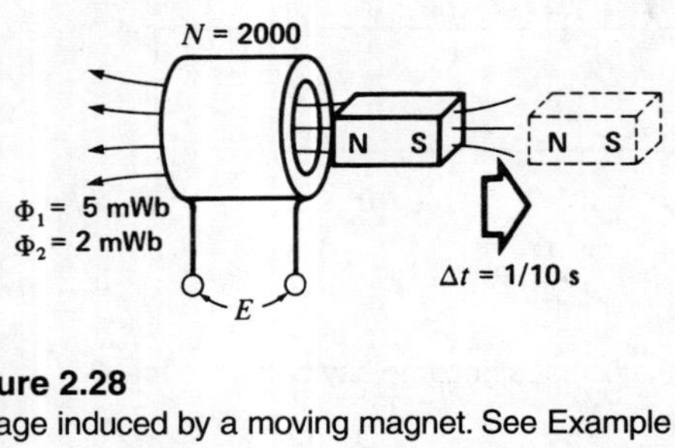

Figure 2.28
Voltage induced by a moving magnet. See Example 2-8.

Because this change takes place uniformly in 1/10 of a second (Δt), the induced voltage is

$$E = N\frac{\Delta\Phi}{\Delta t} = 2000 \times \frac{3}{1000 \times 1/10}$$
$$= 60 \text{ V}$$

The induced voltage falls to zero as soon as the flux ceases to change.

2.21 Voltage induced in a conductor

In many motors and generators, the coils move with respect to a flux that is fixed in space. The relative motion produces a change in the flux linking the coils and, consequently, a voltage is induced according to Faraday's law. However, in this special (although common) case, it is easier to calculate the induced voltage with reference to the *conductors*, rather than with reference to the coil itself. In effect, whenever a conductor cuts a magnetic field, a voltage is induced across its terminals. The value of the induced voltage is given by

$$E = Blv \qquad (2.25)$$

where

E = induced voltage [V]
B = flux density [T]
l = active length of the conductor in the magnetic field [m]
v = relative speed of the conductor [m/s]

Example 2-9

The stationary conductors of a large generator have an active length of 2 m and are cut by a field of 0.6 teslas, moving at a speed of 100 m/s (Fig. 2.29). Calculate the voltage induced in each conductor.

Solution

According to Eq. 2.25, we find

$$E = Blv$$
$$= 0.6 \times 2 \times 100 = 120 \text{ V}$$

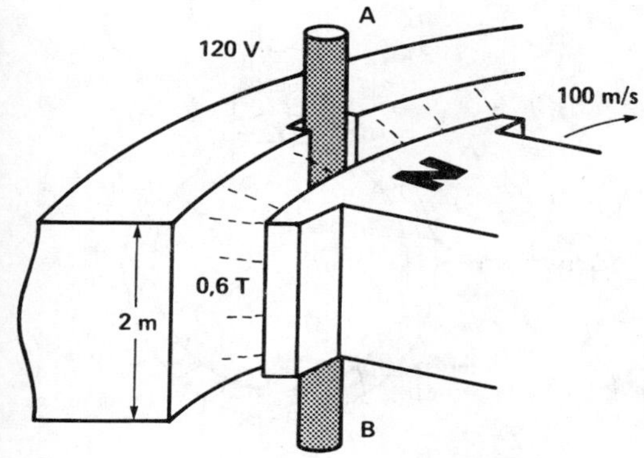

Figure 2.29
Voltage induced in a stationary conductor. See Example 2-9.

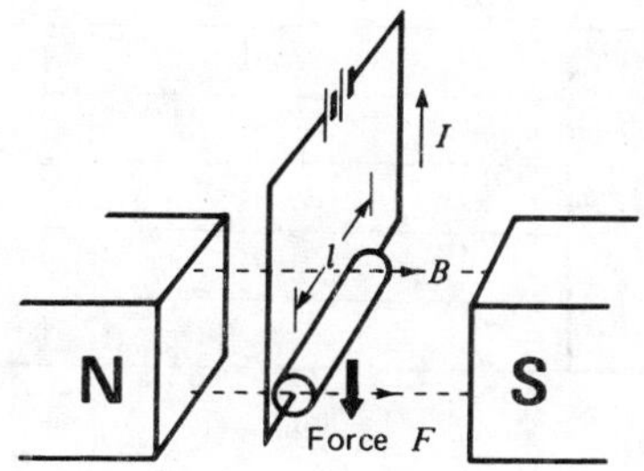

Figure 2.30
Force on a conductor.

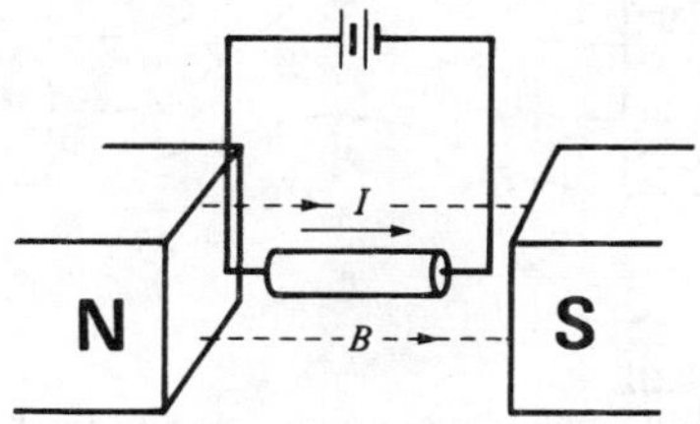

Figure 2.31
Force = 0.

2.22 Lorentz force on a conductor

When a current-carrying conductor is placed in a magnetic field, it is subjected to a force which we call *electromagnetic force,* or Lorentz force. This force is of fundamental importance because it constitutes the basis of operation of motors, of generators, and of many electrical instruments. The magnitude of the force depends upon the orientation of the conductor with respect to the direction of the field. The force is greatest when the conductor is perpendicular to the field (Fig. 2.30) and zero when it is parallel to it (Fig. 2.31). Between these two extremes, the force has intermediate values.

The maximum force acting on a straight conductor is given by

$$F = BlI \tag{2.26}$$

where

F = force acting on the conductor [N]

B = flux density of the field [T]

l = active length of the conductor [m]

I = current in the conductor [A]

Example 2-10

A conductor 3 m long carrying a current of 200 A is placed in a magnetic field whose density is 0.5 T. Calculate the force on the conductor if it is perpendicular to the lines of force (Fig. 2.30).

Solution

$$F = BlI$$
$$= 0.5 \times 3 \times 200 = 300 \text{ N}$$

2.23 Direction of the force acting on a straight conductor

Whenever a conductor carries a current, it is surrounded by a magnetic field. For a current flowing into the page of this book, the circular lines of force have the direction shown in Fig. 2.32a. The same figure shows the magnetic field created between the N, S poles of a powerful permanent magnet.

The magnetic field does not, of course, have the shape shown in the figure because lines of force never cross each other. What, then, is the shape of the resulting field?

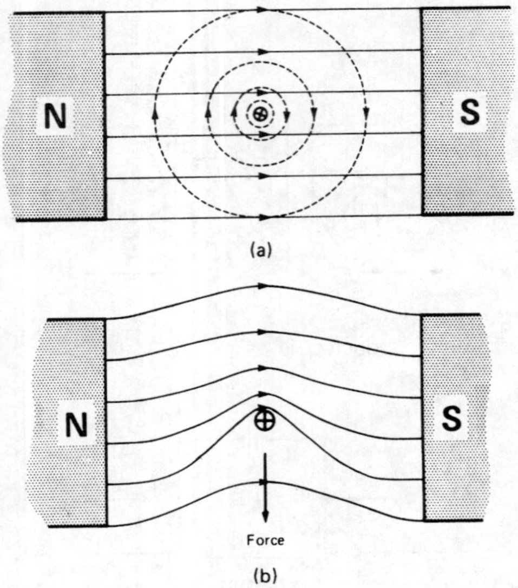

Figure 2.32
a. Magnetic field due to magnet and conductor.
b. Resulting magnetic field pushes the conductor downward.

To answer the question, we observe that the lines of force created respectively by the conductor and the permanent magnet act in the same direction above the conductor and in opposite directions below it. Consequently, the number of lines above the conductor must be greater than the number below. The resulting magnetic field therefore has the shape given in Fig. 2.32b.

Recalling that lines of flux act like stretched elastic bands, it is easy to visualize that a force acts upon the conductor, tending to push it downward.

2.24 Residual flux density and coercive force

Consider the coil of Fig. 2.33a, which surrounds a magnetic material formed in the shape of a ring. A current source, connected to the coil, produces a current whose value and direction can be changed at will. Starting from zero, we gradually increase I, so that H and B increase. This increase traces out

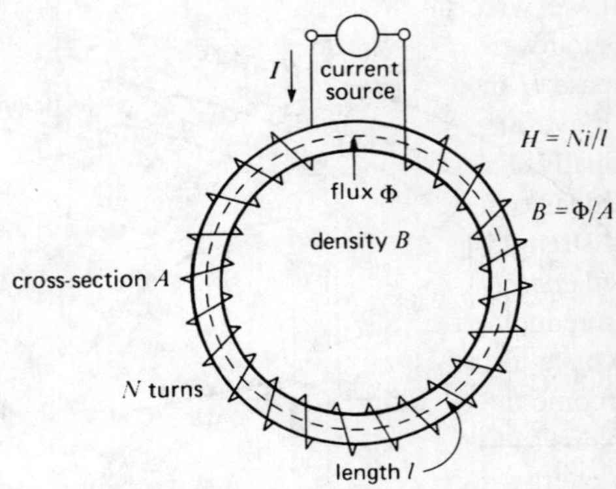

Figure 2.33a
Method of determining the *B-H* properties of a magnetic material.

curve **oa** in Fig. 2.33b. The flux density reaches a value B_m for a magnetic field strength H_m.

If the current is now gradually reduced to zero, the flux density B does not follow the original curve, but moves along a curve **ab** situated above **oa.** In effect, as we reduce the magnetic field strength, the magnetic domains that were lined up under the influence of field H_m tend to retain their origi-nal orientation. This phenomenon is called hysteresis. Consequently, when H is reduced to zero, a substantial flux density remains. It is called residual flux density or *residual induction* (B_r).

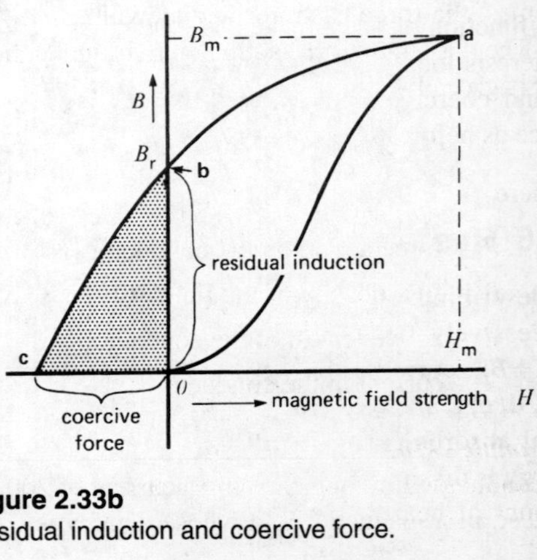

Figure 2.33b
Residual induction and coercive force.

If we wish to eliminate this residual flux, we have to reverse the current in the coil and gradually increase H in the opposite direction. As we do so, we move along curve **bc.** The magnetic domains gradually change their previous orientation until the flux density becomes zero at point **c.** The magnetic field strength required to reduce the flux to zero is called *coercive force* (H_c).

In reducing the flux density from B_r to zero, we also have to furnish energy. This energy is used to overcome the frictional resistance of the magnetic domains as they oppose the change in orientation. The energy supplied is dissipated as heat in the material. A very sensitive thermometer would indicate a slight temperature rise as the ring is being demagnetized.

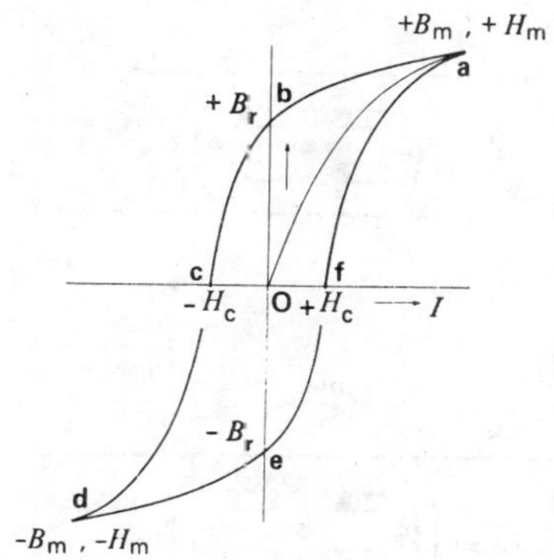

Figure 2.34
Hysteresis loop. If B is expressed in teslas and H in amperes per meter, the area of the loop is the energy dissipated per cycle, in joules per cubic meter.

2.25 Hysteresis loop

Transformers and most electric motors operate on alternating current. In such devices the flux in the iron changes continuously both in value and direction. The magnetic domains are therefore oriented first in one direction, then the other, at a rate that depends upon the frequency. Thus, if the flux has a frequency of 60 Hz, the domains describe a complete cycle every 1/60 of a second, passing successively through peak flux densities $+B_m$ and $-B_m$ as the peak magnetic field strength alternates between $+H_m$ and $-H_m$. If we plot the flux density B as a function of H, we obtain a closed curve called hysteresis loop (Fig. 2.34). The residual induction B_r and coercive force H_c have the same significance as before.

2.26 Hysteresis loss

In describing a hysteresis loop, the flux moves successively from $+B_m$, $+B_r$, 0, $-B_m$, $-B_r$, 0, and $+B_m$, corresponding respectively to points **a, b, c, d, e, f,** and **a,** of Fig. 2.34. The magnetic material absorbs energy during each cycle and this energy is dissipated as heat. We can prove that the amount of heat released per cycle (expressed in J/m^3) is equal to the area (in T·A/m) of the hysteresis loop.

To reduce hysteresis losses, we select magnetic materials that have a narrow hysteresis loop, such as the grain-oriented silicon steel used in the cores of alternating-current transformers.

2.27 Hysteresis losses caused by rotation

Hysteresis losses are also produced when a piece of iron rotates in a constant magnetic field. Consider, for example, an armature AB, made of iron, that revolves in a field produced by permanent magnets N, S (Fig. 2.35). The magnetic domains in the armature tend to line up with the magnetic field, irrespective of the position of the armature. Consequently, as the armature rotates, the N poles of the domains point first toward A and then toward B. A complete reversal occurs therefore every half-revolution, as can be seen in Figs. 2.35a and 2.35b. Consequently, the magnetic domains in the armature reverse periodically, even though the magnetic field is constant. Hysteresis losses are produced just as they are in an ac magnetic field.

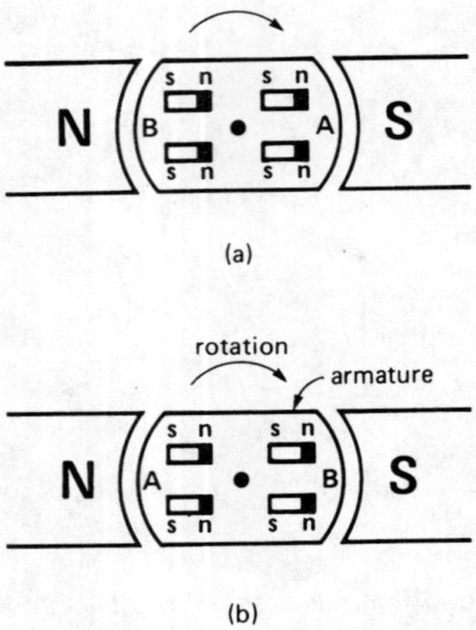

Figure 2.35
Hysteresis losses due to rotation.

2.28 Eddy currents

Consider an ac flux Φ that links a rectangular-shaped conductor (Fig. 2.36). According to Faraday's law, an ac voltage E_1 is induced across its terminals.

If the conductor is short-circuited, a substantial alternating current I_1 will flow, causing the conductor to heat up. If a second conductor is placed inside the first, a smaller voltage is induced because it links a smaller flux. Consequently, the short-circuit current I_2 is less than I_1 and so, too, is the power dissipated in this loop. Fig. 2.37 shows four such concentric loops carrying currents I_1, I_2, I_3, and I_4. The currents are progressively smaller as the area of the loops surrounding the flux decreases.

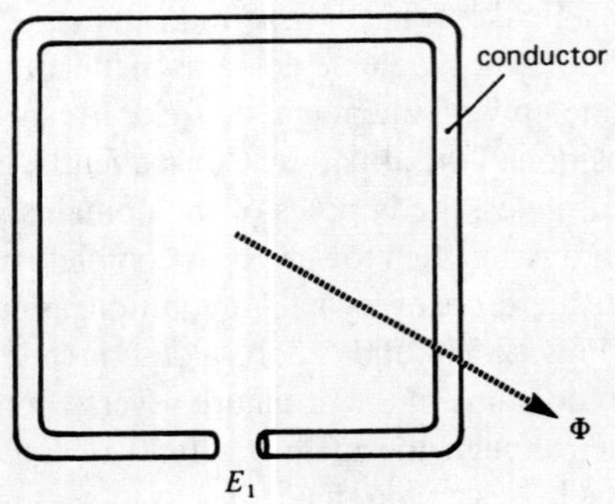

Figure 2.36
An ac flux Φ induces voltage E_1.

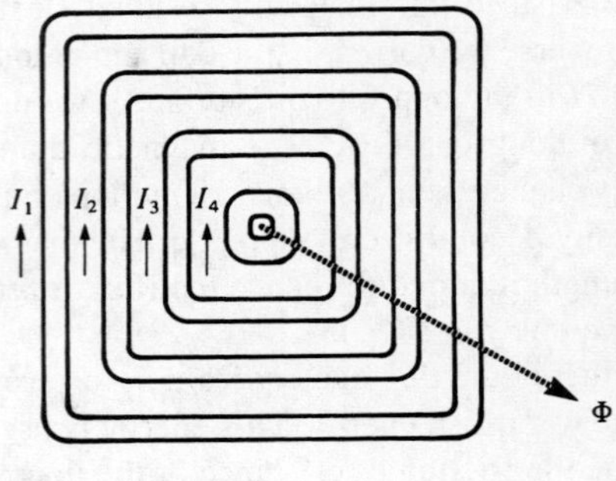

Figure 2.37
Concentric conductors carry ac currents due to ac flux Φ.

In Fig. 2.38 the ac flux passes through a solid metal plate. It is basically equivalent to a densely packed set of rectangular conductors touching each other. Currents swirl back and forth inside the plate, following the paths shown in the figure. These so-called *eddy currents* (or *Foucault currents*) can be very large, due to the low resistance of the plate. Consequently, a metal plate that is penetrated by an ac flux can become very hot. In this regard, special care has to be taken in transformers so that stray leakage fluxes do not cause sections of the enclosing tanks to overheat.

The flux ϕ in Figs. 2.37 and 2.38 is assumed to be increasing. As a result, due to the Lenz's law, the eddy currents flow in such a way as to oppose the increasing flux.

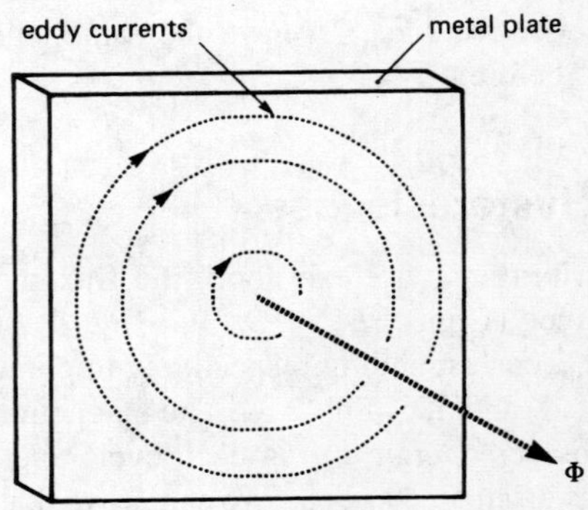

Figure 2.38
Large ac eddy currents are induced in a solid metal plate.

2.29 Eddy currents in a stationary iron core

The eddy-current problem becomes particularly important when iron has to carry an ac flux. This is the case in all ac motors and transformers. Fig. 2.39a shows a coil carrying an ac current that produces an ac flux in a solid iron core. Eddy currents are set up as shown and they flow throughout the entire length of the core. A large core could eventually become red hot (even at a frequency of 60 Hz) due to these eddy-current losses.

We can reduce the losses by splitting the core in two along its length, taking care to insulate the two sections from each other (Fig. 2.39b). The voltage induced in each section is one half of what it was before, with the result that the eddy currents, and the corresponding losses, are considerably reduced.

If we continue to subdivide the core, we find that the losses decrease progressively. In practice, the core is composed of stacked laminations, usually a fraction of a millimeter thick. Furthermore, a small amount of silicon is alloyed with the steel to increase its resistivity, thereby reducing the losses still more (Fig. 2.39c).

The cores of ac motors and generators are therefore always laminated. A thin coating of insulation covers each lamination to prevent electrical contact between them. The stacked laminations are tightly held in place by bolts and appropriate end-pieces. For a given iron core, the eddy-current losses decrease in proportion to the square of the number of laminations.

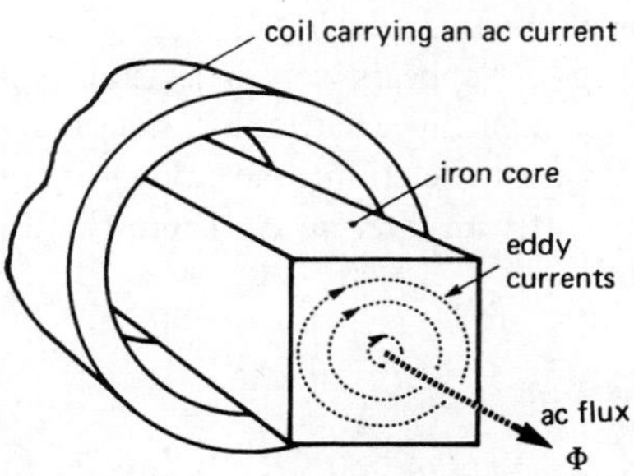

Figure 2.39a
Solid iron core carrying an ac flux.

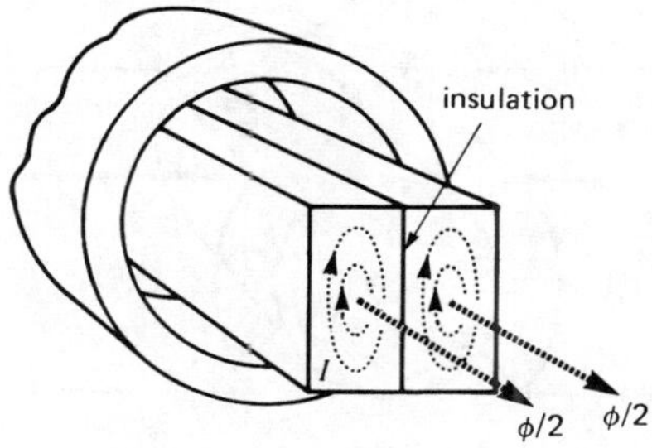

Figure 2.39b
Eddy currents are reduced by splitting the core in half.

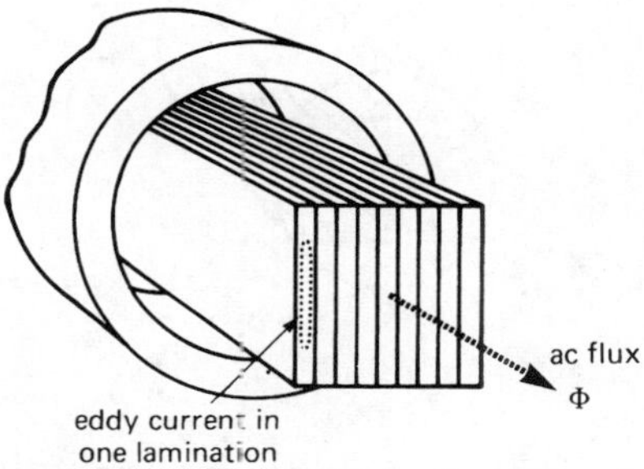

Figure 2.39c
Core built up of thin, insulated laminations.

2.30 Eddy-current losses in a revolving core

The stationary field in direct-current motors and generators produces a constant dc flux. This constant flux induces eddy currents in the revolving armature. To understand how they are induced, consider a solid cylindrical iron core that revolves between the poles of a magnet (Fig. 2.40a). As it turns, the core cuts flux lines and, according to Faraday's law, a voltage is induced along its length having the polarities shown. Owing to this voltage, large eddy currents flow in the core because its resistance is very low (Fig. 2.40b). These eddy currents produce large I^2R losses which are immediately converted into heat. The power loss is proportional to the square of the speed and the square of the flux density.

To reduce the eddy-current losses, we laminate the armature using thin circular laminations that are

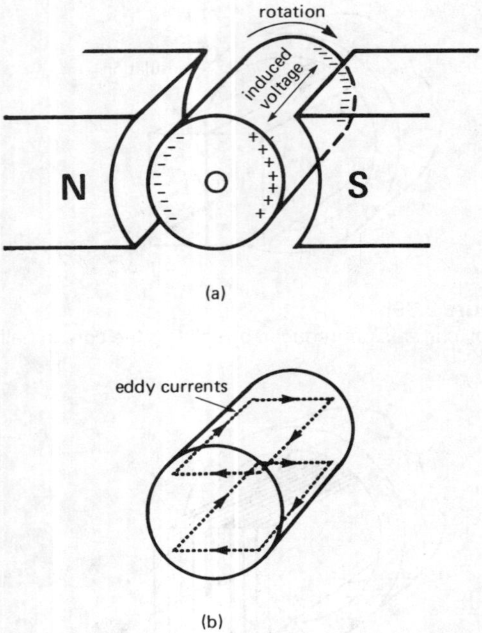

Figure 2.40
a. Voltage induced in a revolving armature.
b. Large eddy currents are induced.

insulated from each other. The laminations are tightly stacked with the flat side running parallel to the flux lines (Fig. 2.41).

2.31 Current in an inductor

It is well known that in an inductive circuit the voltage and current are related by the equation

$$e = L\frac{\Delta i}{\Delta t} \tag{2.27}$$

where

e = instantaneous voltage induced in the circuit [V]

L = inductance of the circuit [H]

$\Delta i/\Delta t$ = rate of change of current [A/s]

This equation enables us to calculate the instantaneous voltage e, when we know the rate of change

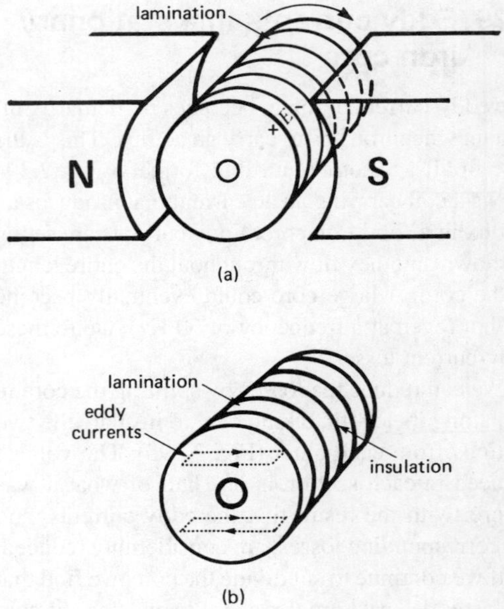

Figure 2.41
a. Armature built up of thin laminations.
b. Much smaller eddy currents are induced.

of current. However, it often happens that e is known and we want to calculate the resulting current I. We can use the same equation, but the solution requires a knowledge of advanced mathematics. To get around this problem, we can use a graphical solution, called the *volt-second method*. It yields the same results and has the advantage of enabling us to visualize how the current in an inductor increases and decreases with time, in response to a known applied voltage.

Consider, for example, Fig. 2.42, in which a variable voltage E appears across an inductance L. Suppose the inductance carries a current I_1 at a time $t = t_1$. We want to determine the current a very short time later, after an interval Δt. From Eq. 2.27 we can write

$$\Delta i = \frac{1}{L}e\Delta t$$

which means that the change in current Δi during a short interval Δt is given by

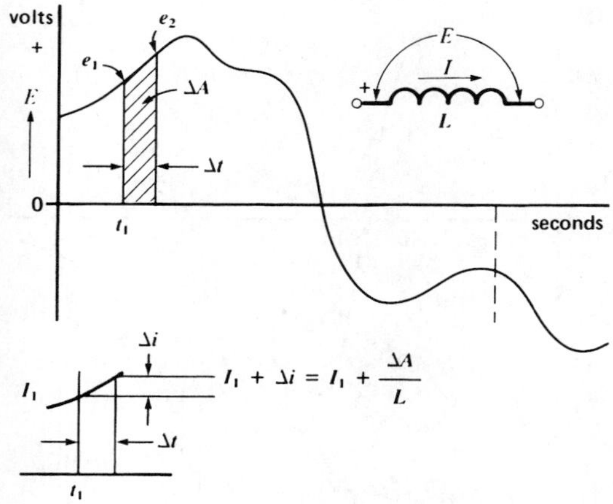

Figure 2.42
Variable voltage applied across an inductor and resulting change in current. Initial current is I_1.

$$\Delta i = \frac{1}{L}\left(\begin{array}{c}\text{average voltage } e \text{ during the interval}\\ \times \text{ duration } \Delta t \text{ of the interval}\end{array}\right)$$

$$\Delta i = \frac{1}{L}\frac{(e_1 + e_2)}{2} \times \Delta t$$

$$\Delta i = \frac{1}{L}\left(\begin{array}{c}\text{area } \Delta A \text{ under the voltage}\\ \text{curve during the interval } \Delta t\end{array}\right)$$

$$\Delta i = \frac{1}{L}\left(\begin{array}{c}\text{volt-seconds across the induc-}\\ \text{tance during the interval } \Delta t\end{array}\right)$$

Therefore, the current in the inductance after the interval Δt is

$$I \text{ at time } (t_1 + \Delta t) = \text{initial current} + \Delta i$$
$$= I_1 + \frac{\Delta A}{L}$$

We are usually more interested in calculating the current at a time t_2, when t_2 is many Δt intervals after t_1 (Fig. 2.43). We then have to add the incre-

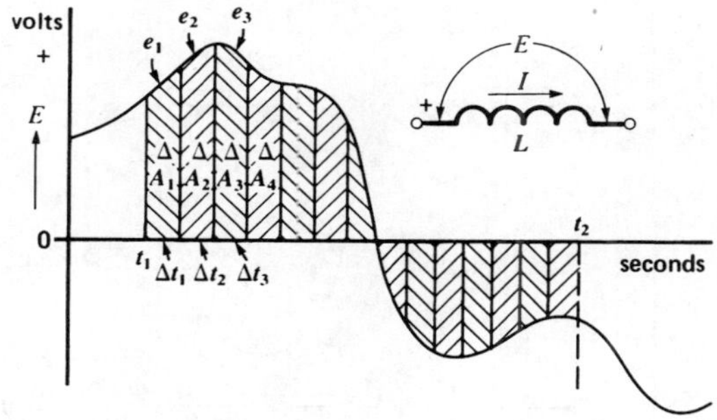

Figure 2.43
Volt-seconds are gained (and lost) when a variable voltage is applied acrcss an inductor.

mental changes in current Δi during the long period $(t_2 - t_1)$. As a result we find current I_2 at time t_2

$$I_2 = \text{initial current } I_1 + (\Delta i_1 + \Delta i_2 + \Delta i_3 + \ldots)$$

$$I_2 = I_1 + \frac{1}{L}(e_1\Delta t_1 + e_2\Delta t_2 + e_3\Delta t_3 + \cdots)$$

$$I_2 = I_1 + \frac{1}{L}(\Delta A_1 - \Delta A_2 + \Delta A_3 + \cdots)$$

$$I_2 = I_1 + \frac{1}{L}\left(\begin{array}{c}\text{algebraic sum of all the little}\\ \text{areas under the voltage curve}\\ \text{between } t_1 \text{ and } t_2\end{array}\right)$$

$$I_2 = I_1 + \frac{1}{L}\left(\begin{array}{c}\text{net area } A \text{ under the voltage}\\ \text{curve between } t_1 \text{ and } t_2\end{array}\right)$$

The values of e_1, e_2, e_3, and so on may be positive (+) or negative (−) and, therefore, the little areas ΔA_1, ΔA_2, ΔA_3, and so on may be (+) or (−). The sum of these (+) and (−) values of the ΔAs gives the net area under the voltage curve between t_1 and t_2.

Thus, in Fig. 2.44 the net area A after time interval T is equal to $(A_1 - A_2)$ volt-seconds. To generalize, the current after an interval T is always given by

$$I = I_1 + A/L \tag{2.28}$$

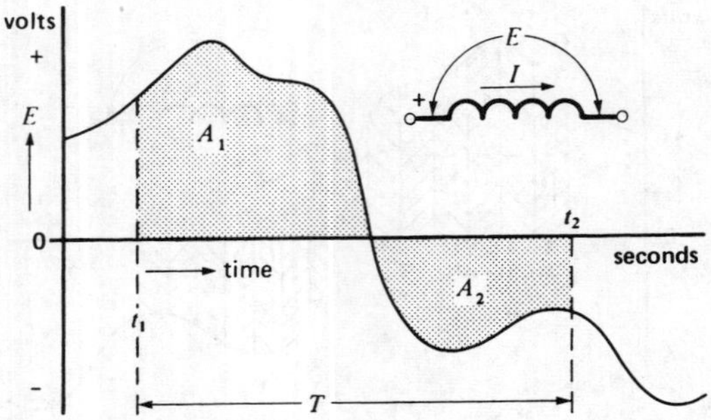

Figure 2.44
The net volt-seconds during interval T is equal to the algebraic sum of the areas A_1 and A_2.

where

I_1 = current at start of interval T
I = current after time interval T [A]
A = net area under the volt-time curve during time T [V·s]
L = inductance [H]

Consider, for example an inductor L, having negligible resistance, connected to a source whose voltage varies according to the curve of Fig. 2.45a. If the initial current is zero, the value at *instant* t_1 is

$$I = A_1/L$$

As time goes by, the area under the curve increases progressively and so does the current. However, the current reaches its maximum value at time t_2 because at this moment the area under the voltage curve ceases to increase any more. Beyond t_2 the voltage becomes negative and, consequently, the net area begins to diminish. At instant t_3, for example, the net area is equal to $(A_1 + A_2 - A_3)$ and the corresponding current is

$$I = (A_1 + A_2 - A_3)/L$$

At instant t_4, the negative area $(A_3 + A_4)$ is exactly equal to the positive area $(A_1 + A_2)$. The net area is zero and so the current is also zero. After instant t_4, the current becomes negative; in other words, it changes direction.

Another way of looking at the situation (Fig. 2.45), is to consider that the inductor accumulates volt-

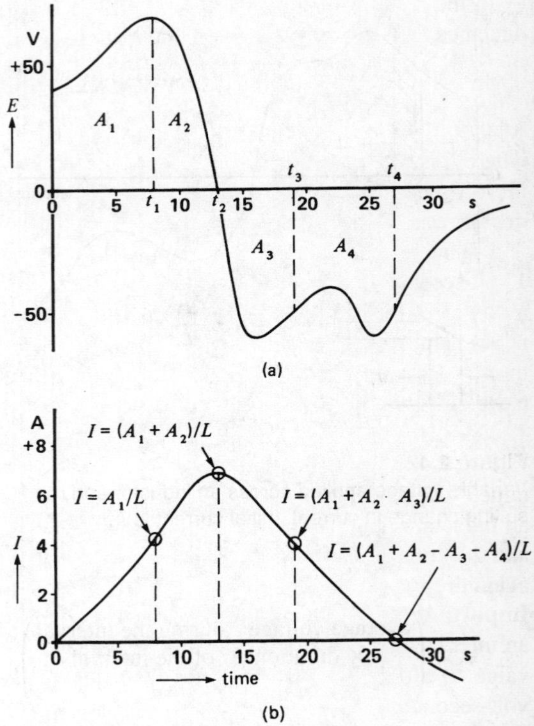

Figure 2.45
a. An inductor stores volt-seconds.
b. Current in the inductor.

seconds during the interval from 0 to t_2. As it becomes *charged up* with volt-seconds, the current increases in direct proportion to the volt-seconds received. Then during the *discharge* period from t_2 to t_4 the inductor loses volt-seconds and the current decreases accordingly. An inductor, therefore, behaves very much like a capacitor. However, instead of storing ampere-seconds (coulombs), an inductor stores volt-seconds. For example, in a capacitor having a capacitance C, it is well known that the voltage E across its terminals is given by

$$E = \frac{Q_c}{C} + E_1$$

where E_1 is the initial voltage and Q_c is the charge in coulombs (ampere seconds, positive or negative) the capacitor received during a given interval.

In the same way, for an inductor having an inductance L, the current I it carries is given by

$$I = \frac{Q_L}{L} + I_1$$

where I_1 is the initial current and Q_L is the "charge" in volt-seconds (positive or negative) that the inductor received during a given interval.

It is interesting to note that 1 weber-turn is equal to 1 volt-second. Thus a coil of 600 turns that surrounds a flux of 20 milliwebers has stored in it a total magnetic charge of 600 turns × 20 mWb = 12 000 mWb turns = 12 volt-seconds. If the inductor has an inductance of 3 henries, it is carrying a current of Q_L/L = 12 V·s/3 H = 4 A.

Fig. 2.45b shows the instantaneous current obtained when the voltage of Fig. 2.45a is applied to an inductance of 100 H. The initial current is zero, and the current rises to a maximum of 6.9 A before again dropping to zero after a time interval of 27 s.

Important Note: If the current at the beginning of an interval T is not zero, we simply add the initial value to all the ampere values calculated by the volt-second method.

Example 2-11

The voltage across the terminals of an inductor of 2 H varies according to the curve given in Fig. 2.46.

a. Calculate the instantaneous current I in the circuit, knowing that the initial current is zero.
b. Repeat the calculations for an initial current of 7 A.

Solution

a. **Interval from zero to 3 s:** During this interval the area in volt-seconds increases uniformly and progressively. Thus, after one second, the area A is 4 V·s; after two seconds it is 8 V·s; and so forth. Using the expression $I = A/L$, the current builds up to the following respective values: 2 A, 4 A, and so on, attaining a final value of 6 A after three seconds.

Interval from 3 s to 5 s: The area continues to increase but at a slower rate, because voltage E is smaller than before. When t = 5 s, the total surface starting from the beginning is 16 V·s; therefore the current is 16 V·s/2 H = 8 A.

Interval from 5 s to 7 s: The surface increases by 4 squares, which is equivalent to 8 V·s.

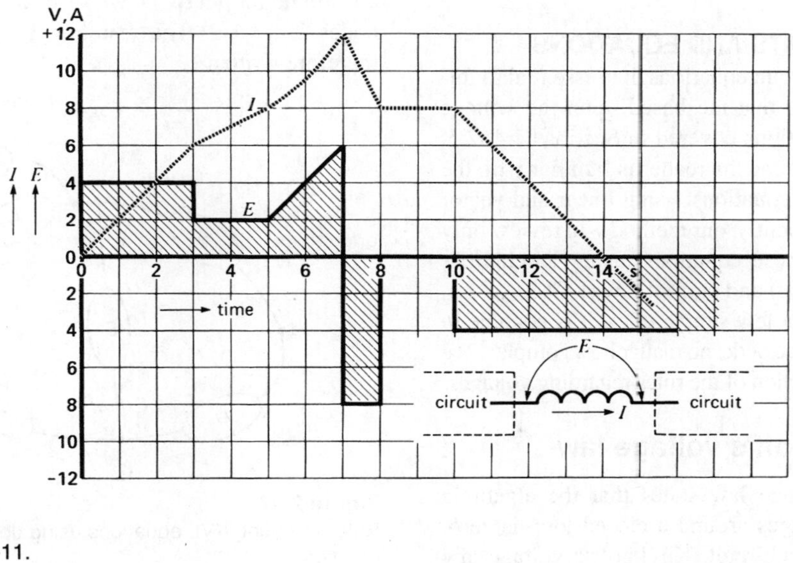

Figure 2.46
See Example 2-11.

Consequently, the current increases by 4 A, thus reaching 12 A. Note that the current no longer follows a straight line because the voltage is not constant during this interval.

Interval from 7 s to 8 s: The voltage suddenly changes polarity with the result that the 8 V·s during this interval subtract from the volt-seconds that were accumulated previously. The net area from the beginning is therefore 24 V·s − 8 V·s = 16 V·s. Consequently, the current at the end of this interval is $I = 16$ V·s/2 $H = 8$ A.

Interval from 8 s to 10 s: Because the terminal voltage is zero during this interval, the net volt-second area does not change and neither does the current (remember that we assumed zero coil resistance).

Interval from 10 s to 14 s: The negative volt-seconds continue to accumulate and at $t = 14$ s, the negative area is equal to the positive area, and so the net current is zero. Beyond this point the current changes direction.

b. With an initial current of +7 A, we have to add 7 A to each of the currents calculated previously. The new current wave is simply 7 A above the curve shown in Fig. 2.46. Thus, the current at $t = 11$ s is 6 + 7 = 13 A.

CIRCUITS AND EQUATIONS

When writing circuit equations, it is essential to follow certain rules that are based upon the voltage and current notations covered in Sections 2.4, 2.5, and 2.7. We presume the reader is familiar with the solution of such equations, using linear and vector algebra. Consequently, our method will review only the writing of these equations, using Kirchhoff's voltage law (KVL) and current law (KCL).

By following a few simple rules, it is possible to solve any circuit, ac or dc, no matter how complex. We begin our explanation of the rules regarding voltages.

2.32 Kirchhoff's voltage law

Kirchhoff's voltage law states that the algebraic sum of the voltages around a closed loop is zero. Thus, in a closed circuit, Kirchhoff's voltage law means that the sum of the voltage rises is equal to the sum of the voltage drops. In our methodology it is not necessary to specify whether there is a "voltage rise" or a "voltage drop."

We have seen that voltages can be expressed in either double-subscript or sign notation. The choice of one or the other is a matter of individual preference. We will begin with the double-subscript notation, followed later by the sign notation.

2.33 Kirchhoff's voltage law and double-subscript notation

Consider Fig. 2.47 in which six circuit elements **A, B, C, D, E,** and **F** are connected together. The elements may be sources or loads, and the connections (nodes) are labeled 1 to 4. In going around a circuit loop, such as the loop involving elements **A, E,** and **D,** we can start with any node and move in either a cw or ccw direction until we come back to the starting point. In so doing, we encounter the labeled nodes one after the other. This ordered set of labels is used to establish the voltage subscripts. We write the voltage subscripts in sequential fashion, following the same order as the nodes we meet.

For example, starting with node 2 and moving cw around loop **ABCD,** we successively encounter nodes 2-4-3-1-2. The resulting KVL equation is therefore written

$$E_{24} + E_{43} + E_{31} + E_{12} = 0$$

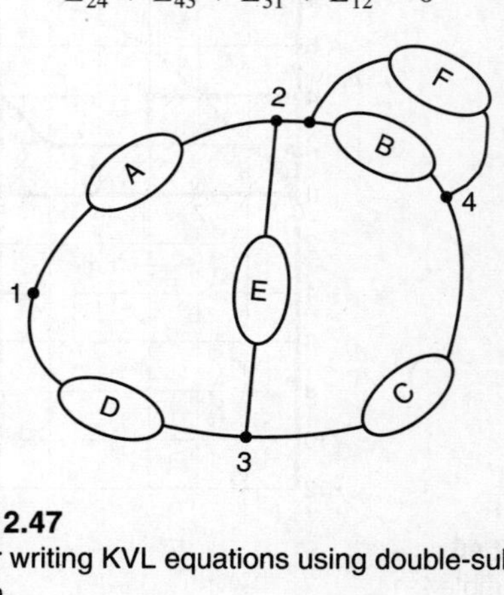

Figure 2.47
Rule for writing KVL equations using double-subscript notation.

If we select loop **CEF** and start with node 4 and move ccw, we successively encounter nodes 4-2-3-4. The resulting KVL equation is

$$E_{42} + E_{23} + E_{34} = 0$$

The set of voltages designated by the KVL equations may be ac or dc. If they are ac, the voltages will usually be expressed as phasors, having certain magnitudes and phase angles. In some cases the set of voltages can even represent instantaneous values. In order to prevent errors, it is essential to equate all KVL equations to zero as we have done so far and will continue to do. We do not recommend attempts to equate voltage rises to voltage drops.

In finding the solution to such double-subscript equations, it is useful to remember that a voltage expressed as E_{XY} can always be expressed as $-E_{YX}$, and vice versa.

Example 2-12

Fig. 2.48 shows two sources connected in series, having terminals (nodes) 1, 2, and 3. The magnitude and polarity of E_{12} and E_{32} are specified as $E_{12} = +40$ V and $E_{32} = +30$ V. We wish to determine the magnitude and polarity of the voltage between the open terminals 1 and 3.

Solution

In writing the loop equation, let us start at terminal 1 and move ccw till we again come back to terminal 1. The resulting KVL equation is

$$E_{12} + E_{23} + E_{31} = 0$$

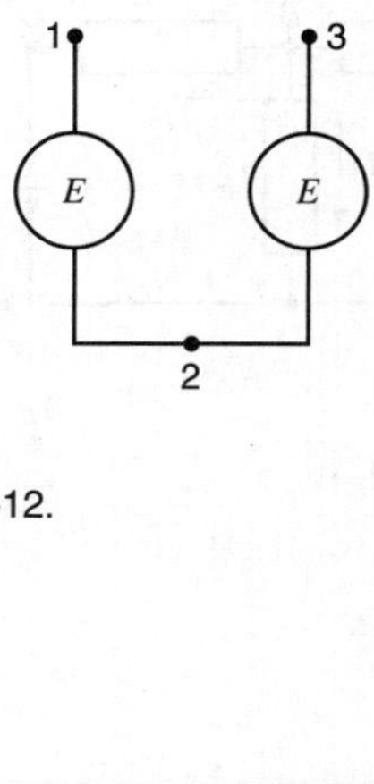

Figure 2.48
See Example 2-12.

Transposing terms,

$$\begin{aligned} E_{31} &= -E_{12} - E_{23} \\ &= -E_{12} + E_{32} \\ &= -40 + 30 \\ &= -10 \text{ V} \end{aligned}$$

and so

$$E_{13} = +10 \text{ V}$$

indicating that terminal 1 is positive with respect to terminal 3 and that the voltage between the two is 10 V.

2.34 Kirchhoff's current law

Kirchhoff's current law states that the algebraic sum of the currents that arrive at a point is equal to zero. This means that the sum of the currents that flow into a terminal is equal to the sum of the currents that leave it.

Fig. 2.49 shows five currents arriving at a common terminal (or node). The sum of the currents flowing into the node is $(I_1 + I_3)$, while the sum that leaves it is $(I_2 + I_4 + I_5)$. Applying KCL, we can write

$$I_1 + I_3 = I_2 + I_4 + I_5$$

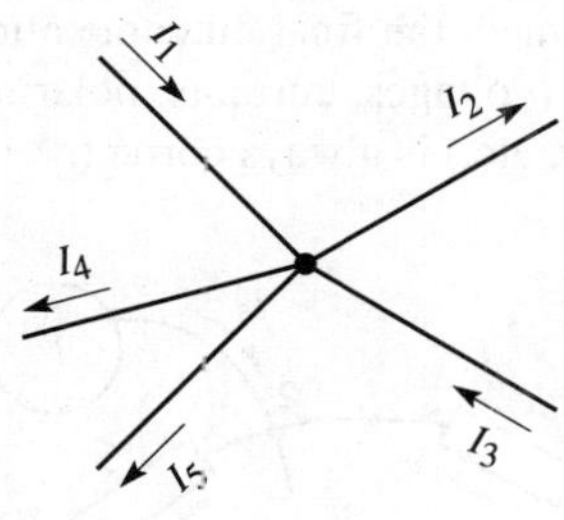

Figure 2.49
Rule for writing KCL equations.

2.35 Currents, impedances, and associated voltages

Consider an impedance Z, carrying a current I, connected between two terminals marked 1 and 2 (Fig. 2.50). A voltage E_{12}, having a magnitude IZ, will appear across the impedance. The question of

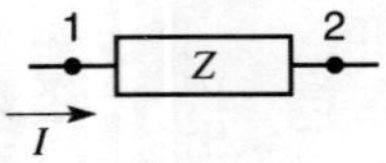

Figure 2.50
$E_{12} = +IZ$.

polarity now arises: Is E_{12} equal to $+IZ$ or $-IZ$? The question is resolved by the following rule:

When moving across an impedance Z in the same direction as the current flow I, the associated voltage IZ is preceded by a positive sign. Thus, in Fig. 2.50, we write $E_{12} = +IZ$. Conversely, when moving across an impedance *against* the direction of current flow, the voltage IZ is preceded by a negative sign. Thus, $E_{21} = -IZ$. The current can be ac or dc, and the impedance can be resistive (R), inductive (jX_L), or capacitive ($-jX_C$).

In most circuits it is impossible to predict the actual direction of current flow in the various circuit elements. Consider for example the circuit of Fig. 2.51 in which two known voltage sources E_{13} and E_{24} are connected to four known impedances Z_1, Z_2, Z_3, and Z_4. Because the actual directions of current flows are presently unknown, we simply assume *arbitrary* directions as shown in the figure. It is a remarkable fact that no matter what directions are assumed, the final outcome after solving the equations (voltages, currents, polarities, phase angles, power, etc.) is always correct.

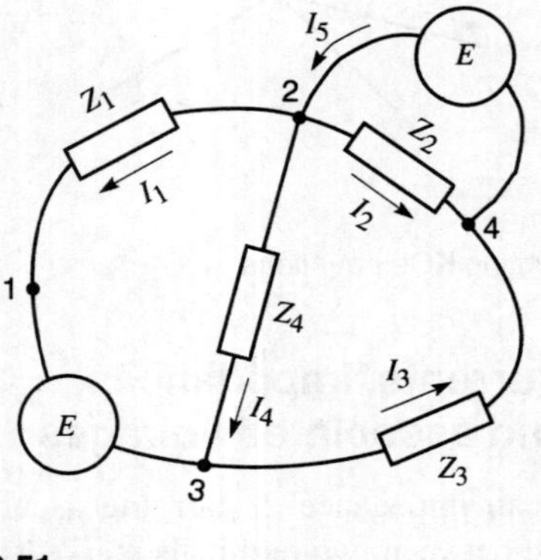

Figure 2.51
Writing KVL and KCL equations.

Let us write the circuit equations for Fig. 2.51.

Loop **2312,** starting with node **2** and moving cw:

$$+I_4Z_4 + E_{31} - I_1Z_1 = 0$$

Voltage I_4Z_4 is preceded by a (+) sign, because in going around the loop we are moving in the direction of I_4. On the other hand, voltage I_1Z_1 is preceded by a negative sign because we are moving against the direction of I_1.

Loop **3423,** starting with node **3** and moving ccw:

$$+I_3Z_3 - I_2Z_2 + I_4Z_4 = 0$$

Voltages I_3Z_3 and I_4Z_4 are preceded by a (+) sign, because in going around the loop we are moving in the direction of the respective currents. Voltage I_2Z_2 is preceded by a negative sign because we are moving against current I_2.

Loop **242,** starting with node **2** and moving cw:

$$E_{24} - I_2Z_2 = 0$$

KCL at node 2:

$$I_5 = I_1 + I_2 + I_4$$

KCL at node 3:

$$I_4 + I_1 = I_3$$

Example 2-13

Write the circuit equations and calculate the currents flowing in the circuit of Fig. 2.52, knowing that $E_{AD} = +108$ V and $E_{CD} = +48$ V.

Solution

We first select arbitrary directions for currents I_1, I_2, and I_3 and write the circuit equations as follows:

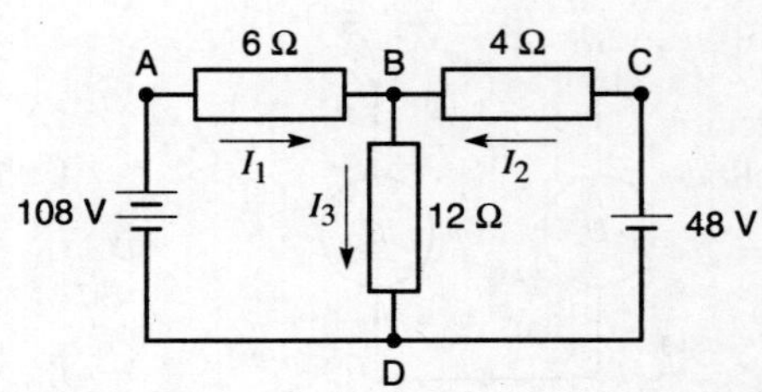

Figure 2.52
See Example 2-13.

For the loop **DABCD** composed of the two sources and the 6 Ω and 4 Ω resistors, we obtain

$$E_{DA} + 6I_1 - 4I_2 + E_{CD} = 0 \qquad \text{(cw)}$$
$$-108 + 6I_1 - 4I_2 + 48 = 0$$

For the loop **DCBD** composed of the 48 V source and the 4 Ω and 12 Ω resistors

$$E_{DC} + 4I_2 + 12I_3 = 0 \qquad \text{(ccw)}$$
$$-48 + 4I_2 + 12I_3 = 0$$

Applying KCL at node B, we get

$$I_1 + I_2 = I_3$$

Solving these simultaneous equations, we find

$$I_1 = +8\ \text{A} I_2 = -3\ \text{A} I_3 = +5\ \text{A}$$

We conclude that the directions we assumed for I_1 and I_3 were correct because both currents carry a positive sign. However, the actual direction of I_2 is opposite to that assumed because I_2 bears a negative sign.

2.36 Kirchhoff's laws and ac circuits

The same basic rules of writing double-subscript equations can be applied to ac circuits, including 3-phase circuits. The only difference is that the resistive elements in dc circuits are replaced by resistive, inductive, or capacitive elements, or a combination of all three. Furthermore, the voltages and currents are expressed as phasors, having magnitudes and phase angles. The solution of phasor equations is more time-consuming, but the equations themselves can be written down almost by inspection. Let us consider two examples.

Example 2-14

In the circuit of Fig. 2.53, two sources A, B generate the following voltages:

$$E_{ac} = 200 \angle 120° \qquad E_{bc} = 100 \angle 150°$$

Calculate

a. The value of the current I in the circuit
b. The value of E_{ab} and its phase angle

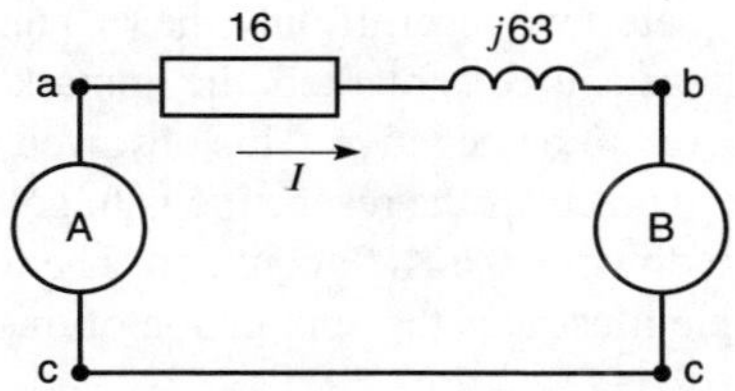

Figure 2.53
See Example 2-14.

Solution

a. To solve the circuit, we first establish an arbitrary direction of current flow. Thus, suppose I flows from left to right between points **a** and **b.** To write the circuit equation, let us move cw around the loop, starting from terminal c. This yields

$$E_{ca} + I\,(16 + j\,63) + E_{bc} = 0$$

Substituting the values of E_{ac} and E_{bc} in this equation and combining the terms in I, we get

$$-200 \angle 120° + I65 \angle 75.8° + 100 \angle 150° = 0$$

Solving this equation, we find that $I = 1.9 \angle 20.5°$.

b. To determine E_{ab}, we write the following equation, moving cw around the loop:

$$E_{ca} + E_{ab} + E_{bc} = 0$$

Transposing terms,

$$E_{ab} = -E_{ca} - E_{bc}$$
$$= E_{ac} - E_{bc}$$
$$= 200 \angle 120° - 100 \angle 150°$$

Using vector algebra, we find

$$E_{ab} = 123.9 \angle 96.2°$$

2.37 KVL and sign notation

Voltages in ac and dc circuits are frequently indicated with sign notation and designated by symbols such as E_1, E_a, e_m, and so on. To write the equations for such circuits, we employ the following rule:

As we cruise around a loop, we observe the polarity (+ or −) of the first terminal of every voltage

(E_1, E_a, e_m, etc.) we meet. If only the (+) terminal of the voltage source is marked, the unmarked terminal is taken to be negative. This observed polarity (+ or −) precedes the respective voltages as we write them down in the KVL equation. The following example illustrates the application of this rule.

Example 2-15

In Fig. 2.54, given the polarity marks of E_A and E_B, it is known that $E_A = +37$ V and $E_B = -15$ V. We wish to determine the value and polarity of the voltage E_C across the open terminals.

Solution

First, we assign an arbitrary polarity (+) to the terminal voltage E_C. We then proceed cw around the loop in Fig. 2.54, starting with voltage E_A. This yields the following equation:

$$-E_A + E_C - E_B = 0 \qquad \text{(cw)}$$

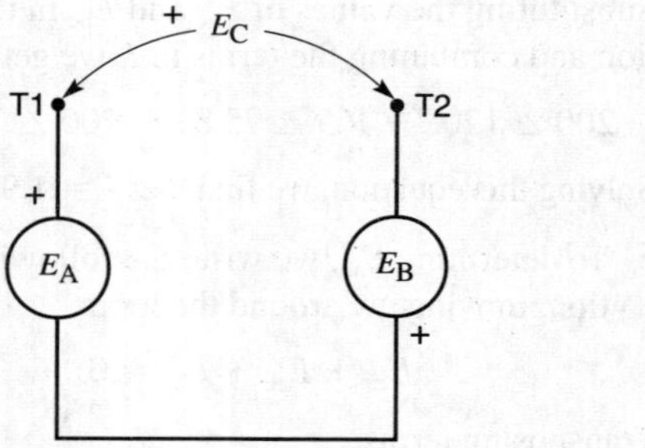

Figure 2.54
Rule for writing KVL equations using sign notations.

Note that the sign preceding each voltage corresponds to the polarity of the terminal that was first encountered in going cw around the loop.

Transposing terms,

$$\begin{aligned} E_C &= E_A + E_B \\ &= +37 - 15 \\ &= +22 \text{ V} \end{aligned}$$

Thus, the magnitude of E_C is 22 V, and the polarity of terminal T1 is indeed positive with respect to terminal T2. The polarity we assumed at the outset happens to have been the correct one.

2.38 Solving ac and dc circuits with sign notation

In circuits using sign notation, we treat the *IZ* voltages in the same way as in circuits using double-subscript notation. In other words, the *IZ* voltage across an impedance *Z* is preceded by a positive sign whenever we move across the impedance in the direction of current flow. Conversely, the *IZ* voltage is preceded by a negative sign whenever we move against the direction of current flow.

The following example illustrates the procedure to be followed.

Example 2-16

The circuit of Fig. 2.55 is powered by an ac source $E = 1600 \angle 60°$. The values of the respective impedances are indicated in the figure.

Calculate

a. The current flowing in each element
b. The voltage E_X across the 72 ohm capacitive reactance.

Solution

a. To solve this problem, the currents are assumed to flow in the arbitrary directions shown. We then write the following equations.

Moving cw around the loop **BDAB,** we obtain

$$-E - I_1(j\,40) - I_1(30) + I_2\,(-j\,37) = 0 \text{ (cw)}$$

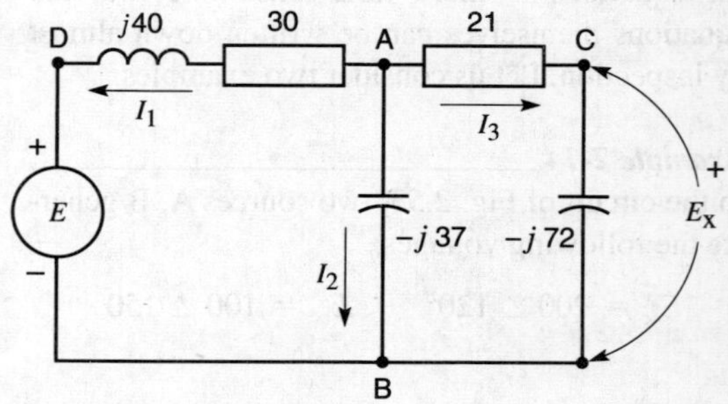

Figure 2.55
See Example 2-15.

Then, moving ccw around the second loop **ABCA,** we obtain

$$I_2(-j\,37) - I_3\,(-\,j\,72) - 21\,I_3 = 0 \quad \text{(ccw)}$$

Finally, applying KCL at node A, we have

$$I_1 + I_2 + I_3 = 0$$

Upon solving these equations, we obtain the following results:

$$I_1 = 44.9 \angle 215° \qquad I_2 = 30.3 \angle 40°$$

$$I_3 = 14.9 \angle 24°$$

b. We can think of E_X as being a voltmeter connected across the capacitor. As a result, the "voltmeter" and capacitor together form a closed loop for which we can write a circuit equation, as for any other loop. Thus, in traveling cw around the loop we write

$$-I_3(-\,j\,72) + E_X = 0$$

Thus

$$E_X = I_3(-j\,72)$$

$$= 14.9 \angle 24°(-j\,72)$$

and so

$$E_X = 1073 \angle -66°$$

2.39 Circuits and hybrid notation

In some circuits it is useful to employ both sign notation and double-subscript notation as shown in the following example.

Example 2-17

Fig. 2.56 shows a 3-phase system in which $E_a = 26 \angle 0°$, $E_b = 26 \angle 120°$, and $E_c = 26 \angle 240°$ (sign notation). We wish to determine the values of E_{12}, E_{23}, and E_{31} (double-subscript notation).

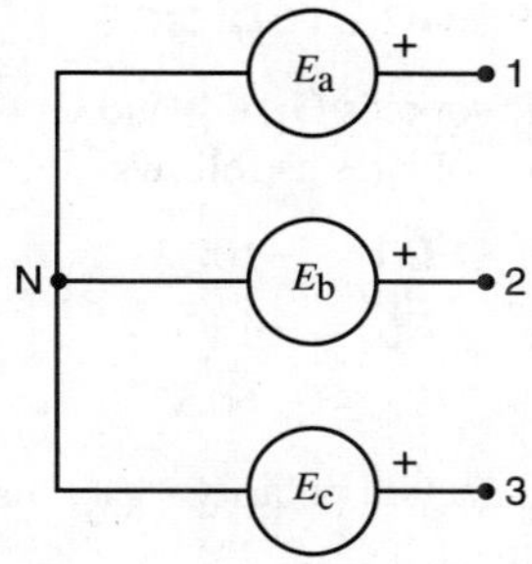

Figure 2.56
See Example 2-16.

Solution

To meet this requirement, we write the following KVL equations, which the reader should verify:

$$E_{12} + E_b - E_a = 0$$

$$E_{23} + E_c - E_b = 0$$

$$E_{31} + E_a - E_c = 0$$

Transposing terms, we obtain

$$E_{12} = E_a - E_b = 26 \angle 0° - 26 \angle 120° = 45 \angle -30°$$

$$E_{23} = E_b - E_c = 26 \angle 120° - 26 \angle 240° = 45 \angle 90°$$

$$E_{31} = E_c - E_a = 26 \angle 240° - 26 \angle 0° = 45 \angle 210°$$

We can even express the sign notation in terms of double-subscript notation. For example, in following the loop created by E_a and terminals N and 1, we can write the KVL equation

$$E_{N1} + E_a = 0$$

Therefore $E_{N1} = -E_a$, which can be expressed as $E_{1N} = E_a$.

This completes our review on the writing of dc and ac circuit equations.

Questions and Problems

2-1 Three dc sources G_1, G_2, and G_3 (Fig. 2.57) generate voltages as follows:

$$E_{12} = -100 \text{ V}$$
$$E_{34} = -40 \text{ V}$$
$$E_{56} = +60 \text{ V}$$

Show the actual polarity (+)(−) of the terminals in each case.

2-2 In Problem 2-1, if the three sources are connected in series, determine the voltage and polarity across the open terminals if the following terminals are connected together.
a. Terminals 2-3 and 4-5
b. Terminals 1-4 and 3-6
c. Terminals 1-3 and 4-6

2-3 Referring to Fig. 2.58, show the voltage and the actual polarity of the generator terminals at instants 1, 2, 3, and 4.

2-4 A conductor 2 m long moves at a speed of 60 km/h through a magnetic field having a flux density of 0.6 T. Calculate the induced voltage.

2-5 A coil having 200 turns links a flux of 3 mWb, produced by a permanent magnet. The magnet is moved, and the flux linking the coil falls to 1.2 mWb in 0.2 s. Calculate the average voltage induced.

2-6 What is the SI unit of
a. magnetic flux
b. magnetic flux density
c. magnetic field intensity
d. magnetomotive force

2-7 Referring to Figure 2.26, calculate the relative permeability of cast iron at 0.2 T, 0.6 T, and 0.7 T.

2-8 We want to produce a flux density of 0.6 T in an air gap having a length of 8 mm. Calculate the mmf required.

2-9 Conductor AB in Figure 2.29 carries a current of 800 A flowing from B to A.
a. Calculate the force on the conductor.
b. Calculate the force on the moving N pole.
c. Does the force on the N pole act in the same direction as the direction of rotation?

2-10 **a.** Draw the waveshape of a sinusoidal voltage having a peak value of 200 V and a frequency of 5 Hz.
b. If the voltage is zero at $t = 0$, what is the voltage at $t = 5$ ms? 75 ms? 150 ms?

2-11 A sinusoidal current has an effective value of 50 A. Calculate the peak value of current.

2-12 A sinusoidal voltage of 120 V is applied to a resistor of 10 Ω.

Calculate

a. the effective current in the resistor
b. the peak voltage across the resistor

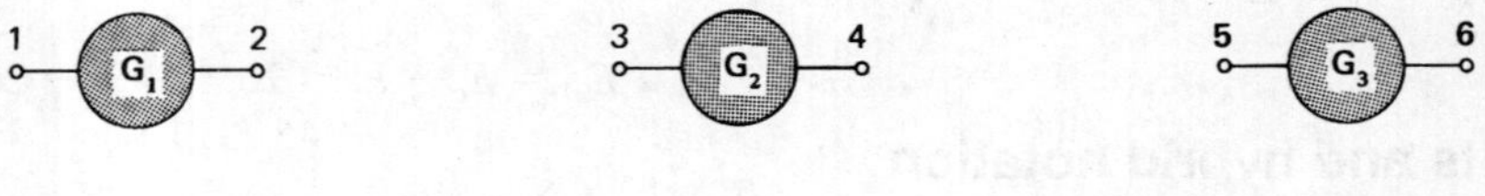

Figure 2.57
See Problems 2-1 and 2-2.

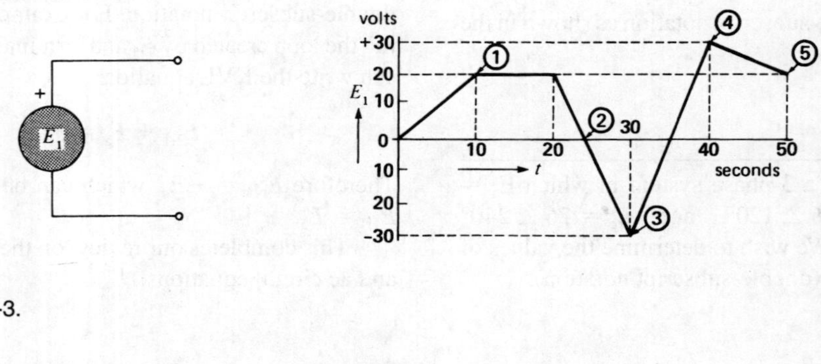

Figure 2.58
See Problem 2-3.

c. the power dissipated by the resistor
d. the peak power dissipated by the resistor

2-13 A distorted voltage contains an 11th harmonic of 20 V, 253 Hz. Calculate the frequency of the fundamental.

2-14 The current in a 60 Hz single-phase motor lags 36 degrees behind the voltage. Calculate the time interval between the positive peaks of voltage and current.

2-15 Referring to Fig. 2.59, determine the phase angle between the following phasors and, in each case, indicate which phasor is lagging.
a. I_1 and I_3
b. I_2 and I_3
c. E and I_1

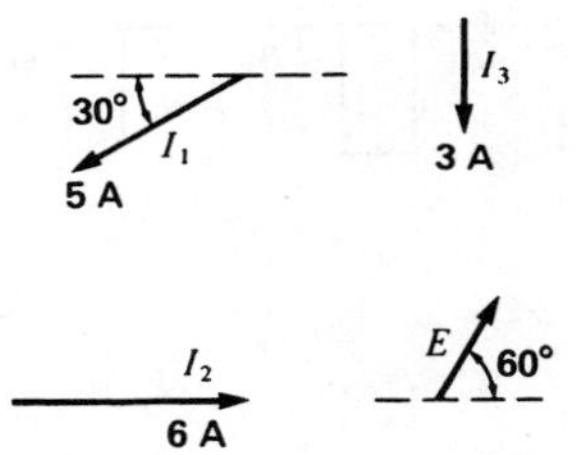

Figure 2.59
See Problem 2-15.

2-16 The voltage applied to an ac magnet is given by the expression $E = 160 \sin \phi$ and the current is $I = 20 \sin (\phi - 60°)$, all angles being expressed in degrees.
a. Draw the phasor diagram for E and I, using effective values.
b. Draw the waveshape of E and I as a function of ϕ.
c. Calculate the peak positive power and the peak negative power in the circuit.

2-17 **a.** Referring to Fig. 2.24, draw the waveshape of the distorted sine wave, if the leads of the third harmonic source are reversed.
b. Calculate the peak voltage of the resulting waveshape.

2-18 In Fig. 2.4, if terminal A_1 is (−) and current flows from A_2 to B_2, which box is the source?

2-19 The resistance of the conductors joining the two boxes in Fig. 2.4 is zero. If A_1 is (+) with respect to A_2, can B_1 be (−) with respect to B_2?

2-20 The alternating voltage e_2 in Fig. 2.24a is given by the expression

$$e_2 = 20 \cos (360\, ft - \theta)$$

If $= 150°$ and $f = 180$ Hz, calculate the value of e_2 at $t = 0$, and at $t = 262.37$ s.

Industrial Application

2-21 In Fig. 2.60 write the KVL circuit equations for parts (a), (b), (c), and (d). (Go cw around the loops.)

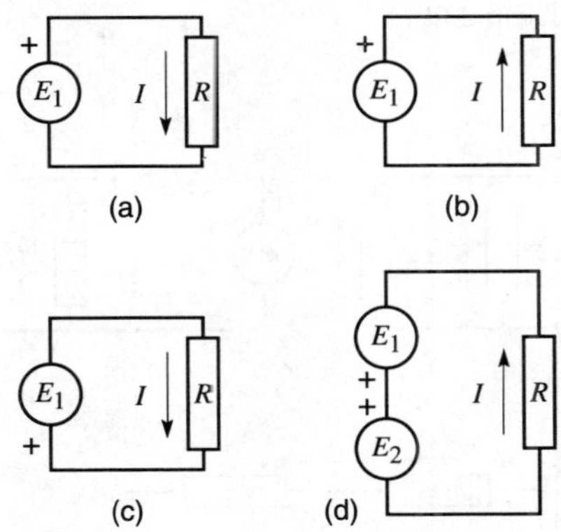

Figure 2.60
See Problem 2-21.

2-22 In Fig. 2.61 write the KCL circuit equations for parts (a), (b), and (c) and determine the true direction of current flow.

2-23 In Fig. 2.62 write the KVL and KCL circuit equations for parts (a), (b), (c) and (d). (Go cw around the loops.)

2-24 An electronic generator produces the output voltage pulses shown in Fig. 2.63. If this voltage is applied across a 10 Ω resistor, calculate

a. the fundamental frequency of the current
b. the peak power, in watts
c. the energy dissipated per cycle, in joules
d. the average power per cycle
e. the value of the dc voltage that would produce the same average power in the resistor
f. the effective value of the voltage in the figure
g. the average voltage

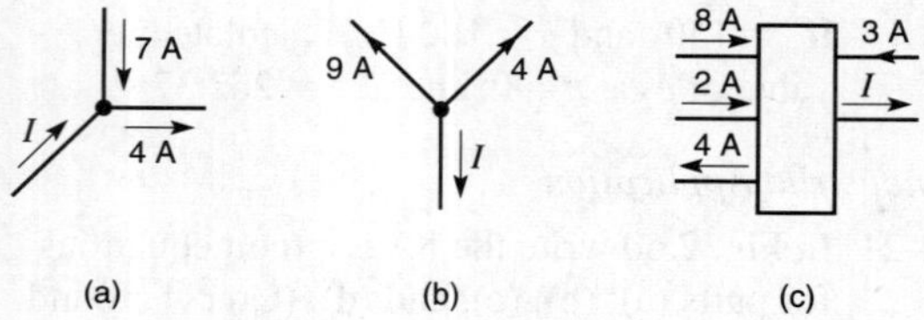

Figure 2.61
See Problem 2-22.

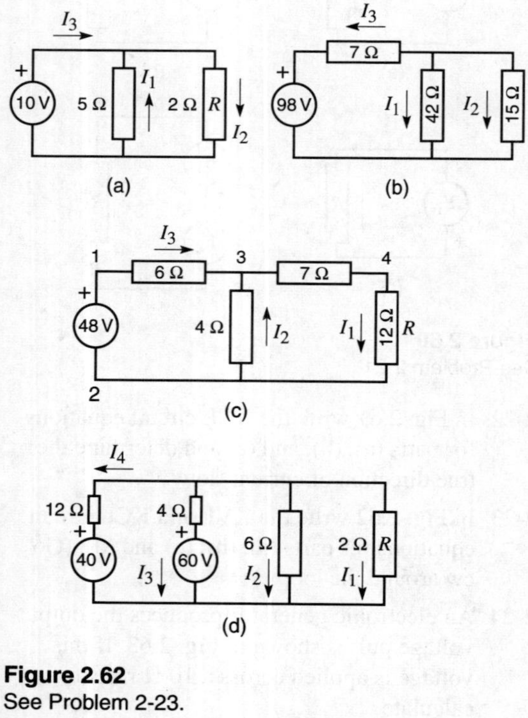

Figure 2.62
See Problem 2-23.

2-25 Repeat the calculations of Problem 2-24 for the waveshape shown in Fig. 2.64.

2-26 In Fig. 2.65 write the KVL and KCL circuit equations for the ac circuits shown in parts (a) to (g). (Go cw around the loops.)

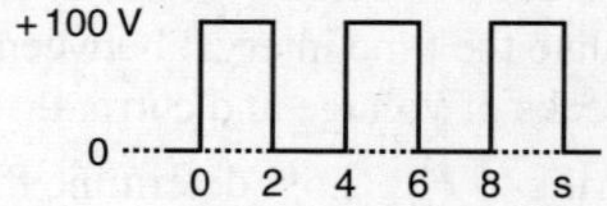

Figure 2.63
See Problem 2-24.

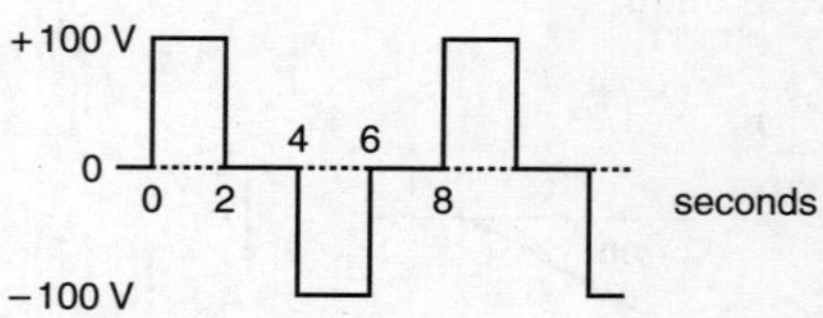

Figure 2.64
See Problem 2-25.

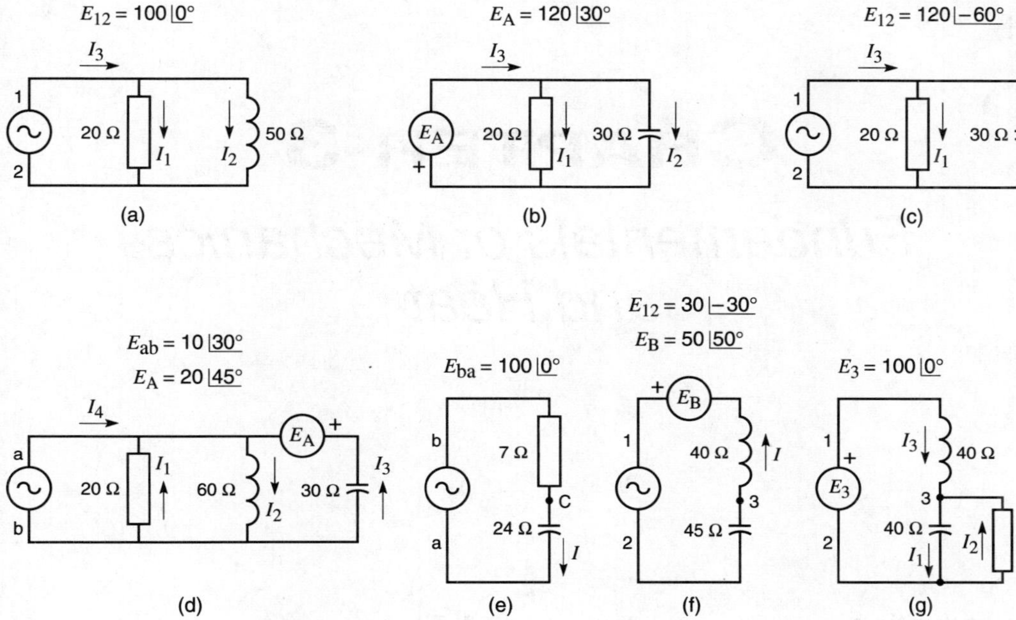

Figure 2.65
See Problem 2-26.

CHAPTER 3

Fundamentals of Mechanics and Heat

3.0 Introduction

In order to get a thorough grasp of electrical power technology, it is essential to know something about mechanics and heat. For example, the starting of large motors is determined not only by the magnitude of the torque, but also by the inertia of the revolving parts. And the overload capacity of an alternator is determined not only by the size of its conductors, but also by the temperature that its windings can safely withstand. And the stringing of a transmission line is determined as much by the ice-loading and mechanical strength of the conductors as by the currents they carry. And we could mention many more cases where the comprehensive approach—the electrical/mechanical/thermal approach—is essential to a thorough understanding of power technology.

For this reason, this introductory chapter covers certain fundamentals of mechanics and heat. The topics are not immediately essential to an understanding of the chapters which follow, but they constitute a valuable reference source, which the reader may wish to consult from time to time. Consequently, we recommend a quick first reading, followed by a closer study of each section, as the need arises.

3.1 Force

The most familiar force we know is the force of gravity. For example, whenever we lift a stone, we exert a muscular effort to overcome the gravitational force that continually pulls it downward. There are other kinds of forces, such as the force exerted by a stretched spring or the forces created by exploding dynamite. All these forces are expressed in terms of the newton (N), which is the SI unit of force.

The magnitude of the force of gravity depends upon the mass of a body, and is given by the approximate equation

$$F = 9.8\, m \tag{3.1}$$

where

F = force of gravity acting on the body [N]

m = mass of the body [kg]

9.8 = an approximate constant that applies when objects are relatively close to the surface of the earth (within 30 km)

Example 3-1

Calculate the approximate value of the force of gravity that acts on a mass of 12 kg.

Solution

The force of gravity is

$$F = 9.8\,m = 9.8 \times 12 = 117.6 \text{ newtons}$$
$$= 117.6 \text{ N}$$

When using the English system of units, we have to make a distinction between the pound (lb) and the pound-force (lbf). A **pound** is a unit of mass equal to 0.453 592 37 kg, exactly. On the other hand, a **pound-force** is equal to (9.806 65 × 0.453 592 37) newtons exactly, or about 4.448 N.

Example 3-2

Calculate the approximate value of the force of gravity that acts on a mass of 140 lb. Express the result in newtons and in pounds-force.

Solution

Using the conversion charts in Appendix AX0, a mass of 140 lb = 140 (÷ 2.205) = 63.5 kg. Using Eq. 3.1 the force of gravity is

$$F = 9.8\,m = 9.8 \times 63.5 = 622.3 \text{ N}$$

Again using the conversion charts, a force of 622.3 N = 622.3 (÷ 4.448) = 139.9 pound-force = 139.9 lbf. Note that the force of gravity of 139.9 lbf is almost exactly equal to the mass of 140 lb. However, although the numbers are nearly the same, a force of 140 lbf is entirely different from a mass of 140 lb.

3.2 Torque

Torque is produced when a force exerts a twisting action on a body, tending to make it rotate. Torque is equal to the product of the force times the perpendicular distance between the axis of rotation and the point of application of the force. For example, suppose a string is wrapped around a pulley having a radius r (Fig. 3.1). If we pull on the string with a force F, the pulley will tend to rotate. The torque exerted on the pulley by the tangential force is given by

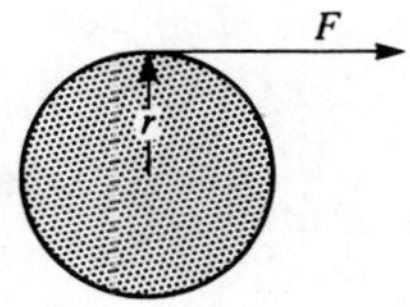

Figure 3.1
Torque $T = Fr$.

$$T = Fr \tag{3.2}$$

where

T = torque [N·m]
F = force [N]
r = radius [m]

If the pulley is free to move, it will begin to rotate around its axis.

Example 3-3

A motor develops a starting torque of 150 N·m. If a pulley on the shaft has a diameter of 1 m, calculate the braking force needed to prevent the motor from turning.

Solution

The radius is 0.5 m; consequently, a braking force $F = T/r = 150/0.5 = 300$ N is required. If the radius were 2 m, a braking force of 75 N would be sufficient to prevent rotation.

3.3 Mechanical work

Mechanical work is done whenever a force F moves a distance d in the direction of the force. The work is given by

$$W = Fd \tag{3.3}$$

where

W = work [J]
F = force [N]
d = distance the force moves [m]

Example 3-4

A mass of 50 kg is lifted to a height of 10 m (Fig. 3.2). Calculate the work done.

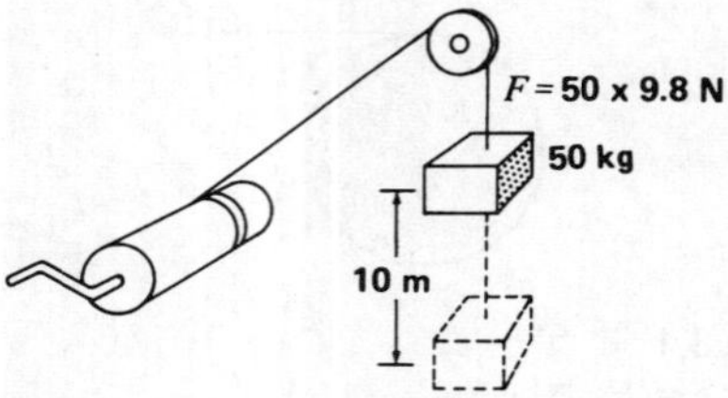

Figure 3.2
Work $W = Fd$.

Solution
The force of gravity acting on the 50 kg mass is

$$F = 9.8\ m = 9.8 \times 50 = 490\ \text{N}$$

The work done is

$$W = Fd = 490 \times 10 = 4900\ \text{J}$$

3.4 Power

Power is the rate of doing work. It is given by the equation

$$P = W/t \tag{3.4}$$

where

P = power [W]
W = work done [J]
t = time taken to do the work [s]

The unit of power is the watt (W). We often use the kilowatt (kW), which is equal to 1000 W. The power output of motors is sometimes expressed in horsepower (hp) units. One horsepower is equal to 746 W. It corresponds to the average power output of a dray horse.

Example 3-5
An electric motor lifts a mass of 500 kg through a height of 30 m in 12 s (Fig. 3.3). Calculate the power developed by the motor, in kilowatts and in horsepower.

Solution
The tension in the cable is equal to the force of gravity acting on the mass that is being lifted:

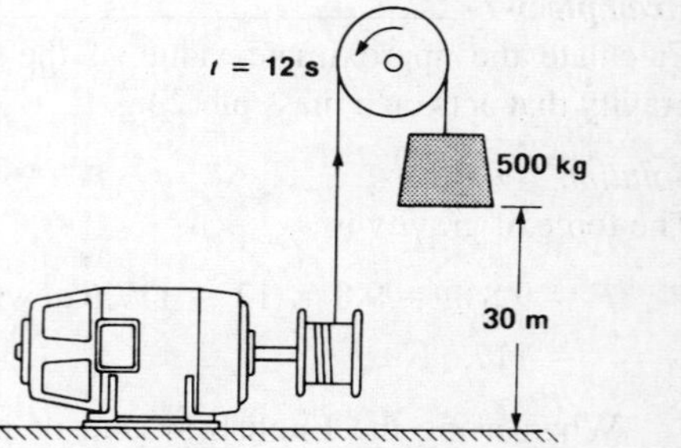

Figure 3.3
Power $P = W/t$.

$$F = 9.8\ m = 9.8 \times 500 = 4900\ \text{N}$$

The work done is

$$W = Fd = 4900 \times 30 = 147\ 000\ \text{J}$$

The power is

$$P = W/t$$
$$= 147\ 000/12 = 12\ 250\ \text{W} = 12.25\ \text{kW}$$

Expressed in horsepower,

$$P = 12\ 250/746 = 16.4\ \text{hp}$$

3.5 Power of a motor

The mechanical power output of a motor depends upon its rotational speed and the torque it develops. The power is given by

$$P = \frac{nT}{9.55} \tag{3.5}$$

where

P = mechanical power [W]
T = torque [N·m]
n = speed of rotation [r/min]
9.55 = a constant to take care of units (exact value = $30/\pi$)

We can measure the power output of a motor by means of a prony brake. It consists of a stationary flat belt that presses against a pulley mounted on the motor shaft. The ends of the belt are connected to two spring scales, and the belt pressure is adjusted by tightening screw V (Fig. 3.4). As the motor turns, we can increase or decrease the power output by adjusting the tension of the belt. The mechanical power developed by the motor is entirely converted into heat by the belt rubbing against the pulley.

When the motor is not running, the spring scales register equal pulls and so the resulting torque is zero. However, when the motor turns clockwise (as it does in Fig. 3.4), pull P_1 exceeds pull P_2. The resultant force acting on the circumference of the pulley is therefore $(P_1 - P_2)$ newtons. If the pulley has a radius r, the net torque $T = (P_1 - P_2)r$ newton meters. Knowing the speed of rotation, we can calculate the power, using Eq. 3.5.

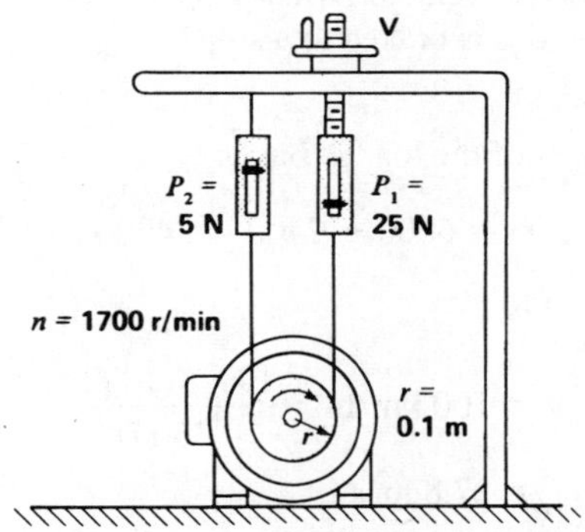

Figure 3.4
Prony brake.

Example 3-6

During a prony brake test on an electric motor, the spring scales indicate 25 N and 5 N, respectively (Fig. 3.4). Calculate the power output if the motor turns at 1700 r/min and the radius of the pulley is 0.1 m.

Solution

The torque is

$$T = Fr$$
$$= (25 - 5) \times 0.1 = 2 \text{ N·m}$$

The power is

$$P = nT/9.55 = 1700 \times 2/9.55 = 356 \text{ W}$$

The motor develops 356 W, or about 0.5 hp.

3.6 Transformation of energy

Energy can exist in one of the following forms:

1. Mechanical energy (potential energy stored in a coiled spring or the kinetic energy of a moving car)
2. Thermal energy (heat released by a stove, by friction, by the sun)
3. Chemical energy (energy contained in dynamite, in coal, or in an electric storage battery)
4. Electrical energy (energy produced by a generator, or by lightning)
5. Atomic energy (energy released when the nucleus of an atom is modified)

Although energy can be neither created nor destroyed, it can be converted from one form to another by means of appropriate devices or machines. For example, the chemical energy contained in coal can be transformed into thermal energy by burning the coal in a furnace. The thermal energy contained in steam can then be transformed into mechanical energy by using a turbine. Finally, the mechanical energy can be transformed into electrical energy by means of a generator.

In the above example, the furnace, the turbine, and the generator are the *machines* that do the energy transformation.

Unfortunately, whenever energy is transformed, the output is always less than the input because all machines have losses. These losses appear in the form of heat, causing the temperature of the machine to rise. Thus, the electrical energy supplied to a motor is partly dissipated as heat in the windings. Furthermore, some of its mechanical energy is also lost, due to bearing friction and air turbulence created by the cooling fan. The mechanical losses are also transformed into heat. Consequently, the useful mechanical power output of a motor is less than the electrical input.

3.7 Efficiency of a machine

The efficiency of a machine is given by the equation

$$\eta = \frac{P_o}{P_i} \times 100 \tag{3.6}$$

where

η = efficiency [percent]

P_o = output power of the machine [W]

P_i = input power to the machine [W]

The efficiency is particularly low when thermal energy is converted into mechanical energy. Thus, the efficiency of steam turbines ranges from 25 to 40 percent, while that of internal combustion engines (automobile engines, diesel motors) lies between 15 and 30 percent. To realize how low these efficiencies are, we must remember that a machine having an efficiency of 20 percent loses, in the form of heat, 80 percent of the energy it receives.

Electric motors transform electrical energy into mechanical energy much more efficiently. Their efficiency ranges between 75 and 98 percent, depending on the size of the motor.

Example 3-7

A 150 kW electric motor has an efficiency of 92 percent when it operates at full-load. Calculate the losses in the machine.

Solution

The 150 kW rating always refers to the mechanical power *output* of the motor.
The input power is

$$P_i = P_o/\eta = 150/0.92 = 163 \text{ kW}$$

The mechanical output power is

$$P_o = 150 \text{ kW}$$

The losses are

$$P_i - P_o = 163 - 150 = 13 \text{ kW}$$

Considering the high efficiency of the motor, the losses are quite moderate, but they would still be enough to heat a large home in the middle of winter.

3.8 Kinetic energy of linear motion

A falling stone or a swiftly moving automobile possess kinetic energy, which is energy due to motion.

Kinetic energy is a form of mechanical energy given by the equation

$$E_k = 1/2mv^2 \quad (3.7)$$

where

E_k = kinetic energy [J]

m = mass of the body [kg]

v = speed of the body [m/s]

Example 3-8

A bus having a mass of 6000 kg moves at a speed of 100 km/h. If it carries 40 passengers having a total mass of 2400 kg, calculate the total kinetic energy of the loaded vehicle. What happens to this energy when the bus is braked to a stop?

Solution

Total mass of the loaded bus is

$$m = 6000 + 2400 = 8400 \text{ kg}$$

The speed is

$$v = 100 \text{ km/h} = \frac{100 \times 1000 \text{ m}}{3600 \text{ s}}$$

$$= 27.8 \text{ m/s}$$

The kinetic energy is

$$E_k = 1/2\, mv^2 = 1/2 \times 8400 \times 27.8^2$$

$$= 3\,245\,928 \text{ J} = 3.25 \text{ MJ}$$

To stop the bus, the brakes are applied and the resulting frictional heat is entirely produced at the expense of the kinetic energy. The bus will finally come to rest when all the kinetic energy (3.25 MJ) has been dissipated as heat.

3.9 Kinetic energy of rotation, moment of inertia

A revolving body also possesses kinetic energy. Its magnitude depends upon the speed of rotation and upon the mass and shape of the body. The kinetic energy of rotation is given by the equation on page 56.

TABLE 3A MOMENT OF INERTIA J AROUND AN AXIS OF ROTATION 0

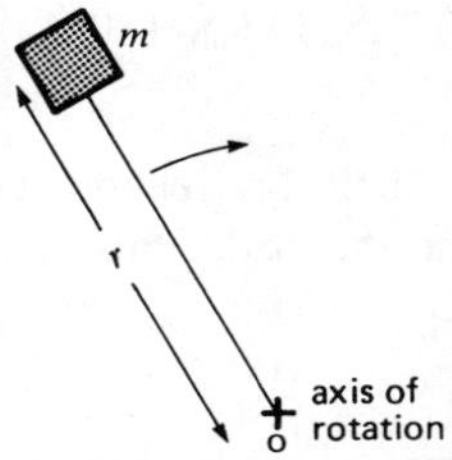

Figure 3.5
Mass m revolving at a distance r around axis 0.

$$J = mr^2 \tag{3.9}$$

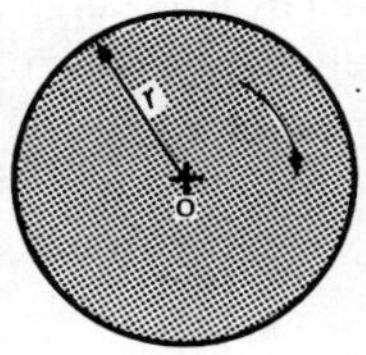

Figure 3.6
Solid disc of mass m and radius r.

$$J = \frac{mr^2}{2} \tag{3.10}$$

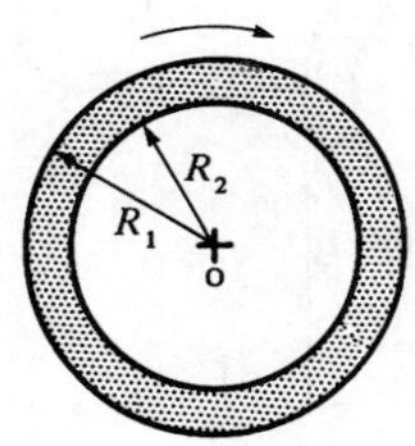

Figure 3.7
Annular ring of mass m having a rectangular crosssection.

$$J = \frac{m}{2}(R_1^2 + R_2^2) \tag{3.11}$$

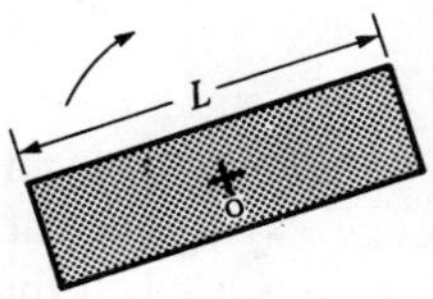

Figure 3.8
Straight bar of mass m pivoted on its center.

$$J = \frac{mL^2}{12} \tag{3.12}$$

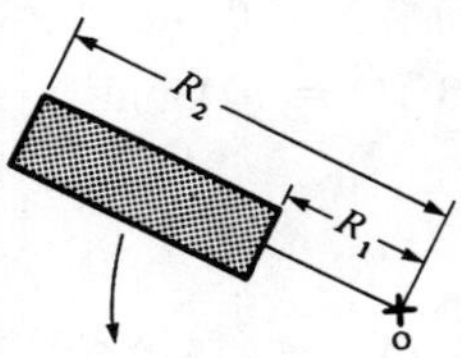

Figure 3.9
Rectangular bar of mass m revolving around axis 0.

$$J = \frac{m}{3}(R_1^2 + R_2^2 + R_1R_2) \tag{3.13}$$

$$E_k = 5.48 \times 10^{-3} Jn^2 \qquad (3.8)$$

where

E_k = kinetic energy [J]
J = moment of inertia [kg·m²]
n = rotational speed [r/min]
5.48×10^{-3} = constant to take care of units [exact value = $\pi^2/1800$]

The moment of inertia J (sometimes simply called *inertia*) depends upon the mass and shape of the body. Its value may be calculated for a number of simple shapes by using Eqs. 3.9 to 3.13 given in Table 3A. If the body has a complex shape, it can always be broken up into two or more of the simpler shapes given in the table. The individual Js of these simple shapes are then added to give the total J of the body.

Inertia plays a very important part in rotating machines; consequently, it is worth our while to solve a few problems.

Example 3-9

A solid 1400 kg steel flywheel has a diameter of 1 m and a thickness of 225 mm (Fig. 3.10).

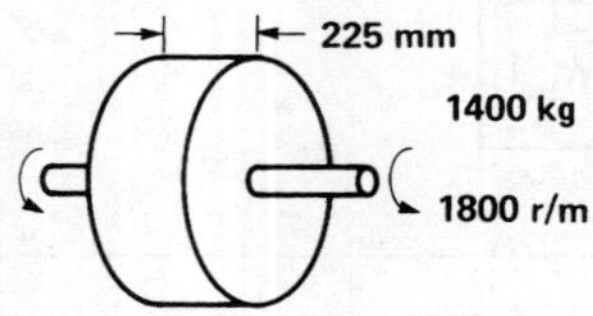

Figure 3.10
Flywheel in Example 3-9.

Calculate

a. Its moment of inertia
b. The kinetic energy when the flywheel revolves at 1800 r/min

Solution

a. Referring to Table 3A, we find the moment of inertia is

$$J = \frac{mr^2}{2} \qquad (3.10)$$

$$= \frac{1400 \times 0.5^2}{2} = 175 \text{ kg·m}^2$$

b. The kinetic energy is

$$E_k = 5.48 \times 10^{-3} Jn^2 \qquad (3.8)$$
$$= 5.48 \times 10^{-3} \times 175 \times 1800^2$$
$$= 3.1 \text{ MJ}$$

Note that this relatively small flywheel possesses as much kinetic energy as the loaded bus mentioned in Example 3-8.

Example 3-10

A flywheel having the shape given in Fig. 3.11 is composed of a ring supported by a rectangular hub. The ring and hub respectively have a mass of 80 kg and 20 kg. Calculate the moment of inertia of the flywheel.

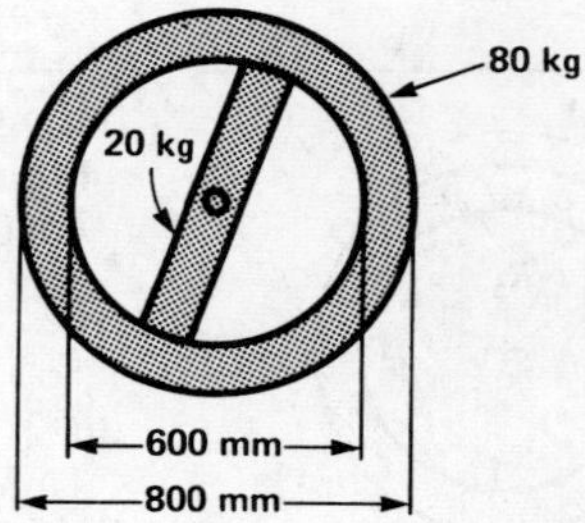

Figure 3.11
Flywheel in Example 3-10.

Solution

For the ring,

$$J_1 = m(R_1^2 + R_2^2)/2 \qquad (3.11)$$
$$= 80(0.4^2 + 0.3^2)/2 = 10 \text{ kg·m}^2$$

For the hub,

$$J_2 = mL^2/12 \qquad (3.12)$$
$$= 20 \times (0.6)^2/12 = 0.6 \text{ kg·m}^2$$

The total moment of inertia of the flywheel is

$$J = J_1 + J_2 = 10.6 \text{ kg·m}^2$$

3.10 Torque, inertia, and change in speed

There is only one way to change the speed of a revolving body, and that is to subject it to a *torque* for a given period of time. The rate of change of speed depends upon the inertia, as well as on the torque. A simple equation relates these factors:

$$\Delta n = 9.55\ T\Delta t/J \qquad (3.14)$$

where

Δn = change in speed [r/min]
T = torque [N·m]
Δt = interval of time during which the torque is applied [s]
J = moment of inertia [kg·m²]
9.55 = constant to take care of units [exact value = $30/\pi$]

If the torque acts in the direction of rotation, the speed rises. Conversely, if it acts against the direction of rotation, the speed falls. The term Δn may therefore represent either an increase or a decrease in speed.

Example 3-11

The flywheel of Fig. 3.11 turns at 60 r/min. We wish to increase its speed to 600 r/min by applying a torque of 20 N·m. For how long must the torque be applied?

Solution

The change in speed is

$$\Delta n = (600 - 60) = 540 \text{ r/min}$$

The moment of inertia is

$$J = 10.6 \text{ kg·m}^2$$

Substituting these values in Eq. 3.14

$$\Delta n = 9.55\ T\Delta t/J \qquad (3.14)$$

$$540 = 9.55 \times 20\ \Delta t/10.6$$

yielding

$$\Delta t = 30 \text{ s}$$

3.11 Speed of a motor/load system

In electric power technology, it often happens that an electric motor drives a mechanical load. In such a system there are three main factors to consider: the torque developed by the motor, the torque exerted by the load, and the speed. We now explain how they interreact.

Consider a load coupled to a motor by means of a shaft (Fig. 3.12). The load exerts a constant torque T_L that always acts in a counterclockwise direction. On the other hand, the torque T_M developed by the motor acts clockwise, and it can be varied by increasing or decreasing the electric current I. Suppose the system is initially at rest and that $T_M = T_L$. Because the torques are equal and opposite, the net torque acting on the shaft is zero, and so it has no tendency to rotate.

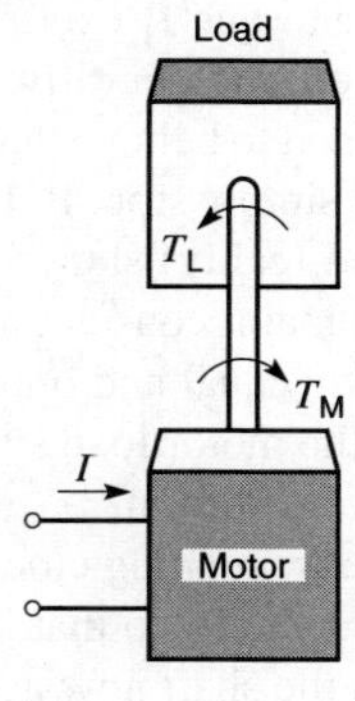

Figure 3.12
Shaft is stationary $T_M = T_L$.

As a result of the opposing torques, the shaft twists and becomes slightly deformed, but otherwise nothing happens.

Suppose we want the load to turn clockwise at a speed n_1. To do so, we increase the motor current so that T_M exceeds T_L. The net torque on the shaft acts clockwise, and so it begins to rotate clockwise. The speed increases progressively with time but as soon as the desired speed n_1 is reached, let us reduce the motor current so that T_M is again exactly equal to T_L. The net torque acting on the system is now zero and the speed n_1 will neither increase or decrease any more (Fig. 3.13).

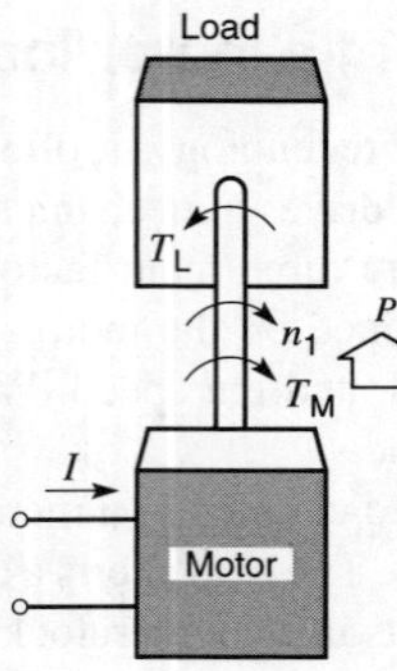

Figure 3.13
Shaft turns cw $T_M = T_L$.

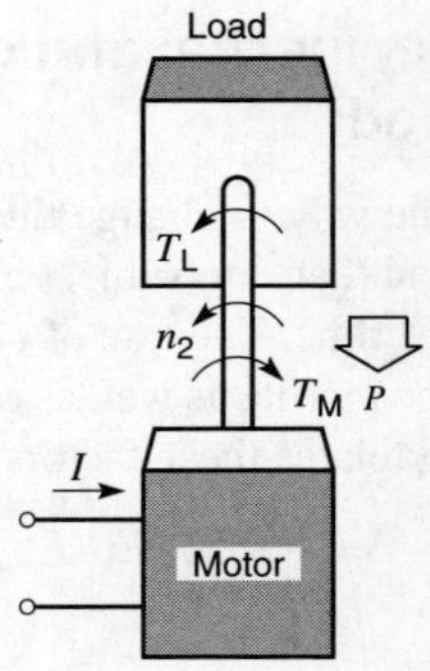

Figure 3.14
Shaft turns ccw $T_M = T_L$.

This brings us to a very important conclusion. The speed of a mechanical load remains constant when the torque T_M developed by the motor is *equal and opposite* to the torque T_L exerted by the load. At first, this conclusion is rather difficult to accept, because we are inclined to believe that when $T_M = T_L$, the system should simply stop. But this is not so, as our reasoning (and reality) shows. We repeat: The speed of a motor remains constant whenever the motor torque is *exactly* equal and opposite to the load torque. In effect, the motor/load system is then in a state of dynamic equilibrium.

With the load now running clockwise at a speed n_1, suppose we reduce T_M so that it is less than T_L. The net torque on the shaft now acts counterclockwise. Consequently, the speed decreases and will continue to decrease as long as T_L exceeds T_M. If the imbalance between T_L and T_M lasts long enough, the speed will eventually become zero and then reverse. If we control the motor torque so that $T_M = T_L$ when the reverse speed reaches a value n_2, the system will continue to run indefinitely at this new speed (Fig. 3.14).

In conclusion, torques T_M and T_L are *identical* in Figs. 3.12, 3.13, and 3.14, and yet the shaft may be turning clockwise, counterclockwise, or not at all. The actual steady-state speed depends upon whether T_M was greater or less than T_L for a certain period of time *before* the actual steady-state condition was reached. The reader should ponder a few moments over this statement.

Whenever the motor torque T_M and load torque T_L are not exactly equal and opposite, the speed will change. The rate of change depends upon the inertia of the rotating parts, and this aspect is covered in more detail in Section 3.13.

3.12 Power flow in a mechanically coupled system

Returning again to Fig. 3.13, we see that motor torque T_M acts in the same direction (clockwise) as speed n_1. This means that the motor *delivers* mechanical power to the shaft. On the other hand, load torque T_L acts opposite to speed n_1. Consequently, the load *receives* mechanical power from the shaft. We can therefore state the following general rule:

When the torque developed by a motor acts in the same direction as the speed, the motor delivers power to the load. For all other conditions, the motor receives power from the load.

In Fig. 3.14, for example, the motor receives power from the load because T_M acts opposite to n_2. Although this is an unusual condition, it occurs for brief periods in electric trains and electric hoists. The behavior of the motor under these conditions will be examined in later chapters.

3.13 Motor driving a load having inertia

When a motor drives a mechanical load, the speed is usually constant. In this state of dynamic equilibrium, the torque T_M developed by the motor is exactly equal and opposite to the torque T_L imposed by the load. The inertia of the revolving parts does not come into play under these conditions. However, if the motor torque is raised so that it exceeds the load torque, the speed will increase, as we have already seen. Conversely, when the motor torque is less than that of the load, the speed drops. The increase or decrease in speed (Δn) is still given by Eq. 3.14, except that torque T is now replaced by the *net* torque $(T_M - T_L)$:

$$\Delta n = 9.55\,(T_M - T_L)\Delta t/J \qquad (3.15)$$

where

Δn = change in speed [r/min]
T_M = motor torque [N·m]
T_L = load torque [N·m]
Δt = time interval during which T_M and T_L are acting [s]
J = moment of inertia of all revolving parts [kg·m^2]

Example 3-12

A large reel of paper installed at the end of a paper machine has a diameter of 1.8 m, a length of 5.6 m, and a moment of inertia of 4500 kg·m^2. It is driven by a directly coupled variable-speed dc motor turning at 120 r/min. The paper is kept under a constant tension of 6000 N.

a. Calculate the power of the motor when the reel turns at a constant speed of 120 r/min.
b. If the speed has to be raised from 120 r/min to 160 r/min in 5 seconds, calculate the torque that the motor must develop during this interval.
c. Calculate the power of the motor after it has reached the desired speed of 160 r/min.

Solution

a. The torque exerted on the reel is

$$T = Fr = 6000 \times 1.8/2 = 5400 \text{ N·m}$$

The power developed by the reel motor is

$$P = \frac{nT}{9.55} = \frac{120 \times 5400}{9.55} \qquad (3.5)$$
$$= 67.85 \text{ kW (about 91 hp)}$$

b. As the speed increases from 120 r/min to 160 r/min, the load torque (5400 N·m) stays constant because the tension in the paper remains unchanged. Let the required motor torque be T_M. It must be greater than the load torque in order for the speed to increase.

We have

$$\Delta n = 160 - 120 = 40 \text{ r/min}$$
$$J = 4500 \text{ kg·m}^2$$
$$\Delta t = 5 \text{ s}$$
$$\Delta n = \frac{9.55(T_M - T_L)\Delta t}{J}$$
$$40 = \frac{9.55(T_M - 5400)\,5}{4500}$$

Thus,

$$T_M - 5400 = 3770$$
$$T_M = 9170$$

The motor must therefore develop a constant torque of 9170 N·m during the acceleration period.

The mechanical power of the accelerating reel motor at 160 r/min is

$$P = \frac{nT}{9.55} = \frac{160 \times 9170}{9.55}$$
$$= 153.6 \text{ kW (equivalent to 206 hp)}$$

c. As soon as the desired speed (160 r/min) is reached, the motor only has to develop a torque equal to the load torque (5400 N·m). The power of the motor is therefore reduced to

$$P = \frac{nT}{9.55} = \frac{160 \times 5400}{9.55}$$
$$= 90.5 \text{ kW (equivalent to 121 hp)}$$

3.14 Electric motors driving linear motion loads

Rotating loads such as fans, pumps, and machine tools are well suited for direct mechanical coupling to electric motors. On the other hand, loads that move in a straight line, such as hoists, trains, wire-drawing machines, etc., must be equipped with a *motion converter* before they can be connected to a rotating machine. The motion converter may be a rope-pulley arrangement, a rack and pinion mechanism, or simply a wheel moving over a track. These converters are so utterly simple that we seldom think of the important part they play.

Straight-line motion involves a linear speed v and a force F, while rotary motion involves a rotational speed n and a torque T. How are these quantities related when a motion converter is used?

Consider a jack driven by a motor that rotates at a speed n while exerting a torque T (Fig. 3.15). This causes a vertical ram to exert a powerful force F while moving at a linear speed v. The power supplied in raising the load is given by

$$P_o = Fv$$

On the other hand, the power input to the jack is given by

$$P_i = \frac{nT}{9.55} \qquad (3.5)$$

Assuming there are no losses in the motion converter, we have

$$P_i = P_o$$

Consequently,

$$nT = 9.55Fv \qquad (3.16)$$

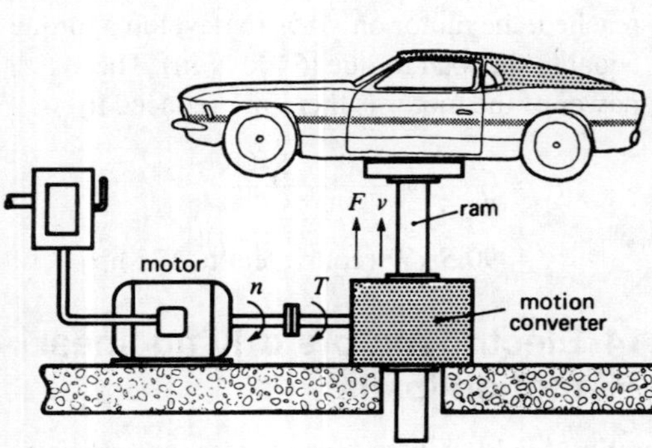

Figure 3.15
Converting rotary motion into linear motion.

where

n = rotational speed [r/min]
T = torque [N·m]
9.55 = a constant [exact value = $30/\pi$]
F = force [N]
v = linear speed [m/s]

Example 3-13

A force of 25 kN is needed to pull an electric train at a speed of 90 km/h. The motor on board the locomotive turns at 1200 r/min. Calculate the torque developed by the motor.

Solution

$$nT = 9.55Fv \qquad (3.16)$$

$$1200\,T = 9.55 \times 25\,000 \times (90\,000/3600)$$

$$T = 4974 \text{ N·m} = 5 \text{ kN·m}$$

3.15 Heat and temperature

Whenever heat is applied to a body, it receives thermal energy. Heat is therefore a form of energy and the SI unit is the joule.

What happens when a body receives this type of energy? First, the atoms of the body vibrate more intensely. Second, its temperature increases, a fact we can verify by touching it or by observing the reading of a thermometer.

For a given amount of heat, the increase in temperature depends upon the mass of the body and the material of which it is made. For example, if we add 100 kJ of heat to 1 kg of water, the temperature rises by 24°C. The same amount of heat supplied to 1 kg of copper raises *its* temperature by 263°C. It is therefore obvious that heat and temperature are two quite different things.

If we remove heat from a body, its temperature drops. However, the temperature cannot fall below a lower limit. This limit is called *absolute zero.* It corresponds to a temperature of 0 kelvin or −273.15°C. At absolute zero all atomic vibrations cease and the only motion that subsists is that of the orbiting electrons.

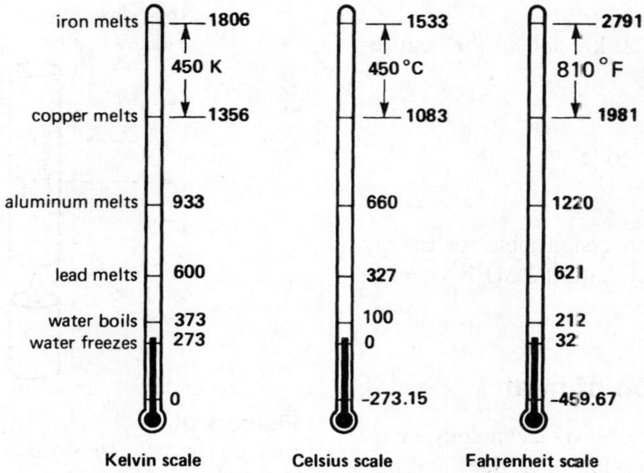

Figure 3.16
Temperature scales.

3.16 Temperature scales

The kelvin and the degree Celsius are the SI units of temperature. Fig. 3.16 shows some interesting relationships between the Kelvin, Celsius, and Fahrenheit temperature scales. For example, iron melts at 1806 K or 1533°C or 2791°F.

3.17 Heat required to raise the temperature of a body

The temperature rise of a body depends upon the heat it receives, its mass, and the nature of the material. The relationship between these quantities is given by the equation

$$Q = mc\,\Delta t \tag{3.17}$$

where

Q = quantity of heat added to (or removed from) a body [J]
m = mass of the body [kg]
c = specific heat capacity of the material making up the body [J/(kg·°C)]
Δt = change in temperature [°C]

The specific heat capacity of several materials is given in Table AX2 in the Appendix.

Example 3-14

Calculate the heat required to raise the temperature of 200 L of water from 10°C to 70°C, assuming the tank is perfectly insulated (Fig. 3.17). The specific heat capacity of water is 4180 J/kg·°C, and one liter weighs 1 kg.

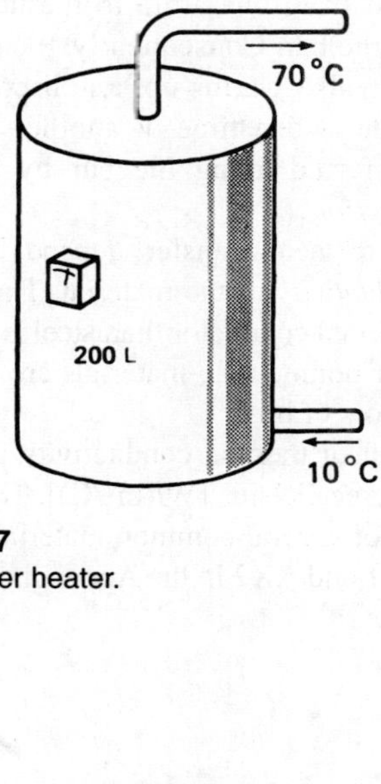

Figure 3.17
Electric water heater.

Solution

The mass of water is 200 kg, and so the heat required is

$$Q = mc\Delta t$$
$$= 200 \times 4180 \times (70 - 10)$$
$$= 50.2 \text{ MJ}$$

Referring to the conversion table for Energy (see Appendix), we find that 50.2 MJ is equal to 13.9 kW·h.

3.18 Transmission of heat

Many problems in electric power technology are related to the adequate cooling of devices and machines. This, in turn, requires a knowledge of the mechanism by which heat is transferred from one body to another. In the sections that follow, we briefly review the elementary physics of heat transmission. We also include some simple but useful equations, enabling us to determine, with reasonable accuracy, the heat loss, temperature rise, and so on of electrical equipment.

3.19 Heat transfer by conduction

If we bring a hot flame near one end of an iron bar, its temperature rises due to the increased vibration of its atoms (Fig. 3.18). This atomic vibration is transmitted from one atom to the next, to the other end of the bar. Consequently, the end opposite the flame also warms up, an observation we have all made at one time or another. In effect, heat is transferred along the bar by a process called *conduction.*

The rate of heat transfer depends upon the *thermal conductivity* of the material. Thus, copper is a better thermal conductor than steel is, and plastics and other nonmetallic materials are especially poor conductors of heat.

The SI unit of thermal conductivity is the watt per meter degree Celsius [W/(m·°C)]. The thermal conductivity of several common materials is given in Tables AX1 and AX2 in the Appendix.

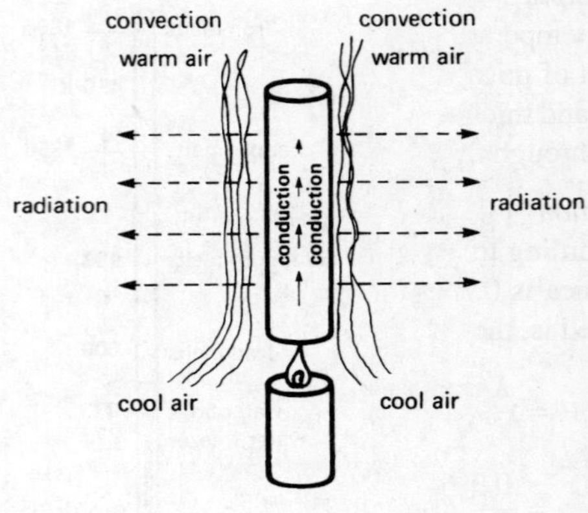

Figure 3.18
Heat transmission by convection, conduction, and radiation.

Referring to Fig. 3.19, we can calculate the thermal power transmitted through a body by using the equation

$$P = \frac{\lambda A(t_1 - t_2)}{d} \tag{3.18}$$

where

P = power (heat) transmitted [W]
λ = thermal conductivity of the body [W/(m·°C)]
A = surface area of the body [m^2]
$(t_1 - t_2)$ = difference of temperature between opposite faces [°C]
d = thickness of the body [m]

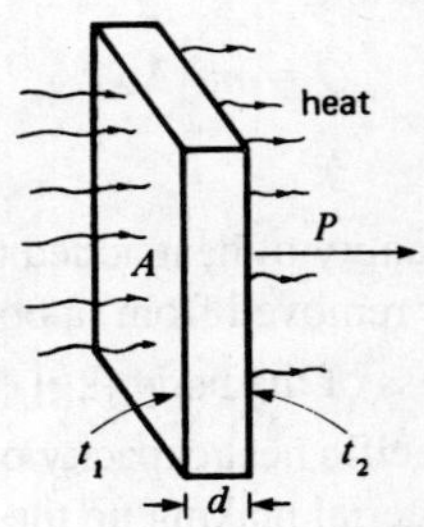

Figure 3.19
Heat transmission by conduction.

Example 3-15

The temperature difference between two sides of a sheet of mica is 50°C (Fig. 3.20). If its area is 200 cm^2 and thickness is 3 mm, calculate the heat flowing through the sheet, in watts.

Solution

According to Table AX1, the thermal conductivity of mica is 0.36 W/m·°C. The thermal power conducted is, therefore,

$$P = \frac{\lambda A(t_1 - t_2)}{d} \quad (3.18)$$

$$= \frac{0.36 \times 0.02(120 - 70)}{0.003} = 120 \text{ W}$$

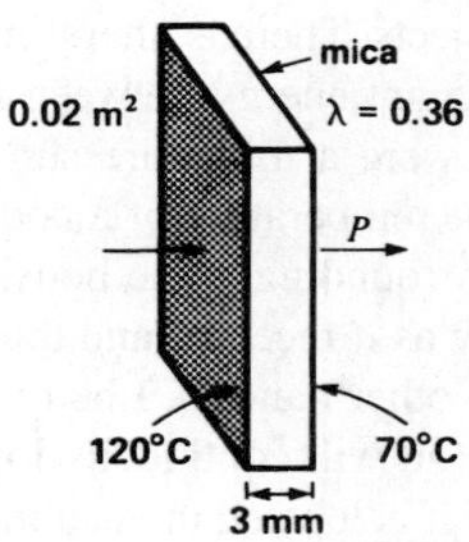

Figure 3.20
Mica sheet, Example 3-15.

3.20 Heat transfer by convection

In Fig. 3.18 the air in contact with the hot steel bar warms up and, becoming lighter, rises like smoke in a chimney. As the hot air moves upward, it is replaced by cooler air which, in turn, also warms up. A continual current of air is therefore set up around the bar, removing its heat by a process called *natural convection.*

The convection process can be accelerated by employing a fan to create a rapid circulation of fresh air. Heat transfer by *forced convection* is used in most electric motors to obtain efficient cooling.

Natural convection also takes place when a hot body is immersed in a liquid, such as oil. The oil in contact with the body heats up, creating convection currents which follow the path shown in Fig. 3.21.

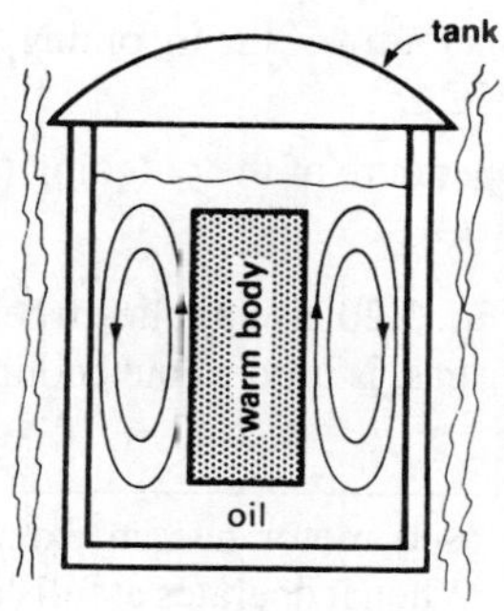

Figure 3.21
Convection currents in oil.

The warm oil comes in contact with the cooler tank, it chills, becomes heavier, sinks to the bottom, and moves upward again to replace the warmer oil now moving away. The heat dissipated by the body is, therefore, carried away by convection to the external tank. The tank, in turn, loses *its* heat by natural convection to the surrounding air.

3.21 Calculating the losses by convection

The heat loss by natural convection in air is given by the approximate equation

$$P = 3A(t_1 - t_2)^{1.25} \quad (3.19)$$

where

P = heat loss by natural convection [W]
A = surface of the body [m]
t_1 = surface temperature of the body [°C]
t_2 = ambient temperature of the surrounding air [°C]

In the case of *forced* convection, such as that produced by a blower, the heat carried away is given approximately by

$$P = 1280\, V_a(t_2 - t_1) \quad (3.20)$$

where

P = heat loss by forced convection [W]
V_a = volume of cooling air [m^3/s]

t_1 = temperature of the incoming (cool) air [°C]

t_2 = temperature of the outgoing (warm) air [°C]

Surprisingly, Eq. 3.20 also applies when hydrogen, a much lighter gas, is used as the cooling medium.

Example 3-16

A totally enclosed motor has an external surface area of 1.2 m². When it operates at full-load, the surface temperature rises to 60°C in an ambient of 20°C (Fig. 3.22). Calculate the heat loss by natural convection.

Solution

$$P = 3A(t_1 - t_2)^{1.25}$$
$$= 3 \times 1.2(60 - 20)^{1.25} = 362 \text{ W}$$

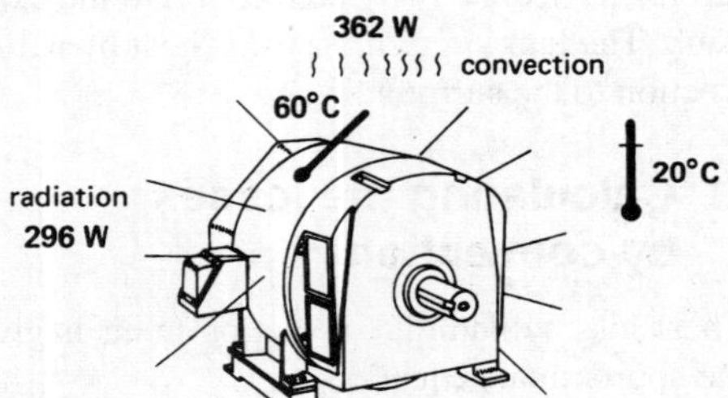

Figure 3.22
Convection and radiation losses in a totally enclosed motor.

Example 3-17

A fan rated at 3.75 kW blows 240 m³/min of air through a 750 kW motor to carry away the heat. If the inlet temperature is 22°C and the outlet temperature is 31°C, estimate the losses in the motor.

Solution

The losses are carried away by the circulating air. Consequently, the losses are

$$P = 1280\ V_a(t_2 - t_1)$$
$$= 1280 \times 240/60(31 - 22) = 46 \text{ kW}$$
(approximate)

3.22 Heat transfer by radiation

We have all basked in the warmth produced by the sun's rays. This radiant heat energy possesses the same properties as light, and it readily passes through the empty space between the sun and the earth. Solar energy is only converted to heat when the sun's rays meet a solid body, such as the physical objects and living things on the surface of the earth. Scientists have discovered that all bodies radiate heat, even those that are very cold. The amount of energy given off depends upon the temperature of the body.

On the other hand, all bodies *absorb* radiant energy from the objects that surround them. The energy absorbed depends upon the temperature of the surrounding objects. There is, therefore, a continual exchange of radiant energy between material bodies, as if each were a miniature sun. Equilibrium sets in when the temperature of a body is the same as that of its surroundings. The body then radiates as much energy as it receives and the net radiation is zero. On the other hand, if a body is hotter than its environment, it will continually lose heat by radiation, even if it is located in vacuum.

3.23 Calculating radiation losses

The heat that a body loses by radiation is given by the equation

$$P = kA\ (T_1^4 - T_2^4) \quad (3.21)$$

where

P = heat radiated [W]

A = surface area of the body [m²]

T_1 = absolute temperature of the body [K]

T_2 = absolute temperature of the surrounding objects [K]

k = a constant, which depends upon the nature of the body surface

Table 3B gives the values of k for surfaces commonly encountered in electrical equipment.

TABLE 3B RADIATION CONSTANTS

Type of surface	Constant k W/(m^2·K^4)
polished silver	0.2×10^{-8}
bright copper	1×10^{-8}
oxidized copper	3×10^{-8}
aluminum paint	3×10^{-8}
oxidized Nichrome	2×10^{-8}
tungsten	2×10^{-8}
oxidized iron	4×10^{-8}
insulating materials	5×10^{-8}
paint or nonmetallic enamel	5×10^{-8}
perfect emitter (blackbody)	5.669×10^{-8}

Example 3-18

The motor in Example 3-16 is coated with a nonmetallic enamel. Calculate the heat lost by radiation, knowing that all surrounding objects are at an ambient temperature of 20°C.

Solution

T_1 = surface temperature = 60°C or (273.15 + 60) = 333 K

T_2 = surrounding temperature = 20°C or (273.15 + 20) = 293 K

From Table 3B, $k = 5 \times 10^{-8}$ W/(m^2·K^4).
The power lost by radiation is, therefore,

$$P = kA\,(T_1^4 - Y_2^4) \tag{3.21}$$

$$= 5 \times 10^{-8} \times 1.2(333^4 - 293^4)$$

$$= 296 \text{ W (approximate)}$$

It is interesting to note that the motor dissipates almost as much heat by radiation (296 W) as it does by convection (362 W).

Questions and Problems

Practical level

3-1 A cement block has a mass of 40 kg. What is the force of gravity acting on it? What force is needed to lift it?

3-2 How much energy is needed to lift a sack of flour weighing 75 kg to a height of 4 m?

3-3 Give the SI unit and the corresponding SI symbol for the following quantities:

force	work
pressure	area
mass	temperature
thermal energy	thermal power
mechanical energy	mechanical power
electrical energy	electrical power

3-4 In tightening a bolt, a mechanic exerts a force of 200 N at the end of a wrench having a length of 0.3 m. Calculate the torque he/she exerts.

3-5 An automobile engine develops a torque of 600 N·m at a speed of 4000 r/min. Calculate the power output in watts and in horsepower.

3-6 A crane lifts a mass of 600 lb to a height of 200 ft in 15 s. Calculate the power in watts and in horsepower.

3-7 An electric motor draws 120 kW from the line and has losses equal to 20 kW. Calculate

a. The power output of the motor [kW] and [hp]

b. The efficiency of the motor

c. The amount of heat released [Btu/h]

3-8 A large flywheel has a moment of inertia of 500 lb·ft^2. Calculate its kinetic energy when it rotates at 60 r/min.

3-9 The rotor of an induction motor has a moment of inertia of 5 kg·m^2. Calculate the energy needed to bring the speed

a. from zero to 200 r/min

b. from 200 r/min to 400 r/min

c. from 3000 r/min to 400 r/min

3-10 Name the three ways whereby heat is carried from one body to another.

3-11 A motor develops a cw torque of 60 N·m, and the load develops a ccw torque of 50 N·m.

a. If this situation persists for some time, will the direction of rotation eventually be cw or ccw?

b. What value of motor torque is needed to keep the speed constant?

3-12 A motor drives a load at cw speed of 1000 r/min. The motor develops a cw torque of 12 N·m, and the load exerts a ccw torque of 15 N·m.

a. Will the speed increase or decrease?

b. If this situation persists for some time, in what direction will the shaft eventually rotate?

3-13 Referring to Fig. 3.12, if $T_M = 40$ N·m, what is the power delivered by the motor?

3-14 Referring to Fig. 3.13, if $T_M = 40$ N·m and $n_1 = 50$ r/min, calculate the power delivered by the motor.

3-15 Referring to Fig. 3.14, if $T_M = 40$ N·m and $n_2 = 50$ r/min, calculate the power received by the motor.

Intermediate level

3-16 During a prony brake test on a motor (see Fig. 3.4), the following scale and speed readings were noted:

$$P_2 = 5 \text{ lbf} \qquad P_1 = 28 \text{ lbf}$$

$$n = 1160 \text{ r/min}$$

If the diameter of the pulley is 12 inches, calculate the power output of the motor in kilowatts and in horsepower.

3-17 A motor drives a flywheel having a moment of inertia of 5 kg·m^2. The speed increases from 1600 r/min to 1800 r/min in 8 s. Calculate

a. the torque developed by the motor [N·m]

b. the energy in the flywheel at 1800 r/min [kJ]

c. the motor power [W] at 1600 r/min

d. the power input [W] to the flywheel at 1750 r/min

3-18 A dc motor coupled to a large grinder develops 120 hp at a constant speed of 700 r/min. The moment of inertia of the revolving parts is 2500 lb·ft^2.

a. Calculate the torque [N·m] developed by the motor.

b. Calculate the motor torque [N·m] needed so that the speed will increase to 750 r/min in 5 s.

(*Note:* The torque exerted by the grinder remains the same.)

3-19 The electric motor in a trolley bus develops a power output of 80 hp at 1200 r/min as the bus moves up a hill at a speed of 30 miles per hour. Assuming that the gear losses are negligible, calculate the following:

a. The torque developed by the motor [N·m]

b. The force opposing the motion of the bus [N]

3-20 Calculate the heat [MJ] required to raise the temperature of 100 kg of copper from 20°C to 100°C.

3-21 Repeat Problem 3-20 for 100 kg of aluminum.

3-22 The motor in Fig. 3.23 drives a hoist, raising a mass m of 800 kg at a uniform rate of 5 m/s. The winch has a radius of 20 cm. Calculate the torque [N·m] and speed [r/min] of the motor.

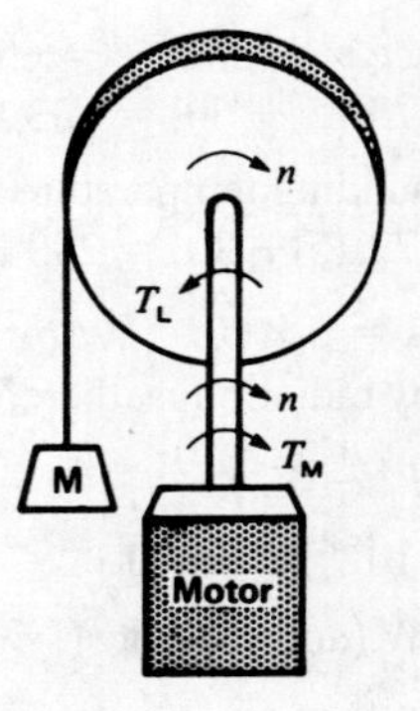

Figure 3.23
Electric hoist, Problem 3-22.

3-23 If the hoisting rate in Problem 3-22 is reduced to 1 m/s, calculate the new speed [r/min] and torque [ft·lbf] of the motor.

Industrial application

3-24 How many Btus are required to raise the temperature of a 50 gallon (U.S.) reservoir of water from 55°F to 180°F, assuming that the tank is perfectly insulated. How long will it take if the tank is heated by a 2 kW electric heater?

3-25 A large indoor transformer is painted a nonmetallic black. It is proposed to refurbish it using an aluminum paint. Will this affect the temperature of the transformer? If so, will it run hotter or cooler?

3-26 An electrically heated cement floor covers an area of 100 m × 30 m. The surface temperature is 25°C and the ambient temperature is 23°C. Approximately how much heat is given off, in kilowatts? *NOTE:* from the point of view of heat radiation, cement is considered to be an insulator.

3-27 The cable and other electrical components inside a sheet metal panel dissipate a total of 2 kW. A blower inside the panel keeps the inside temperature at a uniform level throughout. The panel is 4 ft wide, 8 ft high, 2 ft deep, and totally closed. Assuming that heat is radiated by convection and radiation from all sides except the bottom, estimate the temperature inside the panel if the ambient temperature is 30°C. The panel is painted with a nonmetallic enamel.

PART TWO

Electrical Machines and Transformers

CHAPTER 4
Direct-Current Generators

4.0 Introduction

We begin our study of rotating machinery with the direct-current generator. Direct-current generators are not as common as they used to be, because direct current, when required, is mainly produced by electronic rectifiers. These rectifiers can convert the current of an ac system into direct current without using any moving parts. Nevertheless, an understanding of dc generators is important because it represents a logical introduction to the behavior of dc motors. Indeed, many dc motors in industry actually operate as generators for brief periods.

Commercial dc generators and motors are built the same way; consequently, any dc generator can operate as a motor and vice versa. Owing to their similar construction, the fundamental properties of generators and motors are identical. Consequently, anything we learn about a dc generator can be directly applied to a dc motor.

In this chapter we begin with the basic principles of a 2-pole generator when it operates at no-load. We show the importance of brush position and define what is meant by the *neutral point.* We show how the induced voltage is generated and what determines its magnitude.

This is followed by a study of the behavior of the generator under load. Mechanical torque, direction of current flow, and the importance of armature reaction are discussed. The need for commutating poles and the problem of pole-tip saturation are covered next.

We then discuss the major types of dc generators and their voltage-regulation characteristics.

The chapter ends with a description of the actual physical construction of direct-current machines, including multipole designs.

4.1 Generating an ac voltage

Irrelevant as it may seem, the study of a direct-current (dc) generator has to begin with a knowledge of the alternating-current (ac) generator. The reason is that the voltage generated in any dc generator is inherently alternating and only becomes dc after it has been rectified by the commutator.

Fig. 4.1 shows an elementary ac generator composed of a coil that revolves at 60 r/min between the N, S poles of a permanent magnet. The rotation is due to an external driving force, such as a motor (not shown). The coil is connected to two slip rings mounted on the shaft. The slip rings are connected to an external load by means of two stationary brushes x and y.

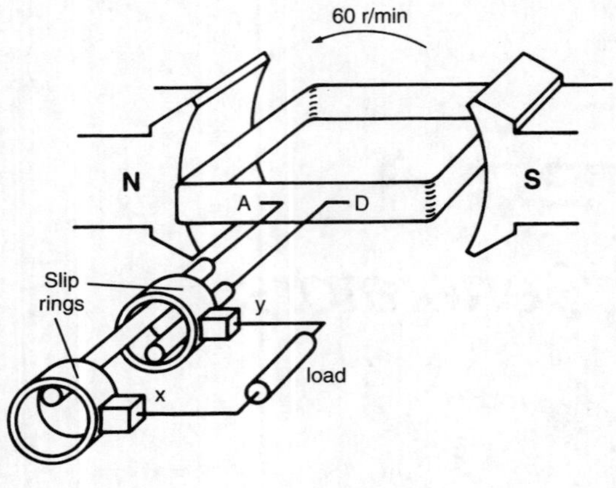

Figure 4.1
Schematic diagram of an elementary ac generator turning at 1 revolution per second.

As the coil rotates, a voltage is induced (Eq. 2.25) between its terminals A and D. This voltage appears between the brushes and, therefore, across the load. The voltage is generated because the conductors of the coil cut across the flux produced by the N, S poles. The induced voltage is therefore maximum (20 V, say) when the coil is momentarily in the horizontal position, as shown. No flux is cut when the coil is momentarily in the vertical position; consequently the voltage at these instants is zero. Another feature of the voltage is that its polarity changes every time the coil makes half a turn. The voltage can therefore be represented as a function of the angle of

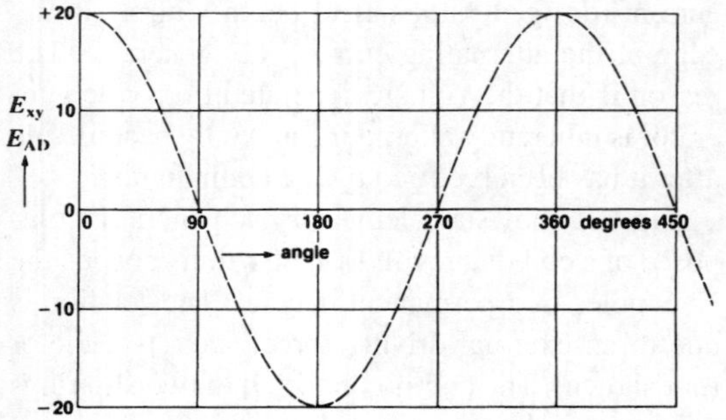

Figure 4.2
Voltage induced in the ac generator as a function of the angle of rotation.

rotation (Fig. 4.2). The waveshape depends upon the shape of the N, S poles. We assume the poles were designed to generate the sinusoidal wave shown.

The coil in our example revolves at uniform speed, therefore each angle of rotation corresponds to a specific interval of time. Because the coil makes one turn per second, the angle of 360° in Fig. 4.2 corresponds to an interval of one second. Consequently, we can also represent the induced voltage as a function of time (Fig. 4.3).

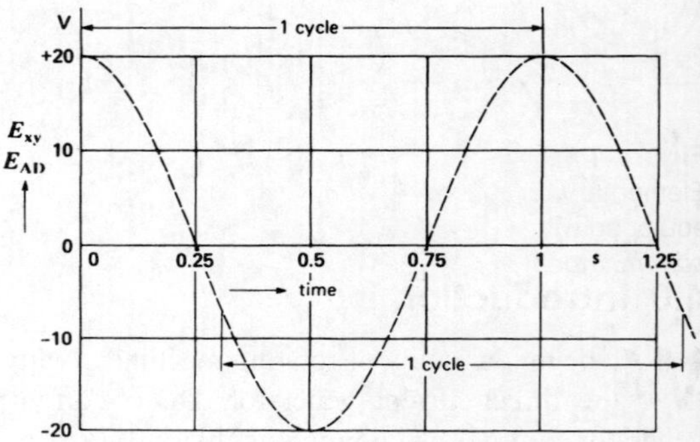

Figure 4.3
Voltage induced as a function of time.

4.2 Direct-current generator

If the brushes in Fig. 4.1 could be switched from one slip ring to the other every time the polarity was about to change, we would obtain a voltage of constant polarity across the load. Brush x would always be positive and brush y negative. We can obtain this result by using a *commutator* (Fig. 4.4). A commutator in its simplest form is composed of a slip ring that is cut in half, with each segment insulated from the other as well as from the shaft. One segment is connected to coil-end A and the other to coil-end D. The commutator revolves with the coil and the voltage between the segments is picked up by two stationary brushes x and y.

The voltage between brushes x and y pulsates but never changes polarity (Fig. 4.5). The alternating voltage in the coil is *rectified* by the commutator, which acts as a mechanical reversing switch.

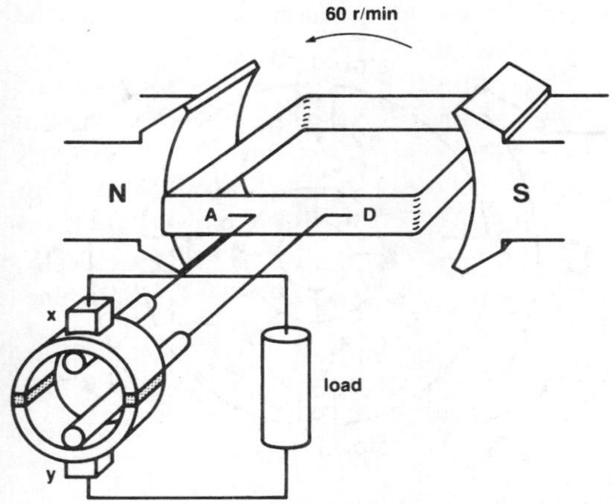

Figure 4.4
Elementary dc generator is simply an ac generator equipped with a mechanical rectifier called a *commutator.*

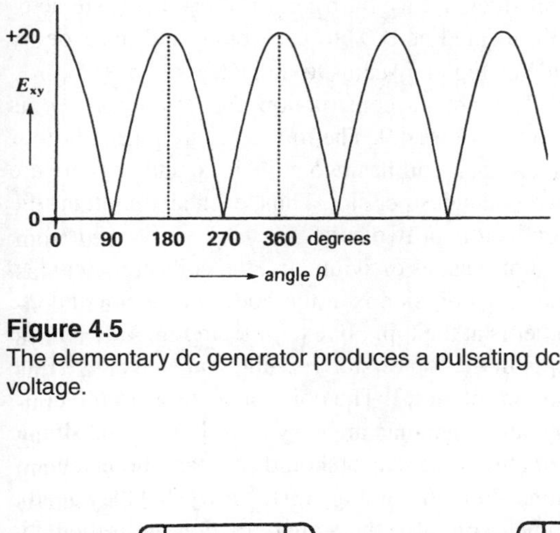

Figure 4.5
The elementary dc generator produces a pulsating dc voltage.

Due to the constant polarity between the brushes, the current in the external load always flows in the same direction. The machine represented in Fig. 4.4 is called a *direct-current generator,* or *dynamo.*

4.3 Difference between ac and dc generators

The elementary ac and dc generators in Figs. 4.1 and 4.4 are essentially built the same way. In each case, a coil rotates between the poles of a magnet and an ac voltage is induced in the coil. The machines only differ in the way the coils are connected to the external circuit (Fig. 4.6): ac generators carry slip rings (Fig. 4.6b) while dc generators require a commutator (Fig. 4.6a). We sometimes build small machines which carry both slip rings and a commutator (Fig. 4.6c). Such machines can function simultaneously as ac and dc generators.

4.4 Improving the waveshape

Returning to the dc generator, we can improve the pulsating dc voltage by using four coils and four segments, as shown in Fig. 4.7. The resulting waveshape is given in Fig. 4.8. The voltage still pulsates but it never falls to zero; it is much closer to a steady dc voltage.

By increasing the number of coils and segments, we can obtain a dc voltage that is very smooth. Modern dc generators produce voltages having a ripple of less than 5 percent. The coils are lodged in the slots of a laminated iron cylinder. The coils and the cylinder constitute the *armature* of the machine. The percent ripple is the ratio of the RMS value of the ac component of voltage to the dc component, expressed in percent.

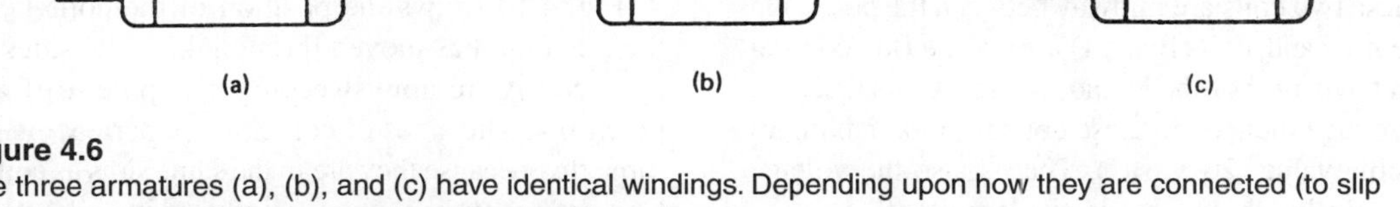

Figure 4.6
The three armatures (a), (b), and (c) have identical windings. Depending upon how they are connected (to slip rings or a commutator), an ac or dc voltage is obtained.

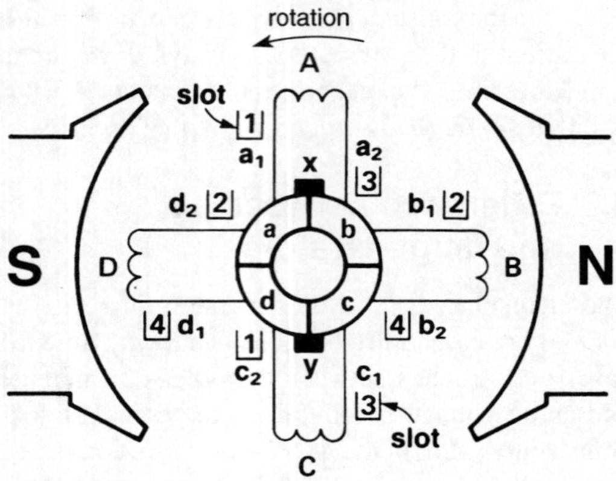

Figure 4.7
Schematic diagram of a dc generator having 4 coils and 4 commutator bars. See Fig. 4.9.

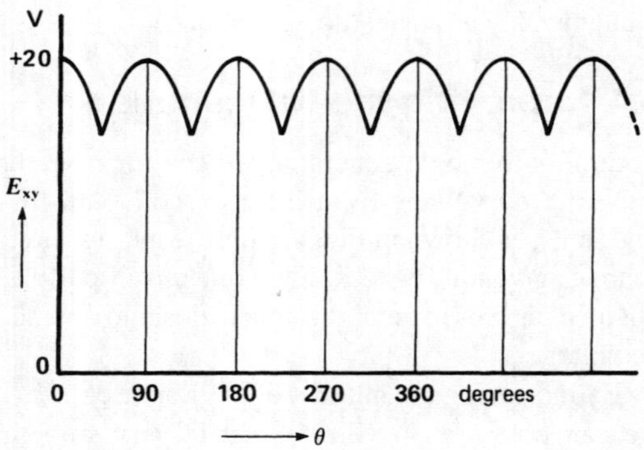

Figure 4.8
The voltage between the brushes is more uniform than in Fig. 4.5.

It is important to understand the physical meaning of Fig. 4.7, because we will be using similar drawings to explain the behavior of dc machines. The four coils in the figure are identical to the coil shown in Fig. 4.1. At the instant shown, coil A is not cutting any flux and neither is coil C. The reason is that the coil sides of these two coils are midway between the poles. On the other hand, coils B and D are cutting flux coming from the center of the N and S poles. Consequently, the voltage induced in these coils is at its maximum possible value (20 V, say). That is also the voltage across the brushes at this particular instant.

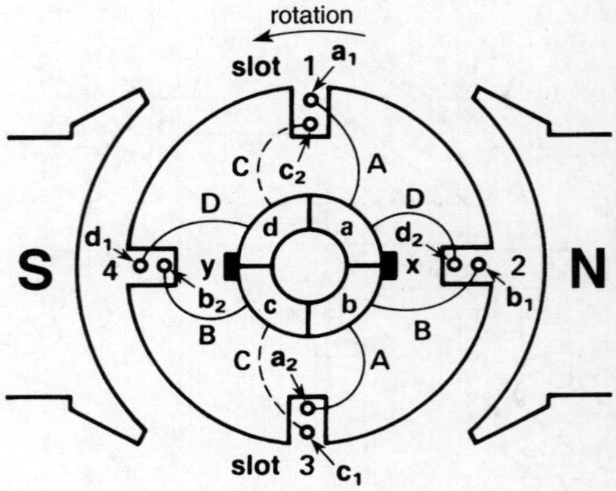

Figure 4.9
The actual physical construction of the generator shown in Fig. 4.7. The armature has 4 slots, 4 coils, and 4 commutator bars.

A schematic diagram such as Fig. 4.7 tells us where the coil sides of the individual coils are located: between the poles, under the poles, near the pole tips, and so on. But we must remember that the coil sides (a_1, a_2; b_1, b_2; etc.) of each coil are actually located at 180° to each other and not side by side as Fig. 4.7 seems to indicate.

The actual construction of this *armature* is shown in Fig. 4.9. The four coils are placed in four slots. Each coil has two coil sides, and so there are two coil sides per slot. Thus, each slot contains the conductors of two coils.

For reasons of symmetry, the coils are wound so that one coil side is at the bottom of a slot and the other is at the top. For example, in Fig. 4.7 coil side a_1 is in the top of slot 1, while coil side a_2 is in the bottom of slot 3. The coil connections to the commutator segments are easy to follow in this simple armature. The reader should compare these connections with those in Fig. 4.9 to verify that they are the same. Note also the actual position and schematic position of the brushes with respect to the poles.

Fig. 4.10 shows the position of the coils when the armature has moved through 45°. The sides a_1, a_2 of coil A are now sweeping past pole tip 1 and pole tip 4. The sides of coil C are experiencing the same flux because they are in the same slots as coil A. Consequently, the voltage e_a induced in coil A is ex-

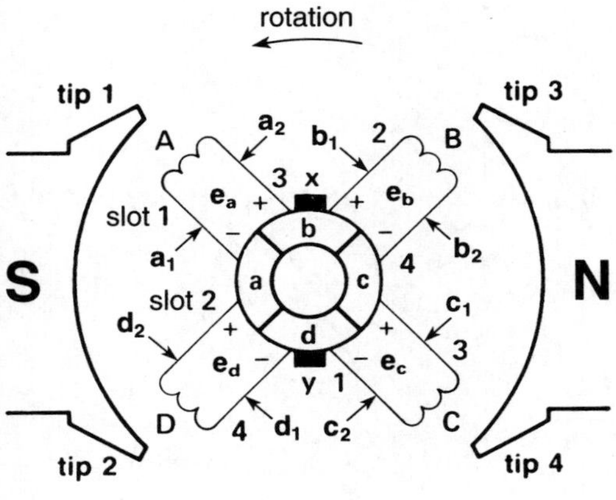

Figure 4.10
Position of the coils when the armature of Fig. 4.9 has rotated through 45°.

actly the same as the voltage e_c induced in coil C. Note, however, that coil A is moving downward, while coil C is moving upward. The polarities of e_a and e_c are, therefore, opposite as shown.

The same reasoning leads us to conclude that e_b and e_d are equal and opposite in polarity. This means that $e_a + e_b + e_c + e_d = 0$ at all times. Consequently, no current will flow in the closed loop formed by the four coils. This is most fortunate, because any such circulating current would produce I^2R losses.

The voltage between the brushes is equal to $e_b + e_c$ (or $e_a + e_d$) at the instant shown. It corresponds to the minimum voltage shown in Fig. 4.8.

The armature winding we have just discussed is called a *lap winding*. It is the most common type of winding used in direct-current generators and motors.

4.5 Induced voltage

Figs. 4.11a and 4.11b show a more realistic armature having 12 coils and 12 slots instead of only 4. When the armature rotates, the voltage E induced in each conductor depends upon the flux density which it cuts. This fact is based upon the equation

$$E = Blv \tag{2.25}$$

Because the density in the air gap varies from point to point, the value of the induced voltage per coil depends upon its instantaneous position.

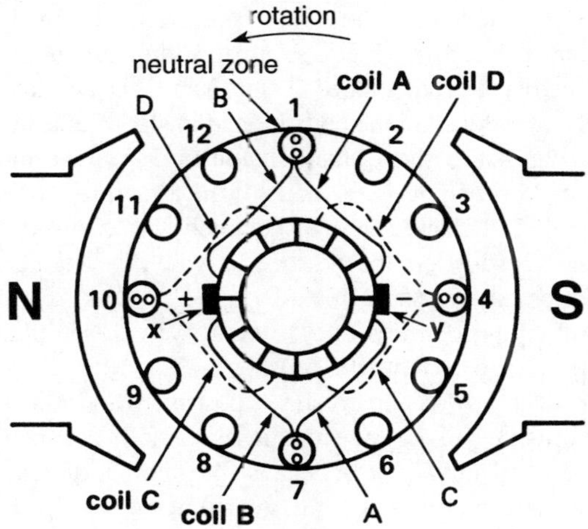

Figure 4.11a
Physical construction of a dc generator having 12 coils, 12 slots, and 12 commutator bars.

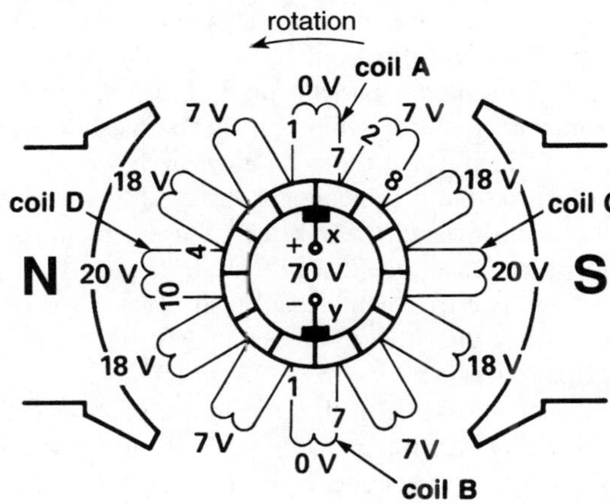

Figure 4.11b
Schematic diagram of the armature and the voltages induced in the 12 coils.

Consider, for example, the voltages induced in the armature when it occupies the position shown in Fig. 4.11. The conductors in slots 1 and 7 are exactly between the poles, where the flux density is zero. The voltage induced in the two coils lodged in slots 1 and 7 is, therefore, zero. On the other hand, the conductors in slots 4 and 10 are directly under the center of the poles, where the flux density is greatest. The voltage induced in the two coils lodged in *these* slots is, therefore, maximum. Finally, due to magnetic symmetry, the voltage induced in the coils lodged in slots 3 and 9 is the same as that induced in the coils lodged in slots 5 and 11.

Fig. 4.11b shows the instantaneous voltage induced in each of the 12 coils of the armature. They are 0, 7, 18, and 20 V, respectively. Note that the brushes short-circuit the coils in which the voltage is momentarily zero.

Taking polarities into account, we can see that the voltage between the brushes is (7 + 18 + 20 + 18 + 7) = 70 V, and brush x is positive with respect to brush y. This voltage remains essentially constant as the armature rotates, because the number of coils between the brushes is always the same, irrespective of armature position.

Note that brush x in Fig. 4.11b straddles two commutator segments that are connected to coil A. Consequently, the brush short-circuits coil A. However, since the induced voltage in this coil is momentarily zero, no current will flow through the brush. The same remarks apply to brush y, which momentarily short-circuits coil B. The brushes are said to be in the *neutral position* when they are positioned on the commutator so as to short-circuit those coils in which the induced voltage is momentarily zero. That is the case in Figs. 4.11a and 4.11b.

If we were to shift the brush yoke by 30° (Fig. 4.12), the voltage between the brushes would become (0 + 7 + 18 + 20 + 18) = 63 V.

Thus, by shifting the brushes the output voltage decreases. Furthermore, in this position, the brushes continually short-circuit coils that generate 7 V. Large currents will flow in the short-circuited coils and brushes, and sparking will result. Thus, shifting the brushes off the neutral position reduces the voltage between the brushes and at the same time causes sparking. When sparking occurs, there is said to be poor commutation.

4.6 Neutral zones

Neutral zones are those places on the surface of the armature where the flux density is zero. When the generator operates at no-load, the neutral zones are located exactly between the poles. No voltage is induced in a coil that cuts through the neutral zone. We always try to set the brushes so they are in contact with coils that are momentarily in a neutral zone.

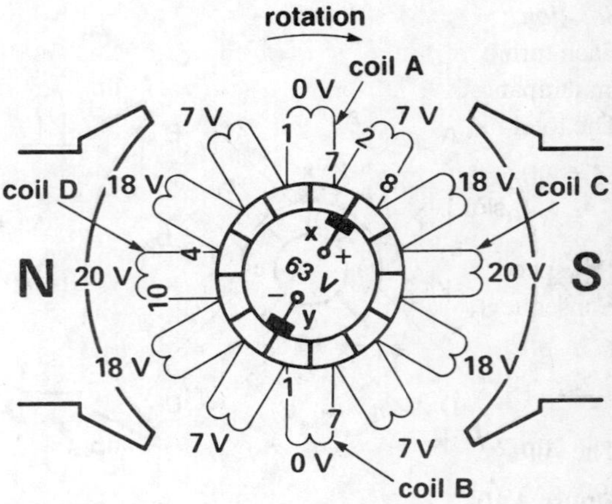

Figure 4.12
Moving the brushes off the neutral point reduces the output voltage and produces sparking.

4.7 Value of the induced voltage

The voltage induced in a dc generator having a lap winding is given by the equation

$$E_o = Zn\Phi/60 \tag{4.1}$$

where

E_o = voltage between the brushes [V]
Z = total number of conductors on the armature
n = speed of rotation [r/min]
Φ = flux per pole [Wb]

This important equation shows that for a given generator the voltage is directly proportional to the flux per pole and to the speed of rotation. The equation only holds true if the brushes are on the neutral position. If the brushes are shifted off neutral, the effect is equivalent to reducing the number of conductors Z.

Example 4-1

The armature of a 6-pole, 600 r/min generator, has 90 slots. Each coil has 4 turns and the flux per pole is 0.04 Wb. Calculate the value of the induced voltage.

Solution

Each turn corresponds to two conductors on the armature, and 90 coils are required to fill the 90 slots. The total number of armature conductors is

$$Z = 90 \text{ coils} \times 4 \text{ turns/coil} \times 2 \text{ conductors/turn}$$
$$= 720$$

The speed is $n = 600$ r/min

Consequently,

$$E_o = Zn\Phi/60 = 720 \times 600 \times 0.04/60$$
$$= 288 \text{ V}$$

The voltage between the brushes at no-load is therefore 288 V, provided the brushes are on neutral.

4.8 Generator under load: the energy conversion process

When a direct-current generator is under load, some fundamental flux and current relationships take place that are directly related to the mechanical-electrical energy conversion process. Consider for example, a 2-pole generator that is driven counterclockwise while delivering current I to a load (Fig. 4.13).

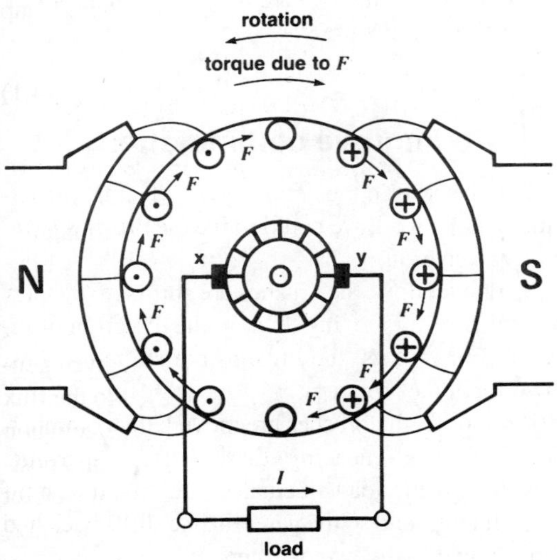

Figure 4.13
The energy conversion process. The electromagnetic torque due to F must be balanced by the applied mechanical torque.

The current delivered by the generator also flows through all the armature conductors. If we could look inside the machine, we would discover that current always flows in the same direction in those conductors that are momentarily under an N pole. The same is true for conductors that are momentarily under an S pole. However, the currents under the N pole flow in the opposite direction to those under an S pole. Referring to Fig. 4.13, the armature conductors under the S pole carry currents that flow *into* the page, *away from* the reader. Conversely, the armature currents under the N pole flow *out* of the page, *toward* the reader.

Because the conductors lie in a magnetic field, they are subjected to a force, according to Lorentz's law (Sections 2.22 and 2.23). If we examine the direction of current flow and the direction of flux, we find that the individual forces F on the conductors all act clockwise. In effect, they produce a torque that acts *opposite* to the direction in which the generator is being driven. To keep the generator going, we must exert a torque on the shaft to overcome this opposing electromagnetic torque. The resulting mechanical power is converted into electrical power, which is delivered to the generator load. That is how the energy conversion process takes place.

4.9 Armature reaction

Until now, we have assumed that the only magnetomotive force (mmf) acting in a dc generator is that due to the field. However, the current flowing in the armature coils also creates a powerful magnetomotive force that distorts and weakens the flux coming from the poles. This distortion and field weakening takes place in both motors and generators. The effect produced by the armature mmf is called *armature reaction.*

To understand the impact of the armature mmf, we return to the generator under load (Fig. 4.13). If we consider the armature alone, it will produce a magnetic field as shown in Fig. 4.14. This field acts at right angles to the field produced by the N, S poles. The intensity of the armature flux depends upon its mmf, which in turn depends upon the current carried by the armature. Thus, contrary to the field flux, the armature flux is not constant but varies with the load.

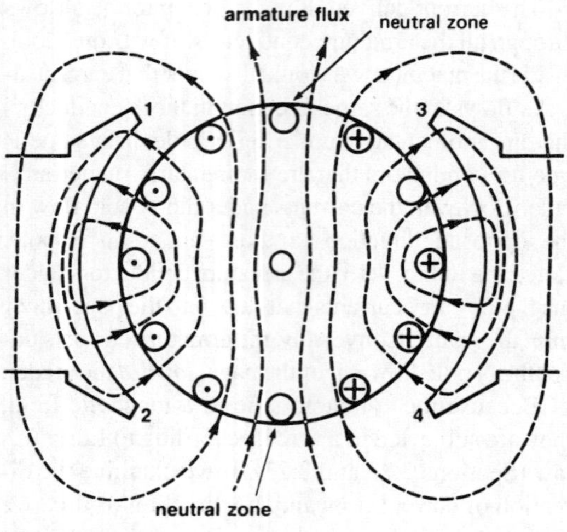

Figure 4.14
Magnetic field produced by the current flowing in the armature conductors.

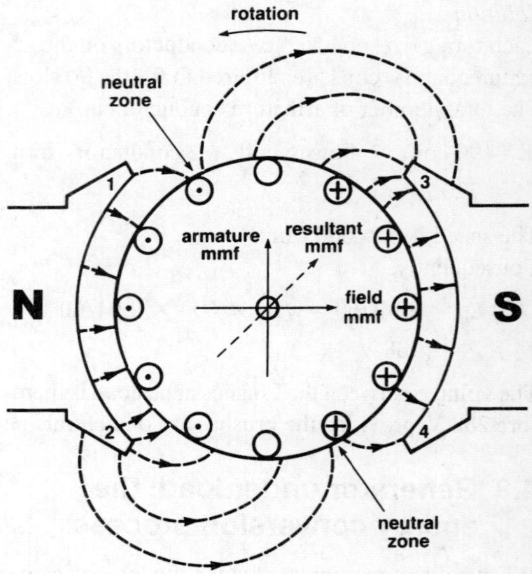

Figure 4.15
Armature reaction distorts the field produced by the N, S poles.

We can immediately foresee a problem which the armature flux will produce. Fig. 4.14 shows that the flux in the neutral zone is no longer zero and, consequently, a voltage will be induced in the coils that are short-circuited by the brushes. As a result, severe sparking may occur. The intensity of the sparking will depend upon the armature flux and hence upon the load current delivered by the generator.

The second problem created by the armature mmf is that it distorts the flux produced by the poles. In effect, the combination of the armature mmf and field mmf produces a magnetic field whose shape is illustrated in Fig. 4.15. The neutral zones have shifted in the direction of rotation of the armature. This occurs in all dc generators.

The flux distortion produces still another effect: the higher flux density in pole tips 2, 3 causes saturation to set in. Consequently, the increase in flux under pole tips 2, 3 is less than the decrease in flux under pole tips 1, 4. As a result, the total flux produced by the N, S poles is less than it was when the generator was running at no-load. This causes a corresponding reduction in the induced voltage given by Eq. 4.1. For large machines, the decrease in flux may be as much as 10 percent.

It is important to note that the orientation of the armature flux remains fixed in space; it does not rotate with the armature.

4.10 Shifting the brushes to improve commutation

Due to the shift in the neutral zone when the generator is under load, we could move the brushes to reduce the sparking.

For generators, the brushes are shifted to the new neutral zone by moving them in the direction of rotation. For motors, the brushes are shifted against the direction of rotation.

As soon as the brushes are moved, the commutation improves, meaning there is less sparking. However, if the load fluctuates, the armature mmf rises and falls and so the neutral zone shifts back and forth between the no-load and full-load positions. We would therefore have to move the brushes back and forth to obtain sparkless commutation. This procedure is not practical and other means are used to resolve the problem. For small dc machines, however, the brushes are set in an intermediate position to ensure reasonably good commutation at all loads.

4.11 Commutating poles

To counter the effect of armature reaction in medium- and large-power dc machines, we always place a set of *commutating poles** between the main poles (Fig. 4.16). These narrow poles carry windings that are connected in series with the armature. The number of turns on the windings is designed so that the poles develop a magnetomotive force mmf_c equal and opposite to the magnetomotive force mmf_a of the armature. As the load current varies, the two magnetomotive forces rise and fall together, exactly bucking each other at all times. By nullifying the armature mmf in this way, the flux in the space between the main poles is always zero and so we no longer have to shift the brushes. In practice, the mmf of the commutating poles is made slightly greater than the armature mmf. This creates a small flux in the neutral zone, which aids the commutation process (see Section 4.28).

Fig. 4.16 shows how the commutating poles of a 2-pole machine are connected. Clearly, the direction of the current flowing through the windings indicates that the mmf of the commutating poles acts opposite to the mmf of the armature and, therefore, neutralizes its effect. However, the neutralization is restricted to the narrow brush zone where commutation takes place. The distorted flux distribution under the main poles, unfortunately, remains the same.

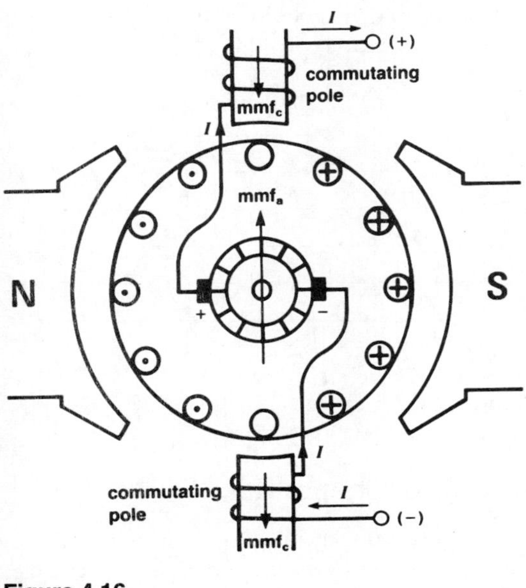

Figure 4.16
Commutating poles produce an mmf_c that opposes the mmf_a of the armature.

* Commutating poles are sometimes called *interpoles.*

4.12 Separately excited generator

Now that we have learned some basic facts about dc generators, we can study the various types and their properties. Thus, instead of using permanent magnets to create the magnetic field, we can use a pair of electromagnets, called *field poles,* as shown in Fig. 4.17. When the dc field current in such a generator is supplied by an independent source (such as a storage battery or another generator, called an *exciter*), the generator is said to be *separately excited.* Thus, in Fig. 4.17 the dc source connected to terminals **a** and **b** causes an exciting current I_x to flow. If the armature is driven by a motor or a diesel engine, a voltage E_o appears between brush terminals **x** and **y.**

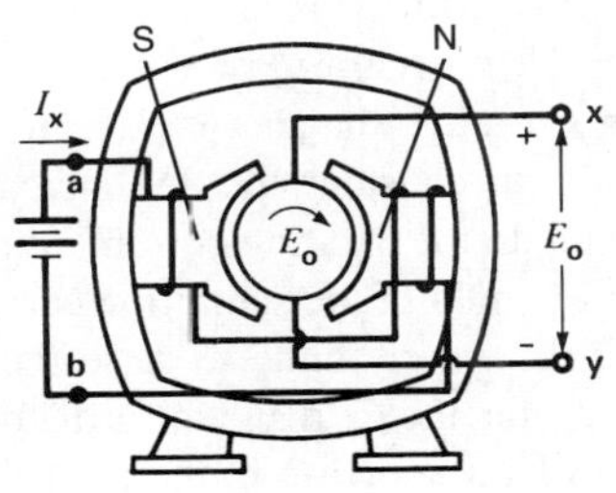

Figure 4.17
Separately excited 2-pole generator. The N, S field poles are created by the current flowing in the field windings.

4.13 No-load operation and saturation curve

When a separately excited dc generator runs at no-load (armature circuit open), a change in the exciting current causes a corresponding change in the induced voltage. We now examine the relationship between the two.

Field flux vs exciting current. Let us gradually raise the exciting current I_x, so that the mmf of the field increases, which increases the flux Φ per pole. If we plot Φ as a function of I_x, we obtain the *saturation curve* of Fig. 4.18a. This curve is obtained whether or not the generator is turning.

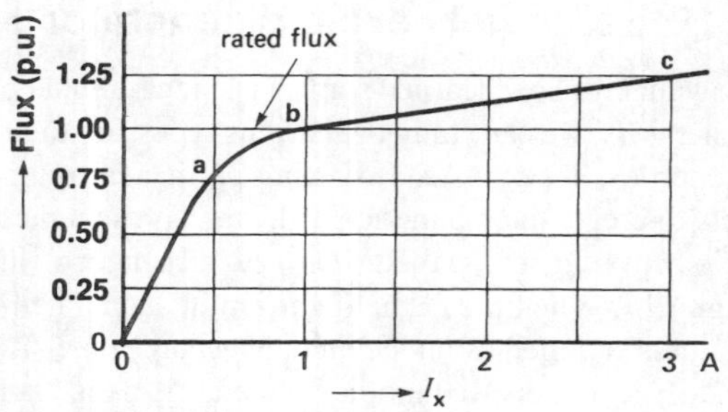

Figure 4.18a
Flux per pole versus exciting current.

When the exciting current is relatively small, the flux is small and the iron in the machine is unsaturated. Very little mmf is needed to establish the flux through the iron, with the result that the mmf developed by the field coils is almost entirely available to drive the flux through the air gap. Because the permeability of air is constant, the flux increases in direct proportion to the exciting current, as shown by the linear portion **0a** of the saturation curve.

However, as we continue to raise the exciting current, the iron in the field and the armature begins to saturate. A large increase in the mmf is now required to produce a small increase in flux, as shown by portion **bc** of the curve. The machine is now said to be saturated. Saturation of the iron begins to be important when we reach the so-called "knee" **ab** of the saturation curve.

How does the saturation curve relate to the induced voltage E_o? If we drive the generator at constant speed, E_o is directly proportional to the flux Φ. Consequently, by plotting E_o as a function of I_x, we obtain a curve whose shape is identical to the saturation curve of Fig. 4.18a. The result is shown in Fig. 4.18b; it is called the *no-load saturation curve* of the generator.

The rated voltage of a dc generator is usually a little above the knee of the curve. In Fig. 4.18b, for example, the rated (or nominal) voltage is 120 V. By varying the exciting current, we can vary the induced voltage as we please. Furthermore, by reversing the current, the flux will reverse and so, too, will the polarity of the induced voltage.

Induced voltage vs speed. For a given exciting current, the induced voltage increases in direct proportion to the speed, a result that follows from Eq. 4.1.

If we reverse the direction of rotation, the polarity of the induced voltage also reverses. However, if we reverse both the exciting current *and* the direction of rotation, the polarity of the induced voltage remains the same.

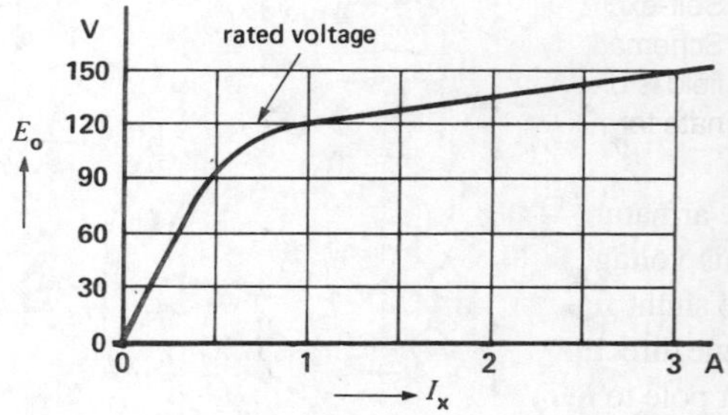

Figure 4.18b
Saturation curve of a dc generator.

4.14 Shunt generator

A shunt-excited generator is a machine whose *shunt-field* winding is connected in parallel with the armature terminals, so that the generator can be self-excited (Fig. 4.19). The principal advantage of this connection is that it eliminates the need for an external source of excitation.

How is self-excitation achieved? When a shunt generator is started up, a small voltage is induced in

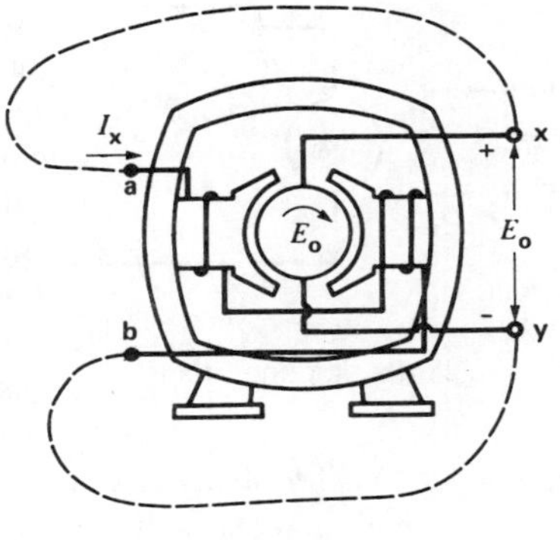

(a)

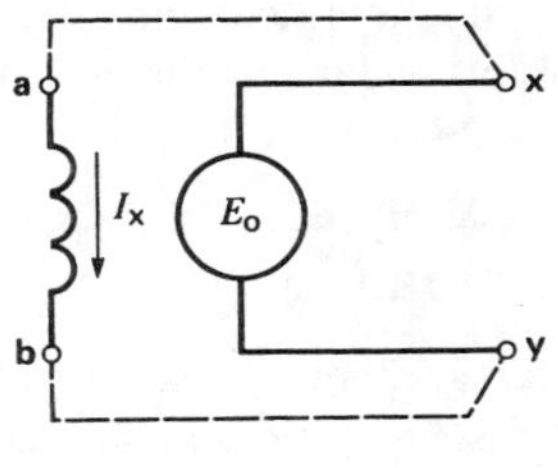

(b)

Figure 4.19
a. Self-excited shunt generator.
b. Schematic diagram of a shunt generator. A shunt field is one designed to be connected in shunt (alternate term for parallel) with the armature winding.

the armature, due to the remanent flux in the poles. This voltage produces a small exciting current I_x in the shunt field. The resulting small mmf acts in the same direction as the remanent flux, causing the flux per pole to increase. The increased flux increases E_o which increases I_x, which increases the flux still more, which increases E_o even more, and so forth. This progressive buildup continues until E_o reaches a maximum value determined by the field resistance and the degree of saturation. See next section.

4.15 Controlling the voltage of a shunt generator

It is easy to control the induced voltage of a shunt-excited generator. We simply vary the exciting current by means of a rheostat connected in series with the shunt field (Fig. 4.20).

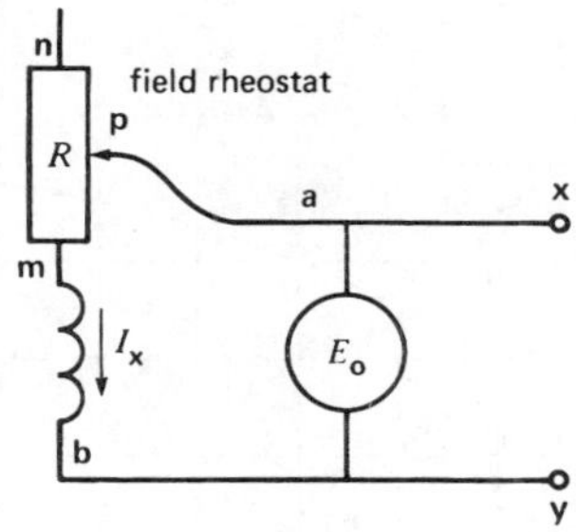

Figure 4.20
Controlling the generator voltage with a field rheostat. A rheostat is a resistor with an adjustable sliding contact.

To understand how the output voltage varies, suppose that E_o is 120 V when the movable contact **p** is in the center of the rheostat. If we move the contact toward extremity **m,** the resistance R_t between points **p** and **b** diminishes, which causes the exciting current to increase. This increases the flux and, consequently, the induced voltage E_o. On the other hand, if we move the contact toward extremity **n,** R_t increases, the exciting current diminishes, the flux diminishes, and so E_o will fall.

We can determine the no-load value of E_o if we know the saturation curve of the generator and the total resistance R_t of the shunt field circuit between points **p** and **b.** We draw a straight line corresponding to the slope of R_t and superimpose it on the saturation curve (Fig. 4.21). This dotted line passes through the origin, and the point where it intersects the curve yields the induced voltage.

For example, if the shunt field has a resistance of 50 Ω and the rheostat is set at extremity **m,** then R_t = 50 Ω. The line corresponding to R_t must pass through the coordinate point E = 50 V, I = 1 A. This line intersects the saturation curve where the voltage is 150 V (Fig. 4.21). That is the maximum voltage the shunt generator can produce.

By changing the setting of the rheostat, the total resistance of the field circuit increases, causing E_o to decrease progressively. For example, if R_t is increased to 120 Ω, the resistance line cuts the saturation curve at a voltage E_o of 120 V.

If we continue to raise R_t, a critical value will be reached where the slope of the resistance line is

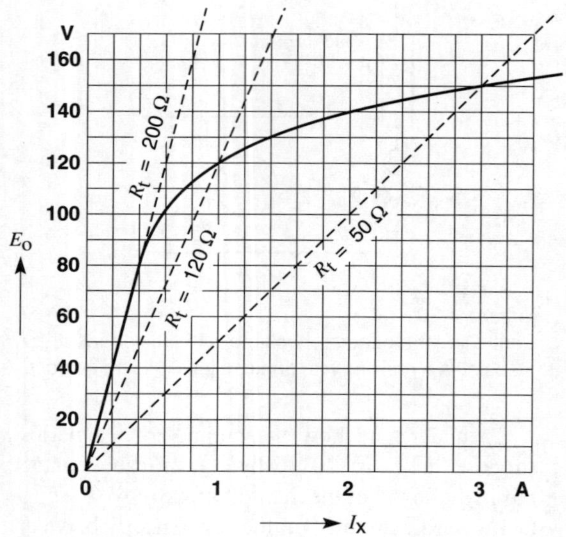

Figure 4.21
The no-load voltage depends upon the resistance of the shunt-field circuit.

equal to that of the saturation curve in its unsaturated region. When this resistance is attained, the induced voltage suddenly drops to zero and will remain so for any R_t greater than this critical value. In Fig. 4.21 the critical resistance corresponds to 200 Ω.

4.16 Equivalent circuit

We have seen that the armature winding contains a set of identical coils, all of which possess a certain resistance. The total armature resistance R_o is that which exists between the armature terminals when the machine is stationary. It is measured on the commutator surface between those segments that lie under the (+) and (−) brushes. The resistance is usually very small, often less than one-hundredth of an ohm. Its value depends mainly upon the power and voltage of the generator. To simplify the generator circuit, we can represent R_o as if it were in series with one of the brushes. If the machine has interpoles, the resistance of these windings is included in R_o.

The equivalent circuit of a generator is thus composed of a resistance R_o in series with a voltage E_o (Fig. 4.22). The latter is the voltage induced in the

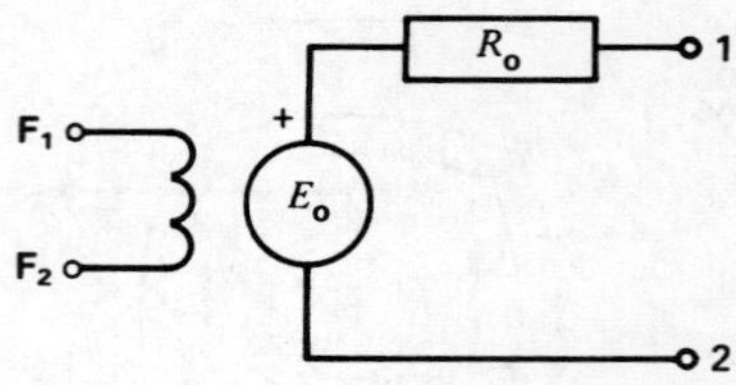

Figure 4.22
Equivalent circuit of a dc generator.

revolving conductors. Terminals 1, 2 are the external armature terminals of the machine, and F_1, F_2 are the field winding terminals. Using this circuit, we will now study the more common types of direct-current generators and their behavior under load.

4.17 Separately excited generator under load

Let us consider a separately excited generator that is driven at constant speed and whose field is excited by a battery (Fig. 4.23). The exciting current is constant and so is the resultant flux. The induced voltage E_o is therefore fixed. When the machine operates at no-load, terminal voltage E_{12} is equal to the induced voltage E_o because the voltage drop in the armature resistance is zero. However, if we connect a load across the armature (Fig. 4.23), the resulting load current I produces a voltage drop across resistance R_o. Terminal voltage E_{12} is now less than the induced voltage E_o. As we increase the load, the terminal voltage diminishes progressively, as shown in Fig. 4.24. The graph of terminal voltage as a function of load current is called the *load curve* of the generator.

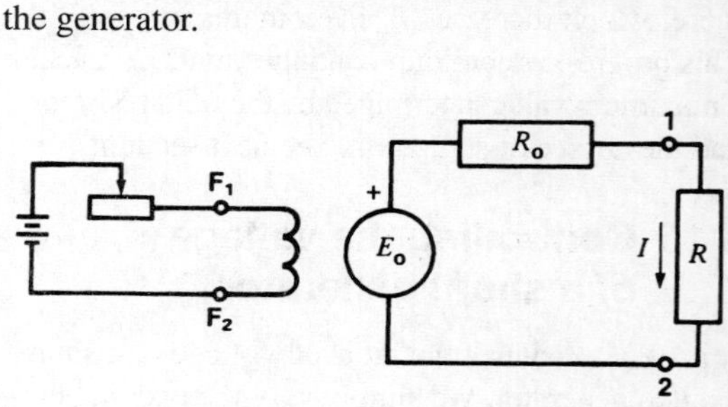

Figure 4.23
Separately excited generator under load.

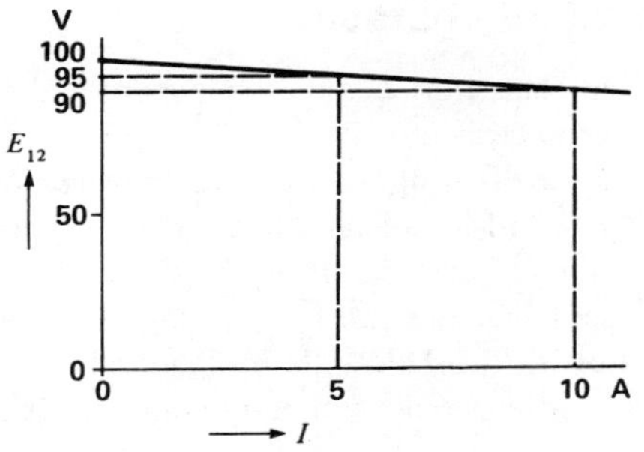

Figure 4.24
Load characteristic of a separately excited generator.

In practice, the induced voltage E_o also decreases slightly with increasing load, because pole-tip saturation tends to decrease the field flux. Consequently, the terminal voltage E_{12} falls off more rapidly than can be attributed to armature resistance alone.

4.18 Shunt generator under load

The terminal voltage of a self-excited shunt generator falls off more sharply with increasing load than that of a separately excited generator. The reason is that the field current in a separately excited machine remains constant, whereas in a self-excited generator the exciting current falls as the terminal voltage drops. For a self-excited generator, the drop in voltage from no-load to full-load is about 15 percent of the full-load voltage, whereas for a separately excited generator it is usually less than 10 percent. The *voltage regulation* is said to be 15% and 10%, respectively.

4.19 Compound generator

The compound generator was developed to prevent the terminal voltage of a dc generator from decreasing with increasing load. Thus, although we can usually tolerate a reasonable drop in terminal voltage as the load increases, this has a serious effect on lighting circuits. For example, the distribution system of a ship supplies power to both dc machinery and incandescent lamps. The current delivered by the generator fluctuates continually, in response to the varying loads. These current variations produce corresponding changes in the generator terminal voltage, causing the lights to flicker. Compound generators eliminate this problem.

A **compound generator** (Fig. 4.25a) is similar to a shunt generator, except that it has additional field coils connected in series with the armature. These *series field* coils are composed of a few turns of heavy wire, big enough to carry the armature current. The total resistance of the series coils is, therefore, small. Fig. 4.25b is a schematic diagram showing the shunt and series field connections.

When the generator runs at no-load, the current in the series coils is zero. The shunt coils, however, carry exciting current I_x which produces the field flux, just as in a standard self-excited shunt generator. As the generator is loaded, the terminal voltage tends to drop, but load current I_c now flows through the series field coils. The mmf developed by these coils acts in the same direction as the mmf of the shunt field. Consequently, the field flux under load rises above its original no-load value, which raises the value of E_o. If the series coils are properly designed, the terminal voltage remains practically constant from no-load to full-load. The

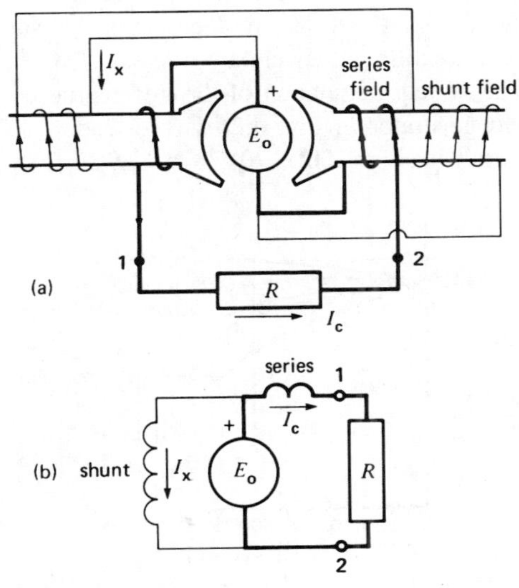

Figure 4.25
a. Compound generator under load.
b. Schematic diagram.

rise in the induced voltage compensates for the armature *IR* drop.

In some cases we have to compensate not only for the armature voltage drop, but also for the *IR* drop in the feeder line between the generator and the load. The generator manufacturer then adds one or two extra turns on the series winding so that the terminal voltage *increases* as the load current rises. Such machines are called *over-compound generators.* If the compounding is too strong, a low resistance can be placed in parallel with the series field. This reduces the current in the series field and has the same effect as reducing the number of turns. For example, if the value of the *diverter* resistance is equal to that of the series field, the current in the latter is reduced by half.

4.20 Differential compound generator

In a *differential compound generator* the mmf of the series field acts opposite to the shunt field. As a result, the terminal voltage falls drastically with increasing load. We can make such a generator by simply reversing the series field of a standard compound generator. Differential compound generators were formerly used in dc arc welders, because they tended to limit the short-circuit current and to stabilize the arc during the welding process.

The voltage regulation of the differential compound generator in Fig. 4.26 is (no-load − full-load)/full-load = (100 − 70)/70 = 42.9%.

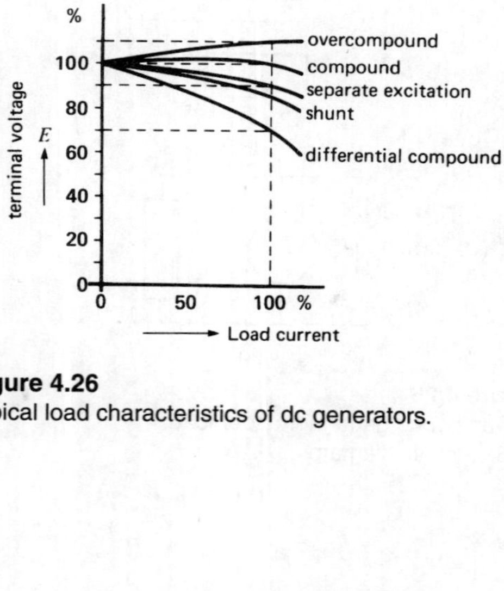

Figure 4.26
Typical load characteristics of dc generators.

4.21 Load characteristics

The load characteristics of some shunt and compound generators are given in Fig. 4.26. The voltage of an over-compound generator increases by 10% when full-load is applied, whereas that of a flat-compound generator remains constant. On the other hand, the full-load voltage of a shunt generator is 15% below its no-load value, while that of a differential-compound generator is 30% lower.

4.22 Generator specifications

The nameplate of a generator indicates the power, voltage, speed, and other details about the machine. These ratings, or *nominal characteristics,* are the values guaranteed by the manufacturer. For example, the following information is punched on the nameplate of a 100 kW generator:

Power	100 kW	Speed	1200 r/min
Voltage	250 V	Type	Compound
Exciting current	20 A	Class	B
Temperature rise	50°C		

These specifications tell us that the machine can deliver, continuously, a power of 100 kW at a voltage of 250 V, without exceeding a temperature rise of 50°C. It can therefore supply a load current of 100 000/250 = 400 A. It possesses a series winding, and the current in the shunt field is 20 A. In practice, the terminal voltage is adjusted to a value close to its rating of 250 V. We may draw any amount of power from the generator, as long as it does not exceed 100 kW and the current is less than 400 A. The class B designation refers to the class of insulation used in the machine.

CONSTRUCTION OF DIRECT-CURRENT GENERATORS

We have described the basic features and properties of direct-current generators. We now look at the mechanical construction of these machines, directing our attention to the field, the armature, the commutator, and the brushes.

4.23 Field

The field produces the magnetic flux in the machine. It is basically a stationary electromagnet composed of a set of salient poles bolted to the inside of a circular frame (Figs. 4.27 and 4.28). Field coils, mounted on the poles, carry the dc exciting current. The frame is usually made of solid cast steel, whereas the pole pieces are composed of stacked iron laminations. In some generators the flux is created by permanent magnets.

In our discussions so far we have considered only 2-pole generators. However, in practice a dc generator or motor may have 2, 4, 6, or as many as 24 poles. The number of poles depends upon the physical size of the machine; the bigger it is, the more poles it will have. By using a multipole design, we can reduce the dimensions and cost of large machines, and also improve their performance.

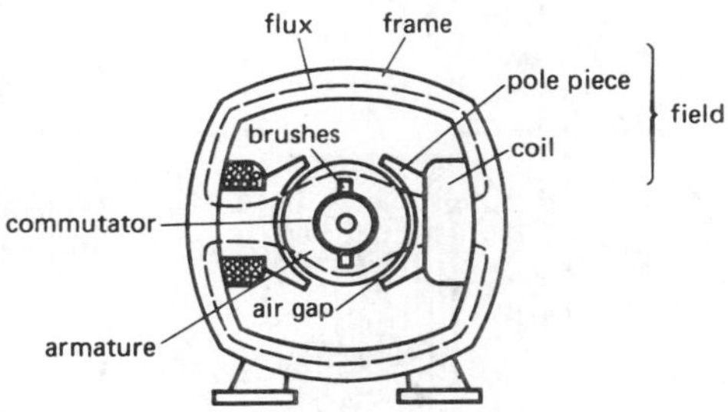

Figure 4.27
Cross section of a 2-pole generator.

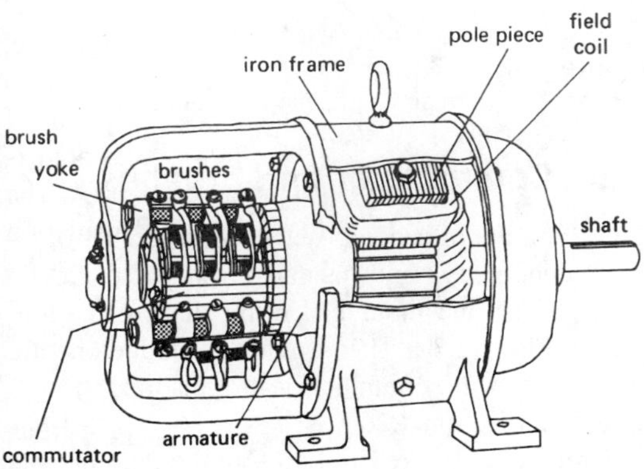

Figure 4.28
Cutaway view of a 4-pole shunt generator. It has 3 brushes per brush set.

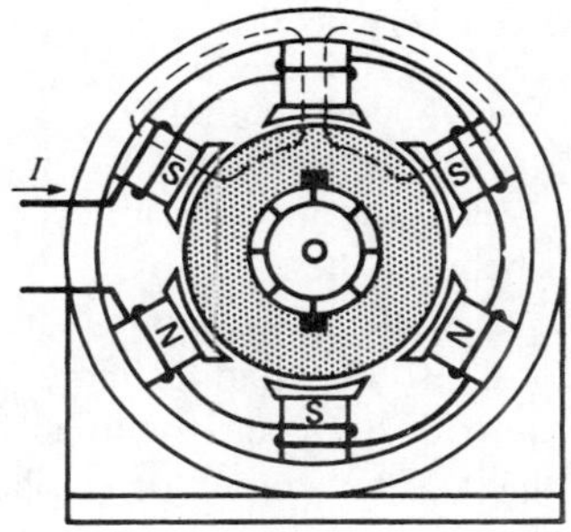

Figure 4.29
Adjacent poles of multipole generators have opposite magnetic polarities.

The field coils of a multipole machine are connected together so that adjacent poles have opposite magnetic polarities (Fig. 4.29). The shunt field coils are composed of several hundred turns of wire carrying a relatively small current. The coils are insulated from the pole pieces to prevent short-circuits.

The mmf developed by the coils produces a magnetic flux that passes through the pole pieces, the frame, the armature, and the air gap. The air gap is the short space between the armature and the pole pieces. It ranges from about 1.5 to 5 mm as the generator rating increases from 1 kW to 100 kW.

Because the armature and field are composed of magnetic materials having excellent permeability, most of the mmf produced by the field is used to drive the flux across the air gap. Consequently, by reducing its length, we can diminish the size of the shunt field coils. However, the air gap cannot be made too short otherwise the armature reaction effect becomes too great.

If the generator has a series field, the coils are wound on top of the shunt-field coils. The conductor size must be large enough so that the winding does not overheat when it carries the full-load current of the generator.

4.24 Armature

The armature is the rotating part of a dc generator. It consists of a commutator, an iron core, and a set of coils (Fig. 4.30). The armature is keyed to a shaft and revolves between the field poles. The iron core is composed of slotted, iron laminations that are stacked to form a solid cylindrical core. The laminations are individually coated with an insulating film so that they do not come in electrical contact with each other. As a result, eddy-current losses are reduced. The slots are lined up to provide the space needed to insert the armature conductors.

The armature conductors carry the load current delivered by the generator. They are insulated from the iron core by several layers of paper or mica and are firmly held in place by fiber slot sticks. If the armature current is below 10 A, round wire is used; but for currents exceeding 20 A, rectangular conductors are preferred because they make better use of the available slot space. The lamination of a small armature is shown in Fig. 4.31. A cross-section view of the slot of a large armature is shown in Fig. 4.32.

Figure 4.30
Armature of a dc generator showing the commutator, stacked laminations, slots, and shaft.
(Courtesy of General Electric Company, USA)

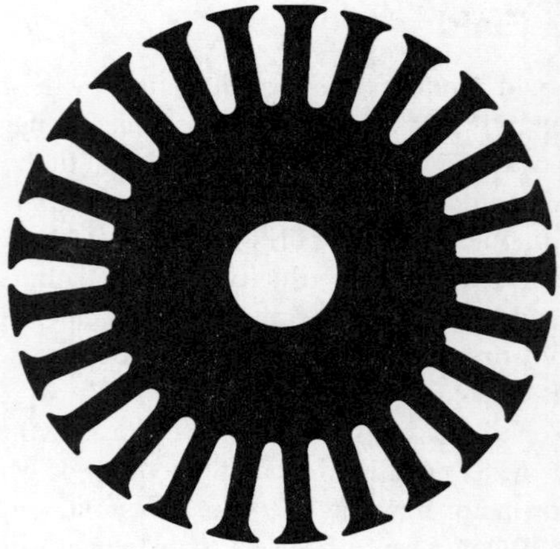

Figure 4.31
Armature lamination with tapered slots.

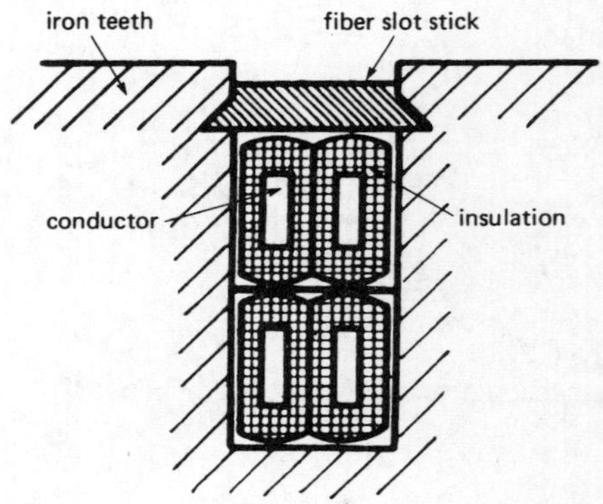

Figure 4.32
Crosssection of a slot containing 4 conductors.

4.25 Commutator and brushes

The commutator is composed of an assembly of tapered copper segments insulated from each other by mica sheets, and mounted on the shaft of the machine (Fig. 4.33). The armature conductors are connected to the commutator in a manner we will explain in Section 4.26.

Great care is taken in building the commutator because any eccentricity will cause the brushes to bounce, producing unacceptable sparking. The sparks burn the brushes and overheat and carbonize the commutator.

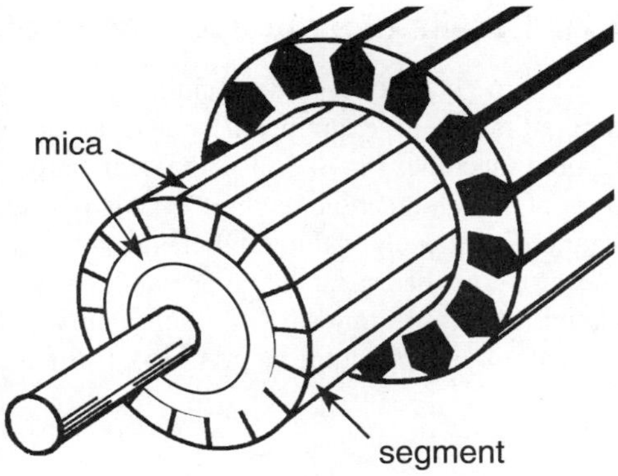

Figure 4.33
Commutator of a dc machine.

A 2-pole generator has two brushes fixed diametrically opposite to each other (Fig. 4.34a). They slide on the commutator and ensure good electrical contact between the revolving armature and the stationary external load.

Multipole machines possess as many brush sets as they have poles. The brush sets, in turn, are composed of one or more brushes, depending upon the current that has to be carried. In Fig. 4.35c, for example, two brushes mounted side by side make up the brush set. The brush sets are spaced at equal intervals around the commutator. They are supported by a movable brush yoke that permits the entire brush assembly to be rotated through an angle and then locked in the neutral position. In going around the commutator, the successive brush sets have positive and negative polarities. Brushes having the same polarity are connected together and the leads are brought out to one positive and one negative terminal (Fig. 4.34b).

The brushes are made of carbon because it has good electrical conductivity and its softness does not score the commutator. To improve the conductivity, a small amount of copper is sometimes mixed with the carbon. The brush pressure is set by means of adjustable springs. If the pressure is too great, the friction produces excessive heating of the commutator and brushes; on the other hand, if it is too weak, the imperfect contact may produce sparking.

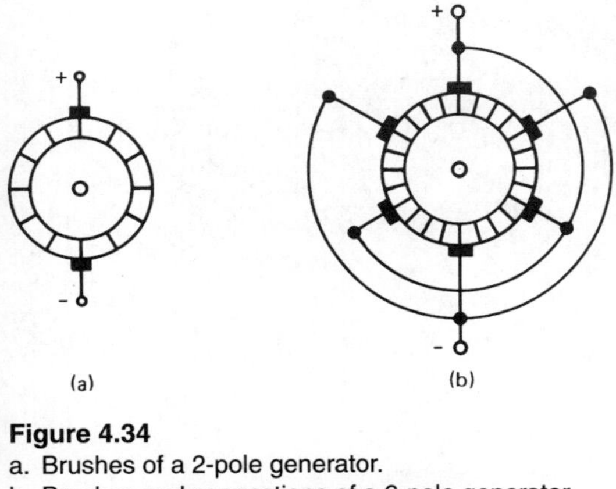

Figure 4.34
a. Brushes of a 2-pole generator.
b. Brushes and connections of a 6-pole generator.

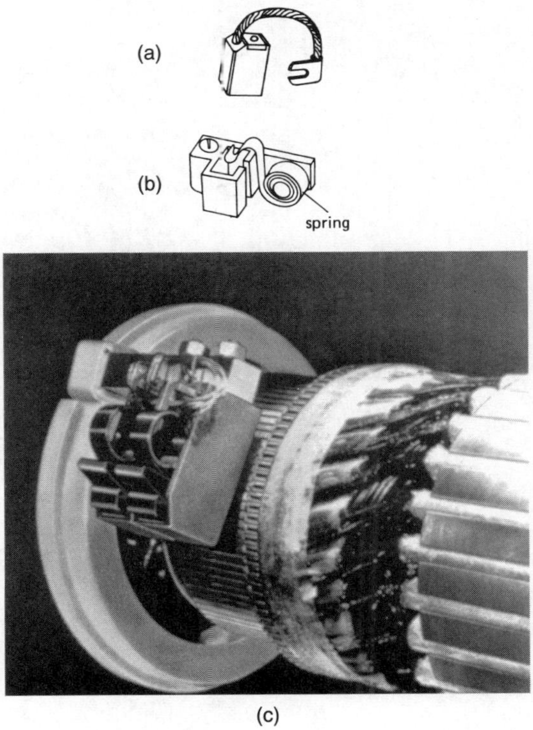

Figure 4.35
a. Carbon brush and ultraflexible copper lead.
b. Brush holder and spring to exert pressure.
c. Brush set composed of two brushes, mounted on rocker arm.
(Courtesy of General Electric Company, USA)

The pressure is usually about 15 kPa ($\approx$ 2 lb/in^2), and the permissible current density is approximately 10 A/cm^2 ($\approx$ 65 A/in^2). Thus, a typical brush having a cross section of 3 cm $\times$ 1 cm ($\approx$ 1.2 in $\times$ 0.4 in) exerts a pressure of 4.5 N ($\approx$ 1 lb) and can carry a current of about 30 A.

Fig. 4.36 shows the construction of a modern 4-pole dc generator. In order to appreciate the progress that has been made, Fig. 4.37 shows a generator that was built in 1889.

4.26 Details of a multipole generator

In order to get a better understanding of multipole generators, let us examine the construction of a 12-pole machine. Fig. 4.38a is the schematic diagram of such a machine having 72 slots on the armature, 72 segments on the commutator, and 72 coils. The armature has a lap winding, and the reader should note how similar it is to the schematic diagram of a 2-pole machine (Fig. 4.11b). Coils A and

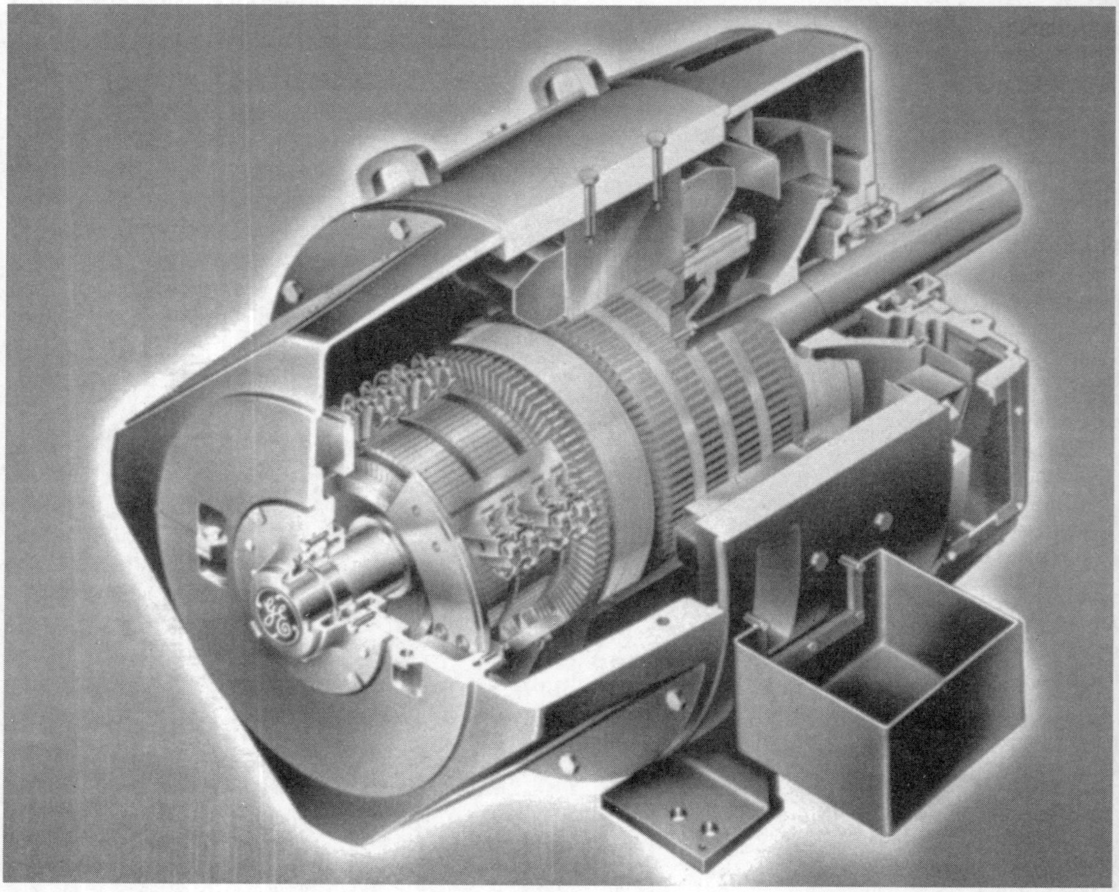

Figure 4.36
Sectional view of a 100 kW, 250 V, 1750 r/min 4-pole dc generator.
(Courtesy of General Electric Company, USA)

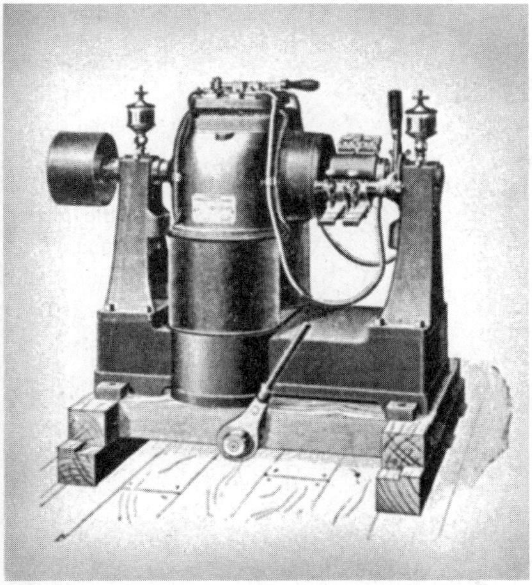

Figure 4.37
This direct-current Thompson generator was first installed in 1889 to light the streets of Montreal. It delivered a current of 250 A at a voltage of 110 V. Other properties of this pioneering machine include the following:

Speed	1300 r/min
Total weight	2390 kg
Armature diameter	292 mm
Stator internal diameter	330 mm
Number of commutator bars	76
Armature conductor size	# 4
Shunt field conductor size	# 14

A modern generator having the same power and speed weighs 7 times less and occupies only 1/3 the floor space.

C are momentarily in the neutral zone, while coil B is cutting the flux coming from the center of the poles.

The coil width (known as *coil pitch*) is such that the coil sides cut the flux coming from adjacent N, S poles. Thus, the coil sides of coil B lie under the center of pole 2 and the center of pole 3. Similarly, the coil sides of coil A are in the neutral zones between poles 1, 2 and poles 2, 3.

The voltage generated between brushes **x** and **y** is equal to the sum of the voltages generated by the five coils connected to commutator segments 1-2, 2-3, 3-4, 4-5, and 5-6. The voltages between the other brush sets are similarly generated by five coils.

The (+) brush sets are connected together to form the (+) terminal. The (−) brush sets are similarly connected to form the (−) terminal. These connections are not shown on the diagram. For similar reasons of clarity, we do not show the interpoles that are placed between the N, S poles.

Fig. 4.38b gives a detailed view of the armature coils lying between brushes **x** and **y.** Only the three coils A, B, and C are shown so as not to complicate the diagram. Coil A has its coil sides in slots 1 and 7, while those of coil B are in slots 4 and 10. Furthermore, coil A is connected to commutator segments 72 and 1, while coil B is connected to segments 3 and 4.

In the position shown, the coil-sides of coil A are in the neutral zone between the poles. Consequently, no voltage is induced in coil A. On the other hand, the coil sides of B are directly under the N and S poles. The voltage in coil B is maximum at this moment. Consequently, the voltage between adjacent commutator segments 3 and 4 is maximum.

The voltage in coil C is also zero because its coil sides are sweeping across the neutral zone. Note that the positive and negative brushes each short-circuit coils having zero induced voltage.

Example 4-2

The generator in Fig. 4.38 generates 240 V between adjacent brushes and delivers a current of 2400 A to the load.

Calculate

a. The current delivered per brush set
b. The current flowing in each coil
c. The average voltage induced per coil

Solution

a. A current of 2400 A flows out of the (+) terminal and back into the (−) terminal of the generator. There are 12 brush sets, 6 positive and 6 negative. The current per brush set is

$$I = 2400/6 = 400 \text{ A}$$

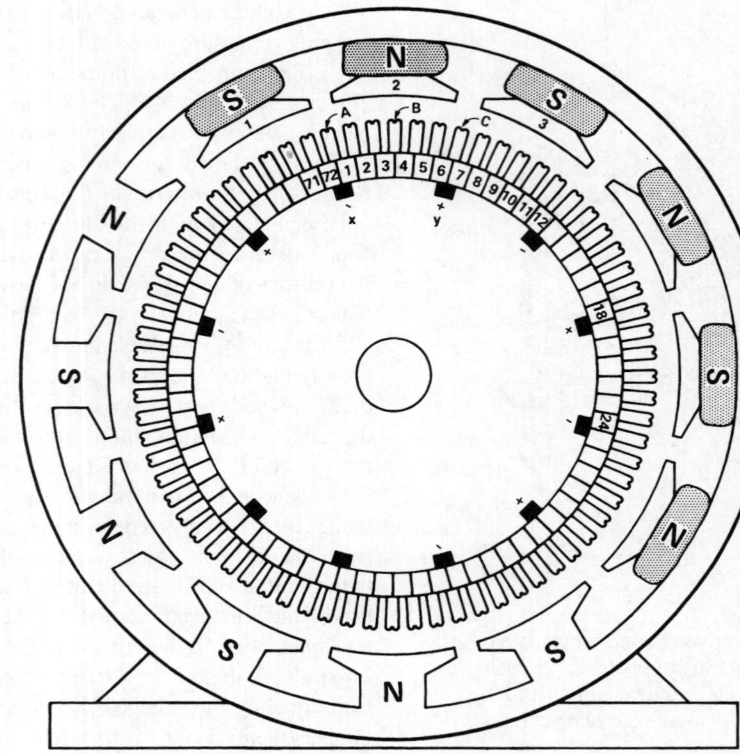

Figure 4.38a
Schematic diagram of a 12-pole, 72-coil dc generator.

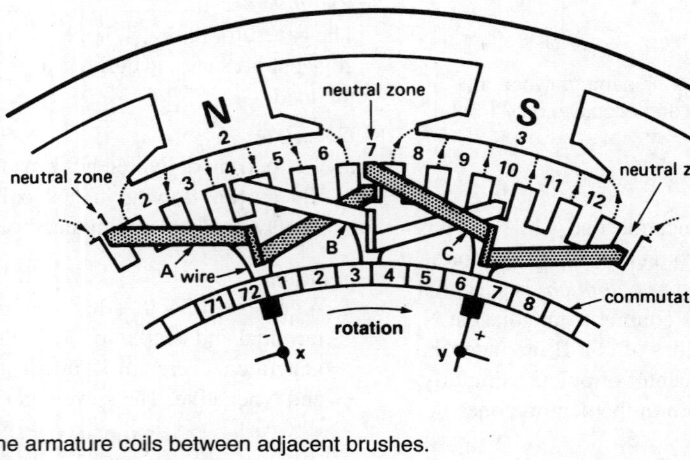

Figure 4.38b
Close-up view of the armature coils between adjacent brushes.

b. Each positive brush set gathers current from the coils to the right and to the left of the brush. Consequently, the current in each coil is

$$I = 400/2 = 200 \text{ A}$$

c. There are six coils between adjacent brush sets. The average voltage per coil is

$$E_{\text{avge}} = 240/6 = 40 \text{ V}$$

4.27 The ideal commutation process

When a generator is under load, the individual coils on the armature carry one-half the load current carried by one brush. The currents flowing in the armature windings next to a positive brush are shown in Fig. 4.39a. Note that the currents in the coils flow toward the brush, coming both from the right and the left. If the load current is 80 A, the coils all carry 40 A.

If the commutator segments are moving from right to left, the coils on the right-hand side of the brush will soon be on the left-hand side. This means that the current in these coils must reverse. The reversal takes place during the millisecond interval that a coil takes to move from one end of the brush to the other. The process whereby the current changes direction in this brief interval is called *commutation.*

To understand how commutation takes place, we refer to Figs. 4.39a to 4.39e.

In Fig. 4.39a the brush is in the middle of segment 1, and the 40 A from the coils on the right and the left of the brush unite to give the 80 A output. The contact resistance between the segment and brush produces a voltage drop of about 1 V.

In Fig. 4.39b the commutator has moved a short distance, and 25 percent of the brush surface is now in contact with segment 2, while 75 percent is in contact with segment 1. Owing to the contact resistance, the *conductivity* between the brush and commutator is proportional to the contact area. The area in contact with segment 2 is only one-fourth of the total contact area, and so the current from segment 2 is only one-fourth of the total current, namely $0.25 \times 80 = 20$ A. By the

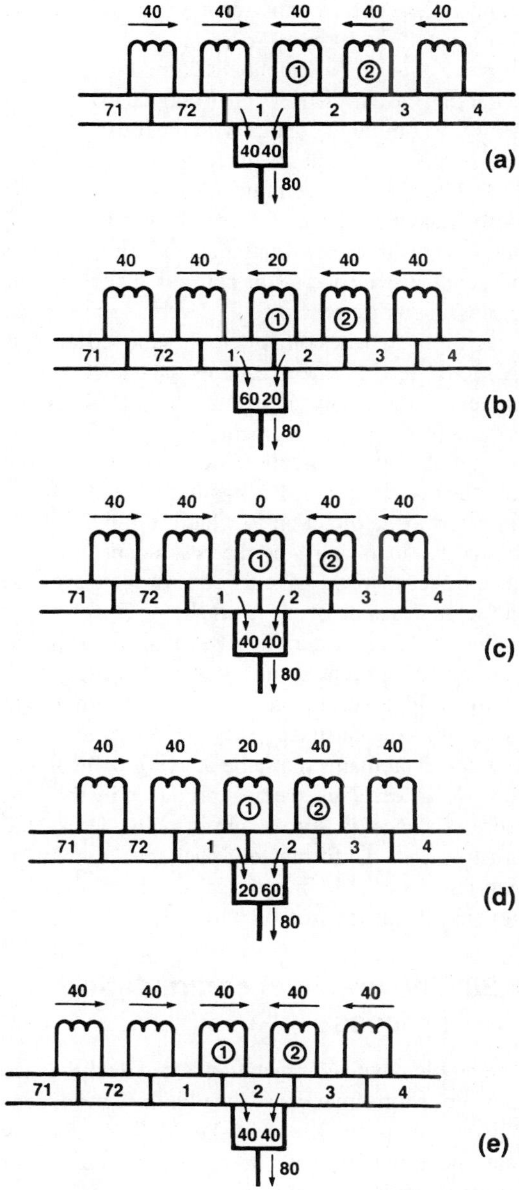

Figure 4.39
Commutation of the current in coil 1. Inductive effects are neglected and current reversal is caused by the brush contact resistance.

same token, the current from segment 1 to the brush is $0.75 \times 80 = 60$ A.

If we now apply Kirchhoff's current law, we discover that the current flowing in coil 1 must be 20 A. Thus, by coming in contact with the brush, the current in this coil has dropped from 40 A to 20 A.

In Fig. 4.39c the commutator has moved a little further, and the brush area in contact with segments 1 and 2 is now the same. Consequently, the conductivities are the same and so the currents are equal. This means that the current in coil 1 is zero at this instant.

In Fig. 4.39d the commutator has moved still farther to the left. Segment 2 is now in contact with 75 percent of the brush, and so the currents divide accordingly: 60 A from segment 2 and 20 A from segment 1. Applying Kirchhoff's current law, we find that the current in coil 1 is again 20 A, but it flows in the opposite direction to what it did before! We can now understand how the brush contact resistance forces a progressive reversal of the current as the segments slide over the brush.

In Fig. 4.39e the current reversal in coil 1 is complete and the current in coil 2 is about to be reversed.

In this ideal commutation process, it is important to note that the current density (amperes per square centimeter) remains the same at every point across the brush face. Thus, the heat produced by the contact resistance is spread uniformally across the brush surface. Unfortunately, such ideal commutation is not possible in practical machines, and we now investigate the reason why.

4.28 The practical commutation process

The problem with commutation is that it takes place in a very short time; consequently, the current cannot reverse as quickly as it should. The reason is that the armature coils have inductance and it strongly opposes a rapid change in current.

Suppose, for example, that the commutator in Fig. 4.39 has 72 bars and that the armature turns at 600 r/min. One revolution is, therefore, completed in 1/10 of a second and during this short period 72 commutator bars sweep past the brush. Thus, the time available to reverse the current in coil 1 is only $1/10 \times 1/72 = 1/720$ s or 1.39 ms!

The voltage induced by self-induction is given by

$$e = L\Delta I/\Delta t \tag{4.2}$$

in which

e = induced voltage [V]

L = inductance of the coil [H]

$\Delta I/\Delta t$ = rate of change of current [A/s]

If coil 1 has an inductance of, say, 100 μH, the induced voltage is

$$\begin{aligned} e &= L\Delta I/\Delta t \\ &= \frac{100 \times 10^{-6} \times [+40 - (-40)]}{1.39 \times 10^{-3}} \\ &= 5.75 \text{ V} \end{aligned}$$

It is the presence of this induced voltage (attributable to L), that opposes the change in current.

Figs. 4.40a to 4.40e illustrate the new currents that flow in coil 1 when the self-inductance of the coil is considered. We have assumed plausible values for these currents in order to determine the resulting current flows in the brush. The currents should be compared with those in Fig. 4.39.

In Fig. 4.40a the brush is in the middle of segment 1, and the currents in the coils are neither increasing or decreasing. As a result, the coil inductance does not come into play.

In Fig. 4.40b the current in coil 1 is changing due to the contact resistance effect. However, the induced voltage e prevents the current from dropping to its ideal value of 20 A. Suppose the coil current is 35 A. From Kirchhoff's current law, the currents flowing from segments 1 and 2 into the brush are then respectively 75 A and 5 A, instead of 60 A and 20 A. Note that the current density is no longer uniform over the brush face. The density is low where the brush touches segment 2, and high where it touches segment 1.

In Fig. 4.40c the brush is momentarily symmetrically placed as regards segments 1 and 2. But the current in coil 1 has not fallen to zero, and is still, say,

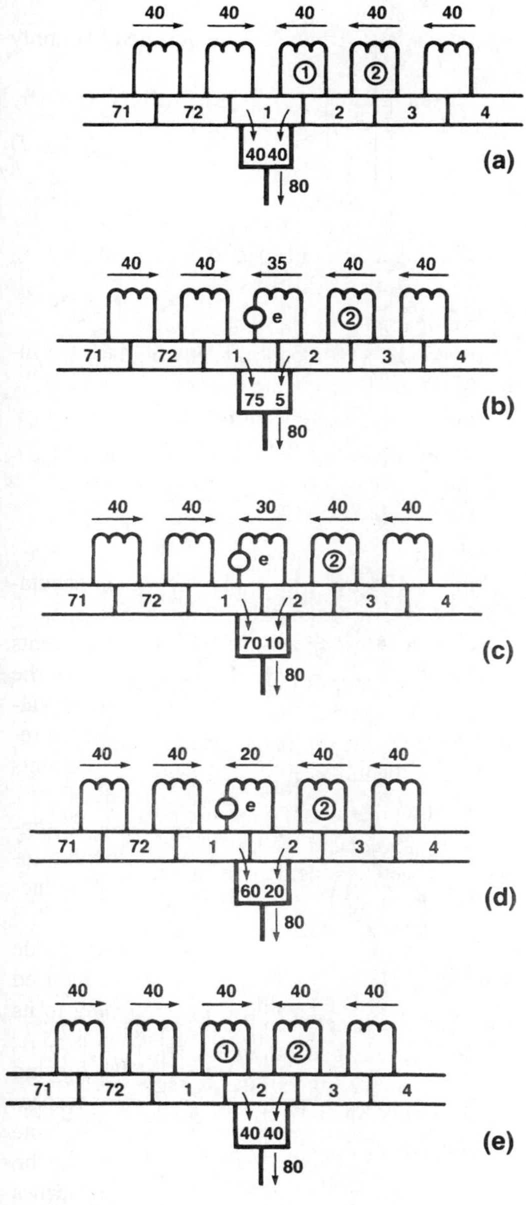

Figure 4.40
Commutation of the current in coil 1. The coil inductance opposes the reversal of current.

30 A. As a result, the current in segment 1 is 70 A while that in segment 2 is only 10 A. The current density on the left-hand side of the brush is, therefore, 7 times greater than on the right-hand side. The left-hand side of the brush will tend to overheat.

In Fig. 4.40d segment 1 has moved beyond the midpoint of the brush and the current in coil 1 has *still* not reversed. Assuming it has a value of 20 A, the current flowing from segment 1 to the brush is now 60 A, despite the fact that the contact area is getting very small. The resulting high current density causes the brush to overheat at the tip. Because 720 coils are being commutated every second, this overheating raises the brush tip to the incandescent point and serious sparking will result.

In designing dc motors and generators, every effort is made to reduce the self-inductance of the coils. One of the most effective ways is to reduce the number of turns per coil. But for a given output voltage, this means that the number of coils must be increased. And more coils implies more commutator bars. Thus, in practice, direct-current generators have a large number of coils and commutator bars—not so much to reduce the ripple in the output voltage but to overcome the problem of commutation.

Another important factor in aiding commutation is that the mmf of the commutating poles is always made slightly greater than the armature mmf. Therefore, a small flux is created in the neutral zone. As the coil side undergoing commutation sweeps through this flux, a voltage is induced in the coil which opposes the voltage due to the selfinductance of the coil.

In addition to these measures, the composition of the brush is carefully chosen. It affects the brush voltage drop, which can vary from 0.2 V to as much as 1.5 V. This drop occurs between the surface of the brush and the commutator surface. A large brush drop helps commutation, but unfortunately it increases the losses. As a result, the commutator and brushes become hotter and the efficiency of the generator is slightly reduced.

Questions and Problems

Practical level

4-1 Sketch the main components of a dc generator.

4-2 Why are the brushes of a dc machine always placed at the neutral points?

4-3 Describe the construction of a commutator.

4-4 How is the induced voltage of a separately excited dc generator affected if
a. the speed increases?
b. the exciting current is reduced?

4-5 How do we adjust the voltage of a shunt generator?

4-6 The terminal voltage of a shunt generator decreases with increasing load. Explain.

4-7 Explain why the output voltage of an over-compound generator increases as the load increases.

4-8 Explain the difference between shunt, compound, and differential compound generators
a. as to construction
b. as to electrical properties

Intermediate level

4-9 A separate excited dc generator turning at 1400 r/min produces an induced voltage of 127 V. The armature resistance is 2 Ω and the machine delivers a current of 12 A.

Calculate

a. the terminal voltage [V]
b. the heat dissipated in the armature [W]
c. the braking torque exerted by the armature [N·m]

4-10 A separately excited dc generator produces a no-load voltage of 115 V. What happens if
a. the speed is increased by 20 percent?
b. the direction of rotation is reversed?
c. the exciting current is increased by 10 percent?
d. the polarity of the field is reversed?

4-11 Each pole of a 100 kW, 250 V flat-compound generator has a shunt field of 2000 turns and a series field of 7 turns. If the total shunt-field resistance is 100 Ω, calculate the mmf when the machine operates at rated voltage
a. at no-load
b. at full-load

4-12 Fig. 4.18b shows the no-load saturation curve of a separately excited dc generator when it revolves at 1500 r/min. Calculate the exciting current needed to generate 120 V at 1330 r/min.

4-13 Referring to Fig. 4.10, the induced voltage in coil D is momentarily 18 V, in the position shown. Calculate the voltages induced in coils A, B, and C at the same instant.

4-14 Referring to Fig. 4.11b, calculate the voltage induced in coil A when the armature has rotated by 90°; by 120°.

4-15 Brush **x** is positive with respect to brush **y** in Fig. 4.11b. Show the polarity of each of the 12 coils. Does the polarity reverse when a coil turns through 180°?

4-16 The generator of Fig. 4.38 revolves at 960 r/min and the flux per pole is 20 mWb. Calculate the no-load armature voltage if each armature coil has 6 turns.

4-17 **a.** How many brush sets are needed for the generator in Fig. 4.38?
b. If the machine delivers a total load current of 1800 A, calculate the current flowing in each armature coil.

Advanced level

4-18 The voltage between brushes **x** and **y** is 240 V in the generator shown in Fig. 4.38. Why can we say that the voltage between segments 3 and 4 *must* be greater than 40 V?

4-19 Referring to Fig. 4.10, determine the polarity of E_{xy} when the armature turns counter-clockwise.

4-20 **a.** In Fig. 4.38 determine the polarity of E_{34} between commutator segments 3 and 4, knowing that the armature is turning clockwise.

b. At the same instant, what is the polarity of segment 35 with respect to segment 34?

4-21 The armature shown in Fig. 5.4 (Chapter 5) has 81 slots, and the commutator has 243 segments. It will be wound to give a 6-pole lap winding having 1 turn per coil. If the flux per field pole is 30 mWb, calculate the following:

a. The induced voltage at a speed of 1200 r/min
b. The average flux density per pole
c. The time needed to reverse the current in each armature coil, knowing that the brushes are 15 mm wide and that the diameter of the commutator is 450 mm

4-22 A 200 W, 120 V, 1800 r/min dc generator has 75 commutator bars. The brush width is such as to cover 3 commutator segments. Show that the duration of the commutation process is equal to 1.33 ms.

4-23 A 4-pole 250 kW, 750V dc generator has a lap winding on the armature.

Calculate

a. the full-load current of the generator
b. the current carried by the armature coils

Industrial Application

4-24 A 240 kW, 500 V 1750 r/min separately excited dc generator has an overall efficiency of 94%. The shunt field resistance is 60 ohms and the rated current is 5 A. The I^2R loss in the armature is 0.023 pu.

Calculate

a. the rated armature current
b. the total losses in the machine
c. the I^2R losses in the armature

4-25 The generator in Problem 4-24 weighs 2600 lb. Calculate the output in watts per kilogram.

4-26 In Problem 4-24 calculate the torque required to drive the generator at 1750 r/min. (The shunt field is powered by a separate source.)

4-27 A 4-pole dc generator delivers a current of 218 A. The average brush voltage drop on each of the four brush sets is found to be 0.6 V. Calculate the total brush loss in the machine, neglecting friction loss.

CHAPTER 5

Direct-Current Motors

5.0 Introduction

Now that we have a good understanding of dc generators, we can begin our study of dc motors. Direct-current motors transform electrical energy into mechanical energy. They drive devices such as hoists, fans, pumps, calendars, punch-presses, and cars. These devices may have a definite torque-speed characteristic (such as a pump or fan) or a highly variable one (such as a hoist or automobile). The torque-speed characteristic of the motor must be adapted to the type of the load it has to drive, and this requirement has given rise to three basic types of motors:

1. Shunt motors
2. Series motors
3. Compound motors

Direct-current motors are seldom used in ordinary industrial applications because all electric utility systems furnish alternating current. However, for special applications such as in steel mills, mines, and electric trains, it is sometimes advantageous to transform the alternating current into direct current in order to use dc motors. The reason is that the torque-speed characteristics of dc motors can be varied over a wide range while retaining high efficiency.

Today, this general statement can be challenged because the availability of sophisticated electronic drives has made it possible to use alternating current motors for variable speed applications. Nevertheless, there are millions of dc motors still in service and thousands more are being produced every year.

5.1 Counter-electromotive force (cemf)

Direct-current motors are built the same way as generators are; consequently, a dc machine can operate either as a motor or as a generator. To illustrate, consider a dc generator in which the armature, initially at rest, is connected to a dc source E_s by means of a switch (Fig. 5.1). The armature has a resistance R, and the magnetic field is created by a set of permanent magnets.

As soon as the switch is closed, a large current flows in the armature because its resistance is very low. The individual armature conductors are immediately subjected to a force because they are immersed in the magnetic field created by the permanent magnets. These forces add up to produce a powerful torque, causing the armature to rotate.

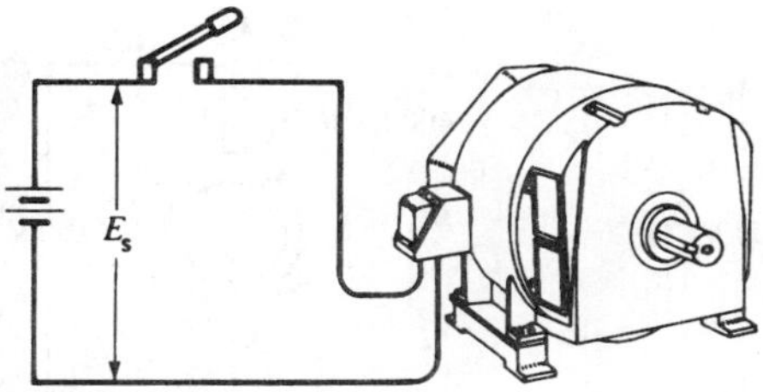

Figure 5.1
Starting a dc motor across the line.

On the other hand, as soon as the armature begins to turn, a second phenomenon takes place: the generator effect. We know that a voltage E_o is induced in the armature conductors as soon as they cut a magnetic field (Fig. 5.2). This is always true, *no matter what causes the rotation.* The value and polarity of the induced voltage are the same as those obtained when the machine operates as a generator. The induced voltage E_o is therefore proportional to the speed of rotation n of the motor and to the flux Φ per pole, as previously given by Eq. 4.1:

$$E_o = Zn\Phi/60 \tag{4.1}$$

As in the case of a generator, Z is a constant that depends upon the number of turns on the armature and the type of winding. For lap windings Z is equal to the number of armature conductors.

In the case of a motor, the induced voltage E_o is called *counter-electromotive force* (cemf) because its polarity always acts *against* the source voltage E_s. It acts against the voltage in the sense that the net voltage acting in the series circuit of Fig. 5.2 is equal to $(E_s - E_o)$ volts and not $(E_s + E_o)$ volts.

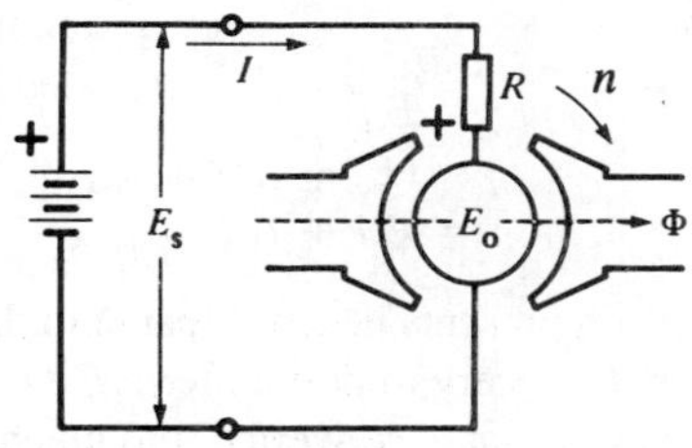

Figure 5.2
Counter-electromotive force (cemf) in a dc motor.

5.2 Acceleration of the motor

The net voltage acting in the armature circuit in Fig. 5.2 is $(E_s - E_o)$ volts. The resulting armature current I is limited only by the armature resistance R, and so

$$I = (E_s - E_o)/R \tag{5.1}$$

When the motor is at rest, the induced voltage $E_o = 0$, and so the starting current is

$$I = E_s/R$$

The starting current may be 20 to 30 times greater than the nominal full-load current of the motor. In practice, this would cause the fuses to blow or the circuit-breakers to trip. However, if they are absent, the large forces acting on the armature conductors produce a powerful starting torque and a consequent rapid acceleration of the armature.

As the speed increases, the counter-emf E_o increases, with the result that the value of $(E_s - E_o)$ diminishes. It follows from Eq. 5.1 that the armature current I drops progressively as the speed increases.

Although the armature current decreases, the motor continues to accelerate until it reaches a definite, maximum speed. At no-load this speed produces a counter-emf E_o slightly less than the source voltage E_s. In effect, if E_o *were* equal to E_s, the net voltage $(E_s - E_o)$ would become zero and so, too, would the current I. The driving forces would cease to act on the armature conductors, and the mechanical drag imposed by the fan and the bearings would immediately cause the motor to slow down. As the speed decreases the net voltage $(E_s - E_o)$ increases and so does the current I. The speed will cease to fall as soon as the torque developed by the armature current is equal to the load torque. Thus, when a motor runs at no-load, the counter-emf must be slightly less than E_s, so as to enable a small current to flow, sufficient to produce the required torque.

Example 5-1

The armature of a permanent-magnet dc generator has a resistance of 1 Ω and generates a voltage of 50 V when the speed is 500 r/min. If the armature

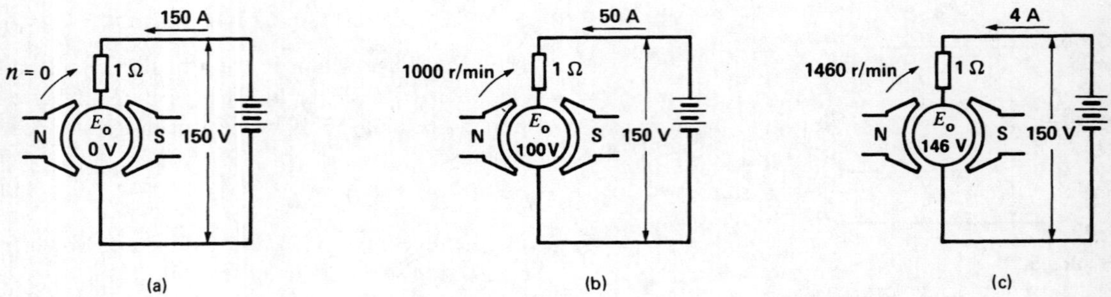

Figure 5.3
See Example 5-1.

is connected to a source of 150 V, calculate the following:

a. The starting current
b. The counter-emf when the motor runs at 1000 r/min. At 1460 r/min.
c. The armature current at 1000 r/min. At 1460 r/min.

Solution

a. At the moment of start-up, the armature is stationary, so $E_o = 0$ V (Fig. 5.3a). The starting current is limited only by the armature resistance:

$$I = E_s/R = 150\text{ V}/1\ \Omega = 150\text{ A}$$

b. Because the generator voltage is 50 V at 500 r/min, the cemf of the motor will be 100 V at 1000 r/min and 146 V at 1460 r/min.
c. The net voltage in the armature circuit at 1000 r/min is

$$E_s - E_o = 150 - 100 = 50\text{ V}$$

The corresponding armature current is

$$\begin{aligned} I &= (E_s - E_o)/R \\ &= 50/1 = 50\text{ A (Fig. 5.3b)} \end{aligned}$$

When the motor speed reaches 1460 r/min, the cemf will be 146 V, almost equal to the source voltage. Under these conditions, the armature current is only

$$\begin{aligned} I &= (E_s - E_o)/R = (150 - 146)/1 \\ &= 4\text{ A} \end{aligned}$$

and the corresponding motor torque is much smaller than before (Fig. 5.3c).

5.3 Mechanical power and torque

The power and torque of a dc motor are two of its most important properties. We now derive two simple equations that enable us to calculate them.

1. According to Eq. 4.1 the cemf induced in a lap-wound armature is given by

$$E_o = Zn\Phi/60 \qquad (4.1)$$

Referring to Fig. 5.2, the electrical power P_a supplied to the armature is equal to the supply voltage E_s multiplied by the armature current I:

$$P_a = E_sI \qquad (5.2)$$

However, E_s is equal to the sum of E_o plus the IR drop in the armature:

$$E_s = E_o + IR \qquad (5.3)$$

It follows that

$$\begin{aligned} P_a &= E_sI \\ &= (E_o + IR)I \\ &= E_oI + I^2R \qquad (5.4) \end{aligned}$$

The I^2R term represents heat dissipated in the armature, but the very important term E_oI is the electrical power that is converted into mechanical power. The mechanical power of the motor is therefore exactly equal to the product of the cemf multiplied by the armature current

$$P = E_o I \quad (5.5)$$

where

P = mechanical power developed by the motor [W]
E_o = induced voltage in the armature (cemf) [V]
I = total current supplied to the armature [A]

2. Turning our attention to torque T, we know that the mechanical power P is given by the expression

$$P = nT/9.55 \quad (3.5)$$

where n is the speed of rotation.

Combining Eqs. 3.5, 4.1, and 5.5, we obtain

$$nT/9.55 = E_o I$$
$$= Zn\Phi I/60$$

and so

$$T = Z\Phi I/6.28$$

The torque developed by a lap-wound motor is therefore given by the expression

$$T = Z\Phi I/6.28 \quad (5.6)$$

where

T = torque [N·m]
Z = number of conductors on the armature
Φ = effective flux per pole [Wb]*
I = armature current [A]
6.28 = constant, to take care of units [exact value = 2π]

Eq. 5.6 shows that we can raise the torque of a motor either by raising the armature current or by raising the flux created by the poles.

Example 5-2

The following details are given on a 225 kW (≈ 300 hp), 250 V, 1200 r/min dc motor (see Figs. 5.4 and 5.5):

armature coils	243
turns per coil	1
type of winding	lap
armature slots	81
commutator segments	243
field poles	6
diameter of armature	559 mm
axial length of armature	235 mm

* The effective flux is given by $\Phi = 60\ E_o/Zn$.

Figure 5.4
Bare armature and commutator of a dc motor rated 225 kW, 250 V, 1200 r/min. The armature core has a diameter of 559 mm and an axial length of 235 mm. It is composed of 400 stacked laminations 0.56 mm thick. The armature has 81 slots and the commutator has 243 bars.
(*H. Roberge*)

Figure 5.5
a. Armature of Fig. 5.4 in the process of being wound; coil-forming machine gives the coils the desired shape.
b. One of the 81 coils ready to be placed in the slots.
c. Connecting the coil ends to the commutator bars.
d. Commutator connections ready for brazing.
(*H. Roberge*)

Calculate

a. The rated armature current
b. The number of conductors per slot
c. The flux per pole

Solution

a. We can assume that the induced voltage E_o is nearly equal to the applied voltage (250 V). The rated armature current is

$$I = P/E_o = 225\,000/250$$
$$= 900 \text{ A}$$

b. Each coil is made up of 2 conductors, so altogether there are $243 \times 2 = 486$ conductors on the armature.

$$\text{Conductors per slot} = 486/81 = 6$$
$$\text{Coil sides per slot} = 6$$

c. The motor torque is

$$T = 9.55\,P/n$$
$$= 9.55 \times 225\,000/1200$$
$$= 1791 \text{ N·m}$$

The flux per pole is

$$\Phi = 6.28\,T/ZI$$
$$= (6.28 \times 1790)/(486 \times 900)$$
$$= 25.7 \text{ mWb}$$

5.4 Speed of rotation

When a dc motor drives a load between no-load and full-load, the *IR* drop due to armature resistance is always small compared to the supply voltage E_s. This means that the counter-emf E_o is very nearly equal to E_s.

On the other hand, we have already seen that E_o may be expressed by the equation

$$E_o = Zn\Phi/60 \qquad (4.1)$$

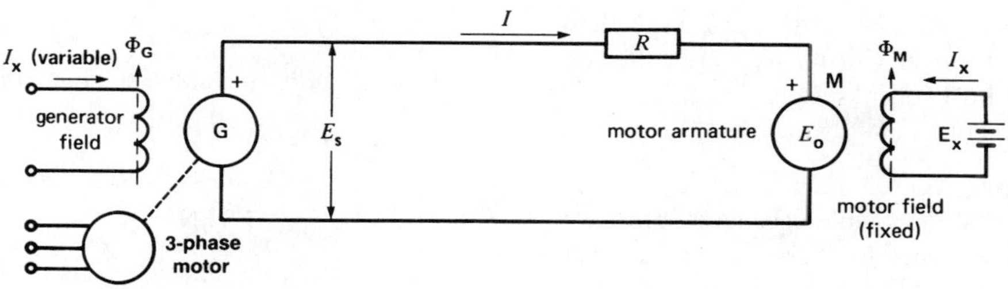

Figure 5.6
Ward-Leonard speed control system.

Replacing E_o by E_s, we obtain

$$E_s = Zn\Phi/60$$

That is,

$$n = \frac{60E_s}{Z\Phi}\text{(approx.)} \tag{5.7}$$

where

n = speed of rotation [r/min]
E_s = armature voltage [V]
Z = total number of armature conductors

This important equation shows that the speed of the motor is directly proportional to the armature supply voltage and inversely proportional to the flux per pole. We will now study how this equation is applied.

5.5 Armature speed control

According to Eq. 5.7, if the flux per pole Φ is kept constant (permanent magnet field or field with fixed excitation), the speed depends only upon the armature voltage E_s. By raising or lowering E_s, the motor speed will rise and fall in proportion.

In practice, we can vary E_s by connecting the motor armature M to a separately excited variable-voltage dc generator G (Fig. 5.6). The field excitation of the motor is kept constant, but the generator excitation I_x can be varied from zero to maximum and even reversed. The generator output voltage E_s can therefore be varied from zero to maximum, with either positive or negative polarity. Consequently, the motor speed can be varied from zero to maximum in either direction. Note that the generator is driven by an ac motor connected to a 3-phase line. This method of speed control, known as the Ward-Leonard system, is found in steel mills, high-rise elevators, mines, and paper mills.

In modern installations the generator is often replaced by a high-power electronic converter that changes the ac power of the electrical utility to dc, by electronic means.

The Ward-Leonard system is more than just a simple way of applying a variable dc voltage to the armature of a dc motor. It can actually force the motor to develop the torque and speed required by the load. For example, suppose E_s is adjusted to be slightly higher than the cemf E_o of the motor. Current will then flow in the direction shown in Fig. 5.6, and the motor develops a positive torque. The armature of the motor absorbs power because I flows into the positive terminal.

Now, suppose we reduce E_s by reducing the generator excitation Φ_G. As soon as E_s becomes less than E_o, current I reverses. As a result, (1) the motor torque reverses and (2) the armature of the motor *delivers* power to generator G. In effect, the dc motor suddenly becomes a generator and generator G suddenly becomes a motor. The electric power that the dc motor now delivers to G is derived at the expense of the kinetic energy of the rapidly decelerating armature and its connected mechanical load. Thus, by reducing E_s, the motor is suddenly forced to slow down.

What happens to the dc power received by generator G? When G receives electric power, it operates as a motor, driving its own ac motor as an asynchronous generator!* As a result, ac power is fed

* The asynchronous generator is explained in Chapter 14.

back into the line that normally feeds the ac motor. The fact that power can be recovered this way makes the Ward-Leonard system very efficient, and constitutes another of its advantages.

Example 5-3

A 2000 kW, 500 V, variable-speed motor is driven by a 2500 kW generator, using a Ward-Leonard control system shown in Fig. 5.6. The total resistance of the motor and generator armature circuit is 10 mΩ. The motor turns at a nominal speed of 300 r/min, when E_o is 500 V.

Calculate

a. The motor torque and speed when

$$E_s = 400 \text{ V and } E_o = 380 \text{ V}$$

b. The motor torque and speed when

$$E_s = 350 \text{ V and } E_o = 380 \text{ V}$$

Solution

a. The armature current is

$$I = (E_s - E_o)/R = (400 - 380)/0.01$$
$$= 2000 \text{ A}$$

The power to the motor armature is

$$P = E_oI = 380 \times 2000 = 760 \text{ kW}$$

The motor speed is

$$n = (380 \text{ V}/500 \text{ V}) \times 300 = 228 \text{ r/min}$$

The motor torque is

$$T = 9.55P/n$$
$$= (9.55 \times 760\,000)/228$$
$$= 31.8 \text{ kN·m}$$

b. Because E_o = 380 V, the motor speed is still 228 r/min.

The armature current is

$$I = (E_s - E_o)/R = (350 - 380)/0.01$$
$$= -3000 \text{ A}$$

The current is negative and so it flows in reverse; consequently, the motor torque also reverses.

Power returned by the motor to the generator and the 10 mΩ resistance:

$$P = E_oI = 380 \times 3000 = 1140 \text{ kW}$$

Braking torque developed by the motor:

$$T = 9.55P/n$$
$$= (9.55 \times 1\,140\,000)/228$$
$$= 47.8 \text{ kN·m}$$

The speed of the motor and its connected mechanical load will rapidly drop under the influence of this electromechanical braking torque.

Rheostat Speed Control Another way to control the speed of a dc motor is to place a rheostat in series with the armature (Fig. 5.7). The current in the rheostat produces a voltage drop which subtracts from the fixed source voltage E_s, yielding a smaller supply voltage across the armature. This method enables us to *reduce* the speed below its nominal speed. It is only recommended for small motors because a lot of power and heat is wasted in the rheostat, and the overall efficiency is low. Furthermore, the speed regulation is poor, even for a fixed setting of the rheostat. In effect, the *IR* drop across the rheostat increases as the armature current increases. This produces a substantial drop in speed with increasing mechanical load.

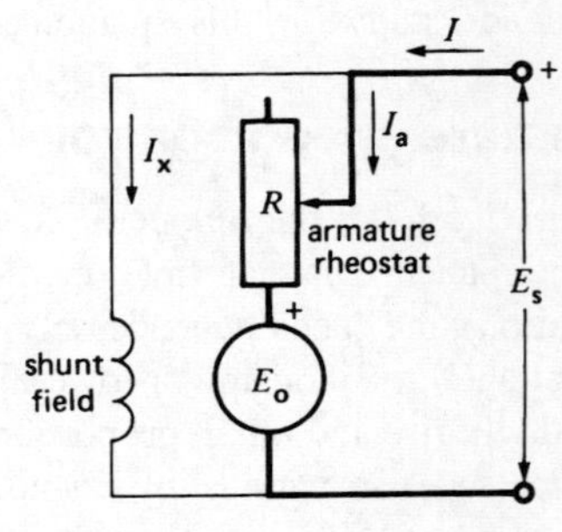

Figure 5.7
Armature speed control using a rheostat.

5.6 Field speed control

According to Eq. 5.7 we can also vary the speed of a dc motor by varying the field flux Φ. Let us now keep the armature voltage E_s constant so that the numerator in Eq. 5.7 is constant. Consequently, the motor speed now changes in inverse proportion to the flux Φ: if we increase the flux the speed will drop, and vice versa.

This method of speed control is frequently used when the motor has to run above its rated speed, called *base speed.* To control the flux (and hence, the speed), we connect a rheostat R_f in series with the field (Fig. 5.8a).

To understand this method of speed control, suppose that the motor in Fig. 5.8a is initially running at constant speed. The counter-emf E_o is slightly less than the armature supply voltage E_s, due to the *IR* drop in the armature. If we suddenly increase the resistance of the rheostat, both the exciting current I_x and the flux Φ will diminish. This immediately reduces the cemf E_o, causing the armature current I to jump to a much higher value. The current changes dramatically because its value depends upon the very small *difference* between E_s and E_o. Despite the weaker field, the motor develops a greater torque than before. It will accelerate until E_o is again almost equal to E_s.

Clearly, to develop the same E_o with a weaker flux, the motor must turn faster. We can therefore raise the motor speed above its nominal value by introducing a resistance in series with the field. For shunt-wound motors, this method of speed control enables high-speed/base-speed ratios as high as 3 to 1. Broader speed ranges tend to produce instability and poor commutation.

Under certain abnormal conditions, the flux may drop to dangerously low values. For example, if the exciting current of a shunt motor is interrupted accidentally, the only flux remaining is that due to the remanent magnetism in the poles.* This flux is so small that the motor has to rotate at a dangerously high speed to induce the required cemf. Safety devices are introduced to prevent such runaway conditions.

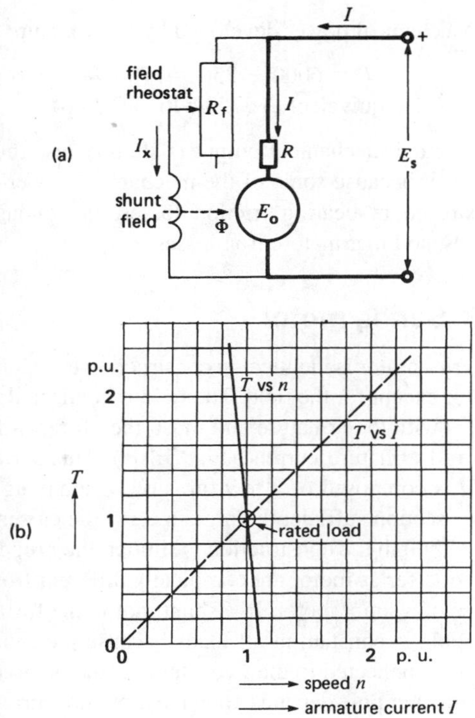

Figure 5.8
a. Schematic diagram of a shunt motor including the field rheostat.
b. Torque-speed and torque-current characteristic of a shunt motor.

5.7 Shunt motor under load

Consider a dc motor running at no-load. If a mechanical load is suddenly applied to the shaft, the small no-load current does not produce enough torque to carry the load and the motor begins to slow down. This causes the cemf to diminish, resulting in a higher current and a corresponding higher torque. When the torque developed by the motor is *exactly* equal to the torque imposed by the mechanical load, then, and only then, will the speed remain constant (see Section 3.11). To sum up, as the mechanical load increases, the armature current rises and the speed drops.

The speed of a shunt motor stays relatively constant from no-load to full-load. In small motors, it only drops by 10 to 15 percent when full-load is

* The term *residual* magnetism is also used. However, the *IEEE Standard Dictionary of Electrical and Electronics Terms* states, ". . . If there are no air gaps . . . in the magnetic circuit, the remanent induction will equal the residual induction; if there are air gaps . . . the remanent induction will be less than the residual induction."

applied. In big machines, the drop is even less, due in part, to the very low armature resistance. By adjusting the field rheostat, the speed can, of course, be kept absolutely constant as the load changes.

Typical torque-speed and torque-current characteristics of a shunt motor are shown in Fig. 5.8b. The speed, torque, and current are given in per-unit values. The torque is directly proportional to the armature current. Furthermore, the speed changes only from 1.1 pu to 0.9 pu as the torque increases from 0 pu to 2 pu.

Example 5-4

A shunt motor rotating at 1500 r/min is fed by a 120 V source (Fig. 5.9a). The line current is 51 A and the shunt-field resistance is 120 Ω. If the armature resistance is 0.1 Ω, calculate the following:

a. The current in the armature
b. The counter-emf
c. The mechanical power developed by the motor

Solution

a. The field current (Fig. 5.9b) is

$$I_x = 120 \text{ V}/120\ \Omega = 1 \text{ A}$$

The armature current is

$$I = 51 - 1 = 50 \text{ A}$$

b. The voltage across the armature is

$$E = 120 \text{ V}$$

Voltage drop due to armature resistance is

$$IR = 50 \times 0.1 = 5 \text{ V}$$

The cemf generated by the armature is

$$E_o = 120 - 5 = 115 \text{ V}$$

c. The total power supplied to the motor is

$$P_i = EI = 120 \times 51 = 6120 \text{ W}$$

Power absorbed by the armature is

$$P_a = EI = 120 \times 50 = 6000 \text{ W}$$

Power dissipated in the armature is

$$P = IR^2 = 50^2 \times 0.1 = 250 \text{ W}$$

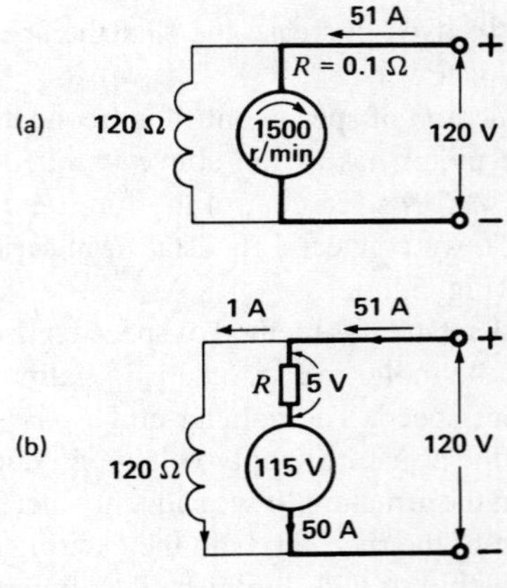

Figure 5.9
See Example 5-4.

Mechanical power developed by the armature is

$$P = 6000 - 250 = 5750 \text{ W}$$
$$(\text{equivalent to } 5750/746 = 7.7 \text{ hp})$$

The actual mechanical output is slightly less than 5750 W because some of the mechanical power is dissipated in bearing friction losses, in windage losses, and in armature iron losses.

5.8 Series motor

A series motor is identical in construction to a shunt motor except for the field. The field is connected in series with the armature and must, therefore, carry the full armature current (Fig. 5.10a). This *series field* is composed of a few turns of wire having a cross section sufficiently large to carry the current.

Although the construction is similar, the properties of a series motor are completely different from those of a shunt motor. In a shunt motor, the flux F per pole is constant at all loads because the shunt field is connected to the line. But in a series motor the flux per pole depends upon the armature current and, hence, upon the load. When the current is large, the flux is large and vice versa. Despite these differences, the same basic principles and equations apply to both machines.

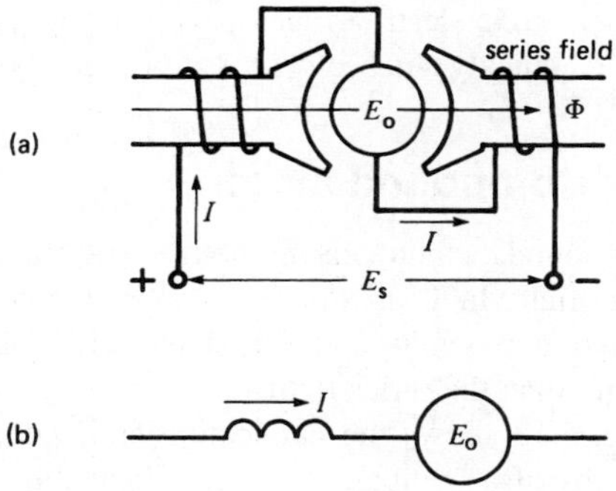

Figure 5.10
a. Series motor connection diagram.
b. Schematic diagram of a series motor.

When a series motor operates at full-load, the flux per pole is the same as that of a shunt motor of identical power and speed. However, when the series motor starts up, the armature current is higher than normal, with the result that the flux per pole is also greater than normal. It follows that the starting torque of a series motor is considerably greater than that of a shunt motor. This can be seen by comparing the *T* versus *I* curves of Figs. 5.8 and 5.11.

On the other hand, if the motor operates at less than full-load, the armature current and the flux per pole are smaller than normal. The weaker field causes the speed to rise in the same way as it would for a shunt motor with a weak shunt field. For example, if the load current of a series motor drops to half its normal value, the flux diminishes by half and so the speed doubles. Obviously, if the load is small, the speed may rise to dangerously high values. For this reason we never permit a series motor to operate at no-load. It tends to run away, and the resulting centrifugal forces could tear the windings out of the armature and destroy the machine.

5.9 Series motor speed control

When a series motor carries a load, its speed may have to be adjusted slightly. Thus, the speed can be increased by placing a low resistance in parallel with the series field. The field current is then smaller than before, which produces a drop in flux and an increase in speed.

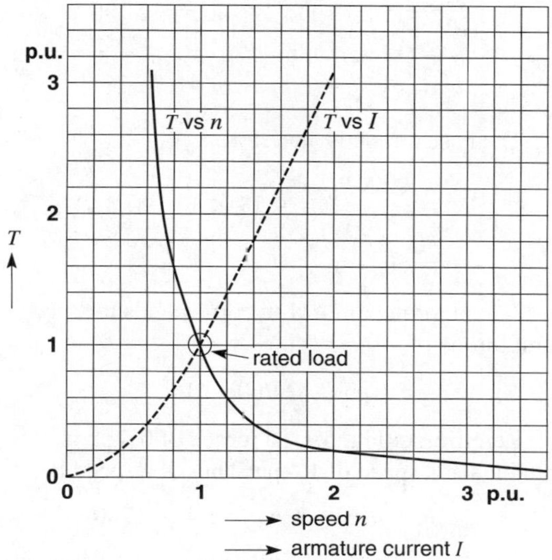

Figure 5.11
Typical speed-torque and current-torque characteristic of a series motor.

Conversely, the speed may be lowered by connecting an external resistor in series with the armature and the field. The total *IR* drop across the resistor and field reduces the armature supply voltage, and so the speed must fall.

Typical torque-speed and torque-current characteristics are shown in Fig. 5.11. They are quite different from the shunt motor characteristics given in Fig. 5.8b.

Example 5-5

A 15 hp, 240 V, 1780 r/min dc series motor has a full-load rated current of 54 A. Its operating characteristics are given by the per-unit curves of Fig. 5.11.

Calculate

a. The current and speed when the load torque is 24 N·m
b. The efficiency under these conditions

Solution

a. We first establish the base power, base speed, and base current of the motor. They correspond to the full-load ratings as follows:

$$P_B = 15 \text{ hp} = 15 \times 746 = 11\,190 \text{ W}$$
$$n_B = 1780 \text{ r/min}$$
$$I_B = 54 \text{ A}$$

The base torque is, therefore,

$$T_B = \frac{9.55\, P_B}{n_B} = 9.55 \times 11\,190/1\,780$$
$$= 60 \text{ N·m}$$

A load torque of 24 N·m corresponds to a per-unit torque of

$$T(\text{pu}) = 24/60 = 0.4$$

Referring to Fig. 5.11, a torque of 0.4 pu is attained at a speed of 1.4 pu. Thus, the speed is

$$n = n(\text{pu}) \times n_B = 1.4 \times 1780$$
$$= 2492 \text{ r/min}$$

From the T vs I curve, a torque of 0.4 pu requires a current of 0.6 pu. Consequently, the load current is

$$I = I(\text{pu}) \times I_B = 0.6 \times 54 = 32.4 \text{ A}$$

b. To calculate the efficiency, we have to know P_o and P_i.

$$P_i = EI = 240 \times 32.4 = 7776 \text{ W}$$
$$P_o = nT/9.55 = 2492 \times 24/9.55$$
$$= 6263 \text{ W}$$
$$\eta = P_o/P_i = 6263/7776 = 0.805 \text{ or } 80.5\%$$

5.10 Applications of the series motor

Series motors are used on equipment requiring a high starting torque. They are also used to drive devices which must run at high speed at light loads. The series motor is particularly well adapted for traction purposes, such as in electric trains. Acceleration is rapid because the torque is high at low speeds. Furthermore, the series motor automatically slows down as the train goes up a grade yet turns at top speed on flat ground. The power of a series motor tends to be constant, because high torque is accompanied by low speed and vice versa. Series motors are also used in electric cranes and hoists: light loads are lifted quickly and heavy loads more slowly.

5.11 Compound motor

A compound dc motor carries both a series field and a shunt field. In a *cumulative compound motor,* the mmf of the two fields add. The shunt field is always stronger than the series field.

Fig. 5.12 shows the connection and schematic diagrams of a compound motor. When the motor runs at no-load, the armature current I in the series winding is low and the mmf of the series field is negligible. However, the shunt field is fully excited by current I_x and so the motor behaves like a shunt machine: it does not tend to run away at no-load.

As the load increases, the mmf of the series field increases but the mmf of the shunt field remains constant. The total mmf (and the resulting flux per pole) is therefore greater under load than at no-load. The motor speed falls with increasing load and the speed drop from no-load to full-load is generally between 10 percent and 30 percent.

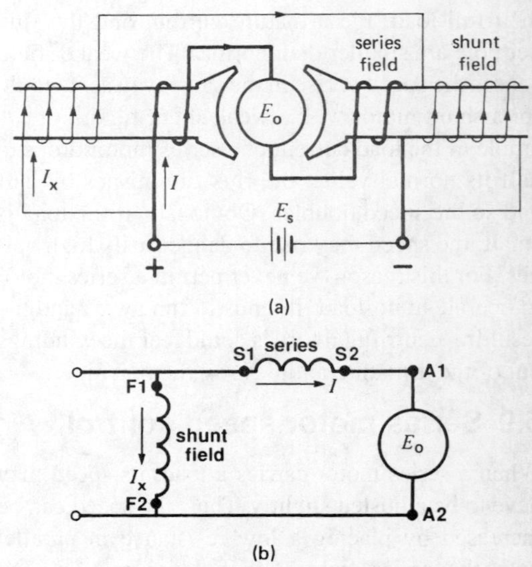

Figure 5.12
a. Connection diagram of a dc compound motor.
b. Schematic diagram of the motor.

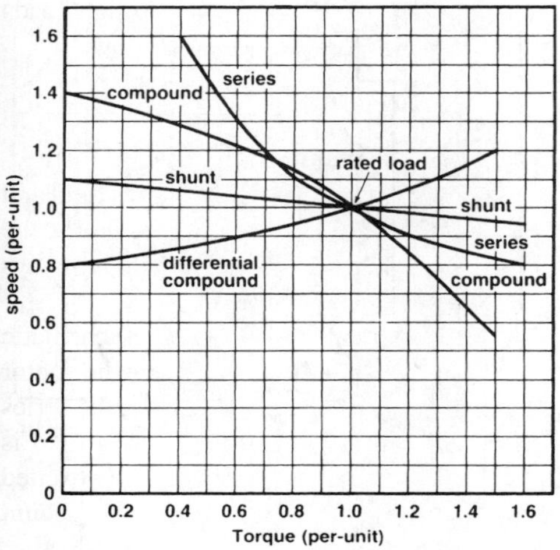

Figure 5.13
Typical speed versus torque characteristics of various dc motors.

If the series field is connected so that it opposes the shunt field, we obtain a *differential compound motor.* In such a motor, the total mmf decreases with increasing load. The speed rises as the load increases, and this may lead to instability. The differential compound motor has very few applications.

Fig. 5.13 shows the typical torque-speed curves of shunt, compound, and series motors on a per-unit basis. Fig. 5.14 shows a typical application of dc motors in a steel mill.

5.12 Reversing the direction of rotation

To reverse the direction of rotation of a dc motor, we must reverse either (1) the armature connections or (2) both the shunt and series field connections. The interpoles are considered to form part of the armature. The change in connections is shown in Fig. 5.15.

Figure 5.14
Hot strip finishing mill composed of 6 stands, each driven by a 2500 kW dc motor. The wide steel strip is delivered to the runout table (left foreground) driven by 161 dc motors, each rated 3 kW.
(Courtesy of General Electric)

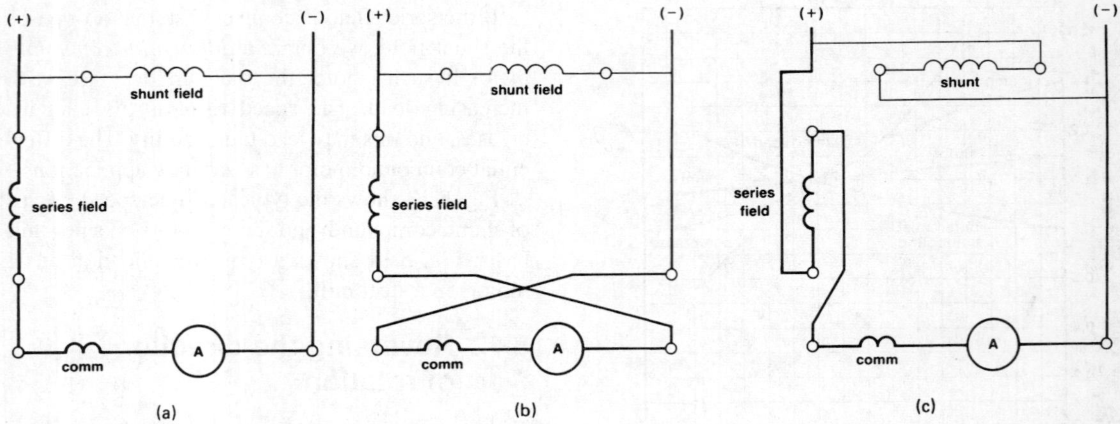

Figure 5.15
a. Original connections of a compound motor.
b. Reversing the armature connections to reverse the direction of rotation.
c. Reversing the field connections to reverse the direction of rotation.

5.13 Starting a shunt motor

If we apply full voltage to a stationary shunt motor, the starting current in the armature will be very high and we run the risk of

a. Burning out the armature;
b. Damaging the commutator and brushes, due to heavy sparking;
c. Overloading the feeder;
d. Snapping off the shaft due to mechanical shock;
e. Damaging the driven equipment because of the sudden mechanical hammerblow.

All dc motors must, therefore, be provided with a means to limit the starting current to reasonable values, usually between 1.5 and twice full-load current. One solution is to connect a rheostat in series with the armature. The resistance is gradually reduced as the motor accelerates and is eventually eliminated entirely, when the machine has attained full speed.

Today, electronic methods are often used to limit the starting current and to provide speed control.

5.14 Face-plate starter

Fig. 5.16 shows the schematic diagram of a manual face-plate starter for a shunt motor. Bare copper contacts are connected to current-limiting resistors R_1, R_2, R_3, and R_4. Conducting arm **1** sweeps across the contacts when it is pulled to the right by means of insulated handle **2.** In the position shown, the arm touches dead copper contact M and the motor circuit is open. As we draw the handle to the right, the conducting arm first touches fixed contact N.

The supply voltage E_s immediately causes full field current I_x to flow, but the armature current I is limited by the four resistors in the starter box. The motor begins to turn and, as the cemf E_o builds up, the armature current gradually falls. When the motor speed ceases to rise any more, the arm is pulled to the next contact, thereby removing resistor R_1 from the armature circuit. The current immediately jumps to a higher value and the motor quickly accelerates to the next higher speed. When the speed again levels off, we move to the next contact, and so forth, until the arm finally touches the last contact. The arm is magnetically held in this position by a small electromagnet **4,** which is in series with the shunt field.

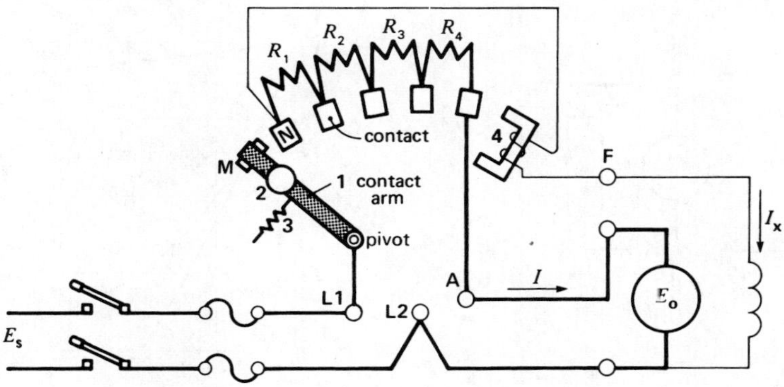

Figure 5.16
Manual face-plate starter for a shunt motor.

If the supply voltage is suddenly interrupted, or if the field excitation should accidentally be cut, the electromagnet releases the arm, allowing it to return to its dead position, under the pull of spring **3.** This safety feature prevents the motor from restarting unexpectedly when the supply voltage is reestablished.

5.15 Stopping a motor

One is inclined to believe that stopping a dc motor is a simple, almost trivial, operation. Unfortunately, this is not always true. When a large dc motor is coupled to a heavy inertia load, it may take an hour or more for the system to come to a halt. For many reasons such a lengthy deceleration time is often unacceptable and, under these circumstances, we must apply a braking torque to ensure a rapid stop. One way to brake the motor is by simple mechanical friction, in the same way we stop a car. A more elegant method consists of circulating a reverse current in the armature, so as to brake the motor electrically. Two methods are employed to create such an electromechanical brake: (1) dynamic braking and (2) plugging.

5.16 Dynamic braking

Consider a shunt motor whose field is directly connected to a source E_s, and whose armature is connected to the same source by means of a double-throw switch. The switch connects the armature to either the line or to an external resistor R (Fig. 5.17).

When the motor is running normally, the direction of the armature current I_1 and the polarity of the cemf E_o are as shown in Fig. 5.17a. Neglecting the armature IR drop, E_o is equal to E_s.

If we suddenly open the switch (Fig. 5.17b), the motor continues to turn, but its speed will gradually drop due to friction and windage losses. On the other hand, because the shunt field is still excited, induced voltage E_o continues to exist, falling at the same rate as the speed. In essence, the motor is now a generator whose armature is on open-circuit.

Let us close the switch on the second set of contacts so that the armature is suddenly connected to the external resistor (Fig. 5.17c). Voltage E_o will immediately produce an armature current I_2. However, this current flows in the *opposite* direction to the original current I_1. It follows that a reverse torque is developed whose magnitude depends upon I_2. The reverse torque brings the machine to a rapid, but very smooth stop.

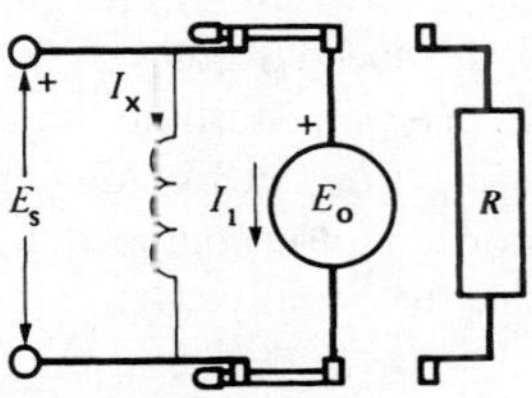

Figure 5.17a
Armature connected to a dc source E_s.

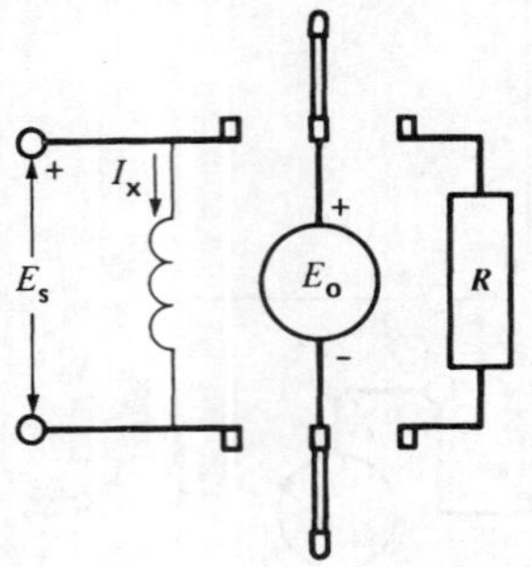

Figure 5.17b
Armature on open circuit generating a voltage E_o.

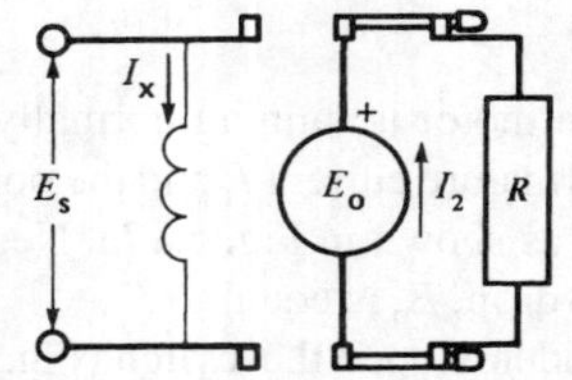

Figure 5.17c
Dynamic braking.

In practice, resistor R is chosen so that the initial braking current is about twice the rated motor current. The initial braking torque is then twice the normal torque of the motor.

As the motor slows down, the gradual decrease in E_o produces a corresponding decrease in I_2. Consequently, the braking torque becomes smaller and smaller, finally becoming zero when the armature ceases to turn. The speed drops quickly at first and then more slowly, as the armature comes to a halt. The speed decreases exponentially, somewhat like the voltage across a discharging capacitor. Consequently, the speed decreases by half in equal intervals of time T_o. To illustrate the usefulness of dynamic braking, Fig. 5.18 compares the speed-time curves for a motor equipped with dynamic braking and one that simply coasts to a stop.

5.17 Plugging

We can stop the motor even more rapidly by using a method called *plugging.* It consists of suddenly

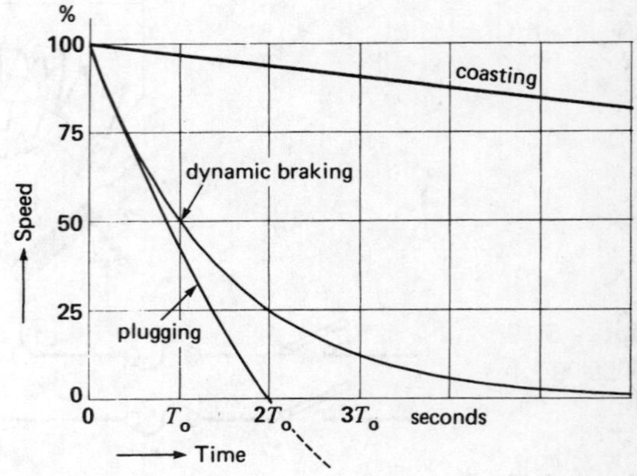

Figure 5.18
Speed versus time curves for various braking methods.

reversing the armature current by reversing the terminals of the source (Fig. 5.19a).

Under normal motor conditions, armature current I_1 is given by

$$I_1 = (E_s - E_o)/R_o$$

where R_o is the armature resistance. If we suddenly reverse the terminals of the source, the net voltage acting on the armature circuit becomes $(E_o + E_s)$. The so-called counter-emf E_o of the armature is no longer counter to anything but actually *adds* to the supply voltage E_s. This net voltage would produce an enormous reverse current, perhaps 50 times greater than the full-load armature current. This current would initiate an arc around the commutator, destroying segments, brushes, and supports, even before the line circuit breakers could open.

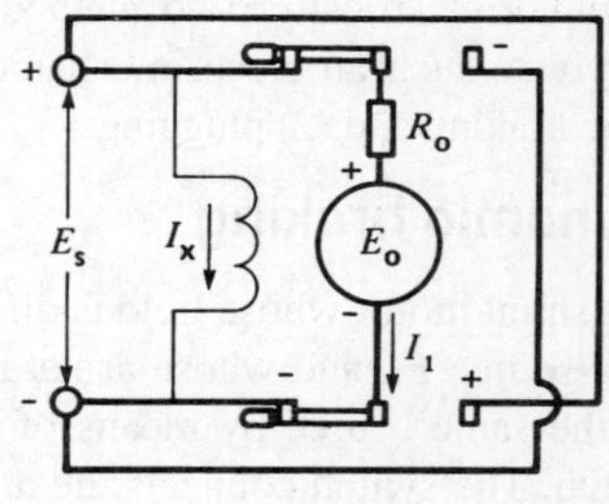

Figure 5.19a
Armature connected to dc source E_s.

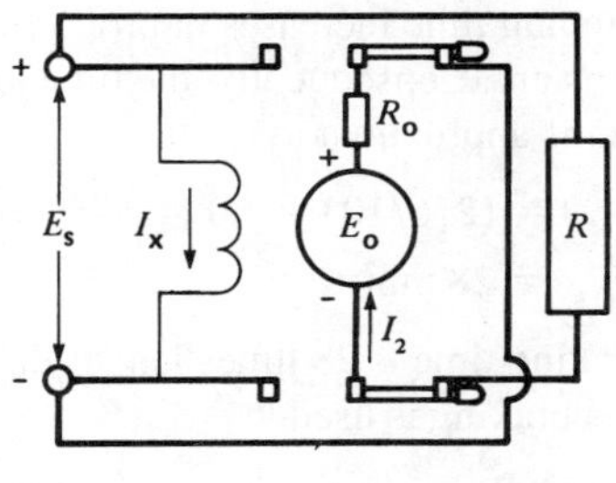

Figure 5.19b
Plugging.

To prevent such a catastrophe, we must limit the reverse current by introducing a resistor R in series with the reversing circuit (Fig. 5.19b). As in dynamic braking, the resistor is designed to limit the initial braking current I_2 to about twice full-load current. With this plugging circuit, a reverse torque is developed even when the armature has come to a stop. In effect, at zero speed, $E_o = 0$, but $I_2 = E_s/R$, which is about one-half its initial value. As soon as the motor stops, we must immediately open the armature circuit, otherwise it will begin to run in reverse. Circuit interruption is usually controlled by an automatic null-speed device mounted on the motor shaft.

The curves of Fig. 5.18 enable us to compare plugging and dynamic braking for the same initial braking current. Note that plugging stops the motor completely after an interval $2T_o$. On the other hand, if dynamic braking is used, the speed is still 25 percent of its original value at this time. Nevertheless, the comparative simplicity of dynamic braking renders it more popular in most applications.

5.18 Dynamic braking and mechanical time constant

We mentioned that the speed decreases exponentially with time when a dc motor is stopped by dynamic braking. We can therefore speak of a mechanical time constant T in much the same way we speak of the electrical time constant of a capacitor that discharges into a resistor.

In essence, T is the time it takes for the speed of the motor to fall to 36.8 percent of its initial value. However, it is much easier to draw the speed-time curves by defining a new time constant T_o which is the time for the speed to decrease to 50 percent of its original value. There is a direct mathematical relationship between the conventional time constant T and the half-time constant T_o. It is given by

$$T_o = 0.693T \tag{5.8}$$

We can prove that this mechanical time constant is given by

$$T_o = \frac{Jn_1^2}{131.5\ P_1} \tag{5.9}$$

where

T_o = time for the motor speed to fall to one-half its previous value [s]
J = moment of inertia of the rotating parts, referred to the motor shaft [kg·m^2]
n_1 = initial speed of the motor when braking starts [r/min]
P_1 = initial power delivered by the motor to the braking resistor [W]
131.5 = a constant [exact value = $(30/\pi)^2/\log_e 2$]
0.693 = a constant [exact value = $\log_e 2$]

This equation is based upon the assumption that the braking effect is entirely due to the energy dissipated in the braking resistor. In general, the motor is subjected to an extra braking torque due to windage and friction, and so the braking time will be less than that given by Eq. 5.9.

Example 5-6

A 225 kW (≈ 300 hp), 250 V, 1280 r/min dc motor has windage, friction, and iron losses of 8 kW. It drives a large flywheel and the total moment of inertia of the flywheel and armature is 177 kg·m^2. The motor is connected to a 210 V dc source, and its speed is 1280 r/min just before the armature is switched across a braking resistor of 0.2 Ω.

Calculate

a. The mechanical time constant T_o of the braking system
b. The time for the motor speed to drop to 20 r/min

c. The time for the speed to drop to 20 r/min if the only braking force is that due to the windage, friction, and iron losses

Solution

a. We note that the armature voltage is 210 V and the speed is 1280 r/min.

When the armature is switched to the braking resistor, the induced voltage is still very close to 210 V. The initial power delivered to the resistor is

$$P_1 = E^2/R = 210^2/0.2 = 220\,500 \text{ W}$$

The time constant T_o is

$$T_o = Jn_1^2/(131.5\,P_1) \quad (5.9)$$

$$= \frac{177 \times 1280^2}{131.5 \times 220\,500}$$

$$= 10 \text{ s}$$

b. The motor speed drops by 50 percent every 10 s. The speed versus time curve follows the sequence given below:

speed (r/min)	time (s)
1280	0
640	10
320	20
160	30
80	40
40	50
20	60

The speed of the motor drops to 20 r/min after an interval of 60 s.

c. The initial windage, friction, and iron losses are 8 kW. These losses do not vary with speed in exactly the same way as do the losses in a braking resistor. However, the behavior is comparable, which enables us to make a rough estimate of the braking time. We have

$$n_1 = 1280 \quad P_1 = 8000$$

The new time constant is

$$T_o = Jn_1^2/(131.5\,P_1)$$

$$= (177 \times 1280^2)/(131.5 \times 8000)$$

$$= 276 \text{ s} = 4.6 \text{ min}$$

The stopping time increases in proportion to the time constant. Consequently, the time to reach 20 r/min is approximately

$$t = (276/10) \times 60 = 1656 \text{ s}$$

$$= 28 \text{ min}$$

This braking time is 28 times longer than when dynamic braking is used.

Theoretically, a motor which is dynamically braked never comes to a complete stop. In practice, however, we can assume that the machine stops after an interval equal to 5 T_o seconds.

If the motor is plugged, the stopping time has a definite value given by

$$t_s = 2T_o \quad (5.10)$$

where

t_s = stopping time using plugging [s]

T_o = time constant as given in Eq. 5.9 [s]

Example 5-7

The motor in Example 5-6 is plugged, and the braking resistor is increased to 0.4 Ω, so that the initial braking current is the same as before.

Calculate

a. The initial braking current and braking power
b. The stopping time

Solution

The net voltage acting across the resistor is

$$E = E_o + E_s = 210 + 210 = 420 \text{ V}$$

The initial braking current is

$$I_1 = E/R = 420/0.4 = 1050 \text{ A}$$

The initial braking power is

$$P_1 = E_o I_1 = 210 \times 1050 = 220.5 \text{ kW}$$

According to Eq. 5.9, T_o has the same value as before:

$$T_o = 10 \text{ s}$$

The time to come to a complete stop is

$$t_s = 2T_o = 20 \text{ s}$$

5.19 Armature reaction

Until now we have assumed that the only mmf acting in a dc motor is that due to the field. However, the current flowing in the armature conductors also creates a magnetomotive force that distorts and weakens the flux coming from the poles. This distortion and field weakening takes place in motors as well as in generators. We recall that the magnetic action of the armature mmf is called *armature reaction.*

5.20 Flux distortion due to armature reaction

When a motor runs at no-load, the small current flowing in the armature does not appreciably affect the flux Φ_1 coming from the poles (Fig. 5.20). But when the armature carries its normal current, it produces a strong magnetomotive force which, if it acted alone, would create a flux Φ_2 (Fig. 5.21). By superimposing Φ_1 and Φ_2, we obtain the resulting flux Φ_3 (Fig. 5.22). In our example the flux density increases under the left half of the pole and it deceases under the right half. This unequal distribution produces two important effects. First the neutral zone shifts toward the left (against the direction of rotation). The result is poor commutation with sparking at the brushes. Second, due to the higher flux density in pole tip A, saturation sets in. Consequently, the increase of flux under the left-hand side of the pole is less than the decrease under the right-hand side. Flux Φ_3 at full-load is therefore slightly less than flux Φ_1 at no-load. For large machines the decrease in flux may be as much as 10 percent and it causes the speed to increase with load. Such a condition tends to be unstable; to eliminate the problem, we sometimes add a series field of one or two turns to increase the flux under load. Such motors are said to have a *stabilized-shunt winding.*

5.21 Commutating poles

To counter the effect of armature reaction and thereby improve commutation, we always place a set of *commutating poles* between the main poles of medium- and large-power dc motors (Fig. 5.23). As

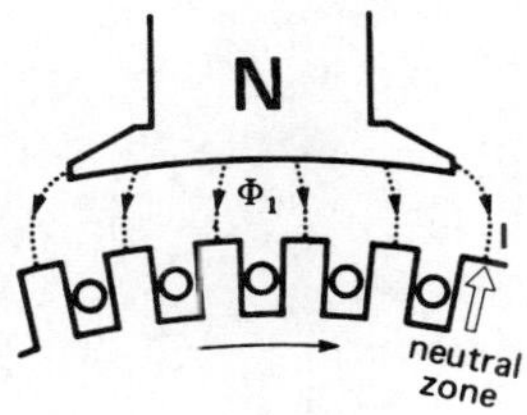

Figure 5.20
Flux distribution in a motor running at no-load.

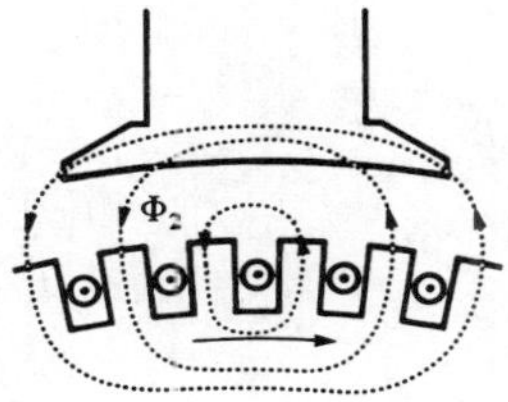

Figure 5.21
Flux created by the full-load armature current.

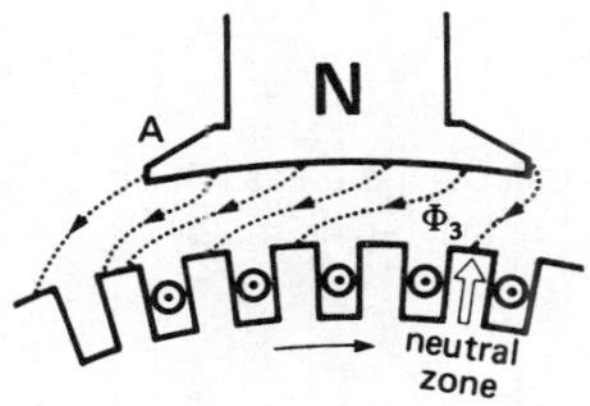

Figure 5.22
Resulting flux distribution in a motor running at full-load.

in the case of a dc generator, these narrow poles develop a magnetomotive force equal and opposite to the mmf of the armature so that the respective magnetomotive forces rise and fall together as the load current varies. In practice, the mmf of the commutating poles is made slightly greater than that of the armature. Consequently, a small flux subsists in the region of the commutating poles. The flux is designed to induce in the coil undergoing commutation a voltage that is equal and opposite to the self-induction voltage mentioned in Section 4.28. As a result, commutation is greatly improved and takes place roughly as described in Section 4.27.

Figure 5.23
The narrow commutating poles are placed between the main poles of this 6-pole motor.

The neutralization of the armature mmf is restricted to the narrow zone covered by the commutating poles, where commutation takes place. The flux distribution under the main poles unfortunately remains distorted. This creates no problem for motors driving ordinary loads. But in special cases it is necessary to add a compensating winding, a feature we will now describe.

5.22 Compensating winding

Some dc motors in the 100 kW to 10 MW (≈ 134 hp to 13 400 hp) range employed in steel mills perform a series of rapid, heavy-duty operations. They accelerate, decelerate, stop, and reverse, all in a matter of seconds. The corresponding armature current increases, decreases, reverses in stepwise fashion, producing very sudden changes in armature reaction.

For such motors the commutating poles and series stabilizing windings do not adequately neutralize the armature mmf. Torque and speed control is difficult under such transient conditions and flash-overs may occur across the commutator. To eliminate this problem, special *compensating windings* are connected in series with the armature. They are distributed in slots, cut into the pole faces of the main field poles (Fig. 5.24). Like commutating poles, these windings produce a mmf equal and opposite to the mmf of the armature. However, because the windings are distributed across the pole faces, the armature mmf is bucked from point to point, which eliminates the field distortion shown in Fig. 5.22. With compensating windings, the field distribution remains essentially undisturbed from no-load to full-load, retaining the general shape shown in Fig. 5.20.

The addition of compensating windings has a profound effect on the design and performance of a dc motor:

1. A shorter air gap can be used because we no longer have to worry about the demagnetizing effect of the armature. A shorter gap means that the shunt field strength can be reduced and hence the coils are smaller.
2. The inductance of the armature circuit is reduced by a factor of 4 or 5; consequently, the armature current can change more quickly and the motor gives a much better response. This is particularly true in big machines.
3. A motor equipped with compensating windings can briefly develop 3 to 4 times its rated torque. The peak torque of an uncompensated motor is much lower when the armature current is large. The reason is that the effective flux in the air gap falls off rapidly with increasing current because of armature reaction.

We conclude that compensating windings are essential in large motors subjected to severe duty cycles.

5.23 Basics of variable speed control

The most important outputs of a dc motor are its speed and torque. It is useful to determine the limits of each as the speed is increased from zero to above

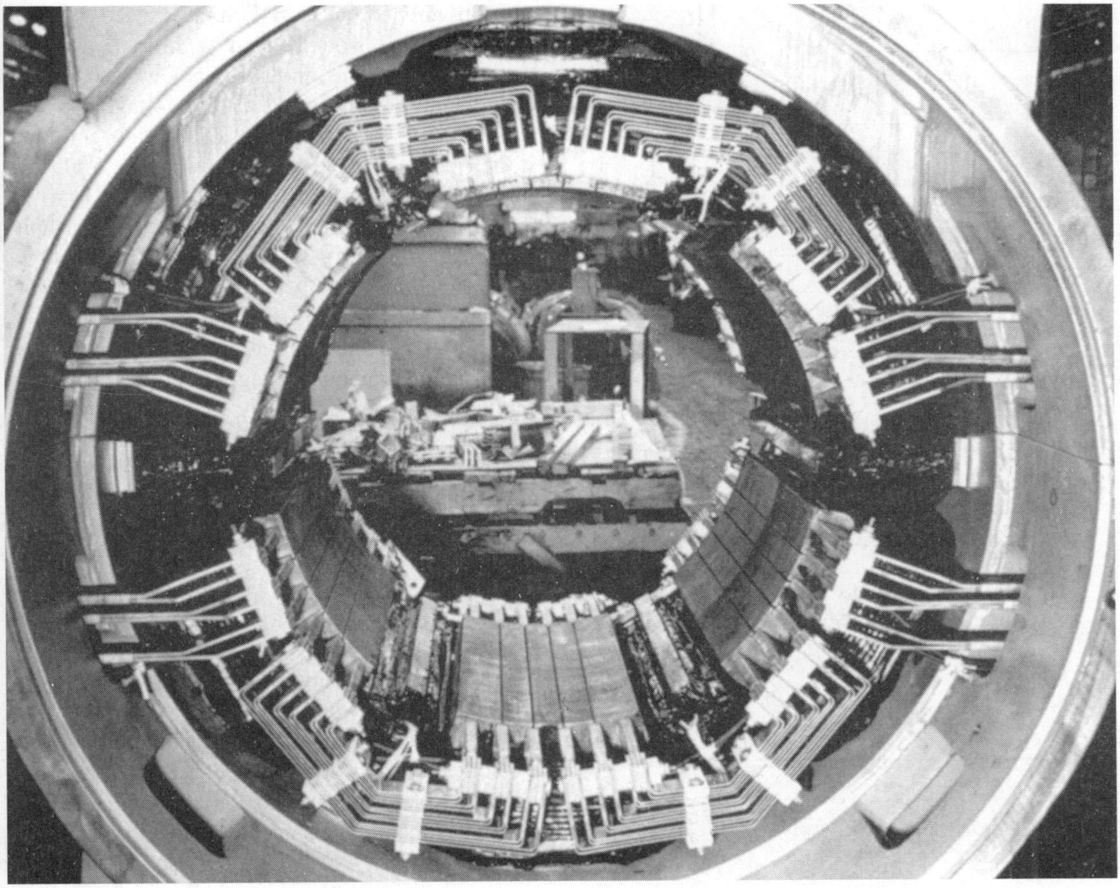

Figure 5.24
Six-pole dc motor having a compensating winding distributed in slots in the main poles. The machine also has 6 commutating poles.
(Courtesy of General Electric Company)

base speed. In so doing, the rated values of armature current, armature voltage, and field flux must not be exceeded, although lesser values may be used.

In making our analysis, we assume an ideal separately excited shunt motor in which the armature resistance is negligible (Fig. 5.25). The armature voltage E_a, the armature current I_a, the flux Φ_f, the exciting current I_f, and the speed n are all expressed in per-unit values. Thus, if the rated armature voltage E_a happens to be 240 V and the rated armature current I_a is 600 A, they are both given a per-unit value of 1. Similarly, the rated shunt field flux Φ_f has a per-unit value of 1. The advantage of the per-unit approach is that it renders the torque-speed curve universal.

Thus, the per-unit torque T is given by the per-unit flux Φ_f times the per-unit armature current I_a

$$T = \Phi_f I_a \tag{5.11}$$

By the same reasoning, the per-unit armature voltage E_a is equal to the per-unit speed n times the per-unit flux Φ_f

$$E_a = n \Phi_f \tag{5.12}$$

The logical starting point of the torque-speed curve (Fig. 5.26), is the condition where the motor

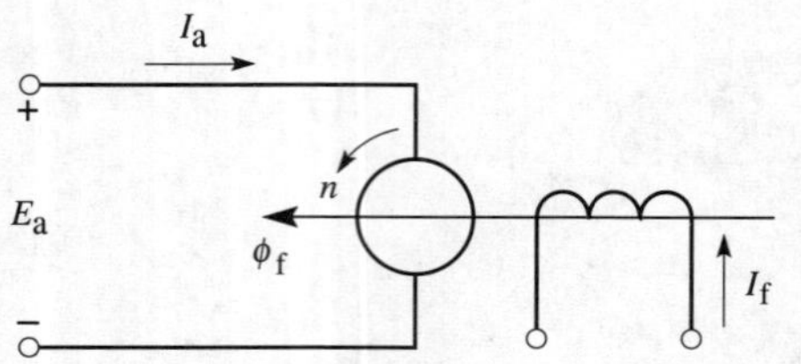

Figure 5.25
Per-unit circuit diagram.

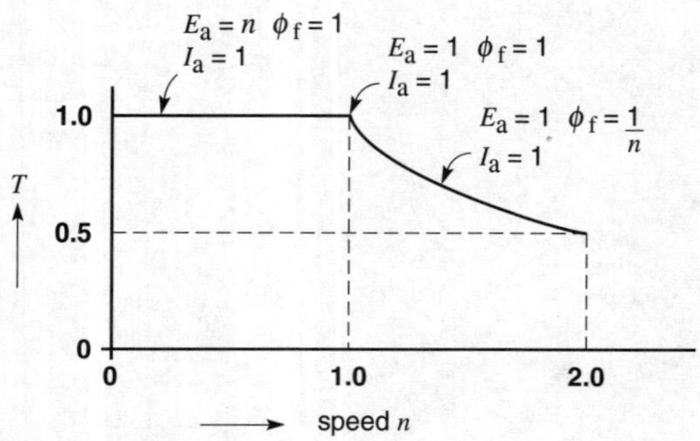

Figure 5.26

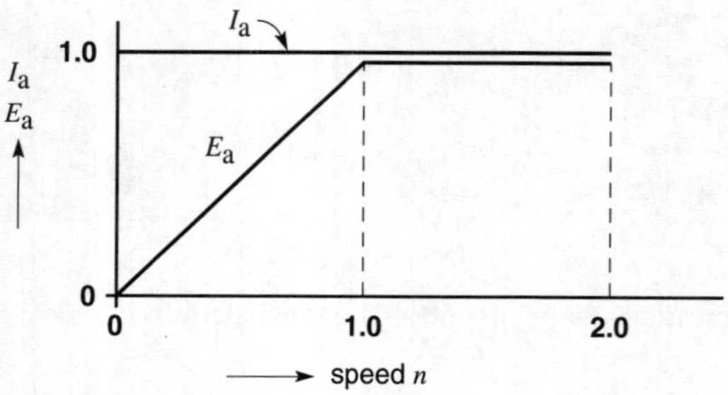

Figure 5.27

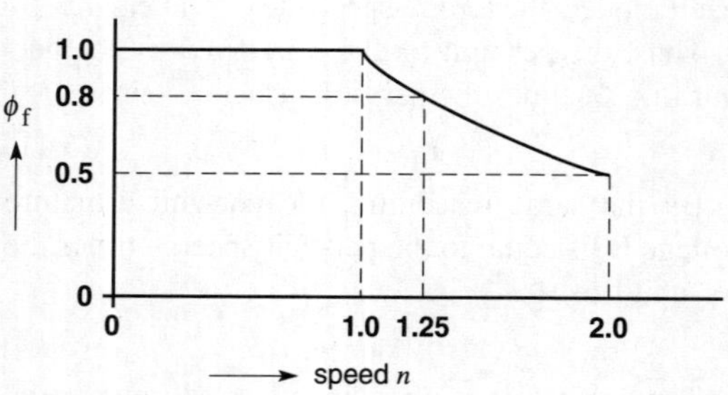

Figure 5.28

develops rated torque ($T = 1$) at rated speed ($n = 1$). The rated speed is often called *base speed.*

In order to reduce the speed below base speed, we gradually reduce the armature voltage to zero, while keeping the rated values of I_a and Φ_f constant at their per-unit value of 1. Applying Eq. 5.11, the corresponding per-unit torque $T = 1 \times 1 = 1$. Furthermore, according to Eq. 5.12, the per-unit voltage $E_a = n \times 1 = n$. Figs. 5.27 and 5.28 show the state of E_a, I_a, and Φ_f during this phase of motor operation, known as the *constant torque* mode.

Next, to raise the speed above base speed, we realize that the armature voltage cannot be increased anymore because it is already at its rated level of 1. The only solution is to keep E_a at its rated level of 1 and reduce the flux. Referring to Eq. 5.12, this means that $n\Phi_f = 1$, and so $\Phi_f = 1/n$. Thus, above base speed, the per-unit flux is equal to the reciprocal of the per-unit speed. During this operating mode, the armature current can be kept at its rated level of 1. Recalling Eq. 5.11, it follows that $T = \Phi_f I_a = (1/n) \times 1 = 1/n$. Consequently, above base speed, the per-unit torque decreases as the reciprocal of the per-unit speed. It is clear that since the per-unit armature current and armature voltage are both equal to 1 during this phase, the power input to the motor is equal to 1. Having assumed an ideal machine, the per-unit mechanical power output is also equal to 1, which corresponds to rated power. That is why the region above base speed is named the *constant horsepower* mode.

We conclude that the ideal dc shunt motor can operate anywhere within the limits of the torque-speed curve depicted in Fig. 5.26.

In practice, the actual torque-speed curve may differ considerably from that shown in Fig. 5.26. The curve indicates an upper speed limit of 2 but some machines can be pushed to limits of 3 and even 4, by reducing the flux accordingly. However, when the speed is raised above base speed, commutation problems develop and centrifugal forces may become dangerous. When the motor runs below base speed, the ventilation becomes poorer and the temperature tends to rise above its rated value. Consequently, the armature current must be reduced, which reduces the torque. Eventually, when the speed is zero, all forced ventilation ceases and even the field current must be reduced to prevent overheating of the shunt field coils. As a result, the permissible stalled torque may only have a per-unit value of 0.25. The resulting practical torque-speed curve is shown in Fig. 5.29.

The drastic fall-off in torque as the speed diminishes can be largely overcome by using an external blower to cool the motor. It delivers a constant stream of air, no matter what the speed of the motor happens to be. Under these conditions, the torque-speed curve approaches that shown in Fig. 5.26.

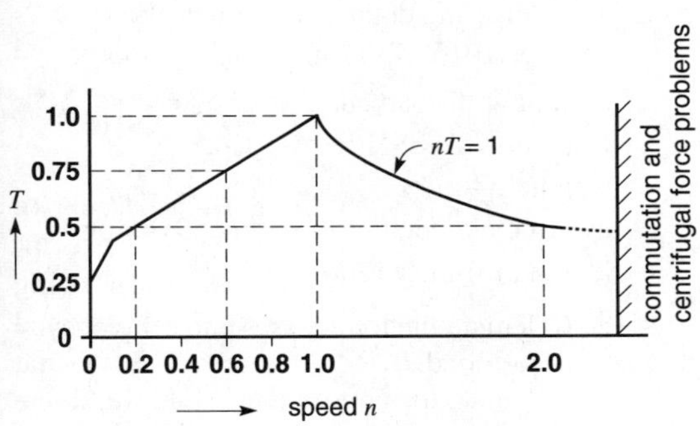

Figure 5.29
Torque-speed curve of a typical dc motor.

5.24 Permanent magnet motors

We have seen that shunt-field motors require coils and a field current to produce the flux. The energy consumed, the heat produced, and the relatively large space taken up by the field poles are disadvantages of a dc motor. By using permanent magnets instead of field coils, these disadvantages are overcome. The result is a smaller motor having a higher efficiency with the added benefit of never risking run-away due to field failure.

A further advantage of using permanent magnets is that the effective air gap is increased many times. The reason is that the magnets have a permeability that is nearly equal to that of air. As a result, the armature mmf cannot create the intense field that is possible when soft-iron pole pieces are employed. Consequently, the field created by the magnets does not become distorted, as shown in Fig. 5.22. Thus, the armature reaction is reduced and commutation is improved, as well as the overload capacity of the motor. A further advantage is that the long air gap reduces the inductance of the armature and hence it responds much more quickly to changes in armature current.

Permanent magnet motors are particularly advantageous in capacities below about 5 hp. The magnets

Figure 5.30
Permanent magnet motor rated 1.5 hp, 90 V, 2900 r/min, 14.5 A. Armature diameter: 73 mm; armature length: 115 mm; slots 20; commutator bars: 40; turns per coil: 5; conductor size: No. 17 AWG, lap winding. Armature resistance at 20°C: 0.34 Ω.
(Courtesy of Baldor Electric Company)

are ceramic or rare-earth/cobalt alloys. Fig. 5.30 shows the construction of a 1.5 hp, 90 V, 2900 r/min PM motor. Its elongated armature ensures low inertia and fast response when used in servo applications.

The only drawback of PM motors is the relatively high cost of the magnets and the inability to obtain higher speeds by field weakening.

Questions and Problems

Practical Level

5-1 Name three types of dc motors and make a sketch of the connections.

5-2 Explain what is meant by the generator effect in a motor.

5-3 What determines the magnitude and polarity of the counter-emf in a dc motor?

5-4 The counter-emf of a motor is always slightly less than the applied armature voltage. Explain.

5-5 Name two methods that are used to vary the speed of a dc motor.

5-6 Explain why the armature current of a shunt motor decreases as the motor accelerates.

5-7 Why is a starting resistor needed to bring a motor up to speed?

5-8 Show one way to reverse the direction of rotation of a compound motor.

5-9 A 230 V shunt motor has a nominal armature current of 60 A. If the armature resistance is 0.15 Ω, calculate the following:
- **a.** The counter-emf [V]
- **b.** The power supplied to the armature [W]
- **c.** The mechanical power developed by the motor, [kW] and [hp]

5-10 **a.** In Problem 5-9 calculate the initial starting current if the motor is directly connected across the 230 V line.
- **b.** Calculate the value of the starting resistor needed to limit the initial current to 115 A.

Intermediate level

5-11 The compound motor of Fig. 5.12 has 1200 turns on the shunt winding and 25 turns on the series winding, per pole. The shunt field has a total resistance of 115 Ω, and the nominal armature current is 23 A. If the motor is connected to a 230 V line, calculate the following:
- **a.** The mmf per pole at full-load
- **b.** The mmf at no-load

5-12 A separately excited dc motor turns at 1200 r/min when the armature is connected to a 115 V source. Calculate the armature voltage required so that the motor runs at 1500 r/min. At 100 r/min.

5-13 The following details are known about a 250 hp, 230 V, 435 r/min dc shunt motor:

nominal full-load current: 862 A
insulation class: H
weight: 3400 kg
external diameter of the frame: 915 mm
length of frame: 1260 mm

- **a.** Calculate the total losses and efficiency at full-load.
- **b.** Calculate the approximate shunt field exciting current if the shunt field causes 20 percent of the total losses.
- **c.** Calculate the value of the armature resistance as well as the counter-emf, knowing that 50 percent of the total losses at full-load are due to armature resistance.
- **d.** If we wish to attain a speed of 1100 r/min, what should be the approximate exciting current?

5-14 We wish to stop a 120 hp, 240 V, 400 r/min motor by using the dynamic braking circuit shown in Fig. 5.17. If the nominal armature current is 400 A, calculate the following:
- **a.** The value of the braking resistor *R* if we want to limit the maximum braking current to 125 percent of its nominal value
- **b.** The braking power [kW] when the motor has decelerated to 200 r/min, 50 r/min, 0 r/min

5-15 **a.** The motor in Problem 5-14 is now stopped by using the plugging circuit of Fig. 5.19. Calculate the new braking resistor *R* so that the maximum braking current is 500 A.

b. Calculate the braking power [kW] when the motor has decelerated to 200 r/min, 50 r/min, 0 r/min.
c. Compare the braking power developed at 200 r/min to the instantaneous power dissipated in resistor *R*.

Advanced level

5-16 The armature of a 225 kW, 1200 r/min motor has a diameter of 559 mm and an axial length of 235 mm. Calculate the following:
a. The approximate moment of inertia, knowing that iron has a density of 7900 kg/m^3
b. The kinetic energy of the armature alone when it turns at 1200 r/min
c. The total kinetic energy of the revolving parts at a speed of 600 r/min, if the *J* of the windings and commutator is equal to the *J* calculated in (a)

5-17 If we reduce the normal exciting current of a practical shunt motor by 50 percent, the speed increases, but it never doubles. Explain why, bearing in mind the saturation of the iron under normal excitation.

5-18 The speed of a series motor drops with rising temperature, while that of a shunt motor increases. Explain.

Industrial Application

5-19 A permanent magnet motor equipped with cobalt-samarium magnets loses 3% of its magnetism per 100°C increase in temperature. The motor runs at a no-load speed of 2500 r/min when connected to a 150 V source in an ambient temperature of 22°C. Estimate the speed if the motor is placed in a room where the ambient temperature is 40°C.

5-20 Referring to Fig. 5.30, calculate the following:
a. The number of conductors on the armature
b. The value of the counter-emf at full load
c. The flux per pole, in milliwebers [mWb]

5-21 A standard 20 hp, 240 V, 1500 r/min self-cooled dc motor has an efficiency of 88%. A requirement has arisen whereby the motor should run at speeds ranging from 200 r/min to 1500 r/min without overheating. It is decided to cool the machine by installing an external blower and channeling the air by means of an air duct. The highest expected ambient temperature is 30°C and the temperature of the air that exits the motor should not exceed 35°C. Calculate the capacity of the blower required, in cubic feet per minute. (Hint: see Section 3.21.)

5-22 A 250 hp, 500 V dc shunt motor draws a nominal field current of 5 A under rated load. The field resistance is 90 Ω. Calculate the ohmic value and power of the series resistor needed so that the field current drops to 4.5 A when the shunt field and resistor are connected to the 500 V source.

5-23 A 5 hp dc motor draws a field current of 0.68 A when the field is connected to a 150 V source. On the other hand, a 500 hp motor draws a field current of 4.3 A when the field is connected to a 300 V dc source.

In each case, calculate the power required for the field as a percentage of the rated power of the motor. What conclusions can you draw from these results?

CHAPTER 6

Efficiency and Heating of Electrical Machines

6.0 Introduction

Whenever a machine transforms energy from one form to another, there is always a certain loss. The loss takes place in the machine itself, causing (1) an increase in temperature and (2) a reduction in efficiency.

From the standpoint of losses, electrical machines may be divided into two groups: those that have revolving parts (motors, generators, etc.) and those that do not (transformers, reactors, etc.). Electrical and mechanical losses are produced in rotating machines, while only electrical losses are produced in stationary machines.

In this chapter we analyze the losses in dc machines, but the same losses are also found in most machines operating on alternating current. The study of power losses is important because it gives us a clue as to how they may be reduced.

We also cover the important topics of temperature rise and the service life of electrical equipment. We show that both are related to the class of insulation used and that these insulation classes have been standardized.

6.1 Mechanical losses

Mechanical losses are due to bearing friction, brush friction, and windage. The friction losses depend upon the speed of the machine and upon the design of the bearings, brushes, commutator, and slip rings. Windage losses depend on the speed and design of the cooling fan and on the turbulence produced by the revolving parts. In the absence of prior information, we usually conduct tests on the machine itself to determine the value of these mechanical losses.

Rotating machines are usually cooled by an internal fan mounted on the motor shaft. It draws in cool air from the surroundings, blows it over the windings, and expels it again through suitable vents. In hostile environments, special cooling methods are sometimes used, as illustrated in Fig. 6.1.

6.2 Electrical losses

Electrical losses are composed of the following:

1. Conductor I^2R losses (sometimes called *copper* losses)

2. Brush losses
3. Iron losses

1. Conductor Losses The losses in a conductor depend upon its resistance and the square of the current it carries. The resistance, in turn, depends upon the length, cross section, resistivity, and temperature of the conductor. The following equations enable us to determine the resistance at any temperature and for any material:

Figure 6.1
Totally enclosed, water-cooled, 450 kW, 3600 r/min motor for use in a hostile environment. Warm air inside the machine is blown upward and through a water-cooled heat exchanger, situated immediately above the Westinghouse nameplate. After releasing its heat to a set of water-cooled pipes, the cool air reenters the machine by way of two rectangular pipes leading into the end bells. The cooling air therefore moves in a closed circuit, and the surrounding contaminated atmosphere never reaches the motor windings. The circular capped pipes located diagonally on the heat exchanger serve as cooling-water inlet and outlet respectively.
(Courtesy of Westinghouse)

$$R = \rho \frac{L}{A} \tag{6.1}$$

$$\rho = \rho_0(1 + \alpha t) \tag{6.2}$$

in which

R = resistance of conductor [Ω]
L = length of conductor [m]
A = cross section of conductor [m^2]
ρ = resistivity of conductor at temperature t [Ω·m]
ρ_0 = resistivity of conductor at 0°C [Ω·m]
α = temperature coefficient of resistance at 0°C [1/°C]
t = temperature of conductor [°C]

The values of ρ and α for different materials are listed in Appendix AX2. In dc motors and generators, copper losses occur in the armature, the series field, the shunt field, the commutating poles, and the compensating winding. These I^2R losses show up as heat, causing the conductor temperatures to rise above ambient temperature.

Instead of using the I^2R equation, we sometimes prefer to express the losses in terms of the number of watts per kilogram of conductor material. The losses are then given by the equation

$$P_c = 1000J^2\rho/\zeta \tag{6.3}$$

where

P_c = specific conductor power loss [W/kg]
J = current density [A/mm^2]
ρ = resistivity of the conductor [n·m]
ζ = density of the conductor [kg/m^3]
1000 = constant, to take care of units

According to this equation, the loss per unit mass is proportional to the square of the current density. For copper conductors, we use densities between 1.5 A/mm^2 and 6 A/mm^2. The corresponding losses vary from 5 W/kg to 90 W/kg (Fig. 6.2). The higher densities require an efficient cooling system to prevent an excessive temperature rise.

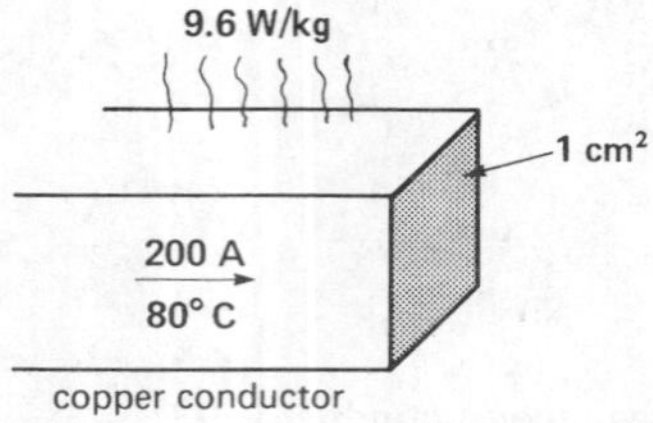

Figure 6.2
Copper losses may be expressed in watts per kilogram.

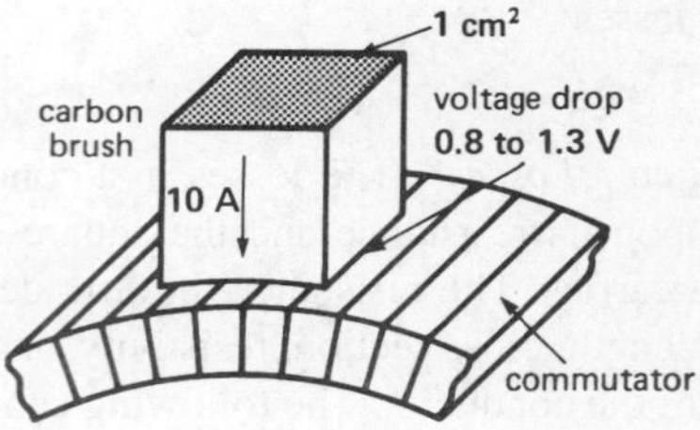

Figure 6.3
Brush contact voltage drop occurs between the brush face and commutator.

2. Brush Losses The I^2R losses in the brushes are negligible because the current density is only about 0.1 A/mm^2, which is far less than that used in copper. However, the *contact* voltage drop between the brushes and commutator may produce significant losses. The drop varies from 0.8 V to 1.3 V, depending on the type of brush, the applied pressure, and the brush current (Fig. 6.3).

3. Iron Losses Iron losses are produced in the armature of a dc machine. They are due to hysteresis and eddy currents, as previously explained in Sections 2.27 and 2.30. Iron losses depend upon the magnetic flux density, the speed of rotation, the quality of the steel, and the size of the armature. They typically range from 0.5 W/kg to 20 W/kg. The higher values occur in the armature teeth, where the flux density may be as high as 1.7 T. The losses in the armature core are usually much lower. The losses can be minimized by annealing the steel (Fig. 6.4).

Figure 6.4
This 150 kW electric oven is used to anneal punched steel laminations. This industrial process, carried out in a controlled atmosphere of 800°C, significantly reduces the iron losses. The laminations are seen as they leave the oven. *(Courtesy of General Electric)*

Some iron losses are also produced in the pole faces. They are due to flux pulsations created as successive armature teeth and slots sweep across the pole face.

Strange as it may seem, iron losses impose a mechanical drag on the armature, producing the same effect as mechanical friction.

Example 6-1

A dc machine turning at 875 r/min carries an armature winding whose total weight is 40 kg. The current density is 5 A/mm^2 and the operating temperature is 80°C. The total iron losses in the armature amount to 1100 W.

Calculate

a. The copper losses
b. The mechanical drag [N·m] due to the iron losses

Solution

a. Referring to Table AX2 in the Appendix, the resistivity of copper at 80°C is

$$\begin{aligned}\rho &= \rho_o(1 + \alpha t)\\ &= 15.88\,(1 + 0.004\,27 \times 80)\\ &= 21.3\ \text{n}\Omega\cdot\text{m}\end{aligned}$$

The density of copper is 8890 kg/m^3

The specific power loss is

$$\begin{aligned}P_c &= 1000J^2\rho/\zeta \qquad (6.1)\\ &= 1000 \times 5^2 \times 21.3/8890\\ &= 60\ \text{W/kg}\end{aligned}$$

Total copper loss is

$$P = 60 \times 40 = 2400\ \text{W}$$

b. The braking torque due to iron losses can be calculated from

$$P = nT/9.55 \qquad (3.5)$$

$$1100 = 875\,T/9.55$$

$$T = 12\ \text{N·m or approximately 8.85 ft·lbf}$$

6.3 Losses as a function of load

A dc motor running at no-load develops no useful power. However, it must absorb some power from the line to continue to rotate. This no-load power overcomes the friction, windage, and iron losses, and provides for the copper losses in the shunt field. The I^2R losses in the armature, series field, and commutating field are negligible because the no-load current is seldom more than 5 percent of the nominal full-load current.

As we load the machine the current increases in the armature circuit. Consequently, the I^2R losses in the armature circuit (consisting of the armature and all the other windings in series with it) will rise. On the other hand, the no-load losses mentioned above remain essentially constant as the load increases, unless the speed of the machine changes appreciably. It follows that the total losses increase with load. Because they are converted into heat, the temperature of the machine rises progressively as the load increases.

However, the temperature must not exceed the maximum allowable temperature of the insulation used in the machine. Consequently, there is a limit to the power that the machine can deliver. This temperature-limited power enables us to establish the *nominal* or *rated power* of the machine. A machine loaded beyond its nominal rating will usually overheat. The insulation deteriorates more rapidly, which inevitably shortens the service life of the machine.

If a machine runs *intermittently,* it can carry heavy overloads without overheating, provided that the operating time is short. Thus, a motor having a nominal rating of 10 kW can readily carry a load of 12 kW for short periods. However, for higher loads the capacity is limited by other factors, usually electrical. For instance, it is physically impossible for a generator rated at 10 kW to deliver an output of 100 kW, even for one millisecond.

6.4 Efficiency curve

The efficiency of a machine is the ratio of the useful output power P_o to the input power P_i (Section 3.7). Furthermore, input power is equal to useful power plus the losses p. We can therefore write

$$\eta = \frac{P_o}{P_i} \times 100 = \frac{P_o}{P_o + p} \times 100 \qquad (6.4)$$

where

η = efficiency [%]
P_o = output power [W]
P_i = input power [W]
p = losses [W]

The following example shows how to calculate the efficiency of a dc machine.

Example 6-2

A dc compound motor having a rating of 10 kW, 1150 r/min, 230 V, 50 A, has the following losses at *full-load:*

	bearing friction loss	=	40 W
	brush friction loss	=	50 W
	windage loss	=	200 W
(1)	total mechanical losses	=	290 W
(2)	iron losses	=	420 W
(3)	copper loss in the shunt field	=	120 W
	copper losses at full-load:		
	a. in the armature	=	500 W
	b. in the series field	=	25 W
	c. in the commutating winding	=	70 W
(4)	total copper loss in the armature circuit at full-load	=	595 W

Calculate the losses and efficiency at no-load and at 25, 50, 75, 100, and 150 percent of the nominal rating of the machine. Draw a graph showing efficiency as a function of mechanical load (neglect the losses due to brush contact drop).

Solution

No-load The copper losses in the armature circuit are negligible at no-load. Consequently, the no-load losses are equal to the sum of the mechanical losses (1), the iron losses (2), and the shunt-field losses (3):

no-load losses = 290 + 420 + 120 = 830 W

These losses remain essentially constant as the load varies.

The efficiency is zero at no-load because no useful power is developed by the motor.

25 percent load When the motor is loaded to 25 percent of its nominal rating, the armature current is approximately 25 percent (or 1/4) of its full-load value. Because the copper losses vary as the square of the current, we have the following:

copper losses in the armature circuit
$= (1/4)^2 \times 595 = 37$ W

no-load losses
= 830 W

total losses
= 37 + 830 = 867 W

Useful power developed by the motor at 25 percent load is

$$P_o = 10 \text{ kW} \times (1/4) = 2500 \text{ W} \ (\approx 3.35 \text{ hp})$$

Power supplied to the motor is

$$P_i = 2500 + 867 = 3367 \text{ W}$$

and the efficiency is

$$\eta = (P_o/P_i) \times 100 \qquad (6.2)$$
$$= (2500/3367) \times 100 = 74\%$$

In the same way, we find the losses at 50, 75, 100, and 150 percent of the nominal load:

At 50 percent load the losses are

$$(1/2)^2 \times 595 + 830 = 979 \text{ W}$$

At 75 percent load the losses are

$$(3/4)^2 \times 595 + 830 = 1165 \text{ W}$$

At 100 percent load the losses are

$$595 + 830 = 1425 \text{ W}$$

At 150 percent load the losses are

$$(1.5)^2 \times 595 + 830 = 2169 \text{ W}$$

The efficiency calculations for the various loads are listed in Table 6A and the results are shown graphically in Fig. 6.5.

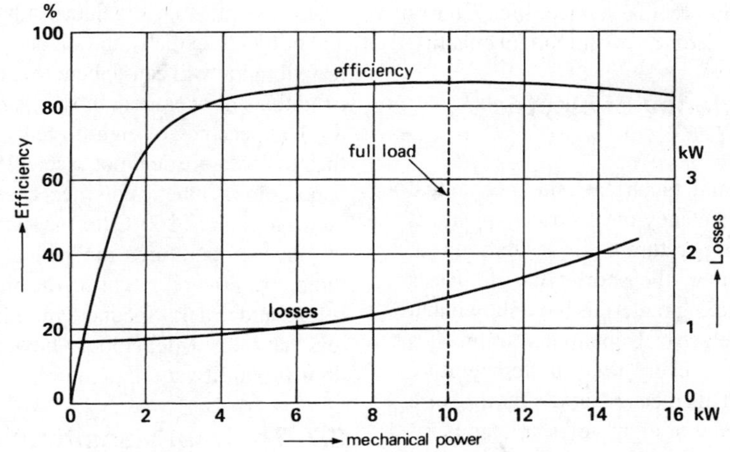

Figure 6.5
Losses and efficiency as a function of mechanical power. See Example 6-2.

TABLE 6A LOSSES AND EFFICIENCY OF A DC MOTOR

Load [%]	Total losses [W]	Output power P_o [W]	Input power P_i [W]	Efficiency [%]
0	830	0	830	0
25	867	2 500	3 367	74
50	979	5 000	5 980	83.6
75	1 165	7 500	8 665	86.5
100	1 425	10 000	11 425	87.5
150	2 169	15 000	17 170	87.4

The efficiency curve rises sharply as the load increases, flattens off over a broad range of power, and then slowly begins to fall. This is typical of the efficiency curves of *all* electric motors, both ac and dc. Electric motor designers usually try to attain the peak efficiency at full-load.

In the above calculation of efficiency we could have included the losses due to brush voltage drop. Assuming a constant drop, say, of 0.8 V per brush, the brush loss at full-load amounts to 0.8 V × 50 A × 2 brushes = 80 W. At 50 percent load, the brush loss would be 40 W. These losses, when added to the other losses, modify the efficiency curve only slightly.

It is important to remember that at light loads the efficiency of any motor is poor. Consequently, when selecting a motor to do a particular job, we should always choose one having a power rating roughly equal to the load it has to drive.

We can prove that the efficiency of any dc machine reaches a maximum at that load where the armature circuit copper losses are equal to the no-load losses. In our example this corresponds to a total loss of (830 + 830) = 1660 W, an output of 11 811 W (15.8 hp) and an efficiency of 87.68 percent. The reader may wish to check these results.

6.5 Temperature rise

The temperature rise of a machine or device is the difference between the temperature of its warmest accessible part and the ambient temperature. It may be measured by simply using two thermometers. However, due to the practical difficulty of placing a thermometer close to the really warmest spot inside the machine, this method is seldom used. We usually rely upon more sophisticated methods, described in the following sections.

Temperature rise has a direct bearing on the power rating of a machine or device. It also has a direct bearing on its useful service life. Consequently, temperature rise is a very important quantity.

6.6 Life expectancy of electric equipment

Apart from accidental electrical and mechanical failures, the life expectancy of electrical apparatus is limited by the temperature of its insulation: the higher the temperature, the shorter its life. Tests made on many insulating materials have shown that the service life of electrical apparatus diminishes approximately by half every time the temperature increases by 10°C. This means that if a motor has a normal life expectancy of eight years at a temperature of 105°C, it will have a service life of only four years at a temperature of 115°C, of two years at 125°C, and of only one year at 135°C!

The factors that contribute most to the deterioration of insulators are (1) heat, (2) humidity, (3) vibration, (4) acidity, (5) oxidation, and (6) time (Fig. 6.6). Because of these factors, the state of the insulation changes gradually; it slowly begins to crystallize and the transformation takes place more rapidly as the temperature rises.

In crystallizing, organic insulators become hard and brittle. Eventually, the slightest shock or mechanical vibration will cause them to break. Under normal conditions of operation, most organic insulators have a life expectancy of eight to ten years provided that their temperature does not exceed 100°C. On the other hand, some synthetic polymers can withstand temperatures as high as 200°C for the same length of time.

Low temperatures are just as harmful as high temperatures are, because the insulation tends to freeze and crack. Special synthetic organic insulators have been developed, however, which retain their flexibility at temperatures as low as −60°C.

6.7 Thermal classification of insulators

Committees and organizations that set standards* have grouped insulators into five classes, depending upon their ability to withstand heat. These classes correspond to the maximum temperature levels of: 105°C, 130°C, 155°C, 180°C, and 220°C (formerly

* Such as IEEE, Underwriters Laboratories, Canadian Standards Association.

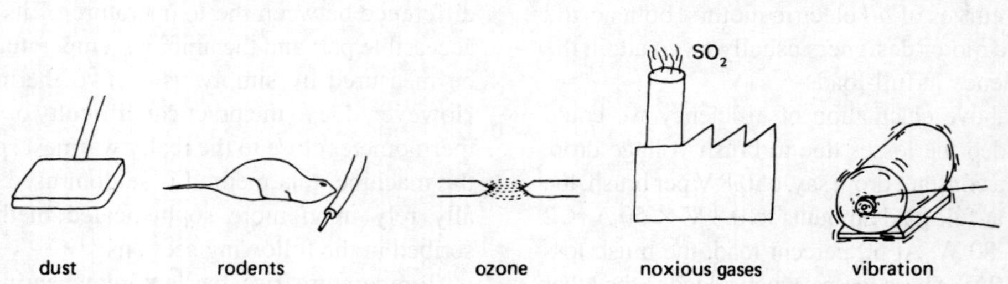

Figure 6.6
Factors that may shorten the service life of an insulator.

represented by the letters A, B, F, H, and R). This thermal classification (Table 6B) is a cornerstone in the design and manufacture of electrical apparatus.

6.8 Maximum ambient temperature and hot-spot temperature rise

Standards organizations have also established a maximum *ambient temperature,* which is usually 40°C. This standardized temperature was established for the following reasons:

1. It enables electrical manufacturers to foresee the worst ambient temperature conditions that their machines are likely to encounter.
2. It enables them to standardize the size of their machines and to give performance guarantees.

TABLE 6B CLASSES OF INSULATION SYSTEMS

Class	Illustrative examples and definitions
105°C A	Materials or combinations of materials such as cotton, silk, and paper when suitably impregnated or coated or when immersed in a dielectric liquid such as oil. Other materials or combinations of materials may be included in this class if by experience or accepted tests they can be shown to have comparable thermal life at 105°C.
130°C B	Materials or combinations of materials such as mica, glass fiber, asbestos, etc., with suitable bonding substances. Other materials or combinations of materials may be included in this class if by experience or accepted tests they can be shown to have comparable thermal life at 130°C.
155°C F	Materials or combinations of materials such as mica, glass fiber, asbestos, etc., with suitable bonding substances. Other materials or combinations of materials may be included in this class if by experience or accepted tests they can be shown to have comparable life at 155°C.
180°C H	Materials or combinations of materials such as silicone elastomer, mica, glass fiber, asbestos, etc., with suitable bonding substances such as appropriate silicone resins. Other materials or combinations of materials may be included in this class if by experience or accepted tests they can be shown to have comparable life at 180°C.
200°C N	Materials or combinations of materials which by experience or accepted tests can be shown to have the required thermal life at 200°C.
220°C R	Materials or combinations of materials which by experience or accepted tests can be shown to have the required thermal life at 220°C.
240°C S	Materials or combinations of materials which by experience or accepted tests can be shown to have the required thermal life at 240°C.
above 240°C C	Materials consisting entirely of mica, porcelain, glass, quartz, and similar inorganic materials. Other materials or combinations of materials may be included in this class if by experience or accepted tests they can be shown to have the required thermal life at temperatures above 240°C.

The above insulation classes indicate a normal life expectancy of 20 000 h to 40 000 h at the stated temperature. This implies that electrical equipment insulated with a class A insulation system would probably last for 2 to 5 years if operated continuously at 105°C. Note that this classification assumes that the insulation system is not in contact with corrosive, humid, or dusty atmospheres.

For a complete explanation of insulation classes, insulation systems, and temperature indices, see IEEE Std 1-1969 and the companion IEEE Standards Publications Nos. 96, 97, 98, 99, and 101. See also IEEE Std 117-1974 and Underwriters Laboratories publication on insulation systems UL 1446, 1978.

The temperature of a machine varies from point to point, but there are places where the temperature is warmer than anywhere else. This *hottest-spot temperature* must not exceed the maximum allowable temperature of the particular class of insulation used.

Figure 6.7 shows the hot-spot temperature limits for class A, B, F, and H insulation (curve 1). They are the temperature limits previously mentioned in Section 6.7. The maximum ambient temperature of 40°C is also shown (curve 3). The temperature difference between curve 1 and curve 3 gives the *maximum permissible temperature rise* for each insulation class. This limiting temperature rise enables the manufacturer to establish the physical size of the motor, relay, and so forth, he intends to put on the market. Thus, for class B insulation, the maximum allowable temperature rise is (130 − 40) = 90°C.

To show how the temperature rise affects the size of a machine, suppose a manufacturer has designed and built a 10 kW motor using class B insulation. To test the motor he places it in a constant ambient temperature of 40°C and loads it up until it delivers 10 kW of mechanical power. Special temperature detectors, located at strategic points inside the machine, record the temperature of the windings. After the temperatures have stabilized (which may take several hours), the hottest temperature is noted, and this is called the *hot-spot temperature.* If the hot-spot temperature so recorded is, say 147°C, the

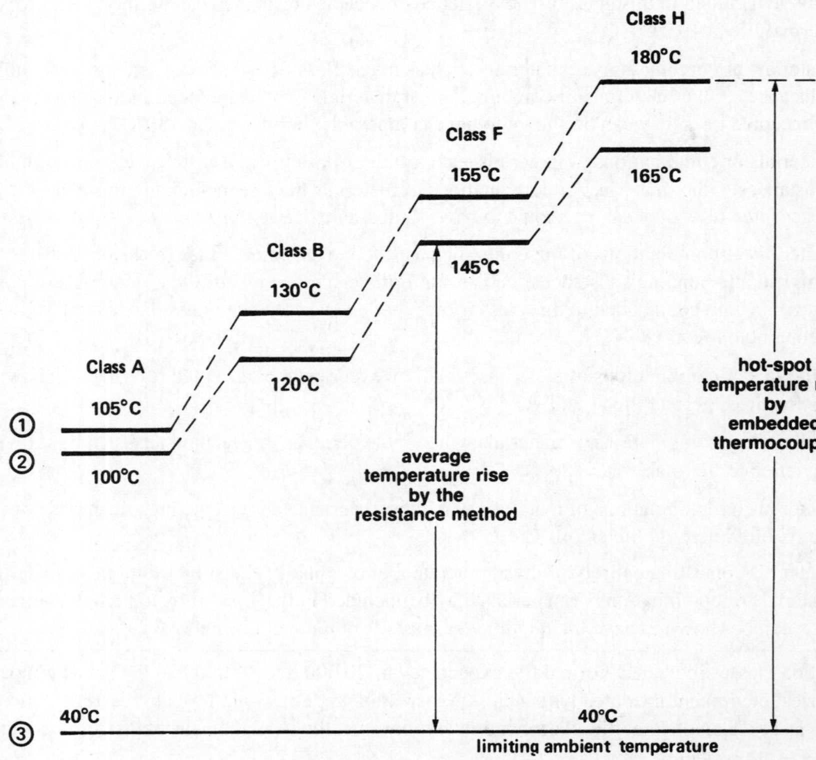

Figure 6.7
Typical limits of some dc and ac industrial machines, according to the insulation class:
1. Shows the maximum permissible temperature of the insulation to obtain a reasonable service life
2. Shows the maximum permissible temperature using the resistance method
3. Shows the limiting ambient temperature

manufacturer would not be permitted to sell his/her product. The reason is that the temperature rise (147° − 40°) = 107°C exceeds the maximum permissible rise of 90°C for class B insulation.

On the other hand, if the hottest-spot temperature is only 100°C, the temperature rise is (100° − 40°) = 60°C. The manufacturer immediately perceives that he/she can make a more economical design and still remain within the permissible temperature rise limits. For instance, he/she can reduce the conductor size until the hot-spot temperature rise is very close to 90°C. Obviously, this reduces the weight and cost of the windings. But the manufacturer also realizes that the reduced conductor size now enables him/her to reduce the size of the slots. This, in turn, reduces the amount of iron. By thus redesigning the motor, the manufacturer ultimately ends up with a machine that operates within the permissible temperature rise limits and has the smallest possible physical size, as well as lowest cost.

In practice, it is not convenient to carry out performance tests in a controlled ambient temperature of 40°C. The motor is usually loaded to its rated capacity in much lower (and more comfortable) ambient temperatures. Toward this end, it has been established by standards-setting bodies that, for testing purposes, the ambient temperature may lie anywhere between 10°C and 40°C. The hottest-spot temperature is recorded as before. If the temperature rise under these conditions is equal to or less than 90°C (for class B insulation), the manufacturer is allowed to sell his product.

Example 6-3

A 75 kW motor, insulated class F, operates at full-load in an ambient temperature of 32°C. If the hot-spot temperature is 125°C, does the motor meet the temperature standards?

Solution

The hot-spot temperature rise is

$$(125° - 32°) = 93°C$$

According to Fig. 6.7, the permissible hot-spot temperature rise for class F insulation is (155° − 40°) = 115°C. The motor easily meets the temperature standards. The manufacturer could reduce the size of the motor and thereby market a more competitive product.

6.9 Temperature rise by the resistance method

The hot-spot temperature rise is rather difficult to measure because it has to be taken at the very inside of a winding. This can be done by embedding a small temperature detector, such as a thermocouple or thermistor. However, this direct method of measuring hot-spot temperature is costly, and is only justified for larger machines.

To simplify matters, accepted standards permit a second method of determining temperature rise. It is based upon the *average* winding temperature, measured by resistance, rather than the hot-spot temperature. The maximum allowable average winding temperatures for the various insulation classes are shown in curve 2, Fig. 6.7. For example, in the case of class B insulation, an *average* winding temperature of 120°C is assumed to correspond to a hot-spot temperature of 130°C. Consequently, an average temperature rise of (120° − 40°) = 80°C is assumed to correspond to a hot-spot temperature rise of (130° − 40°) = 90°C.

The average temperature of a winding is found by the resistance method. It consists of measuring the winding resistance at a known winding temperature, and measuring it again when the machine is hot. For example, if the winding is made of copper, we can use the following equation (derived from Eqs. 6.1 and 6.2) to determine its average temperature:

$$t_2 = \frac{R_2}{R_1}(234 + t_1) - 234 \qquad (6.5)$$

where

t_2 = average temperature of the winding when hot [°C]

234 = a constant equal to $1/\alpha = 1/0.004\,27$

R_2 = hot resistance of the winding [Ω]

R_1 = cold resistance of the winding [Ω]

t_1 = temperature of the winding when cold [°C]

Knowing the hot winding temperature by the resistance method, we can immediately calculate the corresponding temperature rise by subtracting the ambient temperature. If this temperature rise falls within the permissible limit (80°C for class B insulation), the product is acceptable from a standards point of view. Note that when performance tests are carried out using the resistance method, the ambient temperature must again lie between 10°C and 40°C. If the winding happens to be made of aluminum wire, Eq. 6.3 can still be used, but the number 234 must be changed to 228.

Example 6-4

A dc motor that has been idle for several days in an ambient temperature of 19°C, is found to have a shunt-field resistance of 22 Ω. The motor then operates at full-load and, when temperatures have stabilized, the field resistance is found to be 30 Ω. The corresponding ambient temperature is 24°C. If the motor is built with class B insulation, calculate the following:

a. The average temperature of the winding, at full-load
b. The full-load temperature rise by the resistance method
c. Whether the motor meets the temperature standards

Solution

a. The average temperature of the shunt field at full-load is

$$
\begin{aligned}
t_2 &= (R_2/R_1)(234 + t_1) - 234 \\
&= (30/22)(234 + 19) - 234 \\
&= 111°\text{C}
\end{aligned}
$$

b. The average temperature rise at full-load is 111° − 24° = 87°C.
c. The maximum allowable temperature rise by resistance for class B insulation is (120° − 40°) = 80°C. Consequently, the motor does not meet the standards. Either its rating will have to be reduced, or the cooling system improved, before it can be put on the market. Alternatively, it may be rewound using class F insulation. As a very last resort, its size may have to be increased.

A final word of caution: Temperature rise standards depend not only on the class of insulation, but also on the type of apparatus (motor, transformer, relay, etc.), the type of construction (drip-proof, totally enclosed, etc.), and the field of application of the apparatus (commercial, industrial, naval, etc.). Consequently, the pertinent standards must always be consulted before conducting a heat-run test on a specific machine or device (Fig. 6.10).

6.10 Relationship between the speed and size of a machine

Although maximum allowable temperature rise establishes the nominal power rating of a machine, its basic physical size depends upon the power and speed of rotation.

Consider the 100 kW, 250 V, 2000 r/min generator shown in Fig. 6.8. Suppose we have to build another generator having the same power and voltage, but running at half the speed.

To generate the same voltage at half the speed, we either have to double the number of conductors on the armature or double the flux from the poles. Consequently, we must either increase the size of the armature, or increase the size of the poles. In practice, we increase both. We conclude that for a given power output, a low-speed machine is always bigger than a high-speed machine (Fig. 6.9). This is true for both ac and dc machines.

Basically, the size of a machine depends uniquely upon its torque. Thus, a 100 kW, 2000 r/min motor

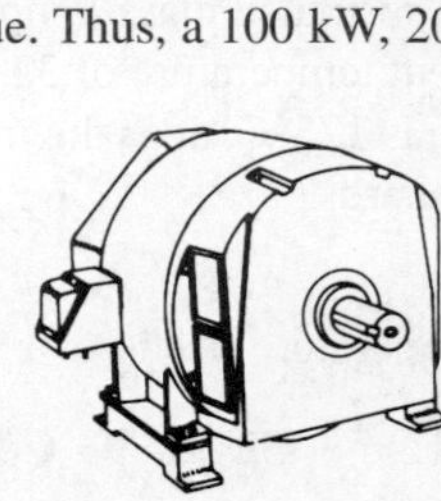

Figure 6.8
100 kW, 2000 r/min motor; mass: 300 kg.

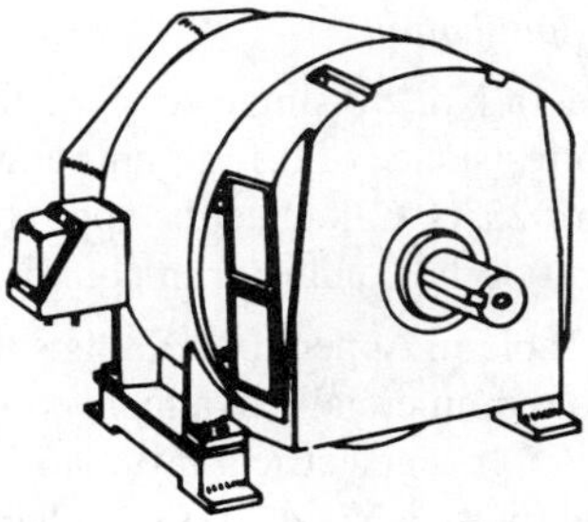

Figure 6.9
100 kW, 1000 r/min motor; mass: 500 kg.

has about the same physical size as a 10 kW motor running at 200 r/min because they develop the same torque.

Low-speed motors are therefore much more costly than high-speed motors of equal power. Consequently, for low-speed drives, it is often cheaper to use a small high-speed motor with a gear box than to use a large low-speed motor directly coupled to its load.

Questions and Problems

Practical level

6-1 Name the losses in a dc motor.

6-2 What causes iron losses and how can they be reduced?

6-3 Explain why the temperature of a machine increases as the load increases.

6-4 What determines the power rating of a machine?

6-5 If we cover up the vents in a motor, its output power must be reduced. Explain.

6-6 If a motor operates in a cold environment, may we load it above its rated power? Why?

6-7 Name some of the factors that contribute to the deterioration of organic insulators.

6-8 A motor is built with class H insulation. What maximum hot-spot temperature can it withstand?

Intermediate level

6-9 A dc motor connected to a 240 V line produces a mechanical output of 160 hp. Knowing that the losses are 12 kW, calculate the input power and the line current.

6-10 A 115 V dc generator delivers 120 A to a load. If the generator has an efficiency of 81 percent, calculate the mechanical power needed to drive it [hp].

6-11 Calculate the full-load current of a 250 hp, 230 V dc motor having an efficiency of 92 percent.

6-12 A machine having class B insulation attains a temperature of 208°C (by resistance) in a torrid ambient temperature of 180°C.
a. What is the temperature rise?
b. Is the machine running too hot and, if so, by how much?

6-13 The efficiency of a motor is always low when it operates at 10 percent of its nominal power rating. Explain.

6-14 Calculate the efficiency of the motor in Example 6-2 when it delivers an output of 1 hp.

6-15 An electric motor driving a skip hoist withdraws 1.5 metric tons of minerals from a trench 20 m deep every 30 seconds. If the hoist has an overall efficiency of 94 percent, calculate the power output of the motor in horsepower and in kilowatts.

6-16 Thermocouples are used to measure the internal hot-spot winding temperature of a 1200 kW ac motor, insulated class F. If the motor runs at full-load, what is the maximum temperature these detectors should indicate in an ambient temperature of 40°C? 30°C? 14°C?

6-17 A 60 hp ac motor with class F insulation has a cold winding resistance of 12 Ω at 23°C. When it runs at rated load in an ambient temperature of 31°C, the hot winding resistance is found to be 17.4 Ω.
a. Calculate the hot winding temperature.
b. Calculate the temperature rise of the motor.

c. Could the manufacturer increase the name plate rating of the motor? Explain.

6-18 An electric motor has a normal life of eight years when the ambient temperature is 30°C. If it is installed in a location where the ambient temperature is 60°C, what is the new probable service life of the motor?

6-19 A No. 10 round copper wire 210 m long carries a current of 12 A. Knowing that the temperature of the conductor is 105°C, calculate the following:

a. The current density [A/mm^2]
b. The specific copper losses [W/kg]

Advanced level

6-20 An aluminum conductor operates at a current density of 2 A/mm^2

a. If the conductor temperature is 120°C, calculate the specific losses [W/kg].
b. Express the current density in circular mils per ampere.

6-21 The temperature rise of a motor is roughly proportional to its losses. On the other hand, its efficiency is reasonably constant in the range between 50 percent and 150 percent of its nominal rating (see, for example, Fig. 6.5). Based on these facts, if a 20 kW motor has a full-load temperature rise of 80°C, what power can it deliver at a temperature rise of 105°C?

6-22 An electromagnet (insulated class A) situated in a particularly hot location has a service life of two years. What is its expected life span if it is rewound using class F insulation?

6-23 An 11 kW ac motor having class B insulation would normally have a service life of 20 000 h, provided the winding temperature by resistance does not exceed 120°C. By how many hours is the service life reduced if the motor runs for 3 h at a temperature (by resistance) of 200°C?

Industrial application

6-24 A reel of No. 2/0 single copper conductor has a resistance of 0.135 ohms at a temperature of 25°C. Calculate the approximate weight of the conductor in pounds.

6-25 The Table in Appendix AX3 lists the properties of commercially available copper conductors. In an electrical installation, it is proposed to use a No. 4 AWG conductor in an area where the operating temperature of the conductor may be as high as 70°C. Using Eq. 6.2, calculate the resistance under these conditions of a 2-conductor cable No. 4 AWG that is 27 meters long.

6-26 The shunt field of a 4-pole dc motor has a total resistance of 56 ohms at 25°C. By scraping off the insulation, it is found that the bare copper wire has a diameter of 0.04 inches. Determine the AWG wire size, and calculate the weight of the wire per pole, in kilograms.

6-27 The National Electrical Code allows a maximum current of 65 A in a No. 6 gauge copper conductor, type RW 75. A 420 ft cable is being used on a 240 V dc circuit to carry a current of 48 A. Assuming a maximum operating temperature of 70°C, calculate the following:

a. The power loss, in watts, in the 2-conductor cable
b. The approximate voltage at the load end if the voltage at the service panel is 243 V.

6-28 In Problem 6-27, if the voltage drop in the cable must not exceed 10 V when it is carrying a current of 60 A, what minimum conductor size would you recommend? Assume a maximum operating temperature of 70°C.

6-29 A dc busbar 4 inches wide, 1/4 inch thick, and 30 feet long carries a current of 2500 A. Calculate the voltage drop if the temperature of the busbar is 105°C. What is the power loss per meter?

6-30 Equation 6.3 gives the resistance/temperature relationship of copper conductors, namely,

$$t_2 = R_2/R_1\,(234 + t_1) - 234$$

Using the information given in Appendix AX2, deduce a similar equation for aluminum conductors.

6-31 The commutator of a 1.5 hp, 2-pole, 3000 r/min dc motor has a diameter of 63 mm. Calculate the peripheral speed in feet per minute and in miles per hour.

6-32 The following information is given on the brushes used in the motor of Problem 6-31:

number of brushes: 2

current per brush: 15 A

brush dimensions: 5/8 in wide, 5/16 in thick, 3/4 in long. (The 5/16 in × 5/8 in area is in contact with the commutator.)

resistivity of brush: 0.0016 Ω

brush pressure: 1.5 lbf

brush contact drop: 1.2 V

coefficient of friction: 0.2

Calculate the following:

a. The resistance of the brush body in ohms
b. The voltage drop in the brush body
c. The total voltage drop in one brush, including the contact voltage drop
d. The total electrical power loss (in watts) due to the two brushes
e. The frictional force of one brush rubbing against the commutator surface (in lbf and in newtons)
f. The frictional energy expended by the two brushes when the commutator makes one revolution (in joules)
g. The power loss due to friction, given the speed of 3000 r/min
h. The total brush loss as a percent of the 1.5 hp motor rating

Figure 6.10
This VARMECA® induction motor, including its variable-speed controller and gear reducer, is housed under a transparent plastic cover. The entire unit is being water-sprayed to demonstrate its ability to operate continuously under harsh environmental conditions.
(Courtesy of Leroy Somer, a division of Emerson Electric)

CHAPTER 7

Active, Reactive, and Apparent Power

7.0 Introduction

The concept of active, reactive, and apparent power plays a major role in electric power technology. In effect, the transmission of electrical energy and the behavior of ac machines are often easier to understand by working with power, rather than dealing with voltages and currents. The reader is therefore encouraged to pay particular attention to this chapter.

The terms *active, reactive,* and *apparent power* apply to steady-state alternating current circuits in which the voltages and currents are sinusoidal. They cannot be used to describe transient-state behavior, nor can we apply them to dc circuits.

Our study begins with an analysis of the instantaneous power in an ac circuit. We then go on to define the meaning of active and reactive power and how to identify sources and loads. This is followed by a definition of apparent power, *power factor,* and the *power triangle.* We then show how ac circuits can be solved using these power concepts. In conclusion, vector notation is used to determine the active and reactive power in an ac circuit.

7.1 Instantaneous power

The instantaneous power supplied to a device is simply the product of the instantaneous voltage across its terminals times the instantaneous current that flows through it.

Instantaneous power is always expressed in watts, irrespective of the type of circuit used. The instantaneous power may be positive or negative. A positive value means that power flows into the device. Conversely, a negative value indicates that power is flowing out of the device.

Example 7-1

A sinusoidal voltage having a peak value of 162 V and a frequency of 60 Hz is applied to the terminals of an ac motor. The resulting current has a peak value of 7.5 A and lags 50° behind the voltage.

a. Express the voltage and current in terms of the electrical angle ϕ.
b. Calculate the value of the instantaneous voltage and current at an angle of 120°.

c. Calculate the value of the instantaneous power at 120°.
d. Plot the curve of the instantaneous power delivered to the motor.

Solution

a. Let us assume that the voltage starts at zero and increases positively with time. We can therefore write

$$e = E_m \sin \phi = 162 \sin \phi$$

The current lags behind the voltage by an angle $\theta = 50°$, consequently, we can write

$$i = I_m \sin (\phi - \theta) = 7.5 \sin (\phi - 50°)$$

b. At $\phi = 120°$ we have

$$e = 162 \sin 120° = 162 \times 0.866$$
$$= 140.3 \text{ V}$$
$$i = 7.5 \sin (120° - 50°) = 7.5 \sin 70°$$
$$= 7.5 \times 0.94$$
$$= 7.05 \text{ A}$$

c. The instantaneous power at 120° is

$$p = ei = 140.3 \times 7.05 = +989 \text{ W}$$

Because the power is positive, it flows at this instant into the motor.

d. In order to plot the curve of instantaneous power, we repeat procedures (b) and (c) for angles ranging from $\phi = 0$ to $\phi = 360°$. Table 7A lists part of the data used.

TABLE 7A VALUES OF *e*, *i*, AND *p* USED TO PLOT FIG. 7.1

Angle ϕ degrees	Voltage $162 \sin \phi$ volts	Current $7.5 \sin (\phi - 50°)$ amperes	Power p watts
0	0	−5.75	0
25	68.5	−3.17	−218
50	124.1	0	0
75	156.5	3.17	497
115	146.8	6.8	1000
155	68.5	7.25	497
180	0	5.75	0
205	−68.5	3.17	−218
230	−124.1	0	0

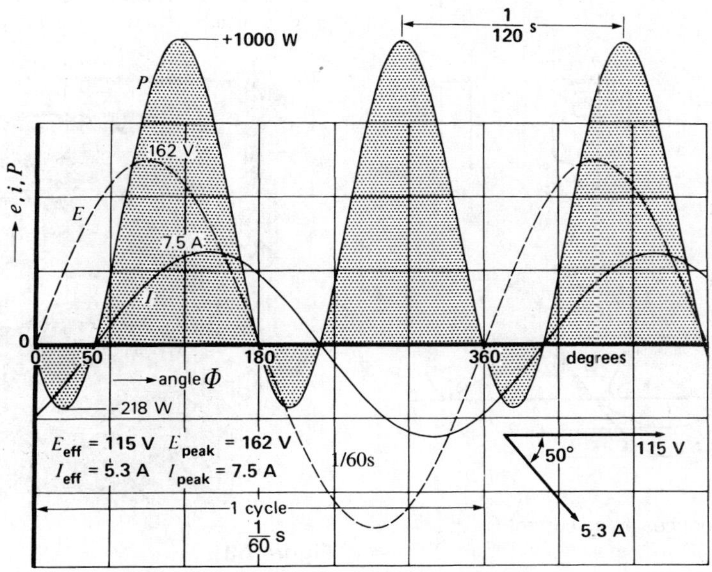

Figure 7.1
Instantaneous voltage, current, and power in an ac circuit. (See Example 7-1.)

The voltage, current, and instantaneous power are plotted in Fig. 7.1. The power attains a positive peak of +1000 W and a negative peak of −218 W. The negative power means that power is actually flowing from the load (motor) to the source. This occurs during the intervals 0–50°, 180°–230°, and 360°–410°. Although a power flow from a device considered to be a load to a device considered to be a source may seem to be impossible, it happens often in ac circuits. The reason is given in the sections that follow.

We also note that the positive peaks occur at intervals of 1/120 s. This means that the frequency of the power cycle is 120 Hz, which is twice the frequency of the voltage and current that produce the power. Again, this phenomenon is quite normal: the frequency of ac power flow is always twice the line frequency.

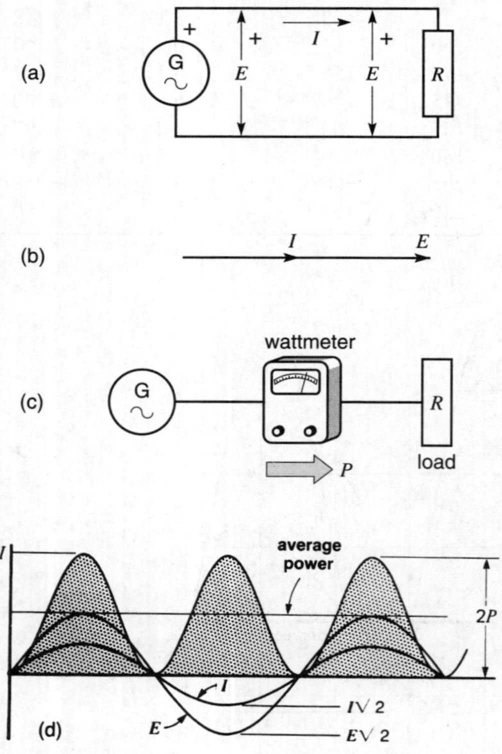

Figure 7.2

a. An ac voltage E produces an ac current I in this resistive circuit.
b. Phasors E and I are in phase.
c. A wattmeter indicates EI watts.
d. The active power is composed of a series of positive power pulses.

7.2 Active power*

The simple ac circuit of Fig. 7.2a consists of a resistor connected to an ac generator. The effective voltage and current are designated E and I, respectively, and as we would expect in a resistive circuit, phasors E and I are in phase (Fig. 7.2b). If we connect a wattmeter (Fig. 7.3) into the line, it will give a reading $P = EI$ watts (Fig. 7.2c).

To get a better picture of what goes on in such a circuit, we have drawn the sinusoidal curves of E and I (Fig. 7.2d). The peak values are respectively $\sqrt{2}E$ volts and $\sqrt{2}I$ amperes because, as stated previously, E and I are *effective* values. By multiplying the instantaneous values of voltage and current as we did in Section 7.1, we obtain the *instantaneous* power in watts.

* Many persons refer to active power as *real power* or *true power,* considering it to be more descriptive. In this book we use the term *active power,* because it conforms to the IEEE designation.

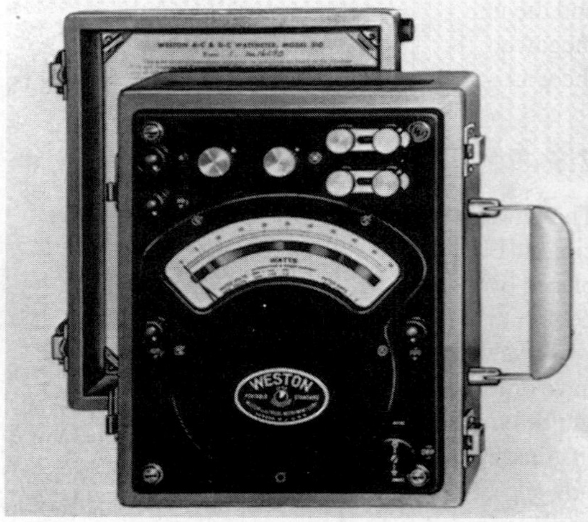

Figure 7.3
Example of a high-precision wattmeter rated 50 V, 100 V, 200 V; 1 A, 5 A. The scale ranges from 0-50 W to 0-1000 W.
(Courtesy of Weston Instruments)

The power wave consists of a series of positive pulses that vary from zero to a maximum value of $(\sqrt{2}E) \times (\sqrt{2}I) = 2EI = 2P$ watts. The fact that power is always positive reveals that it always flows from the generator to the resistor. This is one of the basic properties of what is called *active power:* although it pulsates between zero and maximum, it *never* changes direction. The direction of power flow is shown by an arrow P (Fig. 7.2c).

The average power is clearly midway between $2P$ and zero, and so its value is $P = 2EI/2 = EI$ watts. That is precisely the power indicated by the wattmeter.

The two conductors leading to the resistor in Fig. 7.2a carry the active power. However, unlike current flow, power does not flow down one conductor and return by the other. Power flows over *both* conductors and, consequently, as far as power is concerned, we can replace the conductors by a single line, as shown in Fig. 7.2c.

In general, the line represents any transmission line connecting two devices, irrespective of the number of conductors it may have.

The generator is an *active source* and the resistor is an *active load.* The symbol for active power is P and the unit is the watt (W). The kilowatt (kW) and megawatt (MW) are frequently used multiples of the watt.

7.3 Reactive power

The circuit of Fig. 7.4a is identical to the resistive circuit (Fig. 7.2a) except that the resistor is now replaced by a reactor X_L. As a result, current I lags 90° behind the voltage E (Fig. 7.4b).

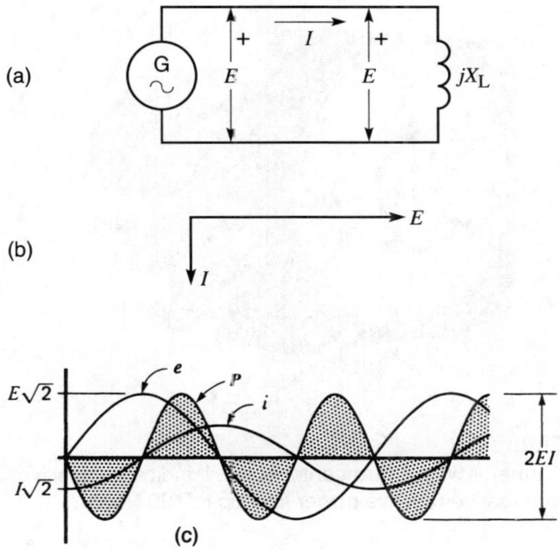

Figure 7.4
a. An ac voltage E produces an ac current I in this inductive circuit.
b. Phasor I lags 90° behind E.
c. Reactive power consists of a series of positive and negative power pulses.

To see what really goes on in such a circuit, we have drawn the waveforms for E and I and, by again multiplying their instantaneous values, we obtain the curve of instantaneous power (Fig. 7.4c). This power p consists of a series of identical positive and negative pulses. The positive waves correspond to instantaneous power delivered by the generator to the reactor and the negative waves represent instantaneous power delivered from the reactor to the generator. The duration of each wave corresponds to one quarter of a cycle of the line frequency. The frequency of the power wave is therefore again twice the line frequency.

Power that surges back and forth in this manner is called *reactive power* (symbol Q), to distinguish it from the unidirectional active power mentioned before. The reactive power in Fig. 7.4 is also given by the product EI. However, to distinguish this power from active power, another unit is used—the **var.** Its multiples are the kilovar (kvar) and megavar (Mvar).

Special instruments, called *varmeters,* are available to measure the reactive power in a circuit (Fig. 7.5). A varmeter registers the product of the effective line voltage E times the effective line current I times sin θ (where θ is the phase angle between E and I). A reading is only obtained when E and I are out of phase; if they are exactly in phase (or exactly 180° out of phase), the varmeter reads zero.

Returning to Fig. 7.4, the dotted area under each pulse is the energy, in joules, transported in one direction or the other. Clearly, the energy is delivered in a continuous series of pulses of very short duration, every positive pulse being followed by a

Figure 7.5
Varmeter with a zero-center scale. It indicates positive or negative reactive power flow up to 100 Mvars.

negative pulse. The energy flows back and forth between the generator and the inductor without ever being used up.

What is the reason for these positive and negative energy surges? The energy flows back and forth because magnetic energy is alternately being stored up and released by the reactor. Thus, when the power is positive, the magnetic field is building up inside the coil. A moment later when the power is negative, the energy in the magnetic field is decreasing and flowing back to the source.

We now have an explanation for the brief negative power pulses in Fig. 7.1. In effect, they represent magnetic energy, previously stored up in the motor windings, that is being returned to the source.

7.4 Definition of a reactive load and reactive source

Reactive power involves real power that oscillates back and forth between two devices over a transmission line. Consequently, it is impossible to say whether the power originates at one end of the line or the other. Nevertheless, it is useful to assume that some devices generate reactive power while others absorb it. In other words, some devices behave like *reactive sources* and others like *reactive loads.*

By definition*, a reactor is considered to be a reactive load that absorbs reactive power.

Example 7-2

A reactor having an inductive reactance of 4 Ω is connected to the terminals of a 120 V ac generator (Fig. 7.6a).

a. Calculate the value of the current in the reactor
b. Calculate the power associated with the reactor
c. Calculate the power associated with the ac generator
d. Draw the phasor diagram for the circuit

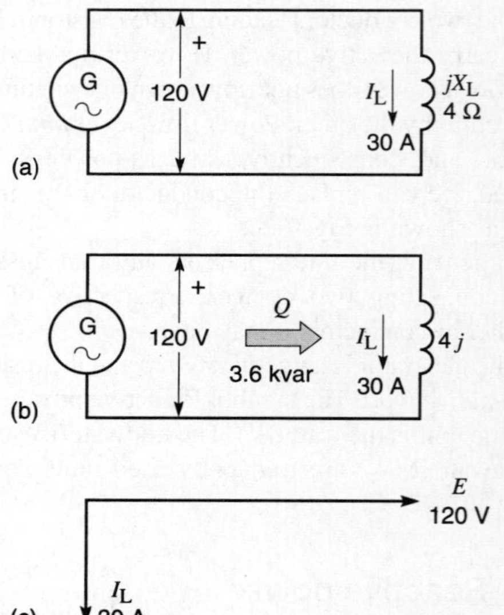

Figure 7.6
See Example 7-2.

Solution

a. Current in the circuit:

$$I_L = \frac{E}{X_L} = \frac{120\ \text{V}}{4\ \Omega} = 30\ \text{A}$$

b. Power associated with the reactor:

$$Q = EI = 120 \times 30 = 3600\ \text{var} = 3.6\ \text{kvar}$$

* This definition is in agreement with IEEE and IEC conventions.

This reactive power is absorbed by the reactor.

c. Because the reactor absorbs 3.6 kvar of reactance power, the ac generator must be supplying it. Consequently, the generator is a source of reactive power: it delivers 3.6 kvar. The reactive power Q flows therefore in the direction shown (Fig. 7.6b).
d. The phasor diagram is shown in Fig. 7.6c. Current I_L lags 90° behind voltage E.

This phasor diagram applies to the reactive load (the reactor) and the reactive source (the ac generator) as well as the line connecting them.

7.5 The capacitor and reactive power

Suppose now that we add a capacitor having a reactance of 4 Ω to the circuit of Fig. 7.6. This yields the circuit of Fig. 7.7a. The current I_c drawn by the capacitor is $I_c = 120\ \text{V}/4\ \Omega = 30\ \text{A}$ and, as we would expect, it leads the voltage by 90° (Fig. 7.7b).

The vector sum of I_L and I_c is zero and so the ac generator is no longer supplying any power at all to the circuit. However, the current in the reactor has not changed; consequently, it continues to absorb $30\ \text{A} \times 120\ \text{V} = 3.6$ kvar of reactive power.

Where is this reactive power coming from? It can only come from the capacitor, which acts as a source of reactive power. The reactive power delivered by the capacitor is equal to the current it carries times the voltage across its terminals, namely

$$Q = EI_c = 120\ \text{V} \times 30\ \text{A} = 3600\ \text{var} = 3.6\ \text{kvar}$$

The reactive power delivered by the capacitor is expressed in vars or kilovars. Reactive power Q now flows from the capacitor to the reactor.

We have arrived at a very important conclusion: a *capacitor is a source of reactive power.* It acts as a reactive power source whenever it is part of a sine-wave-based, steady-state circuit.

Let us take another step and remove the reactor from the circuit in Fig. 7.7a, yielding the circuit of Fig. 7.8a. The capacitor is now alone, connected to the terminals of the ac generator. It still carries a current of 30 A, leading the voltage E by 90° (Fig. 7.8b). Consequently, the capacitor still acts as a source of reactive power, delivering 3.6 kvar. Where does this power go? The answer is that the capacitor delivers reactive power to the very generator to which it is

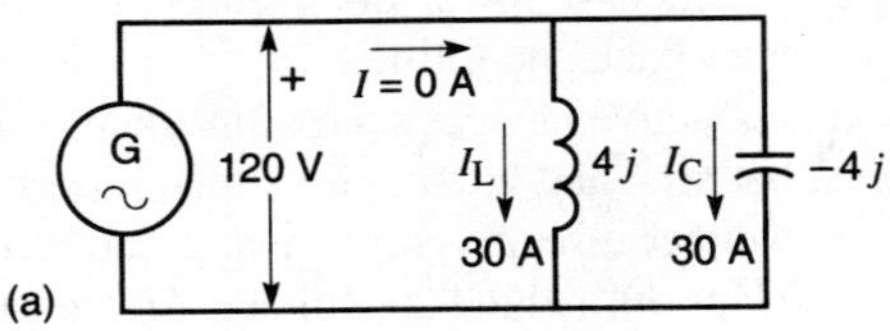

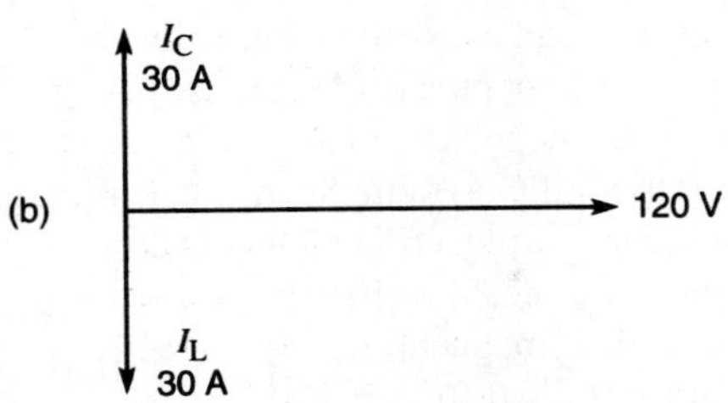

Figure 7.7
See Example 7-3.

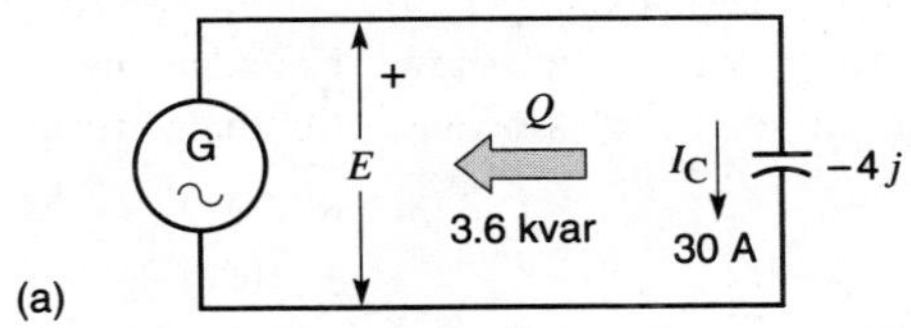

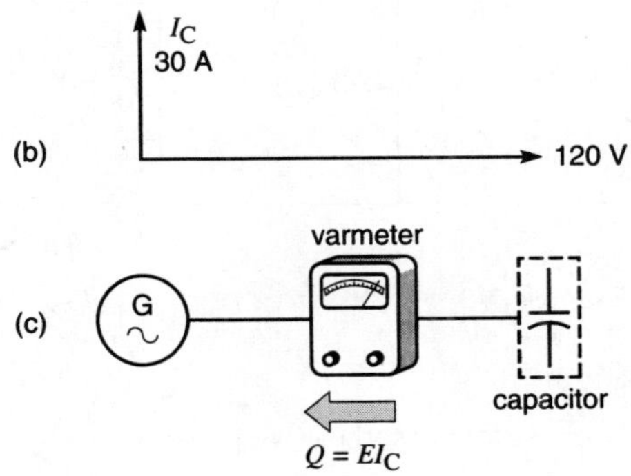

Figure 7.8
a. Capacitor connected to an ac source.
b. Phasor I_C leads E by 90°.
c. Reactive power flows from the capacitor to the generator.

connected! For most people, this takes a little time to accept. How, we may ask, can a passive device like a capacitor possibly produce any power? The answer is that reactive power really represents energy that, like a pendulum, swings back and forth without ever doing any useful work. The capacitor acts as a temporary energy-storing device repeatedly accepting energy for brief periods and releasing it again. However, instead of storing magnetic energy as a reactor does, a capacitor stores electrostatic energy (see Section 2.14).

If we connect a varmeter into the circuit (Fig. 7.8c), it will give a negative reading of $EI = -3600$ var, showing that reactive power is indeed flowing from the capacitor to the generator. The generator is now behaving like reactive load, but we sometimes prefer to call it a *receiver* of reactive power, which, of course, amounts to the same thing. In summary, a capacitive reactance *always* generates reactive power.

Example 7-3

An ac generator G is connected to a group of *R, L, C* circuit elements (Fig. 7.9). The respective elements carry the currents shown. Calculate the active and reactive power associated with the generator.

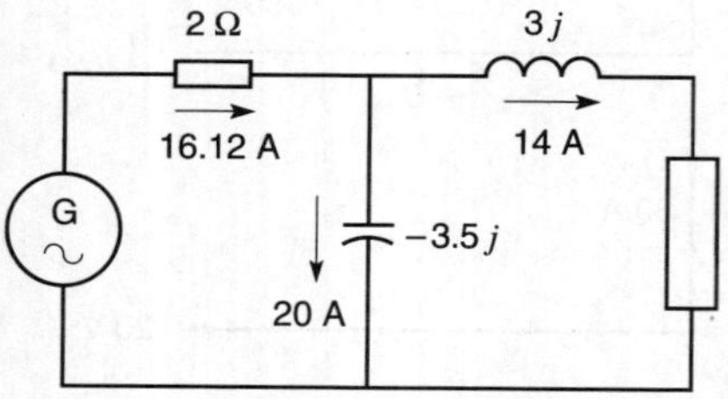

Figure 7.9
See Example 7-3.

Solution

The two resistors absorb active power given by

$$P = I^2R = (14^2 \times 4) + (16.12^2 \times 2) = 784 + 520 = 1304 \text{ W}$$

The 3 Ω reactor absorbs reactive power:
$Q_L = I^2X_L = 14^2 \times 3 = 588$ var

The 3.5 Ω capacitor generates reactive power:
$Q_C = I^2X_C = 20^2 \times 3.5 = 1400$ var.

The *R, L, C* circuit generates a net reactive power of $1400 - 588 = 812$ var.

This reactive power must be absorbed by the generator; hence, as far as reactive power is concerned, the generator acts as a load.

The active power absorbed by the resistors must be supplied by the generator; hence it is a source of active power = 1304 W.

In conclusion, the ac generator is a source of active power (1304 W) and a receiver of reactive power (812 var).

7.6 Distinction between active and reactive power

There is a basic difference between active and reactive power, and perhaps the most important thing to remember is that the one cannot be converted into the other. Active and reactive powers function independently of each other and, consequently, they can be treated as separate quantities in electric circuits.

Both place a burden on the transmission line that carries them, but, whereas active power eventually produces a tangible result (heat, mechanical power, light, etc.), reactive power only represents power that oscillates back and forth.

All ac inductive devices such as magnets, transformers, ballasts, and induction motors, absorb reactive power because one component of the current they draw lags 90° behind the voltage. The reactive power plays a very important role because it produces the ac magnetic field in these devices.

A building, shopping center, or city may be considered to be a huge active/reactive load connected to an electric utility system. Such load centers contain thousands of induction motors and other electromagnetic devices that draw both reactive power (to sustain their magnetic fields) and active power (to do the useful work).

This leads us to the study of loads that absorb both active and reactive power.

7.7 Combined active and reactive loads: apparent power

Loads that absorb both active power P and reactive power Q may be considered to be made up of a resistance and an inductive reactance. Consider, for example, the circuit of Fig. 7.10a in which a resistor and reactor are connected to a source G. The resistor draws a current I_p, while the reactor draws a current I_q.

According to our definitions, the resistor is an active load while the reactor is a reactive load. Consequently, I_p is in phase with E while I_q lags 90° behind. The phasor diagram (Fig. 7.10b) shows that the resultant line current I lags behind E by an angle θ. Furthermore, the magnitude of I is given by

$$I = \sqrt{I_p^2 + I_q^2}$$

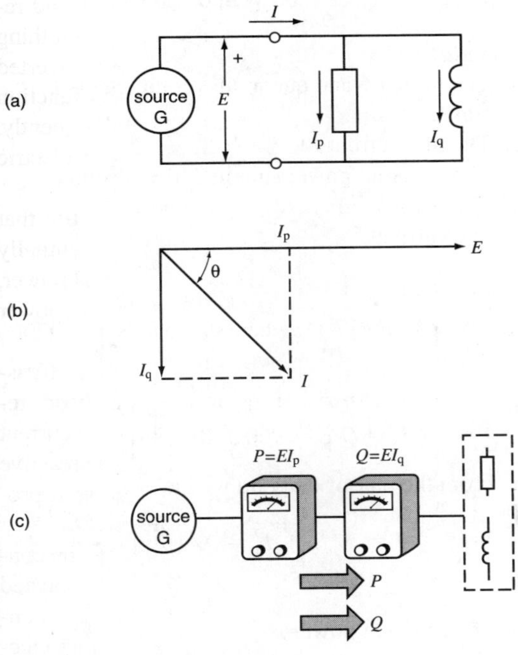

Figure 7.10
a. Circuit consisting of a source feeding an active and reactive load.
b. Phasor diagram of the voltage and currents.
c. Active and reactive power flow from source to load.

The active and reactive power components P and Q both flow in the same direction, as shown by the arrows in Fig. 7.10c. If we connect a wattmeter and a varmeter into the circuit, the readings will both be positive, indicating $P = EI_p$ watts and $Q = EI_q$ vars, respectively.

Furthermore, if we connect an ammeter into the line, it will indicate a current of I amperes. As a result, we are inclined to believe that the power supplied to the load is equal to EI watts. But this is obviously incorrect because the power is composed of an active component (watts) and a reactive component (vars). For this reason the product EI is called *apparent power*. The symbol for apparent power is S.

Apparent power is expressed neither in watts nor in vars, but in *voltamperes*. Multiples are the kilovoltampere (kVA) and megavoltampere (MVA).

7.8 Relationship between *P*, *Q*, and *S*

Consider the single-phase circuit of Fig. 7.11a composed of a source, a load, and appropriate meters. Let us assume that

- the voltmeter indicates E volts
- the ammeter indicates I amperes
- the wattmeter indicates $+P$ watts
- the varmeter indicates $+Q$ vars

Knowing that P and Q are positive, we know that the load absorbs both active and reactive power. Consequently, the line current I lags behind E_{ab} by an angle θ.

Current I can be decomposed into two components I_p and I_q, respectively in phase, and in quadrature, with phasor E (Fig. 7.11b). The numerical values of I_p and I_q can be found directly from the instrument readings

$$I_p = P/E \tag{7.1}$$

$$I_q = Q/E \tag{7.2}$$

Furthermore, the apparent power S transmitted over the line is given by $S = EI$, from which

$$I = S/E \tag{7.3}$$

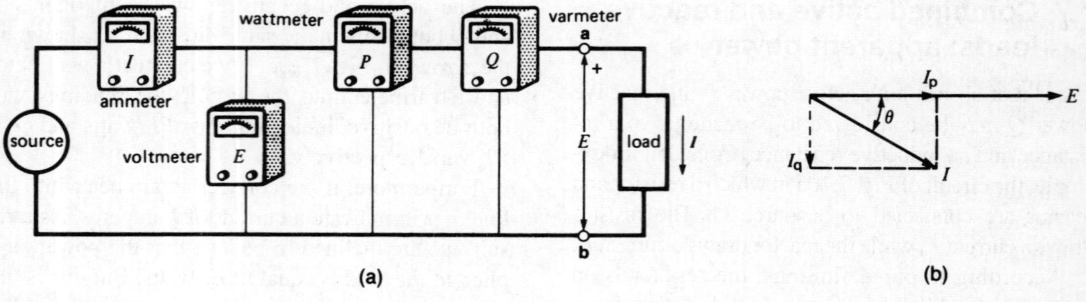

Figure 7.11
a. Instruments used to measure *E, I, P,* and *Q* in a circuit.
b. The phasor diagram can be deduced from the instrument readings.

Referring to the phasor diagram (Fig. 7.11b), it is obvious that

$$I^2 = I_p^{\,2} + I_q^{\,2}$$

Consequently,

$$\left[\frac{S}{E}\right]^2 = \left[\frac{P}{E}\right]^2 + \left[\frac{Q}{E}\right]^2$$

That is,

$$S^2 = P^2 + Q^2 \qquad (7.4)$$

in which

S = apparent power [VA]
P = active power [W]
Q = reactive power [var]

We can also calculate the value of the angle θ because the tangent of θ is obviously equal to I_q/I_p. Thus, we have

$$\theta = \arctan I_q/I_p = \arctan Q/P \qquad (7.5)$$

Example 7-4

An alternating-current motor absorbs 40 kW of active power and 30 kvar of reactive power. Calculate the apparent power supplied to the motor.

Solution

$$S = \sqrt{P^2 + Q^2} \qquad (7.4)$$
$$= \sqrt{40^2 + 30^2}$$
$$= 50 \text{ kVA}$$

Example 7-5

A wattmeter and varmeter are connected into a 120 V single-phase line that feeds an ac motor. They respectively indicate 1800 W and 960 var.

Calculate

a. The in-phase and quadrature components I_p and I_q
b. The line current I
c. The apparent power supplied by the source
d. The phase angle between the line voltage and line current

Solution

Referring to Fig. 7.11, where the load is now a motor, we have

a. $$I_p = P/E = 1800/120 = 15 \text{ A} \qquad (7.1)$$
$$I_q = Q/E = 960/120 = 8 \text{ A} \qquad (7.2)$$

b. From the phasor diagram we have

$$I = \sqrt{I_p^2 + I_q^2} = \sqrt{15^2 + 8^2}$$
$$= 17 \text{ A}$$

c. The apparent power is

$$S = EI = 120 \times 17 = 2040 \text{ VA}$$

d. The phase angle θ between E and I is

$$\theta = \arctan Q/P = \arctan 960/1800$$
$$= 28.1°$$

Example 7-6

A voltmeter and ammeter connected into the inductive circuit of Fig. 7.4a give readings of 140 V and 20 A, respectively.

Calculate

a. The apparent power of the load
b. The reactive power of the load
c. The active power of the load

Solution

a. The apparent power is

$$S = EI = 140 \times 20$$
$$= 2800 \text{ VA} = 2.8 \text{ kVA}$$

b. The reactive power is

$$Q = EI = 140 \times 20$$
$$= 2800 \text{ var} = 2.8 \text{ kvar}$$

If a varmeter were connected into the circuit, it would give a reading of 2800 var.

c. The active power is zero.

If a wattmeter were connected into the circuit, it would read zero.

To recapitulate, the apparent power is 2800 VA, but because the current is 90° out of phase with the voltage, it is also equal to 2800 var.

7.9 Power factor

The power factor of an alternating-current device or circuit is the ratio of the active power P to the apparent power S. It is given by the equation

$$\text{power factor} = P/S \tag{7.6}$$

where

P = active power delivered or absorbed by the circuit or device [W]
S = apparent power of the circuit or device [VA]

Power factor is expressed as a simple number, or as a percentage.

Because the active power P can never exceed the apparent power S, it follows that the power factor can never be greater than unity (or 100 percent).

The power factor of a resistor is 100 percent because the apparent power it draws is equal to the active power. On the other hand, the power factor of an ideal coil having no resistance is zero, because it does not consume any active power.

To sum up, the power factor of a circuit or device is simply a way of stating what fraction of its apparent power is real, or active, power.

In a single-phase circuit the power factor is also a measure of the phase angle θ between the voltage and current. Thus, referring to Fig. 7.11,

$$\begin{aligned}\text{power factor} &= P/S \\ &= EI_p/EI \\ &= I_p/I \\ &= \cos\theta\end{aligned}$$

Consequently,

$$\text{power factor} = \cos\theta = P/S \tag{7.7}$$

where

power factor = power factor of a single-phase circuit or device
θ = phase angle between the voltage and current

If we know the power factor, we automatically know the cosine of the angle between E and I and, hence, we can calculate the angle. The power factor is said to be *lagging* if the current lags behind the voltage. Conversely, the power factor is said to be *leading* if the current leads the voltage.

Example 7-7

Calculate the power factor of the motor in Example 7-5 and the phase angle between the line voltage and line current.

Solution

$$\begin{aligned}\text{power factor} &= P/S \\ &= 1800/2040 \\ &= 0.882 \text{ or } 88.2 \text{ (lagging)} \\ \cos\theta &= 0.882 \\ \text{therefore, } \theta &= 28.1°\end{aligned}$$

Example 7-8

A single-phase motor draws a current of 5 A from a 120 V, 60 Hz line. The power factor of the motor is 65 percent.

Calculate

a. The active power absorbed by the motor
b. The reactive power supplied by the line

Solution

a. The apparent power drawn by the motor is

$$S_m = EI = 120 \times 5 = 600 \text{ VA}$$

The active power absorbed by the motor is

$$P_m = S_m \cos \theta \quad (7.7)$$
$$= 600 \times 0.65 = 390 \text{ W}$$

b. The reactive power absorbed by the motor is

$$Q_m = \sqrt{S_m^2 - P_m^2} \quad (7.4)$$
$$= \sqrt{600^2 - 390^2}$$
$$= 456 \text{ var}$$

Note that the motor draws even more reactive power from the line than active power. This burdens the line with a relatively large amount of nonproductive power.

7.10 Power triangle

The $S^2 = P^2 + Q^2$ relationship expressed by Eq. 7.4, brings to mind a right-angle triangle. Thus, we can show the relationship between *S, P,* and *Q* graphically by means of a *power triangle.* According to convention, the following rules apply:

1. Active power *P* absorbed by a circuit or device is considered to be positive and is drawn horizontally to the right
2. Active power *P* that is delivered by a circuit or device is considered to be negative and is drawn horizontally to the left
3. Reactive power *Q* absorbed by a circuit or device is considered to be positive and is drawn vertically upwards

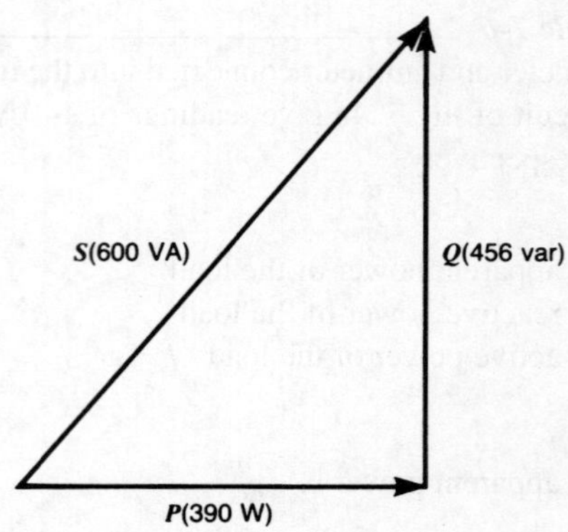

Figure 7.12
Power triangle of a motor. See Example 7-8.

4. Reactive power *Q* that is delivered by a circuit or device is considered to be negative and is drawn vertically downwards

The power triangle for Example 7-8 is shown in Fig. 7.12 in accordance with these rules. The power components *S, P,* and *Q* look like phasors, but they are not. However, we can think of them as convenient vectors. The concept of the power triangle is useful when solving ac circuits that comprise several active and reactive power components.

7.11 Further aspects of sources and loads

Let us consider Fig. 7.13a in which a resistor and capacitor are connected to a source. The circuit is similar to Fig. 7.10 except that the capacitor is a reactive source. As a result, reactive power flows from the capacitor to the source G while active power flows from the source G to the resistor. The active and reactive power components therefore flow in opposite directions over the transmission line. A wattmeter connected into the circuit will give a positive reading $P = EI_p$ watts, but a varmeter will give a negative reading $Q = EI_q$. The source G *delivers* active power *P* but *receives* reactive power *Q*. Thus, G is simultaneously an active source *and* a reactive load.

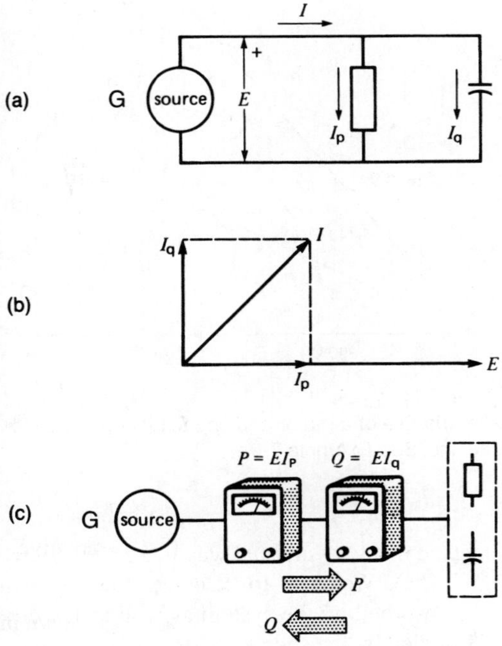

Figure 7.13
a. Source feeding an active and reactive (capacitive) load.
b. Phasor diagram of the circuit.
c. The active and reactive powers flow in opposite directions.

It may seem unusual to have two powers flowing in opposite directions over the same transmission line, but we must again remember that active power P is not the same as a reactive power Q and that each flows independently of the other.

Speaking of sources and loads, a deceptively simple electrical outlet, such as the 120 V receptacle in a home, also deserves our attention. All such outlets are ultimately connected to the huge alternators that power the electrical transmission and distribution systems. Odd as it may seem, an electrical outlet can act not only as an active or reactive source (as we would expect), but it may also behave as an active or reactive load. What factors determine whether it will behave in one way or the other? It all depends upon the type of device (or devices) connected to the receptacle. If the device absorbs active power, the receptacle will provide it; if the device delivers active power, the receptacle will receive it. In other words, a simple receptacle outlet is at all times ready to deliver—or accept—either active power P or reactive power Q in accordance with the devices connected to it.

The same remarks apply to any 3-phase, 480 V service entrance to a factory or the terminals of a high-power 345 kV transmission line.

Example 7-9

A 50 μF paper capacitor is placed across the motor terminals in Example 7-8.

Calculate

a. The reactive power generated by the capacitor
b. The active power absorbed by the motor
c. The reactive power absorbed from the line
d. The new line current

Solution

a. The impedance of the capacitor is

$$X_C = 1/(2\pi fC) \quad (2.11)$$
$$= 1/(2\pi \times 60 \times 50 \times 10^{-6})$$
$$= 53\ \Omega$$

The current in the capacitor is

$$I = E/X_C = 120/53$$
$$= 2.26\ \text{A}$$

The reactive power generated by the capacitor is

$$Q_C = EI_q = 120 \times 2.26$$
$$= 271\ \text{var}$$

b. The motor continues to draw the same active power because it is still fully loaded. Consequently,

$$P_m = 390\ \text{W}$$

The motor also draws the same reactive power as before, because nothing has taken place to change its magnetic field. Consequently,

$$Q_m = 456\ \text{var}$$

c. The motor draws 456 var from the line, but the capacitor furnishes 271 var to the same line. The net reactive power drawn from the line is, therefore,

$$Q_L = Q_m - Q_C$$
$$= 456 - 271$$
$$= 185 \text{ var}$$

The active power drawn from the line is

$$P_L = P_m = 390 \text{ W}$$

d. The apparent power drawn from the line is

$$S_L = \sqrt{P_L^2 + Q_L^2}$$
$$= \sqrt{390^2 + 185^2}$$
$$= 432 \text{ VA}$$

The new line current is

$$I_L = S_L/E = 432/120$$
$$= 3.6 \text{ A}$$

Thus, the line current drops from 5 A to 3.6 A by placing the capacitor in parallel with the motor. This represents a big improvement because the line current is smaller and the operation of the motor has not been changed in the least.

The new power factor of the line is

$$\cos \phi_L = P_L/S_L = 390/432$$
$$= 0.903 \text{ or } 90.3\%$$
$$\phi_L = \arccos 0.903 = 25.5°$$

The power triangle is shown in Fig. 7.14. The reactive power Q_C generated by the capacitor is drawn vertically downward. By comparing this power triangle with that in Fig. 7.12, we can visually observe the effect of the capacitor on the apparent power supplied by the line.

7.12 Systems comprising several loads

The concept of active and reactive power enables us to simplify the solution of some rather complex circuits. Consider, for example, a group of loads

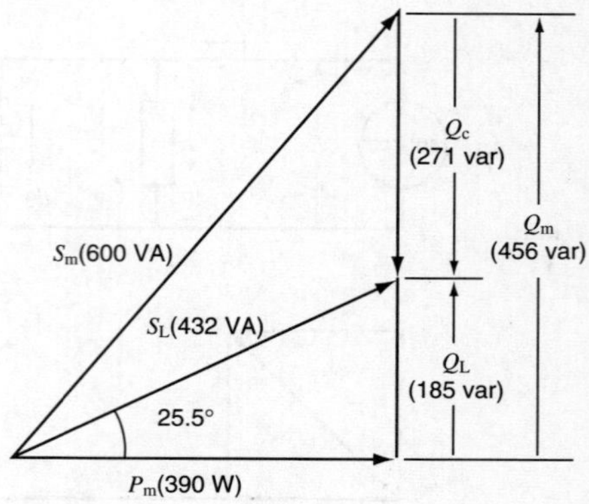

Figure 7.14
Power triangle of a motor and capacitor connected to an ac line. See Example 7-9.

connected in a very unusual way to a 380 V source (Fig. 7.15a). We wish to calculate the apparent power absorbed by the system as well as the current supplied by the source.

Using the power approach, we do not have to worry about the way the loads are interconnected. We simply draw a block diagram of the individual loads, indicating the direction (as far as the source is concerned) of active and reactive power flow (Fig. 7.15b). Thus, because load A is inductive, it absorbs reactive power; consequently, the 5 kvar arrow flows from the source to the load. On the other hand, because load C represents a capacitor, it delivers reactive power to the system. The 16 kvar arrow is directed therefore toward the source.

The distinct (and independent) nature of the active and reactive powers enables us to add all the active powers in a circuit to obtain the total active power P. In the same way, we can add the reactive powers to obtain the total reactive power Q. The resulting total apparent power S is then found by

$$S = \sqrt{P^2 + Q^2} \qquad (7.4)$$

We recall that when adding reactive powers, we assign a positive value to those that are absorbed by the system and a negative value to those that are generated (such as by a capacitor). In the same way,

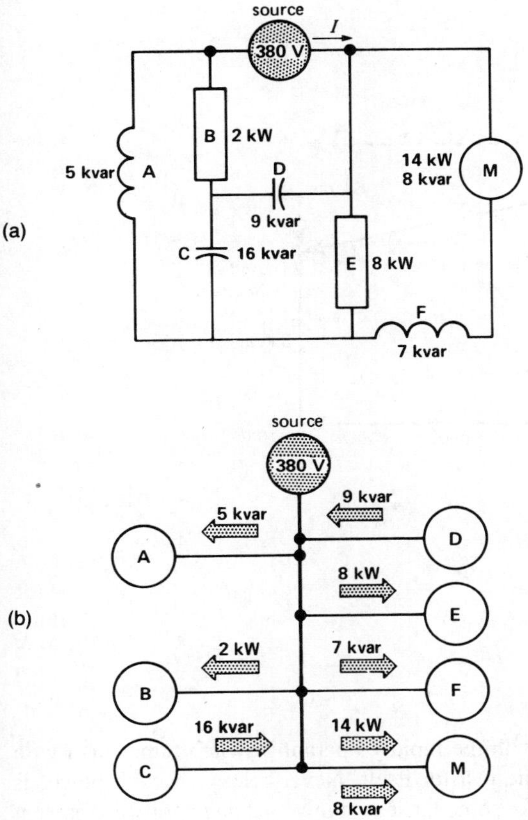

Figure 7.15
a. Example of active and reactive loads connected to a 380 V source.
b. All loads are assumed to be directly connected to the 380 V receptacle.

we assign a positive value to active powers that are absorbed and a negative value to those that are generated (such as by an alternator).

Note that usually we *cannot* add the apparent powers in various parts of a circuit to obtain the total apparent power S. We can only add them if their power factors are identical.

Let us now solve the circuit of Fig. 7.15:

1. Active power absorbed by the system:

$$P = (2 + 8 + 14) = +24 \text{ kW}$$

2. Reactive power absorbed by the system:

$$Q_1 = (5 + 7 + 8) = +20 \text{ kvar}$$

3. Reactive power supplied by the capacitors:

$$Q_2 = (-9 - 16) = -25 \text{ kvar}$$

4. Net reactive power Q absorbed by the system:

$$Q = (+20 - 25) = -5 \text{ kvar}$$

5. Apparent power of the system:

$$S = \sqrt{P^2 + Q^2} = \sqrt{24^2 + (-5)^2}$$
$$= 24.5 \text{ kVA}$$

6. Because the 380 V source furnishes the apparent power, the line current is

$$I = S/E = 24\,500/380 = 64.5 \text{ A}$$

7. The power factor of the system is

$$\cos \phi_L = P/S = 24/24.5 = 0.979 \text{ (leading)}$$

The 380 V source *delivers* 24 kW of active power, but it *receives* 5 kvar of reactive power. This reactive power flows into the local distribution system of the electrical utility company, where it becomes available to create magnetic fields. The magnetic fields may be associated with distribution transformers, transmission lines, or even the electromagnetic relays of customers connected to the same distribution system.

The power triangle for the system is shown in Fig. 7.15c. It is the graphical solution to our problem. Thus, starting with the 5 kvar load, we progressively move from one device to the next around the system. While so doing, we draw the magnitude and direction (up, down, left, right) of each power vector, tail to head, in accordance with the power of each device we meet. When the selection is complete, we can draw a power vector from the starting point to the end point, which yields the inclined vector having a value of 24.5 kVA. The horizontal component of this vector has a value of 24 kW and, because it is directed to the right, we know that it represents power *absorbed* by the system. The vertical component of 5 kvar is directed downward; consequently, it represents reactive power *generated* by the system.

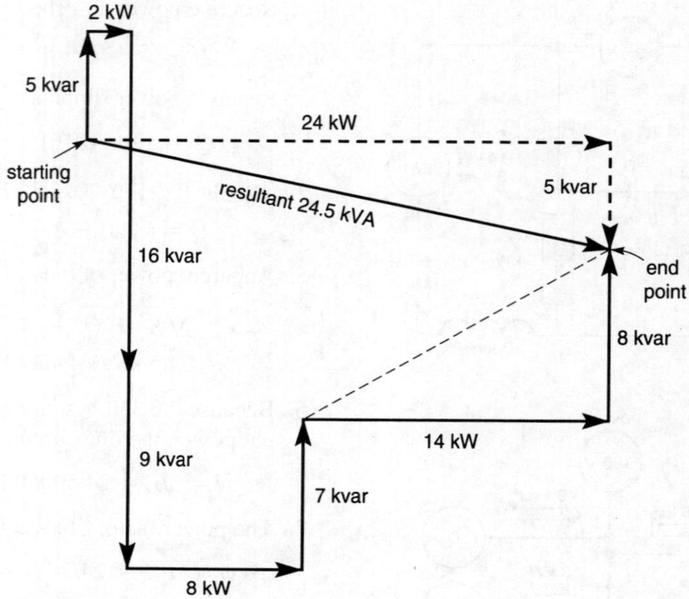

Figure 7.15c
Power triangle of the system.

7.13 Reactive power without magnetic fields

We sometimes encounter situations where loads absorb reactive power without creating any magnetic field at all. This can happen in electronic power circuits when the current flow is delayed by means of a rapid switching device, such as a thyristor.

Consider, for example, the circuit of Fig. 7.16 in which a 100 V, 60 Hz source is connected to a resistive load of 10 Ω by means of a synchronous mechanical switch. The switch opens and closes its contacts so that current only flows during the latter part of each half cycle. We can see, almost by intuition, that this forced delay causes the current to lag behind the voltage. Indeed, if we connected a wattmeter and varmeter between the source and the switch, they would respectively read +500 W and +318 var. This corresponds to a lagging power factor (sometimes called *displacement* power factor) of 84.4 percent. The reactive power is associated with the rapidly operating switch rather than with the resistor itself. Nevertheless, reactive power is consumed just as surely as if a reactor were present in the circuit. This switching circuit will be discussed in detail in Chapter 30.

7.14 Solving ac circuits using the power triangle method

We have seen that active and reactive powers can be added algebraically. This enables us to solve some rather complex ac circuits without ever having to draw a phasor diagram or resorting to vector (j) notation. We calculate the active and reactive powers associated with each circuit element and deduce the corresponding voltages and currents. The following example demonstrates the usefulness of this power triangle approach.

Example 7-10

In Fig. 7.17a, the voltage between terminals 1 and 3 is 60 V.

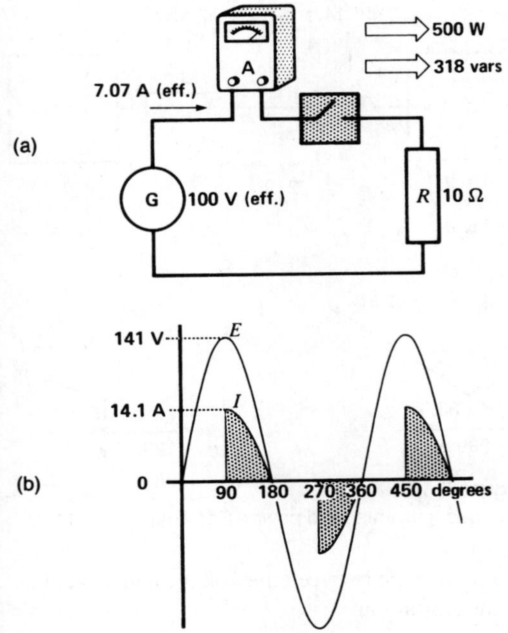

Figure 7.16
a. Active and reactive power flow in a switched resistive load.
b. The delayed current flow is the cause of the reactive power absorbed by the system.

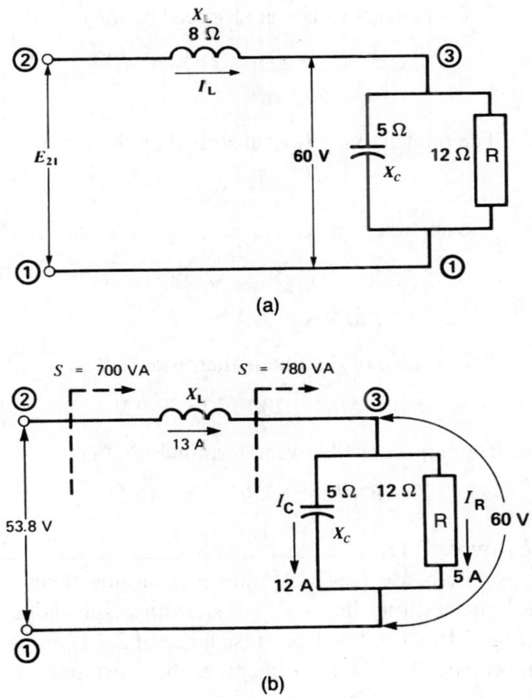

Figure 7.17
a. Solving ac circuits by the power triangle method.
b. Voltages and currents in the circuit. See Example 7-10.

Calculate

a. The current in each circuit element
b. The voltage between terminals 1 and 2
c. The impedance between terminals 1 and 2

Solution

We know the impedances of the elements and that 60 V exists between terminals 3 and 1 (Fig. 7.17b). We now proceed in logical steps, as follows:

a. The current in the capacitor is

$$I_C = 60/5 = 12 \text{ A}$$

from which the reactive power generated is

$$Q_c = 12 \times 60 = -720 \text{ var}$$

The current in the resistor is

$$I_R = 60/12 = 5 \text{ A}$$

from which the active power absorbed is

$$P = 5 \times 60 = 300 \text{ W}$$

The apparent power associated with terminals 1–3:

$$S = \sqrt{P^2 + Q^2} = \sqrt{300^2 + (-720)^2}$$
$$= 780 \text{ VA}$$

The current I_L must, therefore, be

$$I_L = S/E_{31} = 780/60 = 13 \text{ A}$$

The voltage across the inductive reactance is

$$E_{23} = IX_L = 13 \times 8 = 104 \text{ V}$$

The reactive power absorbed by the inductive reactance is

$$Q_L = E_{23} \times I_L = 104 \times 13$$
$$= +1352 \text{ var}$$

The total reactive power absorbed by the circuit is

$$Q = Q_L + Q_C = 1352 - 720$$
$$= +632 \text{ var}$$

The total active power absorbed by the circuit is

$$P = 300 \text{ W}$$

The apparent power absorbed by the circuit is

$$S = \sqrt{P^2 + Q^2} = \sqrt{300^2 + 632^2}$$
$$= 700 \text{ VA}$$

b. The voltage of the line is therefore

$$E_{21} = S/I_L = 700/13 = 53.9 \text{ V}$$

c. The impedance between terminals 2–1 is

$$Z = E_{21}/I_L = 53.9/13 = 4.15\ \Omega$$

Example 7-11

A single-phase 12.47 kV transmission line several kilometers long feeds a load C from a substation (Fig. 7.18). The line has a resistance of 2.4 Ω and a reactance of 15 Ω. Instruments at the substation indicate that the active and reactive power inputs to the line are 3 MW and 2 Mvar, respectively.

Calculate

a. The line current and its phase angle with respect to the line voltage at the substation
b. The active power absorbed by the load
c. The reactive power absorbed by the load
d. The line voltage at the load
e. The phase angle between the voltage at the load and that at the substation

Solution

a. Apparent power delivered to the line:

$$S = \sqrt{P^2 + Q^2} = \sqrt{3^2 + 2^2}$$
$$= 3.60 \text{ MVA}$$

Line current:

$$I = \frac{S}{E} = \frac{3\,600\,000 \text{ VA}}{12\,470 \text{ V}} = 289 \text{ A}$$

Power factor at the substation:

$$FP = \frac{P}{S} = \frac{3 \text{ MW}}{3.6 \text{ MVA}} = 0.833$$

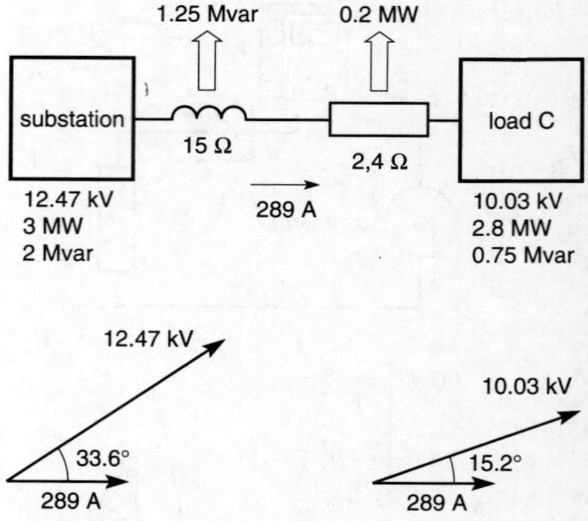

Figure 7.18
Voltages, currents, and power. See Example 7-11.

Phase angle between the voltage and current at the substation:

$$\theta = \arccos 0.833 = 33.6°$$

b. Active power dissipated in the line:

$$P_L = RI^2 = 2.4 \times 289^2$$
$$= 0.2 \times 10^6 = 0.2 \text{ MW}$$

Active power absorbed by the load:

$$P_C = P_{sub} - P_L = 3 \text{ MW} - 0.2 \text{ MW}$$
$$= 2.8 \text{ MW}$$

c. Reactive power absorbed by the line:

$$Q_L = X_L I^2 = 15 \times 289^2 = 1.25 \times 10^6 = 1.25 \text{ Mvar}$$

Reactive power absorbed by the load:

$$Q_C = Q_{sub} - Q_L = 2 \text{ Mvar} - 1.25 \text{ Mvar}$$
$$= 0.75 \text{ Mvar}$$

d. Apparent power at the load:

$$S_C = \sqrt{P_C^2 + Q_C^2} = \sqrt{2.8^2 + 0.75^2}$$
$$= 2.90 \text{ MVA}$$

Voltage at the load end of the line:

$$E_C = \frac{S_C}{I} = \frac{2.90 \text{ MVA}}{289 \text{ A}} = 10.03 \text{ kV}$$

Power factor at the load end of the line:

$$FP = \frac{P_C}{S_C} = \frac{2.8 \text{ MW}}{2.90 \text{ MVA}} = 0.965 \text{ or } 96.5\%$$

Phase angle between the voltage and current at the load:

$$\theta_C = \arccos 0.965 = 15.2°$$

It follows that the phase angle between the voltage at the substation and that at the load is (33.6° − 15.2°) = 18.4°.

Fig. 7.18 summarizes the results of this analysis. We could have found the same values using vector algebra. However, on account of its simplicity, the power method of solving this problem is very appealing.

7.15 Power and vector notation

If vector notation is used to solve an ac circuit, we can readily determine the active and reactive power associated with any component, including the sources. We simply multiply the phasor voltage E across the component by the conjugate (I^*) of the current that flows through it.† The vector product EI^* gives the apparent power S in terms of $P + jQ$, where P is the active power and Q the reactive power absorbed (or delivered) by the component.

A positive value for P or Q means that the component absorbs active or reactive power. Negative values mean that the component delivers active or reactive power.

When calculating the EI^* vector product, it is very important to follow a standard procedure in order to obtain the correct result. The procedure applies to circuits that use the double subscript notation or the sign notation (see Sections 2.4 and 2.5).

Consider Figure 7.19a in which a circuit element Z is part of a larger "rest of circuit." We want to calculate the active and reactive power associated with element Z. We note that current I flows from terminal a to terminal b, i.e. in the sequence ab. Consequently, when calculating the product EI^*, the subscripts of voltage E must be written in the same

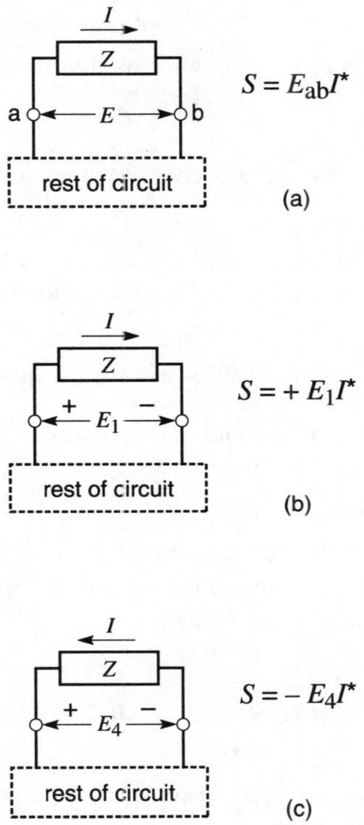

Figure 7.19
Method of writing power equations.

sequence ab (not ba). The apparent power S associated with Z is therefore written

$$S = E_{ab}I^*$$

It would be incorrect to write $S = E_{ba}I.^*$

In Fig. 7.19b, sign notation is used, and it is seen that current I enters Z by the (+) terminal. Consequently, the apparent power is given by

$$S = +E_1I^*$$

The E_1I^* product is preceded by a (+) sign because current I is shown as entering by the (+) terminal of element Z.

In the case of Fig. 7.19c, we write $S = -E_4I^*$ because the current enters Z by the (−) terminal.

If we want to, we can determine the apparent power associated with the "rest of circuit" (roc). Thus, in Fig. 7.19a, because the current circulates from b to a in the roc, we would write:

† If a current has a value $I\angle\theta$, its conjugate $I^* = I\angle-\theta$.

$$S_{roc} = E_{ba}I^*$$

Similarly, in Fig. 7.19c, we would write

$$S_{roc} = +E_4I^*$$

Let us illustrate the procedure by a few examples.

Example 7-12

In the circuit of Fig. 7.19c, the following values are given

$$E_4 = 70\angle 25° \qquad I = 4\angle 40°$$

Calculate the active and reactive power associated with element Z.

Solution

We have $I = 4\angle 40°$; therefore $I^* = 4\angle -40°$ Since the current flows into the (−) terminal, the power equation must bear a (−) sign:

$$\begin{aligned} S &= -E_4I^* \\ &= -70\angle 25° \times 4\angle -40° \\ &= -280\angle -15° \\ &= -280(\cos(-15°) + j\sin(-15°)) \\ &= -270.5 + j\,72.5 \\ &= P + jQ \end{aligned}$$

Thus $P = -270.5$ W and $Q = +72.5$ var

We conclude that element *Z delivers* 270.4 W of active power and *absorbs* 72.5 var of reactive power.

Example 7-13

Given the circuit of Fig. 7.20 in which $E_{12} = 30\angle 78°$, determine the power associated with the capacitor whose reactance is 10 Ω.

Solution

Going cw around the circuit, we can write (see Sections 2.32 to 2.39)

$$E_{21} - I(7 - 10j) = 0$$

$$I = \frac{E_{21}}{7 - 10j} = \frac{-30\angle 78°}{12.5\angle -55°}$$

$$= -2.46\angle 133° = +2.46\angle -47°$$

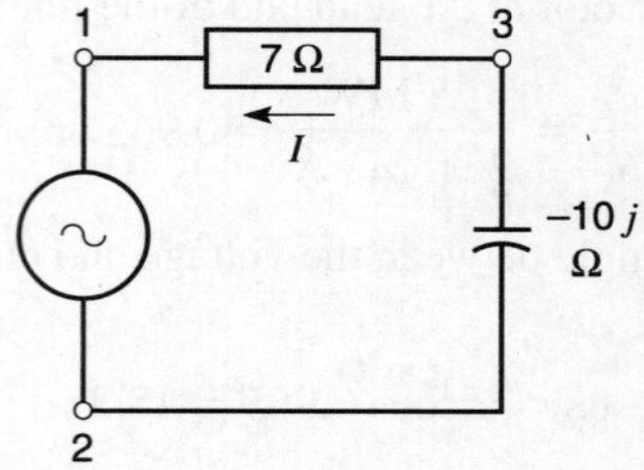

Figure 7.20
See Example 7-13.

The voltage across the capacitor is given by

$$\begin{aligned} E_{32} + I(-10j) &= 0 \\ E_{32} &= 10\,j\,I \\ &= 10\,j \times 2.46\angle -47° \\ &= 24.6\angle(-47° + 90°) \\ &= 24.6\angle 43° \end{aligned}$$

Current in the capacitor flows from terminal 2 to terminal 3. Consequently, the power associated with the capacitor is

$$\begin{aligned} S &= E_{23}I^* \\ &= -24.6\angle 43° \times 2.46\angle 47° \\ &= -60.5\angle 90° \\ &= -60.5(\cos 90° + j\sin 90°) \\ &= 0 - 60.5\,j \\ &= P + jQ \end{aligned}$$

Hence $P = 0$ and $Q = -60.5$. Consequently, the active power associated with the capacitor is zero, and it *delivers* 60.5 var of reactive power.

Example 7-14

The circuit in Fig. 7.21 is composed of a 45 Ω resistor connected in series with a 28 Ω inductive reactance. The source generates a voltage described by the phasor $E_{ab} = 159\angle 65°$.

Calculate

a. The magnitude and phase of the current *I*

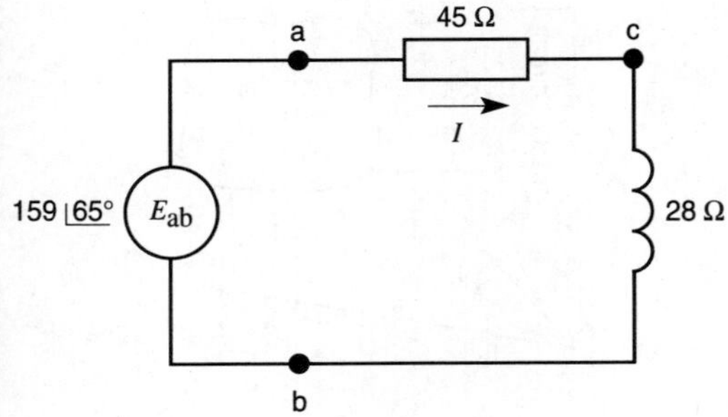

Figure 7.21
Solving an ac circuit using vector notation.

b. The magnitude and phase of the voltage across the resistor and across the reactance
c. The active and reactive power associated with the resistor, the reactance, and the source

Solution

a. Applying Kirchhoff's voltage law (see Section 2.32), we obtain

$$E_{ba} + E_{ac} + E_{cb} = 0$$
$$-E_{ab} + 45\,I + j28\,I = 0$$
$$-159\angle 65° + I(45 + j28) = 0$$
$$I = \frac{159\angle 65°}{45 + j28}$$

Transforming the denominator into polar coordinates, we obtain

$$\text{amplitude} = \sqrt{45^2 + 28^2} = 53$$
$$\text{phase angle} = \arctan 28/45 = 31.89°$$
$$\text{hence } 45 + j28 = 53\angle 31.89°$$

$$\text{and so } I = \frac{159\angle 65°}{53\angle 31.89°} = 3\angle(65° - 31.89°)$$
$$= 3\angle 33.11°$$

b. Voltage across the resistor is

$$E_{ac} = 45\,I$$
$$= 45 \times 3\angle 33.11°$$
$$= 135\angle 33.11°$$

Voltage across the reactance is

$$E_{cb} = j28\,I$$
$$= j28 \times 3\angle 33.11°$$
$$= 84\angle(33.11° + 90°)$$
$$= 84\angle 123.11°$$

c. The conjugate I^* of the current I is

$$I^* = 3\angle -33.11°$$

The apparent power associated with the resistor is

$$S_r = E_{ac}I^*$$
$$= (135\angle 33.11°)(3\angle -33.11°)$$
$$= 405\angle 0°$$
$$= 405\,(\cos 0° + j\sin 0°)$$
$$= 405\,(1 + j0)$$
$$= 405$$

Thus, the resistor absorbs only real power (405 W) because there is no j component in S_r.

The apparent power associated with the reactance is

$$S_x = E_{cb}I^*$$
$$= (84\angle 123.11°)(3\angle -33.11°)$$
$$= 252\angle 90°$$
$$= 252\,(\cos 90° + j\sin 90°)$$
$$= 252\,(0 + j1)$$
$$= j252$$

Thus, the reactance absorbs only reactive power (252 var).

The apparent power associated with the source is

$$S_s = E_{ba}I^* = -E_{ab}I^*$$
$$= -(159\angle 65°)(3\angle -33.11°)$$
$$= -477\angle(65° - 33.11°)$$
$$= -477\angle 31.89°$$
$$= -477\,(\cos 31.89° + j\sin 31.89°)$$
$$= -477\,(0.849 + j\,0.528)$$
$$= -405 - j\,252$$

The active and reactive powers are both negative, which proves that the source *delivers* an active power of 405 W and a reactive power of 252 var.

7.16 Rules on sources and loads (sign notation)

We are often interested in determining whether a device is an active/reactive source or an active/reactive load without making a complete mathematical analysis, such as we performed in Section 7.15. To enable us to positively identify the nature of the source or load, consider Fig. 7.22 in which a device A carries a line current I. The device is part of a circuit.

The voltage between the terminals is E, and one of the terminals bears a (+) sign. The phase angle between E and I can have any value. As a result, I can be decomposed into two components, I_p and I_q that are respectively parallel to, and at right angles to E. Let I_p be the component of I that is parallel to E. It will therefore be either in phase with, or 180° out of phase with E. Similarly, I_q can be either 90° behind or 90° ahead of E.

The circuit diagram, together with the phasor relationships between E and I, enable us to state whether a device is an active load or an active source. The following rule applies*:

1. A device is an active load when
   a. voltage E and component I_p are in phase *and*
   b. the line current I is shown as entering the (+) terminal.

Otherwise, the device is an active source.

The following rule also applies:

2. A device is a reactive load when
   a. component I_q lags 90° behind voltage E *and*
   b. line current I is shown as entering the (+) terminal.

Otherwise, the device is a reactive source.

Based on these rules, and observing the phasor relationships in Fig. 7.22, we deduce that device A is an active load because I_p is in phase with E. Also, device A is a reactive source because I_q is 90° ahead of E.

* These rules are in agreement with IEEE and IEC conventions.

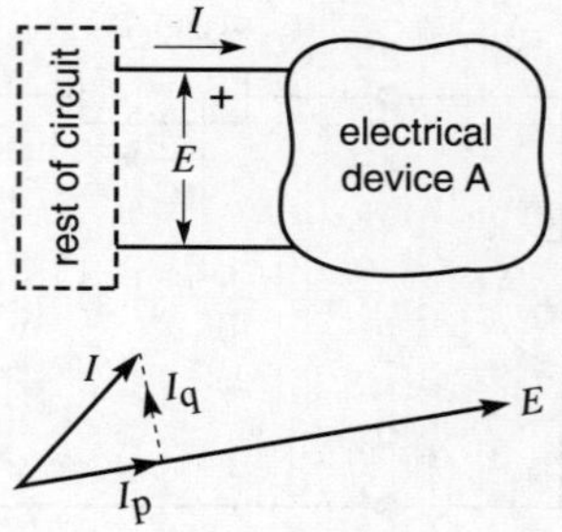

Figure 7.22
Device A may be an active/reactive source or active/reactive load depending upon the phasor relationship between E and I.

7.17 Rules on sources and loads (double subscript notation)

We can also tell whether a device is an active source or active load when double subscript notation is used. Consider Fig. 7.23 in which a device A carries a current I flowing in the direction shown. The voltage between terminals **a** and **b** is E_{ab}. The following rule applies:

3. A device is an active load when:
   a. voltage E_{ab} and component I_p are in phase *and*
   b. line current I is shown as entering terminal a.

Otherwise, the device is an active source.

The following rule also applies:

4. A device is a reactive load when
   a. current I_q lags 90° behind voltage E_{ab} *and*

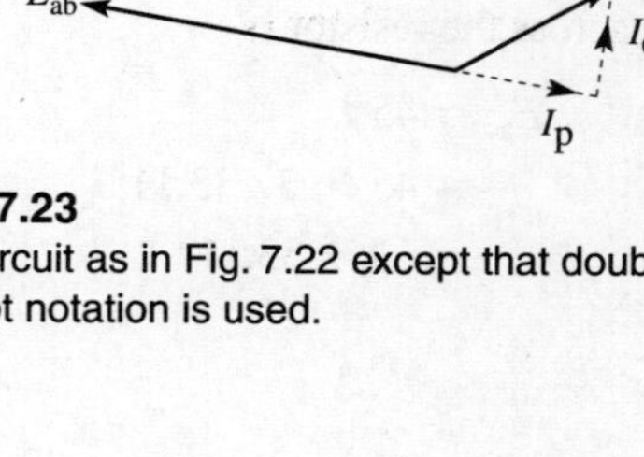

Figure 7.23
Same circuit as in Fig. 7.22 except that double-subscript notation is used.

b. line current I is shown as entering by terminal a.

Otherwise, the device is a reactive source.

Based on these rules, and observing the phasor relationships in Fig. 7.23, we deduce that device A is an active source because I_p is 180° out of phase with E_{ab}.

Also, device A is a reactive load because I_q lags 90° behind E_{ab}.

Questions and Problems

Practical level

7-1 What is the unit of active power? reactive power? apparent power?

7-2 A capacitor of 500 kvar is placed in parallel with an inductor of 400 kvar. Calculate the apparent power of the group.

7-3 Name a static device that can generate reactive power.

7-4 Name a static device that absorbs reactive power.

7-5 What is the approximate power factor, in percent, of a capacitor? of a coil? of an incandescent lamp?

7-6 The current in a single-phase motor lags 50° behind the voltage. What is the power factor of the motor?

Intermediate level

7-7 A large motor absorbs 600 kW at a power factor of 90 percent. Calculate the apparent power and reactive power absorbed by the machine.

7-8 A 200 μF capacitor is connected to a 240 V, 60 Hz source. Calculate the reactive power it generates.

7-9 A 10 Ω resistor is connected across a 120 V, 60 Hz source. Calculate

a. The active power absorbed by the resistor
b. The apparent power absorbed by the resistor
c. The peak power absorbed by the resistor
d. The duration of each positive power pulse

7-10 A 10 Ω reactance is connected to a 120 V, 60 Hz line. Calculate

a. The reactive power absorbed by the reactor
b. The apparent power absorbed by the reactor
c. The peak power input to the reactor
d. The peak power output of the reactor
e. The duration of each positive power pulse

7-11 Using the rules given in Sections 7.16 and 7.17, determine which of the devices in Fig. 7.24a through 7.24f acts as an active (or reactive) power source.

7-12 A single-phase motor draws a current of 12 A at a power factor of 60 percent. Calculate the in-phase and quadrature components of current I_p and I_q with respect to the line voltage.

7-13 A single-phase motor draws a current of 16 A from a 240 V, 60 Hz line. A wattmeter connected into the line gives a reading of 2765 W. Calculate the power factor of the motor and the reactive power it absorbs.

7-14 If a capacitor having a reactance of 30 Ω is connected in parallel with the motor of Problem 7-13, calculate

a. The active power reading of the wattmeter
b. The total reactive power absorbed by the capacitor and motor
c. The apparent power of the ac line
d. The line current
e. The power factor of the motor/capacitor combination

7-15 Using only power triangle concepts (Section 7.14) and without drawing any phasor diagrams, find the impedance of the circuits in Fig. 7.25.

7-16 An induction motor absorbs an apparent power of 400 kVA at a power factor of 80 percent. Calculate

a. The active power absorbed by the motor
b. The reactive power absorbed by the motor
c. What purpose does the reactive power serve

7-17 A circuit composed of a 12 Ω resistor in series with an inductive reactance of 5 Ω carries an ac current of 10 A. Calculate

a. The active power absorbed by the resistor
b. The reactive power absorbed by the inductor
c. The apparent power of the circuit
d. The power factor of the circuit

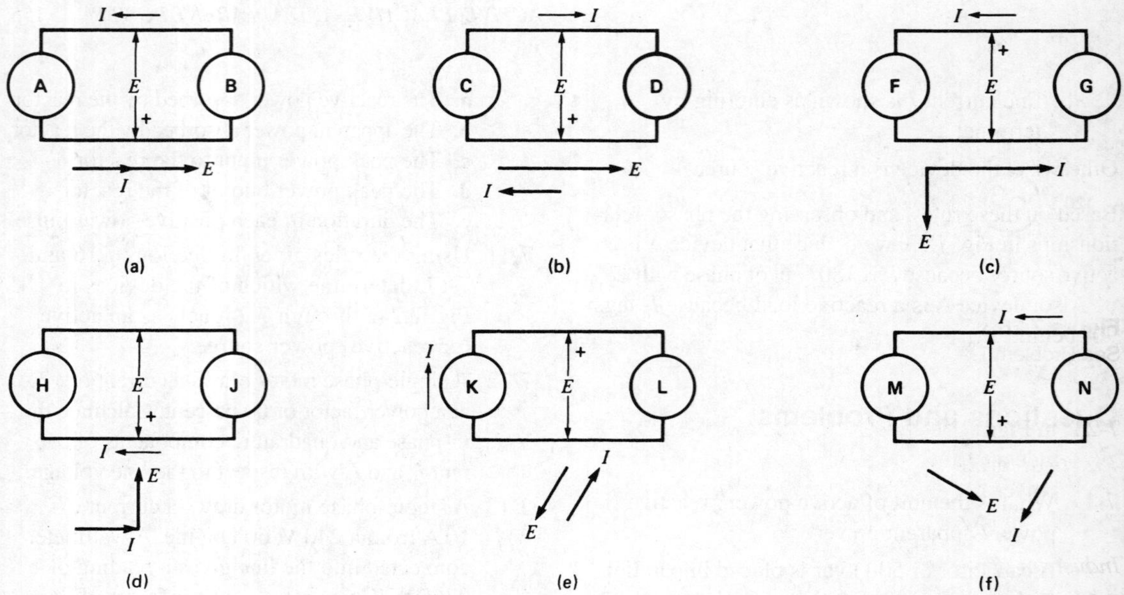

Figure 7.24
See Problem 7-11.

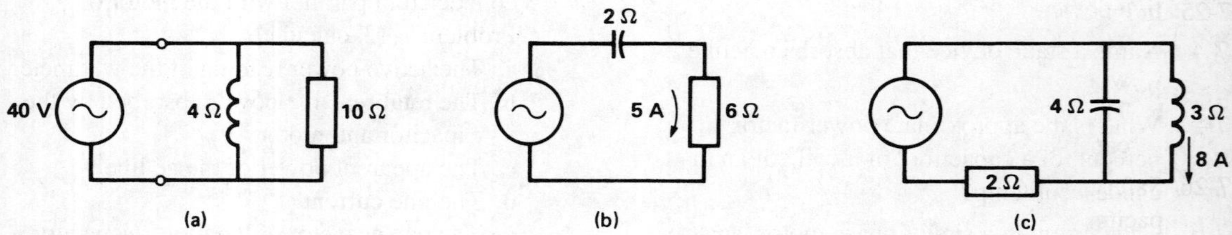

Figure 7.25
See Problem 7-15.

7-18 A coil having a resistance of 5 Ω and an inductance of 2 H carries a direct current of 20 A. Calculate

a. The active power absorbed

b. The reactive power absorbed

Advanced level

7-19 A motor having a power factor of 0.8 absorbs an active power of 1200 W. Calculate the reactive power drawn from the line.

7-20 In Problem 7-13, if we place a capacitor of 500 var in parallel with the motor, calculate

a. The total active power absorbed by the system

b. The apparent power of the system

c. The power factor of the system

7-21 A coil having a reactance of 10 Ω and a resistance of 2 Ω is connected in parallel with a capacitive reactance of 10 Ω. If the supply voltage is 200 V, calculate

a. The reactive power absorbed by the coil

b. The reactive power generated by the capacitor

c. The active power dissipated by the coil

d. The apparent power of the circuit

7-22 The power factor at the terminals of a 120 V source is 0.6 lagging (Fig. 7.26). Without using phasor diagrams, calculate

a. The value of E

b. The impedance of the load Z

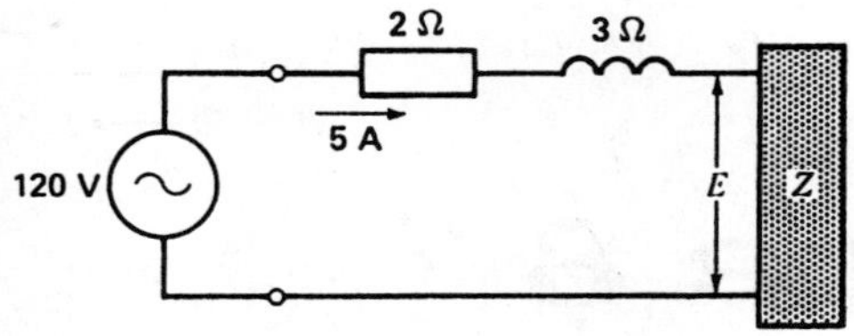

Figure 7.26
See Problem 7-22.

7-23 In Figs. 7.27a and 7.27b, indicate the magnitude and direction of the active and reactive power flow. (Hint: Decompose I into I_p and I_q, and treat them independently.)

Industrial application

7-24 A single-phase capacitor has a rating of 30 kvar, 480 V, 60 Hz. Calculate its capacitance in microfarads.

7-25 In Problem 7-24 calculate

a. The peak voltage across the capacitor when it is connected to a 460 V source

b. The resulting energy stored in the capacitor at that instant, in joules

7-26 Safety rules state that one minute after a capacitor is disconnected from an ac line, the voltage across it must be 50 V or less. The discharge is done by means of a resistor that is permanently connected across the capacitor terminals. Based on the discharge curve of a capacitor, calculate the discharge resistance required, in ohms, for the capacitor in Problem 7-24. Knowing the resistance is subjected to the service voltage when the capacitor is in operation, calculate its wattage rating.

7-27 A 13.2 kV, 60 Hz, single-phase line connects a substation to an industrial load. The line has a resistance of 2.4 Ω and a reactance of 12 Ω. The metering equipment at the substation indicates that the line voltage is 12.5 kV and that the line is drawing 3 MW of active power and 2 Mvar of reactive power. Calculate

a. The current flowing in the line

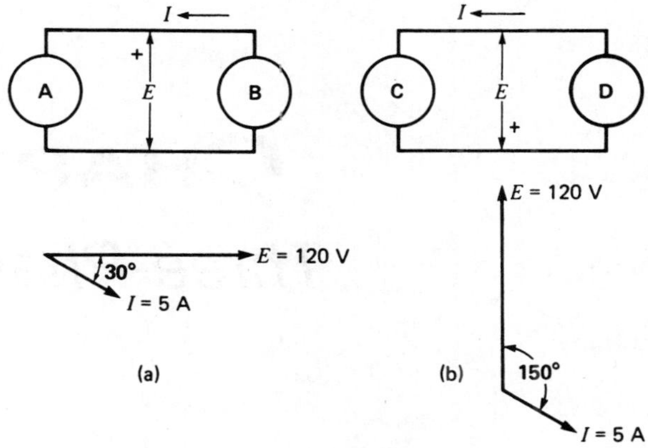

Figure 7.27
See Problem 7-23.

b. The active and reactive, power consumed by the line

c. The active, reactive and apparent power absorbed by the load

d. The voltage across the load

7-28 A 2 hp, 230 V, 1725 r/min, 60 Hz, single-phase washdown duty motor, manufactured by Baldor Electric Company, has the following characteristics:

full-load current: 11.6 A

efficiency: 75.5%

power factor: 74%

weight: 80 lb

a. Calculate the active and reactive power absorbed by this machine when it operates at full load.

b. If a 40 microfarad capacitor is connected across the motor terminals, calculate the line current feeding the motor.

c. Will the presence of the capacitor affect the temperature of the motor?

7-29 A single-phase heater absorbs 4 kW on a 240 V line. A capacitor connected in parallel with the resistor delivers 3 kvar to the line.

a. Calculate the value of the line current.

b. If the capacitor is removed, calculate the new line current.

CHAPTER 8
Three-Phase Circuits

8.0 Introduction

Electric power is generated, transmitted, and distributed in the form of 3-phase power. Homes and small establishments are wired for single-phase power, but this merely represents a tap-off from the basic 3-phase system. Three-phase power is preferred over single-phase power for several important reasons:

a. Three-phase motors, generators, and transformers are simpler, cheaper, and more efficient
b. Three-phase transmission lines can deliver more power for a given weight and cost
c. The voltage regulation of 3-phase transmission lines is inherently better

A knowledge of 3-phase power and 3-phase circuits is, therefore, essential to an understanding of power technology. Fortunately, the basic circuit techniques used to solve single-phase circuits can be directly applied to 3-phase circuits. Furthermore, we will see that most 3-phase circuits can be reduced to elementary single-phase diagrams. In this regard, we assume the reader is familiar with the previous chapters dealing with ac circuits and power.

8.1 Polyphase systems

We can gain an immediate preliminary understanding of polyphase systems by referring to the common gasoline engine. A single-cylinder engine having one piston is comparable to a single-phase machine. On the other hand, a 2-cylinder engine is comparable to a 2-phase machine. The more common 6-cylinder engine could be called a 6-phase machine. In a 6-cylinder engine identical pistons move up and down inside identical cylinders, but they do not move in unison. They are staggered in such a way as to deliver power to the shaft in successive pulses rather than at the same time. As the reader may know from personal experience, this produces a smoother running engine and a much smoother output torque.

Similarly, in a 3-phase electrical system, the three phases are identical, but they deliver power at different times. As a result, the total power flow is very smooth. Furthermore, because the phases are identical, one phase may be used to represent the behavior of all three.

Although we must beware of carrying analogies too far, the above description reveals that a 3-phase system is basically composed of three single-phase systems that operate in sequence. Once this basic fact is realized, much of the mystery surrounding 3-phase systems disappears.

8.2 Single-phase generator

Consider a permanent magnet NS revolving at constant speed inside a stationary iron ring (Fig. 8.1). The magnet is driven by an external mechanical source, such as a turbine. The ring (or stator) reduces the reluctance of the magnetic circuit; consequently, the flux density in the air gap is greater than if the ring were absent. A multiturn rectangular coil having terminals **a, 1** is mounted inside the ring but insulated from it. Each turn corresponds to two conductors, one in each slot.

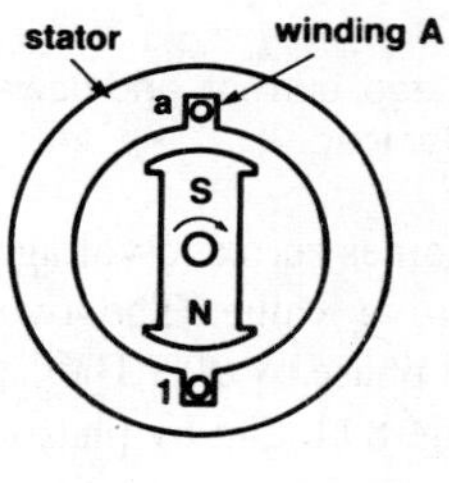

Figure 8.1
A single-phase generator with a multiturn coil embedded in two slots. At this instant E_{a1} is maximum (+).

As the magnet turns, it sweeps across the conductors, inducing a voltage in them according to the equation:

$$E_{a1} = Blv \tag{2.25}$$

wherein

E_{a1} = instantaneous voltage induced in the coil [V]

B = instantaneous flux density cutting across the conductors in the slots [T]

l = length of conductors lying in the magnetic field [m]

v = peripheral speed of the revolving poles [m/s]

The sum of the voltages induced in all the conductors appears across the terminals. The terminal

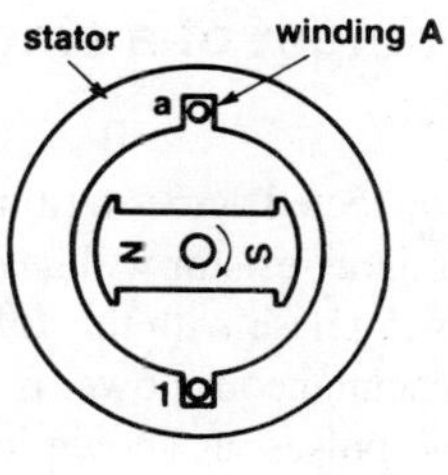

Figure 8.2
At this instant E_{a1} = 0 because the flux does not cut the conductors of winding A.

voltage E_{a1} is maximum when the poles are in the position of Fig. 8.1 because the flux density is greatest at the center of the pole. On the other hand, the voltage is zero when the poles are in the position of Fig. 8.2 because flux does not cut the conductors at this moment.

If we plot E_{a1} as a function of the angle of rotation, and provided the N, S poles are properly shaped, we obtain the sinusoidal voltage shown in Fig. 8.3.* Suppose the alternating voltage has a peak value of 20 V. Machines that produce such voltages are called *alternating-current generators* or *synchronous generators.* The particular machine shown in Fig. 8.1 is called a *single-phase generator.*

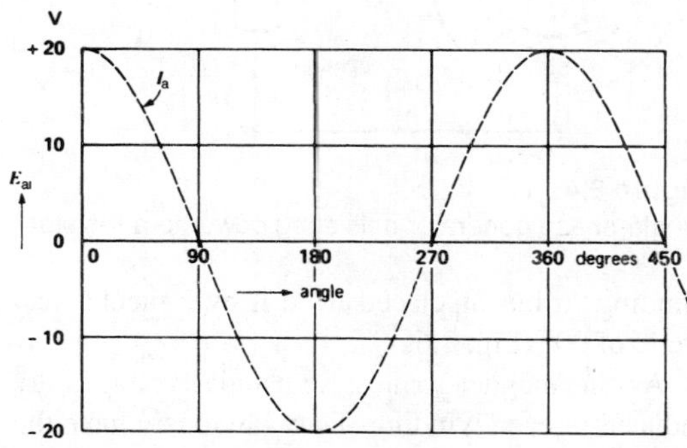

Figure 8.3
Voltage induced in winding A.

* The poles shown in Fig. 8.1 would generate an alternating voltage composed of rather brief flat-topped positive and negative pulses.

8.3 Power output of a single-phase generator

If a resistor is connected across terminals **a, 1** a current will flow and the resistor will heat up (Fig. 8.4). The current I_a is in phase with the voltage and, consequently, the instantaneous power is composed of a series of positive pulses, as shown in Fig. 8.5. The average power is one-half the peak power. This electrical power is derived from the mechanical power provided by the turbine driving the generator. As a result, the turbine must deliver its mechanical energy in pulses, to match the pulsed electrical output. This sets up mechanical vibrations whose frequency is twice the electrical frequency. Consequently, the generator will vibrate and tend to be noisy.

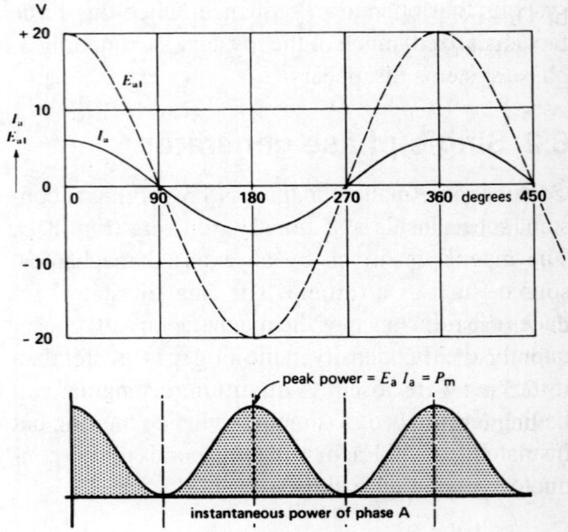

Figure 8.5
Graph of the voltage, current, and power when the generator is under load.

8.4 Two-phase generator

Using the same single-phase generator, let us mount a second winding (B) on the stator, identical to

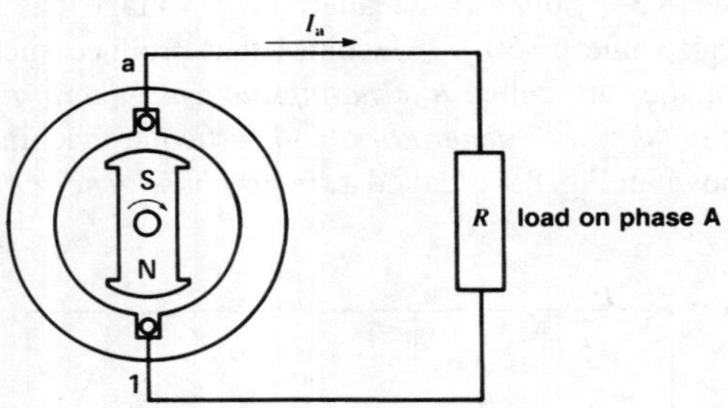

Figure 8.4
Single-phase generator delivering power to a resistor.

winding A, but displaced from it by a mechanical angle of 90° (Fig. 8.6a).

As the magnet rotates, sinusoidal voltages are induced in each winding. They obviously have the same magnitude and frequency but do not reach their maximum value at the same time. In effect, at the moment when the magnet occupies the position shown in Fig. 8.6a, voltage E_{a1} passes through its maximum positive value, whereas voltage E_{b2} is zero. This is because the flux only cuts across the conductors in slots **1** and **a** at this instant. However, after the rotor has made one quarter-turn (or 90°), voltage E_{a1} becomes zero and voltage E_{b2} attains its maximum positive value. The two voltages are therefore out of phase by 90°. They are represented by curves in Fig. 8.6b and by phasors in Fig. 8.6c. Note that E_{a1} leads E_{b2} because it reaches its peak positive value before E_{b2} does.

This machine is called a *two-phase generator,* and the stator windings are respectively called *phase A* and *phase B.*

Example 8-1

The generator shown in Fig. 8.6a rotates at 6000 r/min and generates an effective sinusoidal voltage of 170 V per winding.

Calculate

a. The peak voltage across each phase
b. The output frequency
c. The time interval corresponding to a phase angle of 90°

Solution

a. The peak voltage per phase is

$$E_m = \sqrt{2}E = 1.414 \times 170 \qquad (2.6)$$
$$= 240 \text{ V}$$

b. One cycle is completed every time the magnet makes one turn. The period of one cycle is

$$T = 1/6000 \text{ min}$$
$$= 60/6000 \text{ s} = 0.01 \text{ s}$$
$$= 10 \text{ ms}$$

The frequency is

$$f = 1/T = 1/0.01 = 100 \text{ Hz}$$

c. A phase angle of 90° corresponds to a time interval of one quarter-revolution, or 10 ms/4 = 2.5 ms. Consequently, phasor E_{b2} lags 2.5 ms behind phasor E_{a1}.

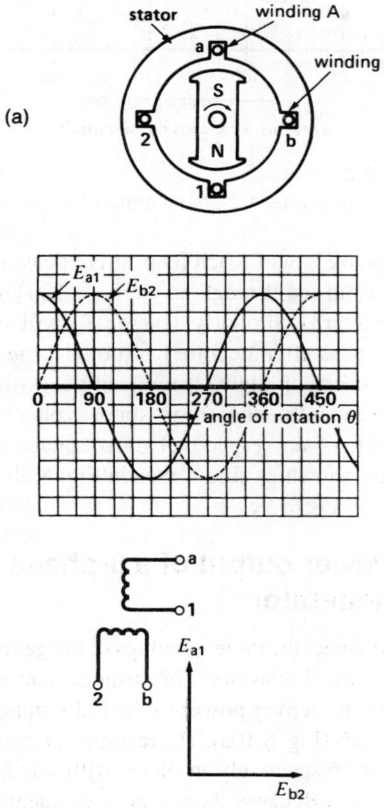

Figure 8.6
a. Schematic diagram of a 2-phase generator.
b. Voltages induced in a 2-phase generator.
c. Phasor diagram of the induced voltages.

8.5 Power output of a 2-phase generator

Let us now connect two identical resistive loads across phases A and B (Fig. 8.7a). Currents I_a and I_b will flow in each resistor. They are respectively in phase with E_{a1} and E_{b2}. The currents are, therefore, 90° out of phase with each other (Fig. 8.7b). This means that I_a reaches its maximum value one quarter-period before I_b does. Furthermore, the generator now produces a 2-phase power output.

The instantaneous power supplied to each resistor is equal to the instantaneous voltage times the instantaneous current. This yields the two power waves shown in Fig. 8.8. Note that when the power of phase A is maximum, that of phase B is zero, and vice versa. If we add the instantaneous powers of both phases, we discover that the resultant power is constant and equal to the peak power P_m of one

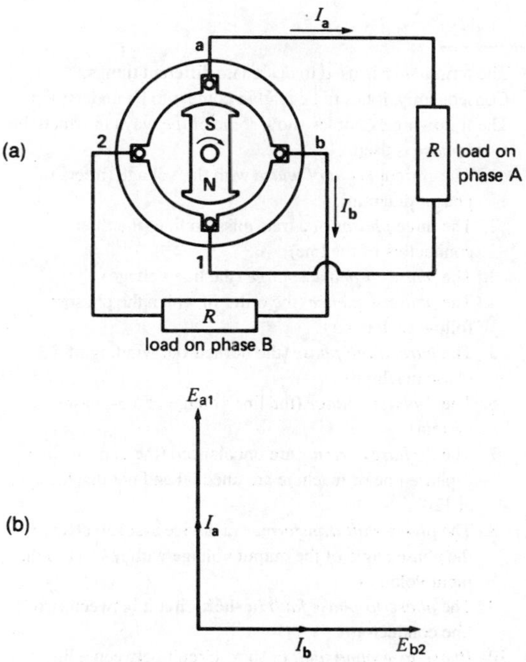

Figure 8.7
a. Two-phase generator under load.
b. Phasor diagram of the voltages and currents.

phase.* In other words, the total power output of the 2-phase generator is the same at every instant. As a result, the mechanical power needed to drive the generator is also constant. A 2-phase generator does not vibrate and so it is less noisy. As an important added benefit, it produces twice the power output without any increase in size, except for the addition of an extra winding.

8.6 Three-phase generator

A 3-phase generator is similar to a 2-phase generator, except that the stator has three identical windings instead of two. The three windings **a-1, b-2,** and **c-3** are placed at 120° to each other, as shown in Fig. 8.9a.

When the magnet is rotated at constant speed, the voltages induced in the three windings have the same effective values, but the peaks occur at different times. At the moment when the magnet is in the position shown in Fig. 8.9a, only voltage E_{a1} is at its maximum positive value.

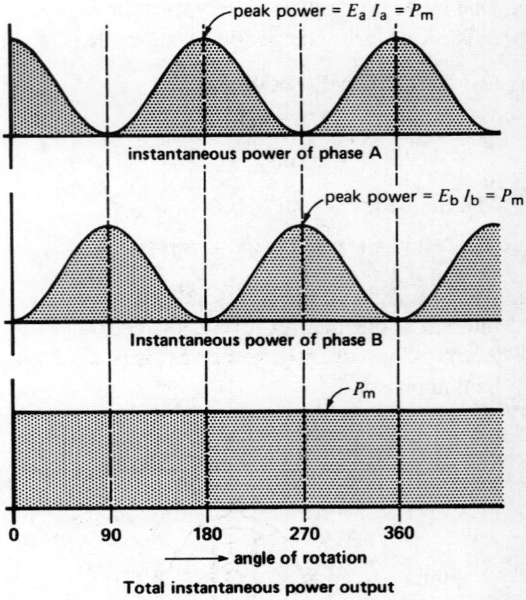

Figure 8.8
Power produced by a 2-phase generator.

Voltage E_{b2} will reach its positive peak after the rotor has turned through an angle of 120° (or one-third of a turn). Similarly, voltage E_{c3} will attain *its* positive peak after the rotor has turned through 240° (or two-thirds of a turn) from its initial position.

Consequently, the three stator voltages—E_{a1}, E_{b2}, and E_{c3}—are respectively out of phase by 120°. They are shown as sine waves in Fig. 8.9b, and as phasors in Fig. 8.9c.

8.7 Power output of a 3-phase generator

Let us connect the three windings of the generator to three identical resistors. This arrangement requires six wires to deliver power to the individual single-phase loads (Fig. 8.10a). The resulting currents I_a, I_b, and I_c are respectively in phase with voltages E_{a1}, E_{b2}, and E_{c3}. Because the resistors are identical, the currents have the same effective values, but they are mutually out of phase by 120° (Fig. 8.10b). The fact that they are out of phase simply means that they reach their positive peaks at different times.

---

* The term *phase* is used to designate different things. Consequently, it has to be read in context to be understood. The following examples show some of the ways in which the word *phase* is used.

1. The current is *out of phase* with the voltage (refers to phasor diagram)
2. The three *phases* of a transmission line (the three conductors of the line)
3. The *phase-to-phase voltage* (the line voltage)
4. The *phase sequence* (the order in which the phasors follow each other)
5. The *burned-out phase* (the burned-out winding of a 3-phase machine)
6. The *3-phase voltage* (the line voltage of a 3-phase system)
7. The *3-phase currents* are unbalanced (the currents in a 3-phase line or machine are unequal and not displaced at 120°)
8. The *phase-shift transformer* (a device that can change the phase angle of the output voltage with respect to the input voltage)
9. The *phase-to-phase fault* (a short-circuit between two line conductors)
10. *Phase-to-ground fault* (a short-circuit between a line or winding and ground)
11. The *phases are unbalanced* (the line voltages, or the line currents, are unequal or not displaced at 120° to each other)

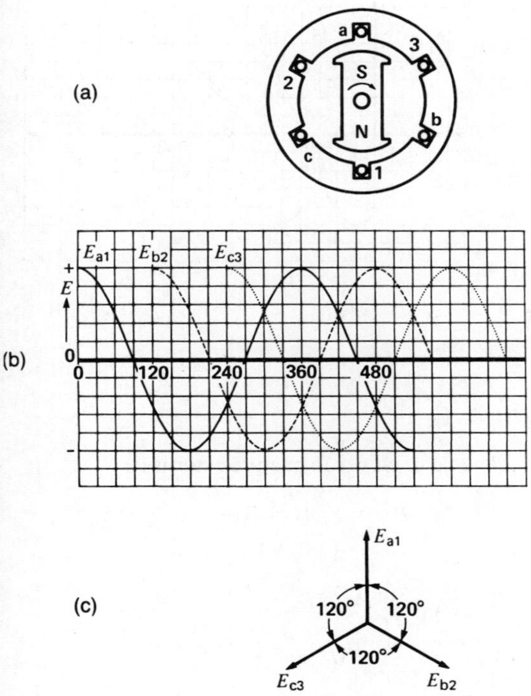

Figure 8.9
a. Three-phase generator.
b. Voltages induced in a 3-phase generator.
c. Phasor diagram of the induced voltages.

The instantaneous power supplied to each resistor is again composed of a power wave that surges between zero and a maximum value P_m. However, the power peaks in the three resistors do not occur at the same time, due to the phase angle between the voltages. If we add the instantaneous powers of all three resistors, we discover that the resulting power is constant, as in the case of a 2-phase generator. However, the total output of a 3-phase generator has a magnitude of 1.5 P_m. Because the electrical output is constant, the mechanical power required to drive the rotor is also constant, and so a 3-phase generator does not vibrate. Furthermore, the power flow over the transmission line, connecting the generator to the load, is constant.

Example 8-2

The 3-phase generator shown in Fig. 8.10a is connected to three 20 Ω load resistors. If the effective voltage induced in each phase is 120 V, calculate the following:

a. The power dissipated in each resistor
b. The power dissipated in the 3-phase load
c. The peak power P_m dissipated in each resistor
d. The total 3-phase power compared to P_m

Solution

a. Each resistor behaves as a single-phase load connected to an effective voltage of 120 V. The power dissipated in each resistor is, therefore,

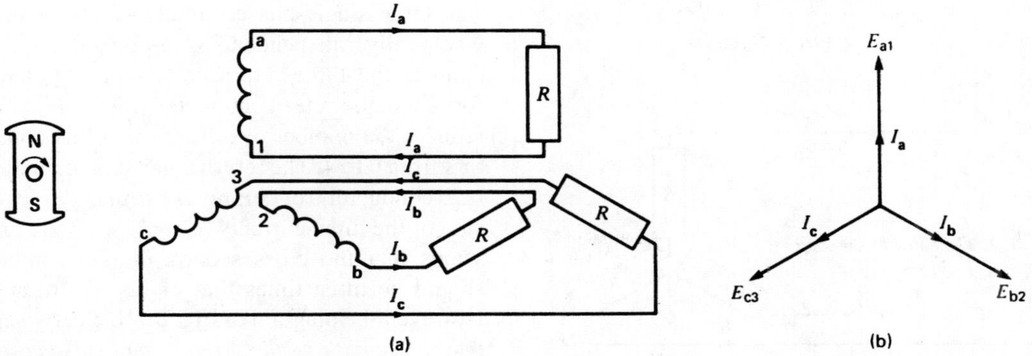

Figure 8.10
a. Three-phase, 6-wire system.
b. Corresponding phasor diagram.

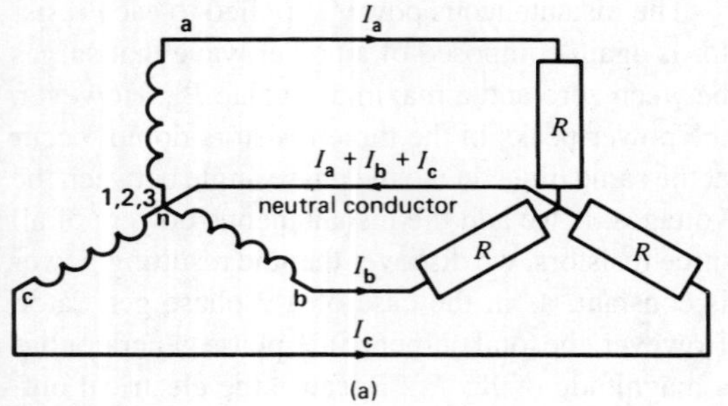

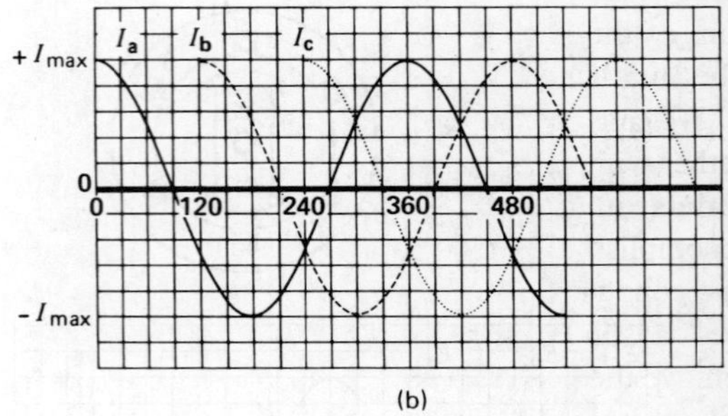

Figure 8.11
a. Three-phase, 4-wire system.
b. Line currents in a 3-phase, 4-wire system.

$$P = E^2/R = 120^2/20$$
$$= 720\text{ W}$$

b. The total power dissipated in the 3-phase load (all three resistors) is

$$P_T = 3P = 3 \times 720$$
$$= 2160\text{ W}$$

This power is absolutely constant from instant to instant.

c. The peak voltage across one resistor is

$$E_m = \sqrt{2}E = \sqrt{2} \times 120$$
$$= 169.7\text{ V}$$

The peak current in each resistor is

$$I_m = E_m/R = 169.7/20$$
$$= 8.485\text{ A}$$

The peak power in each resistor is

$$P_m = E_m I_m = 169.7 \times 8.485$$
$$= 1440\text{ W}$$

d. The ratio of P_T to P_m is

$$P_T/P_m = 2160/1440$$
$$= 1.5$$

Thus, whereas the power in each resistor pulsates between 0 and a maximum of 1440 W, the total power for all three resistors is unvarying and equal to 2160 W.

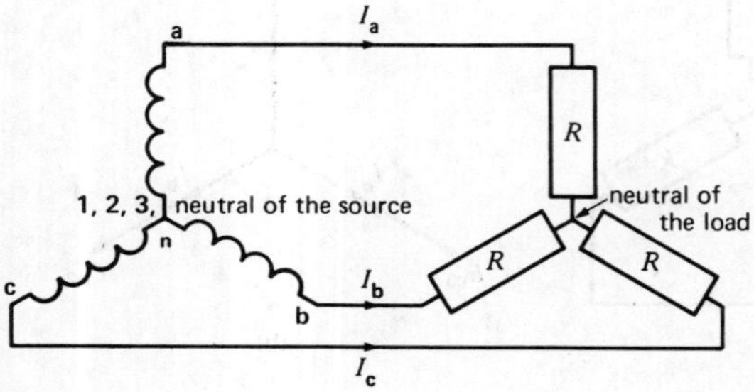

Figure 8.12
Three-phase, 3-wire system showing source and load.

8.8 Wye connection

The three single-phase circuits of Fig. 8.10 are electrically independent. Consequently, we can connect the three return conductors together to form a single return conductor (Fig. 8.11a). This reduces the number of transmission line conductors from 6 to 4. The return conductor, called *neutral* conductor (or simply *neutral*), carries the sum of the three currents ($I_a + I_b + I_c$). At first it seems that the cross section of this conductor should be three times that of lines a, b, and c. However, the diagram of Fig. 8.11b clearly shows that *the sum of the three return currents is zero at every instant.* For example, at the instant corresponding to 240°, $I_c = I_{max}$ and $I_b = I_a = -0.5\ I_{max}$, making $I_a + I_b + I_c = 0$. We arrive at the same result (and much more simply) by taking the sum of the phasors ($I_a + I_b + I_c$) in Fig. 8.10b. The sum is clearly zero.

We can, therefore, remove the neutral wire altogether without in any way affecting the voltages or currents in the circuit (Fig. 8.12). In one stroke we accomplish a great saving because the number of line conductors drops from six to three! However, the loads in Fig. 8.11a must be identical in order to remove the neutral wire. If the loads are not identical, the absence of the neutral conductor produces unequal voltages across the three loads.

The circuit of Fig. 8.12—composed of the generator, transmission line, and load—is called a *3-phase, 3-wire system.* The generator, as well as the load, are said to be connected in *wye,* because the three branches resemble the letter Y. For equally obvious reasons, some people prefer to use the term *connected in star.*

The circuit of Fig. 8.11a is called a *3-phase, 4-wire system.* The neutral conductor in such a system is usually the same size or slightly smaller than the line conductors. Three-phase, 4-wire systems are widely used to supply electric power to commercial and industrial users. The line conductors are often called *phases,* which is the same term applied to the generator windings.

8.9 Voltage relationships

Consider the wye-connected armature windings of a 3-phase generator (Fig. 8.13a). The induced voltage in each winding has an effective value E_{LN} represented by the length of each phasor in the diagram in Fig. 8.13b. Knowing that the line-to-neutral voltages are represented by phasors E_{an}, E_{bn}, and E_{cn} the question is, what are the line-to-line voltages E_{ab}, E_{bc}, and E_{ca}? Referring to Fig. 8.13a, we can write the following equations, based on Kirchhoff's voltage law:

$$E_{ab} = E_{an} + E_{nb} \quad (8.1)$$
$$= E_{an} - E_{bn} \quad (8.1)$$
$$E_{bc} = E_{bn} + E_{nc} \quad (8.2)$$
$$= E_{bn} - E_{cn} \quad (8.2)$$
$$E_{ca} = E_{cn} + E_{na} \quad (8.3)$$
$$= E_{cn} - E_{an} \quad (8.3)$$

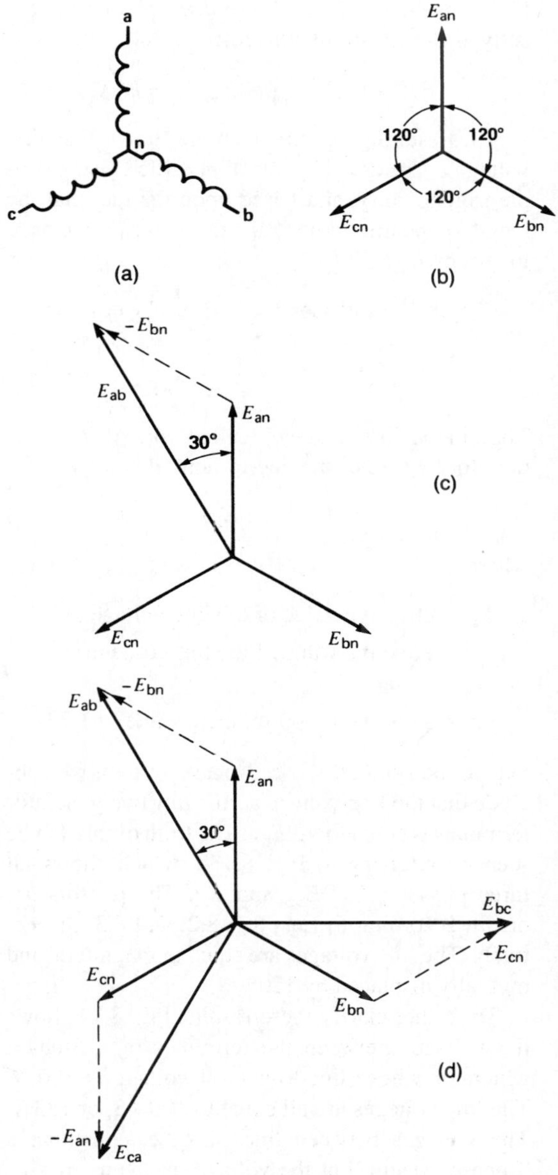

Figure 8.13
a. Wye-connected stator windings of a 3-phase generator.
b. Line-to-neutral voltages of the generator.
c. Method to determine line voltage E_{ab}.
d. Line voltages E_{ab}, E_{bc}, and E_{ca} are equal and displaced at 120°.

Referring first to Eq. 8.1, we draw phasor E_{ab} exactly as the equation indicates:

$$E_{ab} = E_{an} - E_{bn} = E_{an} + (-E_{bn})$$

The resulting phasor diagram shows that line voltage E_{ab} leads E_{an} by 30° (Fig. 8.13c). Using simple trigonometry, and based upon the fact that the length of the line-to-neutral phasors is E_{LN}, we have the following:

$$\begin{aligned} \text{length } E_L \text{ of phasor } E_{ab} &= 2 \times E_{LN} \cos 30° \\ E_L &= 2 \times E_{LN} \sqrt{3}/2 \\ &= \sqrt{3}\, E_{LN} \end{aligned}$$

The line-to-line voltage (called *line voltage*) is therefore $\sqrt{3}$ times the line-to-neutral voltage:

$$E_L = \sqrt{3}\, E_{LN} \tag{8.4}$$

where

E_L = effective value of the line voltage [V]
E_{LN} = effective value of the line-to-neutral voltage [V]
$\sqrt{3}$ = a constant [approximate value = 1.73]

Due to the symmetry of a 3-phase system, we conclude that the line voltage across *any* two generator terminals is equal to $\sqrt{3}\, E_{LN}$. The truth of this can be seen by referring to Fig. 8.13d, which shows all three phasors: E_{ab}, E_{bc}, and E_{ca}. The phasors are drawn according to Eqs. 8.1, 8.2, and 8.3, respectively. The line voltages are equal in magnitude and mutually displaced by 120°.

To further clarify these results, Fig. 8.14 shows the voltages between the terminals of a 3-phase generator whose line-to-neutral voltage is 100 V. The line voltages are all equal to 100 $\sqrt{3}$, or 173 V. The voltages between lines a, b, c, constitute a 3-phase system, but the voltage between any two lines (a and b, b and c, b and n, etc.) is nevertheless an ordinary single-phase voltage.

Example 8-3

A 3-phase, 60 Hz generator, connected in wye, generates a line (line-to-line) voltage of 23 900 V.

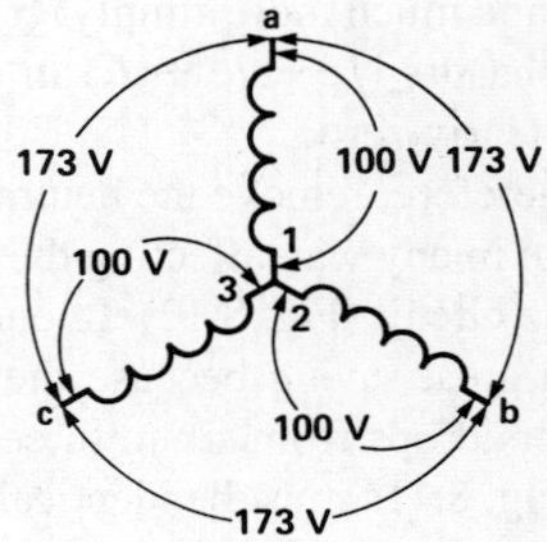

Figure 8.14
Voltages induced in a wye-connected generator.

Calculate

a. The line-to-neutral voltage
b. The voltage induced in the individual windings
c. The time interval between the positive peak voltage of phase A and the positive peak of phase B
d. The peak value of the line voltage

Solution

a. The line-to-neutral voltage is

$$\begin{aligned} E_{LN} &= E_L/\sqrt{3} = 23\,900/\sqrt{3} \\ &= 13\,800 \text{ V} \end{aligned}$$

b. The windings are connected in wye; consequently, the voltage induced in each winding is 13 800 V.

c. One complete cycle (360°) corresponds to 1/60 s. Consequently, a phase angle of 120° corresponds to an interval of

$$\begin{aligned} T &= \frac{120}{360} \times \frac{1}{60} = 1/180 \text{ s} \\ &= 5.55 \text{ ms} \end{aligned}$$

The positive voltage peaks are, therefore, separated by intervals of 5.55 ms.

d. The peak line voltage is

$$\begin{aligned} E_m &= \sqrt{2}\, E_L \\ &= 1.414 \times 23\,900 \qquad (2.6) \\ &= 33\,800 \text{ V} \end{aligned}$$

The same voltage relationships exist in a wye-connected load, such as that shown in Figs. 8.11

and 8.12. In other words, the line voltage is √3 times the line-to-neutral voltage.

Example 8-4

The generator in Fig. 8.12 generates a line voltage of 865 V, and each load resistor has an impedance of 50 Ω.

Calculate

a. The voltage across each resistor
b. The current in each resistor
c. The total power output of the generator

Solution

a. The voltage across each resistor is

$$E_{LN} = E_L/\sqrt{3} = 865/\sqrt{3} \qquad (8.4)$$
$$= 500 \text{ V}$$

b. The current in each resistor is

$$I = E_{LN}/R = 500/50$$
$$= 10 \text{ A}$$

All the line currents are, therefore, equal to 10 A.

c. Power absorbed by each resistor is

$$P = E_{LN}I = 500 \times 10$$
$$= 5000 \text{ W}$$

The power delivered by the generator to all three resistors is

$$P = 3 \times 5000 = 15 \text{ kW}$$

8.10 Delta connection

A 3-phase load is said to be *balanced* when the line voltages are equal and the line currents are equal. This corresponds to three identical impedances connected across the 3-phase line, a condition that is usually encountered in 3-phase circuits.

The three impedances may be connected in wye (as we already have seen) or in *delta* (Fig. 8.15a). The line voltages are produced by an external generator (not shown).

Let us determine the voltage and current relationships in such a delta connection,* assuming a resistive load. The resistors are connected across the line; consequently, resistor currents I_1, I_2, and I_3 are in phase with the respective line voltages E_{ab}, E_{bc}, and E_{ca}. Furthermore, according to Kirchhoff's law, the line currents are given by

$$I_a = I_1 - I_3 \qquad (8.5)$$
$$I_b = I_2 - I_1 \qquad (8.6)$$
$$I_c = I_3 - I_2 \qquad (8.7)$$

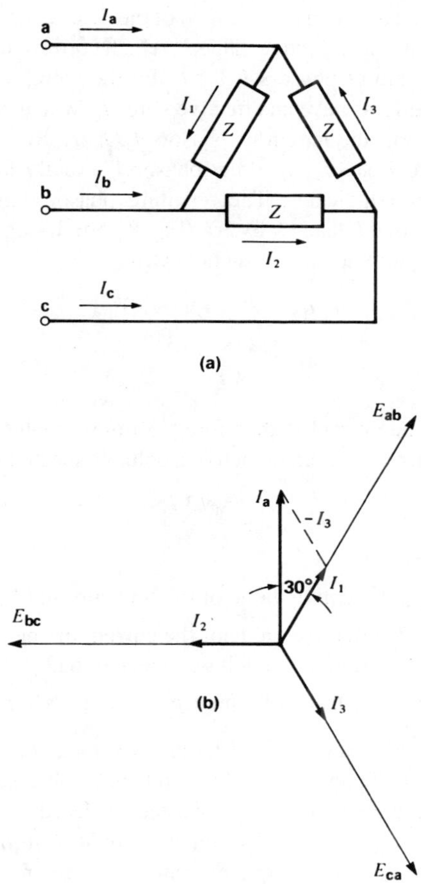

Figure 8.15
a. Impedances connected in delta.
b. Phasor relationships with a resistive load.

* The connection is so named because it resembles the Greek letter Δ.

Let the current in each branch of the delta-connected load have an effective value I_z, which corresponds to the length of phasors I_1, I_2, I_3. Furthermore, let the line currents have an effective value I_L, which corresponds to the length of phasors I_a, I_b, I_c. Referring first to Eq. 8.5, we draw phasor I_a exactly as the equation indicates. The resulting phasor diagram shows that I_a leads I_1 by 30° (Fig. 8.15b). Using simple trigonometry, we can now write

$$\begin{aligned} I_L &= 2 \times I_z \cos 30° \\ &= 2 \times I_z \sqrt{3}/2 \\ &= \sqrt{3}\, I_z \end{aligned}$$

The line current is therefore $\sqrt{3}$ times greater than the current in each branch of a delta-connected load:

$$I_L = \sqrt{3}\, I_z \tag{8.8}$$

where

I_L = effective value of the line current [A]

I_z = effective value of the current in one branch of a delta-connected load [A]

$\sqrt{3}$ = a constant [approximate value = 1.73]

The reader can readily determine the magnitude and position of phasors I_b and I_c, and thereby observe that the three line currents are equal and displaced by 120°.

Table 8A summarizes the basic relationships between the voltages and currents in wye-connected and delta-connected loads. The relationships are valid for any type of circuit element (resistor, capacitor, inductor, motor winding, generator winding, etc.) as long as the elements in the three phases are identical. In other words, the relationships in Table 8A apply to any balanced 3-phase load.

Example 8-5

Three identical impedances are connected in delta across a 3-phase, 550 V line (Fig. 8.15c). If the line current is 10 A, calculate the following:

a. The current in each impedance
b. The value of each impedance [Ω]

Solution

a. The current in each impedance is

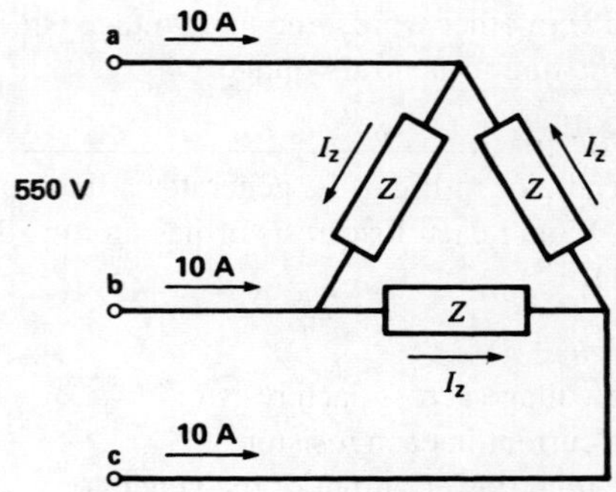

Figure 8.15c
See Example 8-5.

$$I_z = 10/\sqrt{3} = 5.77 \text{ A}$$

b. The voltage across each impedance is 550 V. Consequently,

$$\begin{aligned} Z &= E/I_z = 550/5.77 \\ &= 95\ \Omega \end{aligned}$$

8.11 Power transmitted by a 3-phase line

The apparent power supplied by a single-phase line is equal to the product of the line voltage E times the line current I. The question now arises: What is the apparent power supplied by a 3-phase line having a line voltage E and a line current I?

If we refer to the wye-connected load of Fig. 8.16a, the apparent power supplied to each branch is

$$S_z = \frac{E}{\sqrt{3}} \times I$$

The apparent power supplied to all three branches is obviously three times as great.* Consequently, the total apparent power is

$$S = \frac{E}{\sqrt{3}} \times I \times 3 = \sqrt{3}\, EI$$

* In 3-phase balanced circuits, we can add the apparent powers of the three phases because they have identical power factors. If the power factors are not identical, the apparent powers cannot be added.

TABLE 8A VOLTAGE AND CURRENT RELATIONSHIPS IN 3-PHASE CIRCUITS

Wye connection

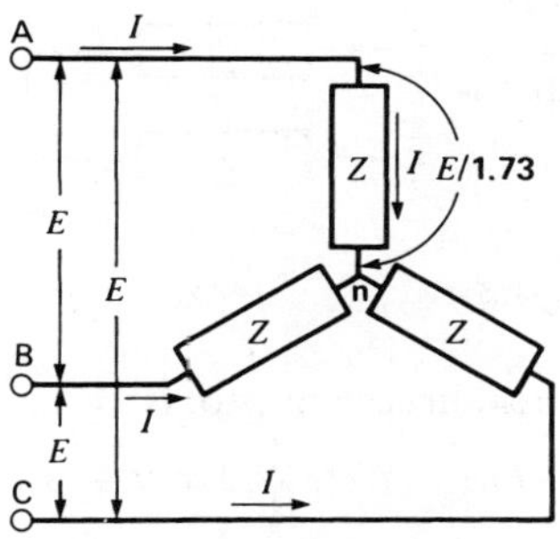

Figure 8.16a
Impedances connected in wye.

- The current in each element is equal to the line current I.
- The voltage across each element is equal to the line voltage E divided by $\sqrt{3}$.
- The voltages across the elements are 120° out of phase.
- The currents in the elements are 120° out of phase.

Delta connection

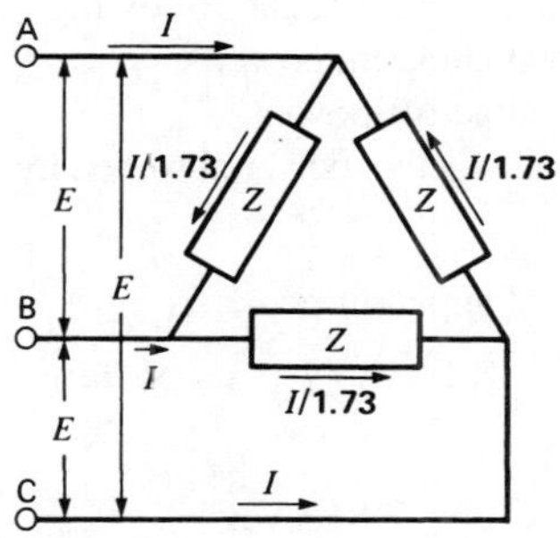

Figure 8.16b
Impedances connected in delta.

- The current in each element is equal to the line current I divided by $\sqrt{3}$.
- The voltage across each element is equal to the line voltage E.
- The voltages across the elements are 120° out of phase.
- The currents in the elements are 120° out of phase.

In the case of a delta-connected load (Fig. 8.16b), the apparent power supplied to each branch is

$$S_z = E \times \frac{I}{\sqrt{3}}$$

which is the same as for a wye-connected load. Consequently, the total apparent power is also the same.
We therefore have

$$S = \sqrt{3}\, EI \qquad (8.9)$$

where

S = total apparent power delivered by a 3-phase line [VA]
E = effective line voltage [V]
I = effective line current [A]
$\sqrt{3}$ = a constant [approximate value = 1.73]

8.12 Active, reactive, and apparent power in 3-phase circuits

The relationship between active power P, reactive power Q, and apparent power S is the same for balanced 3-phase circuits as for single-phase circuits. We therefore have

$$S = \sqrt{P^2 + Q^2} \qquad (8.10)$$

and

$$\cos \theta = P/S \qquad (8.11)$$

where

S = total 3-phase apparent power [VA]
P = total 3-phase active power [W]
Q = total 3-phase reactive power [var]
$\cos \theta$ = power factor of the 3-phase load
θ = phase angle between the line current and the line-to-neutral voltage [°]

Example 8-6

A 3-phase motor, connected to a 440V line, draws a line current of 5 A. If the power factor of the motor is 80 percent, calculate the following:

a. The total apparent power
b. The total active power
c. The total reactive power absorbed by the machine

Solution

a. The total apparent power is

$$S = \sqrt{3}\, EI = \sqrt{3} \times 440 \times 5$$
$$= 3811 \text{ VA}$$
$$= 3.81 \text{ kVA}$$

b. The total active power is

$$P = S \cos \theta = 3.81 \times 0.80$$
$$= 3.05 \text{ kW}$$

c. The total reactive power is

$$Q = \sqrt{S^2 - P^2} = \sqrt{3.81^2 - 3.05^2}$$
$$= 2.28 \text{ kvar}$$

8.13 Solving 3-phase circuits

A *balanced* 3-phase load may be considered to be composed of three identical single-phase loads. Consequently, the easiest way to solve such a circuit is to consider only one phase. The following examples illustrate the method to be employed.

Example 8-7

Three identical resistors dissipating a total power of 3000 W are connected in wye across a 3-phase, 550 V line (Fig. 8.17).

Calculate

a. The current in each line
b. The value of each resistor

Solution

a. The power dissipated by each resistor is

$$P = 3000 \text{ W}/3 = 1000 \text{ W}$$

The voltage across the terminals of each resistor is

$$E = 550 \text{ V}/\sqrt{3} = 318 \text{ V}$$

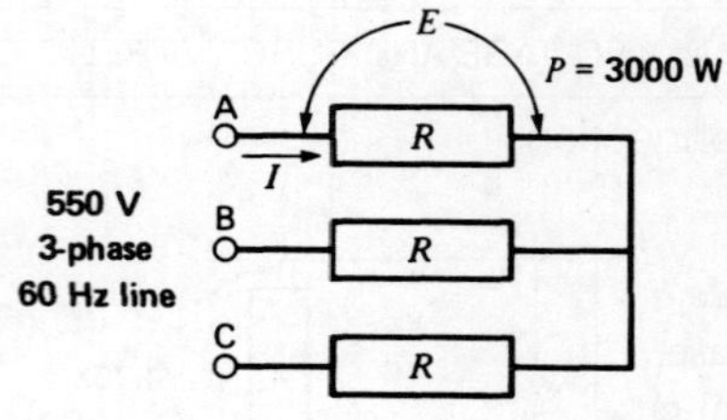

Figure 8.17
See Example 8-7.

The current in each resistor is

$$I = P/E = 1000 \text{ W}/318 \text{ V} = 3.15 \text{ A}$$

The current in each line is also 3.15 A.

b. The resistance of each element is

$$R = E/I = 318/3.15 = 101\ \Omega$$

Example 8-8

In the circuit of Fig. 8.18, calculate the following:

a. The current in each line
b. The voltage across the inductor terminals

Solution

a. Each branch is composed of an inductive reactance $X_L = 4\ \Omega$ in series with a resistance $R = 3\ \Omega$. Consequently, the impedance of each branch is

$$Z = \sqrt{4^2 + 3^2} = 5\ \Omega \quad (2.12)$$

The voltage across each branch is

$$E_{LN} = E_L/\sqrt{3} = 440 \text{ V}/\sqrt{3} = 254 \text{ V}$$

The current in each circuit element is

$$I = E_{LN}/Z = 254/5 = 50.8 \text{ A}$$

(50.8 A is also the line current.)

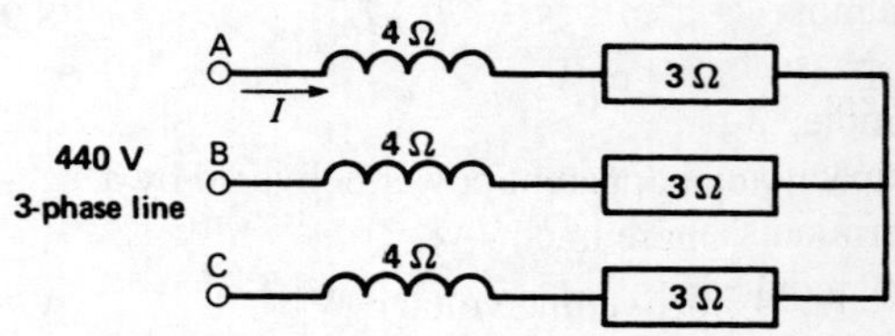

Figure 8.18
See Example 8-8.

b. The voltage across each inductor is

$$E = IX_L = 50.8 \times 4$$
$$= 203.2 \text{ V}$$

Example 8-9

A 3-phase, 550 V, 60 Hz line is connected to three identical capacitors connected in delta (Fig. 8.19). If the line current is 22 A, calculate the capacitance of each capacitor.

Solution

The current in each capacitor is

$$I = I_L/\sqrt{3} = 22 \text{ A}/\sqrt{3} = 12.7 \text{ A}$$

Voltage across each capacitor = 550 V
Capacitive reactance X_c of each capacitor is

$$X_c = E_L/I = 550/12.7 = 43.3 \ \Omega$$

The capacitance of each capacitor is

$$C = 1/2\pi f X_c$$
$$= 1/(2\pi \times 60 \times 43.3) \qquad (2.11)$$
$$= 61.3 \ \mu\text{F}$$

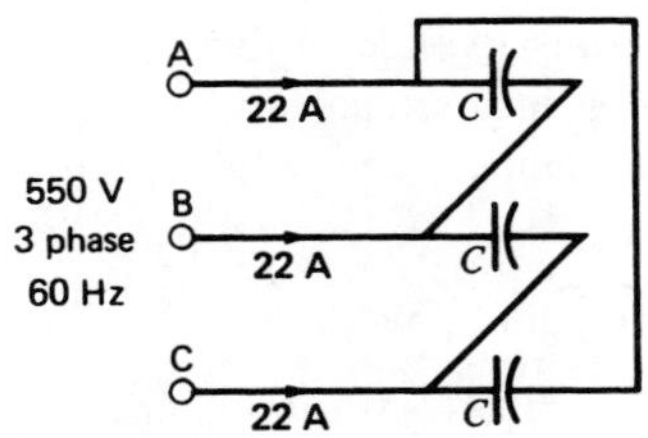

Figure 8.19
See Example 8-9.

8.14 Industrial loads

In most cases, we do not know whether a particular 3-phase load is connected in delta or in wye. For example, 3-phase motors, generators, transformers, capacitors, and so on, often have only three external terminals, and there is no way to tell how the internal connections are made. Under these circumstances, we simply *assume* that the connection is in wye. (A wye connection is slightly easier to handle than a delta connection.)

In a wye connection the impedance per phase is understood to be the line-to-neutral impedance. The voltage per phase is simply the line voltage divided by $\sqrt{3}$. Finally, the current per phase is equal to the line current.

The assumption of a wye connection can be made not only for individual loads, but for entire load centers such as a factory containing motors, lamps, heaters, furnaces, and so forth. We simply assume that the load center is connected in wye and proceed with the usual calculations.

Example 8-10

A manufacturing plant draws a total of 415 kVA from a 2400 V (line-to-line), 3-phase line (Fig. 8.20a). If the plant power factor is 87.5 percent lagging, calculate the following:

a. The impedance of the plant, per phase
b. The phase angle between the line-to-neutral voltage and the line current
c. The complete phasor diagram for the plant

Solution

a. We assume a wye connection composed of three identical impedances Z (Fig. 8.20b). The voltage per branch is

$$E = 2400/\sqrt{3}$$
$$= 1386 \text{ V}$$

The current per branch is

$$I = S/(E\sqrt{3}) \qquad (8.9)$$
$$= 415\,000/(2400\sqrt{3})$$
$$= 100 \text{ A}$$

The impedance per branch is

$$Z = E/I = 1386/100$$
$$= 13.9 \ \Omega$$

b. The phase angle θ between the line-to-neutral voltage (1386 V) and the corresponding line current (100 A) is given by

$$\cos\theta = \text{power factor} = 0.875 \qquad (8.11)$$
$$\theta = 29°$$

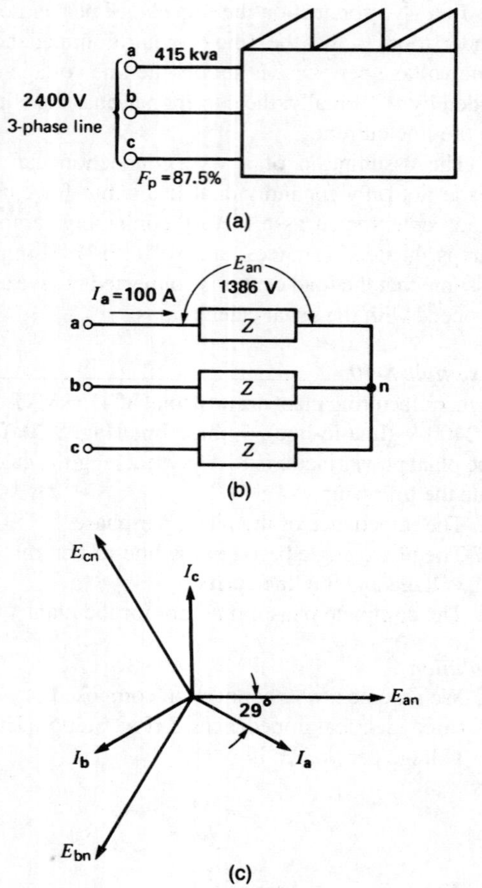

Figure 8.20
a. Power input to a factory. See Example 8-10.
b. Equivalent wye connection of the factory load.
c. Phasor diagram of the voltages and currents.

The current in each phase lags 29° behind the line-to-neutral voltage.

c. The complete phasor diagram is shown in Fig. 8.20c. In practice, we would show only one phase; for example, E_{an}, I_a, and the phase angle between them.

Example 8-11

A 5000 hp, wye-connected motor is connected to a 4000 V (line-to-line), 3-phase, 60 Hz line (Fig. 8.21).

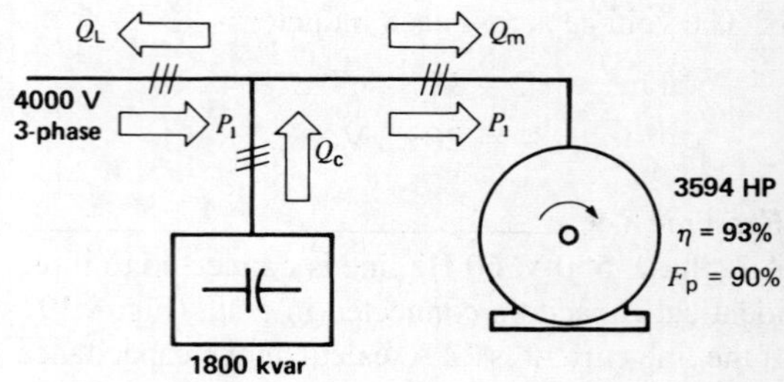

Figure 8.21
Industrial motor and capacitor. See Example 8-11.

A delta-connected capacitor bank rated at 1800 kvar is also connected to the line. If the motor produces an output of 3594 hp at an efficiency of 93 percent and a power factor of 90 percent (lagging), calculate the following:

a. The active power absorbed by the motor
b. The reactive power absorbed by the motor
c. The reactive power supplied by the transmission line
d. The apparent power supplied by the transmission line
e. The transmission line current
f. The motor line current
g. Draw the complete phasor diagram for one phase

Solution

a. Power output of 3594 hp is equivalent to

$$P_2 = 3594 \times 0.746 = 2681 \text{ kW}$$

Active power input to motor:

$$P_m = P_2/\eta = 2681/0.93 \qquad (3.6)$$
$$= 2883 \text{ kW}$$

b. Apparent power absorbed by the motor:

$$S_m = P_m/\cos\theta = 2883/0.90$$
$$= 3203 \text{ kVA}$$

Reactive power absorbed by the motor:

$$Q_m = \sqrt{S_m^2 - P_m^2} = \sqrt{3203^2 - 2883^2}$$
$$= 1395 \text{ kvar}$$

c. Reactive power supplied by the capacitor bank (see Section 7.5):

$$Q_c = -1800 \text{ kvar}$$

Total reactive power absorbed by the load:

$$Q_L = Q_c + Q_m = -1800 + 1395$$
$$= -405 \text{ kvar}$$

This is an unusual situation because reactive power is being returned to the line. In most cases the capacitor bank furnishes no more than Q_m kilovars of reactive power.

d. Active power supplied by the line is

$$P_L = P_m = 2883 \text{ kW}$$

Apparent power supplied by the line is

$$S_L = \sqrt{P_L^2 + Q_L^2} = \sqrt{2883^2 + (-405)^2}$$
$$= 2911 \text{ kVA}$$

e. Transmission line current is

$$I_L = S_L/(E_L\sqrt{3}) \qquad (8.9)$$
$$= 2\,911\,000/(\sqrt{3} \times 4000)$$
$$= 420 \text{ A}$$

f. Motor line current is

$$I_m = S_m/(E_L\sqrt{3})$$
$$= 3\,203\,000/(\sqrt{3} \times 4000)$$
$$= 462 \text{ A}$$

g. The line-to-neutral voltage is

$$E_{LN} = 4000/\sqrt{3} = 2309 \text{ V}$$

Phase angle θ between the motor current and the line-to-neutral voltage is:

$$\cos\theta = \text{power factor} = 0.9$$
$$\theta = 25.8°$$

(The motor current lags 25.8° behind the voltage, as shown in Fig. 8.22a.)
Line current drawn by the capacitor bank is

$$I_c = Q_c/(E_L\sqrt{3})$$
$$= 1\,800\,000/(\sqrt{3} \times 4000)$$
$$= 260 \text{ A}$$

Where should phasor current I_c be located on the phasor diagram? The question is important because the capacitors are connected in delta, and we assumed a wye connection for the motor. This can create unnecessary phase-angle complications if we try to follow the actual currents inside the capacitor bank. The solution is to recognize that *if* the capacitors were connected in wye (while generating the same reactive power), the line current of 260 A would lead E_{LN} by 90°. Consequently, we draw I_c 90° ahead of E_{LN}. That is the correct position for phasor I_c no matter how the capacitor bank is connected internally.

Phase angle θ_L between the transmission line current and E_{LN} is

$$\cos\theta_L = P_L/S_L = 2883/2911$$
$$= 0.99$$
$$\theta_L = 8°$$

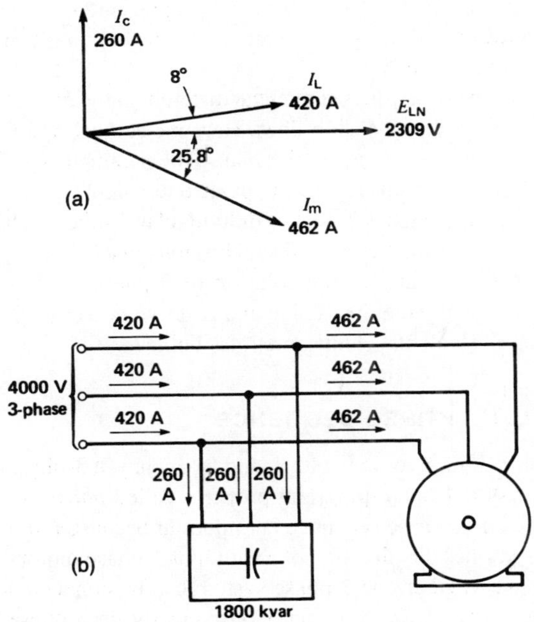

Figure 8.22

a. Phasor relationships for one phase. See Example 8-11.

b. Line currents. Note that the motor currents exceed the currents of the source.

The line current (420 A) leads E_{LN} by 8° because the kvars supplied by the capacitor bank exceed the kvars absorbed by the motor.

The phasor diagram for one phase is shown in Fig. 8.22a.

The circuit diagram and current flows are shown in Fig. 8.22b.

We want to emphasize the importance of assuming a wye connection, irrespective of what the actual connection may be. By assuming a wye connection for all circuit elements, we simplify the calculations and eliminate confusion.

As a final remark, the reader has no doubt noticed that the solution of a 3-phase problem involves active, reactive, and apparent power. The impedance value of devices such as resistors, motors, and capacitors seldom appears on a nameplate. This is to be expected because most industrial loads involve electric motors, furnaces, lights, and so on, which are seldom described in terms of resistance and reactance. They are usually represented as devices that draw a given amount of power at a given power factor.

The situation is somewhat different in the case of 3-phase transmission lines. Here we can define resistances and reactances because the parameters are fixed. The same remarks apply to equivalent circuits describing the behavior of individual machines such as induction motors and synchronous machines.

In conclusion, the solution of 3-phase circuits may involve either active and reactive power or *R, L, C* elements—and sometimes both.

8.15 Phase sequence

In addition to line voltage and frequency, a 3-phase system has an important property called *phase sequence.* Phase sequence is important because it determines the direction of rotation of 3-phase motors and whether one 3-phase system can be connected in parallel with another. Consequently, in 3-phase systems, phase sequence is as important as the frequency and voltage are.

Phase sequence means the order in which the three line voltages become successively positive.

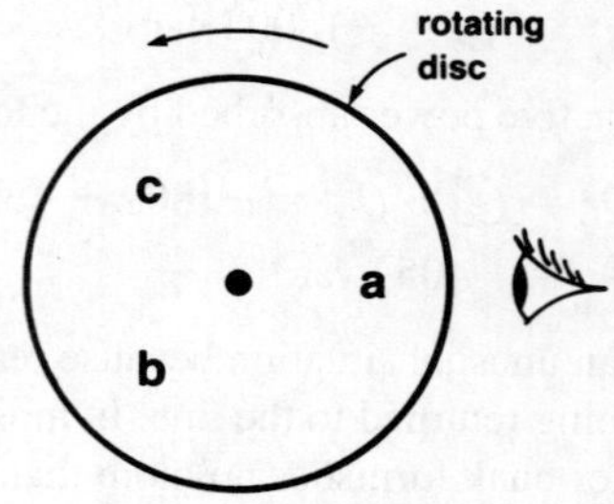

Figure 8.23
The letters are observed in the sequence a-b-c.

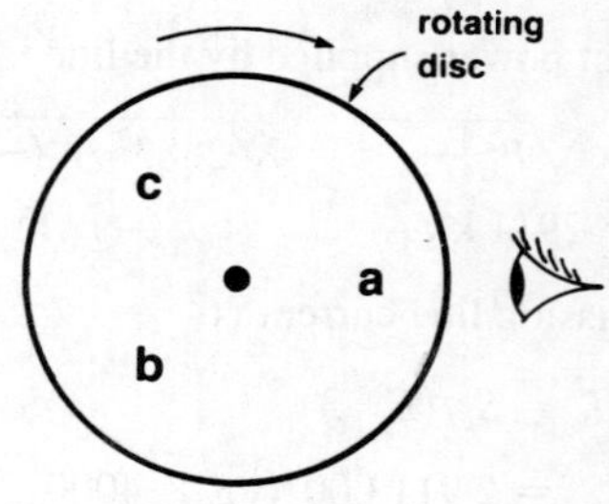

Figure 8.24
The letters are observed in the sequence a-c-b.

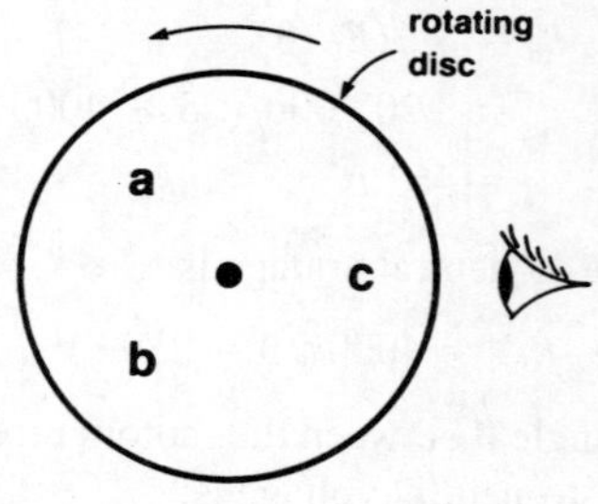

Figure 8.25
The letters are observed in the sequence a-c-b.

We can get a quick intuitive understanding of phase sequence by considering the following analogy.

Suppose the letters **a, b, c** are printed at 120° intervals on a slowly revolving disc (Fig. 8.23). If the disc turns counterclockwise, the letters appear in the sequence **a-b-c-a-b-c.** Let us call this the *positive sequence.* It can be described in any one of three ways: **abc, bca,** or **cab.**

If the same disc turns clockwise, the sequence becomes **a-c-b-a-c-b** . . . (Fig. 8.24). We call this the *negative sequence,* and it can be described by any one of three forms: **acb, cba,** or **bac.** Clearly, there is a difference between a positive sequence and a negative sequence.

Suppose we interchange any two letters on the disc in Fig. 8.23, while retaining the same counterclockwise rotation. If the letters **a** and **c** are interchanged, the result is as shown in Fig. 8.25. The sequence now becomes **c-b-a-c-b-a** . . . , which is the same as the negative sequence generated by the disc in Fig. 8.24.

We conclude that for a given direction of rotation a positive sequence can be converted into a negative sequence by simply interchanging two letters. Similarly, a negative sequence can be converted into a positive sequence by interchanging any two letters.

Let us now consider a 3-phase source having terminals **a, b, c** (Fig. 8.26a). Suppose the line voltages E_{ab}, E_{bc}, E_{ca} are correctly represented by the revolving phasors shown in Fig. 8.26b. As they sweep past the horizontal axis in the conventional counterclockwise direction, they follow the sequence E_{ab}-E_{bc}-E_{ca}-E_{ab}-E_{bc}. . . .

If we direct our attention to the *first* letter in each subscript, we find that the sequence is **a-b-c-a-b-c** . . . The source shown in Fig. 8.26a is said to possess the sequence **a-b-c.** We can, therefore, state the following rule: When using the double-subscript notation, the sequence of the first subscripts corresponds to the phase sequence of the source.

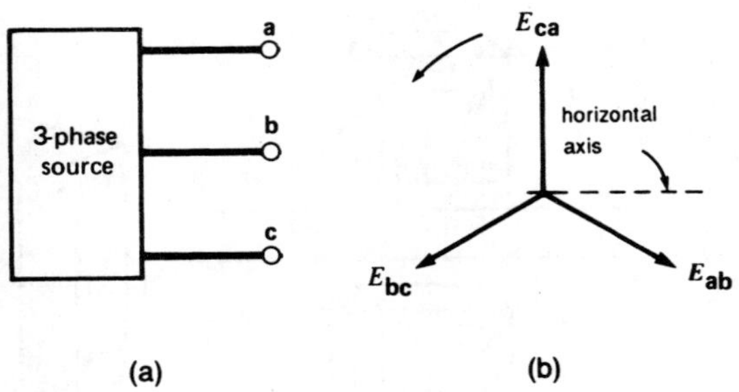

Figure 8.26
a. Determining the phase sequence of a 3-phase source.
b. Phase sequence depends upon the order in which the line voltages reach their positive peaks.

Example 8-12

In Fig. 8.17, the phase sequence of the source is known to be A-C-B. Draw the phasor diagram of the line voltages.

Solution

The voltages follow the sequence A-C-B, which is the same as the sequence AC-CB-BA-AC. . . . Consequently, the line voltage sequence is E_{AC}-E_{CB}-E_{BA} and the corresponding phasor diagram is shown in Fig. 8.27. We can reverse the phase sequence of a 3-phase line by interchanging any two conductors. Although this may appear to be a trivial change, it can become a major problem when large busbars or high-voltage transmission lines have to be interchanged. In practice, measures are taken so that such drastic mechanical changes do not have to be made at the last minute. The phase sequence of all major distribution systems is known in advance, and any future connections are planned accordingly.

8.16 Determining the phase sequence

Special instruments are available to indicate the phase sequence, but we can also determine it by using two incandescent lamps and a capacitor. The three devices are connected in wye. If we connect the circuit to a 3-phase line (without connecting the neutral), one lamp will always burn brighter than the other. The phase sequence is in the following order: *bright lamp—dim lamp—capacitor.*

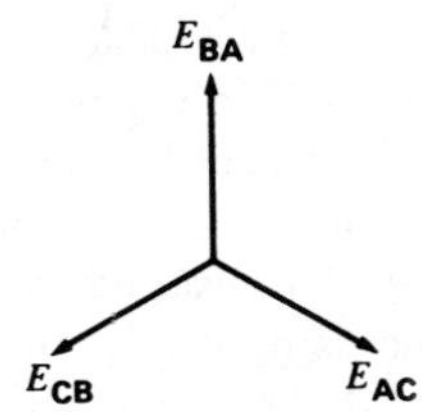

Figure 8.27
See Example 8-12.

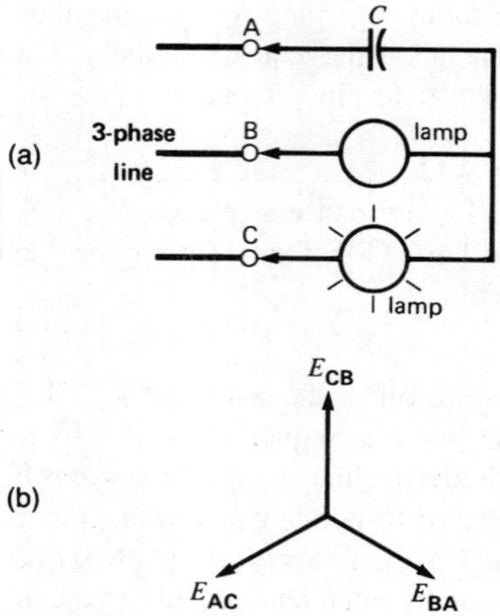

Figure 8.28
a. Determining phase sequence using two lamps and a capacitor.
b. Resulting phasor diagram.

Suppose, for example, that a capacitor/lamp circuit is connected to a 3-phase line, as shown in Fig. 8.28a. If the lamp connected to phase C burns more brightly, the phase sequence is C-B-A. The line voltages follow each other in the sequence CB-BA-AC, which is to say in the sequence E_{CB}, E_{BA}, E_{AC}. The corresponding phasor diagram is shown in Fig. 8.28b.

8.17 Power measurement in ac circuits

Wattmeters are used to measure active power in single-phase and 3-phase circuits.

Owing to its external connections and the way it is built, a wattmeter may be considered to be a voltmeter and ammeter combined in the same box. Consequently, it has 2 potential terminals and 2 current terminals. One of the potential terminals and one of the current terminals bears a ± sign. The ± signs are polarity marks that determine the positive or negative reading of the wattmeter. Thus, when the ± voltage terminal is positive at the same time as current is entering the ± current terminal, then the wattmeter will give a positive (upscale) reading.

The maximum voltage and current the instrument can tolerate are shown on the nameplate.

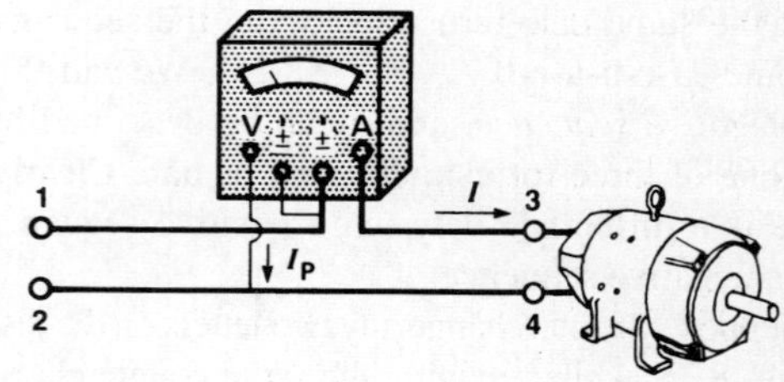

Figure 8.29
Method of connecting a single-phase wattmeter.

In single-phase circuits the pointer moves upscale when the connections between source and load are made as shown in Fig. 8.29. Note that the ± current terminal is connected to the ± potential terminal. When the wattmeter is connected this way, an upscale reading means that power is flowing from supply terminals 1, 2 to load terminals 3, 4.

8.18 Power measurement in 3-phase, 3-wire circuits

In a 3-phase, 3-wire system, the active power supplied to a 3-phase load may be measured by two single-phase wattmeters connected as shown in Fig. 8.30. The total power is equal to the sum of the two wattmeter readings. For balanced loads, if the power factor is less than 100 percent, the instruments will give different readings. Indeed, if the

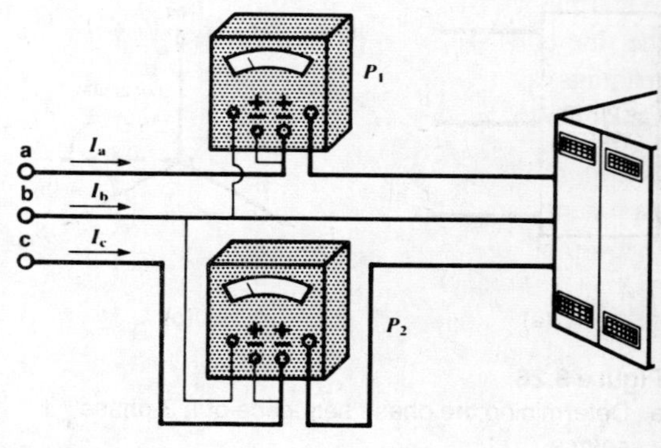

Figure 8.30
Measuring power in a 3-phase, 3-wire circuit using the two-wattmeter method.

power factor is less than 50 percent, one of the wattmeters will give a negative reading. We must then reverse the connections of the potential coil, so as to obtain a reading of this negative quantity. In this case, the power of the 3-phase circuit is equal to the *difference* between the two wattmeter readings.

The two-wattmeter method gives the active power absorbed whether the load is balanced or unbalanced.

Example 8-13

A full-load test on a 10 hp, 3-phase motor yields the following results: $P_1 = +5950$ W; $P_2 = +2380$ W; the current in each of the three lines is 10 A; and the line voltage is 600 V. Calculate the power factor of the motor.

Solution

Apparent power supplied to the motor is

$$S = \sqrt{3}\,EI = \sqrt{3} \times 600 \times 10$$
$$= 10\,390 \text{ VA}$$

Active power supplied to the motor is

$$P = 5950 + 2380$$
$$= 8330 \text{ W}$$
$$\cos\theta = P/S = 8330/10\,390$$
$$= 0.80, \text{ or } 80 \text{ percent}$$

Example 8-14

When the motor in Example 8-13 runs at no-load, the line current drops to 3.6 A and the wattmeter readings are $P_1 = +1295$ W; $P_2 = -845$ W. Calculate the no-load losses and power factor.

Solution

Apparent power supplied to motor

$$S = \sqrt{3}\,EI = \sqrt{3} \times 600 \times 3.6$$
$$= 3741 \text{ VA}$$

No-load losses are

$$P = P_1 + P_2 = 1295 - 845$$
$$= 450 \text{ W}$$

Power factor = P/S = 450/3741 = 0.12 = 12%

8.19 Power measurement in 3-phase, 4-wire circuits

In 3-phase, 4-wire circuits, three single-phase wattmeters are needed to measure the total power. The connections are made as shown in Fig. 8.31. Note that the ± current terminal is again connected to the ± potential terminal. When the wattmeters are connected this way, an upscale reading means that active power is flowing from source A, B, C, N to the load.

The total power supplied to the load is equal to the sum of the three wattmeter readings. The three-wattmeter method gives the active power for both balanced and unbalanced loads.

Some wattmeters, such as those used on switchboards, are specially designed to give a direct readout of the 3-phase power. Figure 8.32 shows a megawatt-range wattmeter circuit that measures the power in a generating station. The current transformers (CT) and potential transformers (PT) step down the line currents and voltages to values compatible with the instrument rating.

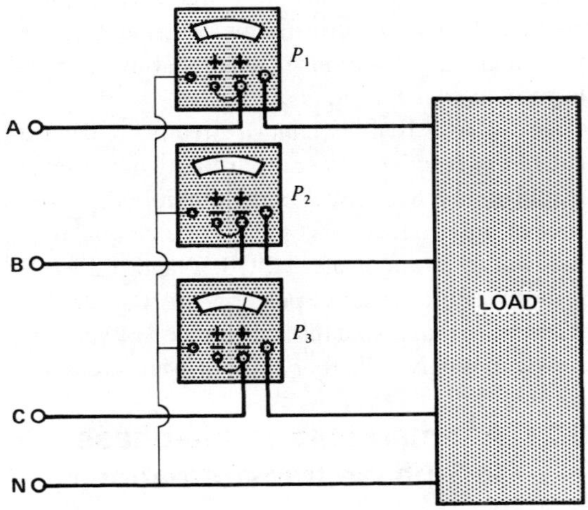

Figure 8.31
Measuring power in a 3-phase, 4-wire circuit.

8.20 Varmeter

A *varmeter* indicates the reactive power in a circuit. It is built the same way as a wattmeter is, but an internal circuit shifts the line voltage by 90° before it

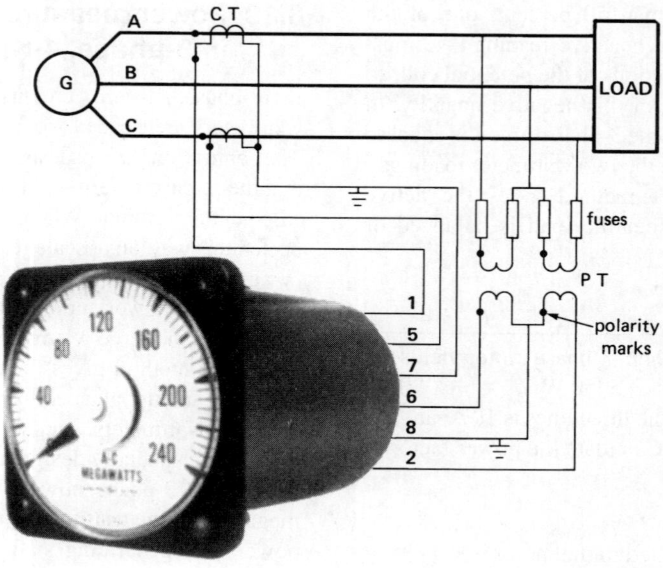

Figure 8.32
Measuring active power in a high-power circuit.

is applied to the potential coil. Varmeters are mainly employed in the control rooms of generating stations and the substations of electrical utilities and large industrial consumers.

In 3-phase, 3-wire *balanced* circuits, we can calculate the reactive power from the two wattmeter readings (Fig. 8.30). We simply multiply the difference of the two readings by $\sqrt{3}$. For example, if the two wattmeters indicate +5950 W and +2380 W respectively, the reactive power is $(5950 - 2380) \times \sqrt{3} = 6176$ vars. Note that this method of var measurement is only valid for *balanced* 3-phase circuits.

8.21 A remarkable single-phase to 3-phase transformation

It sometimes happens that a large single-phase unity power factor load has to be connected to a 3-phase line. This can create a badly unbalanced system. However, it is possible to balance the three phases perfectly by connecting a capacitive reactance and an inductive reactance across the other two lines. The reactances must each have impedances $\sqrt{3}$ times greater than the value of the load resistance (Fig. 8.33). Furthermore, given the 1-2-3-1 phase sequence of the line voltages E_{12}, E_{23}, E_{31}, it is *essential* that the three impedances be connected as indicated. If the capacitive and inductive reactances are interchanged, the 3-phase system becomes completely unbalanced.

Example 8-15

A 800 kW single-phase load is connected between phases 1 and 2 of a 440 V, 3-phase line, wherein $E_{12} = 440 \angle 0$, $E_{23} = 440 \angle -120$, $E_{31} = 440 \angle 120$. Calculate the load currents and line currents

a. When the single-phase load is connected alone on the 3-phase line
b. When balancing reactances are added across the remaining lines, as shown in Fig. 8.34

Solution

a. The resistance of the single-phase load is

$$R = \frac{E^2}{P} = \frac{440^2}{800\ 000} = 0.242\ \Omega$$

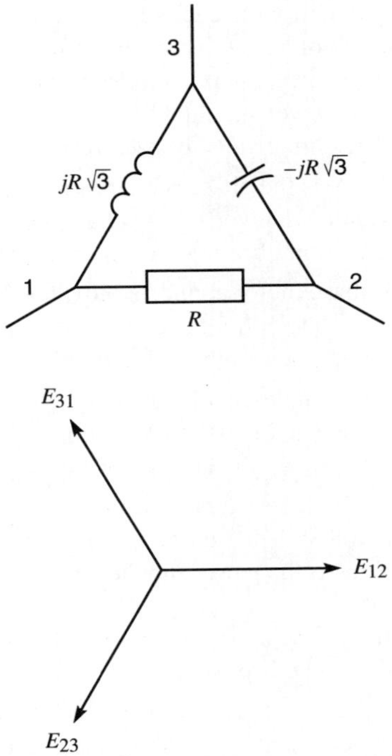

Figure 8.33
A single-phase resistive load can be transformed into a balanced 3-phase load.

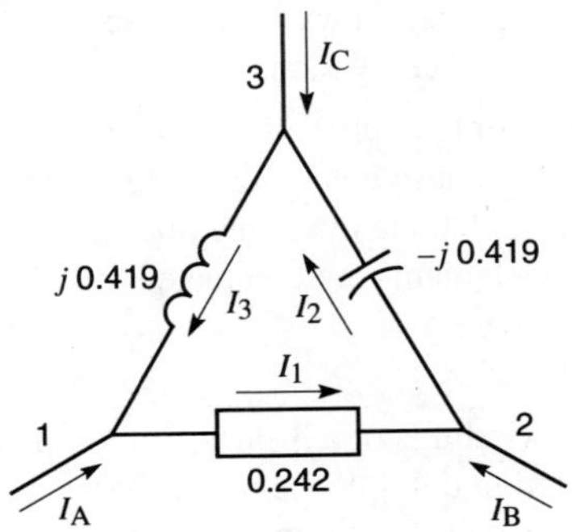

Figure 8.34
See Example 8-14.

The current in the load and in two of the three lines is

$$I = \frac{E}{R} = \frac{440}{0.242} = 1818 \text{ A}$$

The current in the third line is zero, and so the 3-phase system is badly unbalanced.

b. By introducing capacitive and inductive reactances having an impedance of $0.242\sqrt{3} = 0.419\ \Omega$, we obtain a balanced 3-phase line, as demonstrated below. Taking successive loops around the respective circuit elements in Fig. 8.34, and using Kirchhoff's voltage law (see Section 2.32), we obtain the following results:

$$E_{12} - 0.242\, I_1 = 0 \quad \therefore\ I_1 = 4.13\, E_{12} = 4.13 \times 440\angle 0 = 1817\angle 0$$

$$E_{23} + j\,0.419\, I_2 = 0 \quad \therefore\ I_2 = j\,2.38\, E_{23} = 2.38 \times 440\angle(-120 + 90) = 1047\angle -30$$

$$E_{31} - j\,0.419\, I_3 = 0 \quad \therefore\ I_3 = -j\,2.38\, E_{31} = 2.38 \times 440\angle(120 + 90 - 180) = 1047\angle 30$$

Applying Kirchhoff's current law to nodes 1, 2, and 3, we obtain

$$\begin{aligned} I_A &= I_1 - I_3 \\ &= 1817\angle 0 - 1047\angle 30 \\ &= 1817 - 907 - j\,523 \\ &= 1047\angle -30 \end{aligned}$$

$$\begin{aligned} I_B &= I_2 - I_1 \\ &= 1047\angle -30 - 1817\angle 0 \\ &= 907 - j\,523 - 1817 \\ &= -907 - j\,523 \\ &= 1047\angle 210 \end{aligned}$$

$$\begin{aligned} I_C &= I_3 - I_2 \\ &= 1047\angle 30 - 1047\angle -30 \\ &= 907 + j\,523 - 907 + j\,523 \\ &= 1047\, j \\ &= 1047\angle 90 \end{aligned}$$

Thus, I_A, I_B, I_C make up a balanced 3-phase system because they are equal and displaced at 120° to each other (Fig. 8.35).

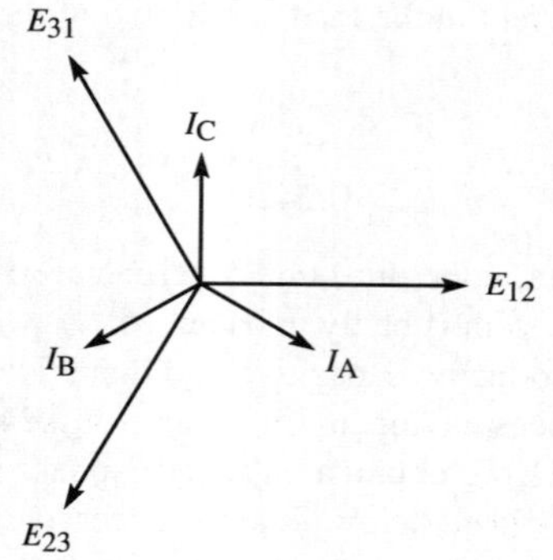

Figure 8.35
See Example 8-14.

Questions and Problems

Practical level

8-1 A 3-phase, wye-connected generator induces 2400 V in each of its windings. Calculate the line voltage.

8-2 The generator in Fig. 8.9 generates a peak voltage of 100 V per phase.
   a. Calculate the instantaneous voltage between terminals **1, a** at 0°, 90°, 120°, 240°, and 330°.
   b. What is the polarity of terminal **a** with respect to terminal **1** at each of these instants?
   c. What is the instantaneous value of the voltage across terminals **2, b** at each of these same instants?

8-3 Referring to Fig. 8.9c, phasor E_{b2} is 120° behind phasor E_{a1}. Could we also say that E_{b2} is 240° ahead of E_{a1}?

8-4 The voltage between lines a-b-c of Fig. 8.12 is 620 V.
   a. What is the voltage across each resistor?
   b. If $R = 15\ \Omega$, what is the current in each line?
   c. Calculate the power supplied to the 3-phase load.

8-5 Three resistors are connected in delta. If the line voltage is 13.2 kV and the line current is 1202 A, calculate the following:
   a. The current in each resistor
   b. The voltage across each resistor
   c. The power supplied to each resistor
   d. The power supplied to the 3-phase load
   e. The ohmic value of each resistor

8-6 **a.** What is the phase sequence in Fig. 8.10?
   b. Could we reverse it by changing the direction of rotation of the magnet?

8-7 A 3-phase motor connected to a 600 V line draws a line current of 25 A. Calculate the apparent power supplied to the motor.

8-8 Three incandescent lamps rated 60 W, 120 V are connected in delta. What line voltage is needed so that the lamps burn normally?

8-9 Three 10 Ω resistors are connected in delta on a 208 V, 3-phase line.
   a. What is the power supplied to the 3-phase load?
   b. If the fuse in one line burns out, calculate the new power supplied to the load.

8-10 If one line conductor of a 3-phase line is cut, is the load then supplied by a single-phase voltage or a 2-phase voltage?

8-11 A 3-phase heater dissipates 15 kW when connected to a 208 V, 3-phase line.
   a. What is the line current if the resistors are connected in wye?
   b. What is the line current if the resistors are connected in delta?
   c. If the resistors are known to be connected in wye, calculate the resistance of each.

8-12 We wish to apply full-load to a 100 kVA, 4 kV, 3-phase generator using a resistive load. Calculate the value of each resistance if the elements are connected
   a. In wye
   b. In delta

8-13 The windings of a 3-phase motor are connected in delta. If the resistance between two terminals is 0.6 Ω, what is the resistance of each winding?

8-14 Three 24 Ω resistors are connected in delta across a 600 V, 3-phase line. Calculate the resistance of three elements connected in wye that would dissipate the same power.

8-15 A 60 hp, 3-phase motor absorbs 50 kW from a 600 V, 3-phase line. If the line current is 60 A, calculate the following:
a. The efficiency of the motor
b. The apparent power absorbed by the motor
c. The reactive power absorbed by the motor
d. The power factor of the motor

8-16 Three 15 Ω resistors and three 8 Ω reactors are connected as shown in Fig. 8.18. If the line voltage is 530 V, calculate the following:
a. The active, reactive, and apparent power supplied to the 3-phase load
b. The voltage across each resistor

8-17 Two 60 W lamps and a 10 μF capacitor are connected in wye. The circuit is connected to the terminals X-Y-Z of a 3-phase, 120 V outlet. The capacitor is connected to terminal Y, and the lamp that burns brighter is connected to terminal X.
a. What is the phase sequence?
b. Draw the phasor diagram for the line voltages.

Advanced level

8-18 Three 10 μF capacitors are connected in wye across a 2300 V, 60 Hz line. Calculate the following:
a. The line current
b. The reactive power generated

8-19 In Problem 8-17, if the capacitor is connected to terminal X, which lamp will be brighter?

8-20 Three delta-connected resistors absorb 60 kW when connected to a 3-phase line. If they are reconnected in wye, calculate the new power absorbed.

8-21 Three 15 Ω resistors (*R*) and three 8 Ω reactors (*X*) are connected in different ways across a 530 V, 3-phase line. Without drawing a phasor diagram, calculate the line current for each of the following connections:
a. *R* and *X* in series, connected in wye
b. *R* and *X* in parallel, connected in delta
c. *R* connected in delta and *X* connected in wye

8-22 In Fig. 8.19, calculate the line current if the frequency is 50 Hz instead of 60 Hz.

8-23 In Problem 8-15, assume that the motor is connected in wye and that each branch can be represented by a resistance *R* in series with an inductive reactance *X*.
a. Calculate the values of *R* and *X*.
b. What is the phase angle between the line current and the corresponding line-to-neutral voltage?

8-24 An industrial plant draws 600 kVA from a 2.4 kV line at a power factor of 80 percent lagging.
a. What is the equivalent line-to-neutral impedance of the plant?
b. Assuming that the plant can be represented by an equivalent circuit similar to Fig. 8.18, determine the values of the resistance and reactance.

8-25 Two wattmeters connected into a 3-phase, 3-wire, 220 V line indicate 3.5 kW and 1.5 kW, respectively. If the line current is 16 A, calculate the following:
a. The apparent power
b. The power factor of the load

8-26 An electric motor having a cos θ of 82 percent draws a current of 25 A from a 600 V, 3-phase line.
a. Calculate the active power supplied to the motor.
b. If the motor has an efficiency of 85 percent, calculate the mechanical power output.
c. How much energy does the motor consume in 3 h?

8-27 The wattmeters in Fig. 8.30 register +35 kW and −20 kW, respectively. If the load is balanced, calculate the following:
a. The load power factor
b. The line current if the line voltage is 630 V

Industrial application

8-28 A 20 Ω resistor is connected between lines A and B of a 3-phase, 480 V line. Calculate the currents that flow in lines A, B, and C, respectively.

8-29 Two 30 Ω resistors are connected between phases AB and BC of a 3-phase, 480 V line. Calculate the currents flowing in lines A, B, and C, respectively.

8-30 A 150 kW, 460 V, 3-phase heater is installed in a hot water boiler. What power does it produce if the line voltage is 470 V?

8-31 Three 5 Ω resistors are connected in wye across a 3-phase, 480 V line. Calculate the current flowing in each. If one of the resistors is disconnected, calculate the current that flows in the remaining two.

8-32 One of the three fuses protecting a 3-phase electric heater rated at 200 kW, 600 V is removed so as to reduce the heat produced by the boiler. What power does the heater develop under these conditions?

8-33 A 450 kW, 575 V, 3-phase steam boiler produces 1300 lb of steam per hour. Estimate the quantity of steam produced if the line voltage is 612 V.

8-34 A 40 hp, 460 V, 1180 r/min, 3-phase, 60 Hz TEFC, premium efficiency induction motor manufactured by Baldor Electric Company has a full-load efficiency of 93.6% and a power factor of 83%. Calculate the following:

a. The active power drawn by the motor.
b. The apparent power drawn by the motor.
c. The full-load line current.

8-35 A 92 in × 24 in × 32 in, 450 kg Square D motor controller is used to drive a 1600 hp, 2400 V, 3-phase, 60 Hz squirrel-cage motor.

a. Assuming the motor has a minimum efficiency and power factor of 96% and 90%, respectively, calculate the full-load current delivered by the controller.
b. What is the reactive power drawn from the line at full-load?
c. What is the phase angle between the line-to-neutral voltage and the line current?

CHAPTER 9
The Ideal Transformer

9.0 Introduction

The transformer is probably one of the most useful electrical devices ever invented. It can raise or lower the voltage or current in an ac circuit, it can isolate circuits from each other, and it can increase or decrease the apparent value of a capacitor, an inductor, or a resistor. Furthermore, the transformer enables us to transmit electrical energy over great distances and to distribute it safely in factories and homes.

We will study some of the basic properties of transformers in this chapter. It will help us understand not only the commercial transformers covered in later chapters but also the basic operating principle of induction motors, alternators, and synchronous motors. All these devices are based upon the laws of electromagnetic induction. Consequently, we encourage the reader to pay particular attention to the subject matter covered here.

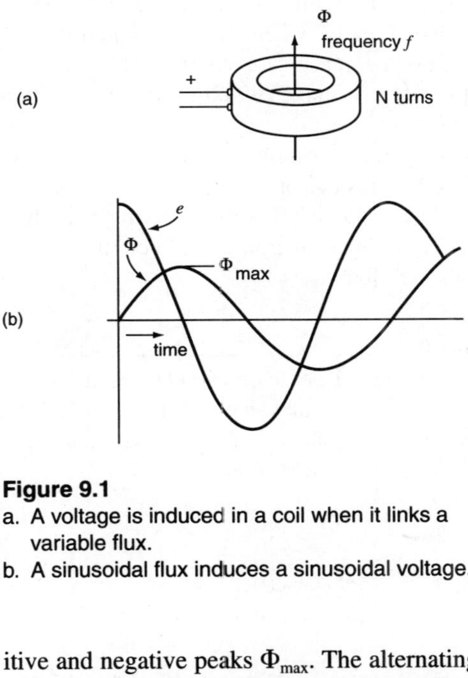

Figure 9.1
a. A voltage is induced in a coil when it links a variable flux.
b. A sinusoidal flux induces a sinusoidal voltage.

9.1 Voltage induced in a coil

Consider the coil of Fig. 9.1a, which surrounds (or links) a variable flux Φ. The flux alternates sinusoidally at a frequency f, periodically reaching positive and negative peaks Φ_{max}. The alternating flux induces a sinusoidal ac voltage in the coil, whose effective value is given by

$$E = 4.44\, fN\Phi_{max} \tag{9.1}$$

where

E = effective voltage induced [V]

f = frequency of the flux [Hz]

N = number of turns on the coil

Φ_{max} = peak value of the flux [Wb]

4.44 = a constant [exact value = $2\pi/\sqrt{2}$]

It does not matter where the ac flux comes from: It may be created by a moving magnet, a nearby ac coil, or even by an ac current that flows in the coil itself.

Eq. 9.1 is derived from Faraday's law equation $e = N\,\Delta\Phi/\Delta t$ in which $\Delta\Phi/\Delta t$ is the rate of change of flux and e is the instantaneous induced voltage. Thus, in Fig. 9.1b, when the flux is increasing with time, the rate of change $\Delta\Phi/\Delta t$ is greater than zero and so the voltage is positive. Conversely, when the flux is decreasing with time, the rate of change $\Delta\Phi/\Delta t$ is less than zero; consequently, the voltage is negative. Finally, when the flux is neither increasing nor decreasing (even for one microsecond), the rate of change $\Delta\Phi/\Delta t$ is zero, and so the voltage is zero.

This question also arises: Why do we use the peak flux Φ_{max} instead of the rms value? The reason is that the peak flux is proportional to the peak flux density B_{max} which, in iron cores, determines the level of saturation.

Example 9-1

The coil in Fig. 9.1 possesses 4000 turns and links an ac flux having a peak value of 2 mWb. If the frequency is 60 Hz, calculate the effective value and frequency of the induced voltage E.

Solution

$$E = 4.44 f N \Phi_{max} \tag{9.1}$$

$$= 4.44 \times 60 \times 4000 \times 0.002$$

$$= 2131 \text{ V}$$

The induced voltage has an effective or RMS value of 2131 V and a frequency of 60 Hz. The peak voltage is $2131\sqrt{2} = 3014$ V.

9.2 Applied voltage and induced voltage

Fig. 9.2a shows a coil of N turns connected to a sinusoidal ac source E_g. The coil has a reactance X_m and draws a current I_m. If the resistance of the coil is negligible, the current is given by

$$I_m = E_g/X_m$$

As in any inductive circuit, I_m lags 90° behind E_g and Φ is in phase with the current (Fig. 9.2b).

The detailed behavior of the circuit can be explained as follows:

The sinusoidal current I_m produces a sinusoidal mmf NI_m, which in turn creates a sinusoidal flux Φ. Consequently, I_m is called the *magnetizing current.* The peak value of this ac flux is Φ_{max}. The flux induces an effective voltage E across the terminals of the coil, whose value is given by Eq. 9.1. On the other hand, the applied voltage E_g and the induced voltage E *must* be identical because they appear between the same pair of conductors. Because $E_g = E$, we can write

$$E_g = 4.44 f N \Phi_{max}$$

from which we obtain

$$\Phi_{max} = \frac{E_g}{4.44 fN} \tag{9.2}$$

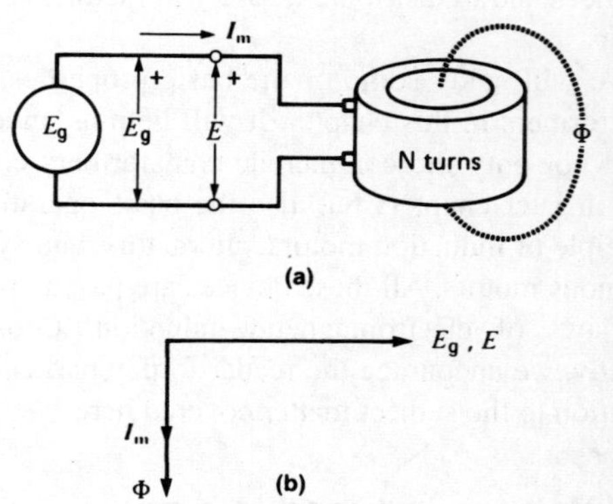

Figure 9.2

a. The voltage E induced in a coil is equal to the applied voltage E_g.

b. Phasor relationships among E_g, E, I_m, and Φ.

This equation shows that for a given frequency and a given number of turns, Φ_{max} varies in proportion to the applied voltage E_g. This means that if E_g is kept constant, the peak flux *must* remain constant.

For example, suppose we gradually insert an iron core into the coil while keeping E_g fixed (Fig. 9.3). The peak value of the ac flux will remain absolutely constant during this operation, retaining its original value Φ_{max} even when the core is completely inside the coil. In effect, if the flux increased (as we would expect), the induced voltage E would also increase. But this is impossible because $E = E_g$ at every instant and, as we said, E_g is kept fixed.

For a given supply voltage E_g, the ac flux in Figs. 9.2 and 9.3 is therefore the same. However, the *magnetizing current* I_m is much smaller when the iron core is inside the coil. In effect, to produce the same flux, a smaller magnetomotive force is needed with an iron core than with an air core. Consequently, the magnetizing current in Fig. 9.3 is much smaller than in Fig. 9.2.

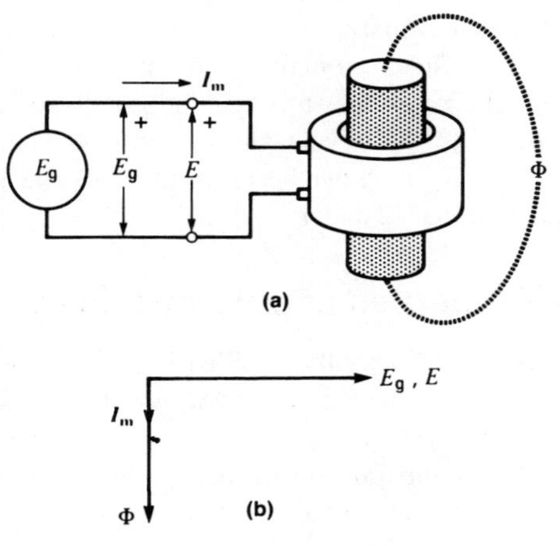

Figure 9.3
a. The flux in the coil remains constant so long as E_g is constant.
b. Phasor relationships.

Example 9-2

A coil having 90 turns is connected to a 120 V, 60 Hz source. If the effective value of the magnetizing current is 4 A, calculate the following:

a. The peak value of flux
b. The peak value of the mmf
c. The inductive reactance of the coil
d. The inductance of the coil

Solution

a.
$$\Phi_{max} = E_g/(4.44\,fN) \quad (9.2)$$
$$= 120/(4.44 \times 60 \times 90)$$
$$= 0.005 = 5 \text{ mWb}$$

b. The peak current is

$$I_{m(peak)} = \sqrt{2}\,I = \sqrt{2} \times 4$$
$$= 5.66 \text{ A}$$

The peak mmf U is

$$U = NI_m = 90 \times 5.66$$
$$= 509.1 \text{ A}$$

The flux is equal to 5 mWb at the instant when the coil mmf is 509.1 ampere-turns.

c. The inductive reactance is

$$X_m = E_g/I_m = 120/4$$
$$= 30\ \Omega$$

d. The inductance is

$$L = X_m/2\pi f \quad (2.10)$$
$$= 30/(2\pi \times 60)$$
$$= 0.0796$$
$$= 79.6 \text{ mH}$$

9.3 Elementary transformer

In Fig. 9.4, a coil having an air core is excited by an ac source E_g. The resulting current I_m produces a total flux Φ, which is dispersed in the space around the coil. If we bring a second coil close to the first, it will surround a portion Φ_{m1} of the total flux. An ac voltage E_2 is therefore induced in the second coil and its value can be measured with a voltmeter. The combination of the two coils is called a *transformer.* The coil connected to the source is called the *primary winding* (or *primary*) and the other one is called the *secondary winding* (or *secondary*).

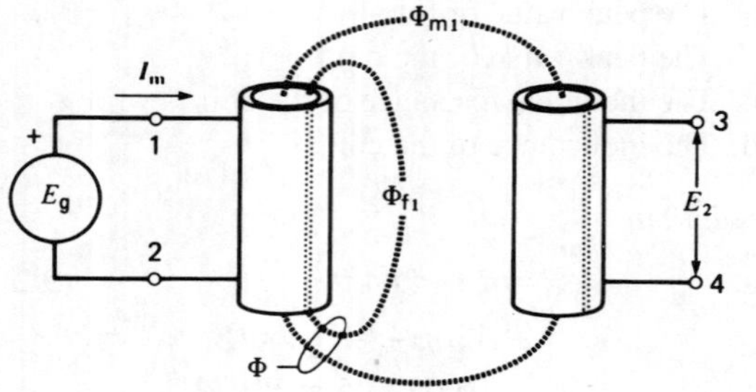

Figure 9.4
Voltage induced in a secondary winding. Mutual flux is Φ_{m1}; leakage flux is Φ_{f1}.

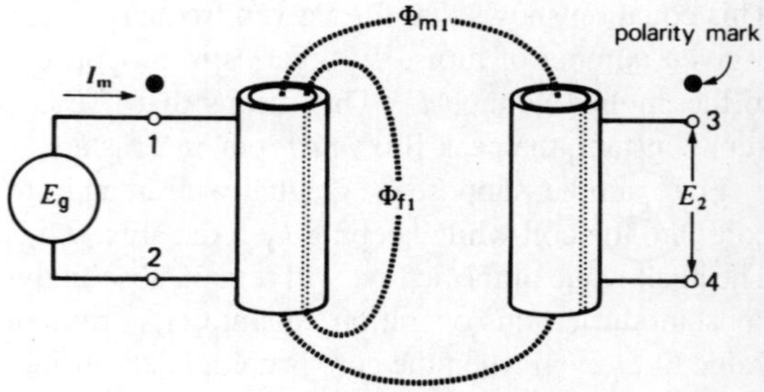

Figure 9.5
Terminals having the same instantaneous polarity are marked with a dot.

A voltage exists only between primary terminals 1-2 and secondary terminals 3-4, respectively. No voltage exists between primary terminal 1 and secondary terminal 3. The secondary is therefore electrically isolated from the primary.

The flux Φ created by the primary can be broken up into two parts: a *mutual flux* Φ_{m1}, which links the turns of both coils; and a *leakage flux* Φ_{f1}, which links only the turns of the primary. If the coils are far apart, the mutual flux is very small compared to the total flux Φ; we then say that the *coupling* between the two coils is weak. We can obtain a better coupling (and a higher secondary voltage E_2) by bringing the two coils closer together. However, even if we bring the secondary right up to the primary so that the two coils touch, the mutual flux will still be small compared to the total flux Φ. When the coupling is weak, voltage E_2 is relatively small and, worse still, it collapses almost completely when a load is connected across the secondary terminals. In most industrial transformers, the primary and secondary windings are wound on top of each other to improve the coupling between them.

9.4 Polarity of a transformer

In Fig. 9.4 fluxes Φ_{f1} and Φ_{m1} are both produced by magnetizing current I_m. Consequently, the fluxes are in phase, both reaching their peak values at the same instant. They also pass through zero at the same instant. It follows that voltage E_2 will reach *its* peak value at the same instant as E_g does. Suppose, during one of these peak moments, that primary terminal 1 is positive with respect to primary terminal 2 and that secondary terminal 3 is positive with respect to secondary terminal 4 (Fig. 9.5). Terminals 1 and 3 are then said to possess the same *polarity.* This sameness can be shown by placing a large dot beside primary terminal 1 and another large dot beside secondary terminal 3. The dots are called polarity marks.

The polarity marks in Fig. 9.5 could equally well be placed beside terminals 2 and 4 because, as the voltage alternates, they too, become simultaneously positive, every half-cycle. Consequently, the polarity marks may be shown beside terminals 1 and 3 *or* beside terminals 2 and 4.

9.5 Properties of polarity marks

A transformer is usually installed in a metal enclosure and so only the primary and secondary terminals are accessible, together with their polarity marks. But although the transformer may not be visible, the following rules always apply to polarity marks:

1. A current entering a polarity-marked terminal produces a mmf that acts in a "positive" direction. As a result, it produces a flux in the "positive" direction* (Fig. 9.6). Conversely, a current flowing out of a polarity-marked terminal

* "Positive" and "negative" are shown in quotation marks because we can rarely look inside a transformer to see in which direction the flux is actually circulating.

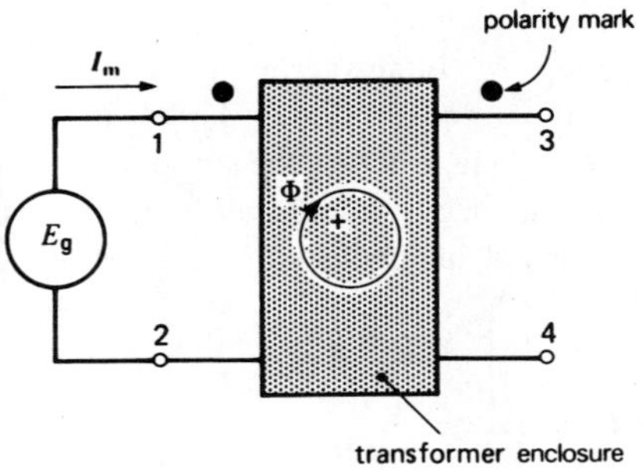

Figure 9.6
A current entering a polarity-marked terminal produces a flux in a "positive" direction.

produces a mmf and flux in the "negative" direction. Thus, currents that respectively flow into and out of polarity-marked terminals of two coils produce magnetomotive forces that buck each other.

2. If one polarity-marked terminal is momentarily positive, then the other polarity-marked terminal is momentarily positive (each with respect to its other terminal). This rule enables us to relate the phasor voltage on the secondary side with the phasor voltage on the primary side. For example, in Fig. 9.7, phasor E_{dc} is in phase with phasor E_{ab}.

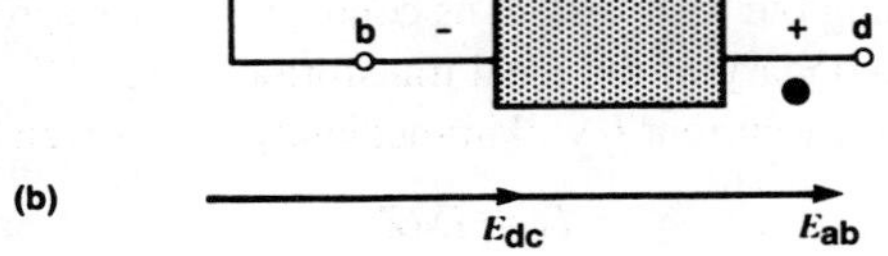

Figure 9.7
a. Instantaneous polarities when the magnetizing current is increasing.
b. Phasor relationship.

9.6 Ideal transformer at no-load; voltage ratio

Before undertaking the study of practical, commercial transformers, we shall examine the properties of the so-called *ideal transformer.* By definition, an ideal transformer has no losses and its core is infinitely permeable. Furthermore, any flux produced by the primary is completely linked by the secondary, and vice versa. Consequently, an ideal transformer has no leakage flux of any kind.

Practical transformers have properties which approach those of an ideal transformer. Consequently, our study of the ideal transformer will help us understand the properties of transformers in general.

Fig. 9.8a shows an ideal transformer in which the primary and secondary respectively possess N_1 and N_2 turns. The primary is connected to a sinusoidal source E_g and the magnetizing current I_m creates a flux Φ_m. The flux is completely linked by the primary and secondary windings and, consequently, it is a *mutual flux.* The flux varies sinusoidally, and reaches a peak value Φ_{max}. According to Eq. 9.1, we can therefore write

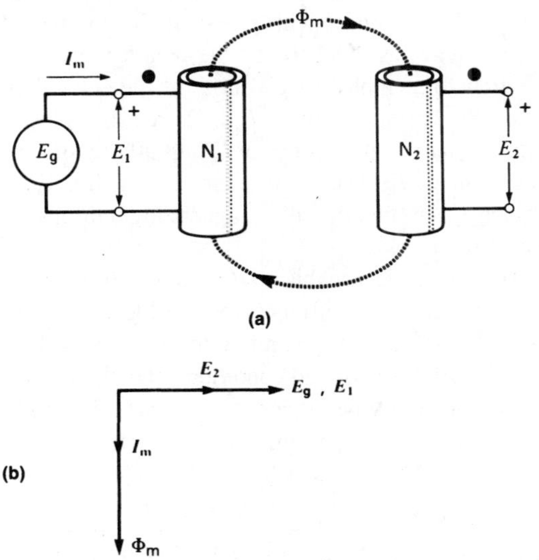

Figure 9.8
a. The ideal transformer at no-load. Primary and secondary are linked by a mutual flux.
b. Phasor relationships at no-load.

$$E_1 = 4.44\, fN_1\Phi_{max} \quad (9.3)$$

and

$$E_2 = 4.44\, fN_2\Phi_{max} \quad (9.4)$$

From these equations, we deduce the expression for the *voltage ratio* and *turns ratio* **a** of an ideal transformer:

$$\frac{E_1}{E_2} = \frac{N_1}{N_2} = a \quad (9.5)$$

where

E_1 = voltage induced in the primary [V]
E_2 = voltage induced in the secondary [V]
N_1 = numbers of turns on the primary
N_2 = numbers of turns on the secondary
a = turns ratio

This equation shows that the ratio of the primary and secondary voltages is equal to the ratio of the number of turns. Furthermore, because the primary and secondary voltages are induced by the same mutual Φ_m, they are necessarily in phase.

The phasor diagram at no-load is given in Fig. 9.8b. Phasor E_2 is in phase with phasor E_1 (and not 180° out of phase) as indicated by the polarity marks. If the transformer has fewer turns on the secondary than on the primary, phasor E_2 is shorter than phasor E_1. As in any inductor, current I_m lags 90° behind applied voltage E_g. The phasor representing flux Φ_m is obviously in phase with magnetizing current I_m which produces it.

However, because this is an *ideal* transformer, the magnetic circuit is infinitely permeable and so no magnetizing current is required to produce the flux Φ_m. Thus, under no-load conditions, the phasor diagram of such a transformer is identical to Fig. 9.8b except that phasor I_m is infinitesimally small.

Example 9-3

A not-quite-ideal transformer having 90 turns on the primary and 2250 turns on the secondary is connected to a 120 V, 60 Hz source. The coupling between the primary and secondary is perfect, but the magnetizing current is 4 A.

Calculate

a. The effective voltage across the secondary terminals
b. The peak voltage across the secondary terminals
c. The instantaneous voltage across the secondary when the instantaneous voltage across the primary is 37 V

Solution

a. The turns ratio is

$$N_2/N_1 = 2250/90 = 25 \quad (9.5)$$

The secondary voltage is therefore 25 times greater than the primary voltage because the secondary has 25 times more turns. Consequently:

$$E_2 = 25 \times E_1 = 25 \times 120 = 3000 \text{ V}$$

Instead of reasoning as above, we can apply Eq. 9.5:

$$E_1/E_2 = N_1/N_2$$
$$120/E_2 = 90/2250 \text{ V}$$

which again yields $E_2 = 3000$ V

b. The voltage varies sinusoidally; consequently, the peak secondary voltage is

$$E_{2(peak)} = \sqrt{2}E = \sqrt{2} \times 3000 = 4242 \text{ V}$$

c. The secondary voltage is 25 times greater than E_1 at every *instant*. Consequently, when $e_1 = 37$ V,

$$e_2 = 25 \times 37 = 925 \text{ V}$$

9.7 Ideal transformer under load; current ratio

Pursuing our analysis, let us connect a load Z across the secondary of the ideal transformer (Fig. 9.9). A secondary current I_2 will immediately flow, given by

$$I_2 = E_2/Z$$

Does E_2 change when we connect the load? To answer this question, we must recall two facts. First, in an ideal transformer the primary and secondary windings are linked by a mutual flux Φ_m, and by no other

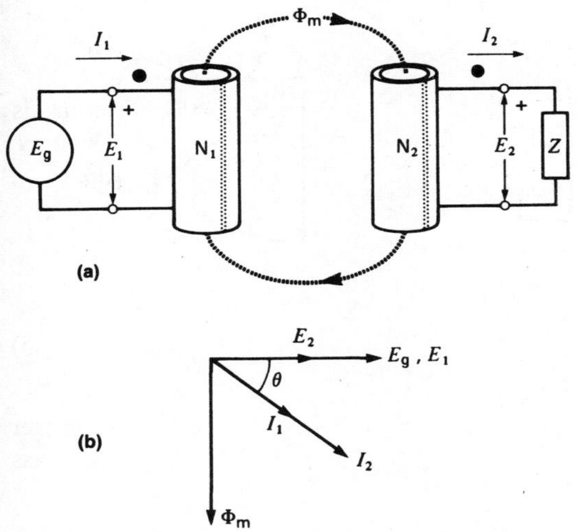

Figure 9.9
a. Ideal transformer under load. The mutual flux remains unchanged.
b. Phasor relationships under load.

flux. In other words, an ideal transformer, by definition, has no leakage flux. Consequently, the voltage ratio under load is the same as at no-load, namely:

$$E_1/E_2 = N_1/N_2$$

Second, if the supply voltage E_g is kept fixed, then the primary induced voltage E_1 remains fixed. Consequently, mutual flux Φ_m also remains fixed. It follows that E_2 also remains fixed. We conclude that E_2 remains fixed whether a load is connected or not.

Let us now examine the magnetomotive forces created by the primary and secondary windings. First, current I_2 produces a secondary mmf N_2I_2. If it acted alone, this mmf would produce a profound change in the mutual flux Φ_m. But we just saw that Φ_m does not change under load. We conclude that flux Φ_m can only remain fixed if the primary develops a mmf which *exactly* counterbalances N_2I_2 at every instant. Thus, a primary current I_1 must flow so that

$$N_1I_1 = N_2I_2 \tag{9.6}$$

To obtain the required instant-to-instant bucking effect, currents I_1 and I_2 must increase and decrease at the same time. Thus, when I_2 goes through zero, I_1 goes through zero, and when I_2 is maximum, (+) I_1 is maximum (+). In other words, the currents must be in phase. Furthermore, in order to produce the bucking effect, when I_1 flows *into* a polarity mark on the primary side, I_2 must flow *out of* the polarity mark on the secondary side (see Fig. 9.9a).

Using these facts, we can now draw the phasor diagram of an ideal transformer under load (Fig. 9.9b). Assuming a resistive-inductive load, current I_2 lags behind E_2 by an angle θ. Flux Φ_m lags 90° behind E_g, but no magnetizing current I_m is needed to produce this flux because this is an idea transformer. Finally, the primary and secondary currents are in phase. According to Eq. 9.6, they are related by the equation

$$\frac{I_1}{I_2} = \frac{N_2}{N_1} = \frac{1}{a} \tag{9.7}$$

where

I_1 = primary current [A]
I_2 = secondary current [A]
N_1 = number of turns on the primary
N_2 = number of turns on the secondary
a = turns ratio

Comparing Eq. 9.5 and Eq. 9.7, we see that the transformer current ratio is the inverse of the voltage ratio. In effect, what we gain in voltage, we lose in current and vice versa. This is consistent with the requirement that the apparent power input E_1I_1 to the primary must equal the apparent power output E_2I_2 of the secondary. If the power inputs and outputs were not identical, it would mean that the transformer itself absorbs power. By definition, this is impossible in an ideal transformer.

Example 9-4

An ideal transformer having 90 turns on the primary and 2250 turns on the secondary is connected to a 200 V, 50 Hz source. The load across the secondary draws a current of 2 A at a power factor of 80 percent lagging (Fig. 9.10a).

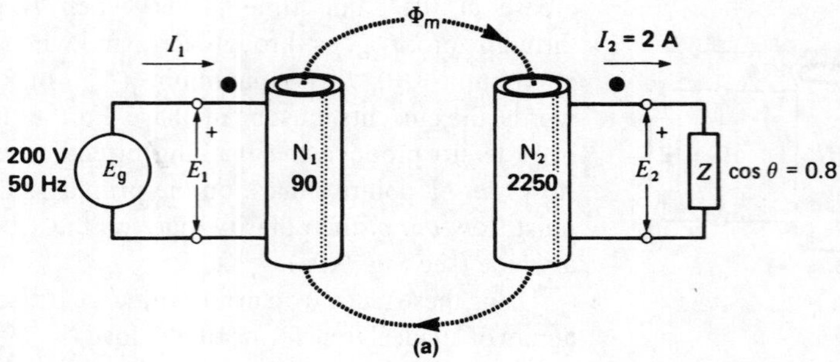

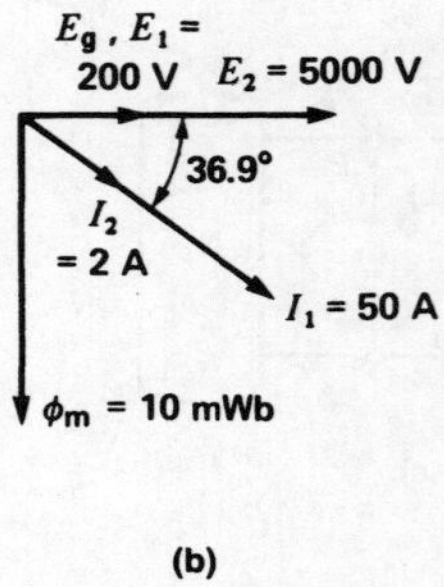

Figure 9.10
a. See Example 9-4.
b. Phasor relationships.

Calculate

a. The effective value of the primary current
b. The instantaneous current in the primary when the instantaneous current in the secondary is 100 mA
c. The peak flux linked by the secondary winding
d. Draw the phasor diagram

Solution

a. The turns ratio is

$$a = N_1/N_2 = 90/2250$$
$$= 1/25$$

The current ratio is therefore 25 and because the primary has fewer turns, the primary current is 25 times greater than the secondary current. Consequently,

$$I_1 = 25 \times 2 = 50 \text{ A}$$

Instead of reasoning as above, we can calculate the current by means of Eq. 9.6.

$$N_1 I_1 = N_2 I_2$$
$$90 I_1 = 2250 \times 2$$
$$I_1 = 50 \text{ A}$$

b. The instantaneous current in the primary is *always* 25 times greater than the instantaneous current in the secondary. Therefore when $I_2 =$ 100 mA, I_1 is

$$I_{1\text{ instantaneous}} = 25\, I_{2\text{ instantaneous}}$$
$$= 25 \times 0.1$$
$$= 2.5 \text{ A}$$

c. In an ideal transformer, the flux linking the secondary is the same as that linking the primary. The peak flux in the secondary is

$$\Phi_{max} = E_g/(4.44\, fN_1)$$
$$= 200/(4.44 \times 50 \times 90)$$
$$= 0.01$$
$$= 10 \text{ mWb}$$

d. To draw the phasor diagram, we reason as follows. Secondary voltage is

$$E_2 = 25 \times E_1 = 25 \times 200$$
$$= 5000 \text{ V}$$

E_2 is in phase with E_1 indicated by the polarity marks. For the same reason, I_1 is in phase with I_2. Phase angle between E_2 and I_2 is

$$\text{power factor} = \cos\theta$$
$$0.8 = \cos\theta$$
$$\theta = 36.9°$$

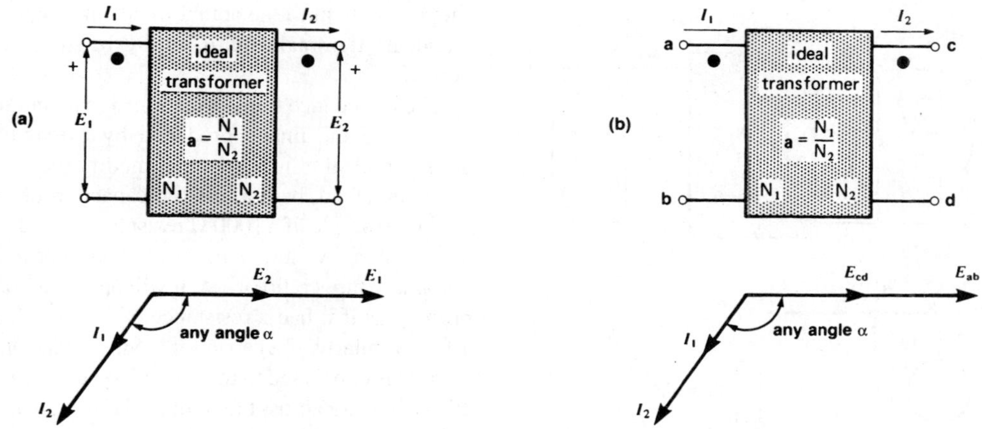

Figure 9.11
a. Symbol for an ideal transformer and phasor diagram using sign notation.
b. Symbol for an ideal transformer and phasor diagram using double-subscript notation.

The phase angle between E_1 and I_1 is also 36.9°.

The mutual flux lags 90° behind E_g (Fig. 9.10b).

9.8 Circuit symbol for an ideal transformer

To highlight the bare essentials of an ideal transformer, it is best to draw it in symbolic form. Thus, instead of drawing the primary and secondary windings and the mutual flux Φ_m, we simply show a box having primary and secondary terminals (Fig. 9.11). Polarity marks are added, enabling us to indicate the direction of current flow as well as the polarities of voltages E_1 and E_2. For example, a current I_1 flowing into one polarity-marked terminal is *always* accompanied by a current I_2 flowing out of the other polarity-marked terminal. Consequently, I_1 and I_2 are always in phase.

Furthermore, if we let the ratio of transformation N_1/N_2 = a, we obtain

$$E_1 = aE_2$$

and

$$I_1 = I_2/a$$

In an ideal transformer, and specifically referring to Fig. 9.11a, E_1 and E_2 are *always* in phase, and so are I_1 and I_2.*

If the double-subscript notation is used (Fig. 9.11b), E_{ab} and E_{cd} are *always* in phase and so are I_1 and I_2.

The angle α depends upon the nature of the load (which may sometimes be a source) connected to the secondary side.

9.9 Impedance ratio

Although a transformer is generally used to transform a voltage or current, it also has the important ability to transform an impedance. Consider, for example, Fig. 9.12a in which an ideal transformer T is connected between a source E_g and a load Z. The ratio of transformation is **a,** and so we can write

---

* Some texts show the respective voltages and currents as being 180° out of phase. This situation can arise depending upon how the behavior of the transformer is described, or how the voltage polarities and current directions are assigned. By using the methodology we have adopted in this book, there is never any doubt as to how the phasors should be drawn.

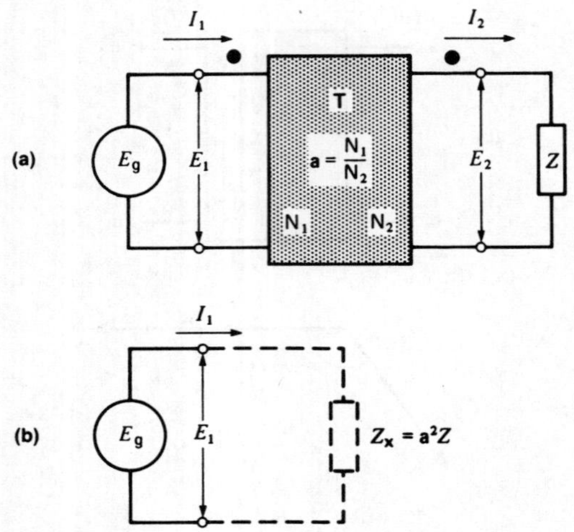

Figure 9.12
a. Impedance transformation using a transformer.
b. The impedance seen by the source differs from Z.

$$E_1/E_2 = a$$

and

$$I_1/I_2 = 1/a$$

As far as the source is concerned, it sees an impedance Z_x between the primary terminals given by:

$$Z_x = E_1/I_1$$

On the other hand, the secondary sees an impedance Z given by

$$Z = E_2/I_2$$

However, Z_x can be expressed in another way:

$$Z_x = \frac{E_1}{I_1} = \frac{aE_2}{I_2/a} = \frac{a^2E_2}{I_2} = a^2Z$$

Consequently,

$$Z_x = a^2Z \qquad (9.8)$$

This means that the impedance seen by the source is a^2 times the real impedance (Fig. 9.12b). Thus, an ideal transformer has the amazing ability to increase or decrease the value of an impedance. In effect, the impedance seen across the primary terminals is identical to the actual impedance across the secondary terminals multiplied by the square of the turns ratio.

The impedance transformation is real, and not illusory like the image produced by a magnifying glass. An ideal transformer can modify the value of any component, be it a resistor, capacitor, or inductor. For example, if a 1000 Ω resistor is placed across the secondary of a transformer having a primary to secondary turns ratio of 1:5, it will appear across the primary as if it had a resistance of $1000 \times (1/5)^2 = 40\ \Omega$. Similarly, if a capacitor having a reactance of 1000 Ω is connected to the secondary, it appears as a 40 Ω capacitor across the primary. However, because the reactance of a capacitor is inversely proportional to its capacitance ($X_c = 1/2\pi fC$), the apparent capacitance between the primary terminals is 25 times greater than its actual value. We can therefore artificially increase (or decrease) the microfarad value of a capacitor by means of a transformer.

9.10 Shifting impedances from secondary to primary and vice versa

As a further illustration of the impedance-changing properties of an ideal transformer, consider the circuit of Fig. 9.13a. It is composed of a source E_g, a transformer T, and four impedances Z_1 to Z_4. The transformer has a turns ratio **a.**

We can progressively shift the secondary impedances to the primary side, as shown in Figs. 9.13b to 9.13e. As the impedances are shifted in this way, the circuit configuration remains the same, but the shifted impedance values are multiplied by $\mathbf{a}^2$.

If all the impedances are transferred to the primary side, the ideal transformer ends up at the extreme right-hand side of the circuit (Fig. 9.13d). In this position the secondary of the transformer is on open-circuit. Consequently, both the primary and secondary currents are zero. We can therefore remove the ideal transformer altogether, yielding the equivalent circuit shown in Fig. 9.13e.

In comparing Figs. 9.13a and 9.13e, we may wonder how a circuit which contains a real transformer T

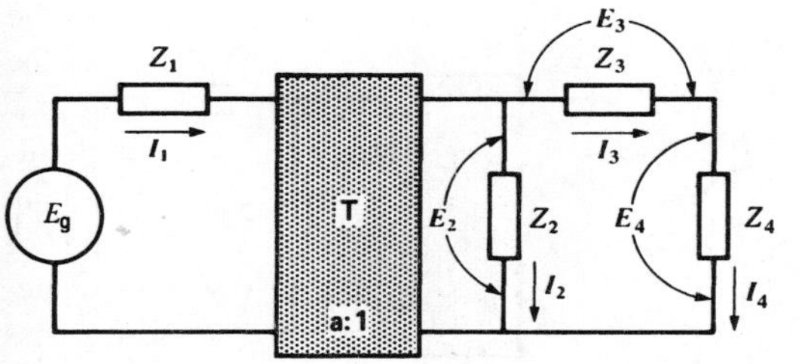

(a)

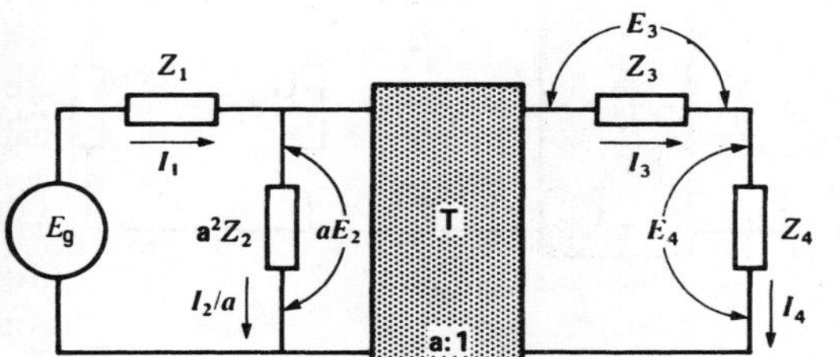

(b)

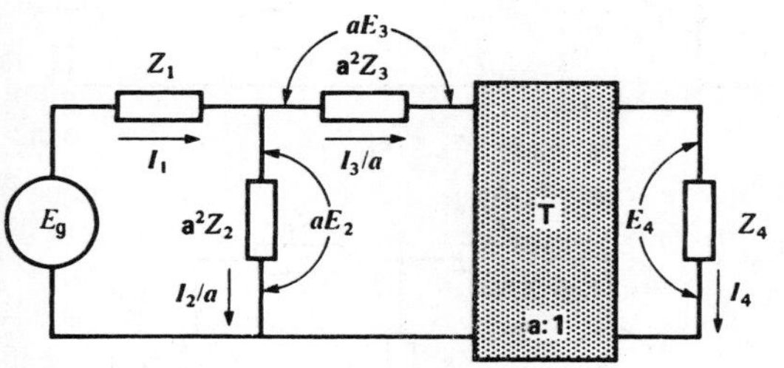

(c)

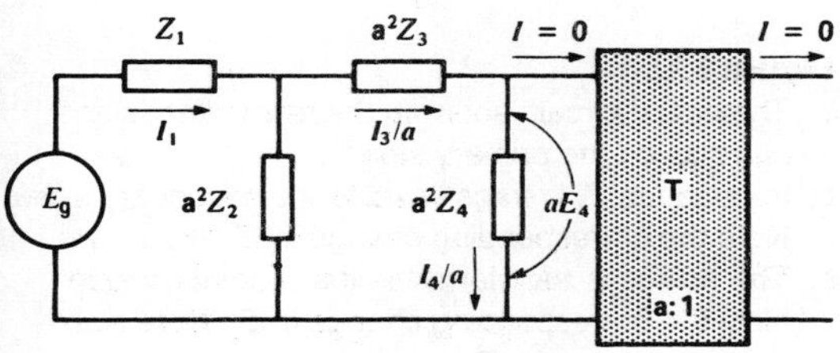

(d)

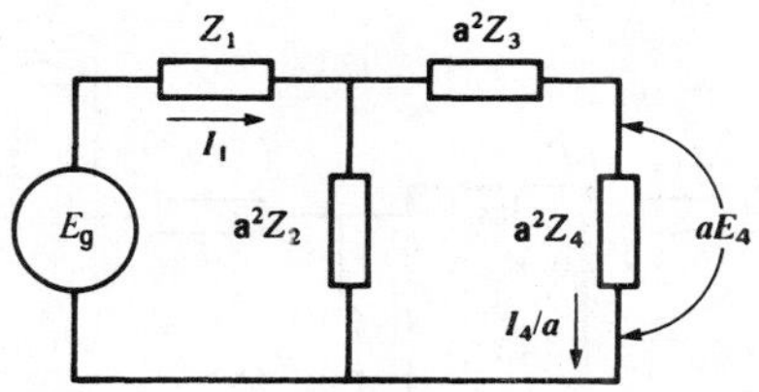

(e)

Figure 9.13

a. The actual circuit showing the actual voltages and currents.
b. Impedance Z_2 is shifted to the primary side. Note the corresponding changes in E_2 and I_2.
c. Impedance Z_3 is shifted to the primary side. Note the corresponding change in E_3 and I_3.
d. Impedance Z_4 is shifted to the primary side. Note the corresponding change in E_4 and I_4. The currents in T are now zero.
e. All the impedances are now transferred to the primary side and the transformer is no longer needed.

can be reduced to a circuit which has no transformer at all. In effect, is there any meaningful relationship between the two circuits? The answer is yes—there is a useful relationship between the real circuit of Fig. 9.13a and the equivalent circuit of Fig. 9.13e. The reason is that the voltage E across each element in the secondary side becomes $\mathbf{a}E$ when the element is shifted to the primary side. Similarly, the current I in each element in the secondary side becomes $I/\mathbf{a}$ when the element is shifted to the primary side.

On account of this relationship, it is easy to solve a real circuit such as the one shown in Fig. 9.13a. We simply reduce it to the equivalent form shown in Fig. 9.13e and solve for all the voltages and currents. These values are then respectively multiplied by $1/\mathbf{a}$ and by $\mathbf{a}$, which yields the actual voltages and currents of each element in the secondary side.

To illustrate, suppose that the real voltage across Z_4 in Fig. 9.14 is E_4 volts and that the real current through it is I_4 amperes. Then, in the equivalent circuit, the voltage across the a^2Z_4 impedance is equal to $E_4 \times \mathbf{a}$ volts. On the other hand, the current through the impedance is equal to $I_4 \div \mathbf{a}$ amperes

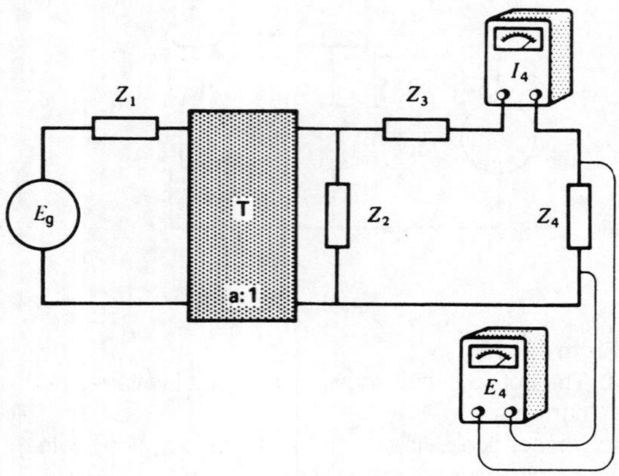

Figure 9.14
Actual voltage and current in impedance Z_4.

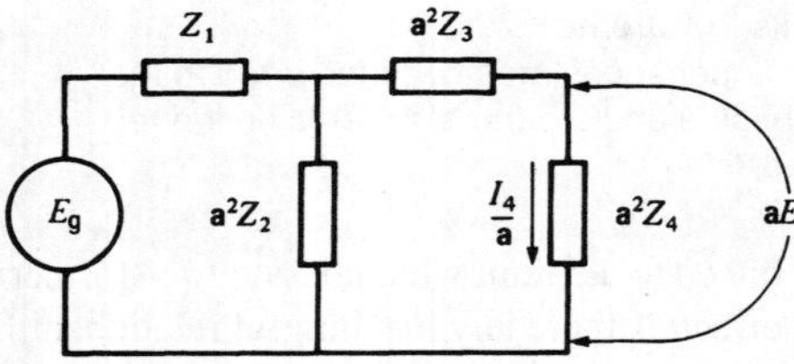

Figure 9.15
Equivalent voltage and current in Z_4.

(Fig. 9.15). In other words, whenever an impedance is transferred to the primary side, the real voltage across the impedance increases by a factor **a,** while the real current decreases by the factor **a.**

In general, whenever an impedance is transferred from one side of a transformer to the other, the real voltage across it changes in proportion to the turns ratio. If the impedance is transferred to the side where the transformer voltage is higher, the voltage across the transferred impedance will also be higher. Conversely, if the impedance is transferred to the side where the transformer voltage is lower, the voltage across the transferred impedance is lower than the real voltage—again, of course, in the ratio of the number of turns.

In some cases it is useful to shift impedances in the opposite way, that is from the primary side to the secondary side (Fig. 9.16a). The procedure is the

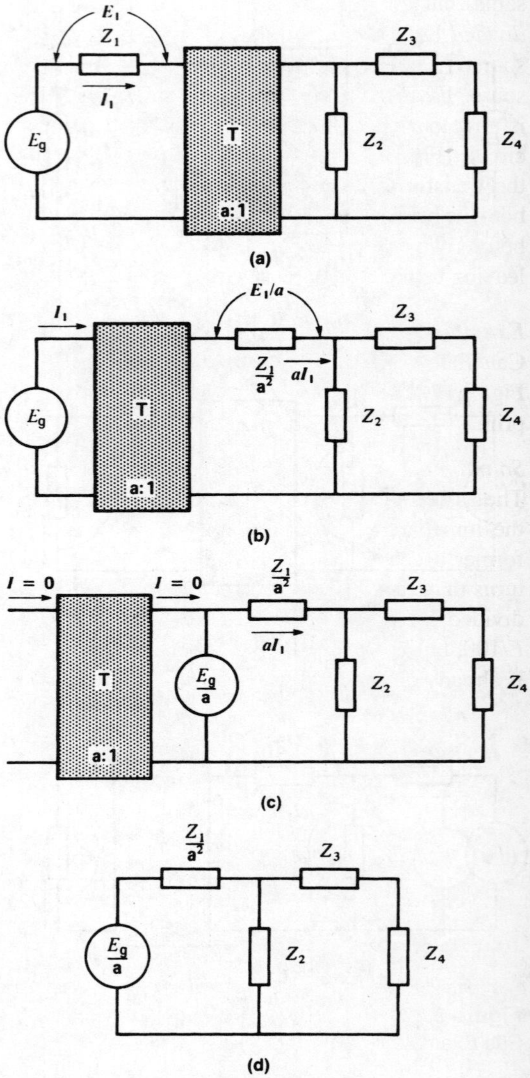

Figure 9.16
a. The actual circuit, showing the real voltages and currents on the primary side.
b. Impedance Z_1 is transferred to the secondary side. Note the corresponding change in E_1 and I_1.
c. The source is transferred to the secondary side. Note the corresponding change in E_g. Note also that the currents in T are zero.
d. All the impedances and even the source are now on the secondary side. The transformer is no longer needed because its currents are zero.

same, but all impedances so transferred are now *divided* by $\mathbf{a}^2$ (Fig. 9.16b). We can even shift the source E_g to the secondary side, where it becomes a source having a voltage E_g/a. The ideal transformer is now located at the extreme left-hand side of the circuit (Fig. 9.16c). In this position the primary of the transformer is on open-circuit. Consequently, both the primary and secondary currents are zero. As before, we can remove the transformer completely, leaving us with the equivalent circuit of Fig. 9.16d.

Example 9-5

Calculate voltage E and current I in the circuit of Fig. 9.17, knowing that ideal transformer T has a primary to secondary turns ratio of 1:100.

Solution

The easiest way to solve this problem is to shift all the impedances to the primary side of the transformer. Because the primary has 100 times fewer turns than the secondary, the impedance values are divided by 100^2, or 10 000. Voltage E becomes $E/100$, but current I remains unchanged because it is already on the primary side (Fig. 9.18).

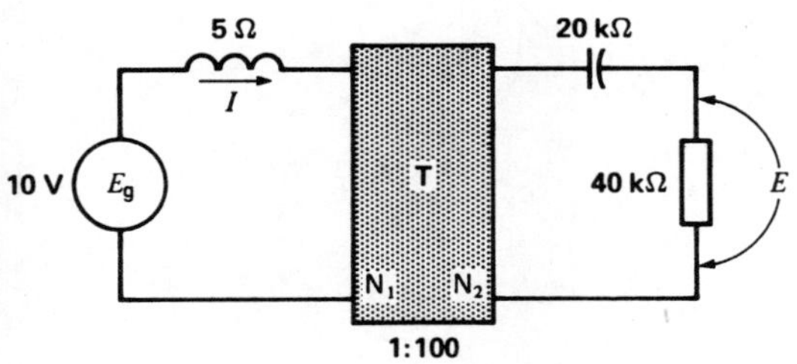

Figure 9.17
See Example 9-5.

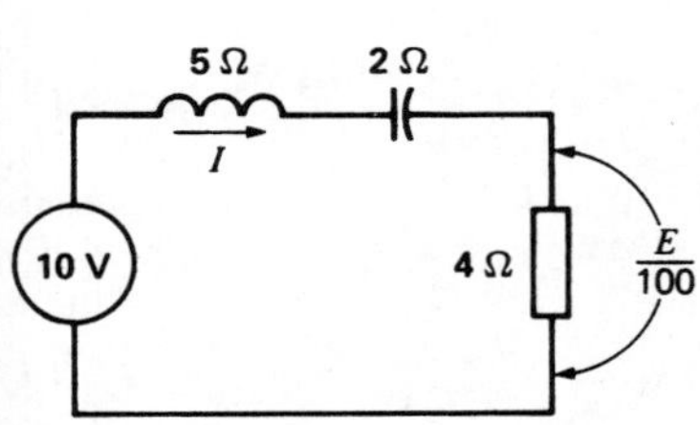

Figure 9.18
Equivalent circuit of Fig. 9.17.

The impedance of the circuit in Fig. 9.18 is

$$Z = \sqrt{R^2 + (X_L - X_C)^2} \quad (2.17)$$
$$= \sqrt{4^2 + (5 - 2)^2}$$
$$= \sqrt{16 + 9}$$
$$= 5\ \Omega$$

The current in the circuit is

$$I = E/Z = 10/5 = 2\text{ A}$$

The voltage across the resistor is

$$E/100 = IR = 2 \times 4 = 8\text{ V}$$

The actual voltage E is, therefore,

$$E = 8 \times 100 = 800\text{ V}$$

Questions and Problems

9-1 The coil in Fig. 9.2a has 500 turns and a reactance of 60 Ω, but negligible resistance. If it is connected to a 120 V, 60 Hz source E_g, calculate the following:
a. The effective value of the magnetizing current I_m
b. The peak value of I_m
c. The peak and mmf produced by the coil
d. The peak flux Φ_{max}

9-2 In Problem 9-1, if the voltage E_g is reduced to 40 V, calculate the new mmf developed by the coil and the peak flux Φ_{max}.

9-3 What is meant by *mutual flux?* by *leakage flux?*

9-4 The ideal transformer in Fig. 9.9 has 500 turns on the primary and 300 turns on the secondary. The source produces a voltage E_g of 600 V, and the load Z is a resistance of 12 Ω. Calculate the following:
a. The voltage E_2
b. The current I_2
c. The current I_1
d. The power delivered to the primary [W]
e. The power output from the secondary [W]

9-5 In Problem 9-4, what is the impedance seen by the source E_g?

9-6 In Fig. 9.17, calculate the voltage across the capacitor and the current flowing through it.

Industrial application

9-7 The nameplate on a 50 kVA transformer shows a primary voltage of 480 V and a secondary voltage of 120 V. We wish to determine the approximate number of turns on the primary and secondary windings. Toward this end, three turns of wire are wound around the external winding, and a voltmeter is connected across this 3-turn coil. A voltage of 76 V is then applied to the 120 V winding, and the voltage across the 3-turn winding is found to be 0.93 V. How many turns are there on the 480 V and 120 V windings (approximately)?

9-8 A coil with an air core has a resistance of 14.7 Ω. When it is connected to a 42 V, 60 Hz ac source, it draws a current of 1.24 A. Calculate the following:

a. The impedance of the coil
b. The reactance of the coil, and its inductance
c. The phase angle between the applied voltage (42 V) and the current (1.24 A).

9-9 Two coils are set up as shown in Fig. 9.4. Their respective resistances are small and may be neglected. The coil having terminals 1, 2 has 320 turns while the coil having terminals 3, 4 has 160 turns. It is found that when a 56 V, 60 Hz voltage is applied to terminals 1-2, the voltage across terminals 3-4 is 22 V. Calculate the peak values of ϕ, ϕ_{f1}, and ϕ_{m1}.

9-10 A 40 μF, 600 V paper capacitor is available, but we need one having a rating of about 300 μF. It is proposed to use a transformer to modify the 40 μF so that it appears as 300 μF. The following transformer ratios are available: 120 V/330 V; 60 V/450 V; 480 V/150 V. Which transformer is the most appropriate and what is the reflected value of the 40 μF capacitance? To which side of the transformer should the 40 μF capacitor be connected?

CHAPTER 10

Practical Transformers

10.0 Introduction

In Chapter 9 we studied the ideal transformer and discovered its basic properties. However, in the real world transformers are not ideal and so our simple analysis must be modified to take this into account. Thus, the windings of practical transformers have resistance and the cores are not infinitely permeable. Furthermore, the flux produced by the primary is not completely captured by the secondary. Consequently, the leakage flux must be taken into account. And finally, the iron cores produce eddy-current and hysteresis losses, which contribute to the temperature rise of the transformer.

In this chapter we discover that the properties of a practical transformer can be described by an equivalent circuit comprising an ideal transformer and resistances and reactances. The equivalent circuit is developed from fundamental concepts. This enables us to calculate such characteristics as voltage regulation and the behavior of transformers that are connected in parallel. The per-unit method is also used to illustrate its mode of application.

10.1 Ideal transformer with an imperfect core

The ideal transformer studied in the previous chapter had an infinitely permeable core. What happens if such a perfect core is replaced by an iron core having hysteresis and eddy-current losses and whose permeability is rather low? We can represent these imperfections by two circuit elements R_m and X_m in parallel with the primary terminals of the ideal transformer (Fig. 10.1a). The primary is excited by a source E_g that produces a voltage E_1.

The resistance R_m represents the iron losses and the resulting heat they produce. To furnish these losses a small current I_f is drawn from the line. This current is in phase with E_1 (Fig. 10.1b).

The magnetizing reactance X_m is a measure of the permeability of the transformer core. Thus, if the permeability is low, X_m is relatively low. The current I_m flowing through X_m represents the magnetizing current needed to create the flux Φ_m in the core. This current lags 90° behind E_1.

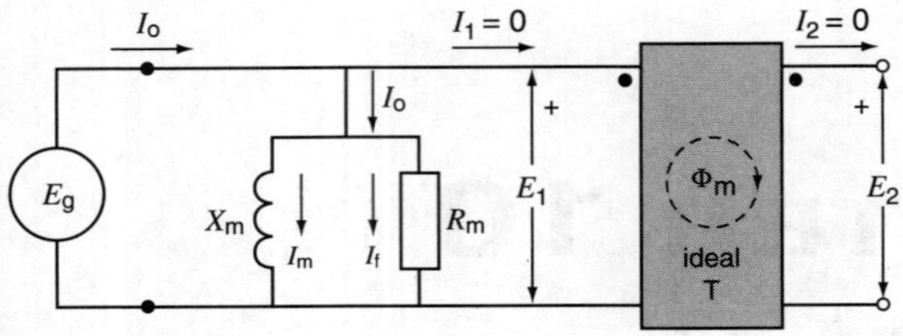

Figure 10.1a
An imperfect core represented by a reactance X_m and a resistance R_m.

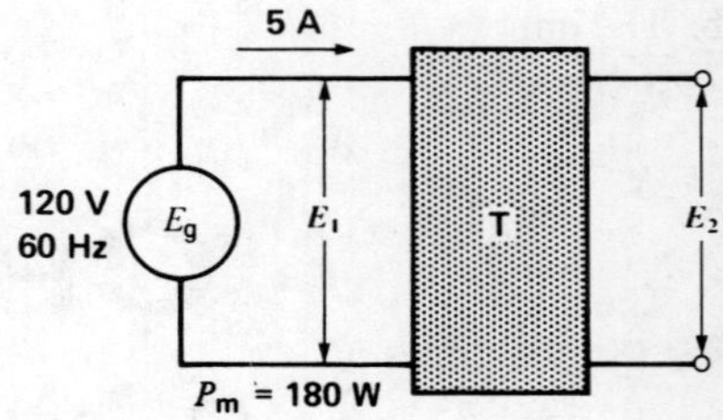

Figure 10.2a
See Example 10-1.

The values of the impedances R_m and X_m can be found experimentally by connecting the transformer to an ac source under no-load conditions and measuring the active power and reactive power it absorbs. The following equations then apply:

$$R_m = E_1^2/P_m \tag{10.1}$$

$$X_m = E_1^2/Q_m \tag{10.2}$$

where

R_m = resistance representing the iron losses [Ω]
X_m = magnetizing reactance of the primary winding [Ω]
E_1 = primary voltage [V]
P_m = iron losses [W]
Q_m = reactive power needed to set up the mutual flux Φ_m [var]

The total current needed to produce the flux Φ_m in an imperfect core is equal to the phasor sum of I_f and I_m. It is called the *exciting current* I_o. It is usually a small percentage of the full-load current. The phasor diagram at no-load for this less-than-ideal transformer is shown in Fig. 10.1b. The peak value of the mutual flux Φ_m is again given by Eq. 9.2:

$$\Phi_m = E_1/(4.44\, fN_1) \tag{9.2}$$

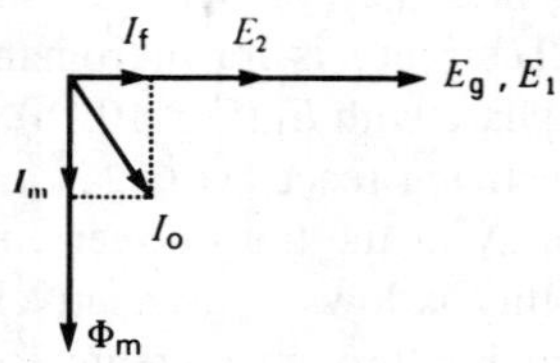

Figure 10.1b
Phasor diagram of a practical transformer at no-load.

Example 10-1

A large transformer operating at no-load draws an exciting current I_o of 5 A when the primary is connected to a 120 V, 60 Hz source (Fig. 10.2a). From a wattmeter test it is known that the iron losses are equal to 180 W.*

Calculate

a. The reactive power absorbed by the core
b. The value of R_m and X_m
c. The value of I_f, I_m, and I_o

Solution

a. The apparent power supplied to the core is

$$S_m = E_1 I_o = 120 \times 5$$
$$= 600 \text{ VA}$$

The iron losses are

$$P_m = 180 \text{ W}$$

The reactive power absorbed by the core is

$$Q_m = \sqrt{S_m^2 - P_m^2} = \sqrt{600^2 - 180^2}$$
$$= 572 \text{ var}$$

* Iron losses are discussed in Sections 2.26 to 2.29.

b. The impedance corresponding to the iron losses is

$$R_m = E_1^2/P_m = 120^2/180 = 80\ \Omega$$

The magnetizing reactance is

$$X_m = E_1^2/Q_m = 120^2/572 = 25.2\ \Omega$$

c. The current needed to supply the iron losses is

$$I_f = E_1/R_m = 120/80 = 1.5\ \text{A}$$

The magnetizing current is

$$I_m = E_1/X_m = 120/25.2 = 4.8\ \text{A}$$

The exciting current I_o is

$$I_o = \sqrt{I_f^2 + I_m^2} = \sqrt{1.5^2 + 4.8^2} = 5\ \text{A}$$

The phasor diagram is given in Fig. 10.2b.

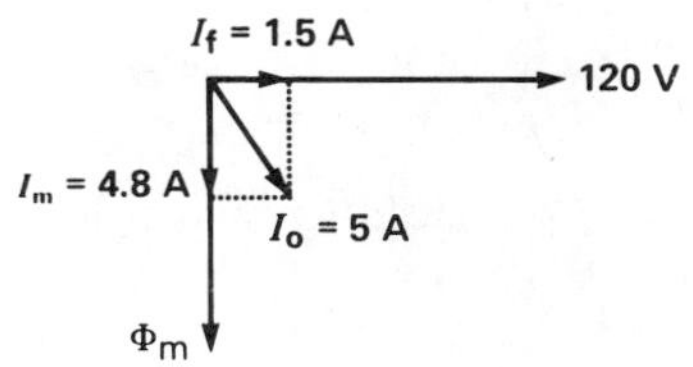

Figure 10.2b
Phasor diagram.

10.2 Ideal transformer with loose coupling

We have just seen how an ideal transformer behaves when it has an imperfect core. We now assume a transformer having a perfect core but rather loose coupling between its primary and secondary windings. We also assume that the primary and secondary windings have negligible resistance and the turns are N_1, N_2.

Consider the transformer in Fig. 10.3 connected to a source E_g and operating at no-load. The voltage

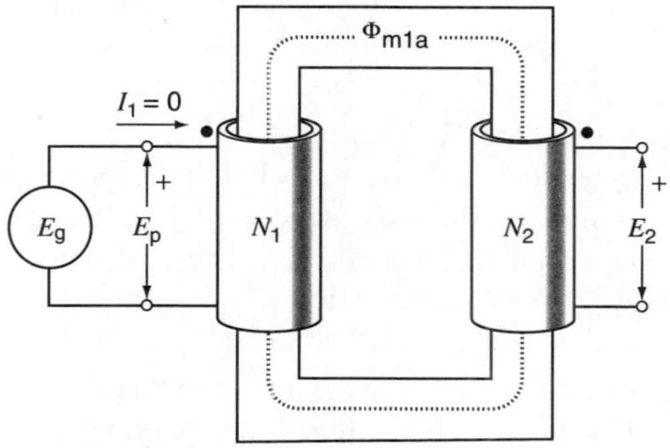

Figure 10.3
Transformer with infinitely permeable core at no-load.

across the primary is E_p and it sets up a mutual flux Φ_{m1a} in the core. This flux lags 90° behind E_p and its peak value is given by $\Phi_{m1a} = E_p/(4.44\ fN_1)$. Because the core is infinitely permeable and because it has no losses, the no-load current $I_1 = 0$. The voltage E_2 is given by $E_2 = (N_2/N_1)\ E_p$. Owing to the current being zero, no mmf is available to drive flux through the air; consequently, there is no leakage flux linking with the primary.

Let us now connect a load Z across the secondary, keeping the source voltage E_p fixed (Fig. 10.4). This simple operation sets off a train of events which we list as follows:

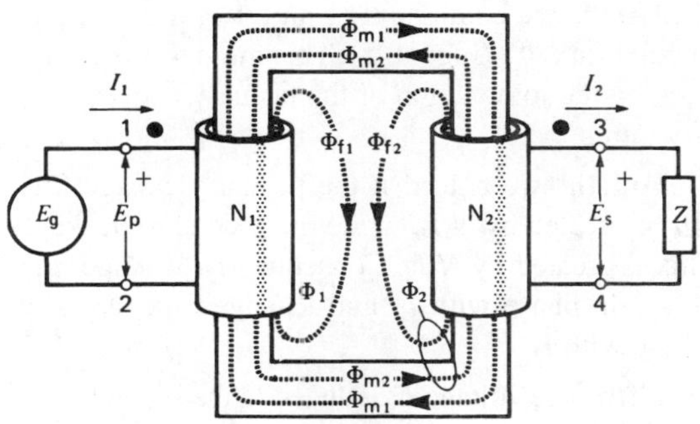

Figure 10.4
Mutual fluxes and leakage fluxes produced by a transformer under load. The leakage fluxes are due to the imperfect coupling between the coils.

1. Currents I_1 and I_2 immediately begin to flow in the primary and secondary windings. They are related by the ideal-transformer equation $I_1/I_2 = N_2/N_1$; hence $N_1I_1 = N_2I_2$.
2. I_2 produces an mmf N_2I_2 while I_1 produces an mmf N_1I_1. These magnetomotive forces are equal and in direct opposition because when I_1 flows into the polarity-marked terminal 1, I_2 flows out of polarity-marked terminal 3.
3. The mmf N_2I_2 produces a total ac flux Φ_2. A portion of Φ_2 (Φ_{m2}) links with the primary winding while another portion (Φ_{f2}) does not. Flux Φ_{f2} is called the *secondary leakage flux.*
4. Similarly, the mmf N_1I_1 produces a total ac flux Φ_1. A portion of Φ_1 (Φ_{m1}) links with the secondary winding, while another portion (Φ_{f1}) does not. Flux Φ_{f1} is called the *primary leakage flux.*

The magnetomotive forces due to I_1 and I_2 upset the magnetic field Φ_{m1a} that existed in the core before the load was connected. The question is, how can we analyze this new situation?

Referring to Fig. 10.4, we reason as follows:

First, the total flux produced by I_1 is composed of two parts: a new mutual flux Φ_{m1} and a leakage flux Φ_{f1}. (The mutual flux Φ_{m1} in Fig. 10.4 is not the same as Φ_{m1a} in Fig. 10.3.)

Second, the total flux produced by I_2 is composed of a mutual flux Φ_{m2} and a leakage flux Φ_{f2}.

Third, we combine Φ_{m1} and Φ_{m2} into a single mutual flux Φ_m (Fig. 10.5). This mutual flux is created by the joint action of the primary and secondary mmfs.

Fourth, we note that the primary leakage flux Φ_{f1} is created by N_1I_1, while the secondary leakage flux is created by N_2I_2. Consequently, leakage flux Φ_{f1} is in phase with I_1, and leakage flux Φ_{f2} is in phase with I_2.

Fifth, the voltage E_s induced in the secondary is actually composed of two parts:

1. A voltage E_{f2} induced by leakage flux Φ_{f2} and given by

$$E_{f2} = 4.44\, fN_2\Phi_{f2} \qquad (10.3)$$

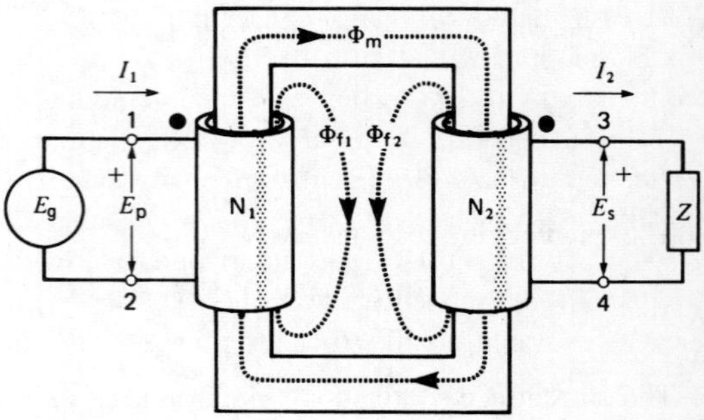

Figure 10.5
A transformer possesses two leakage fluxes and a mutual flux.

2. A voltage E_2 induced by mutual flux Φ_m and given by

$$E_2 = 4.44\, fN_2\Phi_m \qquad (10.4)$$

In general, E_{f2} and E_2 are not in phase.

Similarly, the voltage E_p induced in the primary is composed of two parts:

1. A voltage E_{f1} induced by leakage flux Φ_{f1} and given by

$$E_{f1} = 4.44\, fN_1\Phi_{f1} \qquad (10.5)$$

2. A voltage E_1 induced by mutual flux Φ_m and given by

$$E_1 = 4.44\, fN_1\Phi_m \qquad (10.6)$$

Sixth, induced voltage E_p = applied voltage E_g.

Using these six basic facts, we now proceed to develop the equivalent circuit of the transformer.

10.3 Primary and secondary leakage reactance

We can better identify the four induced voltages E_1, E_2, E_{f1}, and E_{f2} by rearranging the transformer circuit as shown in Fig. 10.6. Thus, the secondary winding is drawn twice to show even more clearly that the N_2 turns are linked by two fluxes, Φ_{f2} and Φ_m. This rearrangement does not change the value of the induced voltages, but it does make each voltage stand out by itself. Thus, it becomes clear that

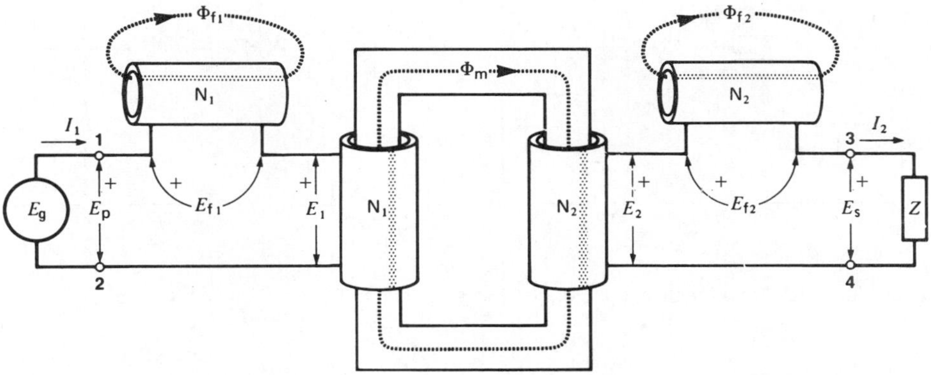

Figure 10.6
Separating the various induced voltages due to the mutual flux and the leakage fluxes.

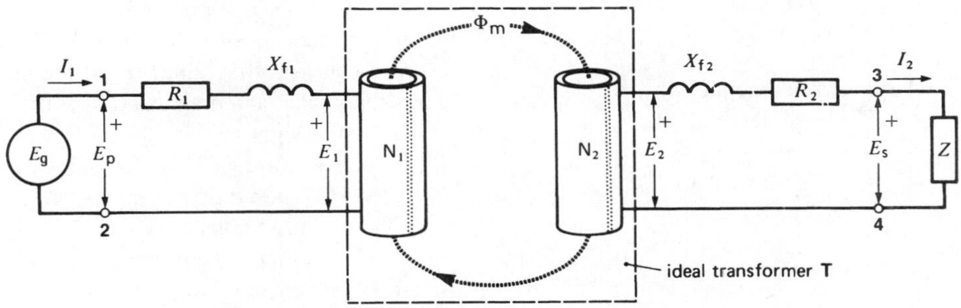

Figure 10.7
Resistance and leakage reactance of the primary and secondary windings.

E_{f2} is really a voltage drop across a reactance. This *secondary leakage reactance* X_{f2} is given by

$$X_{f2} = E_{f2}/I_2 \qquad (10.7)$$

The primary winding is also shown twice, to separate E_1 from E_{f1}. Again, it is clear that E_{f1} is simply a voltage drop across a reactance. This *primary leakage reactance* X_{f1} is given by

$$X_{f1} = E_{f1}/I_1 \qquad (10.8)$$

The primary and secondary leakage reactances are shown in Fig. 10.7. We have also added the primary and secondary winding resistances R_1 and R_2, which, of course, act in series with the respective windings.

Example 10-2

The secondary winding of a transformer possesses 180 turns. When the transformer is under load, the secondary current has an effective value of 18 A, 60 Hz. Furthermore, the mutual Φ_m has a peak value of 20 mWb. The secondary leakage flux Φ_{f2} has a peak value of 3 mWb.

Calculate

a. The voltage induced in the secondary winding by its leakage flux
b. The value of the secondary leakage reactance
c. The value of E_2 induced by the mutual flux Φ_m

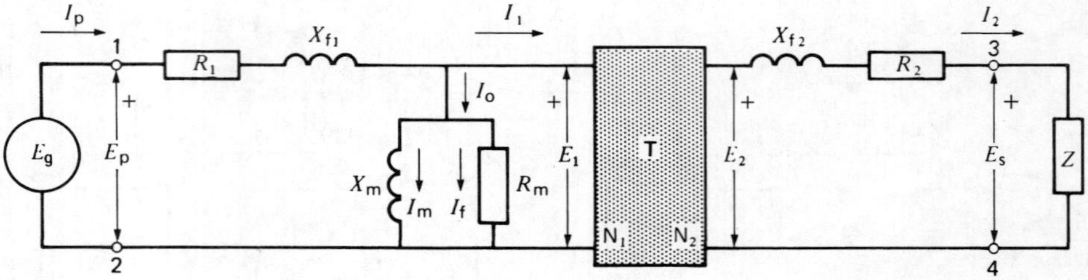

Figure 10.8
Complete equivalent circuit of a practical transformer. The shaded box T is an ideal transformer.

Solution

a. The effective voltage induced by the secondary leakage flux is

$$E_{f2} = 4.44\, fN_2\Phi_{f2} \qquad (10.3)$$
$$= 4.44 \times 60 \times 180 \times 0.003$$
$$= 143.9 \text{ V}$$

b. The secondary leakage reactance is

$$X_{f2} = E_{f2}/I_2 \qquad (10.7)$$
$$= 143.9/18$$
$$= 8\ \Omega$$

c. The voltage induced by the mutual flux is

$$E_2 = 4.44\, fN_2\Phi_m \qquad (10.4)$$
$$= 4.44 \times 60 \times 180 \times 0.02$$
$$= 959 \text{ V}$$

10.4 Equivalent circuit of a practical transformer

The circuit of Fig. 10.7 is composed of resistive and inductive elements (R_1, R_2, X_{f1}, X_{f2}, Z) coupled together by a mutual flux Φ_m, which links the primary and secondary windings. The leakage-free magnetic coupling enclosed in the dotted square is actually an ideal transformer. It possesses the same properties and obeys the same rules as the ideal transformer discussed in Chapter 9. For example, we can shift impedances to the primary side by multiplying their values by $(N_1/N_2)^2$, as we did before.

If we add circuit elements X_m and R_m to represent a practical core, we obtain the complete equivalent circuit of a practical transformer (Fig. 10.8). In this circuit, T is an ideal transformer, but only the primary and secondary terminals 1-2 and 3-4 are accessible; all other components are "buried" inside the transformer itself. However, by appropriate tests we can find the values of all the circuit elements that make up a practical transformer.

Table 10A shows typical values of R_1, R_2, X_{f1}, X_{f2}, X_m, and R_m for transformers ranging from 1 kVA to 400 MVA. The nominal primary and secondary voltages E_{np} and E_{ns} range from 460 V to 424 000 V. The corresponding primary and secondary currents I_{np} and I_{ns} range from 0.417 A to 29 000 A.

The exciting current I_o for the various transformers is also shown. It is always much smaller than the rated primary current I_{np}.

Note that in each case $E_{np}I_{np} = E_{ns}I_{ns} = S_n$, where S_n is the rated power of the transformer.

TABLE 10A ACTUAL TRANSFORMER VALUES

S_n	kVA	1	10	100	1000	400000
E_{np}	V	2400	2400	12470	69000	13800
E_{ns}	V	460	347	600	6900	424000
I_{np}	A	0.417	4.17	8.02	14.5	29000
I_{ns}	A	2.17	28.8	167	145	943
R_1	Ω	58.0	5.16	11.6	27.2	0.0003
R_2	Ω	1.9	0.095	0.024	0.25	0.354
X_{f1}	Ω	32	4.3	39	151	0.028
X_{f2}	Ω	1.16	0.09	0.09	1.5	27
X_m	Ω	200000	29000	150000	505000	460
R_m	Ω	400000	51000	220000	432000	317
I_o	A	0.0134	0.0952	0.101	0.210	52.9

10.5 Construction of a power transformer

Power transformers are usually designed so that their characteristics approach those of an ideal transformer. Thus, to attain high permeability, the core is made of iron (Fig. 10.9a). The resulting magnetizing current I_m is at least 5000 times smaller than it would be if an air core were used. Furthermore, to keep the iron losses down, the core is laminated, and high, resistivity, high-grade silicon steel is used. Consequently, the current I_f needed to supply the iron losses is usually 2 to 4 times smaller than I_m.

Leakage reactances X_{f1} and X_{f2} are made as small as possible by winding the primary and secondary coils on top of each other, and by spacing them as closely together as insulation considerations will permit. The coils are carefully insulated from each other and from the core. Such tight coupling between the coils means that the secondary voltage at no-load is almost exactly equal to N_2/N_1 times the primary voltage. It also guarantees good voltage regulation when a load is connected to the secondary terminals.

Winding resistances R_1 and R_2 are kept low, both to reduce the I^2R loss and resulting heat and to ensure high efficiency. Fig. 10.9a is a simplified version of a power transformer in which the primary and secondary are wound on one leg. In practice, the primary and secondary coils are distributed over both core legs in order to reduce the amount of copper. For the same reason, in larger transformers the cross section of the laminated iron core is not square (as shown) but is built up so as to be nearly round. (See Fig. 12.10a).

Fig. 10.9b shows how the laminations of a small transformer are stacked to build up the core. Fig. 10.9c shows the primary winding of a much bigger transformer.

The number of turns on the primary and secondary windings depends upon their respective voltages. A high-voltage winding has far more turns than a low-voltage winding. On the other hand, the current in an HV winding is much smaller, enabling us to use a smaller size conductor. As a result, the amount of copper in the primary and secondary windings is about the same. In practice, the outer coil (coil 2, in Fig. 10.9a) weighs more because the length per turn is greater. Aluminum or copper conductors are used.

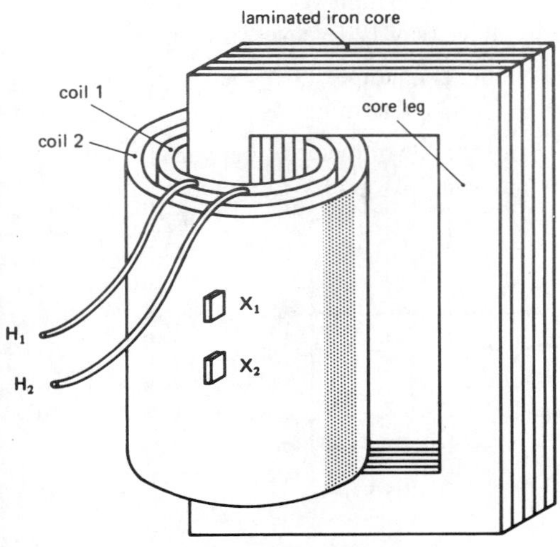

Figure 10.9a
Construction of a simple transformer.

Figure 10.9b
Stacking laminations inside a coil.

Figure 10.9c
Primary winding of a large transformer; rating 128 kV, 290 A.
(Courtesy ABB)

A transformer is reversible in the sense that either winding can be used as the primary winding, where *primary* means the winding that is connected to the source.

10.6 Standard terminal markings

We saw in Section 9.4 that the polarity of a transformer can be shown by means of dots on the primary and secondary terminals. This type of marking is used on instrument transformers. On power transformers, however, the terminals are designated by the symbols H_1 and H_2 for the high-voltage (HV) winding and by X_1 and X_2 for the low-voltage (LV) winding. By convention, H_1 and X_1 have the same polarity.

Although the polarity is known when the symbols H_1, H_2, X_1, and X_2 are given, in the case of power transformers it is common practice to mount the four terminals on the transformer tank in a standard way so that the transformer has either *additive* or *subtractive* polarity. A transformer is said to have

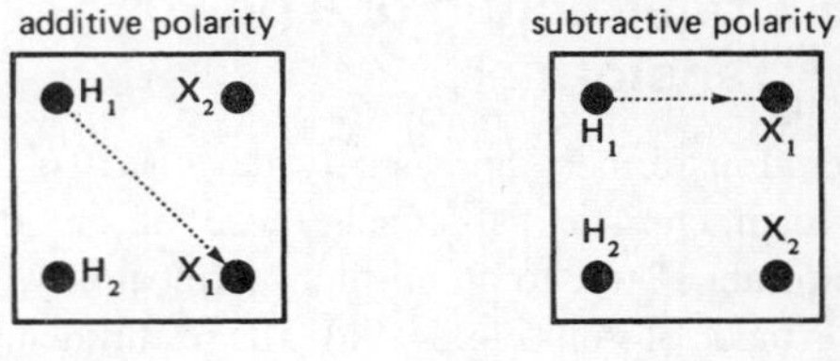

Figure 10.10
Additive and subtractive polarity depend upon the location of the H_1-X_1 terminals.

additive polarity when terminal H_1 is diagonally opposite terminal X_1. Similarly, a transformer has *subtractive* polarity when terminal H_1 is adjacent to terminal X_1 (Fig. 10.10). If we know that a power transformer has additive (or subtractive) polarity, we do not have to identify the terminals by symbols.

Subtractive polarity is standard for all single-phase transformers above 200 kVA, provided the high-voltage winding is rated above 8660 V. All other transformers have additive polarity.

10.7 Polarity tests

To determine whether a transformer possesses additive or subtractive polarity, we proceed as follows (Fig. 10.11):

1. Connect the high-voltage winding to a low-voltage (say 120 V) ac source E_g.
2. Connect a jumper J between any two adjacent HV and LV terminals.
3. Connect a voltmeter E_x between the other two adjacent HV and LV terminals.

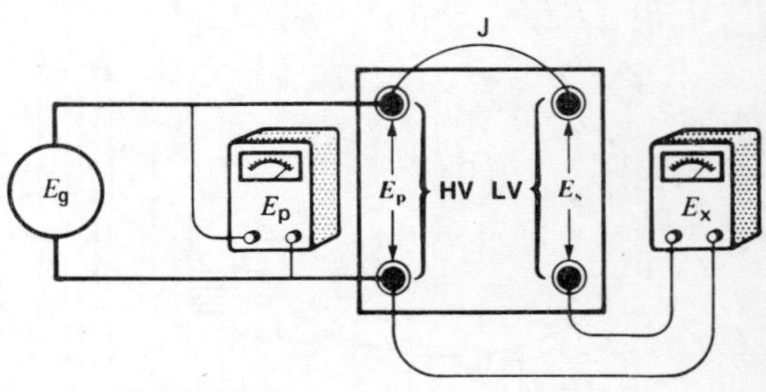

Figure 10.11
Determining the polarity of a transformer using an ac source.

4. Connect another voltmeter E_p across the HV winding. If E_x gives a higher reading than E_p, the polarity is additive. This tells us that H_1 and X_1 are diagonally opposite. On the other hand, if E_x gives a lower reading than E_p, the polarity is subtractive, and terminals H_1 and X_1 are adjacent.

In this polarity text, jumper J effectively connects the secondary voltage E_s in series with the primary voltage E_p. Consequently, E_s either adds to or subtracts from E_p. In other words, $E_x = E_p + E_s$ or $E_x = E_p - E_s$, depending on the polarity. We can now see how the terms additive and subtractive originated.

In making the polarity test, an ordinary 120 V, 60 Hz source can be connected to the HV winding, even though its nominal voltage may be several hundred kilovolts.

Example 10-3

During a polarity test on a 500 kVA, 69 kV/600 V transformer (Fig. 10.11), the following readings were obtained: $E_p = 118$ V, $E_x = 119$ V. Determine the polarity markings of the terminals.

Solution

The polarity is additive because E_x is greater than E_p. Consequently, the HV and LV terminals connected by the jumper must respectively be labelled H_1 and X_2 (or H_2 and X_1).

Fig. 10.12 shows another circuit that may be used to determine the polarity of a transformer. A dc source, in series with an open switch, is connected to the LV winding of the transformer. The transformer terminal connected to the positive side of the source is marked X_1. A dc voltmeter is connected across the HV terminals. When the switch is closed, a voltage is momentarily induced in the HV winding. If, at this moment, the pointer of the voltmeter moves upscale, the transformer terminal connected to the (+) terminal of the voltmeter is marked H_1 and the other is marked H_2.

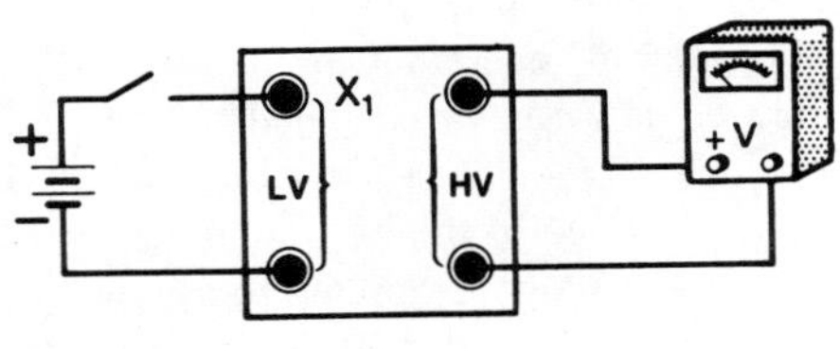

Figure 10.12
Determining the polarity of a transformer using a dc source.

10.8 Transformer taps

Due to voltage drops in transmission lines, the voltage in a particular region of a distribution system may consistently be lower than normal. Thus, a distribution transformer having a ratio of 2400 V/120 V may be connected to a transmission line where the voltage is never higher than 2000 V. Under these conditions the voltage across the secondary is considerably less than 120 V. Incandescent lamps are dim, electric stoves take longer to cook food, and electric motors may stall under moderate overloads.

To correct this problem *taps* are provided on the primary windings of distribution transformers (Fig. 10.13). Taps enable us to change the turns ratio so as to raise the secondary voltage by 4½, 9, or 13½ percent. We can therefore maintain a satisfactory secondary voltage, even though the primary voltage may be 4½, 9, or 13½ percent below normal. Thus, referring to the transformer in Fig. 10.13, if the line voltage is only 2076 V (instead of 2400 V), we would use terminal 1 and tap 5 to obtain 120 V on the secondary side.

Some transformers are designed to change the taps automatically whenever the secondary voltage is above or below a preset level. Such *tap-changing transformers* help maintain the secondary voltage within ±2 percent of its rated value throughout the day.

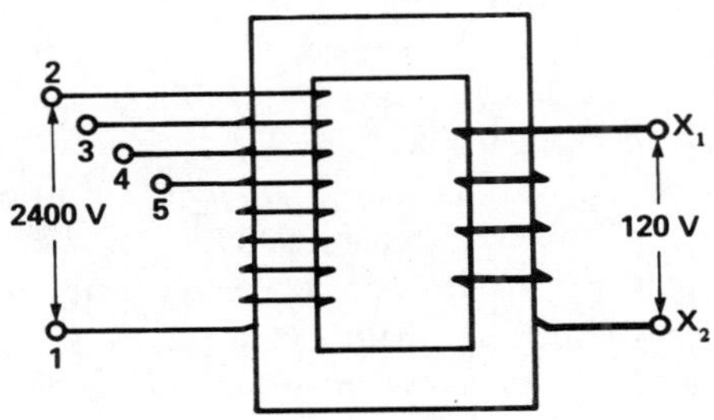

Figure 10.13
Distribution transformer with taps at 2400 V, 2292 V, 2184 V, and 2076 V.

10.9 Losses and transformer rating

Like any electrical machine, a transformer has losses. They are composed of the following:

1. I^2R losses in the windings
2. Hysteresis and eddy-current losses in the core
3. Stray losses due to currents induced in the tank and metal supports by the primary and secondary leakage fluxes

The losses appear in the form of heat and produce 1) an increase in temperature and 2) a drop in efficiency. Under normal operating conditions, the efficiency of transformers is very high; it may reach 99.5 percent for large power transformers.

The heat produced by the iron losses depends upon the peak value of the mutual flux Φ_m, which in turn depends upon the applied voltage. On the other hand, the heat dissipated in the windings depends upon the current they carry. Consequently, to keep the transformer temperature at an acceptable level, we must set limits to both the applied voltage and the current drawn by the load. These two limits determine the *nominal voltage* E_{np} and *nominal current* I_{np} of the transformer winding (primary or secondary).

The *power rating* of a transformer is equal to the product of the nominal voltage times the nominal current of the primary or secondary winding. However, the result is not expressed in watts, because the phase angle between the voltage and current may have any value at all, depending on the nature of the load. Consequently, the power-handling capacity of a transformer is expressed in voltamperes (VA), in kilovoltamperes (kVA), or in megavoltamperes (MVA), depending on the size of the transformer. The temperature rise of a transformer is directly related to the *apparent power* that flows through it. This means that a 500 kVA transformer will get just as hot feeding a 500 kvar inductive load as a 500 kW resistive load.

The rated kVA, frequency, and voltage are always shown on the nameplate. In large transformers the corresponding rated currents are also shown.

Example 10-4

The nameplate of a distribution transformer indicates 250 kVA, 60 Hz, primary 4160 V, secondary 480 V.

a. Calculate the nominal primary and secondary currents.

b. If we apply 2000 V to the 4160 V primary, can we still draw 250 kVA from the transformer?

Solution

a. Nominal current of the 4160 V winding is

$$I_{np} = \frac{\text{nominal } S}{\text{nominal } E_p} = \frac{S_n}{E_{np}} = \frac{250 \times 1000}{4160} = 60 \text{ A}$$

Nominal current of the 480 V winding is

$$I_{ns} = \frac{\text{nominal } S}{\text{nominal } E_s} = \frac{S_n}{E_{ns}} = \frac{250 \times 1000}{480} = 521 \text{ A}$$

b. If we apply 2000 V to the primary, the flux and the iron losses will be lower than normal and the core will be cooler. However, the load current should not exceed its nominal value, otherwise the windings will overheat. Consequently, the maximum power output using this far lower voltage is

$$S = 2000 \text{ V} \times 60 \text{ A} = 120 \text{ kVA}$$

10.10 No-load saturation curve

Let us gradually increase the voltage E_p on the primary of a transformer, with the secondary open-circuited. As the voltage rises, the mutual flux Φ_m increases in direct proportion, in accordance with Eq. 9.2. Exciting current I_o will therefore increase but, when the iron begins to saturate, the magnetizing current I_m has to increase very steeply to produce the required flux. If we draw a graph of E_p versus I_o, we see the dramatic increase in current as we pass the normal operating point (Fig. 10.14). Transformers are usually designed to operate at a peak flux density of about 1.5 T, which corresponds roughly to the knee of the saturation curve. Thus, when nominal voltage is applied to a transformer, the corresponding flux density is about 1.5 T. We can exceed the nominal voltage by perhaps 10 percent, but if we were to apply twice the nominal volt-

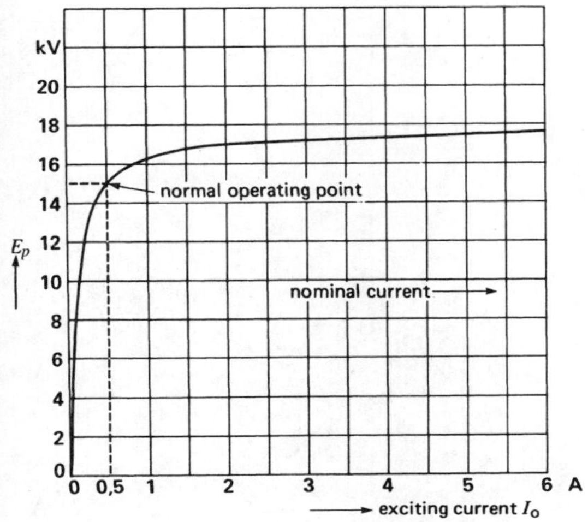

Figure 10.14
No-load saturation curve of a 167 kVA, 14.4 kV/480 V, 60 Hz transformer.

Figure 10.15
Single-phase, dry-type transformer, type AA, rated at 15 kVA, 600 V/240 V, 60 Hz, insulation class 150°C for indoor use. Height: 600 mm; width: 434 mm; depth: 230 mm; weight: 79.5 kg.
(Courtesy of Hammond)

age, the exciting current could become even greater than the nominal full-load current.

The nonlinear relationship between E_p and I_o shows that the exciting branch (composed of R_m and X_m in Fig. 10.1a) is not as constant as it appears. In effect, although R_m is reasonably constant, X_m decreases rapidly with increasing saturation. However, most transformers operate at close to rated voltage, and so R_m and X_m remain essentially constant.

10.11 Cooling methods

To prevent rapid deterioration of the insulating materials inside a transformer, adequate cooling of the windings and core must be provided.

Indoor transformers below 200 kVA can be directly cooled by the natural flow of the surrounding air. The metallic housing is fitted with ventilating louvres so that convection currents may flow over the windings and around the core (Fig. 10.15). Larger transformers can be built the same way, but forced circulation of clean air must be provided. Such *dry-type* transformers are used inside buildings, away from hostile atmospheres.

Distribution transformers below 200 kVA are usually immersed in mineral oil and enclosed in a steel tank. Oil carries the heat away to the tank, where it is dissipated by radiation and convection to the outside air (Fig. 10.16). Oil is a much better insulator than air is; consequently, it is invariably used on high-voltage transformers.

As the power rating increases, external radiators are added to increase the cooling surface of the oil-filled tank (Fig. 10.17). Oil circulates around the transformer windings and moves through the radiators, where the heat is again released to surrounding air. For still higher ratings, cooling fans blow air over the radiators (Fig. 10.18).

For transformers in the megawatt range, cooling may be effected by an oil-water heat exchanger. Hot oil drawn from the transformer tank is pumped to a heat exchanger where it flows through pipes that

Figure 10.16
Two single-phase transformers, type OA, rated 75 kVA, 14.4 kV/240 V, 60 Hz, 55°C temperature rise, impedance 4.2%. The small radiators at the side increase the effective cooling area.

Figure 10.17
Three-phase, type OA grounding transformer, rated 1900 kVA, 26.4 kV, 60 Hz. The power of this transformer is 25 times greater than that of the transformers shown in Fig. 10.16, but it is still self-cooled. Note, however, that the radiators occupy as much room as the transformer itself.

are in contact with cool water. Such a heat exchanger is very effective, but also very costly, because the water itself has to be continuously cooled and recirculated.

Some big transformers are designed to have a multiple rating, depending on the method of cooling used. Thus, a transformer may have a triple rating of 18 000/24 000/32 000 kVA depending on whether it is cooled

1. by the natural circulation of air (AO) (18 000 kVA) or
2. by forced-air cooling with fans (FA) (24 000 kVA) or
3. by the forced circulation of oil accompanied by forced-air cooling (FOA) (32 000 kVA).

These elaborate cooling systems are nevertheless economical because they enable a much bigger output from a transformer of a given size and weight (Fig. 10.19).

The type of transformer cooling is designated by the following symbols:

AA–dry-type, self-cooled

AFA–dry-type, forced-air cooled

OA–oil-immersed, self-cooled

OA/FA–oil-immersed, self-cooled/forced-air cooled

AO/FA/FOA–oil-immersed, self-cooled/forced-air cooled/forced-air, forced-oil cooled

The temperature rise by resistance of oil-immersed transformers is either 55°C or 65°C. The tempera-

Figure 10.18
Three-phase, type FOA, transformer rated 1300 MVA, 24.5 kV/345 kV, 60 Hz, 65°C temperature rise, impedance 11.5%. This step-up transformer, installed at a nuclear power generating station, is one of the largest units ever built. The forced-oil circulating pumps can be seen just below the cooling fans.
(Courtesy of Westinghouse)

Figure 10.19
Three-phase, type OA/FA/FOA transformer rated 36/48/60 MVA, 225 kV/26.4 kV, 60 Hz, impedance 7.4%. The circular tank enables the oil to expand as the temperature rises and reduces the surface of the oil in contact with air. Other details:

weight of core and coils: 37.7 t
weight of tank and accessories: 28.6 t
weight of coil (44.8 m^3): 38.2 t
Total weight: 104.5 t

ture must be kept low to preserve the quality of the oil. By contrast, the temperature rise of a dry-type transformer may be as high as 180°C, depending on the type of insulation used.

10.12 Simplifying the equivalent circuit

The complete equivalent circuit of the transformer as shown in Fig. 10.8 gives far more detail than is needed in most practical problems. Consequently, let us try to simplify the circuit when the transformer operates 1) at no-load and 2) at full-load.

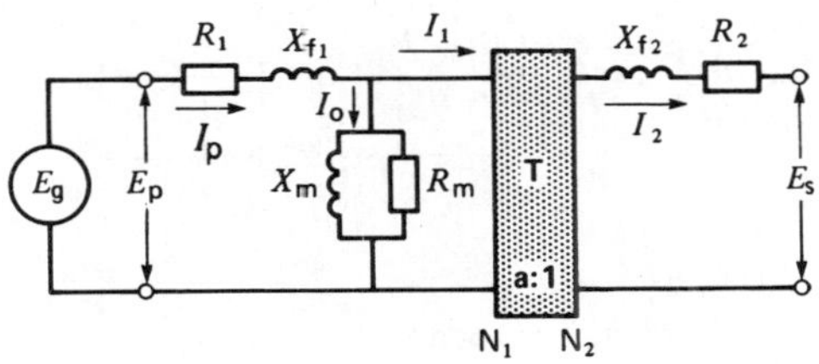

Figure 10.20
Complete equivalent circuit of a transformer at no-load.

1. At *no-load* (Fig. 10.20) I_2 is zero and so is I_1 because T is an ideal transformer. Consequently, only the exciting current I_o flows in R_1 and X_{f1}. These impedances are so small that the voltage drop across them is negligible. Furthermore, the current in R_2 and X_{f2} is zero. We can, therefore, neglect these four impedances, giving us the much simpler circuit of Fig. 10.21. The turns ratio, $\mathbf{a} = N_1/N_2$, is obviously equal to the ratio

of the primary to secondary voltages E_p/E_s measured across the terminals.

2. At *full-load* I_p is at least 20 times larger than I_o. Consequently, we can neglect I_o and the corresponding magnetizing branch. The resulting circuit is shown in Fig. 10.22. This simplified circuit may be used even when the load is only 10 percent of the rated capacity of the transformer.

We can further simplify the circuit by shifting everything to the primary side, thus eliminating transformer T (Fig. 10.23). This technique was explained in Section 9.10. Then, by summing the respective resistances and reactances, we obtain the circuit of Fig. 10.24. In this circuit

$$R_p = R_1 + a^2R_2 \tag{10.9}$$

$$X_p = X_{f1} + a^2X_{f2} \tag{10.10}$$

where

R_p = total transformer resistance referred to the primary side

X_p = total transformer leakage reactance referred to the primary side

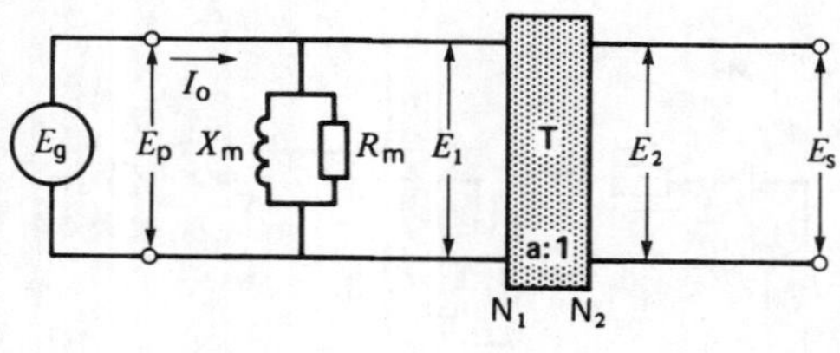

Figure 10.21
Simplified circuit at no-load.

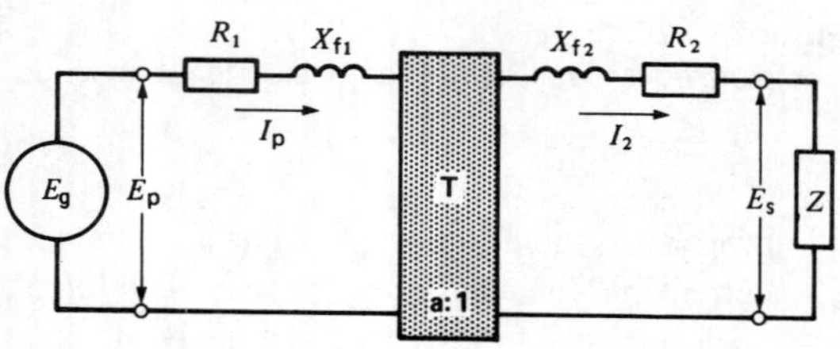

Figure 10.22
Simplified equivalent circuit of a transformer at full-load.

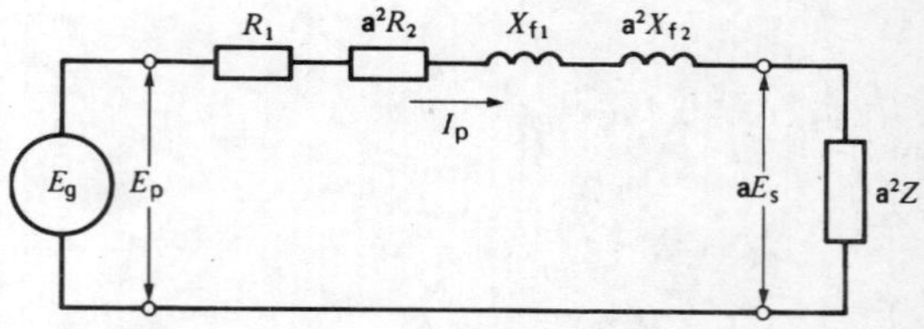

Figure 10.23
Equivalent circuit with impedances shifted to the primary side.

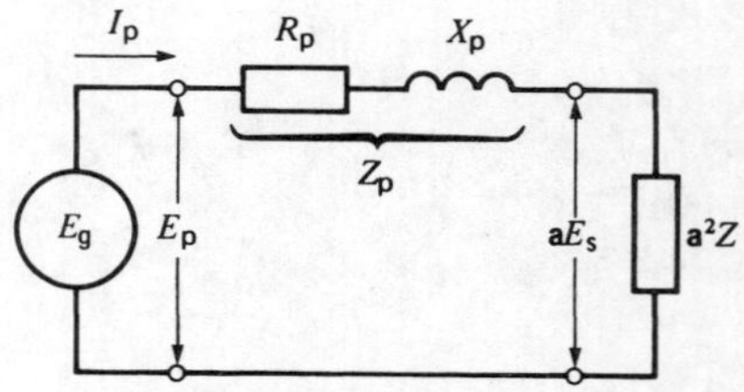

Figure 10.24
The internal impedance of a large transformer is mainly reactive.

The combination of R_p and X_p constitutes the total transformer impedance Z_p referred to the primary side. From Eq. 2.12 we have

$$Z_p = \sqrt{R_p^2 + X_p^2} \tag{10.11}$$

Impedance Z_p is one of the important parameters of the transformer. It produces an internal voltage drop when the transformer is loaded. Consequently, Z_p affects the voltage regulation of the transformer.

Transformers above 500 kVA possess a leakage reactance X_p that is at least five times greater than R_p. In such transformers we can neglect R_p, as far as voltages and currents are concerned.* The equivalent circuit is thus reduced to a simple reactance X_p between the source and the load (Fig. 10.25). It is quite remarkable that the relatively complex circuit of Fig. 10.8 can be reduced to a simple reactance in series with the load.

---

* From the standpoint of temperature rise and efficiency, R_p can never be neglected.

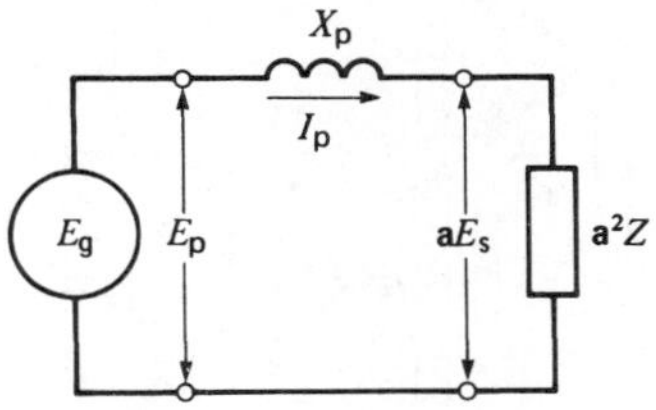

Figure 10.25
The internal impedance of a large transformer is mainly reactive.

10.13 Voltage regulation

An important attribute of a transformer is its voltage regulation. With the primary impressed voltage held constant at its rated value, the voltage regulation, in percent, is defined by the equation:

$$\text{voltage regulation} = \frac{E_{NL} - E_{FL}}{E_{FL}} \times 100 \quad (10.12)$$

where

E_{NL} = secondary voltage at no-load [V]
E_{FL} = secondary voltage at full-load [V]

The voltage regulation depends upon the power factor of the load. Consequently, the power factor must be specified. If the load is capacitive, the no-load voltage may exceed the full-load voltage, in which case the voltage regulation is negative.

Example 10-5

A single-phase transformer rated at 3000 kVA, 69 kV/4.16 kV, 60 Hz has a total internal impedance Z_p of 127 Ω, referred to the primary side.

Calculate

a. The rated primary and secondary currents
b. The voltage regulation from no-load to full-load for a 2000 kW resistive load, knowing that the primary supply voltage is fixed at 69 kV
c. The primary and secondary currents if the secondary is accidentally short-circuited

Solution

a. Rated primary current

$$I_{np} = S_n/E_{np} = 3\,000\,000/69\,000 = 43.5 \text{ A}$$

Rated secondary current

$$I_{ns} = S_n/E_{ns} = 3\,000\,000/4160 = 721 \text{ A}$$

b. Because the transformer exceeds 500 kVA, the windings have negligible resistance compared to their leakage reactance; we can therefore write

$$Z_p = X_p = 127\ \Omega$$

Referring to Fig. 10.26a, the approximate impedance of the 2000 kW load on the secondary side is

$$Z = E_s^2/P = 4160^2/2\,000\,000 = 8.65\ \Omega$$

Load impedance referred to primary side

$$a^2Z = (69/4.16)^2 \times 8.65 = 2380$$

Referring to Fig. 10.26b we have

$$I_p = 69\,000/\sqrt{127^2 + 2380^2} = 28.95 \text{ A}$$

$$aE_s = (a^2Z)I_p = 2380 \times 28.95 = 68\,902 \text{ V}$$

$$E_s = 68\,902 \times (4.16/69) = 4154 \text{ V}$$

Because the primary voltage is held constant at 69 kV, it follows that the secondary voltage at no-load is 4160 V.

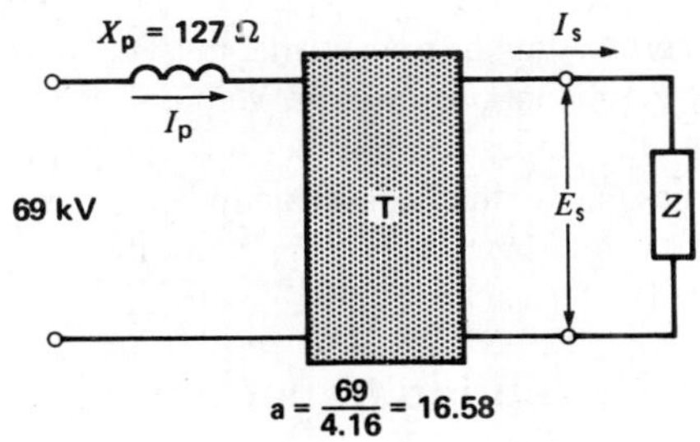

Figure 10.26a
See Example 10-7.

Voltage regulation is

$$\text{voltage regulation} = \frac{E_{NL} - E_{FL}}{E_{FL}} \times 100 \quad (10.12)$$

$$= \frac{4160 - 4154}{4154} \times 100$$

$$= 0.14\%$$

The voltage regulation is excellent.

c. Referring again to Fig. 10.26b, if the secondary is accidentally short-circuited, $aE_s = 0$ and so

$$I_p = E_p/X_p = 69\,000/127$$
$$= 543 \text{ A}$$

The corresponding current I_s on the secondary side

$$I_s = aI_p = (69/4.16) \times 543$$
$$= 9006 \text{ A}$$

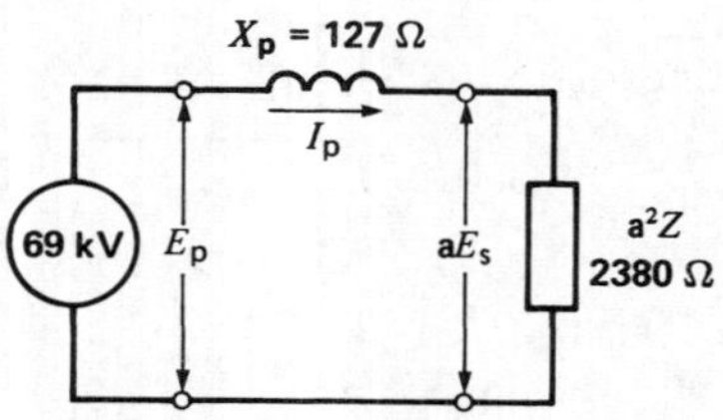

Figure 10.26b
See Example 10-7.

The short-circuit currents in both the primary and secondary windings are 12.5 times greater than the rated values. The I^2R losses are, therefore, 12.5^2 or 156 times greater than normal. The circuit-breaker or fuse protecting the transformer must open immediately to prevent overheating. Very powerful electromagnetic forces are also set up. They, too, are 156 times greater than normal and, unless the windings are firmly braced and supported, they may be damaged or torn apart.

10.14 Measuring transformer impedances

For a given transformer, we can determine the actual values of X_m, R_m, R_p and X_p shown in Figs. 10.21 and 10.24 by means of an open-circuit and a short-circuit test.

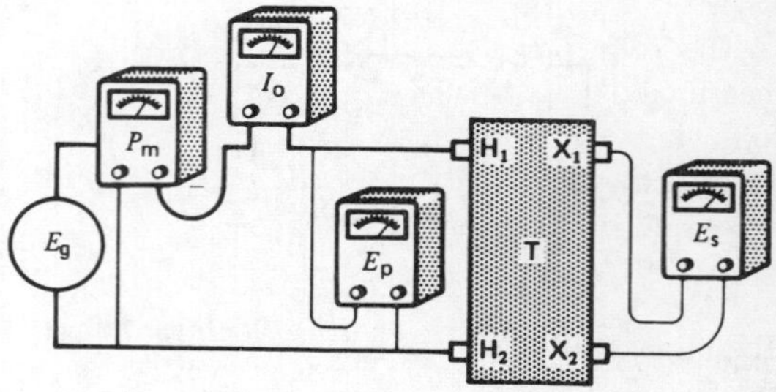

Figure 10.27
Open-circuit test and determination of R_m, X_m, and turns ratio.

During the *open-circuit test,* rated voltage is applied to the primary winding and current I_o, voltage E_p, and active power P_m are measured (Fig. 10.27). The secondary open-circuit voltage E_s is also measured. These test results give us the following information:

active power absorbed by core $= P_m$

apparent power absorbed by core $= S_m = E_pI_o$

reactive power absorbed by core $= Q_m$

$$\text{where } Q_m = \sqrt{S_m^2 - P_m^2}$$

Resistance R_m corresponding to the core loss is

$$R_m = E_p^2/P_m \quad (10.1)$$

Magnetizing reactance X_m is

$$X_m = E_p^2/Q_m \quad (10.2)$$

Turns ratio a is

$$a = N_1/N_2 = E_p/E_s$$

During the *short-circuit test,* the secondary winding is short-circuited and a voltage E_g much lower than normal (usually less than 5 percent of rated voltage) is applied to the primary (Fig. 10.28). The primary current I_{sc} should be less than its nominal value to prevent overheating and, particularly, to prevent a rapid change in winding resistance while the test is being made.

The voltage E_{sc}, current I_{sc}, and power P_{sc} are measured on the primary side (Fig. 10.28) and the following calculations made:

Total transformer impedance referred to the primary side is

$$Z_p = E_{sc}/I_{sc} \quad (10.13)$$

Total transformer resistance referred to the primary side is

$$R_p = P_{sc}/I_{sc}^2 \quad (10.14)$$

Total transformer leakage reactance referred to the primary side is

$$X_p = \sqrt{Z_p^2 - R_p^2} \quad (10.11)$$

Example 10-6

During a short-circuit test on a transformer rated 500 kVA, 69 kV/4.16 kV, 60 Hz, the following voltage, current, and power measurements were made. Terminals X_1, X_2 were in short-circuit (see Fig. 10.28):

$$E_{sc} = 2600 \text{ V}$$
$$I_{sc} = 4 \text{ A}$$
$$P_{sc} = 2400 \text{ W}$$

Calculate the value of the reactance and resistance of the transformer, referred to the HV side.

Solution

Referring to the equivalent circuit of the transformer under short-circuit conditions (Fig. 10.29), we find the following values:

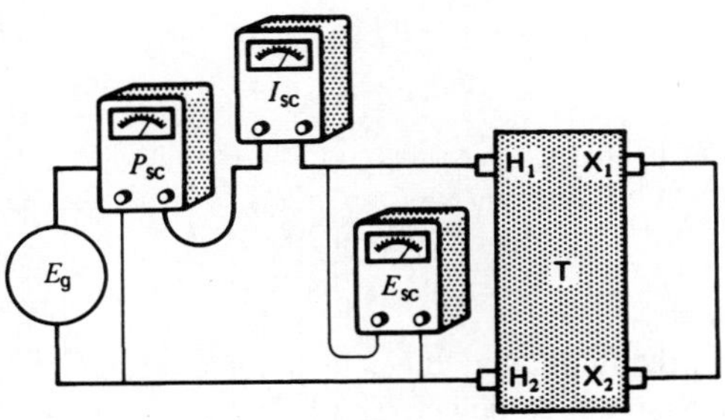

Figure 10.28
Short-circuit test to determine leakage reactance and winding resistance.

Transformer impedance referred to the primary is

$$Z_p = E_{sc}/I_{sc} = 2600/4 = 650\ \Omega$$

Resistance referred to the primary is

$$R_p = P_{sc}/I_{sc}^2 = 2400/16 = 150\ \Omega$$

Leakage reactance referred to the primary is

$$X_p = \sqrt{650^2 - 150^2} = 632\ \Omega$$

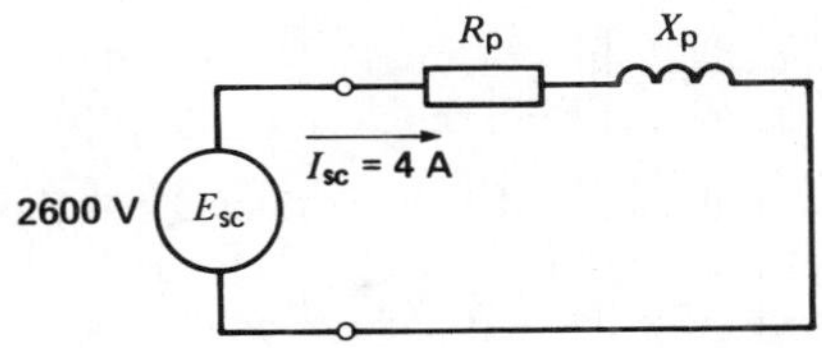

Figure 10.29
See Example 10-6.

Example 10-7

An open-circuit test was conducted on the transformer given in Example 10-6. The following results were obtained when the *low-voltage* winding was excited. (In some cases, such as in a repair shop, a 69 kV voltage may not be available and the open-circuit test has to be done by exciting the LV winding at its rated voltage.)

$$E_s = 4160 \text{ V} \qquad I_o = 2 \text{ A} \qquad P_m = 5000 \text{ W}$$

Using this information and the transformer characteristics found in Example 10-6, calculate:

a. the values of X_m and R_m on the primary side (Fig. 10.21)
b. the efficiency of the transformer when it supplies a load of 250 kVA, whose power factor is 80% (lagging)

Solution

a. Applying Eq. 10.1 to the secondary side

$$R_m = E_s^2/P_m = 4160^2/5000 = 3461\ \Omega$$

The apparent power S_m is

$$S_m = E_s I_0 = 4160 \times 2 = 8320 \text{ VA}$$

$$Q_m = \sqrt{S_m^2 - P_m^2}$$

$$= \sqrt{8320^2 - 5000^2} = 6650 \ \Omega$$

$$X_m = E_s^2/Q_m$$

$$= 4160^2/6650 = 2602 \ \Omega$$

The values of R_m and X_m referred the primary side will be $(69\,000/4160)^2 = 275$ times greater. The values on the primary side are therefore:

$$X_m = 275 \times 2602 \ \Omega = 715 \times 10^3 \ \Omega = 715 \text{ k}\Omega$$

$$R_m = 275 \times 3461 \ \Omega = 952 \times 10^3 \ \Omega = 952 \text{ k}\Omega$$

These are the values that would have been found if the primary had been excited at 69 kV.

b. Industrial loads and voltages fluctuate all the time. Thus, when we state that a load is 250 kVA, with $\cos \theta = 0.8$, it is understood that the load is *about* 250 kVA and that the power factor is *about* 0.8. Furthermore, the primary voltage is *about* 69 kV.

Consequently, in calculating efficiency, there is no point in arriving at a precise mathematical answer, even if we were able to give it. Knowing this, we can make certain assumptions that make it much easier to arrive at a solution.

The equivalent circuit of the transformer and its load is represented by Fig. 10.30. The values of R_p and X_p are already known, and so we only have to add the magnetizing branch. To simplify the calculations, we shifted X_m and R_m from points 3, 4 to the input terminals 1, 2. This change is justified because these impedances are much greater than X_p and R_p. Let us assume that the voltage across the load is 4160 V. We now calculate the efficiency of the transformer.

The load current is

$$I_2 = S/E_s = 250\,000/4160$$

$$= 60 \text{ A}$$

The turns ratio is

$$a = 69 \text{ kV}/4160 \text{ V} = 16.59$$

The current on the primary side is

$$I_1 = I_2/a = 60/16.59 = 3.62 \text{ A}$$

The total copper loss (primary and secondary) is

$$P_{copper} = I_1^2 R_p = 3.62^2 \times 150$$

$$= 1966 \text{ W}$$

The iron loss is the same as that measured at rated voltage on the LV side of the transformer.

$$P_{iron} = 5000 \text{ W}$$

Total losses are

$$P_{losses} = 5000 + 1966$$

$$= 6966 \text{ W} = 7 \text{ kW}$$

The active power delivered by the transformer to the load is

$$P_o = S \cos \theta = 250 \times 0.8$$

$$= 200 \text{ kW}$$

The active power received by the transformer is

$$P_i = P_o + P_{losses} = 200 + 7$$

$$= 207 \text{ kW}$$

The efficiency is therefore

$$\eta = P_o/P_i = 200/207$$

$$= 0.966 \text{ or } 96.6\%$$

Note that in making the calculations, we only consider the active power. The reactive power of the transformer and its load does not enter into efficiency calculations.

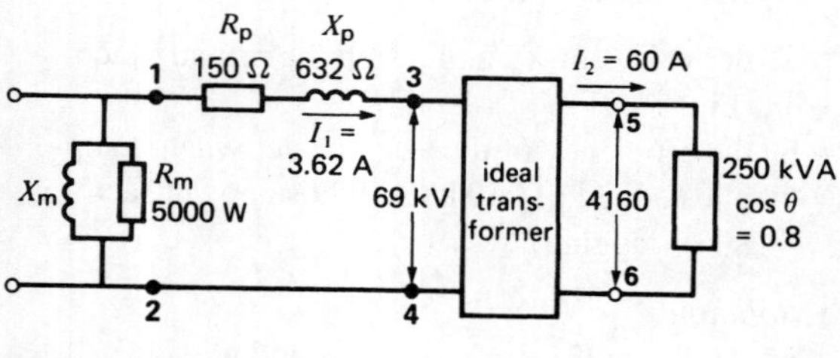

Figure 10.30
See Example 10-7.

10.15 Introducing the per-unit method

Per-unit notation is often encountered when dealing with transformers and other electrical machines. The reason is that per-unit values give us a feel for the *relative* magnitudes of impedances, voltages, currents and powers. Thus, instead of dealing with ohms, amperes, volts and kilowatts, we simply work with numbers. Consequently, we don't have to carry along units when per-unit values are used.

The per-unit method as applied to transformers is easy to understand. However, readers who are not yet familiar with per-unit calculations will find it useful to read Sections 1.9 to 1.11 in Chapter 1 before proceeding further.

Let us begin by looking at Table 10A which is reproduced here for convenience. It displays the actual values of R_1, R_2, X_{f1}, X_{f2}, X_m, and R_m of five transformers ranging from 1 kVA to 400 MVA. In scanning through the table, we see that the impedances vary from 505 000 Ω to 0.0003 Ω, a range in excess of a billion to one. Furthermore, there is no recognizable pattern to the values; they are all over the map. The reason is that the various voltages, currents, and impedances are expressed in actual values using volts, amperes, and ohms.

TABLE 10A ACTUAL TRANSFORMER VALUES

S_n	kVA	1	10	100	1000	400000
E_{np}	V	2400	2400	12470	69000	13800
E_{ns}	V	460	347	600	6900	424000
I_{np}	A	0.417	4.17	8.02	14.5	29000
I_{ns}	A	2.17	28.8	167	145	943
R_1	Ω	58.0	5.16	11.6	27.2	0.0003
R_2	Ω	1.9	0.095	0.024	0.25	0.354
X_{f1}	Ω	32	4.3	39	151	0.028
X_{f2}	Ω	1.16	0.09	0.09	1.5	27
X_m	Ω	200000	29000	150000	505000	460
R_m	Ω	400000	51000	220000	432000	317
I_o	A	0.0134	0.0952	0.101	0.210	52.9

Instead of expressing R_1, R_2, X_{f1}, X_{f2}, X_m, and R_m in ohms, we could express them relative to another ohmic value. The question is: What value should we choose as a basis of comparison?

The best approach is to employ the *nominal* load (voltage and current) of the transformer. We can calculate its ohmic value and use it as a reference.

For example, in the case of the 10 kVA transformer listed in Table 10A, the nominal load impedance on the secondary side is

$$Z_{ns} = \frac{E_{ns}}{I_{ns}} = \frac{347\ \text{V}}{28{,}8\ \text{A}} = 12.0\ \Omega$$

Using this ohmic value as a reference, the *relative* value of the secondary resistance R_2 is

$$R_2(\text{pu}) = \frac{0.095\ \Omega}{12.0\ \Omega} = 0.0079$$

Similarly, the nominal load impedance on the primary side is

$$Z_{np} = \frac{E_{np}}{I_{np}} = \frac{2400\ \text{V}}{4.17\ \text{A}} = 576\ \Omega$$

Using this load impedance as a reference, the *relative* value of the primary resistance R_1 is

$$R_1(\text{pu}) = \frac{5.16\ \Omega}{576\ \Omega} = 0.0090$$

The relative values R_1(pu) and R_2(pu) are pure numbers because they are the ratio of two quantities that bear the same unit.

Circuit elements on the primary side are always compared with the nominal load impedance Z_{np} on the primary side. Similarly, circuit elements on the secondary side are compared with the nominal load impedance Z_{ns} on the secondary side.

Proceeding in this way for the other impedances of the 10 kVA transformer, we obtain the relative values X_{f1}(pu), R_m(pu), etc. displayed in Table 10B.

The relative impedances of the other transformers are calculated the same way. In each case, the respective nominal load impedances Z_{np} and Z_{ns} are chosen as the reference impedances. Using the rated voltage and power of the transformer, they are given by

$$Z_{np} = \frac{E_{np}}{I_{np}} = \frac{E_{np}}{S_n/E_{np}} = \frac{E_{np}^2}{S_n} \tag{10.15a}$$

$$Z_{ns} = \frac{E_{ns}}{I_{ns}} = \frac{E_{ns}}{S_n/E_{ns}} = \frac{E_{ns}^2}{S_n} \tag{10.15b}$$

In practice, the relative values of R_1, R_2, X_{f1}, etc., are called *per-unit* values and are designated by the symbols R_1(pu), R_2(pu), X_{f1}(pu), etc. The quantities used as references are called *base quantities.* Thus, Z_{np}, Z_{ns}, S_n, E_{np}, E_{ns}, I_{np}, I_{ns} listed in Table 10B are all base quantities.

In examining Table 10B, the reader will note that for a given transformer, the values of R_1(pu) and R_2(pu) are nearly the same. Similarly, the values of X_{f1}(pu) and X_{f2}(pu) are nearly the same. This pattern of similarity does not show up in Table 10A.

TABLE 10B PER-UNIT TRANSFORMER VALUES

S_n	kVA	1	10	100	1000	400000
E_{np}	V	2400	2400	12470	69000	13800
E_{ns}	V	460	347	600	6900	424000
I_{np}	A	0.417	4.17	8.02	14.5	29000
I_{ns}	A	2.17	28.8	167	145	943
Z_{np}	Ω	5760	576	1555	4761	0.4761
Z_{ns}	Ω	211.6	12.0	3.60	47.61	449.4
R_1 (pu)	–	0.0101	0.0090	0.0075	0.0057	0.00071
R_2 (pu)	–	0.0090	0.0079	0.0067	0.0053	0.00079
X_{f1} (pu)	–	0.0056	0.0075	0.0251	0.0317	0.0588
X_{f2} (pu)	–	0.0055	0.0075	0.0250	0.0315	0.0601
X_m (pu)	–	34.7	50.3	96.5	106	966
R_m (pu)	–	69.4	88.5	141.5	90.7	666
I_o (pu)	–	0.032	0.023	0.013	0.015	0.0018

There is even a similarity between the per-unit values of transformers whose ratings are quite different. For example, the R_1(pu) of the 1 kVA transformer (0.0101) is of the same order of magnitude as the R_1(pu) of the 1000 kVA transformer (0.0057) despite the fact that the latter is 1000 times more powerful and the voltages are vastly different. Clearly, the per-unit method offers insights that would otherwise not be evident.

10.16 Impedance of a transformer

The total internal impedance Z_p of a transformer was defined in Section 10.12 and highlighted in Fig. 10.24. In power and distribution transformers its value is always indicated on the nameplate. However, it is expressed as a percent of the nominal load impedance. Thus, if the nameplate is marked 3.6%, the per-unit value of Z_p is 0.036.

Example 10-8

A transformer rated 250 kVA, 4160 V/480 V, 60 Hz has an impedance of 5.1%. Calculate

a. the base impedance on the primary and secondary side
b. the total internal impedance Z_p of the transformer referred to the primary side

Solution

a. Base impedance on the primary side is

$$Z_{np} = E_p^{\,2}/S_n = 4160^2/250\,000 = 69\ \Omega$$

Base impedance on the secondary side is

$$Z_{ns} = E_s^{\,2}/S_n = 480^2/250\,000 = 0.92\ \Omega$$

b. The actual value of Z_p on the primary side is

$$Z_p = 5.1\% \times Z_{np} = 0.051 \times 69\ \Omega = 3.52$$

10.17 Typical per-unit impedances

We have seen that we can get a better idea of the relative magnitude of the winding resistance, leakage reactance, etc., of a transformer by comparing these impedances with the base impedance of the transformer. In making the comparison, circuit elements located on the primary side are compared with the primary base impedance. Similarly, circuit elements on the secondary side are compared with the secondary base impedance. The comparison can be made either on a percentage or on a per-unit basis; we shall use the latter. Typical per-unit values are listed in Table 10C for transformers ranging from 3 kVA to 100 MVA. For example, the table shows that the per-unit resistance of the primary winding of a transformer ranges from 0.009 to 0.002 for all power ratings between 3 kVA and 100 MVA. Over this tremendous power range, the per-unit resistance R_1 of the primary or secondary windings varies only from 0.009 to 0.002 of the base impedance of the transformer. Knowing the base impedance of either the primary or the secondary winding, we can readily estimate the order of magnitude of the real values of the transformer impedances. Table 10C is, therefore, a useful source of information.

TABLE 10C TYPICAL PER-UNIT VALUES OF TRANSFORMERS

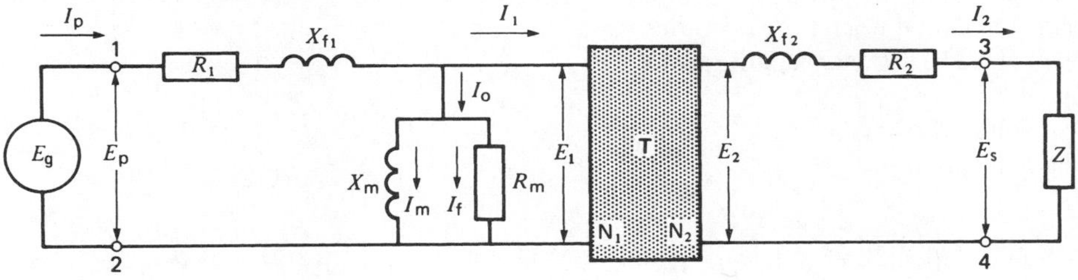

Figure 10.31
Equivalent circuit of a transformer.

Circuit element (see Fig. 10.31)	Typical per-unit values: 3 kVA to 250 kVA	Typical per-unit values: 1 MVA to 100 MVA
R_1 or R_2	0.009–0.005	0.005–0.002
X_{f1} or X_{f2}	0.008–0.025	0.03–0.06
X_m	20–30	50–200
R_m	20–50	100–500
I_o	0.05–0.03	0.02–0.005

Example 10-9

Using the information given in Table 10C and Fig. 10.31, calculate the approximate real values of the impedances of a 250 kVA, 4160 V/480 V, 60 Hz distribution transformer.

Solution

We first determine the base impedances on the primary and secondary side. From the results of Example 10-8, we have

$$Z_{np} = 69\ \Omega$$
$$Z_{ns} = 0.92\ \Omega$$

We now calculate the real impedances by multiplying Z_{np} and Z_{ns} by the per-unit values given in Table 10C. This yields the following results:

$$R_1 = 0.005 \times 69\ \Omega = 0.35\ \Omega$$
$$R_2 = 0.005 \times 0.92\ \Omega = 4.6\ \text{m}\Omega$$
$$X_{f1} = 0.025 \times 69\ \Omega = 1.7\ \Omega$$
$$X_{f2} = 0.025 \times 0.92\ \Omega = 23\ \text{m}\Omega$$
$$X_m = 30 \times 69\ \Omega = 2070\ \Omega = 2\ \text{k}\Omega$$
$$R_m = 50 \times 69\ \Omega = 3450\ \Omega = 3.5\ \text{k}\Omega$$

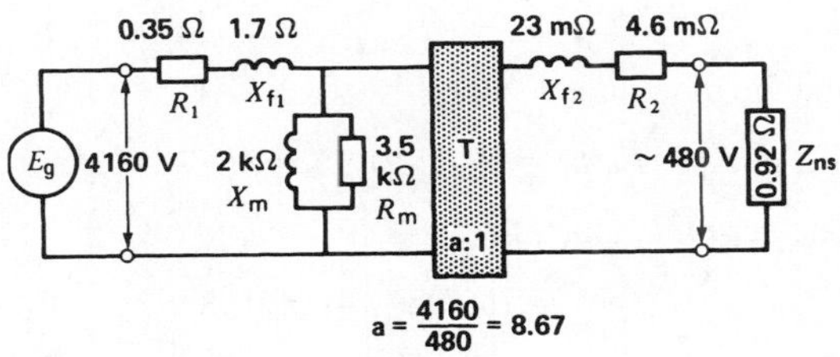

Figure 10.32
See Example 10-9.

This example shows the usefulness of the per-unit method of estimating impedances. The equivalent circuit of the 250 kVA transformer is shown in Fig. 10.32. The true values may be 20 to 50 percent higher or lower than those shown in the figure. The reason is that the per-unit values given in Table 10C are broad estimates covering a wide range of transformers.

Example 10-10

The 500 kVA, 69 kV/4160 V, 60 Hz transformer shown in Fig. 10.30 has a resistance R_p of 150 Ω and a leakage reactance X_p of 632 Ω. Using the per-unit method, calculate

a. the voltage regulation when the load varies between zero and 250 kVA at a lagging power factor of 80%
b. the actual voltage across the 250 kVA load
c. the actual line current I_1

Solution

In examining Fig. 10.30, it is clear that the presence of the magnetizing branch does not affect the voltage drop across R_p and X_p. Consequently, the magnetizing branch does not affect the voltage regulation.

To determine the voltage regulation, we will refer all voltages, impedances, and currents to the HV (69 kV) side. We assume the voltage between terminals 1, 2 is 69 kV, and that it remains fixed.

The base power P_B is 500 kVA.
The base voltage E_B is 69 kV.

Consequently, the base current is

$$I_B = P_B/E_B = 500\,000/69\,000 = 7.25 \text{ A}$$

and the base impedance is

$$Z_B = E_B/I_B = 69\,000/7.25 = 9517\ \Omega$$

The per-unit value of R_p is

$$R_p(\text{pu}) = 150/9517 = 0.0158$$

The per-unit value of X_p is

$$X_p(\text{pu}) = 632/9517 = 0.0664$$

The per-unit value of voltage E_{12} is

$$E_{12}(\text{pu}) = 69\,000/69 \text{ kV} = 1.0$$

The per-unit value of the apparent power absorbed by the load is

$$S(\text{pu}) = 250 \text{ kVA}/500 \text{ kVA} = 0.5$$

The per-unit value of the active power absorbed by the load is

$$P(\text{pu}) = S(\text{pu}) \cos\theta = 0.5 \times 0.8 = 0.4$$

The per-unit value of the reactive power absorbed by the load is

$$Q(\text{pu}) = \sqrt{S^2(\text{pu}) - P^2(\text{pu})} = \sqrt{0.5^2 - 0.4^2} = 0.3$$

The per-unit load resistance R_L corresponding to P is

$$R_L(\text{pu}) = \frac{E^2(\text{pu})}{P(\text{pu})} = \frac{1.0^2}{0.4} = 2.50$$

The per-unit load reactance X_L corresponding to Q is

$$X_L(\text{pu}) = \frac{E^2(\text{pu})}{Q(\text{pu})} = \frac{1.0^2}{0.3} = 3.333$$

We now draw the equivalent per-unit circuit shown in Fig. 10.33. The magnetizing branch is not shown because it does not enter into the calculations. Note that the load appears across the primary terminals 3, 4 of the circuit shown in Fig. 10.30. (These terminals are not accessible; they exist only in the equivalent circuit diagram.) The per-unit impedance between terminals 3, 4 is

$$Z_{34}(\text{pu}) = \frac{2.50 \times j\,3.33}{250 + j\,3.33} = 2\,\angle 36.87° = 1.6 + j\,1.2$$

The per-unit impedance between terminals 1, 2 is

$$Z_{12}(\text{pu}) = 0.0158 + 1.6 + j(1.2 + 0.0664) = 1.616 + j\,1.266 = 2.053\,\angle 38.07°$$

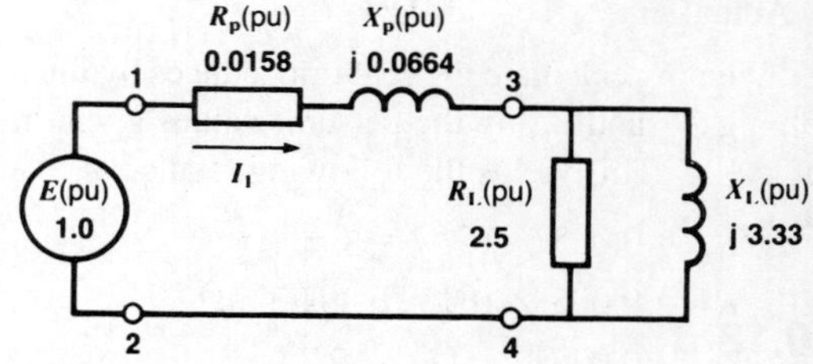

Figure 10.33
Per-unit equivalent circuit of a 500 kVA transformer feeding a 250 kVA load.

The per-unit current I_1 is

$$I_1(\text{pu}) = \frac{E_{12}(\text{pu})}{Z_{12}(\text{pu})} = \frac{1.0}{2.053\ \angle 38.07°}$$
$$= 0.4872\ \angle -38.07°$$

The per-unit voltage E_{34} across the load is

$$E_{34}(\text{pu}) = I_1(\text{pu}) \times Z_{34}(\text{pu})$$
$$= (0.4872\angle -38.07°)(2\angle 36.87°)$$
$$= 0.9744\angle -1.20°$$

The per-unit voltage regulation is

$$\frac{E_{34}(\text{pu}) \text{ at no-load} - E_{34}(\text{pu}) \text{ at full-load}}{E_{34}(\text{pu}) \text{ at full-load}}$$
$$= \frac{1.0 - 0.9744}{0.9744} = 0.0263$$

a. The voltage regulation is therefore 2.63%.

We can now calculate the *actual* values of the voltage and current as follows:

Voltage across terminals 3, 4 is

$$E_{34} = E_{34}(\text{pu}) \times E_B$$
$$= 0.9744 \times 69\,000$$
$$= 67.23 \text{ kV}$$

b. Actual voltage across the load is

$$E_{56} = E_{34} \times (4160/69\,000)$$
$$= 67.23 \times 10^3 \times 0.0603$$
$$= 4054 \text{ V}$$

c. Actual line current is

$$I_1 = I_1(\text{pu}) \times I_B$$
$$= 0.4872 \times 7.246$$
$$= 3.53 \text{ A}$$

10.18 Transformers in parallel

When a growing load eventually exceeds the power rating of an installed transformer, we sometimes connect a second transformer in parallel with it. To ensure proper load-sharing between the two transformers, they must possess the following:

a. The same primary and secondary voltages
b. The same per-unit impedance

Particular attention must be paid to the polarity of each transformer, so that only terminals having the same polarity are connected together (Fig. 10.34). An error in polarity produces a severe short-circuit as soon as the transformers are excited.

In order to calculate the currents flowing in each transformer when they are connected in parallel, we must first determine the equivalent circuit of the system.

Consider first the equivalent circuit when a single transformer feeds a load Z_L (Fig. 10.35a). The primary voltage is E_p and the impedance of the transformer referred to the primary side is Z_{p1}. If the

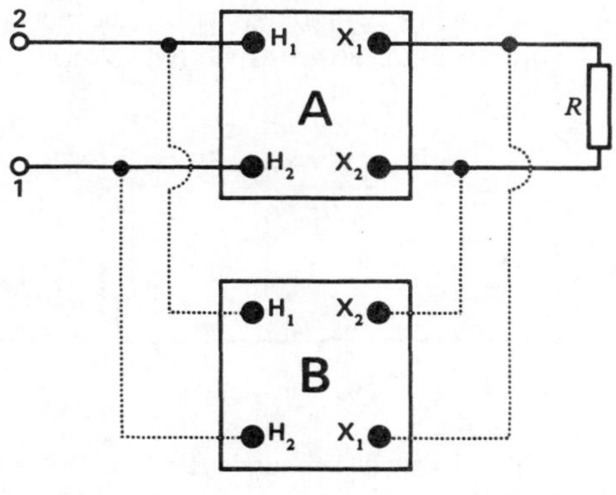

Figure 10.34
Connecting transformers in parallel to share a load.

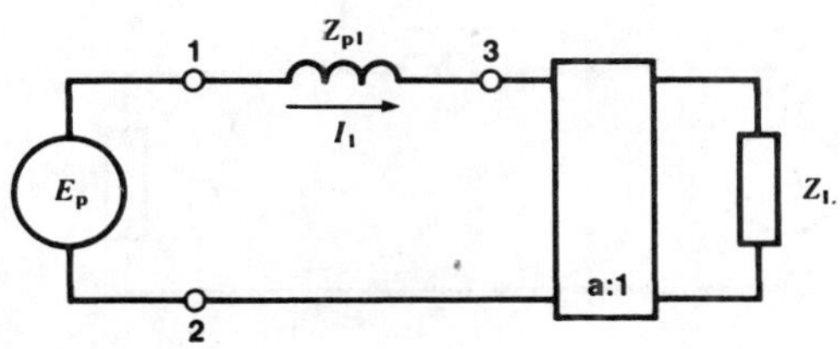

Figure 10.35a
Equivalent circuit of a transformer feeding a load Z_L.

ratio of transformation is **a,** the circuit can be simplified to that shown in Fig. 10.35b, a procedure we are already familiar with.

If a second transformer having an impedance Z_{p2} is connected in parallel with the first, the equivalent circuit becomes that shown in Fig. 10.35c. In effect, the impedances of the transformers are in parallel. The primary currents in the transformers are respectively I_1 and I_2. Because the voltage drop E_{13} across the impedances is the same, we can write

$$I_1Z_{p1} = I_2Z_{p2} \tag{10.16}$$

that is,

$$\frac{I_1}{I_2} = \frac{Z_{p2}}{Z_{p1}} \tag{10.17}$$

The ratio of the primary currents is therefore determined by the magnitude of the respective primary impedances—and not by the ratings of the two transformers. But in order that the temperature rise be the same for both transformers, the currents must be proportional to the respective kVA ratings.

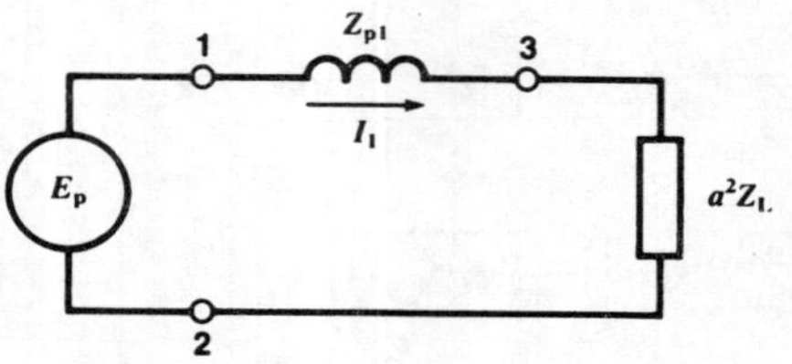

Figure 10.35b
Equivalent circuit with all impedances referred to the primary side.

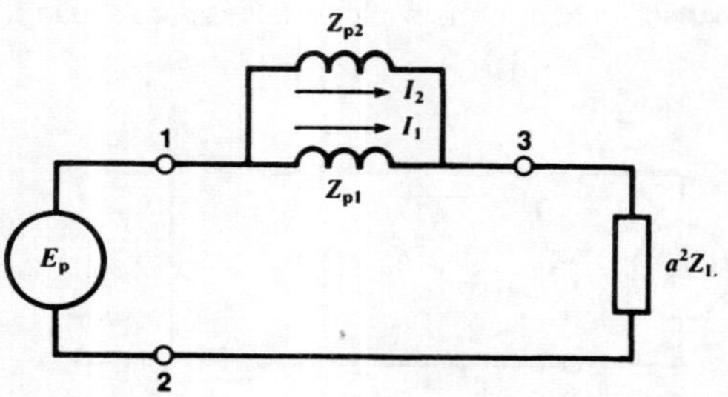

Figure 10.35c
Equivalent circuit of two transformers in parallel feeding a load Z_1. All impedances referred to the primary side.

Consequently, we want to fulfill the following condition:

$$\frac{I_1}{I_2} = \frac{S_1}{S_2} \tag{10.18}$$

From Eqs. 10.17 and 10.18 it can readily be proved that the desired condition is met if the transformers have the same per-unit impedances. The following example shows what happens when the per-unit impedances are different.

Example 10-11

A 100 kVA transformer is connected in parallel with an existing 250 kVA transformer to supply a load of 330 kVA. The transformers are rated 7200 V/240 V, but the 100 kVA unit has an impedance of 4 percent while the 250 kVA transformer has an impedance of 6 percent (Fig. 10.36a).

Calculate

a. The nominal primary current of each transformer
b. The impedance of the load referred to the primary side
c. The impedance of each transformer referred to the primary side
d. The actual primary current in each transformer

Solution

a. Nominal primary current of the 250 kVA transformer is

$$I_{n1} = 250\ 000/7200 = 34.7\ \text{A}$$

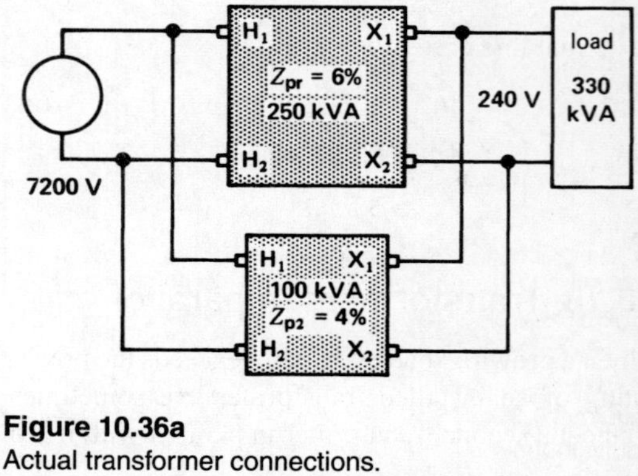

Figure 10.36a
Actual transformer connections.

Nominal primary current of the 100 kVA transformer is

$$I_{n2} = 100\,000/7200 = 13.9 \text{ A}$$

b. The equivalent circuit of the two transformers and the load, referred to the primary side, is given in Fig. 10.35c. Note that transformer impedances Z_{p1} and Z_{p2} are considered to be entirely reactive. This assumption is justified because the transformers are fairly big.
Load impedance referred to the primary side is

$$Z = E_p^2/S_{load} = 7200^2/330\,000$$
$$= 157\ \Omega$$

The approximate load current is

$$I_L = S_{load}/E_p = 330\,000/7200 = 46 \text{ A}$$

c. The base impedance of the 250 kVA unit is

$$Z_{np1} = 7200^2/250\,000 = 207\ \Omega$$

Transformer impedance referred to the primary side is

$$Z_{p1} = 0.06 \times 207 = 12.4\ \Omega$$

Base impedance of the 100 kVA unit is

$$Z_{np2} = 7200^2/100\,000 = 518\ \Omega$$

Transformer impedance referred to the primary side is

$$Z_{p2} = 0.04 \times 518 = 20.7\ \Omega$$

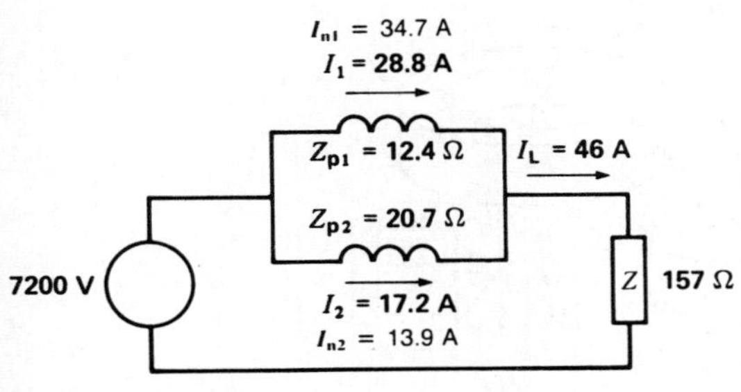

Figure 10.36b
Equivalent circuit. Calculations show that the 100 kVA transformer is seriously overloaded.

d. Referring to Fig. 10.36b, we find that the 46 A load current divides in the following way:

$$I_1 = 46 \times 20.7/(12.4 + 20.7) = 28.8 \text{ A}$$
$$I_2 = 46 - 28.8 = 17.2 \text{ A}$$

The 100 kVA transformer is seriously overloaded because it carries a primary current of 17.2 A, which is 25 percent above its rated value of 13.9 A. The 250 kVA unit is not overloaded because it only carries a current of 28.8 A versus its rated value of 34.7 A. Clearly, the two transformers are not carrying their proportionate share of the load.

The 100 kVA transformer is overloaded because of its low impedance (4 percent), compared to the impedance of the 250 kVA transformer (6 percent). A low-impedance transformer always tends to carry more than its proportionate share of the load. If the percent impedances were equal, the load would be shared between the transformers in proportion to their respective power ratings.

Questions and Problems

Practical level

10-1 Name the principal parts of a transformer.

10-2 Explain how a voltage is induced in the secondary winding of a transformer.

10-3 The secondary winding of a transformer has twice as many turns as the primary. Is the secondary voltage higher or lower than the primary voltage?

10-4 Which winding is connected to the load, the primary or secondary?

10-5 State the voltage and current relationships between the primary and secondary windings of a transformer under load. The primary and secondary windings have N_1 and N_2 turns, respectively.

10-6 Name the losses produced in a transformer.

10-7 What purpose does the no-load current of a transformer serve?

10-8 Name three conditions that must be met in order to connect two transformers in parallel.

10-9 What is the purpose of taps on a transformer?

10-10 Name three methods used to cool transformers.

10-11 The primary of a transformer is connected to a 600 V, 60 Hz source. If the primary has 1200 turns and the secondary has 240, calculate the secondary voltage.

10-12 The windings of a transformer respectively have 300 and 7500 turns. If the low-voltage winding is excited by a 2400 V source, calculate the voltage across the HV winding.

10-13 A 6.9 kV transmission line is connected to a transformer having 1500 turns on the primary and 24 turns on the secondary. If the load across the secondary has an impedance of 5 Ω, calculate the following:

a. The secondary voltage

b. The primary and secondary currents

10-14 The primary of a transformer has twice as many turns as the secondary. The primary voltage is 220 V and a 5 Ω load is connected across the secondary. Calculate the power delivered by the transformer, as well as the primary and secondary currents.

10-15 A 3000 kVA transformer has a ratio of 60 kV to 2.4 kV. Calculate the nominal current of each winding.

Intermediate level

10-16 In Problem 10-11, calculate the peak value of the flux in the core.

10-17 Explain why the peak flux in a 60 Hz transformer remains fixed as long as the ac supply voltage is fixed.

10-18 The transformer in Fig. 10.37 is excited by a 120 V, 60 Hz source and draws a no-load current I_o of 3 A. The primary and secondary windings respectively possess 200 and 600 turns. If 40 percent of the primary flux is linked by the secondary, calculate the following:

a. The voltage indicated by the voltmeter

b. The peak value of flux Φ

c. The peak value of Φ_m

d. Draw the phasor diagram showing E_1, E_2, I_o, Φ_m, and Φ_{f1}

10-19 In Fig. 10.38, when 600 V is applied to terminals H_1 and H_2, 80 V is measured across terminals X_1, X_2.

a. What is the voltage between terminals H_1 and X_2?

b. If terminals H_1, X_1 are connected together, calculate the voltage across terminals H_2, X_2.

c. Does the transformer have additive or subtractive polarity?

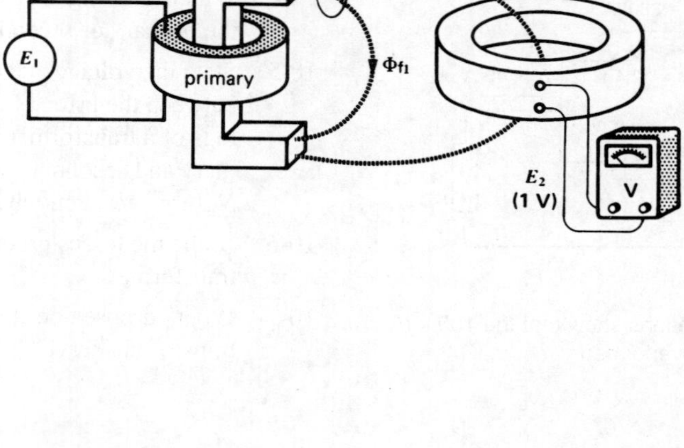

Figure 10.37
See Problem 10-18.

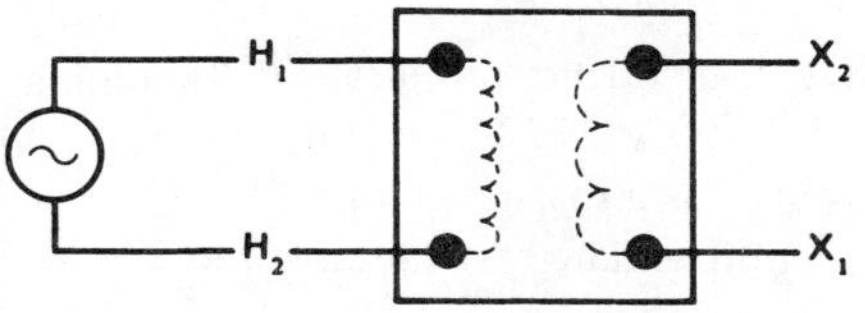

Figure 10.38
See Problem 10-19.

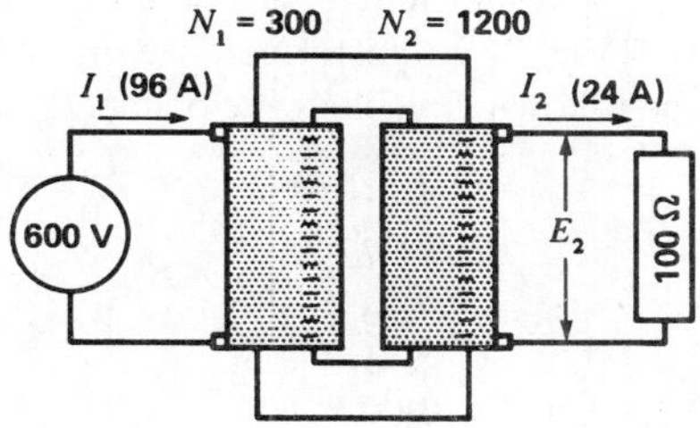

Figure 10.39
See Problem 10-33. The primary is wound on one leg and the secondary on the other.

10-20 **a.** Referring to Fig. 10.34, what would happen if we reversed terminals H_1 and H_2 of transformer B?
b. Would the operation of the transformer bank be affected if terminals H_1, H_2 and X_1, X_2 of transformer B were reversed? Explain.

10-21 Explain why the secondary voltage of a practical transformer decreases with increasing resistive load.

10-22 What is meant by the following terms?
a. Transformer impedance
b. Percent impedance of a transformer

10-23 The transformer in Problem 10-15 has an impedance of 6 percent. Calculate the impedance [Ω] referred to:
a. The 60 kV primary
b. The 2.4 kV secondary

10-24 A 2300 V line is connected to terminals 1 and 4 in Fig. 10.13. Calculate the following:
a. The voltage between terminals X_1 and X_2
b. The current in each winding, if a 12 kVA load is connected across the secondary

10-25 A 66.7 MVA transformer has an efficiency of 99.3 percent when it delivers full power to a load having a power factor of 100 percent.
a. Calculate the losses in the transformer under these conditions.
b. Calculate the losses and efficiency when the transformer delivers 66.7 MVA to a load having a power factor of 80 percent.

10-26 If the transformer shown in Fig. 10.15 were placed in a tank of oil, the temperature rise would have to be reduced to 65°. Explain.

Advanced level

10-27 Referring to Fig. 10.39, calculate the peak value of flux in the core if the transformer is supplied by a 50 Hz source.

10-28 The impedance of a transformer increases as the coupling is reduced between the primary and secondary windings. Explain.

10-29 The following information is given for the transformer circuit of Fig. 10.22.

$R_1 = 18\ \Omega$ $\quad E_p = 14.4$ kV (nominal)
$R_2 = 0.005\ \Omega$ $\quad E_s = 240$ V (nominal)
$X_{f1} = 40\ \Omega$ $\quad X_{f2} = 0.01\ \Omega$

If the transformer has a nominal rating of 75 kVA, calculate the following:
a. The transformer impedance [Ω] referred to the primary side
b. The percent impedance of the transformer
c. The impedance [Ω] referred to the secondary side
d. The percent impedance referred to the secondary side
e. The total copper losses at full load
f. The percent resistance and percent reactance of the transformer

10-30 During a short-circuit test on a 10 MVA, 66 kV/7.2 kV transformer (see Fig. 10.28), the following results were obtained:

$$E_g = 2640 \text{ V}$$
$$I_{sc} = 72 \text{ A}$$
$$P_{sc} = 9.85 \text{ kW}$$

Calculate the following:

a. The total resistance and the total leakage reactance referred to the 66 kV primary side

b. The nominal impedance of the transformer referred to the primary side

c. The percent impedance of the transformer

10-31 In Problem 10-30, if the iron losses at rated voltage are 35 kW, calculate the full-load efficiency of the transformer if the power factor of the load is 85 percent.

10-32 **a.** The windings of a transformer operate at a current density of 3.5 A/mm². If they are made of copper and operate at a temperature of 75°C, calculate the copper loss per kilogram.

b. If aluminum windings were used, calculate the loss per kilogram under the same conditions.

10-33 If a transformer were actually built according to Fig. 10.39, it would have very poor voltage regulation. Explain why and propose a method of improving it.

Industrial application

10-34 A transformer has a rating 200 kVA, 14 400 V/277 V. The high-voltage winding has a resistance of 62 Ω. What is the approximate resistance of the 277 V winding?

10-35 The primary winding of the transformer in Problem 10-34 is wound with No. 11 gauge AWG wire. Calculate the approximate cross section (in square millimeters) of the conductors in the secondary winding.

10-36 An oil-filled distribution transformer rated at 10 kVA weighs 118 kg, whereas a 100 kVA transformer of the same kind weighs 445 kg. Calculate the power output in watts per kilogram in each case.

10-37 The transformer shown in Fig. 10.13 has a rating of 40 kVA. If 80 V is applied between terminals X_1 and X_2, what voltage will appear between terminals 3 and 4? If a single load is applied between terminals 3 and 4 what is the maximum allowable current that can be drawn?

CHAPTER 11
Special Transformers

11.0 Introduction

Many transformers are designed to meet specific industrial applications. In this chapter we study some of the special transformers that are used in distribution systems, neon signs, laboratories, induction furnaces, and high-frequency applications. Although they are special, they still possess the basic properties of the standard transformers discussed in Chapter 10. As a result, the following approximations can be made when the transformers are under load:

1. The voltage induced in a winding is directly proportional to the number of turns, the frequency, and the flux in the core.
2. The ampere-turns of the primary are equal and opposite to the ampere-turns of the secondary.
3. The apparent power input to the transformer is equal to the apparent power output.
4. The exciting current in the primary winding may be neglected.

11.1 Dual-voltage distribution transformer

Transformers that supply electric power to residential areas generally have two secondary windings, each rated at 120 V. The windings are connected in series, and so the total voltage between the lines is 240 V while that between the lines and the center tap is 120 V (Fig. 11.1). The center tap, called *neutral,* is always connected to ground.

Terminal H_2 on the high-voltage winding is usually bonded to the neutral terminal of the secondary winding so that both windings are connected to ground.

The nominal rating of these *distribution transformers* ranges from 3 kVA to 500 kVA. They are mounted on poles of the electrical utility company (Fig. 11.2) to supply power to as many as 20 customers.

The load on distribution transformers varies greatly throughout the day, depending on customer demand. In residential districts a peak occurs in the morning and another peak occurs in the late afternoon. The power peaks never last for more than one or two hours, with the result that during most of the 24-hour day the transformers operate far below their normal rating. Because thousands of such transformers are connected to the public utility system, every effort is made to keep the no-load losses small. This is achieved by using special low-loss silicon steel in the core.

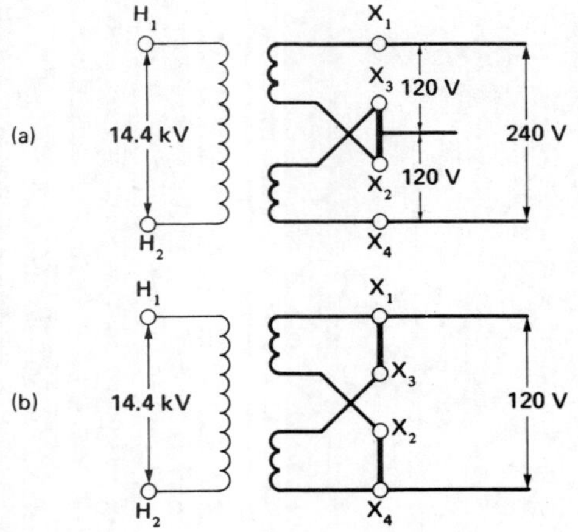

Figure 11.1

a. Distribution transformer with 120 V/240 V secondary. The central conductor is the neutral.
b. Same distribution transformers reconnected to give only 120 V.

Figure 11.2
Single-phase pole-mounted distribution transformer rated 100 kVA, 14.4 kV/240 V/120 V, 60 Hz.

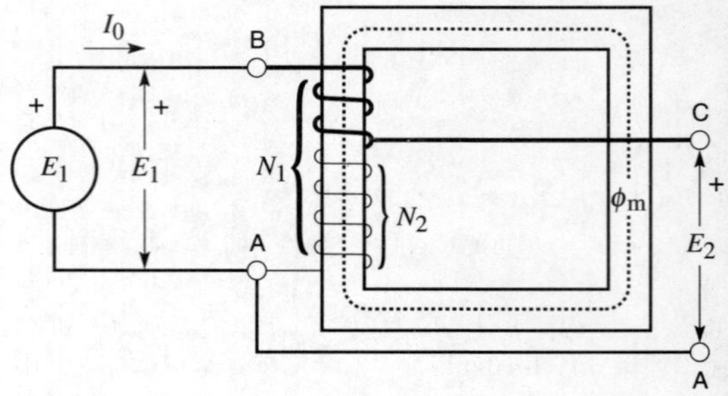

Figure 11.3
Autotransformer having N_1 turns on the primary and N_2 turns on the secondary.

11.2 Autotransformer

Consider a single transformer winding having N_1 turns, mounted on an iron core (Fig. 11.3). The winding is connected to a fixed-voltage ac source E_1, and the resulting exciting current I_o creates an ac flux Φ_m in the core. As in any transformer, the peak value of the flux is fixed so long as E_1 is fixed (Section 9.2).

Suppose a tap C is taken off the winding, so that there are N_2 turns between terminals A and C. Because the induced voltage between these terminals is proportional to the number of turns, E_2 is given by

$$E_2 = (N_2/N_1) \times E_1 \tag{11.1}$$

Clearly, this simple coil resembles a transformer having a primary voltage E_1 and a secondary voltage E_2. However, the primary terminals B, A and the secondary terminals C, A are no longer isolated from each other, because of the common terminal A.

If we connect a load to secondary terminals CA, the resulting current I_2 immediately causes a primary current I_1 to flow (Fig. 11.4).

The BC portion of the winding obviously carries current I_1. Therefore, according to Kirchhoff's current law, the CA portion carries a current $(I_2 - I_1)$. Furthermore, the mmf due to I_1 must be equal and opposite to the mmf produced by $(I_2 - I_1)$. As a result, we have

$$I_1(N_1 - N_2) = (I_2 - I_1)\, N_2$$

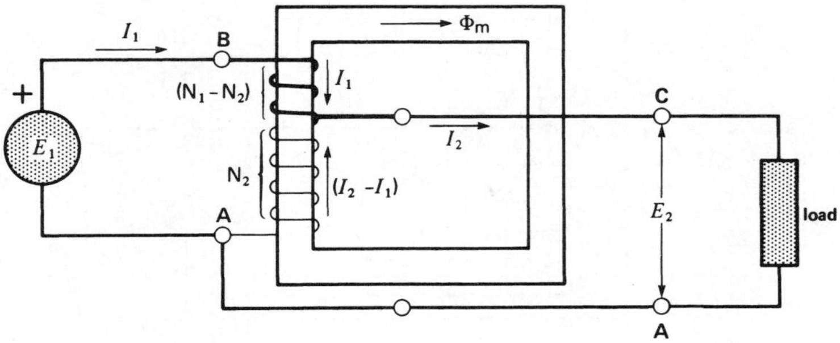

Figure 11.4
Autotransformer under load. The currents flow in opposite directions in the upper and lower windings.

which reduces to

$$I_1 N_1 = I_2 N_2 \quad (11.2)$$

Finally, assuming that both the transformer losses and exciting current are negligible, the apparent power drawn by the load must equal the apparent power supplied by the source. Consequently,

$$E_1 I_1 = E_2 I_2 \quad (11.3)$$

Eqs. 11.1, 11.2, and 11.3 are identical to those of a standard transformer having a turns ratio N_1/N_2. However, in this *autotransformer* the secondary winding is actually part of the primary winding. In effect, an autotransformer eliminates the need for a separate secondary winding. As a result, autotransformers are always smaller, lighter, and cheaper than standard transformers of equal power output. The difference in size becomes particularly important when the ratio of transformation E_1/E_2 lies between 0.5 and 2. On the other hand, the absence of electrical isolation between the primary and secondary windings is a serious drawback in some applications.

Autotransformers are used to start induction motors, to regulate the voltage of transmission lines, and, in general, to transform voltages when the primary to secondary ratio is close to 1.

Example 11-1

The autotransformer in Fig. 11.4 has an 80 percent tap and the supply voltage E_1 is 300 V. If a 3.6 kW load is connected across the secondary, calculate:

a. The secondary voltage and current
b. The currents that flow in the winding
c. The relative size of the conductors on windings BC and CA

Solution

a. The secondary voltage is

$$E_2 = 80\% \times 300 = 240 \text{ V}$$

The secondary current is

$$I_2 = P/E_2 = 3600/240 = 15 \text{ A} \qquad \text{(Fig. 11.5)}$$

b. The current supplied by the source is

$$I_1 = P/E_1 = 3600/300 = 12 \text{ A}$$

The current in winding BC = 12 A

The current in winding CA = 15 − 12 = 3 A

c. The conductors in the secondary winding CA can be one-quarter the size of those in winding BC because the current is 4 times smaller (see Fig. 11.5). However, the voltage across winding BC is equal to the difference between the primary and secondary voltages, namely (300 − 240) = 60 V. Consequently, winding CA has four times as many turns as winding BC. Thus, the two windings require essentially the same amount of copper.

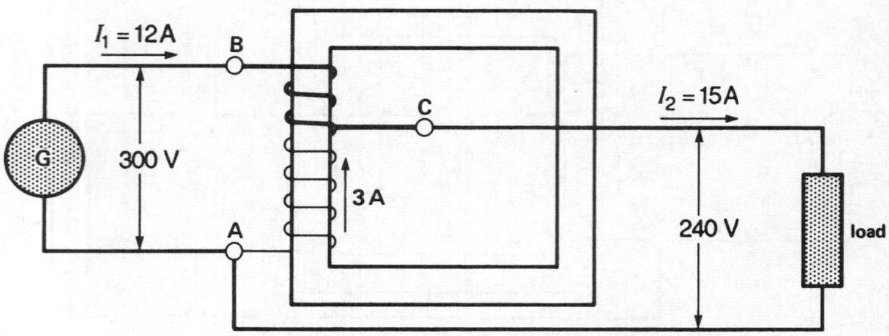

Figure 11.5
Autotransformer of Example 11-1.

11.3 Conventional transformer connected as an autotransformer

A conventional two-winding transformer can be changed into an autotransformer by connecting the primary and secondary windings in series. Depending upon how the connection is made, the secondary voltage may add to, or subtract from, the primary voltage. The basic operation and behavior of a transformer is unaffected by a mere change in external connections. Consequently, the following rules apply whenever a conventional transformer is connected as an autotransformer:

1. The current in any winding should not exceed its nominal current rating.
2. The voltage across any winding should not exceed its nominal voltage rating.
3. If rated current flows in one winding, rated current will *automatically* flow in the other winding (reason: The ampere-turns of the windings are always equal).
4. If rated voltage exists across one winding, rated voltage *automatically* exists across the other winding (reason: The same mutual flux links both windings).
5. If the current in a winding flows from H_1 to H_2, the current in the other winding must flow from X_2 to X_1 and vice versa.
6. The voltages add when terminals of opposite polarity (H_1 and X_2, or H_2 and X_1) are connected together by means of a jumper. The voltages subtract when H_1 and X_1 (or H_2 and X_2) are connected together.

Example 11-2

The standard single-phase transformer shown in Fig. 11.6 has a rating of a 15 kVA, 600 V/120 V, 60 Hz. We wish to reconnect it as an autotransformer in three different ways to obtain three different voltage ratios:

a. 600 V primary to 480 V secondary
b. 600 V primary to 720 V secondary
c. 120 V primary to 480 V secondary

Calculate the maximum load the transformer can carry in each case.

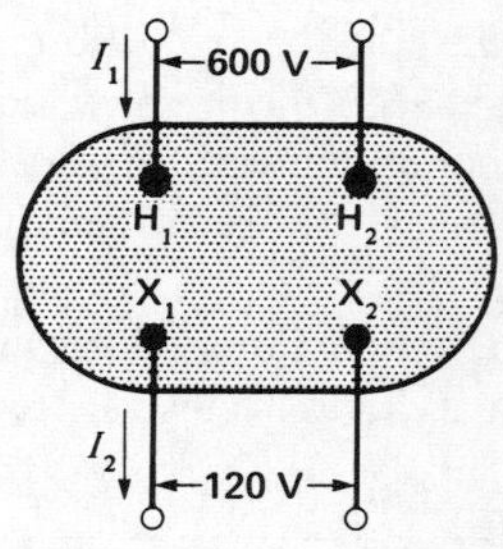

Figure 11.6
Standard 15 kVA, 600 V/120 V transformer.

Solution

Nominal current of the 600 V winding is

$$I_1 = S/E_1 = 15\,000/600 = 25 \text{ A}$$

Nominal current of the 120 V winding is

$$I_2 = S/E_2 = 15\,000/120 = 125 \text{ A}$$

a. To obtain 480 V, the secondary voltage (120 V) between terminals X_1, X_2 must subtract from the primary voltage (600 V). Consequently, we connect terminals having the same polarity together, as shown in Fig. 11.7. The corresponding schematic diagram is given in Fig. 11.8.

Note that the current in the 120 V winding is the same as that in the load. Because this winding has a nominal current rating of 125 A, the load can draw a maximum power.

$$S_a = 125 \text{ A} \times 480 \text{ V} = 60 \text{ kVA}$$

The currents flowing in the circuit at full-load are shown in Fig. 11.8. Note the following:

1. If we assume that the current of 125 A flows from X_1 to X_2 in the winding, a current of 25 A must flow from H_2 to H_1 in the other winding. All other currents are then found by applying Kirchhoff's current law.
2. The apparent power supplied by the source is equal to that absorbed by the load:

$$S = 100 \text{ A} \times 600 \text{ V} = 60 \text{ kVA}$$

b. To obtain a ratio of 600 V/720 V, the secondary voltage must *add* to the primary voltage: 600 + 120 = 720 V. Consequently, terminals of opposite polarity (H_1 and X_2) must be connected together, as shown in Fig. 11.9.

The current in the secondary winding is again the same as that in the load, and therefore the maximum load current is again 125 A. The maximum load is now

$$S_b = 125 \text{ A} \times 720 \text{ V} = 90 \text{ kVA}$$

The previous examples show that when a conventional transformer is connected as an

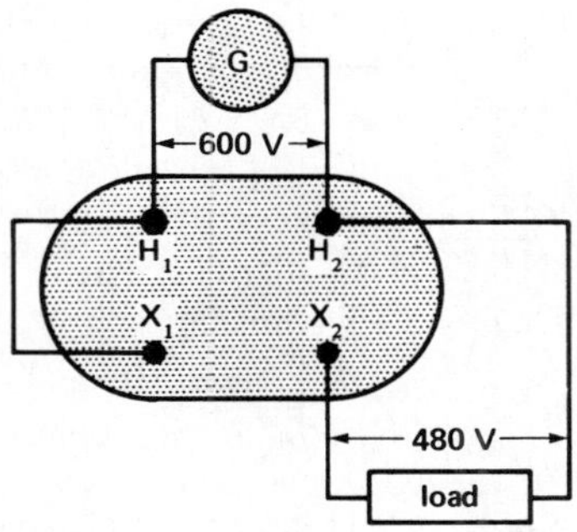

Figure 11.7
Transformer reconnected as an autotransformer to give a ratio of 600 V/480 V.

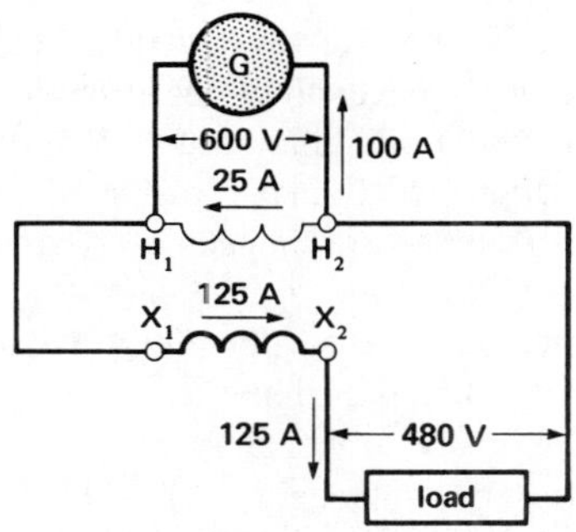

Figure 11.8
Schematic diagram of Fig. 11.7 showing voltages and current flows.

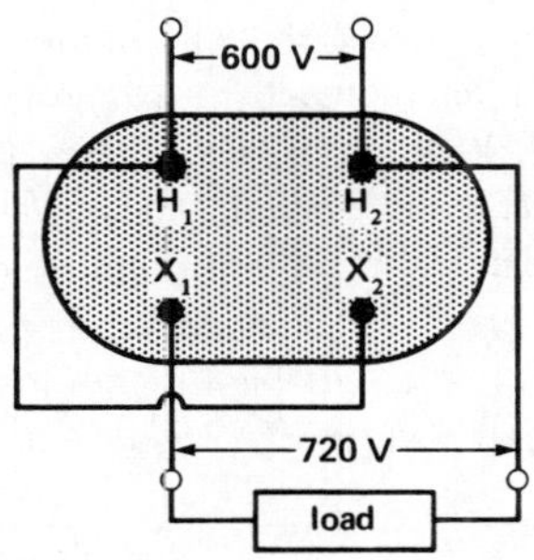

Figure 11.9
Transformer reconnected to give a ratio of 600 V/720 V.

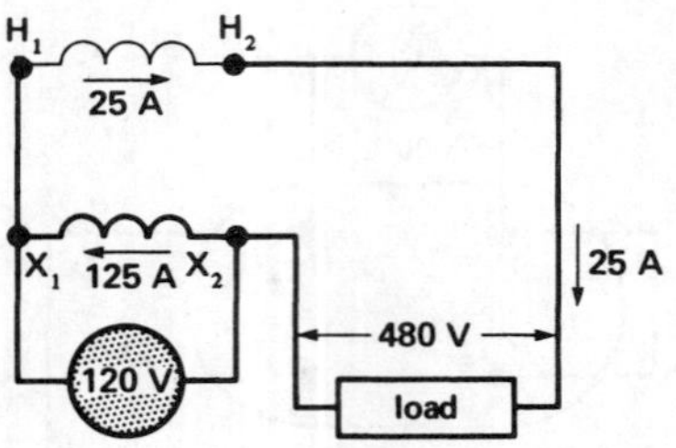

Figure 11.10
Transformer reconnected to give a ratio of 120 V/480 V.

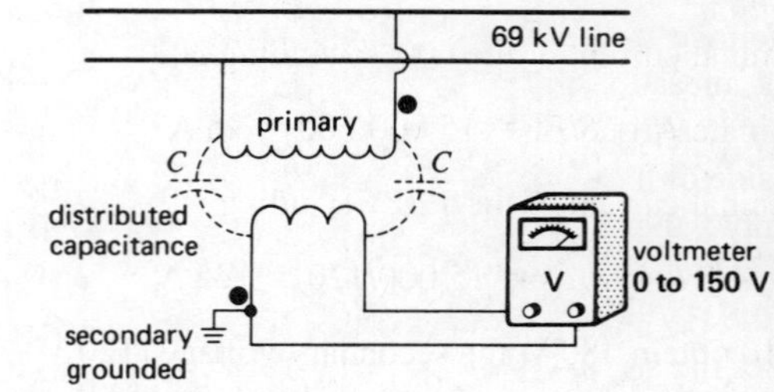

Figure 11.11
Potential transformer installed on a 69 kV line. Note the distributed capacitance between the windings.

autotransformer, it can supply a load far greater than the rated capacity of the transformer. As mentioned earlier, this is one of the advantages of using an autotransformer instead of a conventional transformer. However, this is not always the case, as the next part of our example shows.

c. To obtain the desired ratio of 120 V to 480 V, we again connect H_1 and X_1 (as in solution a), but the source is now connected to terminals X_1, X_2 (Fig. 11.10).
This time, the current in the 600 V winding is the same as that in the load; consequently, the maximum load current cannot exceed 25 A. The corresponding maximum load is, therefore,

$$S_c = 25 \text{ A} \times 480 \text{ V} = 12 \text{ kVA}$$

This load is *less* than the nominal rating (15 kVA) of the standard transformer.

We want to make one final remark concerning these three autotransformer connections. The temperature rise of the transformer is the same in each case, even though the loads are respectively 60 kVA, 90 kVA, and 12 kVA. The reason is that the currents in the windings and the flux in the core are identical in each case and so the losses are the same.

11.4 Voltage transformers

Voltage transformers (also called *potential transformers*) are high-precision transformers in which the ratio of primary voltage to secondary voltage is a known constant, which changes very little with load.* Furthermore, the secondary voltage is almost exactly in phase with the primary voltage. The nominal secondary voltage is usually 115 V, irrespective of what the rated primary voltage may be. This permits standard instruments and relays to be used on the secondary side. Voltage transformers are used to measure or monitor the voltage on transmission lines and to isolate the metering equipment from these lines (Fig. 11.11).

The construction of voltage transformers is similar to that of conventional transformers. However, the insulation between the primary and secondary windings must be particularly great to withstand the full line voltage on the HV side.

In this regard, one terminal of the secondary winding is always connected to ground to eliminate the danger of a fatal shock when touching one of the secondary leads. Although the secondary *appears* to be isolated from the primary, the distributed capacitance between the two windings makes an invisible connection which can produce a very high voltage between the secondary winding and ground. By grounding one of the secondary terminals, the highest voltage between the secondary lines and ground is limited to 115 V.

The nominal rating of voltage transformers is usually less than 500 VA. As a result, the volume of insulation is often far greater than the volume of copper or steel.

* In the case of voltage transformers and current transformers, the load is called *burden*.

Voltage transformers installed on HV lines always measure the line-to-neutral voltage. This eliminates the need for two HV bushings because one side of the primary is connected to ground. For example, the 7000 VA, 80.5 kV transformer shown in Fig. 11.12 has one large porcelain bushing to isolate the HV line from the grounded case. The latter houses the actual transformer.

The basic impulse insulation (BIL) of 650 kV expresses the transformer's ability to withstand lightning and switching surges.

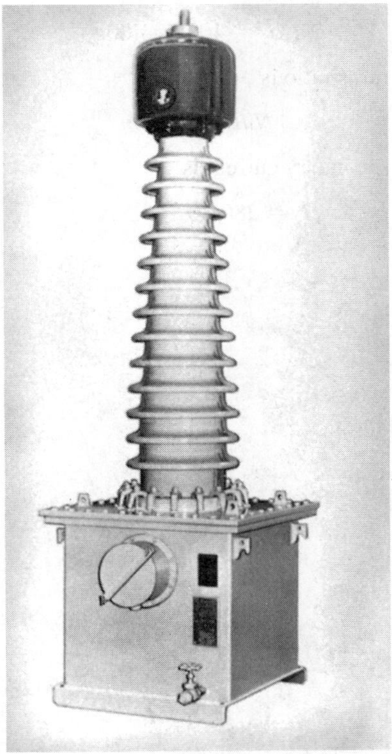

Figure 11.12
7000 VA, 80.5 kV, 50/60 Hz potential transformer having an accuracy of 0.3% and a BIL of 650 kV. The primary terminal at the top of the bushing is connected to the HV line while the other is connected to ground. The secondary is composed of two 115 V windings each tapped at 66.4 V. Other details: total height: 2565 mm; height of porcelain bushing: 1880 mm; oil: 250 L; weight: 740 kg.
(Courtesy of Ferranti-Packard)

11.5 Current transformers

Current transformers are high-precision transformers in which the ratio of primary to secondary current is a known constant that changes very little with the burden. The phase angle between the primary and secondary current is very small, usually much less than one degree. The highly accurate current ratio and small phase angle are achieved by keeping the exciting current small.

Current transformers are used to measure or monitor the current in a line and to isolate the metering and relay equipment connected to the secondary side. The primary is connected in series with the line, as shown in Fig. 11.13. The nominal secondary current is usually 5 A, irrespective of the primary current rating.

Because current transformers (CTs) are only used for measurement and system protection, their power rating is small—generally between 15 VA and 200 VA. As in the case of conventional transformers, the current ratio is inversely proportional to the number of turns on the primary and secondary windings. A current transformer having a ratio of 150 A/5 A has therefore 30 times more turns on the secondary than on the primary.

For safety reasons current transformers must always be used when measuring currents in HV transmission lines. The insulation between the primary and secondary windings must be great enough to withstand the full line-to-neutral voltage, including line surges. The maximum voltage the CT can withstand is always shown on the nameplate.

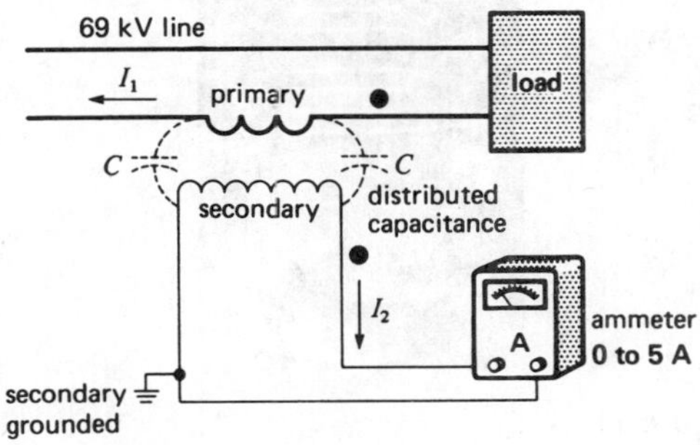

Figure 11.13
Current transformer installed on a 69 kV line.

As in the case of voltage transformers (and for the same reasons) one of the secondary terminals is always connected to ground.

Fig. 11.14 shows a 500 VA, 100 A/5 A current transformer designed for a 230 kV line. The large bushing serves to isolate the HV line from the ground. The CT is housed in the grounded steel case at the lower end of the bushing. The upper end of the bushing has two terminals that are connected in series with the HV line. The line current flows into one terminal, down the bushing, through the primary of the transformer, then up the bushing and out by the other terminal. The internal construction of a CT is shown in Fig. 11.15 and a typical installation is shown in Fig. 11.16.

By way of comparison, the 50 VA current transformer shown in Fig. 11.17 is much smaller, mainly because it is insulated for only 36 kV.

Example 11-3

The current transformer in Fig. 11.17 has a rating of 50 VA, 400 A/5 A, 36 kV, 60 Hz. It is connected into an ac line, having a line-to-neutral voltage of 14.4 kV, in a manner similar to that shown in Fig. 11.13. The ammeters, relays, and connecting wires on the secondary side possess a total impedance (burden) of 1.2 Ω. If the transmission-line current is 280 A, calculate

a. The secondary current
b. The voltage across the secondary terminals
c. The voltage drop across the primary

Solution

a. The current ratio is

$$I_1/I_2 = 400/5 = 80$$

The turns ratio is

$$N_1/N_2 = 1/80$$

The secondary current is

$$I_2 = 280/80 = 3.5 \text{ A}$$

Figure 11.14
500 VA, 100 A/5 A, 60 Hz current transformer, insulated for a 230 kV line and having an accuracy of 0.6%.
(Courtesy of Westinghouse)

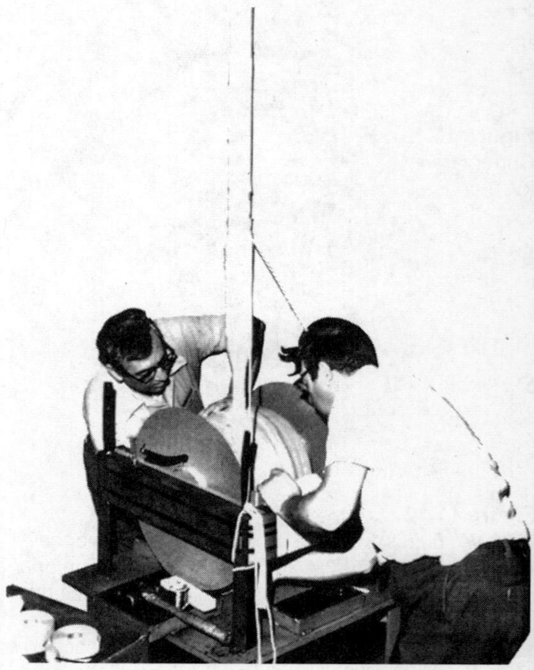

Figure 11.15
Current transformer in the final process of construction.
(Courtesy of Ferranti-Packard)

Figure 11.16
Current transformer in series with one phase of a 220 kV, 3-phase line inside a substation.

Figure 11.17
Epoxy-encapsulated current transformer rated 50 VA, 400 A/5 A, 60 Hz and insulated for 36 kV.
(Courtesy of Montel, Sprecher & Schuh)

b. The voltage across the burden is

$$E_2 = IR = 3.5 \times 1.2 = 4.2 \text{ V}$$

The secondary voltage is therefore 4.2 V.

c. The primary voltage is

$$E_1 = 4.2/80 = 0.0525 = 52.5 \text{ mV}$$

This is a miniscule voltage drop, compared to the 14.4 kV line-to-neutral voltage.

11.6 Opening the secondary of a CT can be dangerous

Every precaution must be taken to *never* open the secondary circuit of a current transformer while current is flowing in the primary circuit. If the secondary is accidentally opened, the primary current I_1 continues to flow unchanged because the impedance of the primary is negligible compared to that of the electrical load. The line current thus becomes the *exciting* current of the transformer because there is no further bucking effect due to the secondary ampere-turns. Because the line current may be 100 to 200 times greater than the normal exciting current, the flux in the core reaches peaks much higher than normal. The flux is so large that the core is totally saturated for the greater part of every half cycle. Referring to Fig. 11.18, as the primary current I_1 rises and falls during the first half cycle, flux Φ in the core also rises and falls, but it remains at a fixed saturation level Φ_s for most of the time. The same thing happens during the second half-cycle. During these saturated intervals, the induced voltage across the secondary winding is negligible because the flux changes very little. However, during the unsaturated intervals, the flux changes at an extremely high rate, inducing voltage peaks of several hundred volts across the open-circuited secondary. This is a dangerous situation because an unsuspecting operator could easily receive a bad shock. The voltage is particularly high in current transformers having ratings above 50 VA.

Thus, for reasons of safety, if a meter or relay in the secondary circuit of a CT has to be disconnected, we must first short-circuit the secondary winding and *then* remove the component. Short-circuiting a current transformer does no harm because the primary current remains unchanged and the secondary current can be no greater than that determined by the turns ratio. The short-circuit across the winding may be removed *after* the secondary circuit is again closed.

11.7 Toroidal current transformers

When the line current exceeds 100 A, we can sometimes use a *toroidal* current transformer. It consists of a laminated ring-shaped core that carries the secondary winding. The primary is composed of a single conductor that simply passes through the center of the ring (Fig. 11.19). The position of the primary conductor is unimportant as long as it is more or less centered. If the secondary possesses N turns, the ratio of transformation is N. Thus, a toroidal CT having a ratio of 1000 A/5 A has 200 turns on the secondary winding.

Toroidal CTs are simple and inexpensive and are widely used in low-voltage (LV) and medium-voltage (MV) indoor installations. They are also incorporated in circuit-breaker bushings to monitor the line current (Fig. 11.20). If the current exceeds a predetermined limit, the CT causes the circuit breaker to trip.

Example 11-4

A potential transformer rated 14 400 V/115 V and a current transformer rated 75 A/5 A are used to measure the voltage and current in a transmission line. If the voltmeter indicates 111 V and the ammeter reads 3 A, calculate the voltage and current in the line.

Solution

The voltage on the line is

$$E = 111 \times (14\,400/115) = 13\,900 \text{ V}$$

The current in the line is

$$I = 3 \times (75/5) = 45 \text{ A}$$

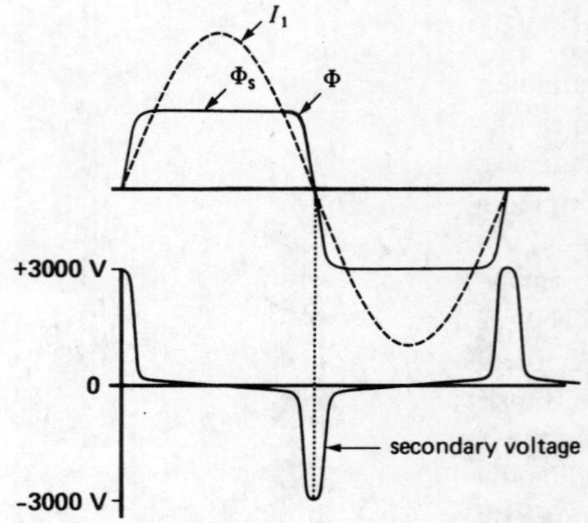

Figure 11.18
Primary current, flux, and secondary voltage when a CT is open-circuited.

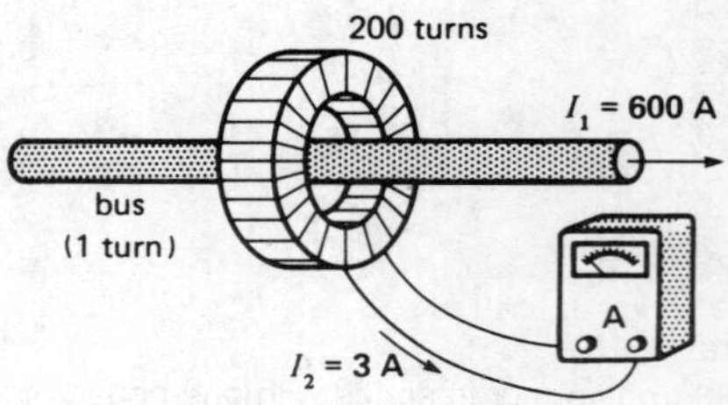

Figure 11.19
Toroidal transformer having a ratio of 1000 A/5 A, connected to measure the current in a line.

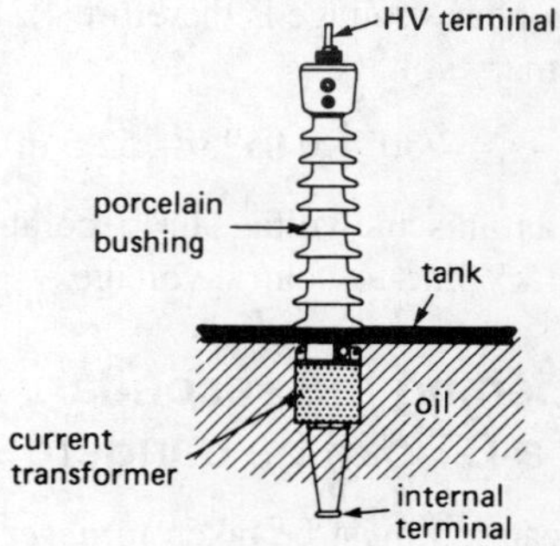

Figure 11.20
Toroidal transformer surrounding a conductor inside a bushing.

11.8 Variable autotransformer

A variable autotransformer is often used when we wish to obtain a variable ac voltage from a fixed-voltage ac source. The transformer is composed of a single-layer winding wound uniformly on a toroidal iron core. A movable carbon brush in sliding contact with the winding serves as a variable tap. The brush can be set in any position between 0 and 330°. Manual or motorized positioning may be used (Figs. 11.21 and 11.23).

As the brush slides over the bared portion of the winding, the secondary voltage E_2 increases in proportion to the number of turns swept out (Fig. 11.22).

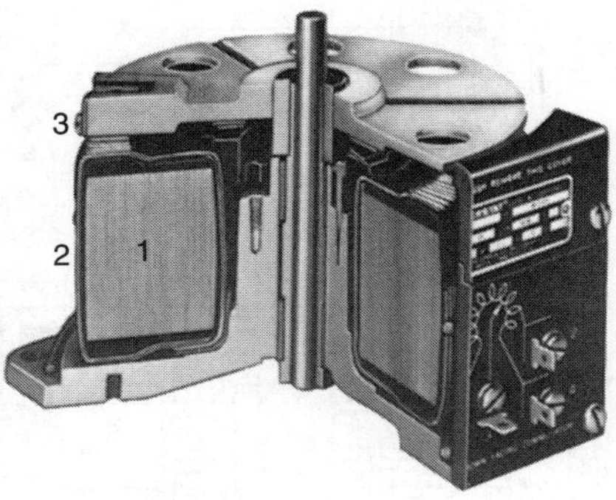

Figure 11.21
Cutaway view of a manually operated 0-140 V, 15 A variable autotransformer showing (1) the laminated toroidal core; (2) the single-layer winding; (3) the movable brush.
(Courtesy of American Superior Electric)

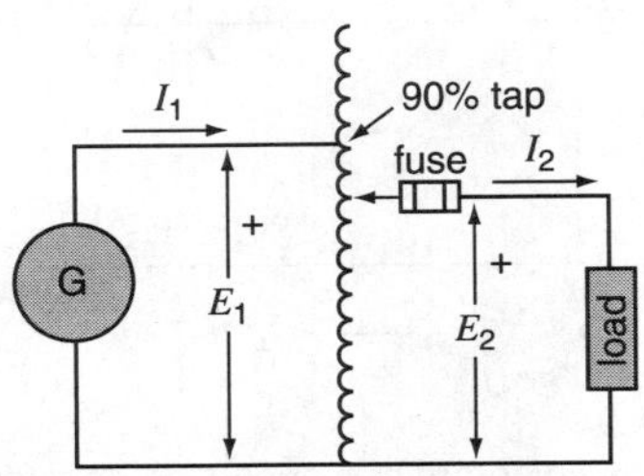

Figure 11.22
Schematic diagram of a variable autotransformer having a fixed 90% tap.

The input voltage E_1 is usually connected to a fixed 90 percent tap on the winding. This enables E_2 to vary from 0 to 110 percent of the input voltage.

Variable autotransformers are efficient and provide good voltage regulation under variable loads. The secondary line should always be protected by a fuse or circuit breaker so that the output current I_2 never exceeds the current rating of the autotransformer.

Figure 11.23
Variable autotransformer rated at 200 A, 0-240 V, 50 Hz/60 Hz. It is composed of eight 50 A, 120 V units, connected in series-parallel. This motorized unit can vary the output voltage from zero to 240 V in 5 s. Dimensions: 400 mm × 1500 mm.
(Courtesy of American Superior Electric)

11.9 High-impedance transformers

The transformers we have studied so far are all designed to have a relatively low leakage reactance, ranging perhaps from 0.03 to 0.1 per unit (Section 10.13). However, some industrial and commercial applications require much higher reactances, sometimes reaching values as high as 0.9 pu. Such high-impedance transformers are used in the following typical applications:

electric toys	arc welders
fluorescent lamps	electric arc furnaces
neon signs	reactive power regulators
oil burners	

Let us briefly examine these special applications.

1. A toy transformer is often accidentally short-circuited, but being used by children it is neither practical nor safe to protect it with a fuse. Consequently, the transformer is designed so that its leakage reactance is so high that even a permanent short-circuit across the low-voltage secondary will not cause overheating.

   The same remarks apply to some bell transformers that provide low-voltage signalling power throughout a home. If a short-circuit occurs on the secondary side, the current is automatically limited by the high reactance so as not to burn out the transformer or damage the fragile annunciator wiring.

2. Electric arc furnaces and discharges in gases possess a negative *E/I* characteristic, meaning that once the arc is struck, the current increases as the voltage falls. To maintain a steady arc, or a uniform discharge, we must add an impedance in series with the load. The series impedance may be either a resistor or reactor, but we prefer the latter because it consumes very little active power.

   However, if a transformer is used to supply the load, it is usually more economical to incorporate the reactance in the transformer itself, by designing it to have a high leakage reactance. A typical example is the neon sign transformer shown in Fig. 11.24.

The primary winding P is connected to a 240 V ac source, and the two secondary windings S are connected in series across the long neon tube. Owing to the large leakage fluxes Φ_a and Φ_b, the secondary voltage E_2 falls rapidly with increasing current, as seen in the regulation curve of the transformer (Fig. 11.24c). The high open-circuit voltage (20 kV) initiates the discharge, but as soon as the neon tube lights up, the secondary current is automatically limited to 15 mA. The corresponding voltage across the neon tube falls to 15 kV. The power of these transformers ranges from 50 VA to 1500 VA. The secondary voltages

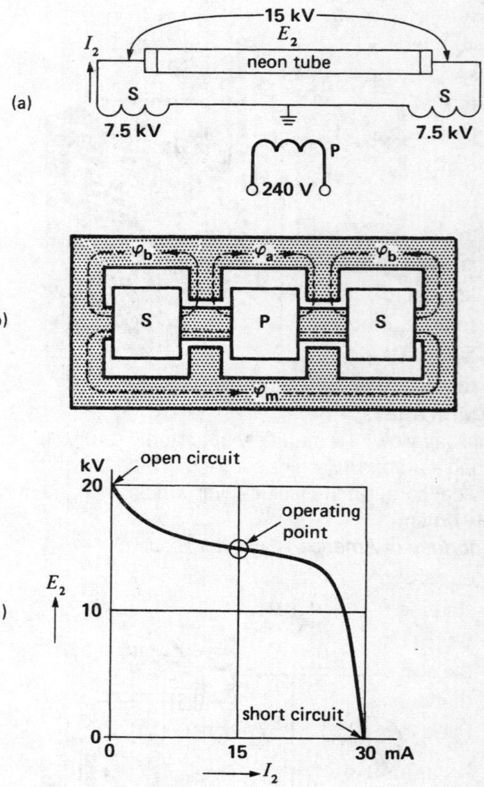

Figure 11.24
a. Schematic diagram of a neon sign transformer.
b. Construction of the transformer.
c. Typical *E-I* characteristic of the transformer.

range from 2 kV to 20 kV, depending mainly upon the length of the tube.

Returning to Fig. 11.24a, we note that the center of the secondary winding is grounded. This ensures that the secondary line-to-ground voltage is only one-half the voltage across the neon tube. As a result, less insulation is needed for the high-voltage winding.

Fluorescent lamp transformers (called ballasts) have properties similar to neon sign transformers. Capacitors are usually added to improve the power factor of the total circuit.

Oil-burner transformers possess essentially the same characteristics as neon sign transformers do. A secondary open-circuit voltage of about 10 kV creates an arc between two closely spaced electrodes situated immediately above the oil jet. The arc continually ignites the vaporized oil while the burner is in operation.

3. Some electric furnaces generate heat by maintaining an intense arc between two carbon electrodes. A relatively low secondary voltage is used and the large secondary current is limited by the leakage reactance of the transformer. Such transformers have ratings between 100 kVA and 500 MVA. In very big furnaces, the leakage reactance of the secondary, together with the reactance of the conductors, is usually sufficient to provide the necessary limiting impedance.
4. Arc-welding transformers are also designed to have a high leakage reactance so as to stabilize the arc during the welding process. The open-circuit voltage is about 70 V, which facilitates striking the arc when the electrode touches the work. However, as soon as the arc is established, the secondary voltage falls to about 15 V, a value that depends upon the length of the arc and the intensity of the welding current.
5. As a final example of high-impedance transformers, we mention the enormous 3-phase units that absorb reactive power from a 3-phase transmission line. These transformers are intentionally designed to produce leakage flux and, consequently, the primary and secondary windings are very loosely coupled. The three primary windings are connected to the HV line (typically between 230 kV and 765 kV) while the three secondary windings (typically 6 kV) are connected to an electronic controller (Fig. 11.25). The controller permits more or less secondary current to flow, causing the leakage flux to vary accordingly. A change in the leakage flux produces a corresponding change in the reactive power absorbed by the transformer. The transformer, incorporated in a static var compensator, is further discussed in Section 25.27.

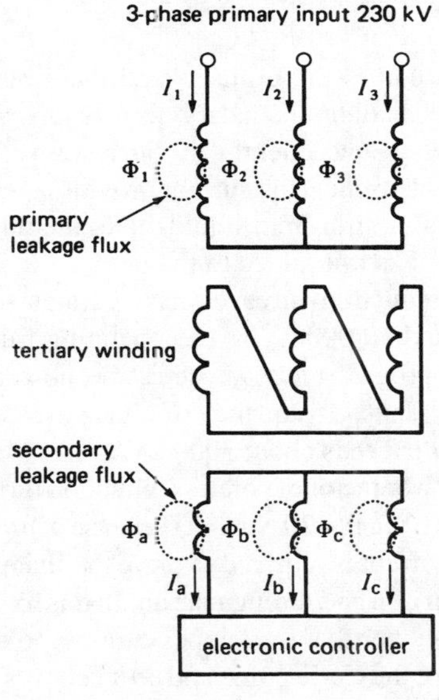

Figure 11.25
Three-phase static var compensator having high leakage reactance.

11.10 Induction heating transformers

High-power induction furnaces also use the transformer principle to produce high-quality steel and other alloys. The induction principle can be understood by referring to Fig. 11.26. A relatively high-frequency 500 Hz ac source is connected to a coil that surrounds a large crucible containing molten

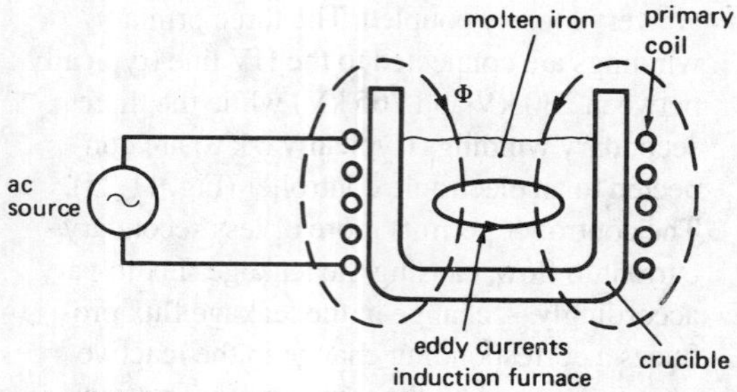

Figure 11.26
Coreless induction furnace. The flux Φ produces eddy currents in the molten metal. The capacitor furnishes the reactive power absorbed by the coil.

iron. The coil is the primary, and the molten iron acts like a single secondary turn, short-circuited upon itself. Consequently, it carries a very large secondary current. This current provides the energy that keeps the iron in a liquid state, melting other scrap metal as it is added to the pool.

Such induction furnaces have ratings between 15 kVA and 40 000 kVA. The operating frequency becomes progressively lower as the power rating increases. Thus, a frequency of 60 Hz is used when the power exceeds about 3000 kVA.

The power factor of coreless induction furnaces is very low (typically 20 percent) because a large magnetizing current is required to drive the flux through the molten iron and through the air. In this regard, we must remember that the temperature of molten iron is far above the Curie point, and so it behaves like air as far as permeability is concerned. That is why these furnaces are often called coreless induction furnaces.

Capacitors are installed close to the coil to supply the reactive power it absorbs.

In another type of furnace, known as a *channel furnace,* a transformer having a laminated iron core is made to link with a channel of molten iron, as shown in Fig. 11.27. The channel is a ceramic pipe that is fitted to the bottom of the crucible. The primary coil is excited by a 60 Hz source, and the secondary current I_2 flows in the liquid channel and through the molten iron in the crucible. In effect, the channel is equivalent to a single turn short-circuited on itself.

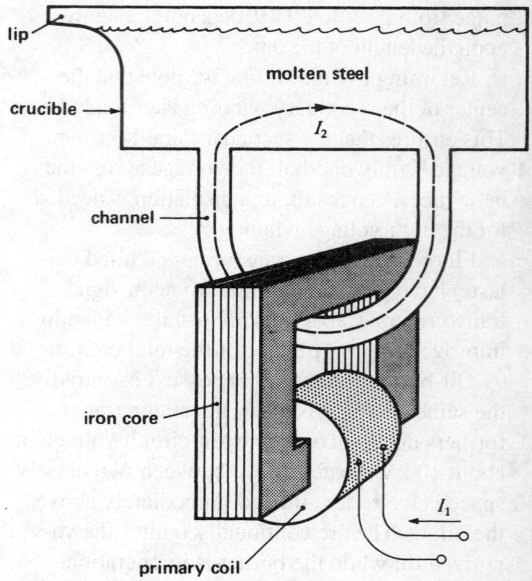

Figure 11.27
Channel induction furnace and its water-cooled transformer.

The magnetizing current is low because the flux is confined to a highly permeable iron core. On the other hand, the leakage flux is large because the secondary turn is obviously not tightly coupled to the primary coil. Nevertheless, the power factor is higher than that in Fig. 11.26, being typically between 60 and 80 percent. As a result, a smaller capacitor bank is required to furnish the reactive power.

Owing to the very high ambient temperature, the primary windings of induction furnace transformers are always made of hollow, water-cooled copper conductors. Induction furnaces are used for melting aluminum, copper, and other metals, as well as iron.

Fig. 11.28 shows a very special application of the induction heating principle.

11.11 High-frequency transformers

In electronic power supplies there is often a need to isolate the output from the input and to reduce the weight and cost of the unit. In other applications, such as in aircraft, there is a strong incentive to min-

Figure 11.28
Special application of the transformer effect. This picture shows one stage in the construction of the rotor of a steam-turbine generator. It consists of expanding the diameter of a 5 t coil-retaining ring. A coil of asbestos-insulated wire is wound around the ring and connected to a 35 kW, 2000 Hz source (left foreground). The coil creates a 2000 Hz magnetic field, which induces large eddy currents in the ring, bringing its temperature up to 280°C in about 3 h. The resulting expansion enables the ring to be slipped over the coil-ends, where it cools and contracts. This method of induction heating is clean and produces a very uniform temperature rise of the large mass.
(Courtesy of ABB)

imize weight. These objectives are best achieved by using a relatively high frequency compared to, say, 60 Hz. Thus, in aircraft the frequency is typically 400 Hz, while in electronic power supplies the frequency may range from 5 kHz to 50 kHz.

An increase in frequency reduces the size of such devices as transformers, inductors, and capacitors. In order to illustrate the reason for this phenomenon, we limit our discussion to transformers. Furthermore, to avoid a cumbersome theoretical analysis, we will take a practical transformer and observe how it behaves when the frequency is raised.

Consider Fig. 11.29, which shows a conventional 120 V/24 V, 60 Hz transformer having a rating of 36 VA. This small transformer weighs 0.5 kg and operates at a peak flux density of 1.5 T. The flux in the core attains a peak of 750 μWb. The laminated core is made of ordinary silicon steel having a thickness of 0.3 mm (12 mils) and the total core loss is about 1 W. The current rating is 300 mA for the primary and 1.5 A for the secondary.

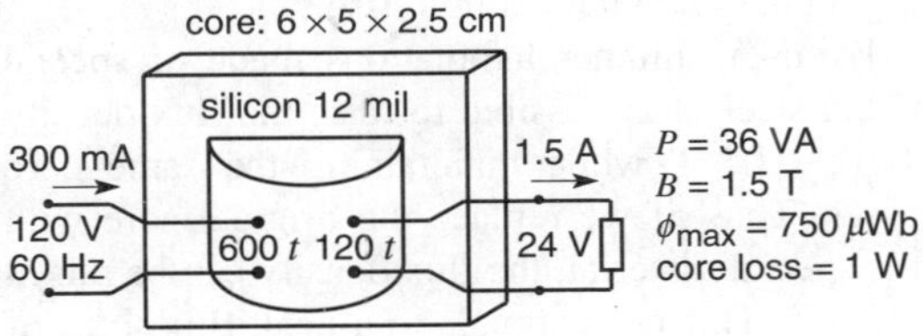

Figure 11.29

Without making any changes to the transformer, let us consider the effect of operating it at a frequency of 6000 Hz, which is 100 times higher than what it was designed for. Assuming the same peak flux density, it follows that the flux Φ_{max} will remain at 750 μWb. However, according to Eq. 9.3, this means that the corresponding primary voltage can be increased to

$$E = 4.44\, fN_1\Phi_{max} \quad (9.3)$$
$$= 4.44 \times 6000 \times 600 \times 750 \times 10^{-6}$$
$$= 12\,000 \text{ V}$$

which is 100 times greater than before! The secondary voltage will likewise be 100 times greater, becoming 2400 V. The operating conditions are shown in Fig. 11.30. The primary and secondary currents remain unchanged and so the power of the transformer is now 3600 VA, 100 times greater than in Fig. 11.29. Clearly, raising the frequency has had a very beneficial effect.

However, the advantage is not as great as it seems because at 6000 Hz the core loss is enormous (about 700 W), due to the increase in eddy current and hysteresis losses. Thus, the transformer in Fig. 11.30 is not feasible because it will quickly overheat.

To get around this problem, we can reduce the flux density so that the core losses are the same as they were in Fig. 11.29. Based upon the properties of 12 mil silicon steel, this requires a reduction in the flux density from 1.5 T to 0.04 T. As a result, according to Eq. 9.3, the primary and secondary voltages will have to be reduced to 320 V and 64 V, respectively. The new power of the transformer will be $P = 320 \times 0.3 = 96$ VA (Fig. 11.31). This is almost 3 times the original power of 36 VA, while retaining the same temperature rise.

By using thinner laminations made of special nickel-steel, it is possible to raise the flux density above 0.04 T while maintaining the same core losses. Thus, if we replace the original core with this special material, the flux density can be raised to 0.2 T. This corresponds to a peak flux Φ_{max} of 750 μWb × (0.2 T/1.5 T) = 100 μWb, which means that the primary voltage can be raised to

$$\begin{aligned} E &= 4.44 f N_1 \Phi_{max} \\ &= 4.44 \times 6000 \times 600 \times 100 \times 10^{-6} \\ &= 1600 \text{ V} \end{aligned}$$

The corresponding secondary voltage is 320 V, and so the enhanced capacity of the transformer is 320 V × 1.5 A = 480 VA (Fig. 11.32).

We are interested, of course, in maintaining the original voltage ratio of 120 V to 24 V. This is readily achieved by rewinding the transformer. Thus, the number of turns on the primary will be reduced from 600 to 600 t × (120 V/1600 V) = 45 turns, while the secondary will have only 9 turns. Such a drastic reduction in the number of turns means that the wire size can be increased significantly. Bearing in mind that the capacity of the transformer is still 480 VA, it follows that the rated primary current can be raised to 4 A while that in the secondary becomes 20 A. This rewound transformer with its special core (Fig. 11.33) has the same size and weight as the one in Fig. 11.29. Furthermore, because the iron and copper losses are the same in both cases, the efficiency of the high-frequency transformer is better.

It is now obvious that the increase in frequency has permitted a very large increase in the power capacity of the transformer. It follows that for a given power output a high-frequency transformer is much smaller, cheaper, more efficient, and lighter than a 60 Hz transformer.

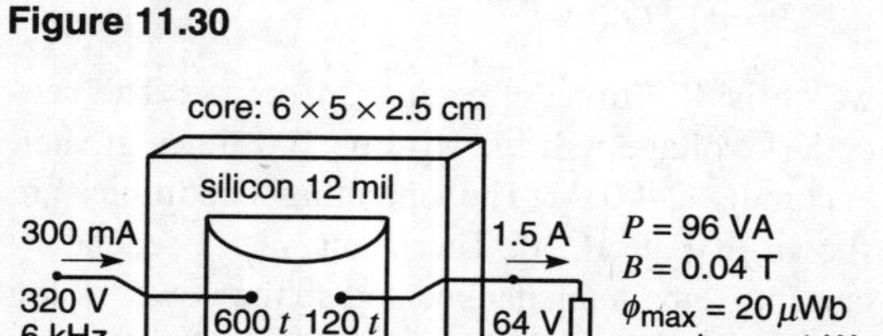

Figure 11.30

Figure 11.31

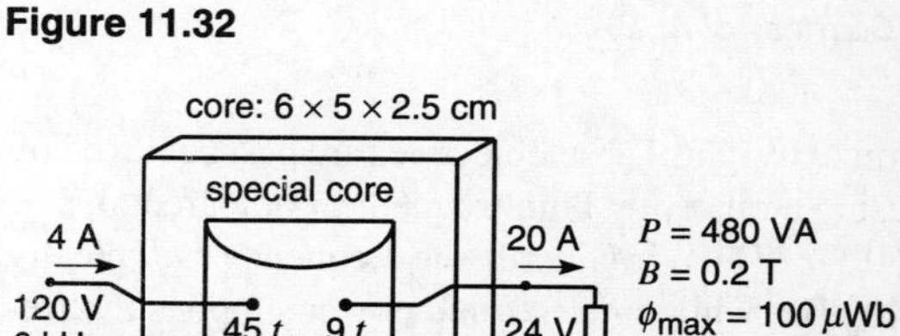

Figure 11.32

Figure 11.33

Questions and Problems

Practical level

11-1 What is the difference between an autotransformer and a conventional transformer?

11-2 What is the purpose of a voltage transformer? of a current transformer?

11-3 Why must we never open the secondary of a current transformer?

11-4 Explain why the secondary winding of a CT or PT must be grounded.

11-5 A toroidal current transformer has a ratio of 1500 A/5 A. How many turns does it have?

11-6 A current transformer has a rating of 10 VA, 50 A/5 A, 60 Hz, 2.4 kV. Calculate the nominal voltage across the primary winding.

Intermediate level

11-7 A single-phase transformer has a rating of 100 kVA, 7200 V/600 V, 60 Hz. If it is reconnected as an autotransformer having a ratio of 7800 V/7200 V, calculate the load it can carry.

11-8 In Problem 11-7, how should the transformer terminals (H_1, H_2, X_1, X_2) be connected?

11-9 The transformer in Problem 11-7 is reconnected again as an autotransformer having a ratio of 6.6 kV/600 V. What load can it carry and how should the connections be made?

Advanced level

11-10 A current transformer has a rating of 100 VA, 2000 A/5 A, 60 Hz, 138 kV. It has a primary to secondary capacitance of 250 pF. If it is installed on a transmission line where the line-to-neutral voltage is 138 kV, calculate the capacitive leakage current that flows to ground (see Fig. 11.13).

11-11 The toroidal current transformer of Fig. 11.19 has a ratio of 1000 A/5 A. The line conductor carries a current of 600 A.

a. Calculate the voltage across the secondary winding if the ammeter has an impedance of 0.15 Ω.

b. Calculate the voltage drop the transformer produces on the line conductor.

c. If the primary conductor is looped four times through the toroidal opening, calculate the new current ratio.

Industrial application

11-12 The nameplate of a small transformer indicates 50 VA, 120 V, 12.8 V. When 118.8 V is applied to the primary, the voltage across the secondary at no-load is 13.74 V. If 120 V were available, what would the secondary voltage be? Why is this voltage higher than the indicated nameplate voltage?

11-13 Referring to Problem 11-12, the windings are encapsulated in epoxy and cannot be seen. However, the resistance of the primary is 15.2 Ω and that of the secondary is 0.306 Ω. Is the 120 V winding wound upon the 12.8 V winding, or vice versa?

11-14 Many airports use series lighting systems in which the primary windings of a large number of current transformers are connected in series across a constant current, 60 Hz source. In one installation, the primary current is kept constant at 20 A. The secondary windings are individually connected to a 100 W, 6.6 A incandescent lamp.

a. Calculate the voltage across each lamp.

b. The resistance of the secondary winding is 0.07 Ω while that of the primary is 0.008 Ω. Knowing that the magnetizing current and the leakage reactance are both negligible, calculate the voltage across the primary winding of each transformer.

c. If 140 lamps, spaced at every 50 m intervals, are connected in series using No. 14 wire, calculate the minimum voltage of the power source. Assume the wire operates at a temperature of 105°C.

11-15 A no-load test on a 15 kVA, 480 V/120 V, 60 Hz transformer yields the following saturation curve data when the 120 V winding is excited by a sinusoidal source. The primary is known to have 260 turns.

a. Draw the saturation curve (voltage versus current in mA).

b. If the experiment were repeated using a 50 Hz source, redraw the resulting saturation curve.

c. Draw the saturation curve at 60 Hz (peak flux in mWb versus current in mA). At what point on the saturation curve does saturation become important? Is the flux distorted under these conditions?

E	14.8	31	49.3	66.7	90.5	110	120	130	136	142	V
I_0	59	99	144	210	430	700	1060	1740	2300	3200	mA

CHAPTER 12

Three-Phase Transformers

12.0 Introduction

Power is distributed throughout North America by means of 3-phase transmission lines. In order to transmit this power efficiently and economically, the voltages must be at appropriate levels. These levels (13.8 kV to 765 kV) depend upon the amount of power that has to be transmitted and the distance it has to be carried. Another aspect is the appropriate voltage levels used in factories and homes. These are fairly uniform, ranging from 120 V/240 V, single-phase systems to 600 V, 3-phase systems. Clearly, this requires the use of 3-phase transformers to transform the voltages from one level to another.

The transformers may be inherently 3-phase, having three primary windings and three secondary windings mounted on a 3-legged core. However, the same result can be achieved by using three single-phase transformers connected together to form a 3-phase transformer bank.

12.1 Basic properties of 3-phase transformer banks

When three single-phase transformers are used to transform a 3-phase voltage, the windings can be connected in several ways. Thus, the primaries may be connected in delta and the secondaries in wye, or vice versa. As a result, the ratio of the 3-phase input voltage to the 3-phase output voltage depends not only upon the turns ratio of the transformers, but also upon how they are connected.

A 3-phase transformer bank can also produce a *phase shift* between the 3-phase input voltage and the 3-phase output voltage. The amount of phase shift depends again upon the turns ratio of the transformers, and on how the primaries and secondaries are interconnected. Furthermore, the phase-shift feature enables us to change the *number* of phases. Thus, a 3-phase system can be converted into a 2-phase, a 6-phase, or a 12-phase system. Indeed, if there were a practical application for it, we could even convert a 3-phase system into a 5-phase system by an appropriate choice of single-phase transformers and interconnections.

In making the various connections, it is important to observe transformer polarities. An error in polarity may produce a short-circuit or unbalance the line voltages and currents.

The basic behavior of balanced 3-phase transformer banks can be understood by making the following simplifying assumptions:

1. The exciting currents are negligible.
2. The transformer impedances, due to the resistance and leakage reactance of the windings, are negligible.
3. The total apparent input power to the transformer bank is equal to the total apparent output power.

Furthermore, when single-phase transformers are connected into a 3-phase system, they retain all their basic single-phase properties, such as current ratio, voltage ratio, and flux in the core. Given the polarity marks X_1, X_2 and H_1, H_2, the phase shift between primary and secondary is zero, in the sense that $E_{X_1 X_2}$ is in phase with $E_{H_1 H_2}$.

12.2 Delta-delta connection

The three single-phase transformers P, Q, and R of Fig. 12.1 transform the voltage of the incoming transmission line A, B, C to a level appropriate for the outgoing transmission line 1, 2, 3. The incoming line is connected to the source, and the outgoing line is connected to the load. The transformers are connected in *delta-delta.* Terminal H_1 of each transformer is connected to terminal H_2 of the next transformer. Similarly, terminals X_1 and X_2 of successive transformers are connected together. The actual physical layout of the transformers is shown in Fig. 12.1. The corresponding schematic diagram is given in Fig. 12.2.

The schematic diagram is drawn in such a way to show not only the connections, but also the phasor

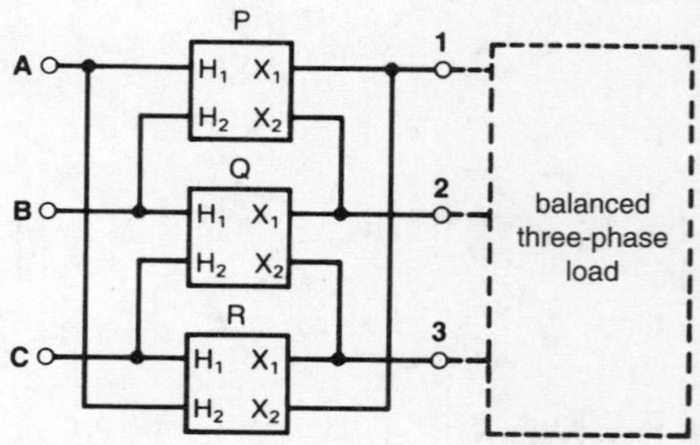

Figure 12.1
Delta-delta connection of three single-phase transformers. The incoming lines (source) are A, B, C and the outgoing lines (load) are 1, 2, 3.

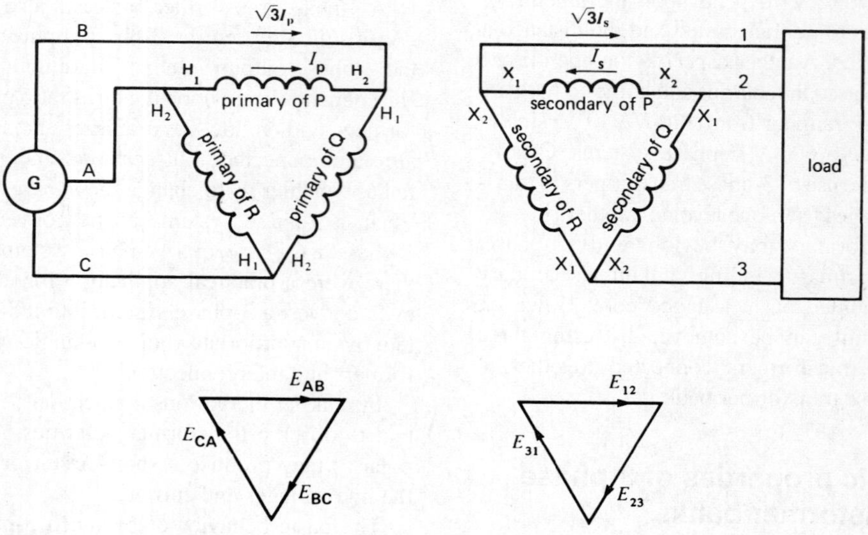

Figure 12.2
Schematic diagram of a delta-delta connection and associated phasor diagram.

relationship between the primary and secondary voltages. Thus, each secondary winding is drawn parallel to the corresponding primary winding to which it is coupled. Furthermore, if source G produces voltages E_{AB}, E_{BC}, E_{CA} according to the indicated phasor diagram, the primary windings are oriented the same way, phase by phase. For example, the primary of transformer P between lines A and B is oriented horizontally, in the same direction as phasor E_{AB}.

Because the primary and secondary voltages $E_{H_1H_2}$ and $E_{X_1X_2}$ of a given transformer must be in phase, it follows that E_{12} (secondary voltage of transformer P) must be in phase with E_{AB} (primary of the same transformer). Similarly, E_{23} is in phase with E_{BC}, and E_{31} with E_{CA}.

In such a *delta-delta* connection, the voltages between the respective incoming and outgoing transmission lines are in phase.

If a balanced load is connected to lines 1-2-3, the resulting line currents are equal in magnitude. This produces balanced line currents in the incoming lines A-B-C. As in any delta connection, the line currents are $\sqrt{3}$ times greater than the respective currents I_p and I_s flowing in the primary and secondary windings (Fig. 12.2). The power rating of the transformer bank is three times the rating of a single transformer.

Note that although the transformer bank constitutes a 3-phase arrangement, each transformer, considered alone, acts as if it were placed in a single-phase circuit. Thus, a current I_p flowing from H_1 to H_2 in the primary winding is associated with a current I_s flowing from X_2 to X_1 in the secondary.

Example 12-1

Three single-phase transformers are connected in delta-delta to step down a line voltage of 138 kV to 4160 V to supply power to a manufacturing plant. The plant draws 21 MW at a lagging power factor of 86 percent.

Calculate

a. The apparent power drawn by the plant
b. The apparent power furnished by the HV line
c. The current in the HV lines
d. The current in the LV lines
e. The currents in the primary and secondary windings of each transformer
f. The load carried by each transformer

Solution

a. The apparent power drawn by the plant is

$$S = P/\cos\theta \qquad (7.7)$$
$$= 21/0.86$$
$$= 24.4 \text{ MVA}$$

b. The transformer bank itself absorbs a negligible amount of active and reactive power because the I^2R losses and the reactive power associated with the mutual flux and the leakage fluxes are small. It follows that the apparent power furnished by the HV line is also 24.4 MVA.

c. The current in each HV line is

$$I_1 = S/(\sqrt{3}E) \qquad (8.9)$$
$$= (24.4 \times 10^6)/(\sqrt{3} \times 138\,000)$$
$$= 102 \text{ A}$$

d. The current in the LV lines is

$$I_2 = S/(\sqrt{3}E)$$
$$= (24.4 \times 10^6)/(\sqrt{3} \times 4160)$$
$$= 3386 \text{ A}$$

e. Referring to Fig. 12.2, the current in each primary winding is

$$I_p = 102/\sqrt{3} = 58.9 \text{ A}$$

The current in each secondary winding is

$$I_s = 3386/\sqrt{3} = 1955 \text{ A}$$

f. Because the plant load is balanced, each transformer carries one-third of the total load, or 24.4/3 = 8.13 MVA.

The individual transformer load can also be obtained by multiplying the primary voltage times the primary current:

$$S = E_pI_p = 138\,000 \times 58.9$$
$$= 8.13 \text{ MVA}$$

Note that we can calculate the line currents and the currents in the transformer windings even though we do not know how the 3-phase load is connected. In effect, the plant load (shown as a box in Fig. 12.2) is composed of hundreds of individual loads, some of which are connected in delta, others in wye. Furthermore, some are single-phase loads operating at much lower voltages than 4160 V, powered by smaller transformers located inside the plant. The sum total of these loads usually results in a reasonably well-balanced 3-phase load, represented by the box.

12.3 Delta-wye connection

When the transformers are connected in *delta-wye*, the three primary windings are connected the same way as in Fig. 12.1. However, the secondary windings are connected so that all the X_2 terminals are joined together, creating a common neutral N (Fig. 12.3). In such a delta-wye connection, the voltage across each primary winding is equal to the incoming line voltage. However, the outgoing line voltage is 3 times the secondary voltage across each transformer.

The relative values of the currents in the transformer windings and transmission lines are given in Fig. 12.4. Thus, the line currents in phases A, B, and C are $\sqrt{3}$ times the currents in the primary windings. The line currents in phases 1, 2, 3 are the same as the currents in the secondary windings.

A delta-wye connection produces a 30° phase shift between the line voltages of the incoming and outgoing transmission lines. Thus, outgoing line

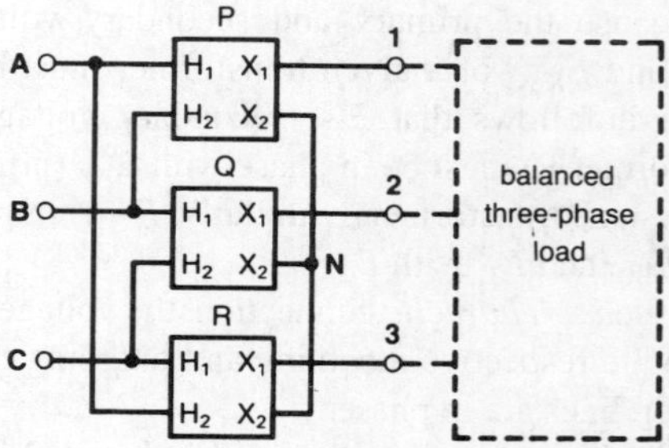

Figure 12.3
Delta-wye connection of three single-phase transformers.

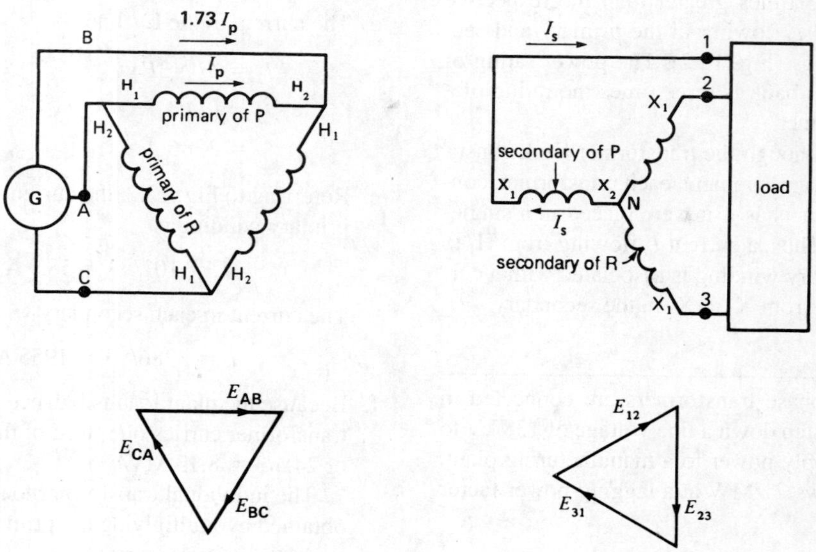

Figure 12.4
Schematic diagram of a delta-wye connection and associated phasor diagram. (The phasor diagrams on the primary and secondary sides are not drawn to the same scale.)

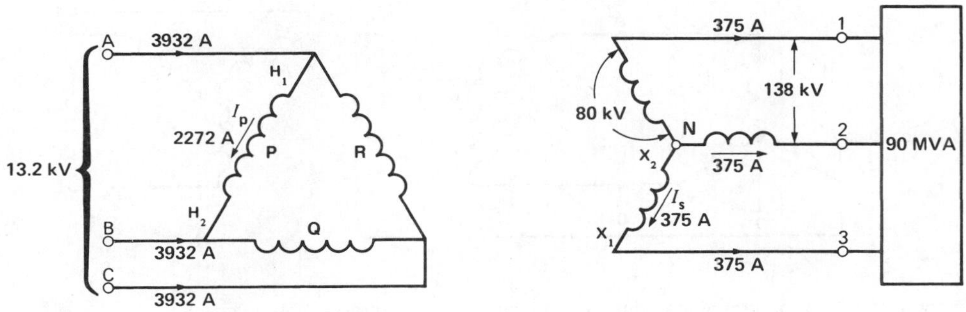

Figure 12.5
See Example 12-2.

voltage E_{12} is 30° ahead of incoming line voltage E_{AB}, as can be seen from the phasor diagram. If the outgoing line feeds an isolated group of loads, the phase shift creates no problem. But, if the outgoing line has to be connected in parallel with a line coming from another source, the 30° shift may make such a parallel connection impossible, even if the line voltages are otherwise identical.

One of the important advantages of the wye connection is that it reduces the amount of insulation needed inside the transformer. The HV winding has to be insulated for only $1/\sqrt{3}$, or 58 percent of the line voltage.

Example 12-2

Three single-phase step-up transformers rated at 40 MVA, 13.2 kV/80 kV are connected in delta-wye on a 13.2 kV transmission line (Fig. 12.5). If they feed a 90 MVA load, calculate the following:

a. The secondary line voltage
b. The currents in the transformer windings
c. The incoming and outgoing transmission line currents

Solution

The easiest way to solve this problem is to consider the windings of only one transformer, say, transformer P.

a. The voltage across the primary winding is obviously 13.2 kV.

The voltage across the secondary is, therefore, 80 kV.

The voltage between the outgoing lines 1, 2, and 3 is

$$E_s = 80\sqrt{3} = 139 \text{ kV}$$

b. The load carried by each transformer is

$$S = 90/3 = 30 \text{ MVA}$$

The current in the primary winding is

$$I_p = 30 \text{ MVA}/13.2 \text{ kV} = 2273 \text{ A}$$

The current in the secondary winding is

$$I_s = 30 \text{ MVA}/80 \text{ kV} = 375 \text{ A}$$

c. The current in each incoming line A, B, C is

$$I = 2273\sqrt{3} = 3937 \text{ A}$$

The current in each outgoing line 1, 2, 3 is

$$I = 375 \text{ A}$$

12.4 Wye-delta connection

The currents and voltages in a *wye-delta* connection are identical to those in the delta-wye connection of Section 12.3. The primary and secondary connections are simply interchanged. In other words, the H_2 terminals are connected together to create a neutral, and the X_1, X_2 terminals are connected in delta. Again, there results a 30° phase shift between the voltages of the incoming and outgoing lines.

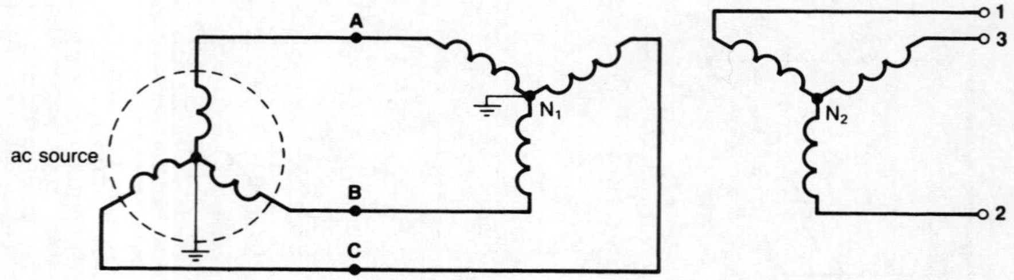

Figure 12.6
Wye-wye connection with neutral of the primary connected to the neutral of the source.

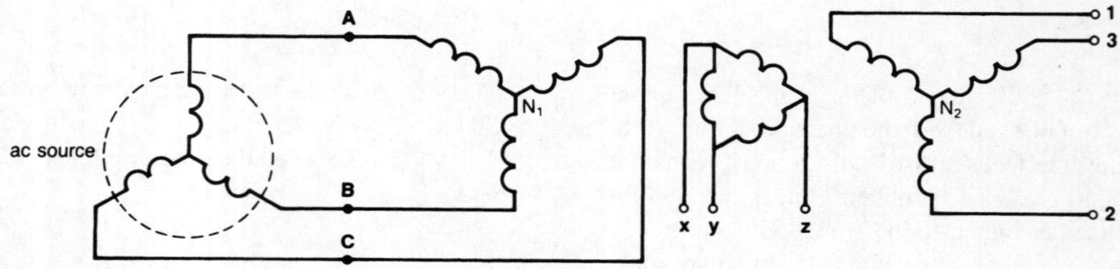

Figure 12.7
Wye-wye connection using a tertiary winding.

12.5 Wye-wye connection

When transformers are connected in wye-wye, special precautions have to be taken to prevent severe distortion of the line-to-neutral voltages. One way to prevent the distortion is to connect the neutral of the primary to the neutral of the source, usually by way of the ground (Fig. 12.6). Another way is to provide each transformer with a third winding, called *tertiary* winding. The tertiary windings of the three transformers are connected in delta (Fig. 12.7). They often provide the substation service voltage where the transformers are installed.

Note that there is no phase shift between the incoming and outgoing transmission line voltages of a wye-wye connected transformer.

12.6 Open-delta connection

It is possible to transform the voltage of a 3-phase system by using only 2 transformers, connected in open-delta. The *open-delta* arrangement is identical to a delta-delta connection, except that one transformer is absent (Fig. 12.8). However, the open-delta connection is seldom used because the load capacity of the transformer bank is only 86.6 percent of the installed transformer capacity. For example, if two 50 kVA transformers are connected in open-delta, the installed capacity of the transformer bank is obviously $2 \times 50 = 100$ kVA. But, strange as it may seem, it can only deliver 86.6 kVA before the transformers begin to overheat.

The open-delta connection is mainly used in emergency situations. Thus, if three transformers

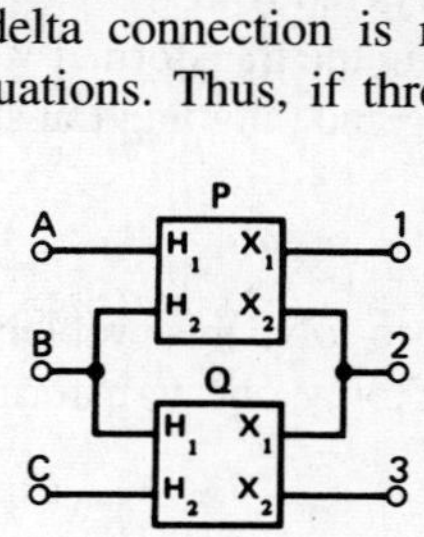

Figure 12.8a
Open-delta connection.

are connected in delta-delta and one of them becomes defective and has to be removed, it is possible to feed the load on a temporary basis with the two remaining transformers.

Example 12-3

Two single-phase 150 kVA, 7200 V/600 V transformers are connected in open-delta. Calculate the maximum 3-phase load they can carry.

Solution

Although each transformer has a rating of 150 kVA, the two together *cannot* carry a load of 300 kVA. The following calculations show why:

The nominal secondary current of each transformer is

$$I_s = 150\ \text{kVA}/600\ \text{V} = 250\ \text{A}$$

The current I_s in lines 1, 2, 3 cannot, therefore, exceed 250 A (Fig. 12.8b). Consequently, the maximum load that the transformers can carry is

$$S = \sqrt{3}\, EI \qquad (8.9)$$

$$= \sqrt{3} \times 600 \times 250 = 259\,800\ \text{VA}$$

$$= 260\ \text{kVA}$$

Thus, the ratio

$$\frac{\text{maximum load}}{\text{installed transformer rating}} = \frac{260\ \text{kVA}}{300\ \text{kVA}}$$

$$= 0.867, \text{ or } 86.7\%$$

12.7 Three-phase transformers

A transformer bank composed of three single-phase transformers may be replaced by one 3-phase transformer (Fig. 12.9). The magnetic core of such a transformer has three legs that carry the primary and secondary windings of each phase. The windings are connected internally, either in wye or in delta, with the result that only six terminals have to be brought outside the tank. For a given total capacity, a 3-phase transformer is always smaller and cheaper than three single-phase transformers. Nevertheless, single-phase transformers are sometimes preferred, particularly when a replacement unit is essential. For example, suppose a manufacturing plant absorbs 5000 kVA. To guarantee continued service we can install one 3-phase 5000 kVA transformer and keep a second one as a spare. Alternatively, we can install three single-phase transformers each rated at 1667 kVA, plus one

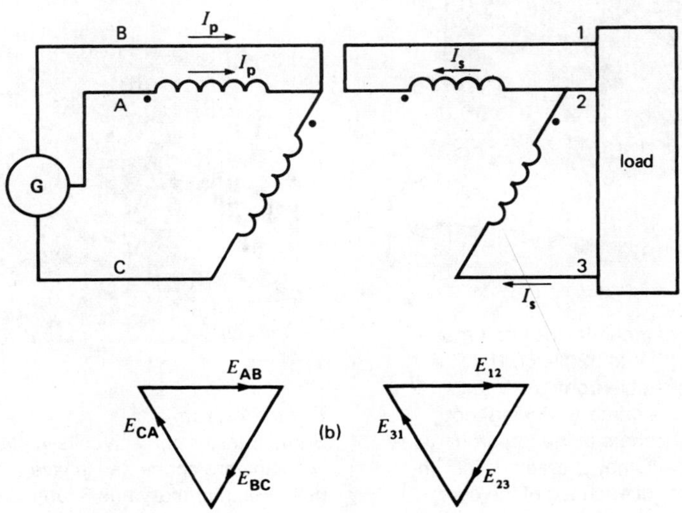

Figure 12.8b
Associated schematic and phasor diagram.

spare. The 3-phase transformer option is more expensive (total capacity: $2 \times 5000 = 10\,000$ kVA) than the single-phase option (total capacity: $4 \times 1667 = 6667$ kVA).

Fig. 12.10 shows successive stages of construction of a 3-phase 110 MVA, 222.5 kV/34.5 kV tap-changing transformer.* Note that in addition to the three main legs, the magnetic core has two additional lateral legs. They enable the designer to reduce the overall height of the transformer, which simplifies the problem of shipping. In effect, whenever large equipment has to be shipped, the designer is faced with the problem of overhead clearances on highways and rail lines.

*A tap-changing transformer regulates the secondary voltage by automatically switching from one tap to another on the primary winding. The tap-changer is a motorized device under the control of a sensor that continually monitors the voltage that has to be held constant.

Figure 12.9
Three-phase transformer for an electric arc furnace, rated 36 MVA, 13.8 kV/160 V to 320 V, 60 Hz. The secondary voltage is adjustable from 160 V to 320 V by means of 32 taps on the primary winding (not shown). The three large busbars in the foreground deliver a current of 65 000 A. Other characteristics: impedance: 3.14%; diameter of each leg of the core: 711 mm; overall height of core: 3500 mm; center line distance between adjacent core legs: 1220 mm. *(Courtesy of Ferranti-Packard)*

Figure 12.10a
Core of a 110 MVA, 222.5 kV/34.5 kV, 60 Hz, 3-phase transformer. By staggering laminations of different widths, the core legs can be made almost circular. This reduces the coil diameter to a minimum, resulting in less copper and lower I^2R losses. The legs are tightly bound to reduce vibration. Mass of core: 53 560 kg.

Figure 12.10b
Same transformer with coils in place. The primary windings are connected in wye and the secondaries in delta. Each primary has 8 taps to change the voltage in steps of $\pm 2.5\%$. The motorized tap-changer can be seen in the right upper corner of the transformer. Mass of copper: 15 230 kg.

The 34.5 kV windings (connected in delta) are mounted next to the core. The 222.5 kV windings (connected in wye) are mounted on top of the 34.5 kV windings. A space of several centimeters separates the two windings to ensure good isolation and to allow cool oil to flow freely between them. The HV bushings that protrude from the oil-filled tank are connected to a 220 kV line. The medium voltage (MV) bushings are much smaller and cannot be seen in the photograph (Fig. 12.10c).

Figure 12.10c
Same transformer ready for shipping. It has been subjected to a 1050 kV impulse test on the HV side and a similar 250 kV test on the LV side. Other details: power rating: 110 MVA/146.7 MVA (OA/FA); total mass including oil: 158.7 t; overall height: 9 m; width: 8.2 m, length: 9.2 m.
(Courtesy of ABB)

12.8 Step-up and step-down autotransformer

When the voltage of a 3-phase line has to be stepped up or stepped down by a moderate amount, it is economically advantageous to use three single-phase transformers to create a wye-connected *autotransformer.* The actual physical connections are shown in Fig. 12.11a, and the corresponding schematic diagram is given in Fig. 12.11b. The respective line-to-neutral voltages of the primary and secondary are obviously in phase. Consequently, the incoming and outgoing transmission line voltages are in phase. The neutral is connected to the system neutral, otherwise a tertiary winding must be added to prevent the line-to-neutral voltage distortion mentioned previously (Section 12.5).

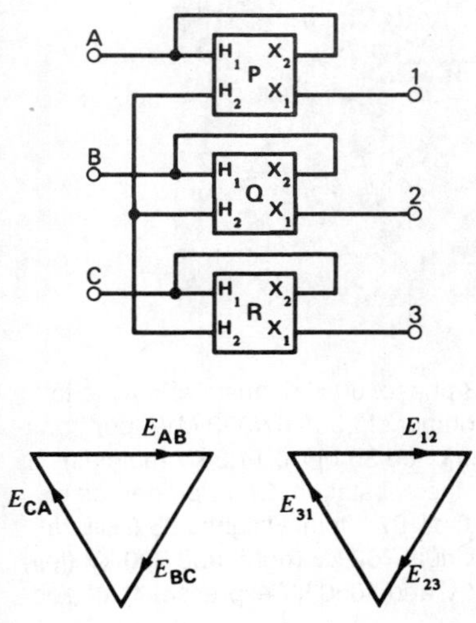

Figure 12.11a
Wye-connected autotransformer.

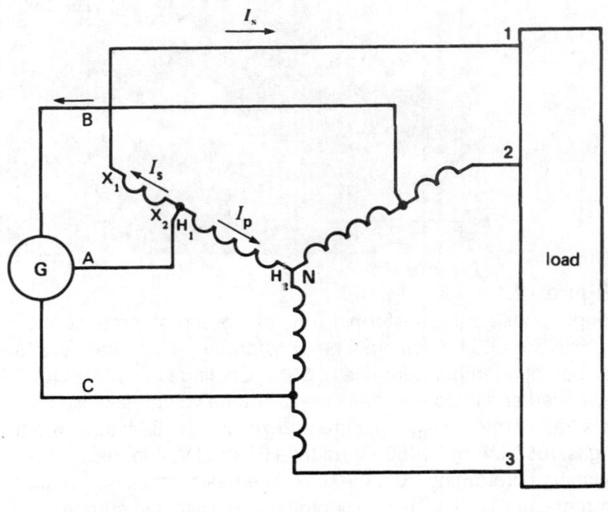

Figure 12.11b
Associated schematic diagram.

Figure 12.11c
Single-phase autotransformer (one of a group of three) connecting a 700 kV, 3-phase, 60 Hz transmission line to an existing 300 kV system. The transformer ratio is 404 kV/173 kV, to give an output of 200/267/333 MVA per transformer, at a temperature rise of 55°C. Cooling is OA/FA/FOA. A tertiary winding rated 35 MVA, 11.9 kV maintains balanced and distortion-free line-to-neutral voltages, while providing power for the substation. Other properties of this transformer: weight of core and windings: 132 t; tank and accessories: 46 t; oil: 87 t; total weight: 265 t. BIL rating is 1950 kV and 1050 kV on the HV and LV side, respectively. Note the individual 700 kV (right) and 300 kV (left) bushings protruding from the tank. The basic impulse insulation (BIL) of 1950 kV and 1050 kV expresses the transformer's ability to withstand lightning and switching surges.
(Courtesy of Hydro-Québec)

For a given power output, an autotransformer is smaller and cheaper than a conventional transformer (see Section 11.2). This is particularly true if the ratio of the incoming line voltage to outgoing line voltage lies between 0.5 and 2.

Fig. 12.11c shows a large single-phase autotransformer rated 404 kV/173 kV with a tertiary winding rated 11.9 kV. It is part of a 3-phase transformer bank used to connect a 700 kV transmission line to an existing 300 kV system.

Example 12-4

The voltage of a 3-phase, 230 kV line has to be stepped up to 345 kV to supply a load of 200 MVA. Three single-phase transformers connected as autotransformers are to be used. Calculate the basic power and voltage rating of each transformer, assuming they are connected as shown in Fig. 12.11b.

Solution

To simplify the calculations, let us consider only one phase (phase A, say).

The line-to-neutral voltage between X_1 and H_2 is

$$E_{IN} = 345/\sqrt{3} = 199 \text{ kV}$$

The line-to-neutral voltage between H_1 and H_2 is

$$E_{AN} = 230/\sqrt{3} = 133 \text{ kV}$$

The voltage of winding X_1X_2 between lines 1 and A is

$$E_{1A} = 199 - 133 = 66 \text{ kV}$$

This means that each transformer has an effective primary to secondary voltage rating of 133 kV to 66 kV.

The current in each phase of the outgoing line is

$$I_s = S/\sqrt{3}\,E \qquad (8.9)$$
$$= (200 \times 10^6)/(\sqrt{3} \times 345\,000)$$
$$= 335 \text{ A}$$

The power associated with winding X_1X_2 is

$$S_a = 66\,000 \times 335 = 22.1 \text{ MVA}$$

Winding H_1H_2 has the same power rating. The basic rating of each single-phase transformer is therefore 22.1 MVA.

The basic rating of the 3-phase transformer bank is $22.1 \times 3 = 66.3$ MVA.

The basic transformer rating (as far as size is concerned) is considerably less than its load-carrying capacity of 200 MVA. This is in keeping with the fact that the ratio of transformation (345/230 = 1.5) lies between 0.5 and 2.0.

12.9 Phase-shift principle

A 3-phase system enables us to shift the phase angle of a voltage very simply. Such phase shifting enables us to create 2-phase, 6-phase, and 12-phase systems from an ordinary 3-phase line. Such multiphase systems are used in large electronic converter stations and in special electric controls. Phase shifting is also used to control power flow over transmission lines that form part of a power grid.

To understand the phase shifting principle, consider a rheostat connected between phases B and C of a 3-phase line (Fig. 12.12). As we slide contact P

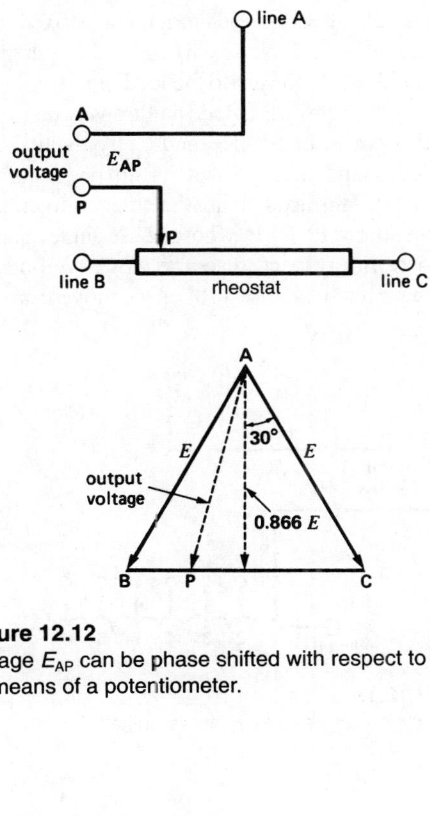

Figure 12.12
Voltage E_{AP} can be phase shifted with respect to E_{AC} by means of a potentiometer.

from phase B toward phase C, voltage E_{AP} changes both in amplitude and phase. We obtain a 60° phase shift in moving from one end of the potentiometer to the other. Thus, as we move from B to C, voltage E_{AP} gradually advances in phase with respect to E_{AB}. At the same time, the magnitude of E_{AP} varies slightly, from E (voltage between the lines) to 0.866 E when the contact is in the middle of the rheostat.

Such a simple phase-shifter can only be used in circuits where the load between terminals A and P draws a few milliamperes. If a heavier load is applied, the resulting IR drop in the rheostat completely changes the voltage and phase angle from what they were on open-circuit.

To get around this problem, we connect a multitap autotransformer between phases B and C (Fig. 12.13). By moving contact P, we obtain the same open-circuit voltages and phase shifts as before, but this time they remain essentially unchanged when a load is connected between terminals A and P. Why is this so? The reason is that the flux in the autotransformer is fixed because E_{BC} is fixed. As a result, the voltage across each turn remains fixed (both in magnitude and phase) whether the autotransformer delivers a current to the load or not.

Fig. 12.14 shows 3 tapped autotransformers connected between lines A, B, and C. Contacts P_1, P_2, P_3 move in tandem as we switch from one set of taps to the next. This arrangement enables us to create a 3-phase source P_1, P_2, P_3 whose phase angle changes stepwise with respect to source ABC. We obtain a maximum phase shift of 120° as we move from one

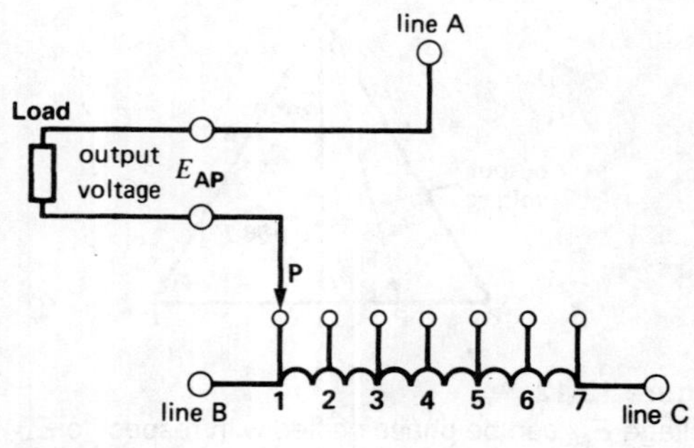

Figure 12.13
Autotransformer used as a phase shifter.

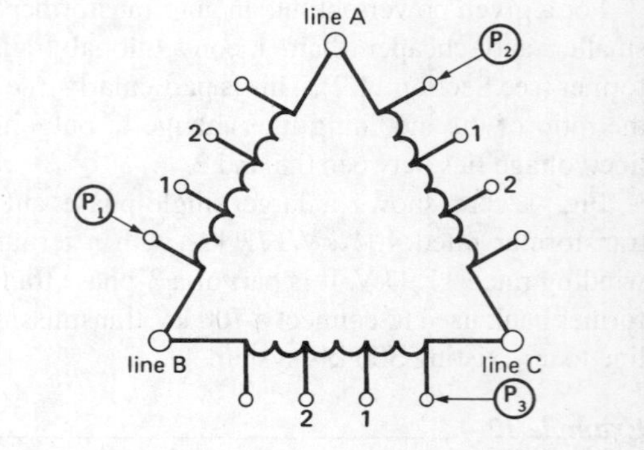

Figure 12.14
Three-phase phase shifter.

extremity of the autotransformers to the other. Also, the magnitude of the 3-phase voltages between cursors P_1, P_2, and P_3 will vary from E_{line} to $0.5E_{line}$ and back to E_{line} as the cursors move smoothly from one end, to midway, to the other end of the autotransformer winding. We now discuss some practical applications of the phase-shift principle.

12.10 Three-phase to 2-phase transformation

The voltages in a 2-phase system are equal but displaced from each other by 90°. There are several ways to create a 2-phase system from a 3-phase source. One of the simplest and cheapest is to use a single-phase autotransformer having taps at 50 percent and 86.6 percent. We connect it between any two phases of a 3-phase line, as shown in Fig. 12.15. If the voltage between lines A, B, C is 100 V, voltages E_{AT} and E_{NC} are both equal to 86.6 V. Furthermore, they are displaced from each other by 90°. This relationship can be seen by referring to the phasor diagram (Fig. 12.15c) and reasoning as follows:

1. Phasors E_{AB}, E_{BC}, and E_{CA} are fixed by the source.
2. Phasor E_{AN} is in phase with phasor E_{AB} because the same ac flux links the turns of the autotransformer.
3. Phasor E_{AT} is in phase with phasor E_{AB} for the same reason.

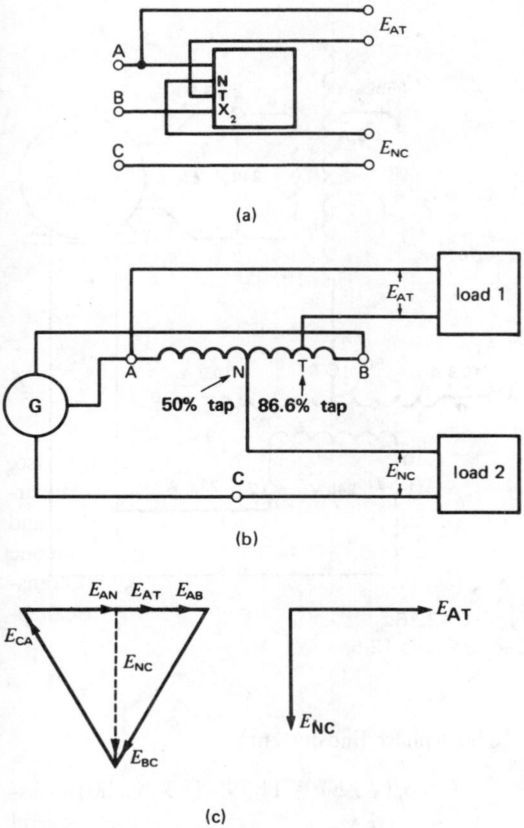

Figure 12.15
a. Simple method to obtain a 2-phase system from a 3-phase line, using a single transformer winding.
b. Schematic diagram of the connections.
c. Phasor diagram of the voltages.

4. From Kirchhoff's voltage law, $E_{AN} + E_{NC} + E_{CA} = 0$. Consequently, phasor E_{NC} must have the value and direction shown in the figure.

Loads 1 and 2 must be isolated from each other, such as the two windings of a 2-phase induction motor. The ratio of transformation (3-phase voltage to 2-phase voltage) is fixed and given by $E_{AB}/E_{AT} = 100/86.6 = 1.15$.

Another way to produce a 2-phase system is to use the *Scott connection.* It consists of two identical single-phase transformers, the one having a 50 percent tap and the other an 86.6 percent tap on the primary winding. The transformers are connected as shown in Fig. 12.16. The 3-phase source is connected to terminals A, B, C and the 2-phase load is connected to the secondary windings. The ratio of transformation (3-phase line voltage to 2-phase line voltage) is given by E_{AB}/E_{12}. The Scott connection has the advantage of isolating the 3-phase and 2-phase systems and providing any desired voltage ratio between them.

Except for servomotor applications, 2-phase systems are seldom encountered today.

Example 12-5

A 2-phase, 7.5 kW (10 hp), 240 V, 60 Hz motor has an efficiency of 0.83 and a power factor of 0.80. It is to be fed from a 600 V, 3-phase line using a Scott-connected transformer bank (Fig. 12.16c).

Calculate

a. The apparent power drawn by the motor
b. The current in each 2-phase line
c. The current in each 3-phase line

Solution

a. The active power drawn by the motor is

$$P = P_o/\eta = 7500/0.83$$
$$= 9036 \text{ W}$$

The apparent power drawn by the motor is

$$S = P/\cos\phi = 9036/0.8$$
$$= 11\,295 \text{ VA}$$

The apparent power per phase is

$$S = 11\,295/2 = 5648 \text{ VA}$$

b. The current in each 2-phase line is

$$I = S/E = 5648/240$$
$$= 23.5 \text{ A}$$

c. The transformer bank itself consumes very little active and reactive power; consequently, the 3-phase line supplies only the active and reactive power absorbed by the motor. The total apparent power furnished by the 3-phase line is, therefore, 11 295 VA.

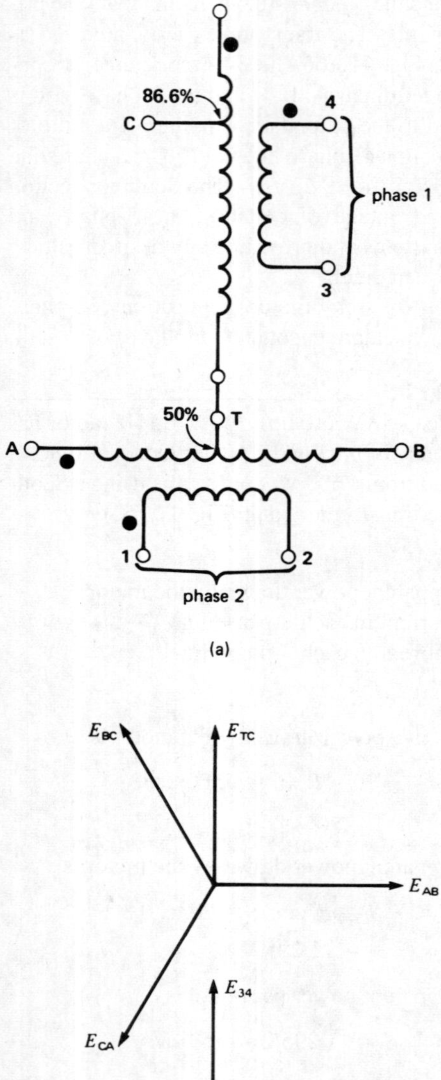

Figure 12.16
a. Scott connection.
b. Phasor diagram of the Scott connection.

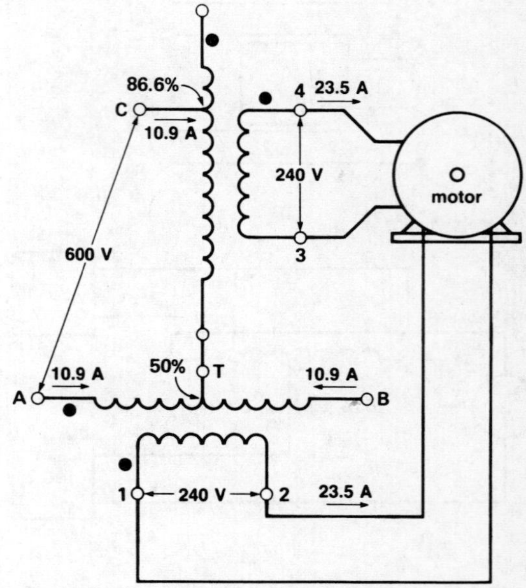

Figure 12.16c
See Example 12-5.

The 3-phase line current is

$$I = S/(\sqrt{3}\,E) = 11\,295/(\sqrt{3} \times 600)$$
$$= 10.9 \text{ A}$$

Figure 12.16c shows the power circuit and the line voltages and currents.

12.11 Phase-shift transformer

A phase-shift transformer is a special type of 3-phase autotransformer that shifts the phase angle between the incoming and outgoing lines without changing the voltage ratio.

Consider a 3-phase transmission line connected to the terminals A, B, C of such a phase-shift transformer (Fig. 12.17). The transformer twists all the incoming line voltages through an angle α without, however, changing their magnitude. The result is that all the voltages of the outgoing transmission line 1, 2, 3 are shifted with respect to the voltages of the incoming line A, B, C. The angle may be lead-

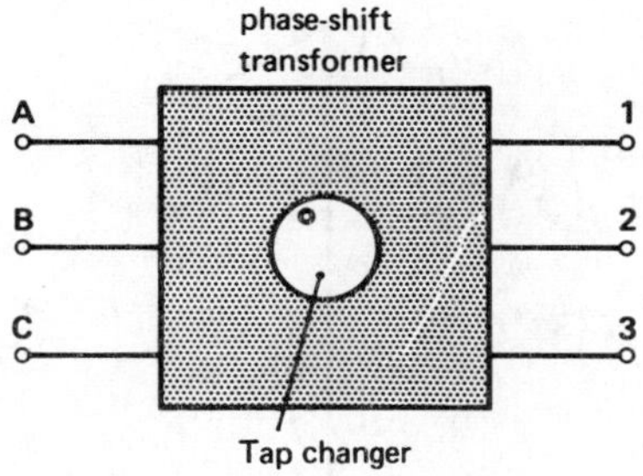

Figure 12.17a
Phase-shift transformer.

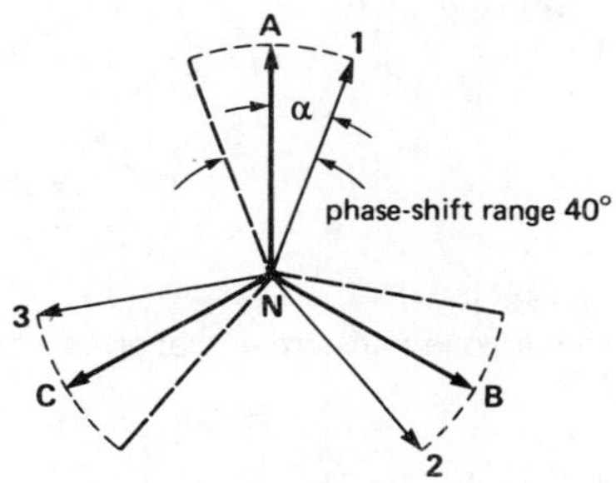

Figure 12.17b
Phasor diagram showing the range over which the phase angle of the outgoing line can be varied.

ing or lagging, and is usually variable between zero and ±20°.

The phase angle is sometimes varied in discrete steps by means of a motorized tap-changer.

The basic power rating of the transformer (which determines its size) depends upon the apparent power carried by the transmission line, and upon the phase shift. For angles less than 20°, it is given by the approximate formula

$$S_T = 0.025\, S_L \alpha_{max} \tag{12.1}$$

where

S_T = basic power rating of the 3-phase transformer bank [VA]

S_L = apparent power carried by the transmission line [VA]

α_{max} = maximum transformer phase shift [°]

0.025 = an approximate coefficient

Example 12-6

A phase-shift transformer is designed to control 150 MVA on a 230 kV, 3-phase line. The phase angle is variable between zero and ±15°.

a. Calculate the approximate basic power rating of the transformer.
b. Calculate the line currents in the incoming and outgoing transmission lines.

Solution

a. The basic power rating is

$$S_T = 0.025\, S_L\, \alpha_{max} \tag{12.1}$$
$$= 0.025 \times 150 \times 15$$
$$= 56 \text{ MVA}$$

Note that the power rating is much less than the power that the transformer carries. This is a feature of all autotransformers.

b. The line currents are the same in both lines, because the voltages are the same. The line current is

$$I = S_L/\sqrt{3}\, E \tag{8.9}$$
$$= (150 \times 10^6)/(\sqrt{3} \times 230\,000)$$
$$= 377 \text{ A}$$

Fig. 12.18a is an example of a 3-phase transformer that could be used to obtain a phase shift of, say, 20 degrees. The transformer has two windings on each leg. Thus, the leg associated with phase A has one winding PN with a tap brought out at terminal A and a second winding having terminals a, 3. The windings of the three phases are interconnected as shown. The incoming line is connected to terminals A, B, C and the outgoing line to terminals 1, 2, 3.

The result is that E_{1N} lags 20° behind E_{AN}. Similarly, E_{2N} lags 20° behind E_{BN}, and E_{3N} lags 20° behind E_{CN} (Fig. 12.18c).

The basic principle of obtaining a phase shift is to connect two voltages in series that are generated by two different phases. Thus, voltage E_{1b} generated by phase B is connected in series with E_{PN} generated by phase A. The values of E_{PN} and E_{1b} are selected so that the output voltage is equal to the input voltage while obtaining the desired phase angle

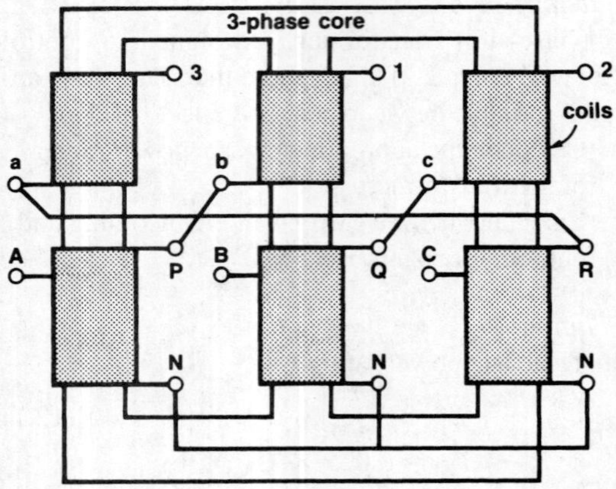

Figure 12.18a
Construction of a 3-phase shift transformer. The incoming terminals are A, B, C; the outgoing terminals are 1, 2, 3.

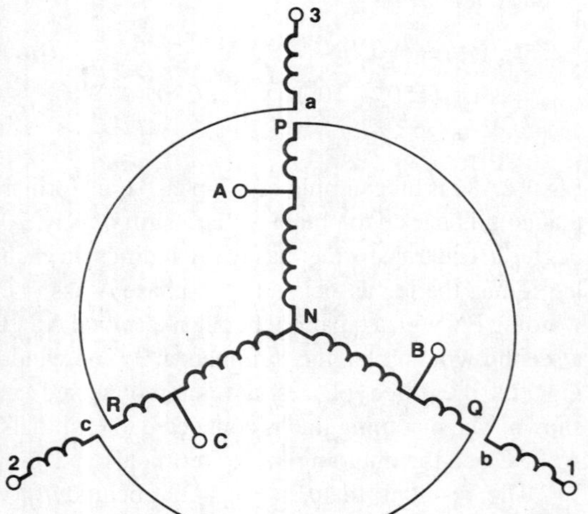

Figure 12.18b
Schematic diagram of the transformer in Fig. 12.18a.

between them. In our particular example, if E is the line-to-neutral voltage of the incoming line, the respective voltages across the windings of phase A are

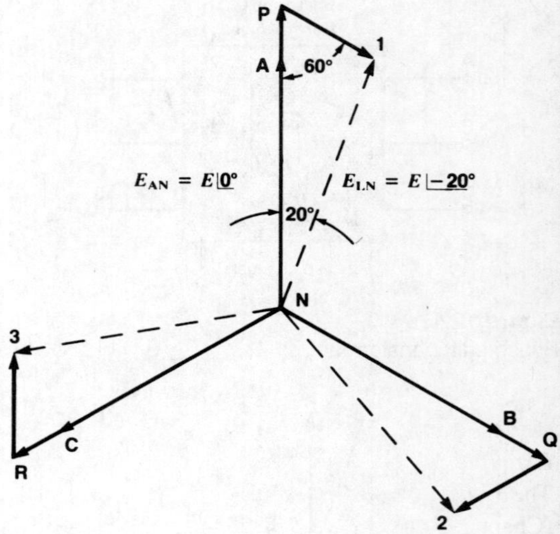

Figure 12.18c
Phasor diagram of a transformer that gives a phase shift of 20°.

$$E_{AN} = E$$
$$E_{PN} = 1.14E$$
$$E_{3a} = 0.40E$$
$$E_{IN} = E_{AN}\angle -20°$$

In practice, the internal circuit of a tap-changing, phase-shift transformer is much more complex. However, it rests upon the basic principles we have just discussed. The purpose of such transformers will be covered in Chapter 25.

12.12 Calculations involving 3-phase transformers

The behavior of a 3-phase transformer bank is calculated the same way as for a single-phase transformer. In making the calculations, we proceed as follows:

1. We assume that the primary and secondary windings are both connected in wye, *even if they are not* (see Section 8.14). This eliminates the problem of having to deal with delta-wye and delta-delta voltages and currents.

2. We consider only one transformer (single phase) of this assumed wye-wye transformer bank.
3. The primary voltage of this hypothetical transformer is the line-to-neutral voltage of the incoming line.
4. The secondary voltage of this transformer is the line-to-neutral voltage of the outgoing line.
5. The nominal power rating of this transformer is one-third the rating of the 3-phase transformer bank.
6. The load on this transformer is one-third the load on the transformer bank.

Example 12-7

The 3-phase step-up transformer shown in Fig. 10.18 (Chapter 10) is rated 1300 MVA, 24.5 kV/345 kV, 60 Hz, impedance 11.5 percent. It steps up the voltage of a generating station to power a 345 kV line.

a. Determine the equivalent circuit of this transformer, per phase.
b. Calculate the voltage across the generator terminals when the HV side of the transformer delivers 810 MVA at 370 kV with a lagging power factor of 0.90.

Solution

a. First, we note that the primary and secondary winding connections are not specified. We don't need this information. However, we assume that both windings are connected in wye.

We shall use the per-unit method to solve this problem. We select the nominal voltage of the secondary winding as our base voltage, E_B.

The base voltage is

$$E_B = 345/\sqrt{3} = 199.2 \text{ kV}$$

Ratio of transformation is

$$a = 345/24.5 = 14.08$$

The nominal power rating of the transformer will be used as the base power S_B. Thus,

$$S_B = 1300/3 = 433.3 \text{ MVA}$$

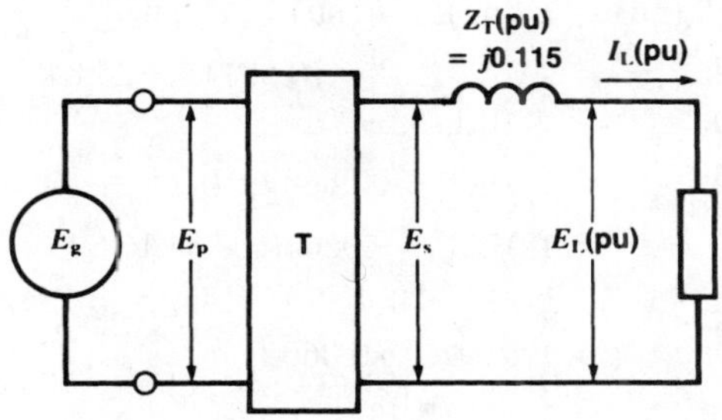

Figure 12.19
See Example 12-7.

This is a very large transformer; consequently, the transformer impedance is almost entirely reactive. The per-unit impedance is, therefore,

$$Z_T(\text{pu}) = j\,0.115$$

The equivalent circuit is shown in Fig. 12.19.

b. The power of the load per phase is

$$S_L = 810/3 = 270 \text{ MVA}$$

The voltage E_L across the load is

$$E_L = 370 \text{ kV}/\sqrt{3} = 213.6 \text{ kV}$$

The per-unit power of the load is

$$S_L(\text{pu}) = 270 \text{ MVA}/433.3 \text{ MVA} = 0.6231$$

By selecting E_L as the reference phasor, the per-unit voltage across the load is

$$E_L(\text{pu}) = 213.6 \text{ kV}/199.2 \text{ kV}$$
$$= 1.0723 \angle 0°$$

The per-unit current in the load is

$$I_L(\text{pu}) = \frac{S_L(\text{pu})}{E_L(\text{pu})} = \frac{0.6231}{1.0723} = 0.5811$$

The power factor of the load is 0.9. Consequently, I_L lags behind E_L by an angle of arcos 0.90 = 25.84°.

Consequently, the amplitude and phase of the per-unit load current is given by

$$I_L(\text{pu}) = 0.5811 \quad -25.84°$$

The per-unit voltage E_s (Fig. 12.19) is

$$
\begin{aligned}
E_s(\text{pu}) &= E_L(\text{pu}) + I_L(\text{pu}) \times Z_T(\text{pu}) \\
&= 1.0723\angle 0° + (0.5811\angle -25.84°) \\
&\quad \times (0.115\angle 90°) \\
&= 1.0723 + 0.0668\angle 64.16° \\
&= 1.0723 + 0.0668(\cos 64.16° + \\
&\quad j \sin 64.16°) \\
&= 1.1014 + j\,0.0601 \\
&= 1.103\angle 3.12°
\end{aligned}
$$

Therefore,

$$E_s = 1.103 \times 345\ \text{kV} = 381\ \text{kV}\angle 3.12°$$

The per-unit voltage on the primary side is also

$$E_p = 1.103\angle 3.12°$$

The effective voltage across the terminals of the generator is, therefore,

$$
\begin{aligned}
E_g &= E_p(\text{pu}) \times E_B(\text{primary}) \\
&= 1.103 \times 24.5\ \text{kV} \\
&= 27.02\ \text{kV}
\end{aligned}
$$

12.13 Polarity marking of 3-phase transformers

The HV terminals of a 3-phase transformer are marked H_1, H_2, H_3 and the LV terminals are marked X_1, X_2, X_3. The following rules have been standardized:

1. If the primary windings and secondary windings are connected wye-wye or delta-delta, the voltages between similarly-marked terminals are in phase. Thus,

   $E_{H_1H_2}$ is in phase with $E_{X_1X_2}$

   $E_{H_2H_1}$ is in phase with $E_{X_2X_1}$

   $E_{H_1H_3}$ is in phase with $E_{X_1X_3}$

and so on.

2. If the primary and secondary windings are connected in wye-delta or delta-wye, there results a 30° phase shift between the primary and secondary line voltages. The internal connections are made so that the voltages on the HV side *always* lead the voltages of similarly marked terminals on the LV side. Thus,

   $E_{H_1H_2}$ leads $E_{X_1X_2}$ by 30°

   $E_{H_2H_1}$ leads $E_{X_2X_1}$ by 30°

   $E_{H_3H_2}$ leads $E_{X_3X_2}$ by 30°

and so on.

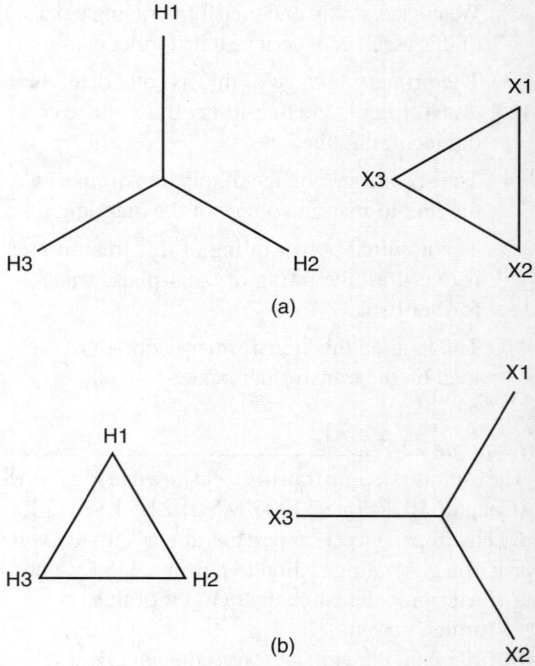

Figure 12.20
Polarity marking of 3-phase transformers.

Fig. 12.20 shows two ways of representing the delta-wye terminal markings.

3. These rules are not affected by the phase sequence of the line voltage applied to the primary side.

Questions and Problems

Practical level

12-1 Assuming that the transformer terminals have polarity marks H_1, H_2, X_1, X_2, make schematic drawings of the following connections:

a. Delta-wye
b. Open-delta

12-2 Three single-phase transformers rated at 250 kVA, 7200 V/600 V, 60 Hz, are connected in wye-delta on a 12 470 V, 3-phase line. If the load is 450 kVA, calculate the following currents:

a. In the incoming and outgoing transmission lines
b. In the primary and secondary windings

12-3 The transformer in Fig. 12.9 has a rating of 36 MVA, 13.8 kV/320 V. Calculate the nominal currents in the primary and secondary lines.

12-4 Calculate the nominal currents in the primary and secondary windings of the transformer shown in Fig. 10.18, knowing that the windings are connected in delta-wye.

Intermediate level

12-5 The transformer shown in Fig. 10.19 operates in the forced-air mode during the morning peaks.

a. Calculate the currents in the secondary lines if the primary line voltage is 225 kV and the primary line current is 150 A.
b. Is the transformer overloaded?

12-6 The transformers in Problem 12-2 are used to raise the voltage of a 3-phase, 600 V line to 7.2 kV.

a. How must they be connected?
b. Calculate the line currents for a 600 kVA load.
c. Calculate the corresponding primary and secondary currents.

12-7 In order to meet an emergency, three single-phase transformers rated 100 kVA, 13.2 kV/2.4 kV are connected in wye-delta on a 3-phase, 18 kV line.

a. What is the maximum load that can be connected to the transformer bank?
b. What is the outgoing line voltage?

12-8 Two transformers rated at 250 kVA, 2.4 kV/600 V are connected in open-delta to supply a load of 400 kVA.

a. Are the transformers overloaded?
b. What is the maximum load the bank can carry on a continuous basis?

12-9 Referring to Figs. 12.3 and 12.4, the line voltage between phases A-B-C is 6.9 kV and the voltage between lines 1, 2, and 3 is balanced and equal to 600 V. Then, in a similar installation the secondary windings of transformer P are by mistake connected in reverse.

a. Determine the voltages measured between lines 1-2, 2-3, and 3-1.
b. Draw the new phasor diagram.

Industrial application

12-10 Three 150 kVA, 480 V/4000 V, 60 Hz single-phase transformers are to be installed on a 4000 V, 3-phase line. The exciting current has a value of 0.02 pu. Calculate the line current when the transformers are operating at no-load.

12-11 The core loss in a 300 kVA, 3-phase distribution transformer is estimated to be 0.003 pu. The copper losses are 0.0015 pu. If the transformer operates effectively at no-load 50 percent of the time, and the cost of electricity is 4.5 cents per kWh, calculate the cost of the no-load operation in the course of one year.

12-12 The bulletin of a transformer manufacturer indicates that a 150 kVA, 230 V/208 V, 60 Hz, 3-phase autotransformer weighs

310 lb, whereas a standard 3-phase transformer having the same rating weighs 1220 lb. Why this difference?

12-13 Three single-phase transformers rated at 15 kVA, 480 V/120 V, 60 Hz are connected in delta to function as autotransformers on a 600 V, 3-phase line. The H_1, H_2, X_1, X_2 polarity marks appear on the metal housing.

a. Show how the transformers should be connected.

b. Determine the 3-phase voltage output of the transformer.

c. Determine the phase shift between the 3-phase voltage output and the 600 V, 3-phase input.

12-14 In Problem 12-13 calculate the maximum line current that can be drawn from the 600 V source. Then calculate the maximum load (kVA) that the autotransformer can carry.

12-15 You wish to operate a 40 hp, 460 V, 3-phase motor from a 600 V, 3-phase supply. The full-load current of the motor is 42 A. Three 5 kVA, 120 V/480 V, single-phase transformers are available. How would you connect them? Are they able to furnish the load current drawn by the motor without overheating?

CHAPTER 13

Three-Phase Induction Machines

13.0 Introduction

Three-phase induction machines comprise both motors and generators.

Three-phase induction motors are the motors most frequently encountered in industry. They are simple, rugged, low-priced, and easy to maintain. They run at essentially constant speed from zero to full-load. The speed is frequency-dependent and, consequently, these motors are not easily adapted to speed control. However, variable frequency electronic drives are being used more and more to control the speed of commercial induction motors.

In this chapter we cover the basic principles of the 3-phase induction motor and develop the fundamental equations describing its behavior. We then discuss its general construction and the way the windings are made.

Squirrel-cage, wound-rotor, and linear induction motors ranging from a few horsepower to several thousand horsepower permit the reader to see that they all operate on the same basic principles.

In this chapter we will also see that 3-phase induction motors can operate as 3-phase induction generators.

13.1 Principal components

A 3-phase induction motor (Fig. 13.1) has two main parts: a stationary stator and a revolving rotor. The rotor is separated from the stator by a small air gap that ranges from 0.4 mm to 4 mm, depending on the power of the motor.

The *stator* (Fig. 13.2) consists of a steel frame that supports a hollow, cylindrical core made up of stacked laminations. A number of evenly spaced slots, punched out of the internal circumference of the laminations, provide the space for the stator winding.

The *rotor* is also composed of punched laminations. These are carefully stacked to create a series of rotor slots to provide space for the rotor winding. We use two types of rotor windings: (1) conventional 3-phase windings made of insulated wire and (2) squirrel-cage windings. The type of winding gives rise to two main classes of motors: *squirrel-cage induction motors* (also called *cage motors*) and *wound-rotor induction motors*.

A **squirrel-cage rotor** is composed of bare copper bars, slightly longer than the rotor, which are pushed into the slots. The opposite ends are welded to two copper end-rings, so that all the bars are short-circuited together. The entire construction (bars and end-rings) resembles a squirrel cage, from which the name is derived. In small and medium-size motors, the bars and end-rings are made of die-cast aluminum, molded to form an integral block (Fig. 13.3a). Figs.13.3b and 13.3c show progressive stages in the manufacture of a squirrel-cage motor.

Figure 13.1
Super-E, premium efficiency induction motor rated 10 hp, 1760 r/min, 460 V, 3-phase, 60 Hz. This totally-enclosed fan-cooled motor has a full-load current of 12.7 A, efficiency of 91.7%, and power factor of 81%. Other characteristics: no-load current: 5 A; locked rotor current: 85 A; locked rotor torque: 2.2 pu; breakdown torque: 3.3 pu; service factor 1.15; total weight: 90 kg; overall length including shaft: 491 mm; overall height: 279 mm.
(Courtesy of Baldor Electric Company)

A **wound rotor** has a 3-phase winding, similar to the one on the stator. The winding is uniformly distributed in the slots and is usually connected in 3-wire wye. The terminals are connected to three slip-rings, which turn with the rotor (Fig. 13.4). The revolving slip-rings and associated stationary brushes enable us to connect external resistors in series with the rotor winding. The external resistors are mainly used during the start-up period; under normal running conditions, the three brushes are short-circuited.

13.2 Principle of operation

The operation of a 3-phase induction motor is based upon the application of Faraday's Law and the Lorentz force on a conductor (Sections 2.20, 2.21, and 2.22). The behavior can readily be understood by means of the following example.

Consider a series of conductors of length l, whose extremities are short-circuited by two bars A and B (Fig. 13.5a). A permanent magnet placed above this conducting ladder, moves rapidly to the right at a speed v, so that its magnetic field B sweeps across the conductors. The following sequence of events then takes place:

Figure 13.2
Exploded view of the cage motor of Fig. 13.1, showing the stator, rotor, end-bells, cooling fan, ball bearings, and terminal box. The fan blows air over the stator frame, which is ribbed to improve heat transfer.
(Courtesy of Baldor Electric Company)

Figure 13.3a
Die-cast aluminum squirrel-cage rotor with integral cooling fan.
(Courtesy of Lab-Volt)

1. A voltage $E = Blv$ is induced in each conductor while it is being cut by the flux (Faraday's law).
2. The induced voltage immediately produces a current I, which flows down the conductor underneath the pole-face, through the end-bars, and back through the other conductors.
3. Because the current-carrying conductor lies in the magnetic field of the permanent magnet, it experiences a mechanical force (Lorentz force).
4. The force always acts in a direction to drag the conductor along with the magnetic field (Section 2.23).

If the conducting ladder is free to move, it will accelerate toward the right. However, as it picks up speed, the conductors will be cut less rapidly by the moving magnet, with the result that the induced voltage E and the current I will diminish. Consequently, the force acting on the conductors will also decrease. If the ladder were to move at the same speed as the magnetic field, the induced voltage E, the current I, and the force dragging the ladder along would all become zero.

In an induction motor the ladder is closed upon itself to form a squirrel-cage (Fig. 13.5b) and the moving magnet is replaced by a rotating field. The field is produced by the 3-phase currents that flow in the stator windings, as we will now explain.

13.3 The rotating field

Consider a simple stator having 6 salient poles, each of which carries a coil having 5 turns (Fig. 13.6). Coils that are diametrically opposite are connected in series by means of three jumpers that respectively connect terminals a-a, b-b, and c-c. This creates three identical sets of windings, AN, BN, CN, that are mechanically spaced at 120° to each other.

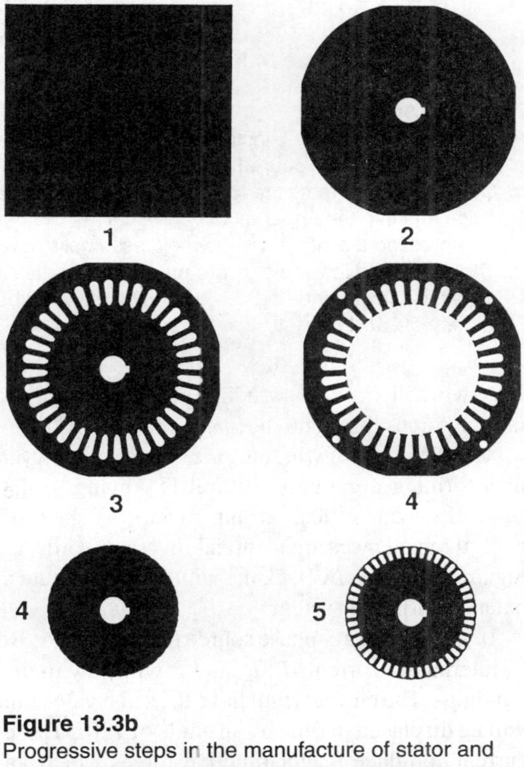

Figure 13.3b
Progressive steps in the manufacture of stator and rotor laminations. Sheet steel is sheared to size (1), blanked (2), punched (3), blanked (4), and punched (5).
(Courtesy of Lab-Volt)

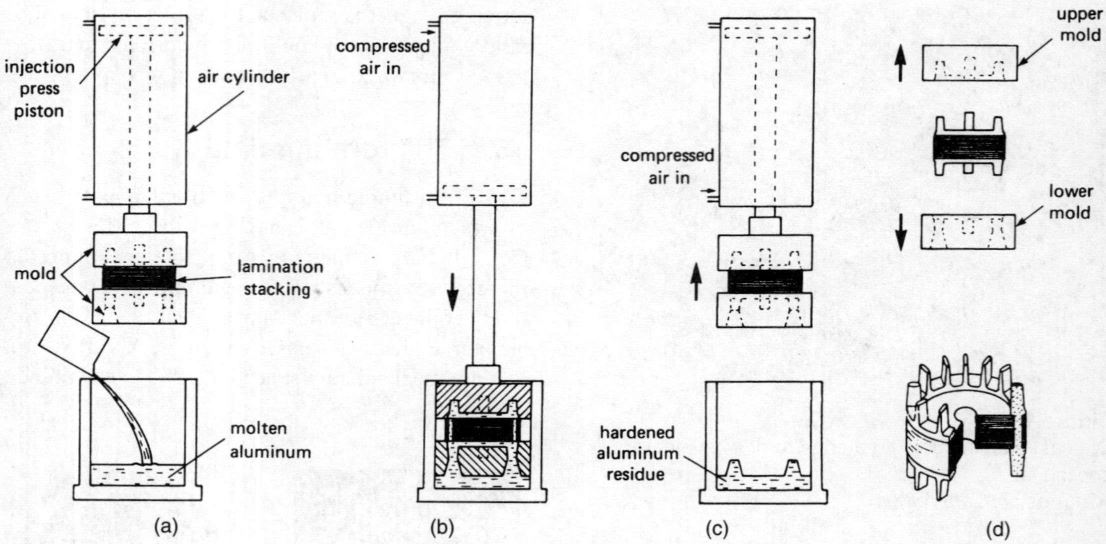

Figure 13.3c
Progressive steps in the injection molding of a squirrel-cage rotor.

a. Molten aluminum is poured into a cylindrical cavity. The laminated rotor stacking is firmly held between two molds.
b. Compressed air rams the mold assembly into the cavity. Molten aluminum is forced upward through the rotor bar holes and into the upper mold.
c. Compressed air withdraws the mold assembly, now completely filled with hot (but hardened) aluminum.
d. The upper and lower molds are pulled away, revealing the die-cast rotor. The cross-section view shows that the upper and lower end-rings are joined by the rotor bars.

(Courtesy of Lab-Volt)

The two coils in each winding produce magnetomotive forces that act in the same direction.

The three sets of windings are connected in wye, thus forming a common neutral N. Owing to the perfectly symmetrical arrangement, the line-to-neutral impedances are identical. In other words, as regards terminals A, B, C, the windings constitute a balanced 3-phase system.

If we connect a 3-phase source to terminals A, B, C, alternating currents I_a, I_b, and I_c will flow in the windings. The currents will have the same value but will be displaced in time by an angle of 120°. These currents produce magnetomotive forces which, in turn, create a magnetic flux. It is this flux we are interested in.

In order to follow the sequence of events, we assume that positive currents (indicated by the arrows) always flow in the windings from line to neutral. Conversely, negative currents flow from neutral to line. Furthermore, to enable us to work with numbers, suppose that the peak current per phase is 10 A. Thus, when $I_a = +7$ A, the two coils of phase A will together produce an mmf of 7 A × 10 turns = 70 ampere-turns and a corresponding value of flux. Because the current is positive, the flux is directed vertically upward, according to the right-hand rule.

As time goes by, we can determine the instantaneous value and direction of the current in each winding and thereby establish the successive flux patterns. Thus, referring to Fig. 13.7 at instant 1, current I_a has a value of +10 A, whereas I_b and I_c both have a value of −5 A. The mmf of phase A is 10 A × 10 turns = 100 ampere-turns, while the mmf

Figure 13.4a
Exploded view of a 5 hp, 1730 r/min, wound-rotor induction motor.

Figure 13.4b
Close-up of the slip-ring end of the rotor.
(Courtesy of Brook Crompton Parkinson Ltd)

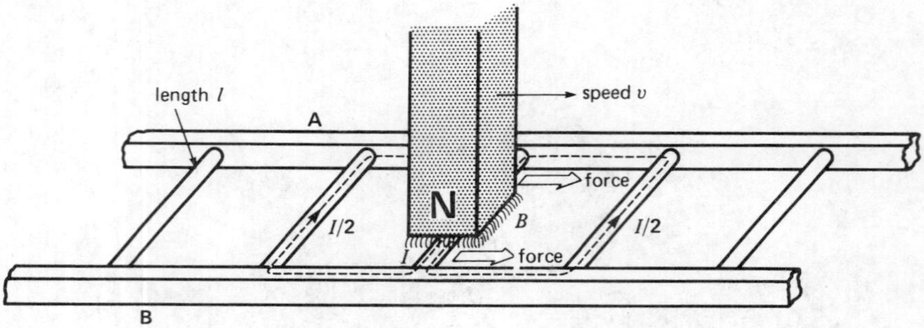

Figure 13.5a
Moving magnet cutting across a conducting ladder.

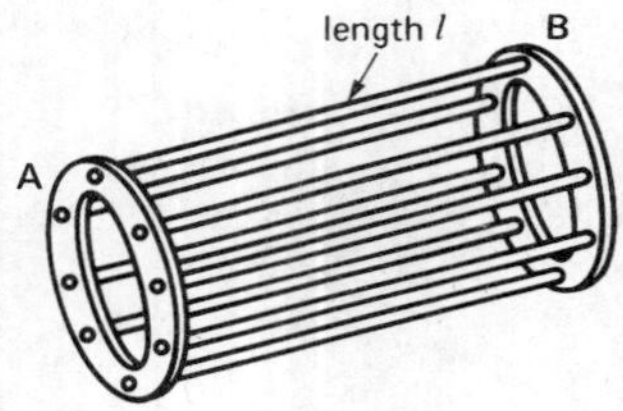

Figure 13.5b
Ladder bent upon itself to form a squirrel cage.

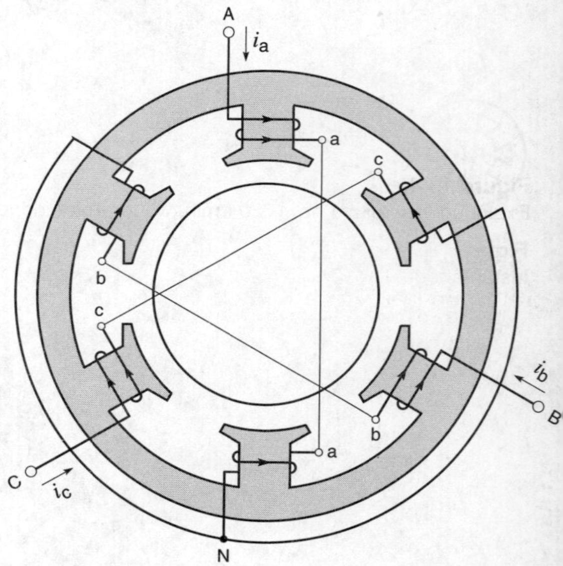

Figure 13.6
Elementary stator having terminals A, B, C connected to a 3-phase source (not shown). Currents flowing from line to neutral are considered to be positive.

of phases B and C are each 50 ampere-turns. The direction of the mmf depends upon the instantaneous current flows and, using the right-hand rule, we find that the direction of the resulting magnetic field is as shown in Fig. 13.8a. Note that as far as the rotor is concerned, the six salient poles together produce a magnetic field having essentially one broad north pole and one broad south pole. This means that the 6-pole stator actually produces a 2-pole field. The combined magnetic field points upward.

At instant 2, one-sixth cycle later, current I_c attains a peak of -10 A, while I_a and I_b both have a value of $+5$ A (Fig. 13.8b). We discover that the new field has the same shape as before, except that it has moved clockwise by an angle of 60°. In other words, the flux makes 1/6 of a turn between instants 1 and 2.

Proceeding in this way for each of the successive instants 3, 4, 5, 6, and 7, separated by intervals of 1/6 cycle, we find that the magnetic field makes one complete turn during one cycle (see Figs. 13.8a to 13.8f).

The rotational speed of the field depends, therefore, upon the duration of one cycle, which in turn depends on the frequency of the source. If the frequency is 60 Hz, the resulting field makes one turn in 1/60 s, that is, 3600 revolutions per minute. On

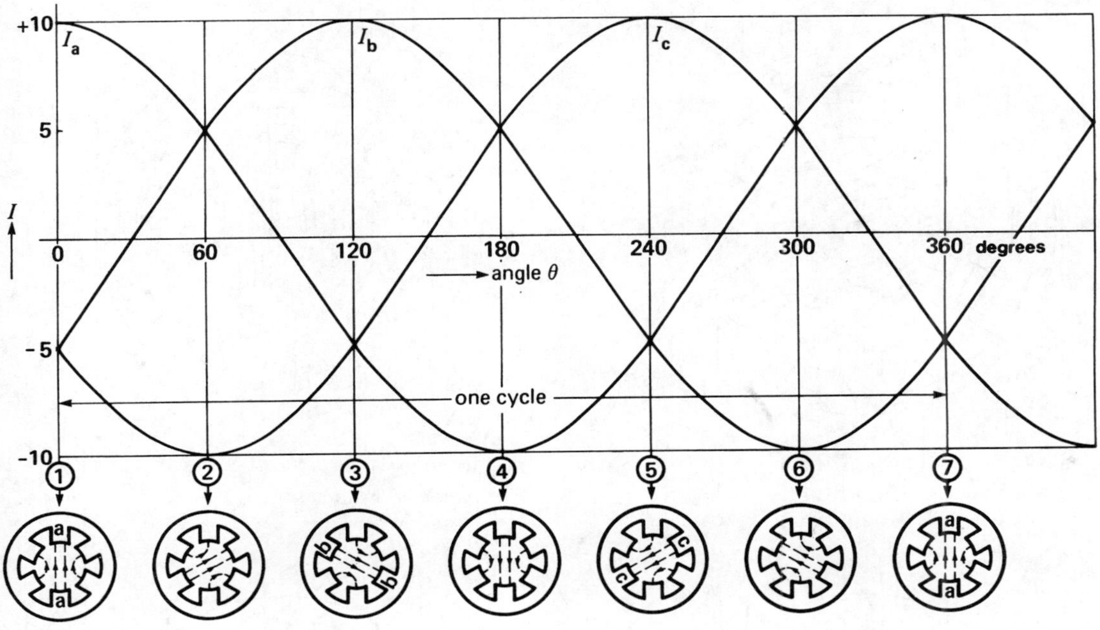

Figure 13.7
Instantaneous values of currents and position of the flux in Fig. 13.6.

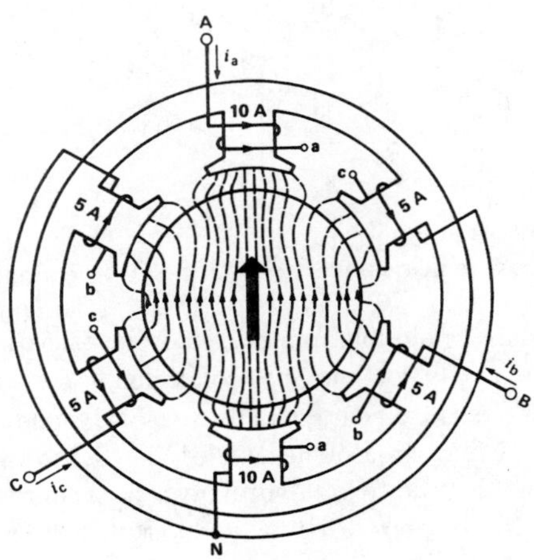

Figure 13.8a
Flux pattern at instant 1.

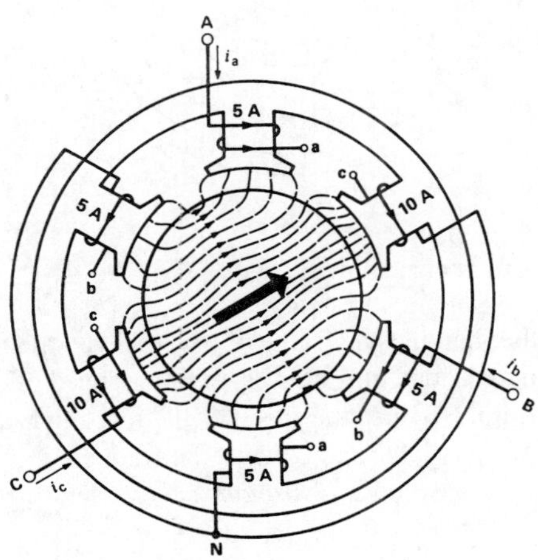

Figure 13.8b
Flux pattern at instant 2.

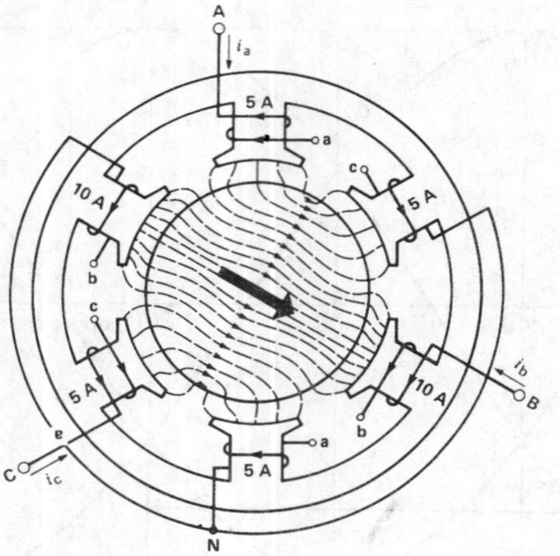

Figure 13.8c
Flux pattern at instant 3.

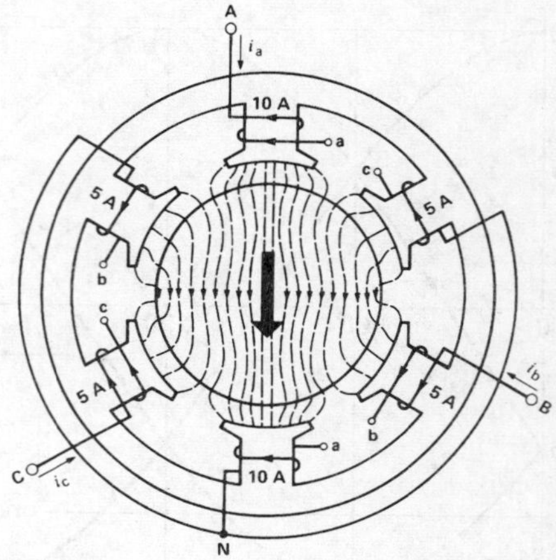

Figure 13.8d
Flux pattern at instant 4.

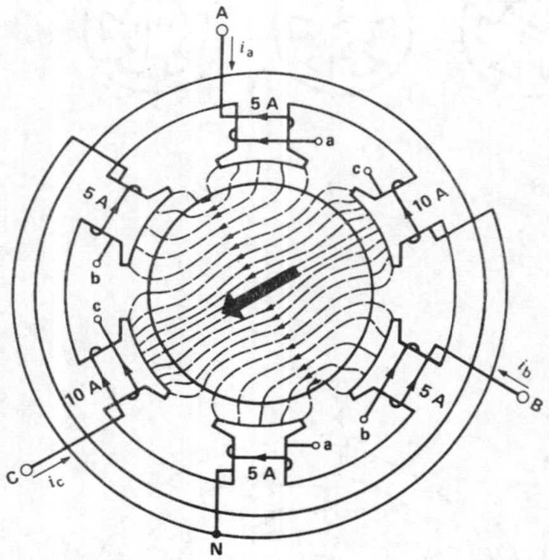

Figure 13.8e
Flux pattern at instant 5.

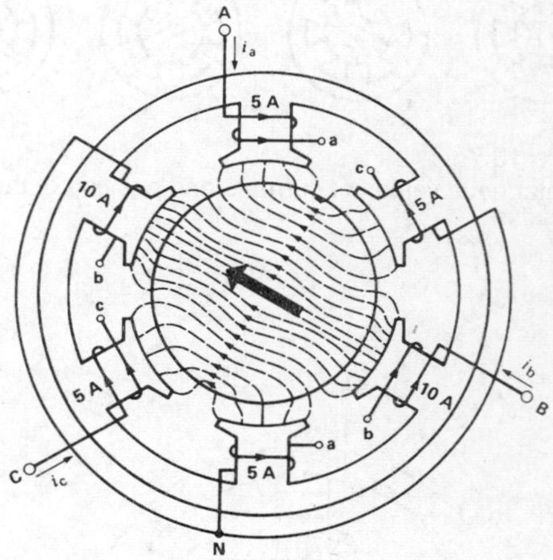

Figure 13.8f
Flux pattern at instant 6.

the other hand, if the frequency were 5 Hz, the field would make one turn in 1/5 s, giving a speed of only 300 r/min. Because the speed of the rotating field is necessarily synchronized with the frequency of the source, it is called *synchronous speed.*

13.4 Direction of rotation

The positive crests of the currents in Fig. 13.7 follow each other in the order A-B-C. This phase sequence produces a field that rotates clockwise. If we interchange any two of the lines connected to the stator, the new phase sequence will be A-C-B. By following the same line of reasoning developed in Section 13.3, we find that the field now revolves at synchronous speed in the opposite, or counterclockwise direction. Interchanging any two lines of a 3-phase motor will, therefore, reverse its direction of rotation.

Although early machines were built with salient poles, the stators of modern motors have internal diameters that are smooth. Thus, the salient-pole stator of Fig. 13.6 is now replaced by a smooth stator such as shown in Figs. 13.2 and 13.24a.

In Fig. 13.6, the two coils of phase A (Aa and An) are replaced by the two coils shown in Fig. 13.9a. They are lodged in two slots on the inner surface of the stator. Note that each coil covers 180° of the circumference whereas the coils in Fig. 13.6 cover only 60°. The 180° coil pitch is more efficient because it produces more flux per turn. A current I_a flowing from terminal A to the neutral N yields the flux distribution shown in the figure.

The coils of phases B and C are identical to those of phase A and, as can be seen in Fig. 13.9b, they are displaced at 120° to each other. The resulting magnetic field due to all three phases again consists of two poles.

In practice, instead of using a single coil per pole as shown in Fig. 13.9a, the coil is subdivided into two, three or more coils lodged in adjacent slots. The staggered coils are connected in series and constitute what is known as a *phase group.* Spreading the coil in this way over two or more slots tends to create a sinusoidal flux distribution per pole, which improves the performance of the motor and makes it less noisy. A phase group (or simply *group*) composed of 5 staggered coils connected in series to be placed in 5 successive slots is shown in Fig. 13.20.

13.5 Number of poles—synchronous speed

Soon after the invention of the induction motor, it was found that the speed of the revolving flux could be reduced by increasing the number of poles.

To construct a 4-pole stator, the coils are distributed as shown in Fig. 13.10a. The four identical groups of phase A now span only 90° of the stator circumference. The groups are connected in series and in such a way that adjacent groups produce magnetomotive forces acting in opposite directions. In other words, when a current I_a flows in the stator winding of phase A (Fig. 13.10a), it creates four alternate N-S poles.

The windings of the other two phases are identical but are displaced from each other (and from phase A) by a mechanical angle of 60°. When the wye-connected windings are connected to a 3-phase source, a revolving field having four poles is created (Fig. 13.10b). This field rotates at only half the speed of the 2-pole field shown in Fig. 13.9b. We will shortly explain why this is so.

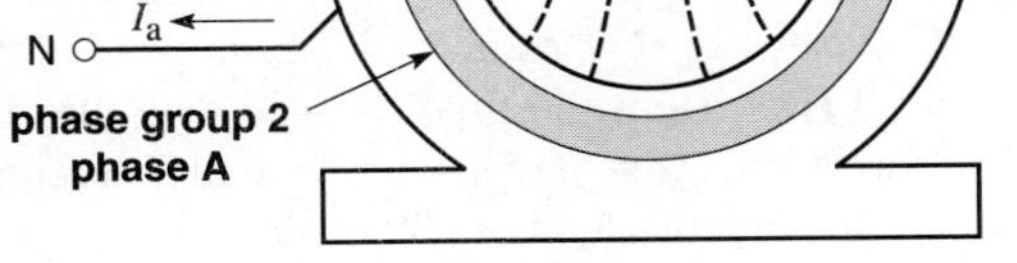

Figure 13.9a
Phase group 1 is composed of a single coil lodged in two slots. Phase group 2 is identical to phase group 1. The two coils are connected in series. In practice, a phase group usually consists of two or more staggered coils.

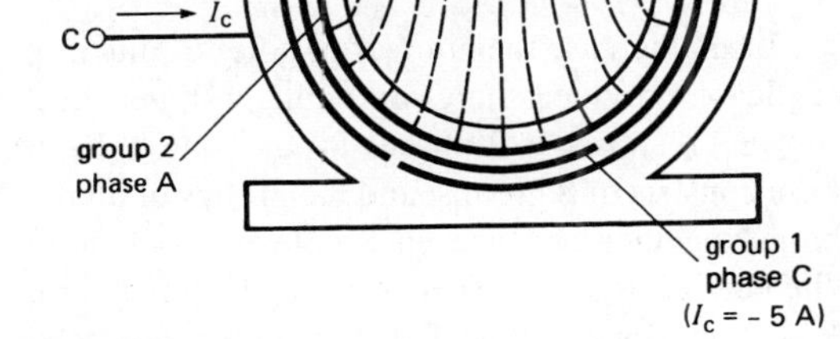

Figure 13.9b
Two-pole, full-pitch, lap-wound stator and resulting magnetic field when the current in phase A = +10 A and $I_b = I_c = -5$ A.

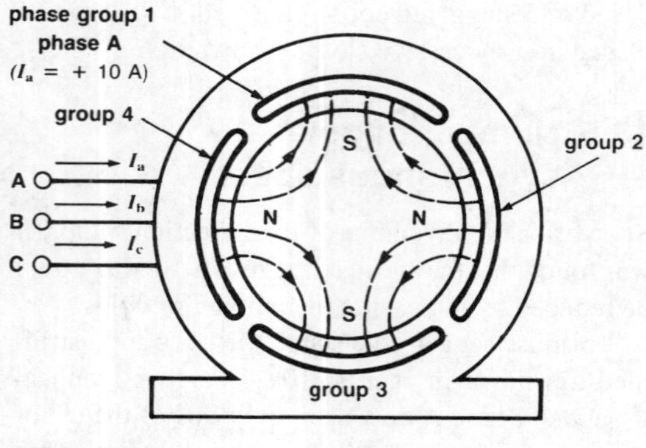

Figure 13.10a
The four phase groups of phase A produce a 4-pole magnetic field.

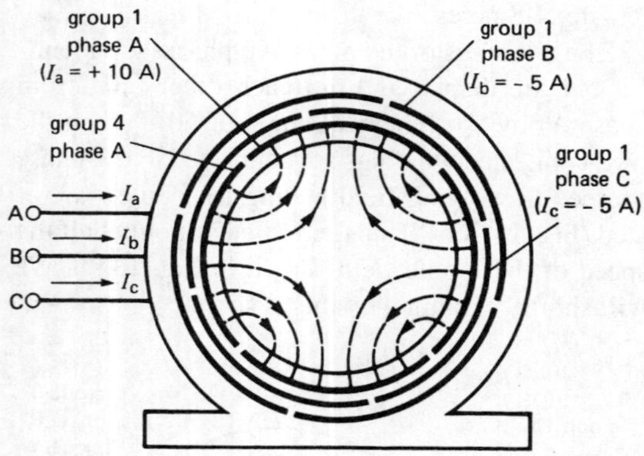

Figure 13.10b
Four-pole, full-pitch, lap-wound stator and resulting magnetic field when $I_a = +10$ A and $I_b = I_c = -5$ A.

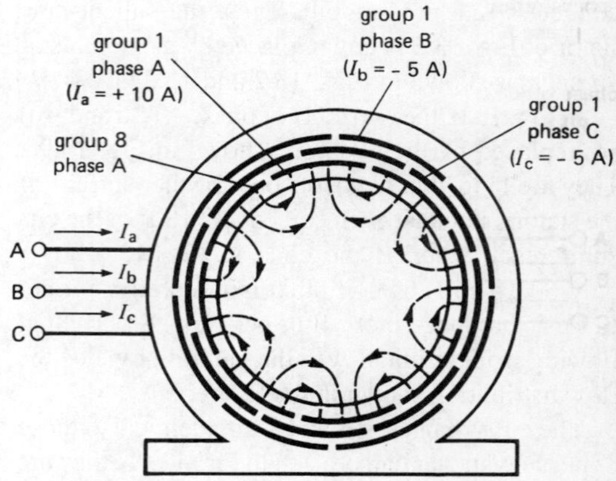

Figure 13.11
Eight-pole, full-pitch, lap-wound stator and resulting magnetic field when $I_a = +10$ A and $I_b = I_c = -5$ A.

We can increase the number of poles as much as we please provided there are enough slots. Thus, Fig. 13.11 shows a 3-phase, 8-pole stator. Each phase consists of 8 groups, and the groups of all the phases together produce an 8-pole rotating field. When connected to a 60 Hz source, the poles turn, like the spokes of a wheel, at a synchronous speed of 900 r/min.

How can we tell what the synchronous speed will be? Without going into all the details of current flow in the three phases, let us restrict our attention to phase A. In Fig. 13.11 each phase group covers a mechanical angle of 360/8 = 45°. Suppose the current in phase A is at its maximum positive value. The magnetic flux is then centered on phase A, and the N-S poles are located as shown in Fig. 13.12a. One-half cycle later, the current in phase A will reach its maximum negative value. The flux pattern will be the same as before, except that all the N poles will have become S poles and vice versa (Fig. 13.12b). In comparing the two figures, it is clear that the entire magnetic field has shifted by an angle of 45°—and this gives us the clue to finding the speed of rotation. The flux moves 45° and so it takes 8 half-cycles (= 4 cycles) to make a complete turn. On a 60 Hz system the time to make one turn is therefore 4 × 1/60 = 1/15 s. Consequently, the flux turns at the rate of 15 r/s or 900 r/min.

The speed of a rotating field depends therefore upon the frequency of the source and the number of poles on the stator. Using the same reasoning as above, we can prove that the synchronous speed is always given by the expression

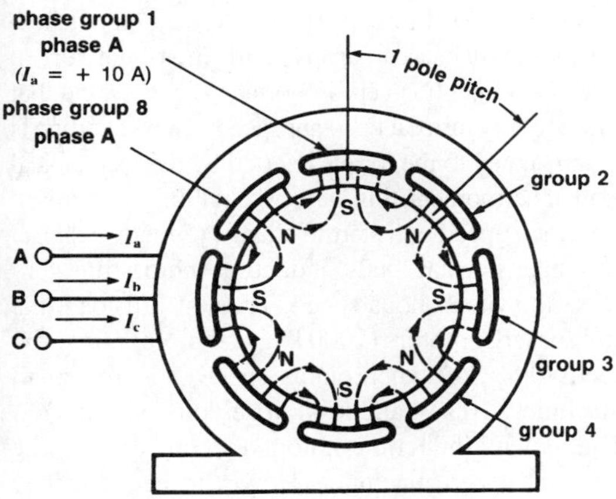

Figure 13.12a
Flux pattern when the current in phase A is at its maximum positive value.

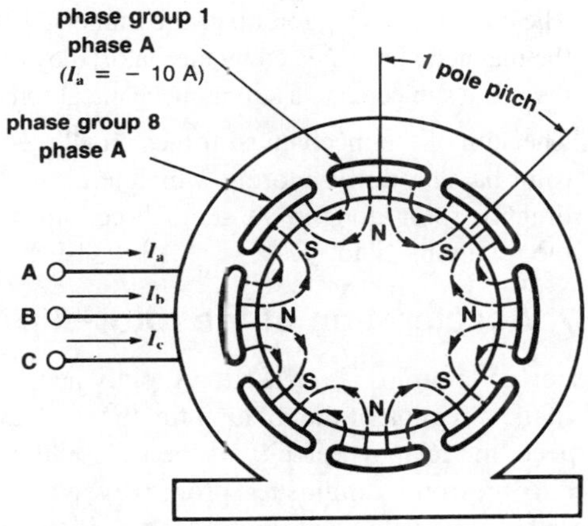

Figure 13.12b
Flux pattern when the current in phase A is at its maximum negative value. The pattern is the same as in Fig. 13.12a but it has advanced by one pole pitch.

$$n_s = \frac{120f}{p} \tag{13.1}$$

where

n_s = synchronous speed [r/min]
f = frequency of the source [Hz]
p = number of poles

This equation shows that the synchronous speed increases with frequency and decreases with the number of poles.

Example 13-1

Calculate the synchronous speed of a 3-phase induction motor having 20 poles when it is connected to a 50 Hz source.

Solution

$$n_s = 120f/p = 120 \times 50/20$$
$$= 300 \text{ r/min}$$

13.6 Starting characteristics of a squirrel-cage motor

Let us connect the stator of an induction motor to a 3-phase source, with the rotor locked. The revolving field created by the stator cuts across the rotor bars and induces a voltage in all of them.

This is an ac voltage because each conductor is cut, in rapid succession, by an N pole followed by an S pole. The frequency of the voltage depends upon the number of N and S poles that sweep across a conductor per second; when the rotor is at rest, it is always equal to the frequency of the source.

Because the rotor bars are short-circuited by the end-rings, the induced voltage causes a large current to flow—usually several hundred amperes per bar in machines of medium power.

The current-carrying conductors are in the path of the flux created by the stator, consequently, they all experience a strong mechanical force. These forces tend to drag the rotor along with the revolving field.

In summary,

1. A revolving magnetic field is set up when a 3-phase voltage is applied to the stator of an induction motor.
2. The revolving field induces a voltage in the rotor bars.
3. The induced voltage creates large circulating currents which flow in the rotor bars and end-rings.

4. The current-carrying rotor bars are immersed in the magnetic field created by the stator; they are therefore subjected to a strong mechanical force.
5. The sum of the mechanical forces on all the rotor bars produces a torque which tends to drag the rotor along in the same direction as the revolving field.

13.7 Acceleration of the rotor-slip

As soon as the rotor is released, it rapidly accelerates in the direction of the rotating field. As it picks up speed, the relative velocity of the field with respect to the rotor diminishes progressively. This causes both the value and the frequency of the induced voltage to decrease because the rotor bars are cut more slowly. The rotor current, very large at first, decreases rapidly as the motor picks up speed.

The speed will continue to increase, but it will never catch up with the revolving field. In effect, if the rotor *did* turn at the same speed as the field (synchronous speed), the flux would no longer cut the rotor bars and the induced voltage and current would fall to zero. Under these conditions the force acting on the rotor bars would also become zero and the friction and windage would immediately cause the rotor to slow down.

The rotor speed is always slightly less than synchronous speed so as to produce a current in the rotor bars sufficiently large enough to overcome the braking torque. At no-load the percent difference in speed between the rotor and field (called *slip*), is small, usually less than 0.1% of synchronous speed.

13.8 Motor under load

Suppose the motor is initially running at no-load. If we apply a mechanical load to the shaft, the motor will begin to slow down and the revolving field will cut the rotor bars at a higher and higher rate. The induced voltage and the resulting current in the bars will increase progressively, producing a greater and greater motor torque. The question is, for how long can this go on? Will the speed continue to drop until the motor comes to a halt?

No, the motor and the mechanical load will reach a state of equilibrium when the motor torque is exactly equal to the load torque. When this state is reached, the speed will cease to drop and the motor will turn at a constant rate. It is very important to understand that a motor only turns at constant speed when its torque is *exactly* equal to the torque exerted by the mechanical load. The moment this state of equilibrium is upset, the motor speed will start to change (Section 3.11).

Under normal loads, induction motors run very close to synchronous speed. Thus, at full-load, the slip for large motors (1000 kW and more) rarely exceeds 0.5% of synchronous speed, and for small machines (10 kW and less), it seldom exceeds 5%. That is why induction motors are considered to be constant speed machines. However, because they never actually turn at synchronous speed, they are sometimes called *asynchronous* machines.

13.9 Slip and slip speed

The slip s of an induction motor is the difference between the synchronous speed and the rotor speed, expressed as a percent (or per-unit) of synchronous speed. The per-unit slip is given by the equation

$$s = \frac{n_s - n}{n_s} \tag{13.2}$$

where

s = slip
n_s = synchronous speed [r/min]
n = rotor speed [r/min]

The slip is practically zero at no-load and is equal to 1 (or 100%) when the rotor is locked.

Example 13-2

A 0.5 hp, 6-pole induction motor is excited by a 3-phase, 60 Hz source. If the full-load speed is 1140 r/min, calculate the slip.

Solution

The synchronous speed of the motor is

$$n_s = 120f/p = 120 \times 60/6 \tag{13.1}$$
$$= 1200 \text{ r/min}$$

The difference between the synchronous speed of the revolving flux and rotor speed is the slip speed:

$$n_s - n = 1200 - 1140 = 60 \text{ r/min}$$

The slip is

$$s = (n_s - n)/n_s = 60/1200 \quad (13.2)$$
$$= 0.05 \text{ or } 5\%$$

13.10 Voltage and frequency induced in the rotor

The voltage and frequency induced in the rotor both depend upon the slip. They are given by the following equations:

$$f_2 = sf \quad (13.3)$$

$$E_2 = sE_{oc} \text{ (approx.)} \quad (13.4)$$

where

f_2 = frequency of the voltage and current in the rotor [Hz]

f = frequency of the source connected to the stator [Hz]

s = slip

E_2 = voltage induced in the rotor at slip s

E_{oc} = open-circuit voltage induced in the rotor when at rest [V]

In a cage motor, the open-circuit voltage E_{oc} is the voltage that *would* be induced in the rotor bars if the bars were disconnected from the end-rings. In the case of a wound-rotor motor the open-circuit voltage is $1/\sqrt{3}$ times the voltage between the open-circuit slip-rings.

It should be noted that Eq. 13.3 *always* holds true, but Eq. 13.4 is valid only if the revolving flux (expressed in webers) remains absolutely constant. However, between zero and full-load the actual value of E_2 is only slightly less than the value given by the equation.

Example 13-3

The 6-pole, wound-rotor induction motor of Example 13-2 is excited by a 3-phase, 60 Hz source. Calculate the frequency of the rotor current under the following conditions:

a. At standstill
b. Motor turning at 500 r/min in the same direction as the revolving field
c. Motor turning at 500 r/min in the opposite direction to the revolving field
d. Motor turning at 2000 r/min in the same direction as the revolving field

Solution

From Example 13-2, the synchronous speed of the motor is 1200 r/min.

a. At standstill the motor speed $n = 0$. Consequently, the slip is

$$s = (n_s - n)/n_s = (1200 - 0)/1200 = 1$$

The frequency of the induced voltage (and of the induced current) is

$$f_2 = sf = 1 \times 60 = 60 \text{ Hz}$$

b. When the motor turns in the same direction as the field, the motor speed n is positive. The slip is

$$s = (n_s - n)/n_s = (1200 - 500)/1200$$
$$= 700/1200 = 0.583$$

The frequency of the induced voltage (and of the rotor current) is

$$f_2 = sf = 0.583 \times 60 = 35 \text{ Hz}$$

c. When the motor turns in the opposite direction to the field, the motor speed is *negative;* thus, $n = -500$. The slip is

$$s = (n_s - n)/n_s$$
$$= [1200 - (-500)]/1200$$
$$= (1200 + 500)/1200 = 1700/1200$$
$$= 1.417$$

A slip greater than 1 implies that the motor is operating as a brake.

The frequency of the induced voltage and rotor current is

$$f_2 = sf = 1.417 \times 60 = 85 \text{ Hz}$$

d. The motor speed is positive because the rotor turns in the same direction as the field: $n = +2000$. The slip is

$$s = (n_s - n)/n_s$$
$$= (1200 - 2000)/1200$$
$$= -800/1200 = -0.667$$

A negative slip implies that the motor is actually operating as a generator.
The frequency of the induced voltage and rotor current is

$$f_2 = sf = -0.667 \times 60 = -40 \text{ Hz}$$

A negative frequency means that the phase sequence of the voltages induced in the rotor windings is reversed. Thus, if the phase sequence of the rotor voltages is A-B-C when the frequency is positive, the phase sequence is A-C-B when the frequency is negative. As far as a frequency meter is concerned, a negative frequency gives the same reading as a positive frequency. Consequently, we can say that the frequency is simply 40 Hz.

13.11 Characteristics of squirrel-cage induction motors

Table 13A lists the typical properties of squirrel-cage induction motors in the power range between 1 kW and 20 000 kW. Note that the current and torque are expressed in per-unit values. The base current is the full-load current and all other currents are compared to it. Similarly, the base torque is the full-load torque and all other torques are compared to it. Finally, the base speed is the synchronous speed of the motor. The following explanations will clarify the meaning of the values given in the table.

*1. **Motor at no-load.*** When the motor runs at no load, the stator current lies between 0.5 and 0.3 pu (of full-load current). The no-load current is similar to the exciting current in a transformer. Thus, it is composed of a magnetizing component that creates the revolving flux Φ_m and a small active component that supplies the windage and friction losses in the rotor plus the iron losses in the stator. The flux Φ_m links both the stator and the rotor; consequently it is similar to the mutual flux in a transformer (Fig. 13.13).

Considerable reactive power is needed to create the revolving field and, in order to keep it within acceptable limits, the air gap is made as short as mechanical tolerances will permit. The power factor at no-load is therefore low; it ranges from 0.2 (or 20%) for small machines to 0.05 for large machines. The efficiency is zero because the output power is zero.

*2. **Motor under load.*** When the motor is under load, the current in the rotor produces an mmf which tends to change the mutual flux Φ_m. This sets up an opposing current flow in the stator. The opposing mmfs of the rotor and stator are very similar to the opposing mmfs of the secondary and primary in a transformer. As a result, leakage fluxes Φ_{f1} and Φ_{f2} are created, in addition to the mutual flux Φ_m (Fig. 13.14). The total reactive power needed to produce these three fluxes is slightly greater than when the motor is operating at no-load. However, the active power (kW) absorbed by the motor increases in almost direct proportion to

TABLE 13A TYPICAL CHARACTERISTICS OF SQUIRREL-CAGE INDUCTION MOTORS

Loading	Current (per-unit)		Torque (per-unit)		Slip (per-unit)		Efficiency		Power factor	
Motor size →	Small*	Big*	Small	Big	Small	Big	Small	Big	Small	Big
Full-load	1	1	1	1	0.03	0.004	0.7 to 0.9	0.96 to 0.98	0.8 to 0.85	0.87 to 0.9
No-load	0.5	0.3	0	0	≈0	≈0	0	0	0.2	0.05
Locked rotor	5 to 6	4 to 6	1.5 to 3	0.5 to 1	1	1	0	0	0.4	0.1

*__*Small*__ means under 11 kW (15 hp); ***big*** means over 1120 kW (1500 hp) and up to 25 000 hp.

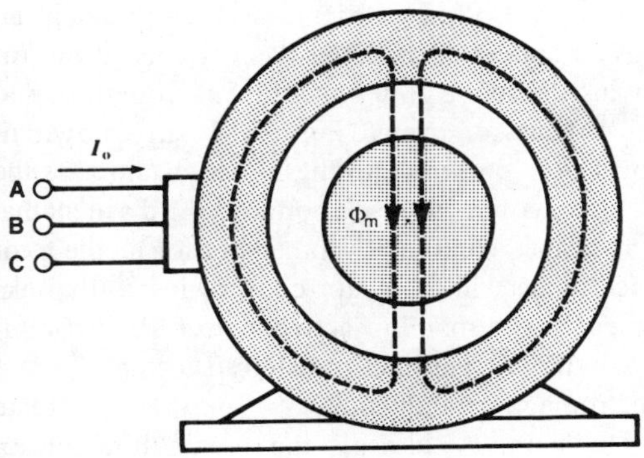

Figure 13.13
At no-load the flux in the motor is mainly the mutual flux Φ_m. To create this flux, considerable reactive power is needed.

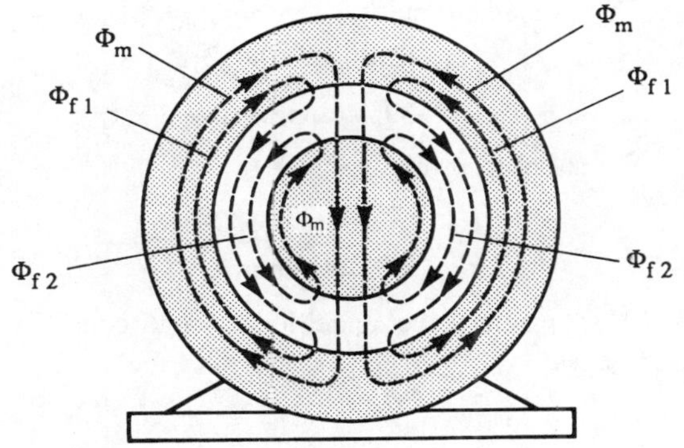

Figure 13.14
At full-load the mutual flux decreases, but stator and rotor leakage fluxes are created. The reactive power needed is slightly greater than in Fig. 13.13.

the mechanical load. It follows that the power factor of the motor improves dramatically as the mechanical load increases. At full-load it ranges from 0.80 for small machines to 0.90 for large machines. The efficiency at full-load is particularly high; it can attain 98% for very large machines.

3. Locked-rotor characteristics. The locked-rotor current is 5 to 6 times the full-load current, making the I^2R losses 25 to 36 times higher than normal. The rotor must therefore never remain locked for more than a few seconds.

Although the mechanical power at standstill is zero, the motor develops a strong torque. The power factor is low because considerable reactive power is needed to produce the leakage flux in the rotor and stator windings. These leakage fluxes are much larger than in a transformer because the stator and the rotor windings are not as tightly coupled (see Section 10.2).

13.12 Estimating the currents in an induction motor

The full-load current of a 3-phase induction motor may be calculated by means of the following approximate equation:

$$I = 600\ P_h/E \tag{13.5}$$

where

I = full-load current [A]
P_h = output power [horsepower]
E = rated line voltage (V)
600 = empirical constant

Recalling that the starting current is 5 to 6 pu and that the no-load current lies between 0.5 and 0.3 pu, we can readily estimate the value of these currents for any induction motor.

Example 13-4

a. Calculate the approximate full-load current, locked-rotor current, and no-load current of a 3-phase induction motor having a rating of 500 hp, 2300 V.
b. Estimate the apparent power drawn under locked-rotor conditions.
c. State the nominal rating of this motor, expressed in kilowatts.

Solution

a. The full-load current is

$$I = 600\ P_h/E \tag{13.5}$$
$$= 600 \times 500/2300$$
$$= 130 \text{ A (approx.)}$$

The no-load current is

$$I_o = 0.3I = 0.3 \times 130$$
$$= 39 \text{ A (approx.)}$$

The starting current is

$$I_{LR} = 6I = 6 \times 130$$
$$= 780 \text{ A (approx.)}$$

b. The apparent power under locked-rotor conditions is

$$S = \sqrt{3}\ EI$$
$$= \sqrt{3} \times 2300 \times 780 \qquad (8.9)$$
$$= 3100 \text{ kVA (approx.)}$$

c. When the power of a motor is expressed in kilowatts, it always relates to the mechanical output and *not* to the electrical input. The nominal rating of this motor expressed in SI units is, therefore,

$P = 500/1.34$

$= 373$ kW (see Power conversion chart in Appendix AX0)

13.13 Active power flow

Voltages, currents, and phasor diagrams enable us to understand the detailed behavior of an induction motor. However, it is easier to see how electrical energy is converted into mechanical energy by following the active power as it flows through the machine. Thus, referring to Fig. 13.15, active power P_e flows from the line into the 3-phase stator. Due to the stator copper losses, a portion P_{js} is dissipated as heat in the windings. Another portion P_f is dissipated as heat in the stator core, owing to the iron losses. The remaining active power P_r is carried across the air gap and transferred to the rotor by electromagnetic induction.

Due to the I^2R losses in the rotor, a third portion P_{jr} is dissipated as heat, and the remainder is finally available in the form of mechanical power P_m. By subtracting a small fourth portion P_v, representing windage and bearing-friction losses, we finally obtain P_L, the mechanical power available at the shaft to drive the load.

The power flow diagram of Fig. 13.15 enables us to identify and to calculate three important properties of the induction motor: (1) its *efficiency,* (2) its *power,* and (3) its *torque.*

1. Efficiency. By definition, the efficiency of a motor is the ratio of the output power to the input power:

$$\text{efficiency } (\eta) = P_L/P_e \qquad (13.6)$$

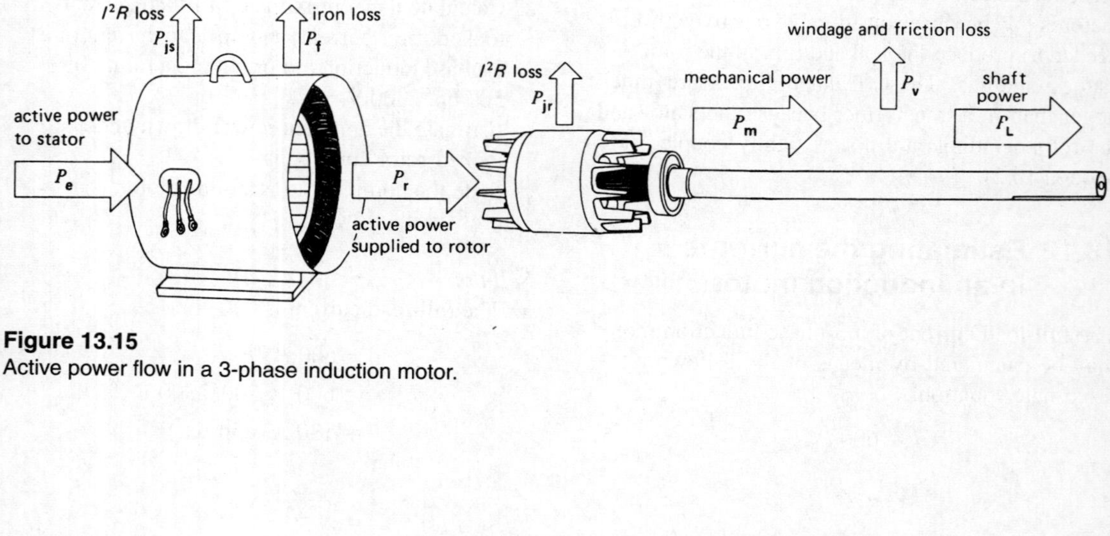

Figure 13.15
Active power flow in a 3-phase induction motor.

2. I^2R losses in the rotor. It can be shown* that the rotor I^2R losses P_{jr} are related to the rotor input power P_r by the equation

$$P_{jr} = sP_r \qquad (13.7)$$

where

P_{jr} = rotor I^2R losses [W]
s = slip
P_r = power transmitted to the rotor [W]

Eq. 13.7 shows that as the slip increases, the rotor I^2R losses consume a larger and larger proportion of the power P_r transmitted across the air gap to the rotor. A rotor turning at half-synchronous speed (s = 0.5) dissipates in the form of heat 50 percent of the active power it receives. When the rotor is locked (s = 1), all the power transmitted to the rotor is dissipated as heat.

3. Mechanical power. The mechanical power P_m developed by the motor is equal to the power transmitted to the rotor minus its I^2R losses. Thus,

$$\begin{aligned} P_m &= P_r - P_{jr} \\ &= P_r - sP_r \end{aligned} \qquad (13.7)$$

whence

$$P_m = (1 - s)P_r$$

The actual mechanical power available to drive the load is slightly less than P_m, due to the power needed to overcome the windage and friction losses. In most calculations we can neglect this small loss.

4. Motor torque. The torque T_m developed by the motor at *any* speed is given by

$$\begin{aligned} T_m &= \frac{9.55\ P_m}{n} \qquad (3.5) \\ &= \frac{9.55(1 - s)\ P_r}{n_s(1 - s)} = 9.55\ P_r/n_s \end{aligned}$$

therefore,

$$T_m = 9.55\ P_r/n_s \qquad (13.9)$$

where

T_m = torque developed by the motor at *any* speed [N·m]
P_r = power transmitted to the rotor [W]
n_s = synchronous speed [r/min]
9.55 = multiplier to take care of units [exact value: $60/2\pi$]

The actual torque T_L available at the shaft is slightly less than T_m, due to the torque required to overcome the windage and friction losses. However, in most calculations we can neglect this small difference.

Eq. 13.9 shows that the torque is directly proportional to the active power transmitted to the rotor. Thus, to develop a high locked-rotor torque, the rotor must absorb a large amount of active power. The latter is dissipated in the form of heat, consequently, the temperature of the rotor rises very rapidly.

Example 13-5

A 3-phase induction motor having a synchronous speed of 1200 r/min draws 80 kW from a 3-phase

---

$$* \begin{bmatrix} \text{mechanical} \\ \text{power output} \\ \text{of rotor} \end{bmatrix} = \begin{bmatrix} \text{electromagnetic} \\ \text{power transferred} \\ \text{to rotor} \end{bmatrix} - \begin{bmatrix} \text{electrical} \\ \text{losses} \\ \text{in rotor} \end{bmatrix}$$

$$P_m = P_r - P_{jr} \qquad \text{(i)}$$

but from Eq. 3.5

$$P_m = \frac{\text{rotor speed} \times \text{mechanical torque}}{9.55}$$

Hence,

$$P_m = \frac{nT_m}{9.55} \qquad \text{(ii)}$$

Also from Eq. 3.5 we can write

$$P_r = \frac{\text{speed of flux} \times \text{electromagnetic torque}}{9.55}$$

$$P_r = \frac{n_s T_{mag}}{9.55} \qquad \text{(iii)}$$

but the mechanical torque T_m must equal the electromagnetic torque T_{mag}.

Thus

$$T_m = T_{mag} \qquad \text{(iv)}$$

Substituting (ii), (iii), and (iv) in (i), we find

$$P_{jr} = sP_r$$

feeder. The copper losses and iron losses in the stator amount to 5 kW. If the motor runs at 1152 r/min, calculate the following:

a. The active power transmitted to the rotor
b. The rotor I^2R losses
c. The mechanical power developed
d. The mechanical power delivered to the load, knowing that the windage and friction losses are equal to 2 kW
e. The efficiency of the motor

Solution

a. Active power to the rotor is

$$P_r = P_e - P_{js} - P_f$$
$$= 80 - 5 = 75 \text{ kW}$$

b. The slip is

$$s = (n_s - n)/n_s$$
$$= (1200 - 1152)/1200$$
$$= 48/1200 = 0.04$$

Rotor I^2R losses are

$$P_{jr} = sP_r = 0.04 \times 75 = 3 \text{ kW}$$

c. The mechanical power developed is

$$P_m = P_r - I^2R \text{ losses in rotor}$$
$$= 75 - 3 = 72 \text{ kW}$$

d. The mechanical power P_L delivered to the load is slightly less than P_m, due to the friction and windage losses.

$$P_L = P_m - P_v = 72 - 2 = 70 \text{ kW}$$

e. The efficiency is

$$\eta = P_L/P_e = 70/80$$
$$= 0.875 \text{ or } 87.5\%$$

Example 13-6

A 3-phase, 8-pole, squirrel-cage induction motor, connected to a 60 Hz line, possesses a synchronous speed of 900 r/min. The motor absorbs 40 kW, and the copper and iron losses in the stator amount to 5 kW and 1 kW, respectively. Calculate the torque developed by the motor.

Solution

The power transmitted across the air gap to the rotor is

$$P_r = P_e - P_{js} - P_f$$
$$= 40 - 5 - 1 = 34 \text{ kW}$$
$$T_m = 9.55\, P_r/n_s \tag{13.9}$$
$$= 9.55 \times 34\,000/900$$
$$= 361 \text{ N·m}$$

Note that the solution to this problem (the torque) is independent of the speed of rotation. The motor could be at a standstill or running at full speed, but as long as the power P_r transmitted to the rotor is equal to 34 kW, the motor develops a torque of 361 N·m.

Example 13-7

A 3-phase induction motor having a nominal rating of 100 hp (~75 kW) and a synchronous speed of 1800 r/min is connected to a 600 V source (Fig. 13.16a). The two-wattmeter method shows a total power con-

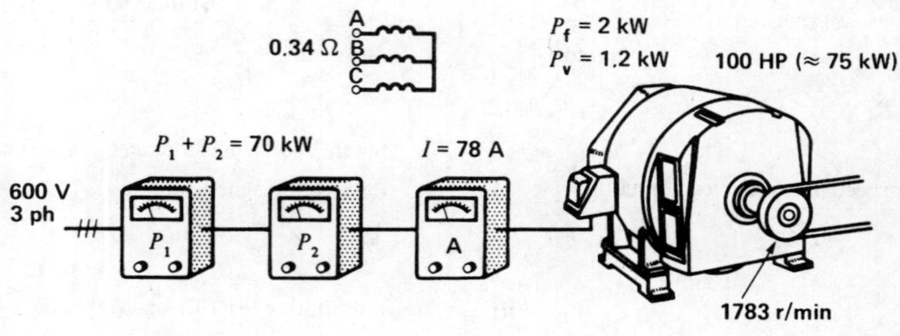

Figure 13.16a
See Example 13-7.

sumption of 70 kW, and an ammeter indicates a line current of 78 A. Precise measurements give a rotor speed of 1763 r/min. In addition, the following characteristics are known about the motor:

stator iron losses $P_f = 2$ kW
windage and friction losses $P_v = 1.2$ kW
resistance between two stator terminals = 0.34 Ω

Calculate

a. Power supplied to the rotor
b. Rotor I^2R losses
c. Mechanical power supplied to the load, in horsepower
d. Efficiency
e. Torque developed at 1763 r/min

Solution

a. Power supplied to the stator is

$$P_e = 70 \text{ kW}$$

Stator resistance per phase (assume a wye connection) is

$$R = 0.34/2 = 0.17 \ \Omega$$

Stator I^2R losses are

$$P_{js} = 3\ I^2R = 3 \times (78)^2 \times 0.17 = 3.1 \text{ kW}$$

Iron losses $P_f = 2$ kW
Power supplied to the rotor

$$P_r = P_e - P_{js} - P_f = (70 - 3.1 - 2) = 64.9 \text{ kW}$$

b. The slip is

$$s = (n_s - n)/n_s = (1800 - 1763)/1800 = 0.0205$$

Rotor I^2R losses

$$P_{jr} = sP_r = 0.0205 \times 64.9 = 1.33 \text{ kW}$$

c. Mechanical power developed is

$$P_m = P_r - P_{jr} = 64.9 - 1.33 = 63.5 \text{ kW}$$

Mechanical power P_L to the load

$$P_L = 63.5 - P_v = 63.5 - 1.2 = 62.3 \text{ kW} = 62.3 \times 1.34 \text{ (hp)} = 83.5 \text{ hp}$$

d. Efficiency of the motor is

$$\eta = P_L/P_e = 62.3/70 = 0.89 \text{ or } 89\%$$

e. Torque at 1763 r/min

$$T = 9.55\ P_r/n_s = 9.55 \times 64\,900/1800 = 344 \text{ N·m}$$

The above calculations are summarized in Fig. 13.16b.

13.14 Torque versus speed curve

The torque developed by a motor depends upon its speed, but the relationship between the two cannot be expressed by a simple equation. Consequently, we prefer to show the relationship in the form of a

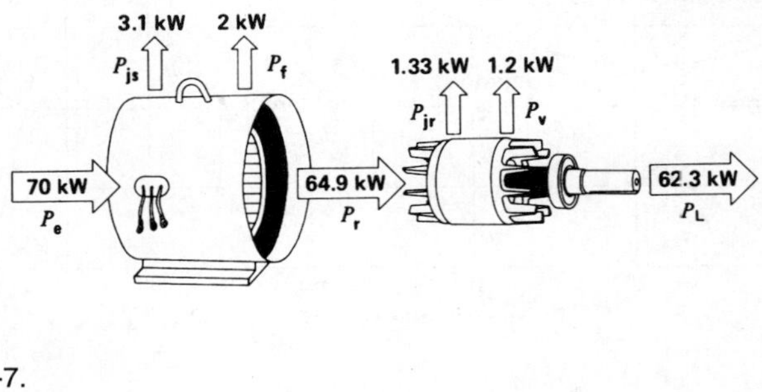

Figure 13.16b
Power flow in Example 13-7.

curve. Fig. 13.17 shows the torque-speed curve of a conventional 3-phase induction motor whose nominal full-load torque is *T*. The starting torque is 1.5 *T* and the maximum torque (called *breakdown* torque) is 2.5 *T*. Pull-up torque is the minimum torque developed by the motor while it is accelerating from rest to the breakdown torque.

At full-load the motor runs at a speed *n*. If the mechanical load increases slightly, the speed will drop until the motor torque is again equal to the load torque. As soon as the two torques are in balance, the motor will turn at a constant but slightly lower speed. However, if the load torque exceeds 2.5 *T* (the breakdown torque), the motor will quickly stop.

Small motors (15 hp and less) develop their breakdown torque at a speed n_d of about 80% of synchronous speed. Big motors (1500 hp and more) attain their breakdown torque at about 98% of synchronous speed.

13.15 Effect of rotor resistance

The rotor resistance of a squirrel-cage rotor is essentially constant from no-load to full-load, except that it increases with temperature. Thus, the resistance increases with increasing load because the temperature rises.

In designing a squirrel-cage motor, the rotor resistance can be set over a wide range by using copper, aluminum, or other metals in the rotor bars and end-rings. The torque-speed curve is greatly affected by such a change in resistance. The only characteristic that remains unchanged is the breakdown torque. The following example illustrates the changes that occur.

Fig. 13.18a shows the torque-speed curve of a 10 kW (13.4 hp), 50 Hz, 380 V motor having a synchronous speed of 1000 r/min and a full-load torque of 100 N·m (~73.7 ft·lbf). The full-load current is 20 A and the locked-rotor current is 100 A. The rotor has an arbitrary resistance *R*.

Let us increase the rotor resistance by a factor of 2.5. This can be achieved by using a material of higher resistivity, such as bronze, for the rotor bars and end-rings. The new torque-speed curve is shown in Fig. 13.18b. It can be seen that the starting torque doubles and the locked-rotor current decreases from 100 A to 90 A. The motor develops its breakdown torque at a speed n_d of 500 r/min, compared to the original breakdown speed of 800 r/min.

If we again double the rotor resistance so that it becomes 5 *R*, the locked-rotor torque attains a maximum value of 250 N·m for a corresponding current of 70 A (Fig. 13.18c).

A further increase in rotor resistance decreases both the locked-rotor torque and locked-rotor current. For example, if the rotor resistance is increased 25 times (25 *R*), the locked-rotor current drops to 20 A, but the motor develops the same

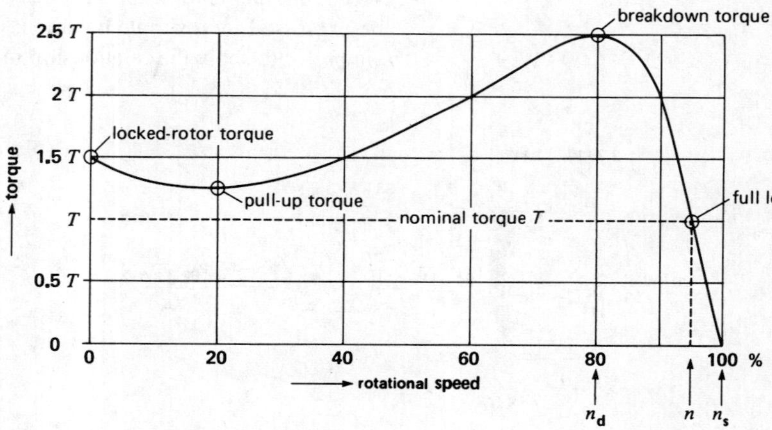

Figure 13.17
Typical torque-speed curve of a 3-phase squirrel-cage induction motor.

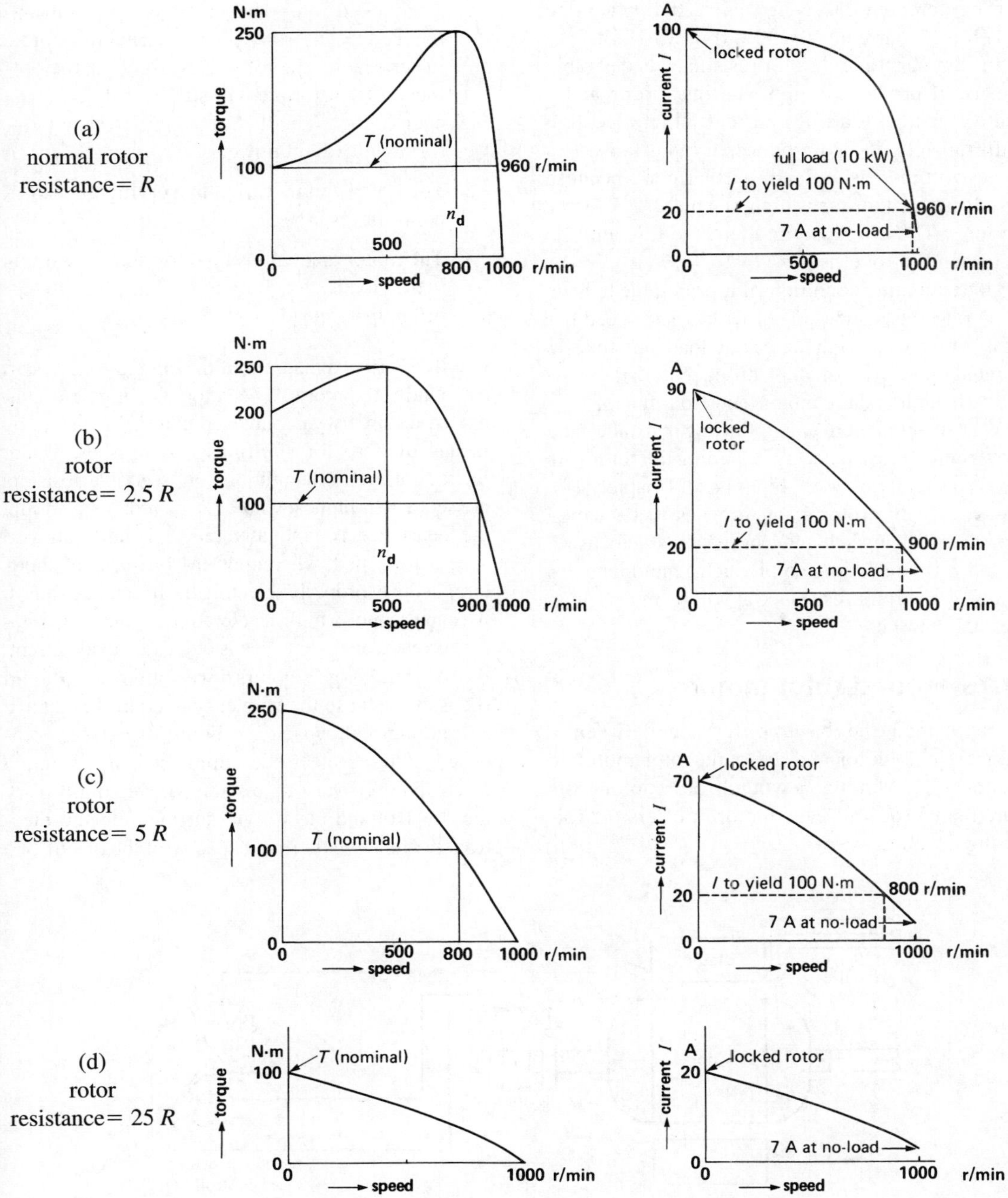

Figure 13.18
Rotor resistance affects the motor characteristics.

starting torque (100 N·m), as it did when the locked-rotor current was 100 A (Fig. 13.18d).

In summary, a high rotor resistance is desirable because it produces a high starting torque and a relatively low starting current (Fig. 13.18c). Unfortunately, it also produces a rapid fall-off in speed with increasing load. Furthermore, because the slip at rated torque is high, the motor I^2R losses are high. The efficiency is therefore low and the motor tends to overheat.

Under running conditions it is preferable to have a low rotor resistance (Fig. 13.18a). The speed decreases much less with increasing load, and the slip at rated torque is small. Consequently, the efficiency is high and the motor tends to run cool.

We can obtain both a high starting resistance and a low running resistance by designing the rotor bars in a special way (see Fig. 14.5, Chapter 14). However, if the rotor resistance has to be varied over a wide range, it may be necessary to use a wound-rotor induction motor. Such a motor enables us to vary the rotor resistance at will by means of an external rheostat.

13.16 Wound-rotor motor

We explained the basic difference between a squirrel-cage motor and a wound-rotor motor in Section 13.1. Although a wound-rotor motor costs more than a squirrel-cage motor, it offers the following advantages:

1. The locked-rotor current can be drastically reduced by inserting three external resistors in series with the rotor. Nevertheless, the locked-rotor torque will still be as high, or even higher, than that of a squirrel-cage motor of equivalent power.
2. The speed can be varied by varying the external rotor resistors.
3. The motor is ideally suited to accelerate high-inertia loads, which require a long time to bring up to speed.

Fig. 13.19 is a diagram of the circuit used to start a wound-rotor motor. The rotor windings are connected to three wye-connected external resistors by means of a set of slip-rings and brushes. Under locked-rotor (LR) conditions, the variable resistors are set to their highest value. As the motor speeds up, the resistance is gradually reduced until full-load speed is reached, whereupon the brushes are short-circuited. By properly selecting the resistance values, we can produce a high accelerating torque with a stator current that never exceeds twice full-load current.

To start large motors, we often use liquid rheostats because they are easy to control and have a large thermal capacity. A liquid rheostat is composed of three electrodes immersed in a suitable electrolyte. To vary its resistance, we simply vary the level of the electrolyte surrounding the electrodes. The large thermal capacity of the electrolyte

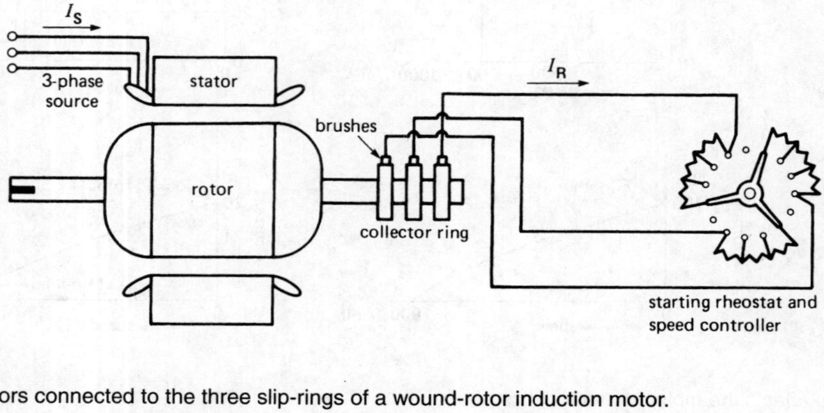

Figure 13.19
External resistors connected to the three slip-rings of a wound-rotor induction motor.

limits the temperature rise. For example, in one application a liquid rheostat is used in conjunction with a 1260 kW wound-rotor motor to bring a large synchronous machine up to speed.

We can also regulate the speed of a wound-rotor motor by varying the resistance of the rheostat. As we increase the resistance, the speed will drop. This method of speed control has the disadvantage that a lot of heat is dissipated in the resistors; the efficiency is therefore low. Furthermore, for a given rheostat setting, the speed varies considerably if the mechanical load varies.

The power rating of a self-cooled wound-rotor motor depends upon the speed at which it operates. Thus, for the same temperature rise, a motor that can develop 100 kW at 1800 r/min can deliver only about 40 kW at 900 r/min. However, if the motor is cooled by a separate fan, it can deliver 50 kW at 900 r/min.

13.17 Three-phase windings

In 1883 a 27-year-old Yugoslav scientist named Nikola Tesla invented the 3-phase induction motor. His first model had a salient-pole stator winding similar to the one shown in Fig. 13.6. Since then the design of induction motors has evolved considerably; modern machines are built with *lap windings* distributed in slots around the stator.

A lap winding consists of a set of phase groups evenly distributed around the stator circumference. The number of groups is given by the equation

$$\text{groups} = \text{poles} \times \text{phases}$$

Thus, a 4-pole, 3-phase stator must have $4 \times 3 = 12$ phase groups. Because a group must have at least one coil, it follows that the minimum number of coils is equal to the number of groups. A 4-pole, 3-phase stator must therefore have at least 12 coils. Furthermore, in a lap winding the stator has as many slots as it has coils. Consequently, a 4-pole, 3-phase stator must have at least 12 slots. However, motor designers have discovered that it is preferable to use two, three, or more coils per group rather than only one. The number of coils and slots increases in proportion. For example, a 4-pole, 3-phase stator having 5 coils per group must have a total of $(4 \times 3 \times 5) =$ 60 coils, lodged in 60 slots. The coils in each group are connected in series and are staggered at one-slot intervals (Fig. 13.20). The coils are identical and may possess one or more turns. The width of each coil is called the *coil pitch*.

Such a *distributed* winding is obviously more costly to build than a concentrated winding having only one coil per group. However, it improves the starting torque and reduces the noise under running conditions.

When the stator windings are excited from a 3-phase source, a multipolar revolving field is produced. The distance between adjacent poles is called the *pole pitch*. It is equal to the internal circumference of the stator divided by the number of poles. For example, a 12-pole stator having a circumference of 600 mm has a pole-pitch of 600/12 or 50 mm.

In practice, the coil pitch is between 80% and 100% of the pole pitch. The coil pitch is usually made less than the pole pitch in order to save copper and to improve the flux distribution in the air gap. The shorter coil width reduces the cost and weight of the windings, while the more sinusoidal flux distribution improves the torque during start-up, and often results in a quieter machine. In the case of 2-pole machines, the shorter pitch also makes the coils much easier to insert in the slots.

To get an overall picture of a lap winding, let us suppose a 24-slot stator is laid out flat as shown in Fig. 13.21a. The 24 coils are held upright, with one

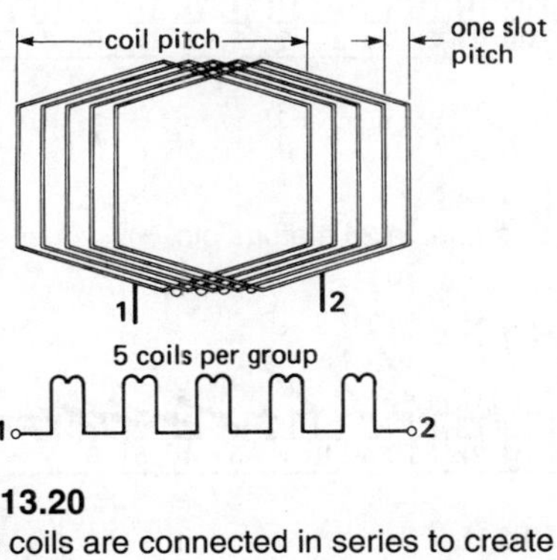

Figure 13.20
The five coils are connected in series to create one phase group.

coil side set in each slot. If the windings are now laid down so that all the other coil sides fall into the slots, we obtain the classical appearance of a 3-phase lap winding having two coil sides per slot (Fig. 13.21b). The coils are connected together to create three identical windings, one for each phase. Each winding consists of a number of groups equal to the number of poles. The groups of each phase are symmetrically distributed around the circumference of the stator. The following examples show how this is done.

Example 13-8

The stator of a 3-phase, 10-pole induction motor possesses 120 slots. If a lap winding is used, calculate the following:

a. The total number of coils
b. The number of coils per phase
c. The number of coils per group
d. The pole pitch
e. The coil pitch (expressed as a percentage of the pole pitch), if the coil width extends from slot 1 to slot 11

Solution

a. A 120-slot stator requires 120 coils.
b. Coils per phase $= 120 \div 3 = 40$.

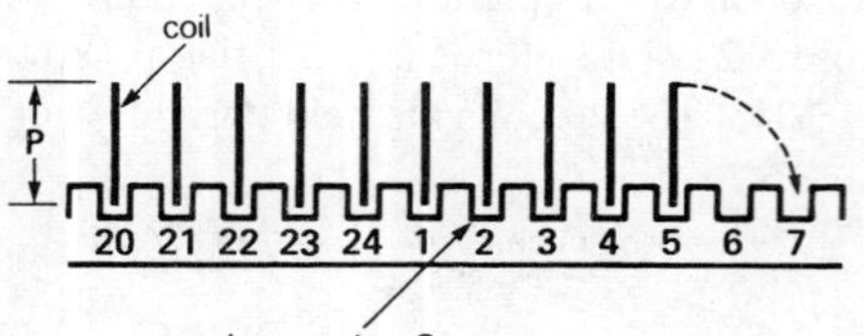

Figure 13.21a
Coils held upright in 24 stator slots.

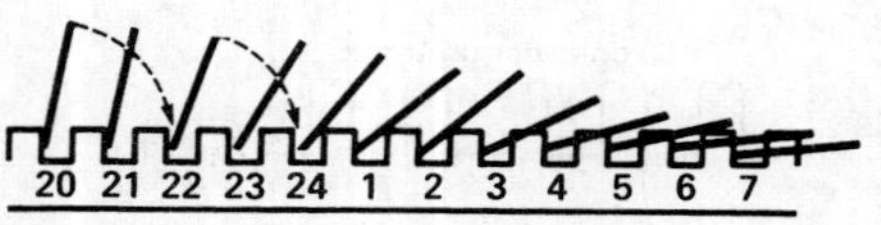

Figure 13.21b
Coils laid down to make a typical lap winding.

c. Number of groups per phase = number of poles = 10
   Coils per group $= 40 \div 10 = 4$.
d. The pole pitch corresponds to

$$\text{pole pitch} = \text{slots/poles} = 120/10 = 12 \text{ slots}$$

   One pole pitch extends therefore from slot 1 (say) to slot 13.
e. The coil pitch covers 10 slots (slot 1 to slot 11). The percent coil pitch $= 10/12 = 83.3\%$.

The next example shows in greater detail how the coils are interconnected in a typical 3-phase stator winding.

Example 13-9

A stator having 24 slots has to be wound with a 3-phase, 4-pole winding. Determine the following:

1. The connections between the coils
2. The connections between the phases

Solution

The 3-phase winding has 24 coils. Assume that they are standing upright, with one coil side in each slot (Fig. 13.22). We will first determine the coil distribution for phase A and then proceed with the connections for that phase. Similar connections will then be made for phases B and C. Here is the line of reasoning:

a. The revolving field creates 4 poles; the motor therefore has 4 groups per phase, or $4 \times 3 = 12$ phase groups in all. Each rectangle in Fig. 13.22a represents one group. Because the stator contains 24 coils, each group consists of $24/12 = 2$ consecutive coils.
b. The groups (poles) of each phase must be uniformly spaced around the stator. The group distribution for phase A is shown in Fig. 13.22b. Each shaded rectangle represents two upright coils connected in series, producing the two terminals shown. Note that the mechanical distance between two successive groups always corresponds to an *electrical* phase angle of 180°.
c. Successive groups of phase A must have opposite magnetic polarities. Consequently, the

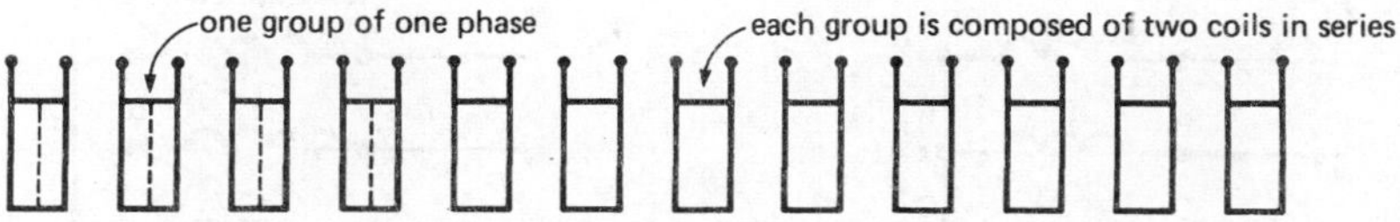

Figure 13.22a
The 24 coils are grouped two-by-two to make 12 groups.

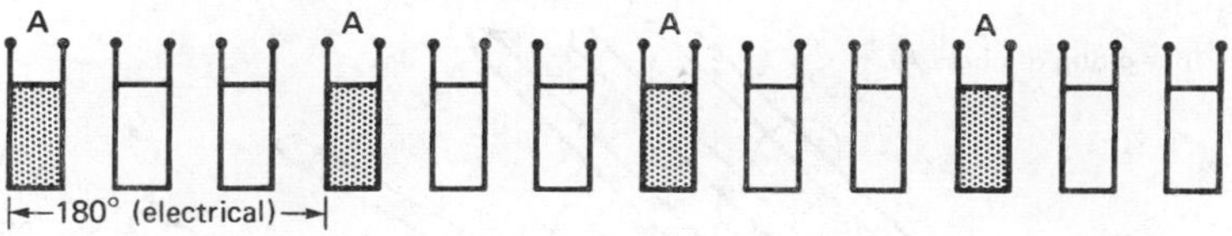

Figure 13.22b
The four groups of phase A are selected so as to be evenly spaced from each other.

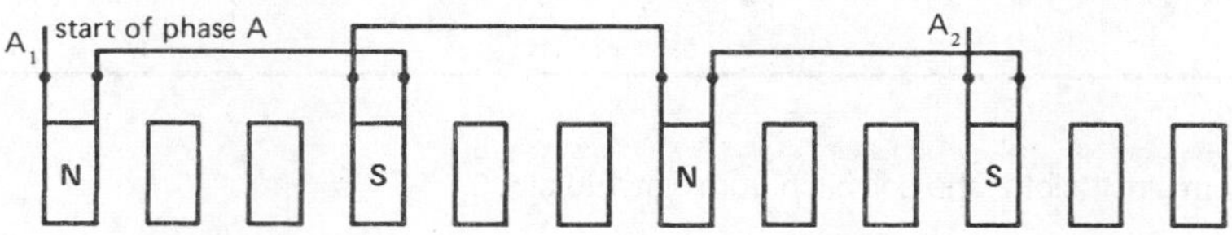

Figure 13.22c
The groups of phase A are connected in series to create alternate N-S poles.

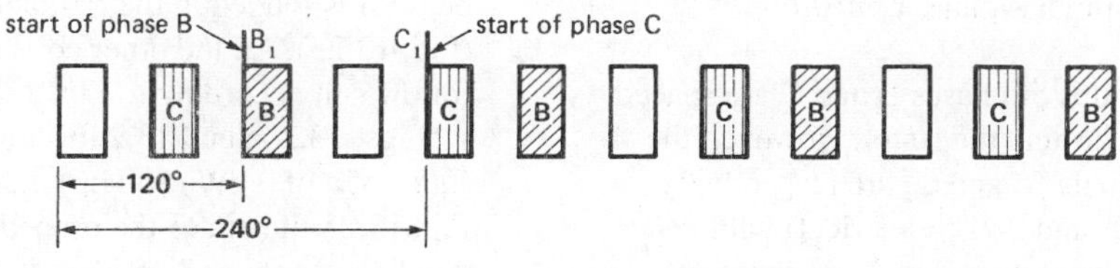

Figure 13.22d
The start of phases B and C begin 120° and 240°, respectively, after the start of phase A.

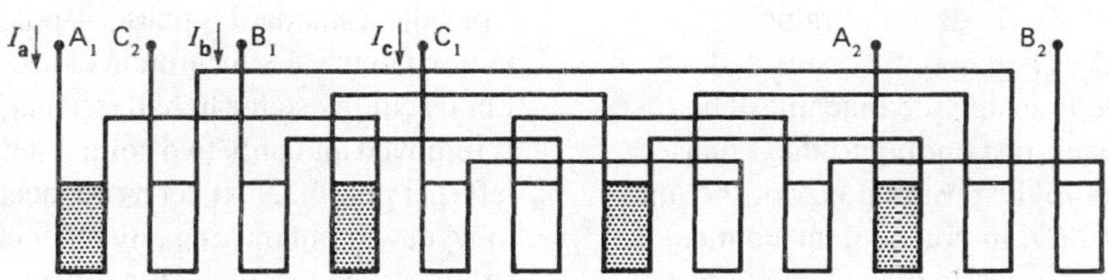

Figure 13.22e
When all phase groups are connected, only six leads remain.

Figure 13.22f
The phase may be connected in wye or in delta, and three leads are brought out to the terminal box.

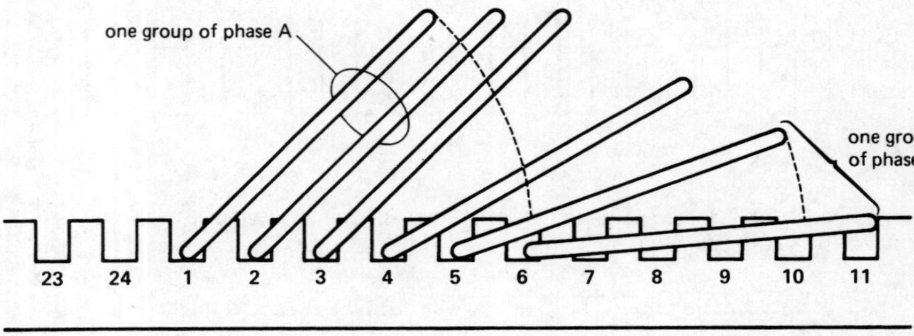

Figure 13.23
The pole pitch is from slot 1 slot 7; the coil pitch from slot 1 to slot 6.

four groups of phase A are connected in series to produce successive N-S-N-S poles (Fig. 13.22c). Phase A now has two terminals, a *starting* terminal A_1 and a *finishing* terminal A_2.

d. The phase groups of phases B and C are spaced the same way around the stator. However, the *starting* terminals B_1 and C_1 are respectively located at 120° and 240° (electrical) with respect to the starting terminal A_1 of phase A (Fig. 13.22d).

e. The groups in phases B and C are connected in series in the same way as those of phase A are (Fig. 13.22e). This yields six terminals: A_1A_2, B_1B_2, and C_1C_2. They may be connected either in wye or in delta inside the machine. The resulting 3 wires corresponding to the 3 phases are brought out to the terminal box of the machine (Fig. 13.22f). In practice, the connections are made, not while the coils are upright (as shown) but only after they have been laid down in the slots.

f. Because the pole pitch corresponds to a span of $24/4 = 6$ slots, the coil pitch may be shortened to 5 slots (slot 1 to slot 6). Thus, the first coil of phase A is lodged in the first and sixth slots (Fig. 13.23). All the other coils and connections follow suit according to Fig. 13.22e.

Figs. 13.24a and 13.24b show the coil and stator of a 450 kW (600 hp) induction motor. Fig. 13.25 illustrates the procedure used in winding a smaller 37.5 kW (50 hp) stator.

13.18 Sector motor

Consider a standard 3-phase, 4-pole, wye-connected motor having a synchronous speed of 1800 r/min. Let us cut the stator in half, so that half the winding is removed and only two complete N and S poles are left (per phase). Next, let us connect the three phases in wye, without making any other changes to the existing coil connections. Finally, we mount the original rotor above this *sector stator,* leaving a small air gap (Fig. 13.26).

Figure 13.24a
Stator of a 3-phase, 450 kW, 1180 r/min, 575 V, 60 Hz induction motor. The lap winding is composed of 108 preformed coils having a pitch from slots 1 to 15. One coil side falls into the bottom of a slot and the other at the top. Rotor diameter: 500 mm; axial length: 460 mm. *(Courtesy of Services Électromécaniques Roberge)*

Figure 13.24b
Close-up view of the preformed coil in Fig. 13.24a.

If we connect the stator terminals to a 3-phase, 60 Hz source, the rotor will again turn at close to 1800 r/min. To prevent saturation, the voltage should be reduced to half its original value because the stator winding now has only one-half the original number of turns. Under these conditions, this remarkable truncated *sector motor* still develops about 20 percent of its original rated power.

The sector motor produces a *revolving* field that moves at the same peripheral speed as the flux in the original 3-phase motor. However, instead of making a complete turn, the field simply travels continuously from one end of the stator to the other.

13.19 Linear induction motor

It is obvious that the sector stator could be laid out flat, without affecting the shape or speed of the magnetic field. Such a flat stator produces a field that moves at constant speed, in a straight line. Using the same reasoning as in Section 13.5, we can prove that the flux travels at a linear synchronous speed given by

$$v_s = 2\,wf \qquad (13.10)$$

where

v_s = linear synchronous speed [m/s]
w = width of one pole-pitch [m]
f = frequency [Hz]

Note that the linear speed does not depend upon the number of poles but only on the pole-pitch. Thus, it is possible for a 2-pole linear stator to create a field moving at the same speed as that of a 6-pole linear stator (say), provided they have the same pole-pitch.

If a flat squirrel-cage winding is brought near the flat stator, the travelling field drags the squirrel cage along with it (Section 13.2). In practice, we generally use a simple aluminum or copper plate as a rotor (Fig. 13.27). Furthermore, to increase the power and to reduce the reluctance of the magnetic path, two flat stators are usually mounted, face-to-face, on opposite sides of the aluminum plate. The combination is called a *linear induction motor.* The direction of the motor can be reversed by interchanging any two stator leads.

In many practical applications, the rotor is stationary while the stator moves. For example, in some high-speed trains, the rotor is composed of a

(a) (c) (b) (d)

Figure 13.25

Stator winding of a 3-phase, 50 hp, 575 V, 60 Hz, 1764 r/min induction motor. The stator possesses 48 slots carrying 48 coils connected in wye.

a. Each coil is composed of 5 turns of five No. 15 copper wires connected in parallel. The wires are covered with a high-temperature polyimide insulation. Five No. 15 wires in parallel is equivalent to one No. 8 wire.
b. One coil side is threaded into slot 1 (say) and the other side goes into slot 12. The coil pitch is, therefore, from 1 to 12.
c. Each coil side fills half a slot and is covered with a paper spacer so that it does not touch the second coil side placed in the same slot. Starting from the top, the photograph shows 3 empty and uninsulated slots and 4 empty slots insulated with a composition paper liner. The remaining 10 slots each carry one coil side.
d. A varnished cambric cloth, cut in the shape of a triangle, provides extra insulation between adjacent phase groups.

(Courtesy of Services Électromécaniques Roberge)

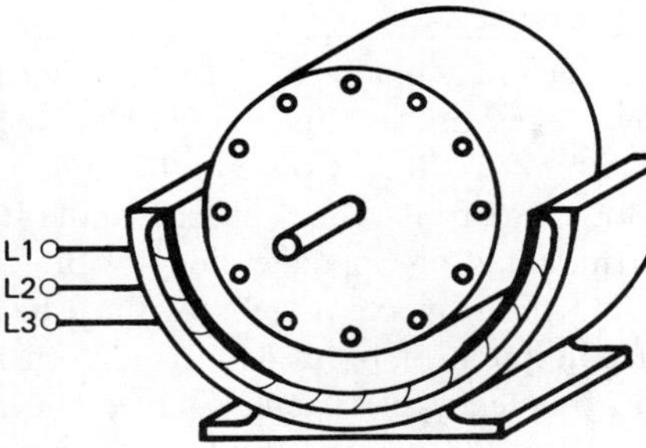

Figure 13.26
Two-pole sector induction motor.

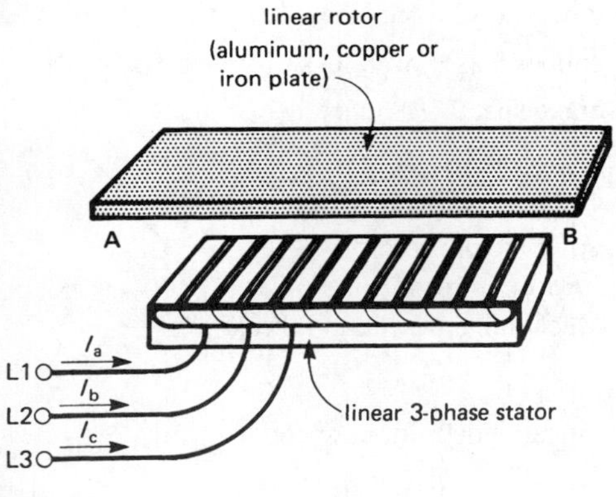

Figure 13.27
Components of a 3-phase linear induction motor.

thick aluminum plate fixed to the ground and extending over the full length of the track. The linear stator is bolted to the undercarriage of the train and straddles the plate. Train speed is varied by changing the frequency applied to the stator (Fig. 13.31).

Example 13-10

The stator of a linear induction motor is excited from a 75 Hz electronic source. If the distance between consecutive phase groups of phase A is 300 mm, calculate the linear speed of the magnetic field.

Solution

The pole-pitch is 300 mm. Consequently,

$$v_s = 2\,wf \qquad (13.10)$$

$$= 2 \times 0.3 \times 75$$

$$= 45 \text{ m/s or } 162 \text{ km/h}$$

13.20 Travelling waves

We are sometimes left with the impression that when the flux reaches the end of a linear stator, there must be a delay before it returns to restart once more at the beginning. This is not the case. The linear motor produces a traveling wave of flux which moves continuously and smoothly from one end of the stator to the other. Fig. 13.28 shows how the flux moves from left to right in a 2-pole linear motor. The flux cuts off sharply at extremities A, B of the stator. However, as fast as a N or S pole disappears at the right, it builds up again at the left.

13.21 Properties of a linear induction motor

The properties of a linear induction motor are almost identical to those of a standard rotating machine. Consequently, the equations for slip, thrust, power, etc., are also similar.

1. ***Slip.*** Slip is defined by

$$s = (v_s - v)/v_s \qquad (13.11)$$

where

s = slip
v_s = synchronous linear speed [m/s]
v = speed of rotor (or stator) [m/s]

2. ***Active power flow.*** With reference to Fig. 13.15, active power flows through a linear motor in the same way it does through a rotating motor, except that the stator and rotor are flat. Consequently, Eqs. 13.6, 13.7, and 13.8 apply to both types of machines:

$$\eta = P_L/P_c \qquad (13.6)$$

$$P_{jr} = sP_r \qquad (13.7)$$

$$P_m = (1 - s)P_r \qquad (13.8)$$

3. ***Thrust.*** The thrust or force developed by a linear induction motor is given by

$$F = P_r/v_s \qquad (13.12)$$

where

F = thrust [N]
P_r = power transmitted to the rotor [W]
v_s = linear synchronous speed [m/s]

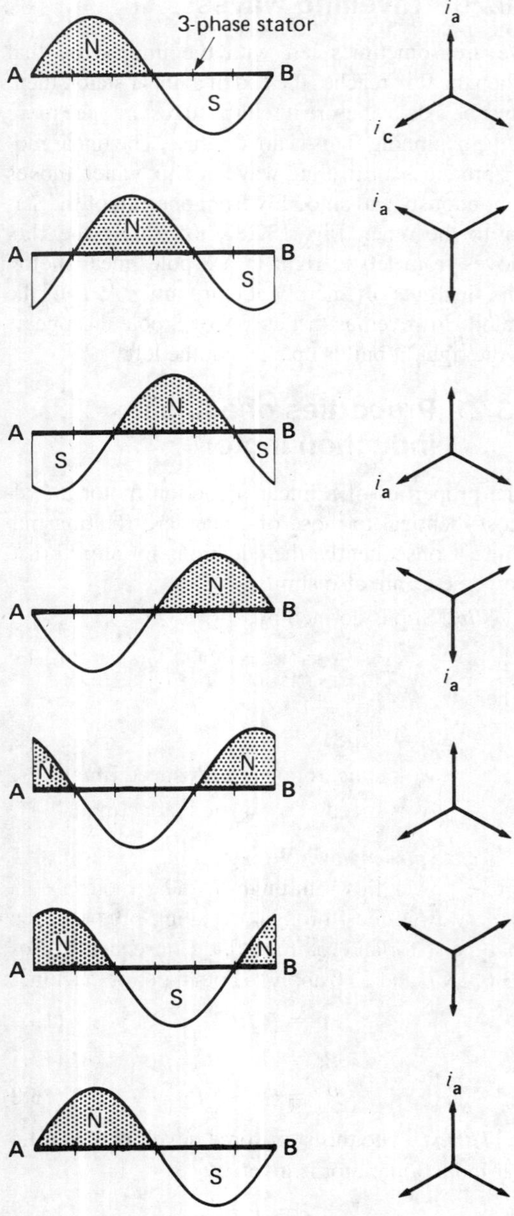

Figure 13.28
Shape of the magnetic field created by a 2-pole, 3-phase linear stator, over one complete cycle. The successive frames are separated by an interval of time equal to 1/6 cycle or 60%.

Example 13-11

An overhead crane in a factory is driven horizontally by means of two linear induction motors whose rotors are the two steel I-beams upon which the crane rolls. The 3-phase, 4-pole linear stators (mounted on opposite sides of the crane and facing the respective webs of the I-beams) have a pole-pitch of 8 cm and are driven by a variable frequency electronic source. During a test on one of the motors, the following results were obtained:

stator frequency: 15 Hz

power to stator: 5 kW

copper loss + iron loss in stator: 1 kW

crane speed: 1.8 m/s

Calculate

a. Synchronous speed and slip
b. Power to the rotor
c. I^2R loss in rotor
d. Mechanical power and thrust

Solution

a. Linear synchronous speed

$$v_s = 2\,wf \qquad (13.10)$$
$$= 2 \times 0.08 \times 15$$
$$= 2.4 \text{ m/s}$$

The slip is

$$s = (v_s - v)/v_s \qquad (13.11)$$
$$= (2.4 - 1.8)/2.4$$
$$= 0.25$$

b. Power to the rotor is

$$P_r = P_c - P_{js} - P_f \qquad \text{(see Fig. 13.15)}$$
$$= 5 - 1$$
$$= 4 \text{ kW}$$

c. I^2R loss in the rotor is

$$P_{jr} = sP_r \qquad (13.7)$$
$$= 0.25 \times 4$$
$$= 1 \text{ kW}$$

d. Mechanical power is

$$P_m = P_r - P_{jr} \quad \text{(Fig. 13.15)}$$
$$= 4 - 1$$
$$= 3 \text{ kW}$$

The thrust is

$$F = P_r/v_s \quad (13.12)$$
$$= 4000/2.4$$
$$= 1667 \text{ N} = 1.67 \text{ kN} (\sim 375 \text{ lb})$$

13.22 Magnetic levitation

In Section 13.2 we saw that a moving permanent magnet, sweeping across a conducting ladder, tends to drag the ladder along with the magnet. We will now show that this horizontal tractive force is also accompanied by a *vertical* force, which tends to push the magnet away from the ladder.

Referring to Fig. 13.29, suppose that conductors 1, 2, 3 are three conductors of the stationary ladder. The center of the N pole of the magnet is sweeping across the top of conductor 2. The voltage induced in this conductor is maximum because

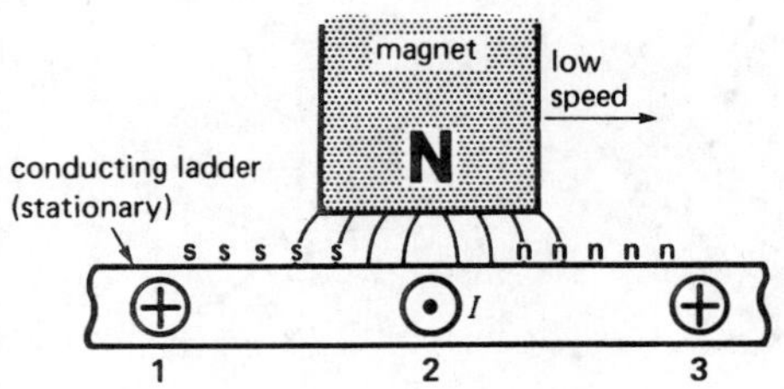

Figure 13.29
Currents and magnetic poles at low speed.

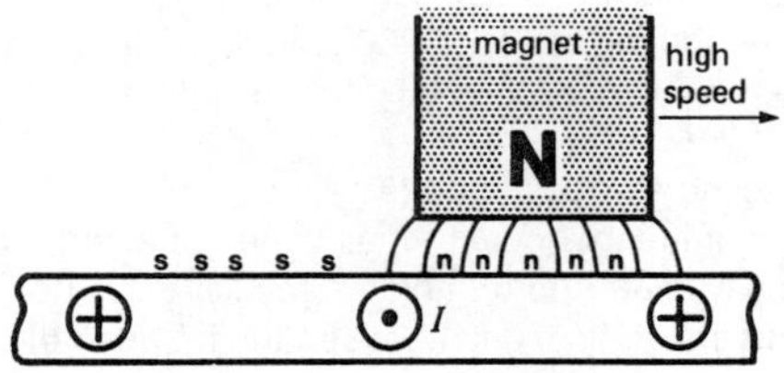

Figure 13.30
Currents and magnetic poles at high speed.

the flux density is greatest at the center of the pole. If the magnet moves very slowly, the resulting induced current reaches *its* maximum value at virtually the same time. This current, returning by conductors 1 and 3, creates magnetic poles nnn and sss as shown in Fig. 13.29. According to the laws of attraction and repulsion, the front half of the magnet is repelled upward while the rear half is attracted downward. Because the distribution of the nnn and sss poles is symmetrical with respect to the center of the magnet, the vertical forces of attraction and repulsion are equal, and the resulting vertical force is nil. Consequently, there is only a horizontal tractive force.

But suppose now that the magnet moves very rapidly. Owing to its inductance, the current in conductor 2 reaches its maximum value a fraction of a second after the voltage has attained *its* maximum. Consequently, by the time the current in conductor 2 is maximum, the center of the magnet is already some distance ahead of the conductor (Fig. 13.30). The current returning by conductors 1 and 3 again creates nnn and sss poles; however, the N pole of the magnet is now directly above an nnn pole, with the result that a strong vertical force tends to push the magnet upward.* This effect is called the principle of *magnetic levitation.*

Magnetic levitation is used in some ultra-high-speed trains that glide on a magnetic cushion rather than on wheels. A powerful electromagnet fixed underneath the train moves above a conducting rail inducing currents in the rail in the same way as in our ladder. The force of levitation is always accompanied by a small horizontal braking force which must, of course, be overcome by the linear motor that propels the train. See Figs. 13.31 and 13.32.

* The current is always delayed (even at low speeds) by an interval of time Δt, which depends upon the L/R time constant of the rotor. This delay is so brief that, at low speeds, the current reaches its maximum at virtually the same time and place as the voltage does. On the other hand, at high speeds, the same delay Δt produces a significant shift in *space* between the points where the voltage and current reach their respective maximum values.

Figure 13.31
This 17 t electric train is driven by a linear motor. The motor consists of a stationary rotor and a flat stator fixed to the undercarriage of the train. The rotor is the vertical aluminum plate mounted in the center of the track. The 3-tonne stator is energized by a 4.7 MVA electronic dc to ac inverter whose frequency can be varied from zero to 105 Hz. The motor develops a maximum thrust of 35 kN (7800 lb) and the top speed is 200 km/h. Direct-current power at 4 kV is fed into the inverter by means of a brush assembly in contact with 6 stationary dc busbars mounted on the left-hand side of the track.

Electromagnetic levitation is obtained by means of a superconducting electromagnet. The magnet is 1300 mm long, 600 mm wide, and 400 mm deep, and weighs 500 kg. The coils of the magnet are maintained at a temperature of 4 K by the forced circulation of liquid helium. The current density is 80 A/mm^2, and the resulting flux density is 3 T. The vertical force of repulsion attains a maximum of 60 kN and the vertical gap between the magnet and the reacting metallic track varies from 100 mm to 300 mm depending on the current.
(Courtesy of Siemens)

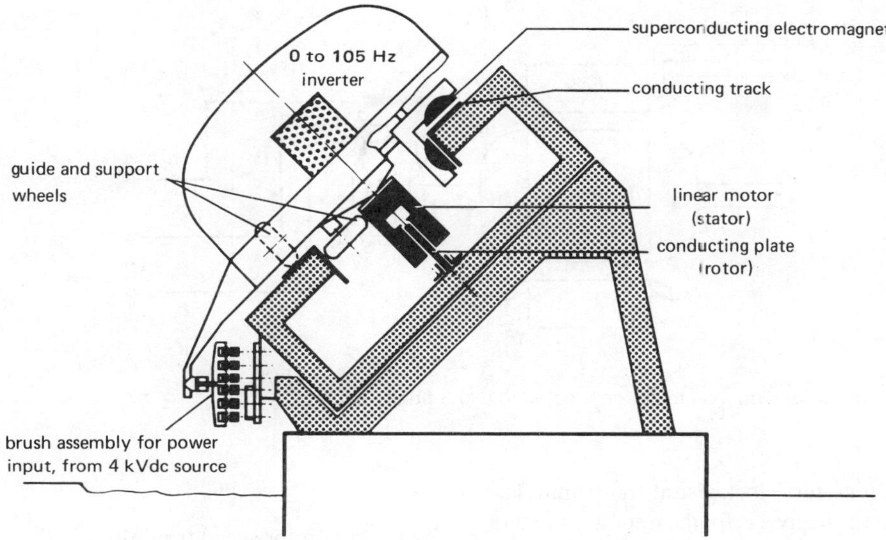

Figure 13.32
Cross-section view of the main components of the high-speed train shown in Fig. 13.31.
(Courtesy of Siemens)

THE DOUBLY-FED INDUCTION MACHINE

Wound-rotor induction machines may have the stator and rotor connected to separate ac sources having different frequencies. They are said to be doubly-fed machines. Such machines, when operating as motors, can be used to drive variable-speed pumps. They can also be used as variable-speed generators driven by wind turbines. The following sections describe the principles and operation of these special machines.

13.23 Doubly-fed wound-rotor motor (speed relationships)

In order to discuss the doubly-fed wound-rotor motor, let us return to the 3-phase wound-rotor motor described in Section 13.16. As always, the stator is connected to a power line whose frequency f is either 60 Hz or 50 Hz. However, instead of connecting the slip-rings to a resistive load, such as illustrated in Fig. 13.19, let us connect them to a second source having a frequency, say, of 14 Hz (Fig. 13.33). What happens under these conditions of such a doubly-fed induction motor?

Suppose we are dealing with a 3-phase, 4-pole machine whose stator is connected to a 60 Hz source. The flux created by the stator will rotate at the usual synchronous speed $n_s = 120\ f/p = 120 \times 60/4 = 1800$ r/min. Let us further suppose that the flux rotates clockwise. Thus, as far as an outside observer is concerned, the stator flux rotates clockwise at a speed of 1800 r/min.

Since the rotor is connected to a 14 Hz source, the rotor flux will rotate at a speed $n_2 = 120 \times 14/4 = 420$ r/min with respect to the rotor. Suppose it rotates clockwise with respect to the rotor.

In order for the N poles of the stator to lock with the S poles of the rotor, it is clear that they must rotate at the same speed as far as an outside observer is concerned. This means that to an outside observer

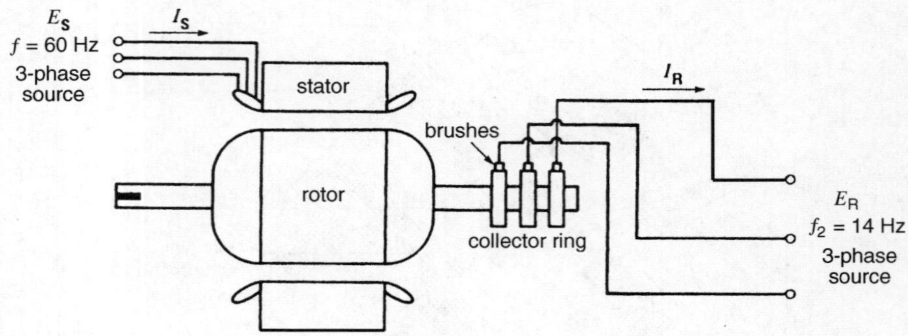

Figure 13.33
Doubly-fed wound-rotor induction motor connected to two 3-phase sources.

the rotor flux must turn clockwise at 1800 r/min. The only way this can happen is for the rotor itself to turn clockwise at a speed of 1800 − 420 = 1380 r/min. If the rotor were to run at any other speed, the rotor poles would slip past the stator poles and the average torque would be zero. The motor would come to a stop.

It is seen that the machine can operate as a motor if, and only if, its speed is *exactly* 1380 r/min. It is said to be running at *subsynchronous* speed.

By interchanging any two leads connected to the slip-rings, we can cause the rotor flux to turn counterclockwise with respect to the rotor. Under these conditions, the N poles of the stator can only lock with the S poles of the rotor provided the rotor turns clockwise at a speed of 1800 + 420 = 2220 r/min. Under these conditions, the motor is said to be running at *supersynchronous* speed.

Based upon this example, and to generalize, we can show that the motor can run at either one of two possible speeds given by

$$n = \frac{120}{p}(f + f_2) \qquad (13.13a)$$

or

$$n = \frac{120}{p}(f - f_2) \qquad (13.13b)$$

where

n = rotor speed [r/min]
f = frequency applied to the stator [Hz]
f_2 = frequency applied to the rotor [Hz]
p = number of poles
120 = numerical value to take care of units

For a given frequency f_2, the speed n depends upon the phase sequence of the 3-phase voltage applied to the rotor. A negative sequence yields supersynchronous speed (Eq. 13.13a), while a positive sequence produces subsynchronous speed (Eq. 13.13b).

How does power flow in such a doubly-fed machine? To answer the question, let us first examine the flow of active power in a wound-rotor motor whose rotor is connected to an external load resistor *R*. Fig. 13.34 shows the power flow through the various components:

1. The 3-phase source E_S delivers power P_e to the stator.
2. After subtracting the stator joule losses P_{js} and iron losses P_f, the resulting active power P_r is transmitted to the rotor.
3. Owing to the slip *s*, a portion of P_r is dissipated in the form of rotor losses sP_r. These losses are equal to the sum of the I^2R losses in the rotor itself (P_{jr}) and the losses (P_{jR}) in the external resistors *R*.

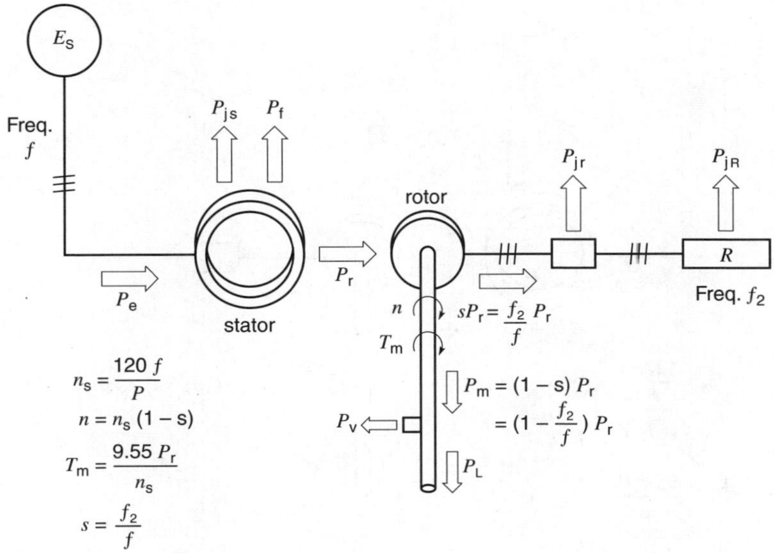

Figure 13.34
Power flow in a wound-rotor induction motor having an external resistance *R*.

4. The difference between P_r and sP_r is converted into mechanical power P_m delivered to the shaft. Hence $P_m = (1 - s)P_r$.
5. The windage and friction losses P_v subtract from P_m to produce the mechanical power P_L that drives the load.
6. We now bring into the picture the relationship between the slip *s*, the stator frequency *f*, and the rotor frequency f_2. As stated in Section 13.10, $f_2 = sf$, from which we obtain the important expression $s = f_2/f$.
7. The mechanical power can now be expressed in terms of the stator frequency *f*, the rotor frequency f_2, and P_m. Thus, $P_m = (1 - f_2/f)\, P_r$. Also, the active electric power delivered by the rotor windings is dissipated in the form of heat P_{jr} and P_{jR} and is always equal to $(f_2/f)\, P_r$.
8. The torque T_m developed by the motor is again given by the equation

$$T_m = 9.55\, P_r/n_s \tag{13.9}$$

With these introductory remarks, we can now look at the power flow in a doubly-fed wound-rotor motor when it operates in the subsynchronous and supersynchronous modes.

13.24 Doubly-fed wound-rotor motor (power relationships at subsynchronous speed)

When the rotor of a wound-rotor motor is connected to a source E_R having a frequency f_2, the slip $s = f_2/f$ is automatically fixed. Consequently, the speed of the motor is also fixed. Indeed, the machine is a special type of synchronous motor. Nevertheless, the power relationships we described for the wound-rotor induction motor (Fig. 13.34) still apply. Referring to Fig. 13.35, we see that the power P_m delivered to the shaft is still given by

$$P_m = (1 - f_2/f)P_r \tag{13.14}$$

Furthermore, the electric power delivered by the rotor is again $(f_2/f)\, P_r$. A portion P_{jr} of this power is

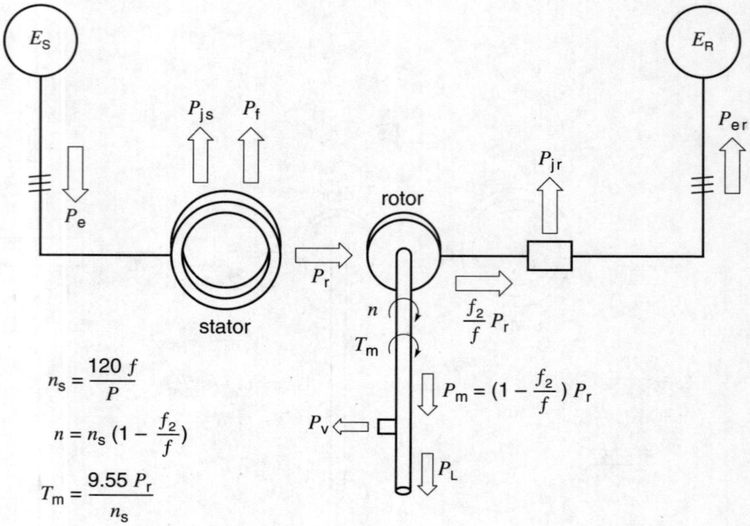

Figure 13.35
Power flow in a doubly-fed wound-rotor induction motor in subsynchronous mode.

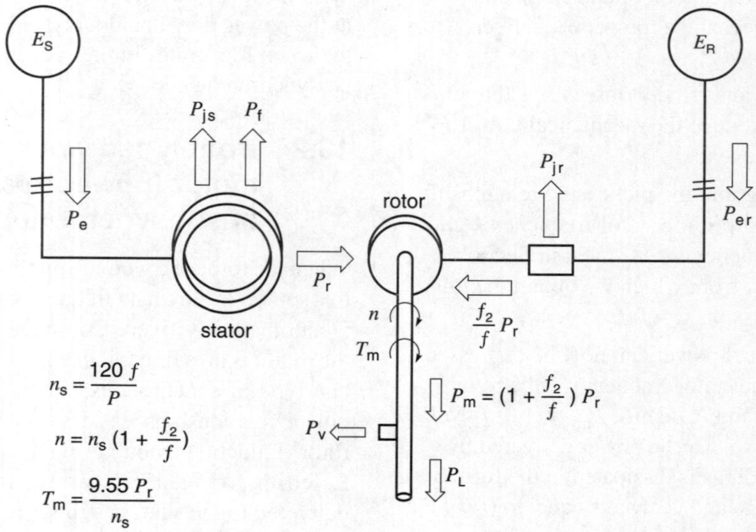

Figure 13.36
Power flow in a doubly-fed wound-rotor induction motor in supersynchronous mode.

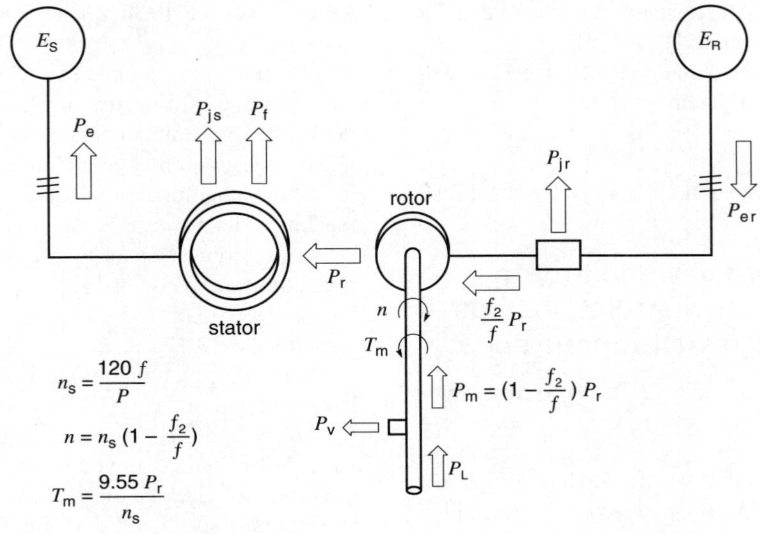

Figure 13.37
Power flow in a doubly-fed wound-rotor induction generator in subsynchronous mode.

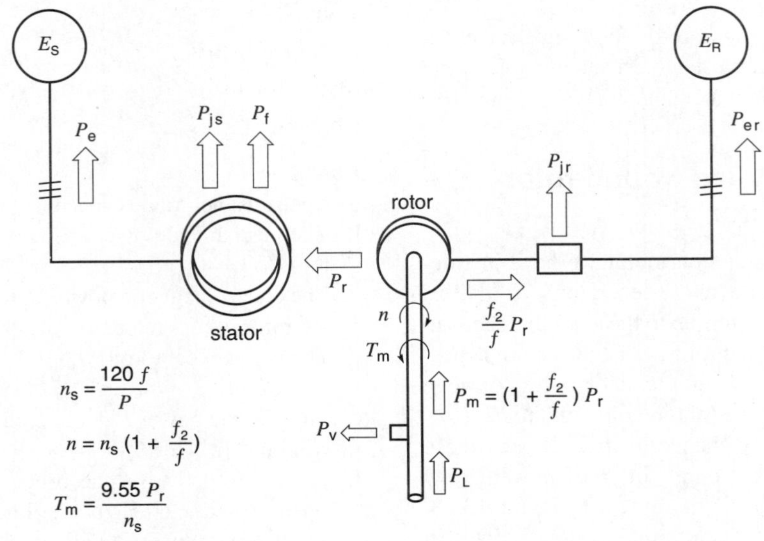

Figure 13.38
Power flow in a doubly-fed wound-rotor induction generator in supersynchronous mode.

dissipated in the rotor resistance, and the remainder P_{er} is fed into the source E_R.

It is interesting to note that the torque T_m developed by the motor is again given by

$$T_m = 9.55\ P_r/n_s \tag{13.9}$$

wherein n_s is the synchronous speed of the stator flux.

13.25 Doubly-fed wound-rotor motor (power relationships at supersynchronous speed)

When the phase sequence of E_R is reversed, the motor runs at supersynchronous speed. Under these conditions, the power flow in the rotor circuit reverses, but the quantitative power relationships still hold (Fig. 13.36). Active power $(f_2/f)\ P_r$ (provided by source E_R) now flows *into* the rotor and the mechanical power P_m is therefore

$$P_m = (1 + f_2/f)\ P_r$$

Note that the torque T_m is again given by

$$T_m = 9.55\ P_r/n_s$$

The doubly-fed wound-rotor motor we have described is sometimes used to drive a variable-speed load, such as a pump (see Fig. 14.17).

13.26 Doubly-fed wound-rotor generator

The doubly-fed induction motor we have just described can operate as a generator. All that is needed is to apply a torque to the shaft that tends to increase the subsynchronous or the supersynchronous speed. This causes the rotor poles to move slightly ahead of the stator poles, without, however, producing any change in speed. Under these conditions, the direction of the power flow changes, as indicated in Figs. 13.37 and 13.38. Fig. 13.37 applies when the generator operates in the subsynchronous mode; Fig. 13.38 is for the supersynchronous mode. The transition from subsynchronous to supersynchronous operation is effected by varying the frequency f_2 and the phase sequence of E_R.

The following example of a wind-turbine generator shows the respective power flows when the doubly-fed generator operates in the subsynchronous mode. A similar reasoning can be applied to any of the other modes of operation of a doubly-fed machine. The power P_e supplied to the line can be set to unity power factor by properly adjusting the magnitude and phase of E_R.

Example 13-12

A 3-phase, 6-pole, doubly-fed induction generator has a rating of 800 kW. The stator is connected to a 60 Hz line and the rotor winding is connected to a variable-frequency converter that produces a frequency of 24 Hz. The machine is operating at subsynchronous speed and the wind turbine develops 500 hp. The wind turbine is connected to the rotor shaft by way of a speed-raising gear box.

The following information is also given (please refer to Fig. 13.39):

Gear box and other friction losses	$P_v = 11$ kW
Rotor I^2R losses	$P_{jr} = 3$ kW
Stator I^2R losses	$P_{js} = 12$ kW
Stator iron losses	$P_f = 7$ kW
Converter losses	$P_c = 2$ kW

Calculate

a. The subsynchronous speed of the rotor [r/min]
b. The mechanical power P_m delivered to the rotor [kW]
c. The electromagnetic power P_r transferred from the rotor to the stator [kW]
d. The mechanical torque T_m at the input to the rotor [kN·m]
e. The electric power P_{er} delivered to the rotor windings [kW]
f. The electric power P_2 absorbed by the converter from the 60 Hz power line [kW]
g. The electric power P_e delivered by the stator to the 60 Hz power line [kW]
h. The efficiency P_1/P_L of the wind-turbine assembly [%]

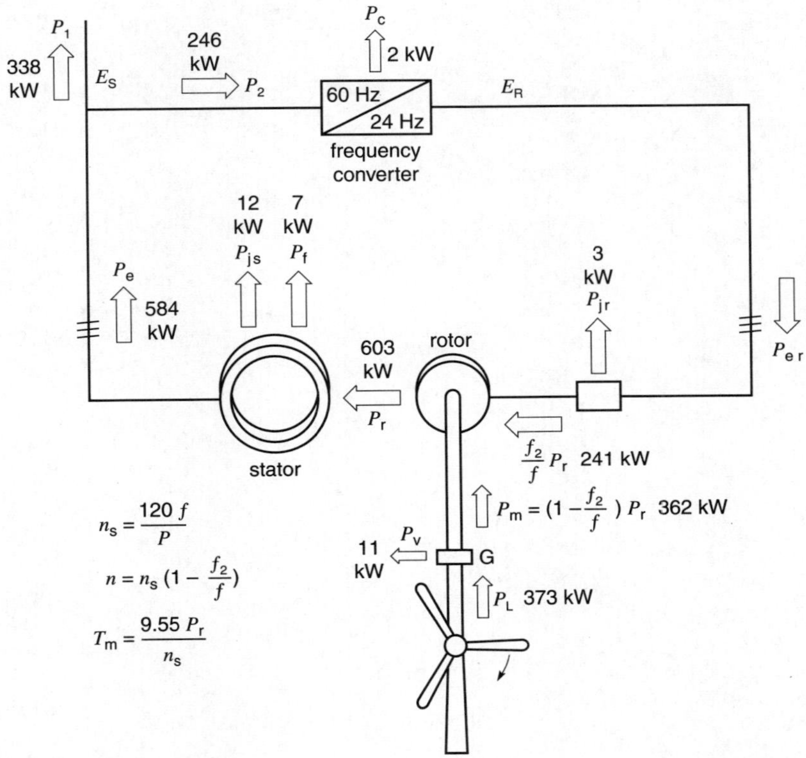

Figure 13.39
See Example 13-12.

Solution

a. The subsynchronous speed:

$$n = \frac{120}{p}(f - f_2) \tag{13.13b}$$

$$= \frac{120}{6}(60 - 24) = 720 \text{ r/min}$$

b. Mechanical power delivered by the turbine to the gear box:

$$P_L = 500 \text{ hp} = 50 \times 746 \text{ W} = 373 \text{ kW}$$

Loss in the gear box $P_v = 11$ kW
Mechanical power input P_m to the rotor

$$P_m = P_L - P_v = 373 - 11 = 362 \text{ kW}$$

c. P_r can be found from the expression

$$P_m = \left(1 - \frac{f_2}{f}\right) P_r \tag{13.14}$$

$$362 = \left(1 - \frac{24}{60}\right) P_r$$

$$362 = 0.6\, P_r$$

and so $$P_r = \frac{362}{0.6} = 603 \text{ kW}$$

Note that this power is considerably greater than the power delivered by the wind turbine.

d. The synchronous speed is $n_s = 120\, f/p = 120 \times 60/6 = 1200$ r/min

Figure 13.40
This Middelgrunden Offshore Wind Farm is located just outside Copenhagen Harbour, in Denmark. It consists of twenty 2 MW turbines yielding a total output of 40 MW. The blades are 38 m long, revolving at a hub height of 64 m. The twenty turbines are equipped with squirrel-cage induction generators that together produce a guaranteed minimum of 89 000 MW h per year.
(Photo © BONUS Energy A/S)

$$T_m = \frac{9.55\, P_r}{n_s} \qquad (13.9)$$

$$= \frac{9.55 \times 603\,000}{1200} = 4.8 \text{ kN·m}$$

e. Electric power input to rotor = $(f_2/f)P_r$ = (24/60) × 603 kW = 241 kW

f. I^2R losses in rotor P_{jr} = 3 kW
Hence, from Fig. 13.39, P_{er} = 241 + 3 = 244 kW.
Electric power P_2 absorbed by the frequency converter

$$P_2 = P_{er} + P_c = 244 + 2 = 246 \text{ kW}$$

g. Electric power delivered by the stator to the power line

$$P_e = P_r - P_{js} - P_f = 603 - 12 - 7 = 584 \text{ kW}$$

Note that the electric power P_e delivered to the 60 Hz source exceeds the turbine power input P_L to the shaft. The reason is that when the generator operates in the subsynchronous mode, the rotor draws power from the 24 Hz converter at the same time as it receives mechanical power from the shaft.

h. Net power P_1 delivered to the power line

$$P_1 = P_e - P_2 = 584 - 246 = 338 \text{ kW}$$

Power developed by turbine: P_L = 373 kW
Efficiency of the wind-turbine assembly = P_1/P_L = 338 kW/373 kW = 0.906 = 90.6%

In addition to doubly-fed induction generators, other methods of transforming wind power into electricity are used. They are described in Chapter 24, Section 24.28.
Fig. 13.40 is one example of an important offshore wind farm.

Questions and Problems

Practical level

13-1 Name the principal components of an induction motor.

13-2 Explain how a revolving field is set up in a 3-phase induction motor.

13-3 If we double the number of poles on the stator of an induction motor, will its synchronous speed also double?

13-4 The rotor of an induction should never be locked while full voltage is being applied to the stator. Explain.

13-5 Why does the rotor of an induction motor turn slower than the revolving field?

13-6 What happens to the rotor speed and rotor current when the mechanical load on an induction motor increases?

13-7 Would you recommend using a 50 hp induction motor to drive a 10 hp load? Explain.

13-8 Give two advantages of a wound-rotor motor over a squirrel-cage motor.

13-9 Both the voltage and frequency induced in the rotor of an induction motor decrease as the rotor speeds up. Explain.

13-10 A 3-phase, 20-pole induction motor is connected to a 600 V, 60 Hz source.
a. What is the synchronous speed?
b. If the voltage is reduced to 300 V, will the synchronous speed change?
c. How many groups are there, per phase?

13-11 Describe the principle of operation of a linear induction motor.

13-12 Calculate the approximate values of the starting current, full-load current, and no-load current of a 150 horsepower, 575 V, 3-phase induction motor.

13-13 Make a drawing of the magnetic field created by a 3-phase, 12-pole induction motor.

13-14 How can we change the direction of rotation of a 3-phase induction motor?

Intermediate level

13-15 **a.** Calculate the synchronous speed of a 3-phase, 12-pole induction motor that is excited by a 60 Hz source.
b. What is the nominal speed if the slip at full-load is 6 percent?

13-16 A 3-phase, 6-pole induction motor is connected to a 60 Hz supply. The voltage induced in the rotor bars is 4 V when the rotor is locked. If the motor turns in the same direction as the flux, calculate the approximate voltage induced and its frequency:
a. At 300 r/min
b. At 1000 r/min
c. At 1500 r/min

13-17 **a.** Calculate the approximate values of full-load current, starting current, and no-load current of a 75 kW, 4000 V, 3-phase, 900 r/min, 60 Hz induction motor.
b. Calculate the nominal full-load speed and torque knowing that the slip is 2 percent.

13-18 A 3-phase, 75 hp, 440 V induction motor has a full-load efficiency of 91 percent and a power factor of 83 percent. Calculate the nominal current per phase.

13-19 An open-circuit voltage of 240 V appears across the slip-rings of a wound-rotor induction motor when the rotor is locked. The stator has 6 poles and is excited by a 60 Hz source. If the rotor is driven by a variable-speed dc motor, calculate the open-circuit voltage and frequency across the slip-rings if the dc motor turns
a. At 600 r/min, in the same direction as the rotating field
b. At 900 r/min, in the same direction as the rotating field
c. At 3600 r/min, opposite to the rotating field

13-20 **a.** Referring to Fig. 13.7, calculate the instantaneous values of I_a, I_b, and I_c for an angle of 150°.
b. Determine the actual direction of current flow in the three phases at this instant and calculate the mmf developed by the windings.
c. Does the resulting mmf point in a direction intermediate between the mmf's corresponding to instants 3 and 4?

13-21 A 3-phase lap-wound stator possessing 72 slots produces a synchronous speed of 900 r/min when connected to a 60 Hz source. Calculate the number of coils per phase group as well as the probable coil pitch. Draw the complete coil connection diagram, following steps (a) to (f) in Fig. 13.22.

13-22 The 3-phase, 4-pole stator of Fig. 13.25 has an internal diameter of 250 mm and a stacking (axial length) of 200 mm. If the maximum flux density per pole is 0.7 T, calculate the following:
a. The peripheral speed [m/s] of the revolving field when the stator is connected to a 60 Hz source
b. The peak voltage induced in the rotor bars
c. The pole-pitch

13-23 A large 3-phase, 4000 V, 60 Hz, squirrel-cage induction motor draws a current of 385 A and a total active power of 2344 kW when operating at full-load. The corresponding speed is accurately measured and is found to be 709.2 r/min. The stator is connected in wye and the resistance between two stator terminals is 0.10 Ω. The total iron losses are 23.4 kW and the windage and friction losses are 12 kW. Calculate the following:
a. The power factor at full-load
b. The active power supplied to the rotor
c. The total I^2R losses in the rotor
d. The load mechanical power [kW], torque [kN·m], and efficiency [%]

13-24 If we slightly increase the rotor resistance of an induction motor, what effect does this have (increase or decrease) upon
a. Starting torque
b. Starting current
c. Full-load speed
d. Efficiency
e. Power factor
f. Temperature rise of the motor at its rated power output

13-25 Explain the principle of magnetic levitation.

Advanced level

13-26 In Fig. 13.5a the permanent magnet has a width of 100 mm and moves at 30 m/s. The flux density in the air gap is 0.5 T and the effective resistance per rotor bar is 1 mΩ. Calculate the current I and the tractive force.

13-27 If the conducting ladder in Fig. 13.5a is pulled along with a force of 20 N, what is the braking force exerted on the magnet?

13-28 A 3-phase, 5000 hp, 6000 V, 60 Hz, 12-pole, wound-rotor induction motor turns at 594 r/min. What are the approximate rotor I^2R losses at rated load?

13-29 The motor in Problem 13-28 has the following characteristics:

1. dc resistance between stator terminals = 0.112 Ω at 17°C
2. dc resistance between rotor slip-rings = 0.0073 Ω at 17°C
3. open-circuit voltage induced between slip-rings with rotor locked = 1600 V
4. line-to-line stator voltage = 6000 V
5. no-load stator current, per phase = 100 A
6. active power supplied to motor at no-load = 91 kW
7. windage and friction losses = 51 kW
8. iron losses in the stator = 39 kW
9. locked-rotor current at 6000 V = 1800 A
10. active power to stator with rotor locked = 2207 kW

Calculate

a. Rotor and stator resistance per phase at 75°C (assume a wye connection)
b. Voltage and frequency induced in the rotor when it turns at 200 r/min and at 594 r/min
c. Reactive power absorbed by the motor to create the revolving field, at no-load
d. I^2R losses in the stator when the motor runs at no-load (winding temperature 75°C)
e. Active power supplied to the rotor at no-load

13-30 Referring to the motor described in Problem 13-29, calculate under full-voltage LR (locked-rotor) conditions:

a. Reactive power absorbed by the motor
b. I^2R losses in the stator
c. Active power supplied to the rotor
d. Mechanical power output
e. Torque developed by the rotor

13-31 We wish to control the speed of the motor given in Problem 13-29 by inserting resistors in series with the rotor (see Fig. 13.19). If the motor has to develop a torque of 20 kN·m at a speed of 450 r/min, calculate the following:

a. Voltage between the slip rings
b. Rotor resistance (per phase) and the total power dissipated
c. Approximate rotor current, per phase

13-32 The train shown in Fig. 13.31 moves at 200 km/h when the stator frequency is 105 Hz. By supposing a negligible slip, calculate the length of the pole-pitch of the linear motor [mm].

13-33 A 3-phase, 300 kW, 2300 V, 60 Hz, 1780 r/min induction motor is used to drive a compressor. The motor has a full-load efficiency and power factor of 92 percent and 86 percent, respectively. If the terminal voltage rises to 2760 V while the motor operates at full-load, determine the effect (increase or decrease) upon

a. Mechanical power delivered by the motor
b. Motor torque
c. Rotational speed
d. Full-load current
e. Power factor and efficiency
f. Starting torque
g. Starting current
h. Breakdown torque
i. Motor temperature rise
j. Flux per pole
k. Exciting current
l. Iron losses

13-34 A 3-phase, 60 Hz linear induction motor has to reach a top no-load speed of 12 m/s and it must develop a standstill thrust of 10 kN. Calculate the required pole-pitch and the minimum I^2R loss in the rotor, at standstill.

Industrial application

13-35 A 10 hp, 575 V, 1160 r/min, 3-phase, 60 Hz induction motor has a rotor made of aluminum, similar to the rotor shown in Fig. 13.3a. The end-rings are trimmed in a lathe, cutting off the cooling fins and also a portion of the rings, making them less thick. What effect will this have on the following?

a. The full-load speed of the motor
b. The starting torque
c. The temperature rise at full-load

13-36 The stator of a 600 hp, 1160 r/min, 575 V, 3-phase, 60 Hz induction motor has 90 slots, an internal diameter of 20 inches, and an axial length of 16 inches.

Calculate

a. The number of coils on the stator
b. The number of coils per phase
c. The number of coils per group
d. The coil pitch (in millimeters)
e. The area of one pole
f. The flux per pole if the average flux density is 0.54 T

13-37 A 25 hp, 1183 r/min, 575 V, 3-phase, 60 Hz, wound-rotor induction motor produces at standstill 320 V between the open-circuit lines of the rotor. It is known that the RMS brush voltage drop is about 0.6 V. Estimate the no-load speed of the motor.

13-38 The rotor of a 60 hp, 1760 r/min, 60 Hz induction motor has 117 bars and a diameter of 11 inches. Calculate the average force on each bar (in newtons) when the motor is running at full-load.

13-39 The stator of a 2-pole wound-rotor motor is powered by a 3-phase, 50 Hz source. If the rotor is connected to a 3-phase, 11 Hz source, at what speeds can the rotor turn? If the motor operates at the lower speed does the 11 Hz source absorb or deliver active power?

13-40 A doubly-fed induction generator runs at supersychronous speed. Does the rotor deliver or absorb active power from the source to which the rotor is connected?

13-41 The stator of a 4-pole doubly-fed induction motor is connected to a 3-phase, 60 Hz source. A tachometer indicates that the rotor is turning at a speed of 2367 r/min. A 3-phase wattmeter inserted in the feeder to the stator indicates an active power flow of 460 kW. Calculate

a. The frequency of the source that is connected to the rotor.
b. The approximate mechanical power developed by the motor.

CHAPTER 14

Selection and Application of Three-Phase Induction Machines

14.0 Introduction

We have seen that 3-phase induction machines can operate as motors or generators.

When purchasing a 3-phase induction motor for a particular application, we often discover that several types can fill the need. Consequently, we have to make a choice. The selection is generally simplified because the manufacturer of the lathe, fan, pump, and so forth indicates the type of motor that is best suited to drive the load. Nevertheless, it is useful to know something about the basic construction and characteristics of the various types of 3-phase induction motors that are available on the market.

In this chapter we also cover some special applications of induction machines, such as asynchronous generators and frequency converters. These interesting devices will enable the reader to gain a better understanding of induction machines in general.

14.1 Standardization and classification of induction motors*

The frames of all industrial motors under 500 hp have standardized dimensions. Thus, a 25 hp, 1725 r/min, 60 Hz motor of one manufacturer can be replaced by that of any other manufacturer, without having to change the mounting holes, the shaft height, or the type of coupling. The standardization covers not only frame sizes, but also establishes limiting values for electrical, mechanical, and thermal characteristics. Thus, motors must satisfy minimum requirements as to starting torque, locked-rotor current, overload capacity, and temperature rise.

14.2 Classification according to environment and cooling methods

Motors are grouped into several categories, depending upon the environment in which they have to operate. We limit our discussion to five important classes.

1. Drip-proof motors. The frame in a drip-proof motor protects the windings against liquid drops and solid particles which fall at any angle between 0 and 15 degrees downward from the vertical. The motors are cooled by means of a fan directly coupled to the rotor. Cool air, drawn into the motor

* Standards in the United States are governed by National Electrical Manufacturers (NEMA) publication MG-1 titled *Motors and Generators.* Standards in Canada are similarly governed by Canadian Standards Association (CSA) publication C 154. The two standards are essentially identical.

through vents in the frame, is blown over the windings and then expelled. The maximum allowable temperature rise (measured by the change in winding resistance) may be 60°C, 80°C, 105°C, or 125°C, depending on the type of insulation used in the windings. Drip-proof motors (Fig. 14.1) can be used in most locations.

*2. **Splash-proof motor.*** The frame in a splash-proof motor protects the windings against liquid drops and solid particles that fall at any angle between 0 and 100° downward from the vertical. Cooling is similar to that in drip-proof motors and the maximum temperature rise is also the same. These motors are mainly used in wet locations.

*3. **Totally enclosed, nonventilated motors.*** These motors have closed frames that prevent the free exchange of air between the inside and the outside of the case. They are designed for very wet and dusty locations. Most are rated below 10 kW because it is difficult to get rid of the heat of larger machines. The motor losses are dissipated by natural convection and radiation from the frame. The permissible temperature rise is 65°C, 85°C, 110°C, or 130°C, depending on the class of insulation (see Fig. 14.2).

Figure 14.1
Energy-efficient, drip-proof, 3-phase, squirrel-cage induction motor rated 230 V/460 V, 3 hp, 1750 r/min, 60 Hz.
(Courtesy of Gould)

*4. **Totally enclosed, fan-cooled motors.*** Medium- and high-power motors that are totally enclosed are usually cooled by an external blast of air. An external fan, directly coupled to the shaft, blows air over the ribbed motor frame (Fig. 14.3). A concentric outer shield prevents physical contact with the fan and serves to channel the airstream. The permissible temperature rise is the same as for drip-proof motors.

*5. **Explosion-proof motors.*** Explosion-proof motors are used in highly inflammable or explosive surroundings, such as coal mines, oil refineries, and grain elevators. They are totally enclosed (but not

Figure 14.2
Two totally enclosed nonventilated (TENV) 2 hp, 1725 r/min cage motors are shown in foreground and two 30 hp, 1780 r/min totally enclosed blower-cooled motors (TEBC) in background. These 3-phase, 460 V motors are intended to operate at variable speeds ranging from a few revolutions per minute to about 3 times rated speed.

The 2 hp motors have a full-load current of 2.9 A, efficiency of 84 percent and power factor of 76 percent. Other characteristics: no-load current: 1.7 A; locked-rotor current: 26 A; locked-rotor torque: 4.2 pu; breakdown torque: 5.0 pu; service factor: 1.0; total weight: 39 kg; overall length including shaft: 377 mm; overall height: 235 mm.

The 30 hp motors have a full-load current of 34 A, efficiency of 93 percent, and power factor of 84 percent. Other characteristics: no-load current: 12 A; locked-rotor current: 214 A; locked rotor torque: 1.6 pu; breakdown torque: 2.84 pu; service factor: 1.0; total weight: 200 kg; overall length including shaft: 834 mm; overall height: 365 mm.
(Courtesy of Baldor Electric Company)

Figure 14.3
Totally enclosed fan-cooled induction motor rated 350 hp, 1760 r/min, 440 V, 3-phase, 60 Hz.
(Courtesy of Gould)

Figure 14.4
Totally enclosed, fan-cooled, explosion-proof motor. Note the particularly rugged construction of this type of motor.
(Courtesy of Brook Crompton-Parkinson Ltd)

airtight) and the frames are designed to withstand the enormous pressure that may build up inside the motor due to an internal explosion. Furthermore, the flanges on the end-bells are made extra long in order to cool any escaping gases generated by such an explosion. Such explosions may be initiated by the spark or a short-circuit within the windings. The permissible temperature rise is the same as for totally enclosed motors (see Fig. 14.4).

14.3 Classification according to electrical and mechanical properties

In addition to the various enclosures just mentioned, 3-phase, squirrel-cage motors can have special electrical and mechanical characteristics, as listed below.

1. Motors with standard locked-rotor torque (NEMA Design B). Most induction motors belong to this group. The per-unit locked-rotor torque decreases as the size of the motor increases. Thus, it ranges from 1.3 to 0.7, as the power increases from 20 hp to 200 hp (15 kW to 150 kW). The corresponding locked-rotor current should not exceed 6.4 times the rated full-load current. These general-purpose motors are used to drive fans, centrifugal pumps, machine tools, and so forth.

2. High starting-torque motors (NEMA Design C). These motors are employed when starting conditions are difficult. Pumps and piston-type compressors that have to start under load are two typical applications. In the range from 20 hp to 200 hp, the locked-rotor torque is 200% of full-load torque, which corresponds to a per-unit torque of 2. The locked-rotor current should not exceed 6.4 times the rated full-load current.

In general, these motors are equipped with a double-cage rotor. The excellent performance of a double-cage rotor (Fig. 14.5) is based upon the following facts:

a. The frequency of the rotor current diminishes as the motor speeds up
b. A conductor that lies close to the rotor surface (cage 1) has a lower inductive reactance than one buried deep inside the iron core (cage 2)
c. The conductors of cage 1 are much smaller than those of cage 2

When the motor is connected to the line with the rotor at standstill, the frequency of the rotor current is equal to line frequency. Owing to the high inductive reactance of squirrel-cage 2, the rotor current flows mainly in the small bars of cage 1. The effective motor resistance is therefore high, being essentially equal to that of cage 1. Consequently, a high starting torque is developed.

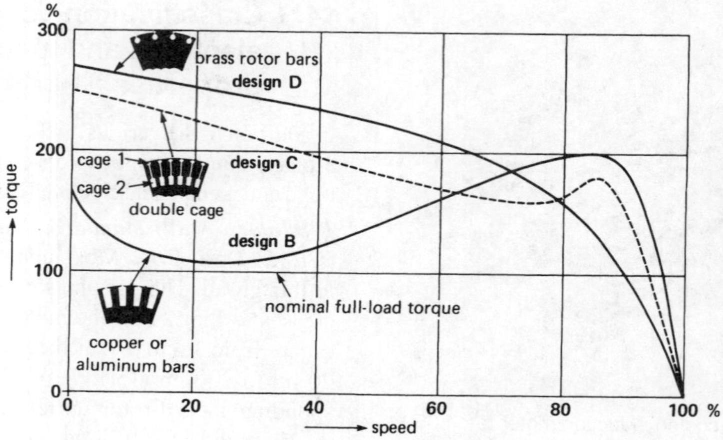

Figure 14.5
Typical torque-speed curves of NEMA Design B, C, and D motors. Each curve corresponds to the minimum NEMA values of locked-rotor torque, pull-up torque, and breakdown torque of a 3-phase, 1800 r/min, 10 hp, 60 Hz, squirrel-cage induction motor. The cross section of the respective rotors indicates the type of rotor bars used.

As the motor speeds up, the rotor frequency falls, with the result that the inductive reactance of both squirrel-cage windings diminishes. At rated speed the rotor frequency is so low (typically 1 Hz) that the reactance of both windings is negligible. The rotor current is then limited only by the *resistance* of cage 1 and cage 2 operating in parallel. Because the conductors of cage 2 are much larger than those of cage 1, the effective rotor resistance at rated speed is much lower than at standstill. For this reason the double-cage rotor develops both a high starting torque and a low slip at full-load.

Despite their high torque, Design C motors are not recommended for starting high-inertia loads. The reason is that most of the rotor I^2R losses during start-up are concentrated in cage 1. Owing to its small size, it tends to overheat and the bars may melt.

3. High-slip motors (NEMA Design D). The rated speed of high-slip, Design D motors usually lies between 85% and 95% of synchronous speed. These motors are used to accelerate high-inertia loads (such as centrifugal dryers), which take a relatively long time to reach full speed. The high-resistance squirrel-cage is made of brass, and the motors are usually designed for intermittent duty to prevent overheating.

The large drop in speed with increasing load is also ideal to drive impact-type machine tools that punch holes in sheet metal. When the worker initiates the operation, a clutch engages the flywheel, causing the punch to descend and pierce the sheet.

Punching a hole requires a tremendous amount of power, sometimes exceeding 1000 hp. The reason is that the punching energy is delivered in a fraction of a second. The energy is furnished by the flywheel rather than by the motor itself. As the punch does its work, the speed of the flywheel drops immediately, thus releasing a lot of kinetic energy in a very short time. The speed of the motor also drops considerably, along with that of the flywheel. However, the Class D design ensures that the current drawn from the line at the lower speed will not exceed its rated value.

As soon as the hole is pierced, the only load on the motor is the flywheel, which is now gradually brought back up to speed. During the acceleration period, the motor delivers energy to the flywheel, thus restoring the energy it lost during the impact. A powerful motor will quickly accelerate the flywheel, permitting rapid, repetitive operation of the punch press. On the other hand, if the repetition rate is low, a much smaller motor will suffice; it will only take longer to bring the flywheel up to speed.

The torque-speed curves of Fig. 14.5 enable us to compare the characteristics of NEMA Design B, C, and D motors. The rotor construction is also shown, and it can be seen that the distinguishing properties are obtained by changing the rotor design. For example, if the rotor resistance is increased (by using brass instead of copper or aluminum), the locked-rotor torque increases, but the speed at rated torque is lower.

14.4 Choice of motor speed

The choice of motor speed is rather limited because the synchronous speed of induction motors changes by quantum jumps, depending upon the frequency and the number of poles. For example, it is impossible to build a conventional induction motor having an acceptable efficiency and running at a speed, say, of 2000 r/min on a 60 Hz supply. Such a motor would require 2 poles and a corresponding synchronous speed of 3600 r/min. The slip of (3600 − 2000)/3600 = 0.444 means that 44.4% of the power supplied to the rotor would be dissipated as heat. (See Section 13.13.)

The speed of a motor is obviously determined by the speed of the machine it has to drive. However, for low-speed machines, it is often preferable to use a high-speed motor and a gearbox instead of directly coupling a low-speed motor to the load. There are several advantages to using a gearbox:

1. For a given output power, the size and cost of a high-speed motor is less than that of a low-speed motor, and its efficiency and power factor are higher.
2. The locked-rotor torque of a high-speed motor is always greater (as a percentage of full-load torque) than that of a similar low-speed motor of equal power.

By way of example, Table 14A compares the properties of two 10 hp, 3-phase, 60 Hz, totally enclosed, fan-cooled induction motors having different synchronous speeds. The difference in price alone would justify the use of a high-speed motor and a gearbox to drive a load operating at, say, 900 r/min.

When equipment has to operate at very low speeds (100 r/min or less), a gearbox is mandatory. The gears are often an integral part of the motor, making for a very compact unit (Fig. 14.6).

A gearbox is also mandatory when equipment has to run above 3600 r/min. For example, in one industrial application a large gear unit is used to drive a 1200 hp, 5000 r/min centrifugal compressor coupled to a 3560 r/min induction motor.

14.5 Two-speed motors

The stator of a squirrel-cage induction motor can be designed so that the motor can operate at two different speeds. Such motors are often used on drill presses, blowers, and pumps. One way to obtain two speeds is to wind the stator with two separate windings having, say, 4 poles and 6 poles. The problem is that only one winding is in operation at a time and so only half the copper in the slots is being utilized.

However, special windings have been invented whereby the speed is changed by simply changing the external stator connections. The synchronous

TABLE 14A COMPARISON BETWEEN TWO MOTORS OF DIFFERENT SPEEDS

Power		Synchronous speed	Power factor	Efficiency	Locked-rotor torque	Mass	Price (2004)
hp	kW	r/min	%	%	%	kg	U.S. $
10	7.5	3600	89	90	150	50	715
10	7.5	900	75	85	125	170	2300

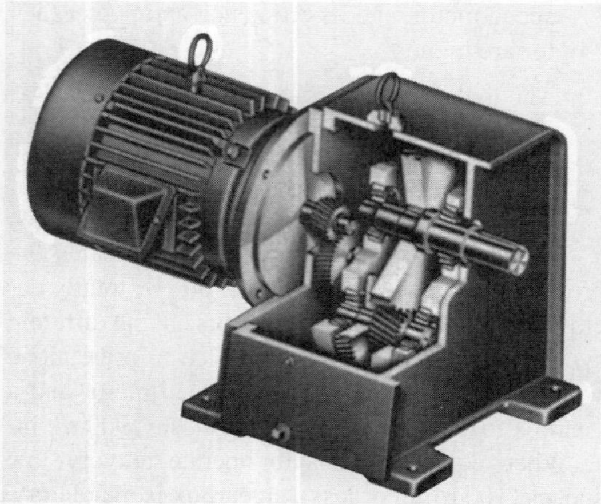

Figure 14.6
Gear motor rated at 2.25 kW, 1740 r/min, 60 Hz. The output torque and speed are respectively 172 N·m and 125 r/min.
(Courtesy of Reliance Electric)

speeds obtained are usually in the ratio 2:1 (3600/1800 r/min, 1200/600 r/min, etc.). The lower speed is produced by the creation of *consequent poles.*

Consider, for example, one phase of a two-pole, 3-phase motor (Fig. 14.7a). When the two poles are connected in series to a 60 Hz ac source, current I_1 flows into terminal 1 and current I_2 $(= I_1)$ flows out of terminal 2. As a result, one N pole and one S pole are created and the flux has the pattern shown. The synchronous speed is

$$\begin{aligned} n_s &= 120f/p = 120 \times 60/2 \\ &= 3600 \text{ r/min} \end{aligned}$$

Note that each pole covers only one-quarter of the stator circumference instead of the usual one-half. This is achieved by using a coil pitch equal to 50 percent of the pole-pitch.

Let us now connect the two poles in parallel, as shown in Fig. 14.7b. In this case, at the instant current I_1 flows into terminal 1, current I_2 flows into terminal 2. As a result, two N poles are created by the windings.

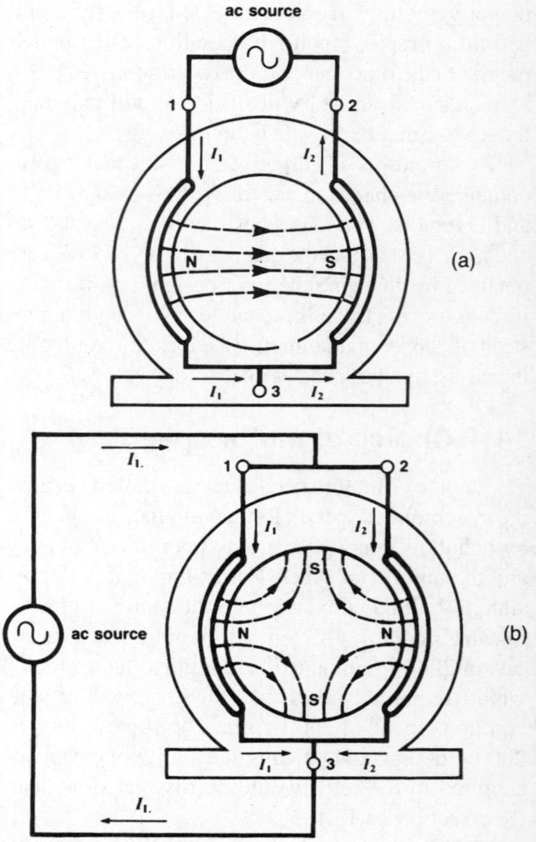

Figure 14.7
a. Two short-pitch coils connected in series produce a two-pole motor.
b. When the coils are connected in parallel, a 4-pole motor is produced. Two of the poles are consequent poles.

Because every N pole must be accompanied by an S pole, it follows that two S poles will appear between the two N poles. The south poles created in this ingenious way are called *consequent poles.* The new connection produces 4 poles in all, and the synchronous speed is 1800 r/min. Thus, we can double the number of poles by simply changing the stator connections. It is upon this principle that 2-speed motors are built.

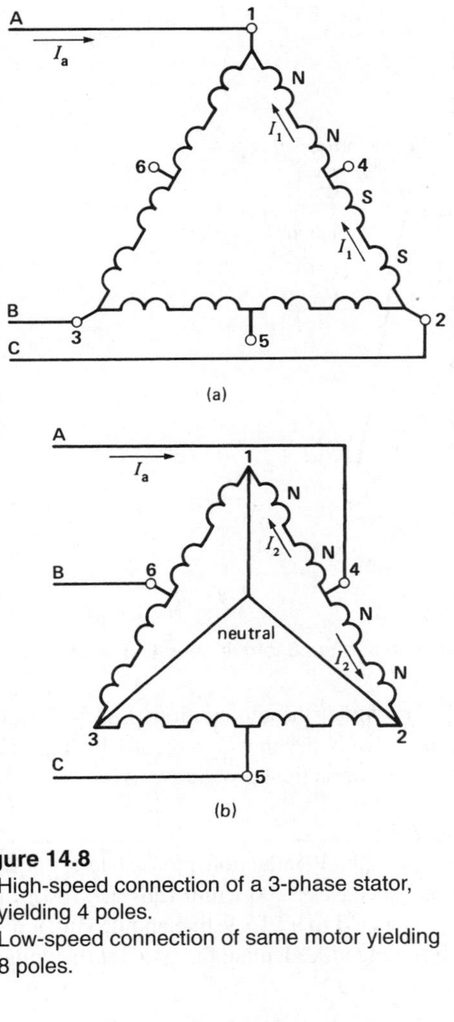

Figure 14.8
a. High-speed connection of a 3-phase stator, yielding 4 poles.
b. Low-speed connection of same motor yielding 8 poles.

Fig. 14.8 shows the stator connections for a 2-speed, 4-pole/8-pole, 3-phase motor. Six leads, numbered 1 to 6, are brought out from the stator winding. For the high-speed connection, power is applied to terminals 1-2-3, and terminals 4-5-6 are open. The resulting delta connection produces 4 poles per phase having two N and two S poles (Fig. 14.8a). Note that the four poles are connected in series.

The low-speed connection is made by short-circuiting terminals 1-2-3 and applying power to terminals 4-5-6. The resulting double-wye connection again produces 4 poles per phase, but now they all possess the same polarity (Fig. 14.8b).

Two-speed motors have a relatively lower efficiency and power factor than single-speed motors do. They can be designed to develop (at both speeds) either constant power, constant torque, or variable torque. The choice depends upon the load that has to be driven.

The 2-speed motors described so far have pole ratios of 2:1. If the motor drives a fan, this may be too big a change in speed. The reason is that the power of a fan varies as the cube of the speed. Consequently, if the speed is reduced by half, the power drops to one-eighth, which is often too low to be of interest.

To overcome this problem, some 3-phase windings are designed to obtain lower pole ratios such as 8/10, 14/16, 26/28, 10/14, and 38/46. These *pole amplitude modulation,* or PAM, motors are particularly useful in driving 2-speed fans in the hundred horsepower range and more. PAM motors enable a moderate reduction in fan power by simply reconnecting the windings to give the lower speed.

14.6 Induction motor characteristics under various load conditions

The complete torque-speed curves displayed in Fig. 14.5 are important, but it must be recognized that most of the time a motor runs at close to synchronous speed, supplying a torque that varies from zero to full-load torque T_n. It so happens that between these limits the torque-speed curve is essentially a straight line (Fig. 14.9). The slope of the line depends mainly upon the rotor resistance—the lower the resistance, the steeper the slope.

In effect, it can be shown that at rated frequency, the slip s, torque T, line voltage E, and rotor resistance R are related by the expression

$$s = kTR/E^2 \tag{14.1}$$

where k is a constant that depends upon the construction of the motor.

This expression enables us to establish a simple formula showing how the line voltage and rotor

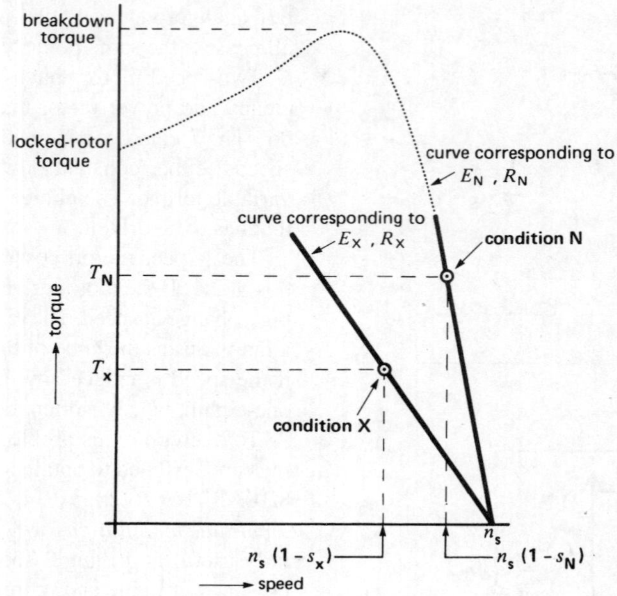

Figure 14.9
The torque-speed curve is essentially a straight line between the no-load and rated torque operating points.

resistance affect the behavior of the motor under load. In effect, once we know the characteristics of a motor for a given load condition, we can predict its speed, torque, power, and so on, for any other load condition. These quantities are related by the formula

$$s_x = s_n \left[\frac{T_x}{T_n}\right]\left[\frac{R_x}{R_n}\right]\left[\frac{E_n}{E_x}\right]^2 \tag{14.2}$$

where

n = subscript referring to the initial, or given load conditions (the given conditions may correspond to the nominal rating of the motor)

x = subscript referring to the new load conditions

s = slip

T = torque [N·m]

R = rotor resistance [Ω]

E = stator voltage [V]

In applying the formula, the only restriction is that the new torque T_x must not be greater than $T_n(E_x/E_n)^2$. Under these conditions Eq. 14.2 yields an accuracy of better than 5 percent which is sufficient for most practical problems.

Example 14-1

A 3-phase, 208 V induction motor having a synchronous speed of 1200 r/min runs at 1140 r/min when connected to a 215 V line and driving a constant torque load. Calculate the speed if the voltage increases to 240 V.

Solution

The slip at 215 V is

$$\begin{aligned} s &= (n_s - n)/n_s \\ &= (1200 - 1140)/1200 \\ &= 0.05 \end{aligned}$$

When the voltage rises to 240 V, the load torque and rotor resistance remain the same. Consequently, in applying Eq. 14.2, we can write

$$\begin{aligned} s_x &= s_n(E_n/E_x)^2 = 0.05\,(215/240)^2 \\ &= 0.04 \end{aligned}$$

The slip speed is, therefore,

$$0.04 \times 1200 = 48 \text{ r/min}$$

The new speed at 240 V is

$$n_x = 1200 - 48 = 1152 \text{ r/min}$$

Example 14-2

A 3-phase, 8-pole induction motor driving a compressor runs at 873 r/min immediately after it is connected to a fixed 460 V, 60 Hz line. The initial cold rotor temperature is 23°C. The speed drops to 864 r/min after the machine has run for several hours.

Calculate

a. The hot rotor resistance in terms of the cold resistance
b. The approximate hot temperature of the rotor bars, knowing they are made of copper

Solution

a. The synchronous speed is

$$n_s = 120\, f/p = 120 \times 60/8 = 900 \text{ r/min}$$

The initial and final slips are

$$s_n = (900 - 873)/900 = 0.03$$
$$s_x = (900 - 864)/900 = 0.04$$

The voltage and torque are fixed; consequently, the speed change is entirely due to the change in rotor resistance. We can therefore write

$$s_x = s_n\,(R_x/R_n)$$
$$0.04 = 0.03\,(R_x/R_n)$$
$$R_x = 1.33\,R_n$$

The hot rotor resistance is 33% greater than the cold rotor resistance.

b. The hot rotor temperature is

$$t_2 = \frac{R_2}{R_1}(234 + T_1) - 234 \qquad (6.5)$$
$$= 1.33\,(234 + 23) - 234$$
$$= 108°\text{C}$$

Example 14-3

A 3-phase, 4-pole, wound-rotor induction motor has a rating of 110 kW, 1760 r/min, 2.3 kV, 60 Hz. Three external resistors of 2 Ω are connected in wye across the rotor slip-rings. Under these conditions the motor develops a torque of 300 N·m at a speed of 1000 r/min.

a. Calculate the speed for a torque of 400 N·m.
b. Calculate the value of the external resistors so that the motor develops 10 kW at 200 r/min.

Solution

a. The given conditions are

$$T_n = 300 \text{ N·m}$$
$$s_n = (1800 - 1000)/1800 = 0.444$$

All other conditions being fixed, we have for a torque of 400 N·m the following:

$$s_x = s_n(T_x/T_n) = 0.444\,(400/300)$$
$$= 0.592$$

The slip speed = 0.592 × 1800 = 1066 r/min. Consequently, the motor speed is

$$n = 1800 - 1066$$
$$= 734 \text{ r/min}$$

Note that the speed drops from 1000 r/min to 734 r/min with increasing load.

b. The torque corresponding to 10 kW at 200 r/min is

$$T_x = 9.55\, P/n \qquad (3.5)$$
$$= 9.55 \times 10\,000/200$$
$$= 478 \text{ N·m}$$

The rated torque is

$$T_{rated} = 9.55\, P/n$$
$$= 9.55 \times 110\,000/1760$$
$$= 597 \text{ N·m}$$

Because T_x is less than T_{rated}, we can apply Eq. 14.2. The slip is

$$s_x = (1800 - 200)/1800 = 0.89$$

All other conditions being fixed, we have, from Eq. 14.2

$$s_x = s_n (T_x/T_n)(R_x/R_n)$$
$$0.89 = 0.44 (478/300)(R_x/2)$$

and so

$$R_x = 2.5\ \Omega$$

Three 2.5 Ω, wye-connected resistors in the rotor circuit will enable the motor to develop 10 kW at 200 r/min.

14.7 Starting an induction motor

High-inertia loads put a strain on induction motors because they prolong the starting period. The starting current in both the stator and rotor is high during this interval so that overheating becomes a major problem. For motors of several thousand horsepower, a prolonged starting period may even overload the transmission line feeding the plant where the motor is installed. The line voltage may fall below normal for many seconds, thus affecting other connected loads. To relieve the problem, induction motors are often started on reduced voltage. This limits the power drawn by the motor, and consequently reduces the line voltage drop as well as the heating rate of the windings. Reduced voltage lengthens the start-up time, but this is usually not important. However, whether the start-up time is long or short, it is worth remembering the following rule for a motor that is not loaded mechanically:

Rule 1 - The heat dissipated in the rotor during the starting period (from zero speed to final rated speed) is equal to the final kinetic energy stored in all the revolving parts.

This rule holds true, irrespective of the stator voltage or the torque-speed curve of the motor. Thus, if a motor brings a massive flywheel up to speed, and if the energy stored in the flywheel is then 5000 joules, the rotor will have dissipated 5000 joules in the form of heat. Depending upon the size of the rotor and its cooling system, this energy could easily produce overheating.

14.8 Plugging an induction motor

In some industrial applications, the induction motor and its load have to be brought to a quick stop. This can be done by interchanging two stator leads, so that the revolving field suddenly turns in the opposite direction to the rotor. During this *plugging* period, the motor acts as a *brake*.

It absorbs kinetic energy from the still-revolving load, causing its speed to fall. The associated mechanical power P_m is entirely dissipated as heat in the rotor. Unfortunately, the rotor also continues to receive electromagnetic power P_r from the stator, which is also dissipated as heat (Fig. 14.10). Consequently, plugging produces I^2R losses in the rotor that even exceed those when the rotor is locked. Motors should not be plugged too frequently because high rotor temperatures may melt the rotor bars or overheat the stator winding. In this regard it is worth

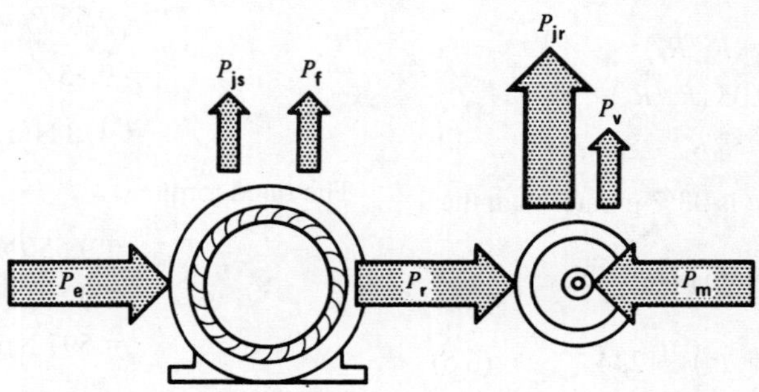

Figure 14.10
When a 3-phase induction motor is plugged, the rotor I^2R losses are very high.

remembering the following rule for plugging operations for a motor that is not loaded mechanically:

Rule 2 - The heat dissipated in the rotor during the plugging period (initial rated speed to zero speed) is *three* times the original kinetic energy of all the revolving parts.

Example 14-4

A 100 kW, 60 Hz, 1175 r/min motor is coupled to a flywheel by means of a gearbox. The kinetic energy of all the revolving parts is 300 kJ when the motor runs at rated speed. The motor is plugged to a stop and allowed to run up to 1175 r/min in the reverse direction. Calculate the energy dissipated in the rotor if the flywheel is the only load.

Solution

During the plugging period, the motor speed drops from 1175 r/min to zero. The heat dissipated in the rotor is 3×300 kJ $= 900$ kJ. The motor then accelerates to nominal speed in the reverse direction. The energy dissipated in the rotor during this period is 300 kJ. By reversing the speed this way, the total heat dissipated in the rotor from start to finish is therefore $900 + 300 = 1200$ kJ.

14.9 Braking with direct current

An induction motor and its high-inertia load can also be brought to a quick stop by circulating dc current in the stator winding. Any two stator terminals can be connected to the dc source.

The direct current produces stationary N, S poles in the stator. The number of poles created is equal to the number of poles which the motor develops normally. Thus, a 3-phase, 4-pole induction motor produces 4 dc poles, no matter how the motor terminals are connected to the dc source.

When the rotor sweeps past the stationary field, an ac voltage is induced in the rotor bars. The voltage produces an ac current and the resulting rotor I^2R losses are dissipated at the expense of the kinetic energy stored in the revolving parts. The motor finally comes to rest when all the kinetic energy has been dissipated as heat in the rotor.

The advantage of dc braking is that it produces far less heat than does plugging. In effect, the energy dissipated in the rotor is only equal to the original kinetic energy stored in the revolving masses, and not three times that energy. The energy dissipated in the rotor is independent of the magnitude of the dc current. However, a smaller dc current increases the braking time. The dc current can be two or three times the rated current of the motor. Even larger values can be used, provided that the stator does not become too hot. The braking torque is proportional to the square of the dc braking current.

Example 14-5

A 50 hp, 1760 r/min, 440 V, 3-phase induction motor drives a load having a total moment of inertia of 25 kg·m^2. The dc resistance between two stator terminals is 0.32 Ω, and the rated motor current is 62 A. We want to stop the motor by connecting a 24 V battery across the terminals.

Calculate

a. The dc current in the stator
b. The energy dissipated in the rotor
c. The average braking torque if the stopping time is 4 min

Solution

a. The dc current is

$$I = E/R = 24/0.32 = 75 \text{ A}$$

This current is slightly higher than the rated current of the motor. However, the stator will not overheat, because the braking time is short.

b. The kinetic energy in the rotor and load at 1760 r/min is

$$\begin{aligned} E_k &= 5.48 \times 10^{-3}\, Jn^2 \qquad (3.8) \\ &= 5.48 \times 10^{-3} \times 25 \times 1760^2 \\ &= 424 \text{ kJ} \end{aligned}$$

Consequently, the rotor absorbs 424 kJ during the braking period.

c. The average braking torque T can be calculated from the equation

$$\Delta n = 9.55\, T\Delta t/J \qquad (3.14)$$

$$1760 = 9.55\, T \times (4 \times 60)/25$$

$$T = 19.2 \text{ N}\cdot\text{m}$$

14.10 Abnormal conditions

Abnormal motor operation may be due to internal problems (short-circuit in the stator, overheating of the bearings, etc.) or to external conditions. External problems may be caused by any of the following:

1. Mechanical overload
2. Supply voltage changes
3. Single phasing
4. Frequency changes

We will examine the nature of these problems in the sections that follow.

According to national standards, a motor shall operate satisfactorily on any voltage within ±10% of the nominal voltage, and for any frequency within ±5% of the nominal frequency. If the voltage and frequency *both* vary, the sum of the two percentage changes must not exceed 10 percent. Finally, all motors are designed to operate satisfactorily at altitudes up to 1000 m above sea level. At higher altitudes the temperature may exceed the permissible limits due to the poor cooling afforded by the thinner air.

14.11 Mechanical overload

Although standard induction motors can develop as much as twice their rated power for short periods, they should not be allowed to run continuously beyond their rated capacity. Overloads cause overheating, which deteriorates the insulation and reduces the service life of the motor. In practice, the overload causes the thermal overload relays in the starter box to trip, bringing the motor to a stop before its temperature gets too high.

Some drip-proof motors are designed to carry a continuous overload of 15 percent. This overload capacity is shown on the nameplate by the *service factor* 1.15. The allowable temperature rise is then 10°C higher than that permitted for drip-proof motors operating at normal load.

During emergencies a drip-proof motor can be made to carry overloads as much as 125 percent, as long as supplementary external ventilation is provided. This is not recommended for long periods because even if the external frame is cool, the temperature of the windings may be excessive.

14.12 Line voltage changes

The most important consequence of a line voltage change is its effect upon the torque-speed curve of the motor. In effect, the torque at any speed is proportional to the *square* of the applied voltage. Thus, if the stator voltage decreases by 10%, the torque at every speed will drop by approximately 20%. A line voltage drop is often produced during start-up, due to the heavy starting current drawn from the line. As a result of the lower voltage, the starting torque may be much less than its rated value.

On the other hand, if the line voltage is too high when the motor is running, the flux per pole will be above normal. For a motor running at full-load, this increases both the iron losses and the magnetizing current, with the result that the temperature increases slightly and the power factor is slightly reduced.

If the 3-phase voltages are unbalanced, they can produce a serious unbalance of the three line currents. This condition increases the stator and rotor losses, yielding a higher temperature. A voltage unbalance of as little as 3.5% can cause the temperature to increase by 15°C. The utility company should be notified whenever the phase-to-phase line voltages differ by more than 2 percent.

14.13 Single-phasing

If one line of a 3-phase line is accidentally opened, or if a fuse blows while the 3-phase motor is running, the machine will continue to run as a *single-phase motor.* The current drawn from the remaining two lines will almost double, and the motor will begin to overheat. The thermal relays protecting the motor will eventually trip the circuit-breaker, thereby disconnecting the motor from the line.

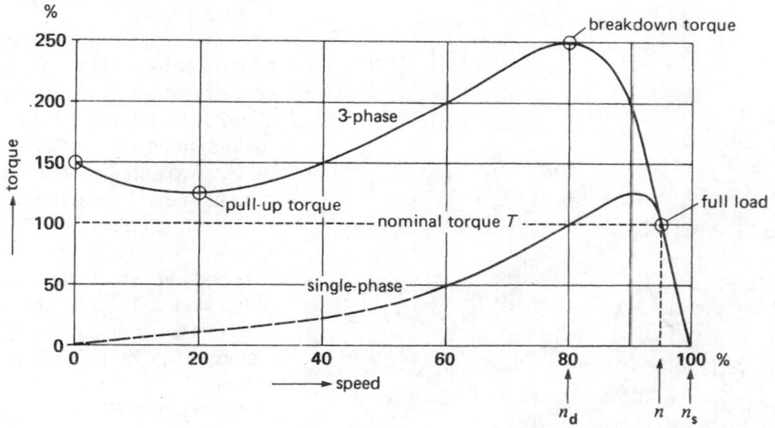

Figure 14.11
Typical torque-speed curves when a 3-phase, squirrel-cage motor operates normally and when it operates on single-phase.

The torque-speed curve is seriously affected when a 3-phase motor operates on single phase. The breakdown torque decreases to about 40% of its original value, and the motor develops no starting torque at all. Consequently, a fully loaded 3-phase motor may simply stop if one of its lines is suddenly opened. The resulting locked-rotor current is about 90% of the normal 3-phase LR current. It is therefore large enough to trip the circuit breaker or to blow the fuses.

Fig. 14.11 shows the typical torque-speed curves of a 3-phase motor when it runs normally and when it is single-phasing. Note that the curves follow each other closely until the torque approaches the single-phase breakdown torque.

14.14 Frequency variation

Important frequency changes never take place on a large distribution system, except during a major disturbance. However, the frequency may vary significantly on isolated systems where electrical energy is generated by diesel engines or gas turbines. The emergency power supply in a hospital, the electrical system on a ship, and the generators in a lumber camp, are examples of this type of supply.

The most important consequence of a frequency change is the resulting change in motor speed: If the frequency drops by 5%, the motor speed drops by 5%.

Machine tools and other motor-driven equipment imported from countries where the frequency is 50 Hz may cause problems when they are connected to a 60 Hz system. Everything runs 20% faster than normal, and this may not be acceptable in some applications. In such cases we either have to gear down the motor speed or supply an expensive auxiliary 50 Hz source.

A 50 Hz motor operates well on a 60 Hz line, but its terminal voltage should be raised to 6/5 (or 120%) of the nameplate rating. The new breakdown torque is then equal to the original breakdown torque and the starting torque is only slightly reduced. Power factor, efficiency, and temperature rise remain satisfactory.

A 60 Hz motor can also operate on a 50 Hz line, but its terminal voltage should be reduced to 5/6 (or 83%) of its nameplate value. The breakdown torque and starting torque are then about the same as before, and the power factor, efficiency, and temperature rise remain satisfactory.

14.15 Induction motor operating as a generator

Consider an electric train powered by a squirrel-cage induction motor that is directly coupled to the wheels. As the train climbs up a hill, the motor will

Figure 14.12
The electric train makes the round trip between Zermatt (1604 m) and Gornergrat (3089 m) in Switzerland. The drive is provided by four 3-phase, wound-rotor induction motors, rated 78 kW, 1470 r/m, 700 V, 50 Hz. Two aerial conductors constitute phases A and B, and the rails provide phase C. A toothed gear-wheel 573 mm in diameter engages a stationary rack on the roadbed to drive the train up and down the steep slopes. The speed can be varied from zero to 14.4 km/h by means of variable resistors in the rotor circuit. The rated thrust is 78 kN.
(Courtesy of ABB)

run at slightly less than synchronous speed, developing a torque sufficient to overcome both friction and the force of gravity. At the top of the hill, on level ground, the force of gravity no longer comes into play and the motor has only to overcome the friction of the rails and the air. The motor runs at light load and very close to synchronous speed.

What happens when the train begins to move downhill? The force of gravity causes the train to accelerate and because the motor is coupled to the wheels, it begins to rotate *above* synchronous speed. However, as soon as this takes place, the motor develops a counter torque that *opposes* the increase in speed. This torque has the same effect as a brake. However, instead of being dissipated as heat, the mechanical braking power is returned to the 3-phase line in the form of electrical energy. An induction motor that turns faster than synchronous speed acts, therefore, as a generator. It converts the mechanical energy it receives into electrical energy, and this energy is returned to the line. Such a machine is called an *asynchronous generator.*

Although induction motors running off a 3-phase line are rarely used to drive trains (Fig. 14.12), there are several industrial applications that may cause a motor to run above synchronous speed. In cranes, for example, during the lowering cycle, the motor receives power from the mechanical "load" and returns it to the line.

We can make an asynchronous generator by connecting an ordinary squirrel-cage motor to a 3-phase line and coupling it to a gasoline engine (Fig. 14.13). As soon as the engine speed exceeds the synchronous speed, the motor becomes a generator, delivering active power P to the electrical system to which it is connected. However, to create its magnetic field, the motor has to absorb reactive power Q. This power can only come from the ac line, with the result that the reactive power Q flows in the opposite direction to the active power P (Fig. 14.13).

The active power delivered to the line is directly proportional to the slip above synchronous speed. Thus, a higher engine speed produces a

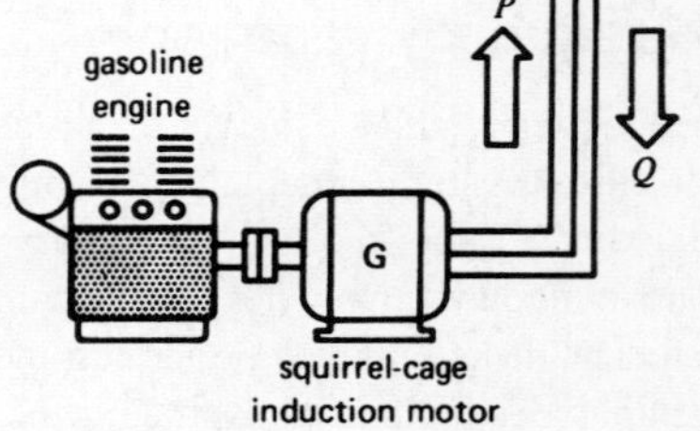

Figure 14.13
Gasoline engine driving an asynchronous generator connected to a 3-phase line. Note that P and Q flow in opposite directions.

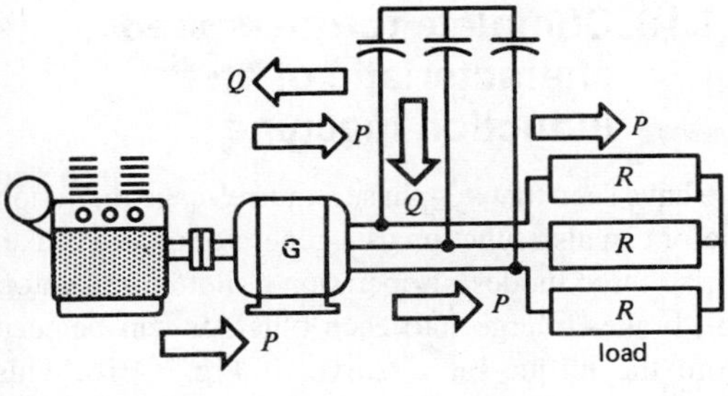

Figure 14.14
Capacitors can provide the reactive power for any asynchronous generator. This eliminates the need for a 3-phase external source.

greater electrical output. However, the rated output is reached at very small slips, typically less than 3%.

The reactive power may be supplied by a group of capacitors connected to the terminals of the motor. With this arrangement we can supply a 3-phase load without using an external 3-phase source (Fig. 14.14). The frequency generated is slightly less than that corresponding to the speed of rotation. Thus, a 4-pole motor driven at a speed of 2400 r/min produces a frequency slightly less than $f = pn/120 = 4 \times 2400/120 = 80$ Hz.

The terminal voltage of the generator increases with the capacitance, but its magnitude is limited by saturation in the iron. If the capacitance is insufficient, the generator voltage will not build up. The capacitor bank must be able to supply at least as much reactive power as the machine normally absorbs when operating as a motor.

Example 14-6

We wish to use a 40 hp, 1760 r/min, 440 V, 3-phase squirrel-cage induction motor as an asynchronous generator. The rated current of the motor is 41 A, and the full-load power factor is 84%.

a. Calculate the capacitance required per phase if the capacitors are connected in delta.
b. At what speed should the driving engine run to generate a frequency of 60 Hz?

Solution

a. The apparent power drawn by the machine when it operates as a motor is

$$S = \sqrt{3}\, EI$$
$$= 1.73 \times 440 \times 41$$
$$= 31.2 \text{ kVA}$$

The corresponding active power absorbed is

$$P = S \cos \theta$$
$$= 31.2 \times 0.84$$
$$= 26.2 \text{ kW}$$

The corresponding reactive power absorbed is

$$Q = \sqrt{S^2 - P^2}$$
$$= \sqrt{31.2^2 - 26.2^2}$$
$$= 17 \text{ kvar}$$

When the machine operates as an asynchronous generator, the capacitor bank must supply *at least* $17 \div 3 = 5.7$ kvar per phase. The voltage per phase is 440 V because the capacitors are connected in delta. Consequently, the capacitive current per phase is

$$I_c = Q/E = 5700/440$$
$$= 13 \text{ A}$$

The capacitive reactance per phase is

$$X_c = E/I = 440/13$$
$$= 34\ \Omega$$

The capacitance per phase must be at least

$$C = 1/2\pi f X_c$$
$$= 1/(2\pi \times 60 \times 34)$$
$$= 78\ \mu\text{F}$$

Fig. 14.15 shows how the generating system is connected. Note that if the load also absorbs reactive power, the capacitor bank must be increased to provide it.

b. The driving engine must turn at slightly more than synchronous speed. Typically, the slip

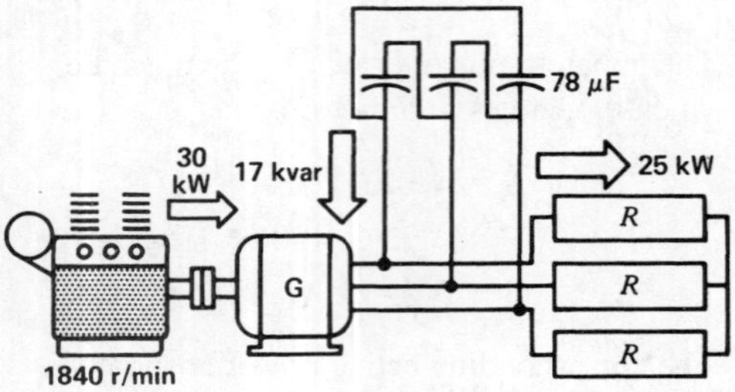

Figure 14.15
See Example 14-6.

should be equal to the full-load slip when the machine operates as a motor. Consequently,

$$\text{slip} = 1800 - 1760$$
$$= 40 \text{ r/min}$$

The engine should therefore run at an approximate speed of

$$n = 1800 + 40$$
$$= 1840 \text{ r/min}$$

14.16 Complete torque-speed characteristic of an induction machine

We have seen that a 3-phase, squirrel-cage induction motor can also function as a generator or as a brake. These three modes of operation—motor, generator, and brake—merge into each other, as can be seen from the torque-speed curve of Fig. 14.16. This curve, together with the adjoining power flow diagrams, illustrates the overall properties of a 3-phase, squirrel-cage induction machine.

We see, for example, that when the shaft turns in the *same* direction as the revolving field, the induction machine operates in either the motor or the generator mode. But to operate in the generator mode, the shaft must turn faster than synchronous speed. Similarly, to operate as a motor, the shaft must turn at less than synchronous speed.

Finally, in order to operate as a brake, the shaft must turn in the opposite direction to the revolving flux.

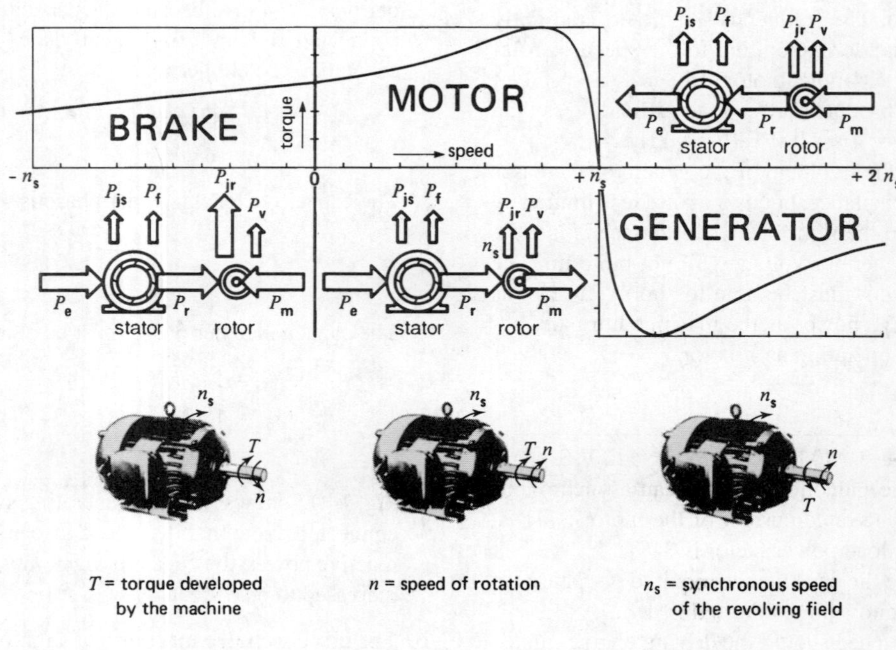

Figure 14.16
Complete torque-speed curve of a 3-phase induction machine.

14.17 Features of a wound-rotor induction motor

So far, we have directed our attention to the squirrel-cage induction motor and its related properties as a generator and brake. The reason is that this type of motor is the one most frequently used in industry. However, the wound-rotor induction motor has certain features that make it attractive in special industrial applications. These may be listed as follows:

1. Start-up of very high-inertia loads
2. Variable-speed drives
3. Frequency converter

We now examine these applications.

14.18 Start-up of high-inertia loads

We recall that whenever a load is brought up to speed by means of an induction motor, the energy dissipated in the rotor is equal to the kinetic energy imparted to the load. This means that a high-inertia load will produce very high losses in the rotor, causing it to become excessively hot. The advantage of the wound-rotor motor is that the heat is dissipated in the external resistors connected to the slip-rings. Thus, the rotor itself remains cool.

Another advantage is that the external resistors can be varied as the motor picks up speed. As a result, it is possible for the motor to develop its maximum torque during the entire acceleration period. Thus, the final speed can be reached in the shortest possible time.

14.19 Variable-speed drives

We have already seen that for a given load, an increase in rotor resistance will cause the speed of an induction motor to fall. Thus, by varying the external resistors of a wound-rotor motor we can obtain any speed we want, so long as it is below synchronous speed. The problem is that the power dissipated as heat in the resistors makes for a very inefficient system, which becomes too costly when the motors have ratings of several thousand horsepower. We get around this problem by connecting the slip-rings to an electronic converter. The converter changes the power at low rotor frequency into power at line frequency and feeds this power back into the 3-phase system (Fig. 14.17). As a result, such a variable-speed control system is very efficient, in the sense that little power is lost in the form of heat.

14.20 Frequency converter

A conventional wound-rotor motor may be used as a *frequency converter* to generate a frequency different from that of the utility company. The stator of

Figure 14.17
The water supply in the City of Stuttgart, Germany, is provided by a pipeline that is 1.6 m in diameter and 110 km long. The water is pumped from Lake Constance in the Alps. The pump in the background is driven by a wound-rotor induction motor rated at 3300 kW, 425 to 595 r/min, 5 kV, 50 Hz. The variable speed enables the water supply to be varied according to the needs of the city.

The enclosed motor housing seen in the foreground contains an air/water heat exchanger that uses the 5°C water for cooling purposes. During start-up, liquid rheostats are connected to the slip-rings, but when the motor is up to speed the slip-rings are connected to an electronic converter which feeds the rotor power back into the line.
(Courtesy of Siemens)

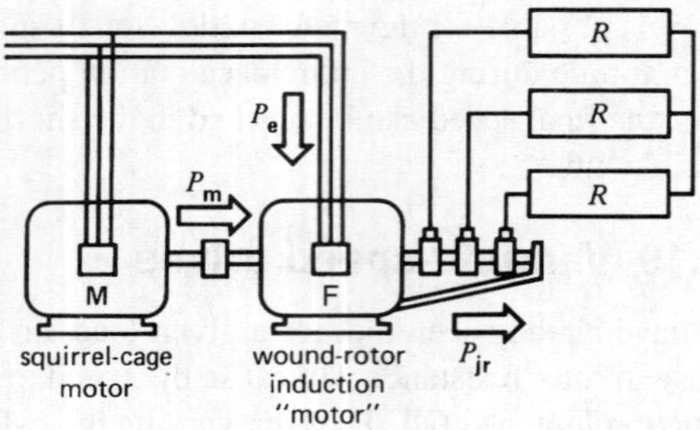

Figure 14.18
Wound-rotor motor used as a frequency converter.

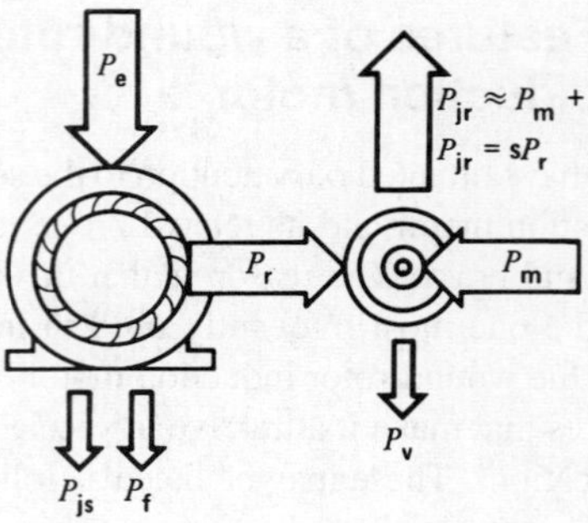

Figure 14.19
Power flow in a frequency converter when the output frequency is greater than the line frequency.

the wound-rotor machine is connected to the utility line, and the rotor is driven at an appropriate speed by a motor M (Fig. 14.18). The rotor supplies power to the 3-phase load at a voltage E_2 and frequency f_2, both of which depend upon the slip. Thus, according to Eqs. 13.3 and 13.4, we have

$$f_2 = sf \qquad (13.3)$$

$$E_2 = sE_{oc} \qquad (13.4)$$

In general, the desired frequency is two or three times that of the utility company. According to Eq. 13.3, in order to attain this frequency the slip must be positive and greater than 1. As a result, the shaft must be rotated against the direction of the revolving flux.

The operation of the frequency converter is then identical to that of an induction motor operating as a brake. However, the power P_{jr}, usually dissipated as heat in the rotor, is now available to supply power to the load. The converter acts as a generator, and the active power flow is as shown in Fig. 14.19. Note how similar this is to the power flow when an induction motor runs as a brake (Fig. 14.16).

Example 14-7

A 3-phase, wound-rotor induction motor has a rating of 150 hp (~110 kW), 1760 r/min, 2.3 kV, 60 Hz. Under locked-rotor conditions, the open-circuit rotor voltage between the slip-rings is 500 V. The rotor is driven by a variable-speed dc motor.

Calculate

a. The turns ratio of the stator to rotor windings
b. The rotor voltage and frequency when the rotor is driven at 720 r/min in the same direction as the revolving field
c. The rotor voltage and frequency when the rotor is driven at 720 r/min opposite to the revolving field

Solution

a. The turns ratio is

$$a = E_1/E_{oc} = 2300/500 = 4.6$$

b. The slip at 720 r/min is

$$s = (n_s - n)/n_s = (1800 - 720)/1800 = 0.6$$

The rotor voltage at 720 r/min is

$$E_2 = sE_{oc} = 0.6 \times 500 = 300 \text{ V}$$

The rotor frequency is

$$f_2 = sf = 0.6 \times 60 = 36 \text{ Hz}$$

c. The motor speed is considered to be negative (−) when it turns opposite to the revolving field. The slip at −720 r/min is

$$s = (n_s - n)/n_s$$
$$= (1800 - (-720))/1800$$
$$= (1800 + 720)/1800$$
$$= 1.4$$

The rotor voltage and frequency at −720 r/min are

$$E_2 = sE_{oc} = 1.4 \times 500$$
$$= 700 \text{ V}$$
$$f_2 = sf = 1.4 \times 60$$
$$= 84 \text{ Hz}$$

Example 14-8

We wish to use a 30 kW, 880 r/min, 60 Hz, wound-rotor motor as a frequency converter (F) to generate 60 kW at an approximate frequency of 180 Hz (see Fig. 14.18). If the supply-line frequency is 60 Hz, calculate the following:

a. The speed of the induction motor (M) that drives the frequency converter
b. The active power delivered to the stator of the frequency converter
c. The power of the induction motor (M)
d. Will the frequency converter overheat under these conditions

Solution

a. To generate 180 Hz the slip must be

$$f_2 = sf \quad (13.3)$$
$$180 = s \times 60$$

from which

$$s = 3$$

The stator is still fed from the 60 Hz line, consequently, the synchronous speed of the converter is 900 r/min. The converter must be driven at a speed n given by

$$s = (n_s - n)/n_s \quad (13.2)$$
$$3 = (900 - n)/900$$

from which

$$n = -1800 \text{ r/min}$$

The converter must therefore be driven at a speed of 1800 r/min. The negative sign indicates that the rotor must run opposite to the revolving field. The induction motor driving the converter must, therefore, have a synchronous speed of 1800 r/min.

b. The rotor delivers an output of 60 kW. This corresponds to P_{jr}, but instead of being dissipated in the rotor, P_{jr} is useful power delivered to a load (Fig. 14.20). The power P_r transferred from the stator to the rotor is

$$P_r = P_{jr}/s = 60/3 \quad (13.7)$$
$$= 20 \text{ kW}$$

The power input to the stator of the frequency converter is equal to 20 kW plus the small copper and iron losses in the stator.

c. The remaining power input to the rotor amounting to (60 − 20) = 40 kW, is derived from the mechanical input to the shaft. By referring to Fig. 14.19 and Fig. 14.20, we can see how the active power flows into (and out of) the converter.

In summary, the rotor receives 20 kW of electrical power from the stator and 40 kW of mechanical power from the driving motor M. The rotor converts this power into 60 kW of electrical power at a frequency of 180 Hz. Induction motor M must therefore have a rating of 40 kW, 60 Hz, 1800 r/min.

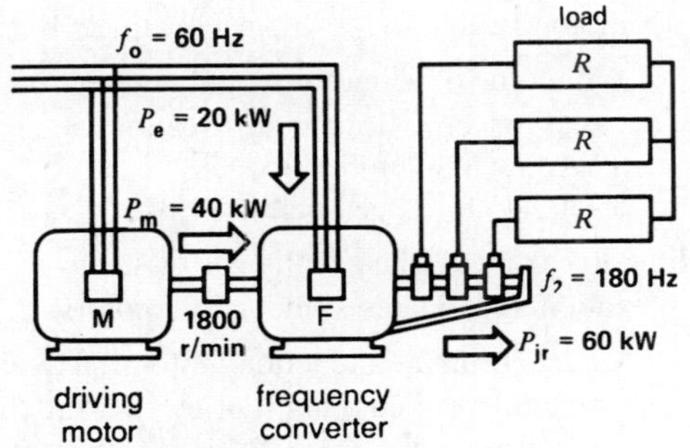

Figure 14.20
See Example 14-8.

d. The stator of the converter will not overheat because the 20 kW it absorbs is much less than its nominal rating of 30 kW. The rotor will not overheat either, even though it delivers 60 kW. The increased power arises from the fact that the voltage induced in the rotor is three times higher than at standstill. The iron losses in the rotor will be high because the frequency is 180 Hz; however, because the rotor turns at twice normal speed, the cooling is more effective, and the rotor will probably not overheat. The stator frequency is 60 Hz, consequently, the iron losses in the stator are normal.

Questions and Problems

Practical level

14-1 What is the difference between a drip-proof motor and an explosion-proof motor?

14-2 What is the approximate life expectancy of a motor?

14-3 Explain why a NEMA Design D motor is unsatisfactory for driving a pump.

14-4 Identify the motor components shown in Fig. 14.3.

14-5 Show the flow of active power in a 3-phase induction motor when it operates
a. As a motor
b. As a brake

14-6 Will a 3-phase motor continue to rotate if one of the lines becomes open? Will the motor be able to start on such a line?

14-7 What type of ac motor would you recommend for the following applications:
a. A saw in a lumber mill
b. A variable speed pump

14-8 Give some of the advantages of standardization as it relates to induction motors.

14-9 We can bring an induction motor to a quick stop either by plugging it or by exciting the stator from a dc source. Which method produces the least amount of heat in the motor? Explain.

14-10 A standard squirrel-cage induction motor rated at 50 hp, 440 V, 60 Hz, 1150 r/min is connected to a 208 V, 3-phase line. By how much are the breakdown torque and locked-rotor torque reduced?

14-11 A 3-phase, squirrel-cage induction motor having a rated voltage of 575 V, is connected to a 520 V line. Explain how the following parameters are affected:
a. Locked-rotor current
b. Locked-rotor torque
c. No-load current
d. No-load speed
e. Full-load current
f. Full-load power factor
g. Full-load efficiency

14-12 **a.** Referring to Fig. 14.6, if we eliminated the gearbox and used another motor directly coupled to the load, what would its power output have to be [hp]?
b. How many poles would the motor have?

14-13 Draw the typical torque-speed curve of a NEMA Design C squirrel-cage induction motor, rated at 30 hp, 900 r/min (see Fig. 14.5). Give the values of the LR, pull-up, and breakdown torques and the corresponding speeds [ft·lbf and r/min].

14-14 A 300 hp, 2300 V, 3-phase, 60 Hz, squirrel-cage induction motor turns at a full-load speed of 590 r/min. Calculate the approximate value of the rotor I^2R losses. If the line voltage then drops to 1944 V, calculate the following:
a. The new speed, knowing that the load torque remains the same
b. The new power output
c. The new I^2R losses in the rotor

14-15 We wish to make an asynchronous generator using a standard squirrel-cage induction motor rated at 40 hp, 208 V, 870 r/min, 60 Hz (Fig. 14.14). The generator is driven at 2100 r/min by a gasoline engine, and the load consists of three 5 Ω resistors connected in wye. The generator voltage builds up when three 100 μF capacitors are connected in wye across the terminals. If the line voltage is 520 V, calculate the following:

a. The approximate frequency generated
b. The active power supplied to the load
c. The reactive power supplied by the capacitor bank
d. The stator current
e. If the following gasoline engines are available—30 hp, 100 hp, and 150 hp—which one is best suited to drive the generator?

14-16 A 30 000 hp, 13.2 kV, 3-phase, 60 Hz, air-to-water cooled induction motor drives a turbo compressor in a large oxygen-manufacturing plant. The motor runs at an exact full-load speed of 1792.8 r/min and by means of a gearbox, it drives the compressor at a speed of 4930 r/min. The motor has an efficiency of 98.1% and a power factor of 0.90. The LR torque and current are respectively 0.7 pu and 4.7 pu. Calculate the following:

a. The full-load current
b. The total losses at full load
c. The exact rotor I^2R losses if the windage and friction losses amount to 62 kW
d. The LR current and torque
e. The torque developed at the compressor shaft

14-17 The motor in Problem 14-16 is cooled by circulating 350 gallons (U.S.) of water through the heat exchanger per minute. Calculate the increase in water temperature as the water flows through the heat exchanger.

14-18 The motor and compressor in Problem 14-16 are started on reduced voltage, and the average starting torque during the acceleration period is 0.25 pu. The compressor has a moment of inertia of 130 000 lb·ft^2 referred to the motor shaft. The squirrel-cage rotor alone has a J of 18 000 lb·ft^2.

a. How long will it take to bring the motor and compressor up to speed, at no-load?
b. What is the energy dissipated in the rotor during the starting period [Btu]?

14-19 A 3-phase induction motor rated at 10 kW, 1450 r/min, 380 V, 50 Hz has to be connected to a 60 Hz line.

a. What line voltage should be used, and what will be the approximate speed of the motor?
b. What power [hp] can the motor deliver without overheating?

Advanced level

14-20 A 1 hp, squirrel-cage, Design B induction motor accelerates an inertia load of 1.4 kg·m^2, from 0 to 1800 r/min. Could this motor be replaced by a Class D motor and, if so,

a. Which motor has the shortest acceleration time from zero to 1200 r/min?
b. Which of the two rotors will be the hottest, after reaching the no-load speed?

14-21 A 3-phase, wound-rotor induction motor having a rating of 150 hp, 1760 r/min, 2.3 kV, 60 Hz, drives a belt conveyor. The rotor is connected in wye and the nominal open-circuit voltage between the slip rings is 530 V. Calculate the following:

a. The rotor winding resistance per phase
b. The resistance that must be placed in series with the rotor (per phase) so that the motor will deliver 40 hp at a speed of 600 r/min, knowing that the line voltage is 2.4 kV

14-22 A 150 hp, 1165 r/min, 440 V, 60 Hz, 3-phase induction motor is running at no-load, close to its synchronous speed of 1200 r/min. The stator leads are suddenly reversed, and the stopping time is clocked at 1.3 s. Assuming that the torque exerted during the plugging interval is equal to the starting torque (1.2 pu), calculate the following:

a. The magnitude of the plugging torque
b. The moment of inertia of the rotor

14-23 In Problem 14-22 calculate the energy dissipated in the rotor during the plugging interval.

14-24 A 3-phase, 8-pole induction motor has a rating of 40 hp, 575 V, 60 Hz. It drives a steel flywheel having a diameter of 31.5 inches and a thickness of 7.875 in. The torque-speed curve corresponds to that of a design D motor given in Fig. 14.5.

a. Calculate the mass of the flywheel and its moment of inertia [lb·ft^2].
b. Calculate the rated speed of the motor and the corresponding torque [ft·lbf].
c. Calculate the locked-rotor torque [ft·lbf].
d. Draw the torque-speed curve of the 40 hp motor and give the torques [N·m] at 0, 180, 360, 540, 720, and 810 r/min.

14-25 **a.** In Problem 14-24 calculate the average torque between 0 and 180 r/min.
b. Using Eq. 3.14 calculate the time required to accelerate the flywheel from 0 to 180 r/min, assuming no other load on the motor.
c. Using Eq. 3.8 calculate the kinetic energy in the flywheel at 180 r/min.
d. Calculate the time required to accelerate the flywheel from 0 to 540 r/min, knowing that this time the load exerts a fixed counter-torque of 300 N·m in addition to the flywheel load.

14-26 The train in Fig. 14.12 has a mass of 78 500 lb and can carry 240 passengers. Calculate the following:
a. The speed of rotation of the gear wheel when the train moves at 9 miles per hour
b. The speed ratio between the motor and the gear wheel
c. The approximate transmission line current when the motors are operating at full-load
d. The total mass of the loaded train if the average weight of a passenger is 60 kg
e. The energy required to climb from Zermatt to Gornergrat [MJ]
f. The minimum time required to make the trip [min]
g. Assuming that 80 percent of the electrical energy is converted into mechanical energy when the train is going uphill and that 80 percent of the mechanical energy is reconverted to electrical energy when going downhill, calculate the total electrical energy consumed during a round trip [kW·h]

Industrial application

14-27 The bearings in a motor have to be greased regularly, but not too often. The following schedule applies to two motors:

Motor A: 75 hp, 3550 r/min; lubricate every 2200 hours of running time.

Motor B: 75 hp, 900 r/min; lubricate every 10 000 hours of running time.

Motor A runs continually, 24 hours per day. Motor B drives a compressor and operates about 6 hours per day. How often should the bearings of each motor be greased per year?

14-28 A 40 hp, 1780 r/min, 460 V, 3-phase, 60 Hz, drip-proof Baldor Super E premium energy induction motor has a power factor of 86% and an efficiency of 93.6%. The motor, priced at $2243, runs at full-load 12 hours per day, 5 days a week. Calculate the cost of driving the motor during a 3-year period, knowing that the cost of energy is $0.06/kWh.

14-29 A standard 40 hp motor, similar to the one described in Problem 14-28, costs $1723 and has an efficiency of 90.2% and power factor of 82%. Calculate the energy savings that accrue to the high-efficiency motor during the 3-year period.

14-30 A constant horsepower, 2-speed induction motor rated 2 hp, 1760/870 r/min, 460 V has windings similar to those shown in Fig. 14.8. The resistance measured between terminals 1 and 2 in the high-speed connection is 12 Ω. What resistance would you expect to measure between terminals 4 and 6 in the low-speed connection?

14-31 A 150 hp, 1175 r/min, 460 V, 3-phase, 60 Hz induction motor has the following properties:

no-load current: 71 A

full-load current: 183 A

locked-rotor current: 1550 A

full-load torque: 886 ft·lbf

breakdown torque: 2552 ft·lbf

locked-rotor torque: 1205 ft·lbf

locked-rotor power factor: 32%

A 3-conductor 250 kcmil copper cable stretches from the main panelboard to the motor, 850 ft away. The voltage at the panelboard is 480 V and the average temperature of the cable is estimated to be 25°C.

a. Determine the equivalent circuit of the motor under locked-rotor conditions.
b. Assuming the cable impedance is purely resistive, calculate the approximate current when the motor is started up across the line.
c. Estimate the resulting starting torque.
d. Compare it with the rated starting torque, percentagewise.

14-32 In Problem 14-31 express the currents and torques in per-unit values.

CHAPTER 15
Equivalent Circuit of the Induction Motor

15.0 Introduction

The preceding three chapters have shown that we can describe the important properties of squirrel-cage and wound-rotor induction motors without using a circuit diagram. However, if we want to gain even a better understanding of the properties of the motor, an equivalent circuit diagram is indispensible. In this chapter* we develop the equivalent circuit from basic principles. We then analyze the characteristics of a low-power and high-power motor and observe their basic differences.

Finally, we develop the equivalent circuit of an asynchronous generator and determine its properties under load.

15.1 The wound-rotor induction motor

A 3-phase, wound-rotor induction motor is very similar in construction to a 3-phase transformer. Thus, the motor has 3 identical primary windings and 3 identical secondary windings—one set for each phase. On account of the perfect symmetry, we can consider a single primary winding and a single secondary winding in analyzing the behavior of the motor.

When the motor is at standstill, it acts exactly like a conventional transformer, and so its equivalent circuit (Fig. 15.1) is the same as that of a transformer, previously developed in Chapter 10, Fig. 10.20.

We assume a wye connection for the stator and the rotor, and a turns ratio of 1:1. The circuit parameters, *per phase,* are identified as follows:

E_g = source voltage, line to neutral

r_1 = stator winding resistance

x_1 = stator leakage reactance

x_2 = rotor leakage reactance

r_2 = rotor winding resistance

R_x = external resistance, effectively connected between one slip-ring and the neutral of the rotor

X_m = magnetizing reactance

R_m = resistance whose losses correspond to the iron losses and windage and friction losses

T = ideal transformer having a turns ratio of 1:1

* This chapter can be skipped by the reader who does not have time to study the more theoretical aspects of induction motor behavior.

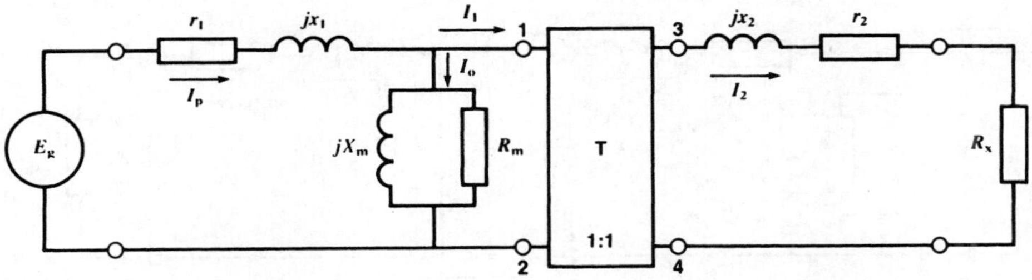

Figure 15.1
Equivalent circuit of a wound-rotor induction motor at standstill.

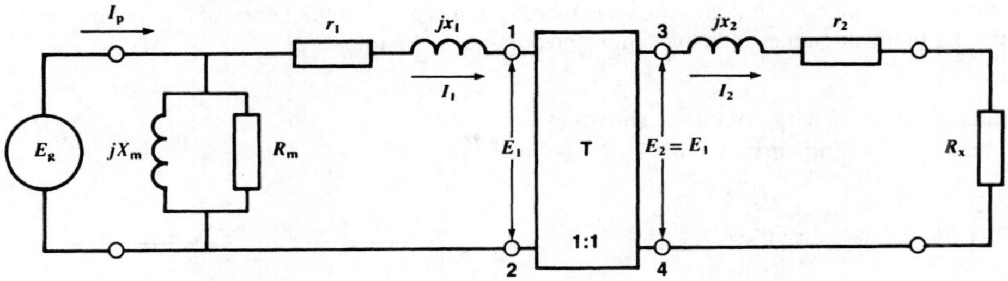

Figure 15.2
Approximation of the equivalent circuit is acceptable for motors above 2 hp.

In the case of a conventional 3-phase transformer, we would be justified in removing the magnetizing branch composed of jX_m and R_m because the exciting current I_o is negligible compared to the load current I_p. However, in a motor this is no longer true: I_o may be as high as 40 percent of I_p because of the air gap. Consequently, we cannot eliminate the magnetizing branch. However, for motors exceeding 2 hp, we can shift it to the input terminals, as shown in Fig. 15.2. This greatly simplifies the equations that describe the behavior of the motor, without compromising accuracy.* Fig. 15.2 is a true representation of the motor when the rotor is locked. How is it affected when the motor starts turning?

Suppose the motor runs at a slip s, meaning that the rotor speed is $n_s(1 - s)$, where n_s is the synchronous speed. This will modify the values of E_1, I_1 and E_2, I_2 on the primary and secondary side of the ideal transformer T. Furthermore, the frequency in the secondary winding will become sf, where f is the frequency of the source E_g. Fig. 15.3 shows these new operating conditions.

Directing our attention to the secondary side, the amplitude of the induced voltage E_2 would be equal to E_1 (the turns ratio is 1:1) if the motor were stationary. But because the slip is s, the actual voltage induced is

$$E_2 = sE_1$$

The frequency is sf and this changes the impedance of the secondary leakage reactance from jx_2 to jsx_2. Because resistors are not frequency-sensitive, the values of r_2 and R_x remain the same. Let us lump the two together to form a single secondary resistance R_2, given by

$$R_2 = r_2 + R_x \tag{15.1}$$

* For motors under 2 hp the exact circuit of Fig. 15.1 should be used.

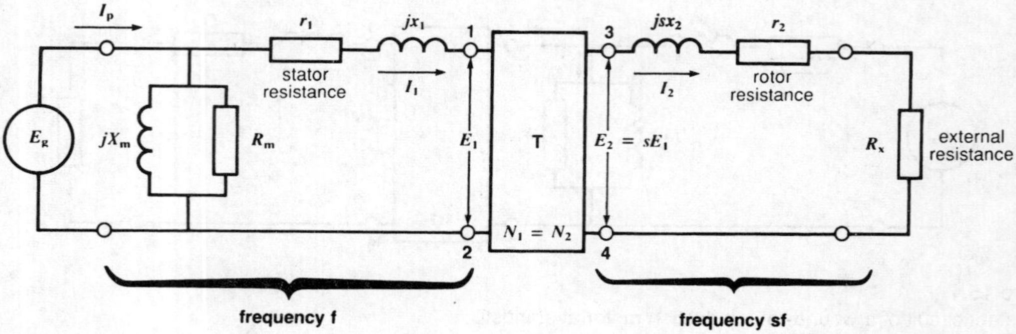

Figure 15.3
Equivalent circuit of a wound-rotor motor when it is running at a slip *s*. The frequency of the voltages and currents in the stator is *f*. But the frequency of the voltages and currents in the rotor is *sf*.

The details of the secondary circuit are shown in Fig. 15.4a, and the resulting current I_2 is

$$I_2 = \frac{sE_1}{R_2 + jsx_2} = \frac{sE_1 \angle -\beta}{\sqrt{R_2^2 + (sx_2)^2}} \quad (15.2)$$

where

$$\beta = \arctan sx_2/R_2 \quad (15.3)$$

The corresponding phasor diagram is shown in Fig. 15.4b. It is important to realize that this phasor diagram relates to the frequency *sf*. Consequently, it cannot be integrated into the phasor diagram on the primary side, where the frequency is *f*. Nevertheless, there is a direct relationship between I_2 (frequency *sf*) in the rotor and I_1 (frequency *f*) in the stator. In effect, the absolute value of I_1 is exactly the same as that of I_2. Furthermore, the phase angle β between E_1 and I_1 is exactly the same as that between E_2 and I_2. This enables us to draw the phasor diagram for E_1 and I_1 as shown in Fig. 15.5.

To summarize

1. The effective value of I_1 is equal to the effective value of I_2, even though their frequencies are different.
2. The effective value of E_1 is equal to the effective value of E_2 divided by the slip *s*.
3. The phase angle between E_1 and I_1 is the same as that between E_2 and I_2.

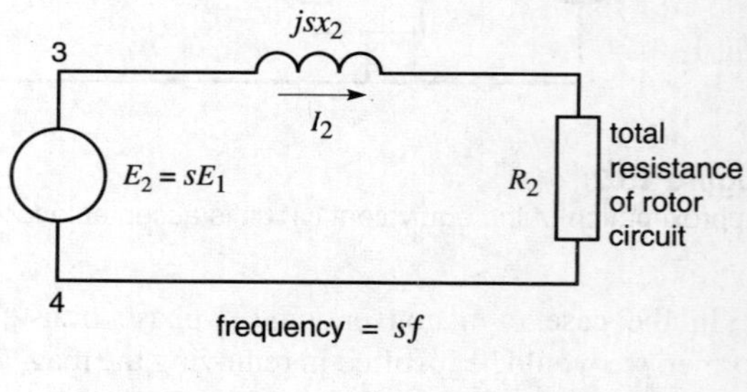

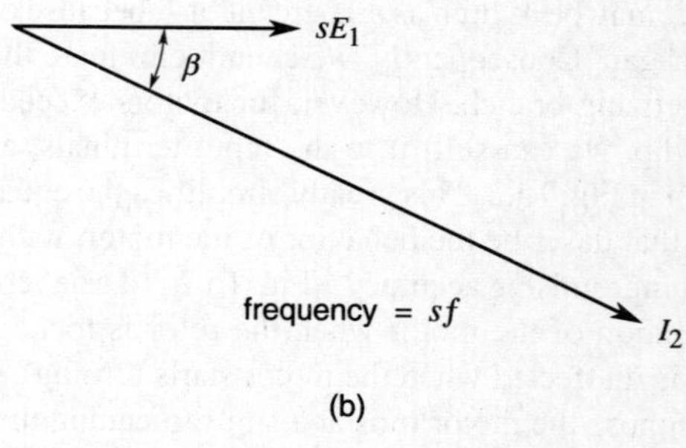

Figure 15.4
a. Equivalent circuit of the rotor; E_2 and I_2 have a frequency *sf*.
b. Phasor diagram showing the current lagging behind the voltage by angle β.

Thus, on the primary side we can write

$$I_1 = I_2 = \frac{sE_1}{R_2 + jsx_2} \tag{15.4}$$

Therefore,

$$I_1 = \frac{E_1}{\frac{R_2}{s} + jx_2} = \frac{E_1}{Z_2} \tag{15.5}$$

The impedance Z_2 seen between the primary terminals 1, 2 of the ideal transformer is, therefore,

$$Z_2 = \frac{E_1}{I_1} = \frac{R_2}{s} + jx_2 \tag{15.6}$$

As a result, we can simplify the circuit of Fig. 15.3 to that shown in Fig. 15.6. The leakage reactances jx_1, jx_2 can now be lumped together to create a single total leakage reactance jx. It is equal to the total leakage reactance of the motor referred to the stator side.

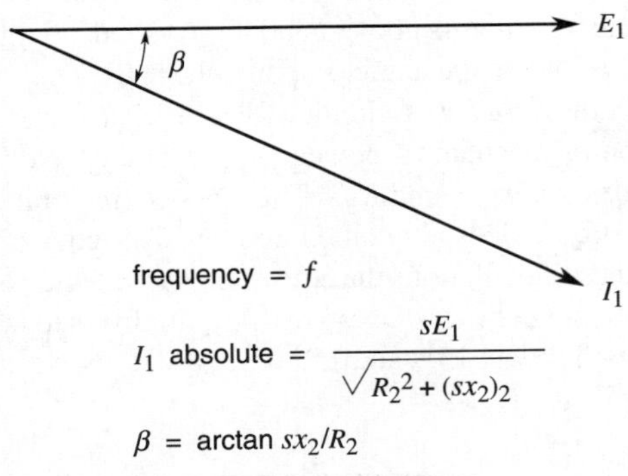

Figure 15.5
The voltage and current in the stator are separated by the same phase angle β, even though the frequency is different.

The final equivalent circuit of the wound-rotor induction motor is shown in Fig. 15.7. In this diagram, the circuit elements are fixed, except for the resistance R_2/s. Its value depends upon the slip and hence upon the speed of the motor. Thus, the value of R_2/s will vary from R_2 to infinity as the motor goes from start-up ($s = 1$) to synchronous speed ($s = 0$).

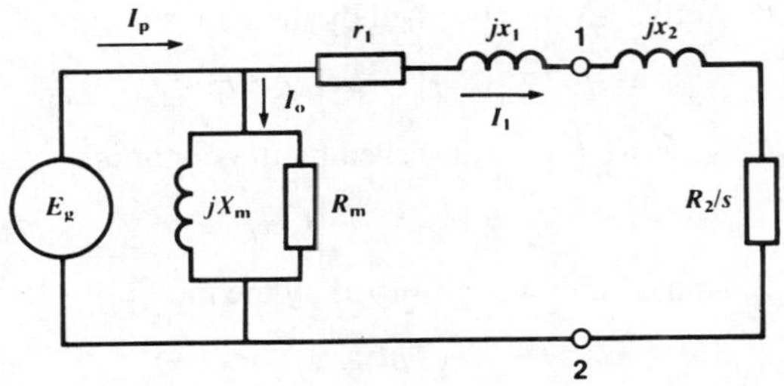

Figure 15.6
Equivalent circuit of a wound-rotor motor referred to the primary (stator) side.

This equivalent circuit of a wound-rotor induction motor is so similar to that of a transformer that it is not surprising that the wound-rotor induction motor is sometimes called a rotary transformer.

The equivalent circuit of a squirrel-cage induction motor is the same, except that R_2 is then equal to the equivalent resistance r_2 of the rotor alone referred to the stator, there being no external resistor.

15.2 Power relationships

The equivalent circuit enables us to arrive at some basic electromechanical power relationships for the 3-phase induction motor. The following equations can be deduced by visual inspection of the equivalent circuit of the wound-rotor motor (Fig. 15.7):

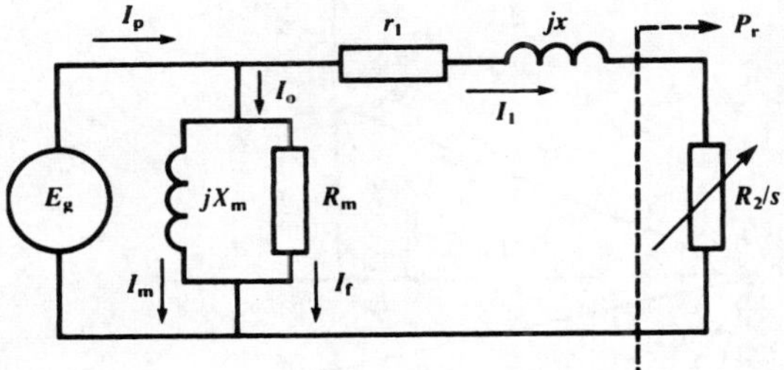

Figure 15.7
The primary and secondary leakage reactances x_1 and x_2 are combined to form an equivalent total leakage reactance x.

1. Active power absorbed by the motor is

$$P = E_g^2/R_m + I_1^2 r_1 + I_1^2 + I_1^2 R_2/s$$

2. Reactive power absorbed by the motor is

$$Q = E_g^{\,2}/X_m + I_1^{\,2}x$$

3. Apparent power absorbed by the motor is

$$S = \sqrt{P^2 + Q^2}$$

4. Power factor of the motor is

$$\cos\theta = P/S$$

5. Line current is

$$I_p = S/E_g$$

6. Active power supplied to the rotor is

$$P_r = I_1^{\,2}R_2/s$$

7. Power dissipated as I^2R losses in the rotor circuit is

$$P_{jr} = I_1^{\,2}R_2 = sP_r$$

8. Mechanical power developed by the motor is

$$P_m = P_r - P_{jr} = P_r(1 - s)$$

9. Torque developed by the motor is

$$T = \frac{9.55\,P_m}{n} = \frac{9.55\,P_r(1 - s)}{n_s(1 - s)} = \frac{9.55\,P_r}{n_s}$$

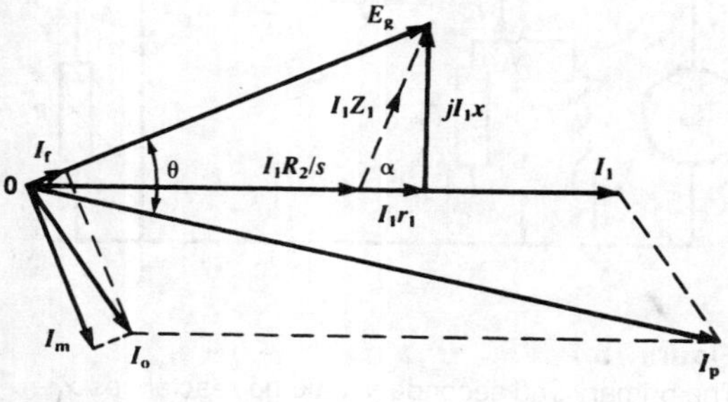

Figure 15.8
Phasor diagram of the voltages and currents in Fig. 15.7. The power factor of the motor is cos θ.

10. Efficiency of the motor is

$$\eta = P_m/P$$

Note: The preceding quantities are "per phase"; some must be multiplied by 3 to obtain the total motor quantities.

15.3 Phasor diagram of the induction motor

If we use current I_1 in Fig. 15.7 as the reference phasor, we obtain the complete phasor diagram of the wound-rotor motor shown in Fig. 15.8. In this diagram (and also in future calculations) it is useful to define an impedance Z_1 and angle as follows:

$$Z_1 = \sqrt{r_1^2 + x^2} \qquad (15.7a)$$

$$\alpha = \arctan x/r_1 \qquad (15.7b)$$

In these equations r_1 is the stator resistance and jx is the total leakage reactance of the motor referred to the stator. Because r_1 and jx are fixed, it follows that Z_1 and α are fixed, irrespective of the speed of the motor.

In large motors above 1000 hp, jx is much larger than r_1 and so the angle α approaches 90°.

In the equivalent circuit of Fig. 15.7, the calculation of mechanical power, torque, and speed depends upon r_1 jx, and R_2/s. The magnetizing branch R_m and jX_m does not come into play. Consequently, for these calculations the equivalent circuit and corresponding phasor diagram can be simplified to that shown in Figs. 15.9 and 15.10.

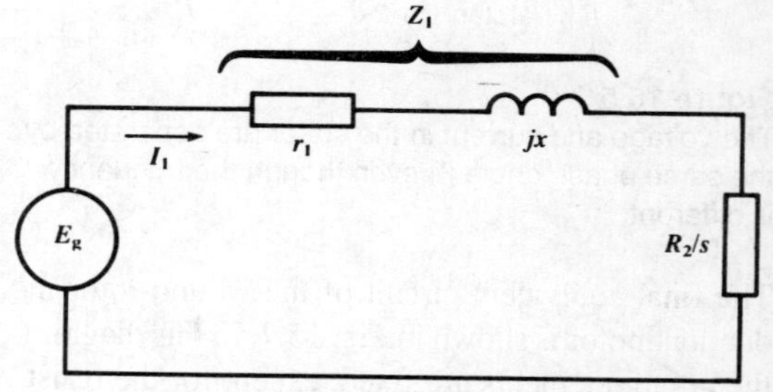

Figure 15.9
As far as mechanical power, torque, and speed are concerned, we can neglect the magnetizing branch X_m and R_m. This yields a simpler circuit for the analysis of motor behavior.

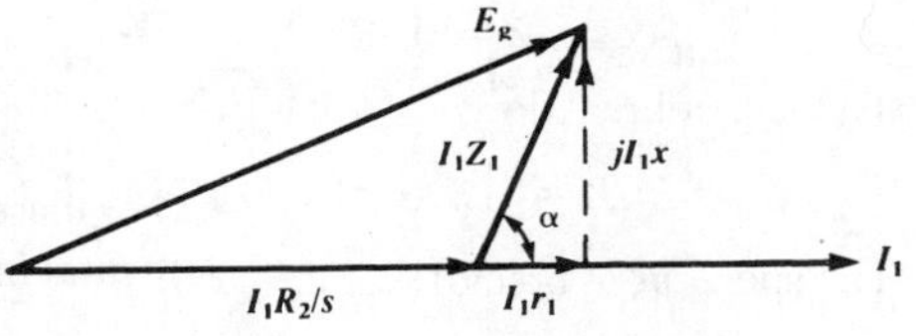

Figure 15.10
Phasor diagram of the circuit of Fig. 15.9. Note that phasor I_1Z_1 is always a degree ahead of phasor I_1.

15.4 Breakdown torque and speed

We have seen that the torque developed by the motor is given by $T = 9.55\ P_r/n_s$ where P_r is the power delivered to the resistance R_2/s (Fig. 15.9). According to a basic power transfer theorem, the power is maximum (and therefore the torque is maximum) when the value of R_2/s is equal to the absolute value of impedance Z_1. Thus, for maximum torque

$$R_2/s = Z_1 \qquad (15.8)$$

Under these circumstances, the magnitude of the voltage drop across Z_1 is equal to that across R_2/s. We can therefore write

$$I_1\frac{R_2}{s} = I_1Z_1$$

The phasor diagram corresponding to this special condition is shown in Fig. 15.11. It is a special case of the phasor diagram of Fig. 15.10. Simple geometry yields the following results:

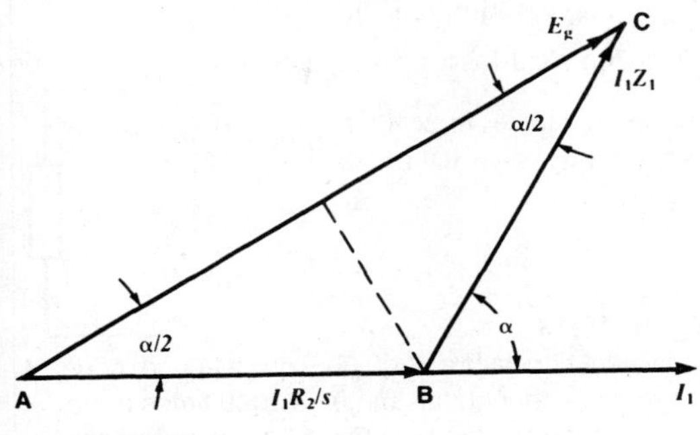

Figure 15.11
Phasor diagram when the motor develops its maximum torque. Under these conditions $R_2/s = Z_1$.

1. Phasors AB and BC have the same length and the angle between them is $(180 - \alpha)°$.
2. angle CAB = angle ACB = $\alpha/2$

Consequently,

$$I_1\frac{R_2}{s}\cos\frac{\alpha}{2} = E_g/2$$

$$I_1Z_1\cos\frac{\alpha}{2} = E_g/2$$

The slip at breakdown torque is

$$s_b = R_2/Z_1 \qquad (15.9)$$

The current at the breakdown torque is

$$I_{1b} = E_g/(2\ Z_1\cos\alpha/2) \qquad (15.10)$$

The breakdown torque is

$$T_b = \frac{9.55\ E_g{}^2}{n_s(4\ Z_1\cos^2\alpha/2)} \qquad (15.11)$$

We note that the magnitudes of both the breakdown torque T_b and the breakdown current I_{1b} are fixed, in the sense that they are independent of the rotor circuit resistance R_2.

However, the slip at the breakdown torque depends upon R_2. Indeed, if $R_2 = Z_1$, the breakdown torque coincides with the starting torque because s_b is then equal to 1. These conclusions are all borne out by the torque-speed curves in Fig. 13.18 (Chapter 13).

In the case of squirrel-cage motors, the resistance R_2 becomes equal to r_2, which is the resistance of the rotor alone reflected into the stator. In practice, the angle α lies between 80° and 89°. The larger angles correspond to medium- and high-power cage motors. In such machines the ratio R_2/Z_1 can be as low as 0.02. Consequently, the breakdown torque occurs at slips as small as 2 percent.

15.5 Equivalent circuit of two practical motors

The impedances and resulting equivalent circuits of two squirrel-cage motors, rated 5 hp and 5000 hp are given in Figs. 15.12 and 15.13, together with the motor ratings. The motors are both connected in wye and the impedances are given per phase.

15.6 Calculation of the breakdown torque

We will now calculate the breakdown torque T_b and the corresponding speed n_b and current I_{1b} for the 5 hp motor.

1. $Z_1 = \sqrt{r_1^2 + x^2} = \sqrt{1.5^2 + 6^2} = 6.18\ \Omega$
2. $\alpha = \arctan x/r_1 = \arctan 6/1.5 = 76°$
3. $\alpha/2 = 38°$, $\cos \alpha/2 = 0.788$
4. The slip at breakdown is

$$s_b = R_2/Z_1 = 1.2/6.18 = 0.194$$

5. The speed n_b at breakdown is

$$\begin{aligned} n_b &= n_s(1 - s_b) \\ &= 1800(1 - 0.194) \\ &= 1450 \text{ r/min} \end{aligned}$$

6. The current at breakdown is

$$I_{1b} = \frac{E_L}{2\ Z_1 \cos \alpha/2}$$

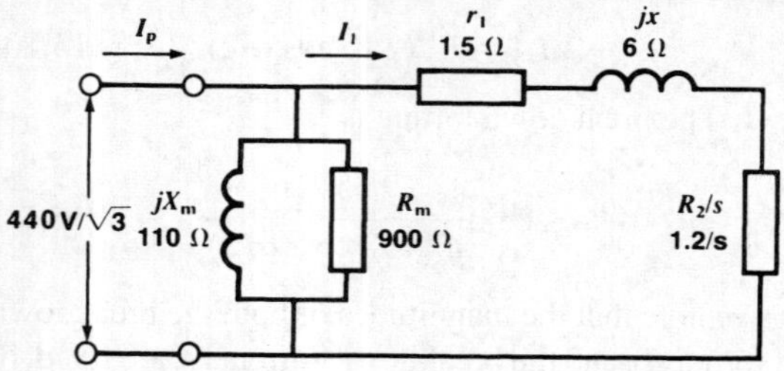

Motor rating:

5 hp, 60 Hz, 1800 r/min, 440 V, 3-phase
full-load current: 7 A
locked-rotor current: 39 A

r_1 = stator resistance 1.5 Ω
r_2 = rotor resistance 1.2 Ω
jx = total leakage reactance 6 Ω
jX_m = magnetizing reactance 110 Ω
R_m = no-load losses resistance 900 Ω

The no-load losses include the iron losses plus windage and friction losses.

Figure 15.12
Equivalent circuit of a 5 hp, squirrel-cage induction motor. Because there is no external resistor in the rotor, $R_2 = r_2$.

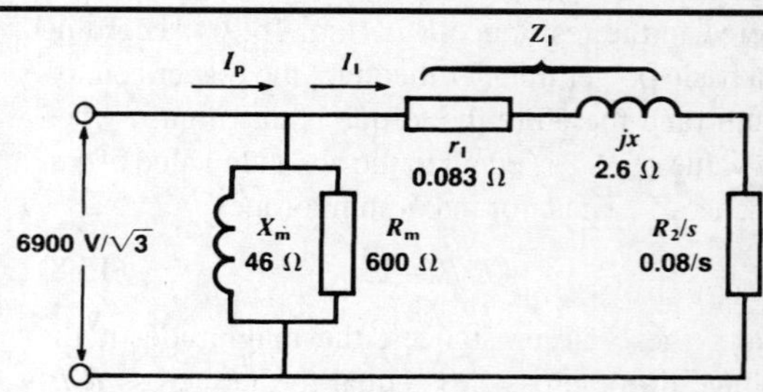

Motor rating:

5000 hp, 60 Hz, 600 r/min, 6900 V, 3-phase
full-load current: 358 A
locked-rotor current: 1616 A

r_1 = stator resistance 0.083 Ω
r_2 = rotor resistance 0.080 Ω
jx = total leakage reactance 2.6 Ω
jX_m = magnetizing reactance 46 Ω
R_m = no-load losses resistance 600 Ω

The no-load losses of 26.4 kW (per phase) consist of 15 kW for windage and friction and 11.4 kW for the iron losses.

Figure 15.13
Equivalent circuit of a 5000 hp, squirrel-cage induction motor. Although this motor is 1000 times more powerful than the motor in Fig. 15.12, the circuit diagram remains the same.

$$= \frac{440/\sqrt{3}}{2 \times 6.18 \times 0.788} = 26.1 \text{ A}$$

7. The power to the rotor is

$$P_r = I_1^2R_2/s = I_1^2Z_1$$
$$= 26.1^2 \times 6.18 = 4210 \text{ W}$$

8. The breakdown torque T_b is

$$T_b = \frac{9.55\ P_r}{n_s}$$
$$= \frac{9.55 \times 4210}{1800} = 22.3 \text{ N·m}$$

Note that this is the torque developed *per phase.* The total torque is, therefore, $3 \times 22.3 = 67$ N·m.

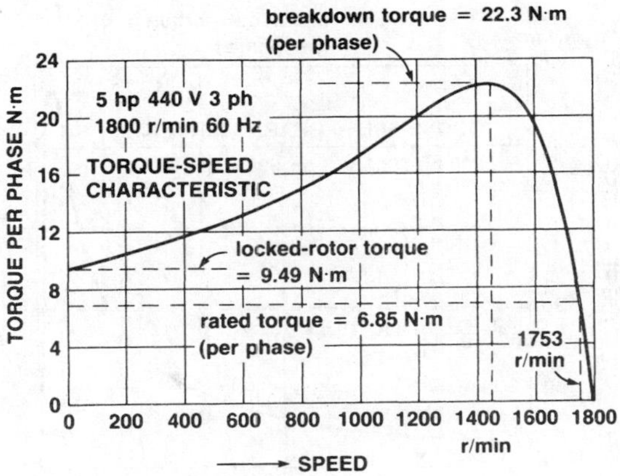

Figure 15.14
Torque-speed curve of a 5 hp motor.

15.7 Torque-speed curve and other characteristics

We can determine the complete torque-speed curve of the 5 hp motor by selecting various values of slip and solving the circuit of Fig. 15.12. The results are listed in Table 15A, and the curve is given in Fig. 15.14.

The same calculations are made for the 5000 hp motor. Table 15B lists the results and Fig. 15.15 shows the torque-speed curve. Note the relatively low starting torque for this large motor, as well as the near-synchronous speed from no-load right up to the breakdown torque. These characteristics are typical for large squirrel-cage induction motors.

TABLE 15A TORQUE-SPEED CHARACTERISTIC

5 hp, 440 V, 1800 r/min, 60 Hz, squirrel-cage induction motor

s	I_1	P_r	T	n
	[A]	[W]	[N·m]	[r/min]
0.0125	2.60	649	3.44	1777
0.025	5.09	1243	6.60	1755
0.026	5.29	1291	6.85	1753
0.05	9.70	2256	12.0	1710
0.1	17.2	3547	18.8	1620
0.2	26.4	4196	22.3	1440
0.4	33.9	3441	18.3	1080
0.6	36.6	2674	14.2	720
0.8	37.9	2150	11.4	360
1	38.6	1788	9.49	0

The rated power of 5 hp is developed at $s = 0.026$.

TABLE 15B TORQUE-SPEED AND LOAD CHARACTERISTIC

5000 hp, 6900 V, 600 r/min, 60 Hz, squirrel-cage induction motor

s	Torque	Total power	Speed	cos θ	Eff'cy	I_p
	[kN·m]	[hp]	[r/min]	[%]	[%]	[A]
2	1.49	−377	−600	4.9	—	1617
1	2.98	0	0	6.3	0	1616
0.6	4.95	500	240	8.2	23.4	1614
0.4	7.39	1120	360	10.6	40.8	1610
0.2	14.4	2921	480	17.7	64.7	1593
0.1	26.8	6095	540	30.8	80.4	1535
0.05	42.1	10114	570	51.7	89.5	1363
0.03077	47.0	11520	581.5	68.2	93.1	1133
0.02	43.1	10679	588	79.8	95.1	878
0.0067	19.9	5000	596	90.1	96.6	358
0.0033	10.2	2577	598	85.1	95.4	198

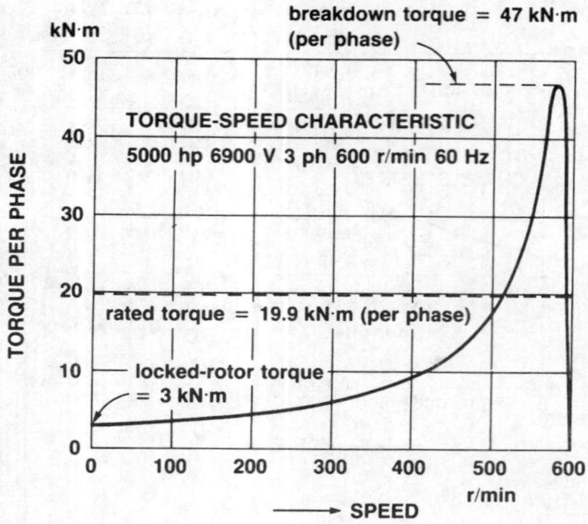

Figure 15.15
Torque-speed curve of a 5000 hp motor.

15.8 Properties of an asynchronous generator

We have already learned that a squirrel-cage induction motor can act as a generator if it is driven above synchronous speed. Now that we have the equivalent circuit for the 5 hp motor, we can calculate the power it can generate, together with its other properties as a generator.

Let us connect the motor to a 440 V, 3-phase line and drive it at a speed of 1845 r/min, which is 45 r/min above synchronous speed. The slip is

$$\begin{aligned} s &= (n_s - n)/n_s \\ &= (1800 - 1845)/1800 \\ &= -0.025 \end{aligned}$$

The value of R_2/s in the equivalent circuit is, therefore,

$$\begin{aligned} R_2/s &= 1.2/(-0.025) \\ &= -48\ \Omega \end{aligned}$$

The negative resistance indicates that power is flowing from the rotor to the stator rather than from the stator to the rotor. Referring to Fig. 15.16 we make the following calculations:

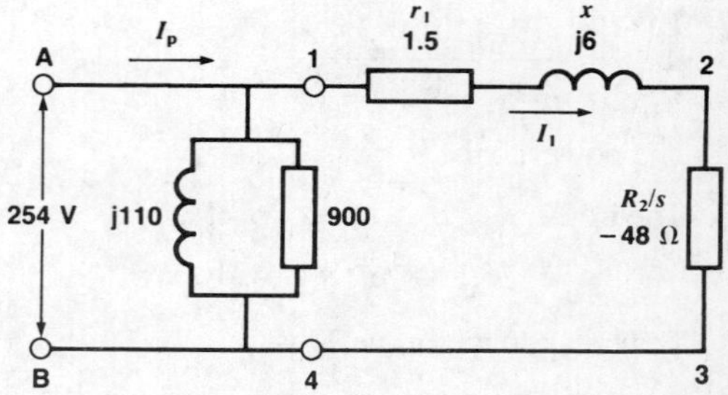

Figure 15.16
Equivalent circuit of a 5 hp motor operating as an asynchronous generator. Note that a negative resistance is reflected into the primary circuit.

1. Net resistance of branch 1-2-3-4 is

$$R_n = -48 + 1.5 = -46.5\ \Omega$$

2. Impedance of branch 1-2-3-4 is

$$\begin{aligned} Z &= \sqrt{R_n^2 + x^2} \\ &= \sqrt{(-46.5)^2 + 6^2} \\ &= 46.88\ \Omega \end{aligned}$$

3. Current in branch 1-2-3-4 is

$$\begin{aligned} I_1 &= E/Z = 254/46.88 \\ &= 5.42\ \text{A} \end{aligned}$$

4. Active power delivered to the rotor is

$$\begin{aligned} P_r &= I_1{}^2 R_2/s = 5.42^2(-48) \\ &= -1410\ \text{W} \end{aligned}$$

This negative power means that 1410 W is flowing from the rotor to the stator.

5. The I^2R losses in the rotor are

$$\begin{aligned} P_{jr} &= I_1{}^2 r_2 = 5.42^2 \times 1.2 \\ &= 35.2\ \text{W} \end{aligned}$$

6. The mechanical power input to the shaft is equal to P_r plus the losses P_{jr} in the rotor:

$$\begin{aligned} P_m &= P_r + P_{jr} \\ &= 1410 + 35.2 \\ &= 1445\ \text{W} \end{aligned}$$

7. The I^2R losses in the stator are

$$P_{js} = I_1{}^2 r_1 = 5.42^2 \times 1.5$$
$$= 44.1 \text{ W}$$

8. The iron plus windage and friction losses are

$$P_f + P_v = E^2/R_m = 254^2/900$$
$$= 71.7 \text{ W}$$

9. The active power delivered to the line *feeding* the motor is

$$P_e = \text{power delivered from rotor to stator minus losses}$$
$$= P_r - P_{js} - P_f - P_v$$
$$= 1410 - 44.1 - 71.7$$
$$= 1294 \text{ W}$$

(P_e for the 3 phases $= 3 \times 1294 = 3882$ W)

10. Reactive power absorbed by the leakage reactance is

$$Q_1 = I_1{}^2 x = 5.42^2 \times 6$$
$$= 176 \text{ var}$$

11. Reactive power absorbed by the magnetizing reactance is

$$Q_2 = E^2/X_m = 254^2/110$$
$$= 586 \text{ var}$$

12. Total reactive power absorbed by the motor is

$$Q = Q_1 + Q_2$$
$$= 176 + 586 = 762 \text{ vars}$$

13. Apparent power at the generator terminals A, B is

$$S = \sqrt{P_e^2 + Q^2} = \sqrt{1294^2 + 762^2}$$
$$= 1502 \text{ VA}$$

14. The line current I_p is

$$I_p = S/E = 1502/254$$
$$= 5.91 \text{ A}$$

15. The power factor at the generator terminals is

$$\cos\theta = P_e/S = 1294/1502$$
$$= 0.861 = 86.1\%$$

16. The efficiency of the asynchronous generator is

$$\eta = \frac{\text{useful electric power}}{\text{mechanical input}} = \frac{P_e}{P_m}$$
$$= \frac{1294}{1445} = 0.895 = 89.5\%$$

17. The horsepower needed to drive the generator is

$$P_m = 3\,P_m/746 = 3 \times 1445/746$$
$$= 5.81 \text{ hp}$$

18. Torque exerted by the driving motor is

$$T = \frac{9.55 \times P}{n} = \frac{9.55 \times 3 \times 1445}{1854} = 22.3 \text{ N·m}$$

15.9 Tests to determine the equivalent circuit

The approximate values of r_1, r_2, X_m, R_m, and x in the equivalent circuit can be found by means of the following tests.

No-load test. When an induction motor runs at no-load, the slip is exceedingly small. Referring to Fig. 15.6, this means that the value of R_2/s is very high and so current I_1 is negligible compared to I_o. Thus, at no-load the circuit consists essentially of the magnetizing branch X_m, R_m. Their values can be determined by measuring the voltage, current, and power at no-load, as follows:

a. Measure the stator resistance R_{LL} between any two terminals. Assuming a wye connection, the value of r_1 is

$$r_1 = R_{LL}/2$$

b. Run the motor at no-load using rated line-to-line voltage, E_{NL} (Fig. 15.17). Measure the no-load current I_{NL} and the total 3-phase active power P_{NL}.

The following calculations of total apparent power S_{NL} and total reactive power Q_{NL} are then made:

$$S_{NL} = E_{NL} I_{NL} \sqrt{3}$$
$$Q_{NL} = \sqrt{S_{NL}^2 - P_{NL}^2}$$

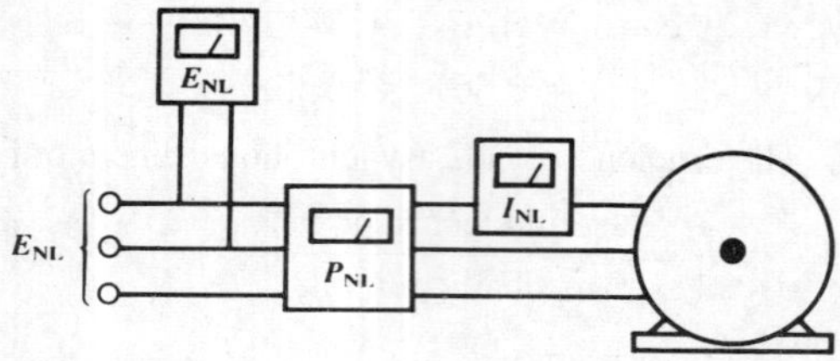

Figure 15.17
A no-load test permits the calculation of X_m and R_m of the magnetizing branch.

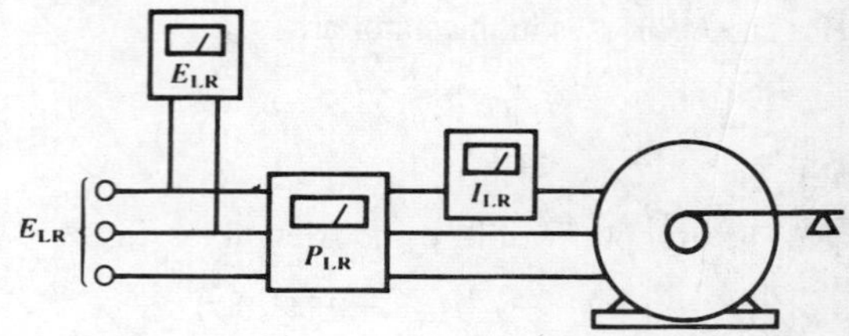

Figure 15.18
A locked-rotor test permits the calculation of the total leakage reactance x and the total resistance $(r_1 + r_2)$. From these results we can determine the equivalent circuit of the induction motor.

$$P_f + P_v = \text{windage, friction, and iron losses}$$
$$= P_{NL} - 3\, I_{NL}^2 r_1$$

The resistance R_m representing $P_f + P_v$ is

$$R_m = E_{NL}^2/(P_f + P_v)$$

The magnetizing reactance is

$$X_m = E_{NL}^2/Q_{NL}$$

Locked-rotor test. Under rated line voltage, when the rotor of an induction motor is locked, the stator current I_p is almost six times its rated value. Furthermore, the slip s is equal to one. This means that r_2/s is equal to r_2, where r_2 is the resistance of the rotor reflected into the stator. Because I_p is much greater than the exciting current I_o, we can neglect the magnetizing branch. This leaves us with the circuit of Fig. 15.9, composed of the leakage reactance x, the stator resistance r_1, and the reflected rotor resistance $R_2/s = r_2/1 = r_2$. Their values can be determined by measuring the voltage, current, and power under locked-rotor conditions, as follows:

a. Apply reduced 3-phase voltage to the stator so that the stator current is about equal to its rated value.
b. Take readings of E_{LR} (line-to-line), I_{LR}, and the total 3-phase power P_{LR} (Fig. 15.18).

The following calculations are then made:

$$S_{LR} = E_{LR} I_{LR} \sqrt{3}$$
$$Q_{LR} = \sqrt{S_{LR}^2 - P_{LR}^2}$$
$$x = Q_{LR}/3\, I_{LR}^2$$
$$3\, I_{LR}^2 (r_1 + r_2) = P_{LR}$$

Hence,

$$r_2 = P_{LR}/(3\, I_{LR}^2) - r_1$$

More elaborate tests are conducted on large machines, but the above-mentioned procedure gives results that are adequate in most cases.

Example 15-1

A no-load test conducted on a 30 hp, 835 r/min, 440 V, 3-phase, 60 Hz, squirrel-cage induction motor yielded the following results:

No-load voltage (line-to-line): 440 V

No-load current: 14 A

No-load power: 1470 W

Resistance measured between two terminals: 0.5 Ω

The locked-rotor test, conducted at reduced voltage, gave the following results:

Locked-rotor voltage (line-to-line): 163 V

Locked-rotor power: 7200 W

Locked-rotor current: 60 A

Determine the equivalent circuit of the motor.

Solution

Assuming the stator windings are connected in wye, the resistance per phase is

$$r_1 = 0.5\ \Omega/2 = 0.25\ \Omega$$

From the no-load test we find

$$S_{NL} = E_{NL}I_{NL}\sqrt{3} = 440 \times 14\sqrt{3}$$
$$= 10\,669 \text{ VA}$$
$$P_{NL} = 1470 \text{ W}$$
$$Q_{NL} = \sqrt{S_{NL}^2 - P_{NL}^2} = \sqrt{10\,669^2 - 1470^2}$$
$$= 10\,568 \text{ var}$$
$$X_m = E_{NL}^2/Q_{NL} = 440^2/10\,568$$
$$= 18.3\ \Omega$$
$$R_m = E_{NL}^2/P_{NL} = 440^2/(1470 - 3 \times 14^2 \times 0.25)$$
$$= 146\ \Omega$$

From the locked-rotor test we find

$$S_{LR} = E_{LR}I_{LR}\sqrt{3} = 163 \times 60\sqrt{3}$$
$$= 16\,939 \text{ VA}$$
$$P_{LR} = 7200 \text{ W}$$
$$Q_{LR} = \sqrt{S_{LR}^2 - P_{LR}^2} = \sqrt{16\,939^2 - 7200^2}$$
$$= 15\,333 \text{ var}$$
$$I_{LR} = 60 \text{ A}$$

Total leakage reactance referred to stator is

$$x = \frac{Q_{LR}}{3\,I_{LR}^2} = \frac{15\,333}{3 \times 60^2} = 1.42\ \Omega$$

Total resistance referred to stator is

$$r_1 + r_2 = P_{LR}/3\,I_{LR}^2 = 7200/(3 \times 60^2)$$
$$= 0.67\ \Omega$$
$$r_1 = 0.25\ \Omega$$
$$r_2 = 0.67 - 0.25 = 0.42\ \Omega$$

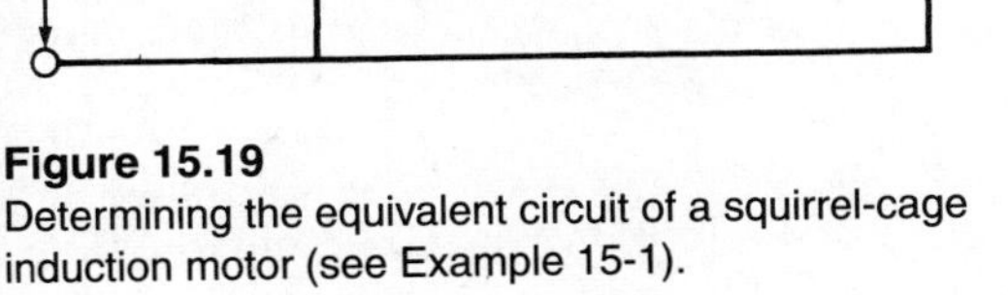

Figure 15.19
Determining the equivalent circuit of a squirrel-cage induction motor (see Example 15-1).

(In a squirrel-cage motor, $R_2 = r_2$ because $R_x = 0$; see Eq. 15.1.)

The equivalent circuit is shown in Fig. 15.19.

Questions and Problems

15-1 Without referring to the text, explain the meaning of the impedances, currents, and voltages in Fig. 15.2.

15-2 A wye-connected squirrel-cage motor having a synchronous speed of 900 r/min has a stator resistance of 0.7 Ω and an equivalent rotor resistance of 0.5 Ω. If the total leakage reactance is 5 Ω and the line-to-neutral voltage is 346 V, calculate the following:
a. The value of Z_1 and the angle α
b. The speed when the breakdown torque is reached
c. The current I_1 at the breakdown torque (see Fig. 15.9)
d. The value of the breakdown torque [N·m]

15-3 **a.** In Problem 15-2, draw the equivalent circuit if the motor runs at 950 r/min in the same direction as the revolving flux. Does the machine operate as a generator? Calculate the torque of the machine.
b. Draw the equivalent circuit if the motor runs at 950 r/min opposite to the revolving flux. Does the machine operate as a generator? Calculate the torque.

15-4 A 550 V, 1780 r/min, 3-phase, 60 Hz, squirrel-cage induction motor running at no-load draws a current of 12 A and a total power of 1500 W. Calculate the value of X_m and R_m per phase (see Fig. 15.2).

15-5 The motor in Problem 15-4 draws a current of 30 A and a power of 2.43 kW when connected to a 90 V, 3-phase line under locked-rotor conditions. The resistance between two stator terminals is 0.8 Ω. Calculate the values of r_1, r_2, and x and the locked-rotor torque [N·m] at rated voltage.

15-6 If the line voltage for the motor in Fig. 15.15 dropped to 6200 V, calculate the new breakdown torque and starting torque.

15-7 A 440 V, 3-phase, 1800 r/min, squirrel-cage motor has the following characteristics:

$r_1 = 1.5\ \Omega$

$r_2 = 1.2\ \Omega$

$x = 6$

If the magnetizing branch can be neglected, calculate the value of the starting torque and the breakdown torque if a 4.5 Ω resistor is connected in series with each line.

15-8 In Problem 15-7 calculate the starting torque and the breakdown torque if a 4.5 Ω reactor is connected in series with each line.

Industrial application

15-9 Consider the 5 hp motor whose equivalent circuit is shown in Fig. 15.12.

a. Calculate the values of the inductances (in millihenries) of the leakage and magnetizing reactances.

b. Determine the values of the leakage reactance and the magnetizing reactance at a frequency of 50 Hz.

c. Calculate the 50 Hz line-to-neutral voltage to obtain the same magnetizing current and compare it with the voltage at 60 Hz.

15-10 The 5 hp motor represented by the equivalent circuit of Fig. 15.12 is connected to a 503 V (line-to-line), 3-phase, 80 Hz source. The stator and rotor resistances are assumed to remain the same.

a. Determine the equivalent circuit when the motor runs at 2340 r/min.

b. Calculate the value of the torque [N·m] and power [hp] developed by the motor.

CHAPTER 16
Synchronous Generators

16.0 Introduction

Three-phase synchronous generators are the primary source of all the electrical energy we consume. These machines are the largest energy converters in the world. They convert mechanical energy into electrical energy, in powers ranging up to 1500 MW. In this chapter we will study the construction and characteristics of these large, modern generators. They are based upon the elementary principles covered in Section 8.6, and the reader may wish to review this material before proceeding further.

16.1 Commercial synchronous generators

Commercial synchronous generators are built with either a stationary or a rotating dc magnetic field.

A *stationary-field* synchronous generator has the same outward appearance as a dc generator. The salient poles create the dc field, which is cut by a revolving armature. The armature possesses a 3-phase winding whose terminals are connected to three slip-rings mounted on the shaft. A set of brushes, sliding on the slip-rings, enables the armature to be connected to an external 3-phase load. The armature is driven by a gasoline engine, or some other source of motive power. As it rotates, a 3-phase voltage is induced, whose value depends upon the speed of rotation and upon the dc exciting current in the stationary poles. The frequency of the voltage depends upon the speed and the number of poles on the field. Stationary-field generators are used when the power output is less than 5 kVA. However, for greater outputs, it is cheaper, safer, and more practical to employ a revolving dc field.

A *revolving-field* synchronous generator has a stationary armature called a stator. The 3-phase stator winding is directly connected to the load, without going through large, unreliable slip-rings and brushes. A stationary stator also makes it easier to insulate the windings because they are not subjected to centrifugal forces. Fig. 16.1 is a schematic diagram of such a generator, sometimes called an *alternator*. The field is excited by a dc generator, usually mounted on the same shaft. Note that the brushes on the commutator have to be connected to another set of brushes riding on slip-rings to feed the dc current I_x into the revolving field.

16.2 Number of poles

The number of poles on a synchronous generator depends upon the speed of rotation and the frequency

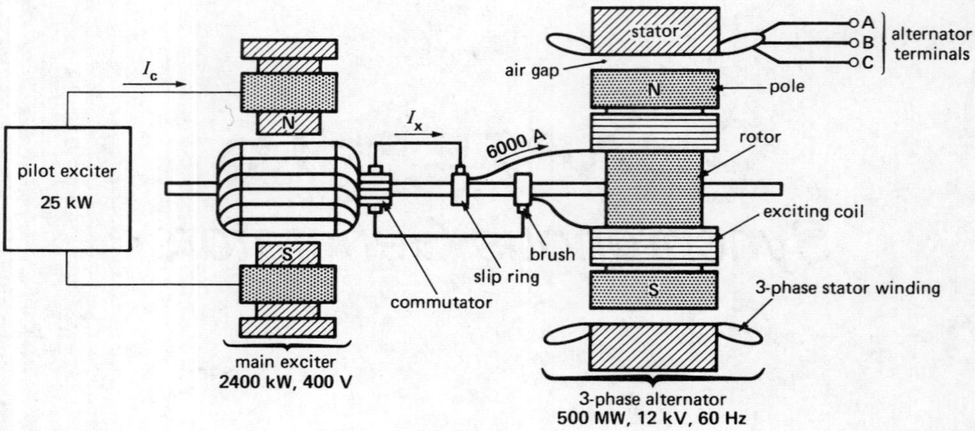

Figure 16.1
Schematic diagram and cross-section view of a typical 500 MW synchronous generator and its 2400 kW dc exciter. The dc exciting current I_x (6000 A) flows through the commutator and two slip-rings. The dc control current I_c from the pilot exciter permits variable field control of the main exciter, which, in turn, controls I_x.

we wish to produce. Consider, for example, a stator conductor that is successively swept by the N and S poles of the rotor. If a *positive* voltage is induced when an N pole sweeps across the conductor, a similar *negative* voltage is induced when the S pole speeds by. Thus, every time a complete pair of poles crosses the conductor, the induced voltage goes through a *complete cycle*. The same is true for every other conductor on the stator; we can therefore deduce that the alternator frequency is given by

$$f = \frac{pn}{120} \tag{16.1}$$

where

f = frequency of the induced voltage [Hz]
p = number of poles on the rotor
n = speed of the rotor [r/min]

Example 16-1

A hydraulic turbine turning at 200 r/min is connected to a synchronous generator. If the induced voltage has a frequency of 60 Hz, how many poles does the rotor have?

Solution

From Eq. 16.1, we have

$$\begin{aligned} p &= 120\, f/n \\ &= 120 \times 60/200 \\ &= 36 \text{ poles, or 18 pairs of N and S poles} \end{aligned}$$

16.3 Main features of the stator

From an electrical standpoint, the stator of a synchronous generator is identical to that of a 3-phase induction motor (Section 13.17). It is composed of a cylindrical laminated core containing a set of slots that carry a 3-phase lap winding (Figs. 16.2, 16.3). The winding is always connected in wye and the neutral is connected to ground. A wye connection is preferred to a delta connection because

1. The voltage per phase is only $1/\sqrt{3}$ or 58% of the voltage between the lines. This means that the highest voltage between a stator conductor and the grounded stator core is only 58% of the line voltage. We can therefore reduce the amount of insulation in the slots which, in turn, enables us to increase the cross section of the conductors. A larger conductor permits us to increase the current and, hence, the power output of the machine.

Figure 16.2a
Stator of a 3-phase, 500 MVA, 0.95 power factor, 15 kV, 60 Hz, 200 r/min generator. Internal diameter: 9250 mm; effective axial length of iron stacking: 2350 mm; 378 slots.
(Courtesy of Marine Industrie)

2. When a synchronous generator is under load, the voltage induced in each phase becomes distorted, and the waveform is no longer sinusoidal. The distortion is mainly due to an undesired *third harmonic* voltage whose frequency is three times that of the fundamental frequency. With a wye connection, the distorting line-to-neutral harmonics do not appear between the lines because they effectively cancel each other. Consequently, the *line voltages* remain sinusoidal under all load conditions. Unfortunately, when a delta connection is used, the harmonic voltages do not cancel, but add up. Because the delta is closed on itself, they produce a third-harmonic circulating current, which increases the I^2R losses.

The nominal line voltage of a synchronous generator depends upon its kVA rating. In general, the greater the power rating, the higher the voltage. However, the nominal line-to-line voltage seldom exceeds 25 kV because the increased slot insulation takes up valuable space at the expense of the copper conductors.

Figure 16.2b
The copper bars connecting successive stator poles are designed to carry a current of 3200 A. The total output is 19 250 A per phase.
(Courtesy of Marine Industrie)

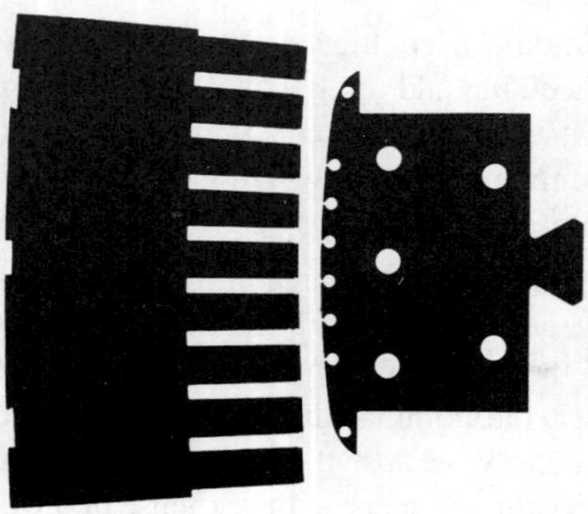

Figure 16.2c
The stator is built up from toothed segments of high-quality silicon-iron steel laminations (0.5 mm thick), covered with an insulating varnish. The slots are 22.3 mm wide and 169 mm deep. The salient poles of the rotor are composed of much thicker (2 mm) iron laminations. These laminations are not insulated because the dc flux they carry does not vary. The width of the poles from tip to tip is 600 mm and the air gap length is 33 mm. The 8 round holes in the face of the salient pole carry the bars of a squirrel-cage winding.

Figure 16.3
Stator of a 3-phase, 722 MVA, 3600 r/min, 19 kV, 60 Hz, steam-turbine generator during the construction phase. The windings are water-cooled. The stator will eventually be completely enclosed in a metal housing (see background). The housing contains hydrogen under pressure to further improve the cooling.
(Courtesy of ABB)

16.4 Main features of the rotor

Synchronous generators are built with two types of rotors: salient-pole rotors and smooth, cylindrical rotors. Salient-pole rotors are usually driven by low-speed hydraulic turbines, and cylindrical rotors are driven by high-speed steam turbines.

1. Salient-pole rotors. Most hydraulic turbines have to turn at low speeds (between 50 and 300 r/min) in order to extract the maximum power from a waterfall. Because the rotor is directly coupled to the waterwheel, and because a frequency of 50 Hz or 60 Hz is required, a large number of poles are required on the rotor. Low-speed rotors always possess a large diameter to provide the necessary space for the poles. The salient poles are mounted on a large circular steel frame which is fixed to a revolving vertical shaft (Fig. 16.4). To ensure good cooling, the field coils are made of bare copper bars, with the turns insulated from each other by strips of mica (Fig. 16.5). The coils are connected in series, with adjacent poles having opposite polarities.

In addition to the dc field winding, we often add a squirrel-cage winding, embedded in the pole-faces (Fig. 16.6). Under normal conditions, this winding does not carry any current because the rotor turns at synchronous speed. However, when the load on the generator changes suddenly, the rotor speed begins to fluctuate, producing momentary speed variations above and below synchronous speed. This induces a voltage in the squirrel-cage winding, causing a large current to flow therein. The current reacts with the magnetic field of the stator, producing forces which dampen the oscillation of the rotor. For this reason, the squirrel-cage winding is sometimes called a *damper winding.*

Figure 16.4
This 36-pole rotor is being lowered into the stator shown in Fig. 16.2. The 2400 A dc exciting current is supplied by a 330 V, electronic rectifier. Other details are: mass: 600 t; moment of inertia: 4140 t·m^2; air gap: 33 mm.
(Courtesy of Marine Industrie)

Figure 16.5
This rotor winding for a 250 MVA, salient-pole generator is made of 18 turns of bare copper bars having a width of 89 mm and a thickness of 9 mm.

Figure 16.6
Salient-pole of a 250 MVA generator showing 12 slots to carry the squirrel-cage winding.

Figure 16.7a
Rotor of a 3-phase, steam-turbine generator rated 1530 MVA, 1500 r/min, 27 kV, 50 Hz. The 40 longitudinal slots are being milled out of the solid steel mass. They will carry the dc winding. Effective axial magnetic length: 7490 mm; diameter: 1800 mm.
(Courtesy of Allis-Chalmers Power Systems Inc., West Allis, Wisconsin)

Figure 16.7b
Rotor with its 4-pole dc winding. Total mass: 204 t; moment of inertia: 85 t·m^2; air gap: 120 mm. The dc exciting current of 11.2 kA is supplied by a 600 V dc brushless exciter bolted to the end of the main shaft.
(Courtesy of Allis-Chalmers Power Systems Inc., West Allis, Wisconsin)

The damper winding also tends to maintain balanced 3-phase voltages between the lines, even when the line currents are unequal due to unbalanced load conditions.

2. Cylindrical rotors. It is well known that high-speed steam turbines are smaller and more efficient than low-speed turbines. The same is true of high-speed synchronous generators. However, to generate the required frequency we cannot use less than 2 poles, and this fixes the highest possible speed. On a 60 Hz system it is 3600 r/min. The next lower speed is 1800 r/min, corresponding to a 4-pole machine. Consequently, these *steam-turbine generators* possess either 2 or 4 poles.

The rotor of a turbine-generator is a long, solid steel cylinder which contains a series of longitudinal slots milled out of the cylindrical mass (Fig. 16.7). Concentric field coils, firmly wedged into the slots and retained by high-strength end-rings,* serve to create the N and S poles.

The high speed of rotation produces strong centrifugal forces, which impose an upper limit on the diameter of the rotor. In the case of a rotor turning at 3600 r/min, the elastic limit of the steel requires the manufacturer to limit the diameter to a maximum of 1.2 m. On the other hand, to build the powerful 1000 MVA to 1500 MVA generators the volume of the rotors has to be large. It follows that high-power, high-speed rotors have to be very long.

16.5 Field excitation and exciters

The dc field excitation of a large synchronous generator is an important part of its overall design. The

* See Fig. 11.28 (Chapter 11).

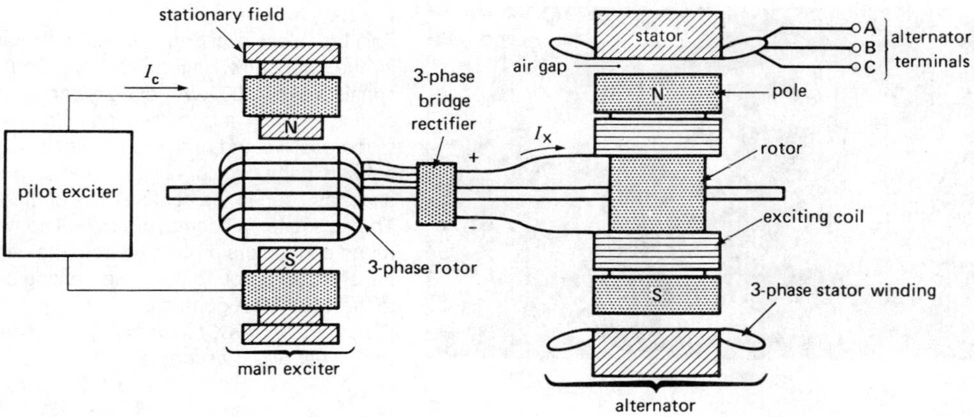

Figure 16.8
Typical brushless exciter system.

reason is that the field must ensure not only a stable ac terminal voltage, but must also respond to sudden load changes in order to maintain system stability. Quickness of response is one of the important features of the field excitation. In order to attain it, two dc generators are used: a main exciter and a *pilot exciter.* Static exciters that involve no rotating parts at all are also employed.

The main exciter feeds the exciting current to the field of the synchronous generator by way of brushes and slip-rings. Under normal conditions the exciter voltage lies between 125 V and 600 V. It is regulated manually or automatically by control signals that vary the current I_c, produced by the pilot exciter (Fig. 16.1).

The power rating of the main exciter depends upon the capacity of the synchronous generator. Typically, a 25 kW exciter is needed to excite a 1000 kVA alternator (2.5% of its rating) whereas a 2500 kW exciter suffices for an alternator of 500 MW (only 0.5% of its rating).

Under normal conditions the excitation is varied automatically. It responds to the load changes so as to maintain a constant ac line voltage or to control the reactive power delivered to the electric utility system. A serious disturbance on the system may produce a sudden voltage drop across the terminals of the alternator. The exciter must then react very quickly to keep the ac voltage from falling. For example, the exciter voltage may have to rise to twice its normal value in as little as 300 to 400 milliseconds. This represents a very quick response, considering that the power of the exciter may be several thousand kilowatts.

16.6 Brushless excitation

Due to brush wear and carbon dust, we constantly have to clean, repair, and replace brushes, slip-rings, and commutators on conventional dc excitation systems. To eliminate the problem, *brushless excitation systems* have been developed. Such a system consists of a 3-phase, stationary-field generator whose ac output is rectified by a group of rectifiers. The dc output from the rectifiers is fed directly into the field of the synchronous generator (Fig. 16.8).

The armature of the ac exciter and the rectifiers are mounted on the main shaft and turn together with the synchronous generator. In comparing the excitation system of Fig. 16.8 with that of Fig. 16.1, we can see they are identical, except that the 3-phase rectifier replaces the commutator, slip-rings, and brushes. In other words, the commutator (which is really a mechanical rectifier) is replaced by an electronic rectifier. The result is that the brushes and slip-rings are no longer needed.

The dc control current I_c from the pilot exciter regulates the main exciter output I_x, as in the case of

Figure 16.9
This brushless exciter provides the dc current for the rotor shown in Fig. 16.7. The exciter consists of a 7000 kVA generator and two sets of diodes. Each set, corresponding respectively to the positive and negative terminals, is housed in the circular rings mounted on the shaft, as seen in the center of the photograph. The ac exciter is seen to the right. The two round conductors protruding from the center of the shaft (foreground) lead the exciting current to the 1530 MVA generator.
(Courtesy of Allis-Chalmers Power Systems Inc., West Allis, Wisconsin)

a conventional dc exciter. The frequency of the main exciter is generally two to three times the synchronous generator frequency (60 Hz). The increase in frequency is obtained by using more poles on the exciter than on the synchronous generator. Fig. 16.9 shows the rotating portion of a typical brushless exciter. Static exciters that involve no rotating parts at all are also employed.

16.7 Factors affecting the size of synchronous generators

The prodigious amount of energy generated by electrical utility companies has made them very conscious about the efficiency of their generators. For example, if the efficiency of a 1000 MW generating station improves by only 1%, it represents extra revenues of several thousand dollars per day. In this regard, the size of the generator is particularly important because its efficiency automatically improves as the power increases. For example, if a small 1 kilowatt synchronous generator has an efficiency of 50%, a larger, but similar model having a capacity of 10 MW *inevitably* has an efficiency of about 90%. This improvement in efficiency with size is the reason why synchronous generators of 1000 MW and up possess efficiencies of the order of 99%.

Another advantage of large machines is that the power output per kilogram increases as the power increases. For example, if a 1 kW generator weighs 20 kg (yielding 1000 W/20 kg = 50 W/kg), a 10 MW

Figure 16.10
Partial view of a 3-phase, salient-pole generator rated 87 MVA, 428 r/min, 50 Hz. Both the rotor and stator are water-cooled. The high resistivity of pure water and the use of insulating plastic tubing enables the water to be brought into direct contact with the live parts of the machine.
(Courtesy of ABB)

generator of similar construction will weigh only 20 000 kg, thus yielding 500 W/kg. From a power standpoint, large machines weigh relatively less than small machines; consequently, they are cheaper. Section 16.24 at the end of this chapter explains why the efficiency and output per kilogram increase with size.

Everything, therefore, favors the large machines. However, as they increase in size, we run into serious cooling problems. In effect, large machines inherently produce high power losses per unit surface area (W/m^2); consequently, they tend to overheat. To prevent an unacceptable temperature rise, we must design efficient cooling systems that become ever more elaborate as the power increases. For example, a circulating cold-air system is adequate to cool synchronous generators whose rating is below 50 MW, but between 50 MW and 300 MW, we have to resort to hydrogen cooling. Very big generators in the 1000 MW range have to be equipped with hollow, water-cooled conductors. Ultimately, a point is reached where the increased cost of cooling exceeds the savings made elsewhere, and this fixes the upper limit to size.

To sum up, the evolution of big alternators has mainly been determined by the evolution of sophisticated cooling techniques (Figs. 16.10 and 16.11). Other technological breakthroughs, such as better materials and novel windings, have also played a major part in modifying the design of early machines (Fig. 16.12).

As regards speed, low-speed generators are always bigger than high-speed machines of equal power. Slow-speed bigness simplifies the cooling problem; a good air-cooling system, completed with a heat exchanger, usually suffices. For example, the large, slow-speed 500 MVA, 200 r/min synchronous generators installed in a typical hydropower plant are air-cooled whereas the much smaller high-speed 500 MVA, 1800 r/min units installed in a steam plant have to be hydrogen-cooled.

16.8 No-load saturation curve

Fig. 16.13a shows a 2-pole synchronous generator operating at no-load. It is driven at constant speed by a turbine (not shown). The leads from the 3-phase, wye-connected stator are brought out to terminals A, B, C, N, and a variable exciting current I_x produces the flux in the air gap.

Let us gradually increase the exciting current while observing the ac voltage E_o between terminal A,

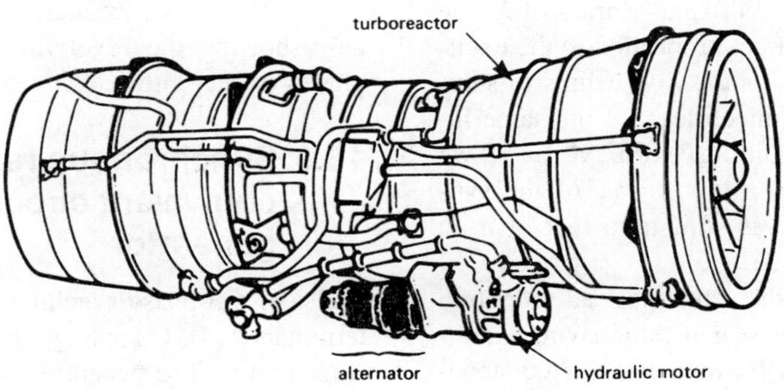

Figure 16.11
The electrical energy needed on board the Concord aircraft is supplied by four 3-phase generators rated 60 kVA, 200/115 V, 12 000 r/min, 400 Hz. Each generator is driven by a hydraulic motor, which absorbs a small portion of the enormous power developed by the turboreactor engines. The hydraulic fluid streaming from the hydraulic motor is used to cool the generator and is then recycled. The generator itself weighs only 54.5 kg.
(Courtesy of Air France)

Figure 16.12
This rotating-field generator was first installed in North America in 1888. It was used in a 1000-lamp street lighting system. The alternator was driven by an 1100 r/min steam engine and had a rated output of 2000 V, 30 A at a frequency of 110 Hz. It weighed 2320 kg, which represents 26 W/kg. A modern generator of equal speed and power produces about 140 W/kg and occupies only one-third the floor space.

say, and the neutral N. For small values of I_x, the voltage increases in direct proportion to the exciting current. However, as the iron begins to saturate, the voltage rises much less for the same increase in I_x. If we plot the curve of E_o versus I_x, we obtain the *no-load saturation curve* of the synchronous generator. It is similar to that of a dc generator (Section 4.13).

Fig. 16.13b shows the actual no-load saturation curve of a 36 MW, 3-phase generator having a nominal voltage of 12 kV (line to neutral). Up to about 9 kV, the voltage increases in proportion to the current, but then the iron begins to saturate. Thus, an exciting current of 100 A produces an output of 12 kV, but if the current is doubled, the voltage rises only to 15 kV.

Fig. 16.13c is a schematic diagram of the generator showing the revolving rotor and the three phases on the stator.

16.9 Synchronous reactance—equivalent circuit of an ac generator

Consider a 3-phase synchronous generator having terminals A, B, C feeding a balanced 3-phase load (Fig. 16.14). The generator is driven by a turbine (not shown), and is excited by a dc current I_x. The machine and its load are both connected in wye, yielding the circuit of Fig. 16.15. Although neutrals N_1 and N_2 are not connected, they are at the same potential because the load is balanced. Consequently,

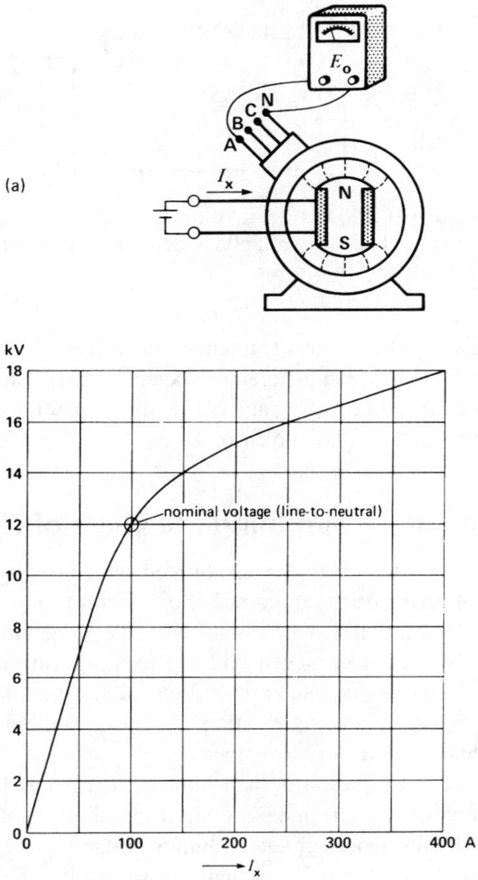

Figure 16.13
a. Generator operating at no-load.
b. No-load saturation curve of a 36 MVA, 21 kV, 3-phase generator.

we *could* connect them together (as indicated by the short dash line) without affecting the behavior of the voltages or currents in the circuit.

The field carries an exciting current which produces a flux Φ. As the field revolves, the flux induces in the stator three equal voltages E_o that are 120° out of phase (Fig. 16.16).

Each phase of the stator winding possesses a resistance R and a certain inductance L. Because this

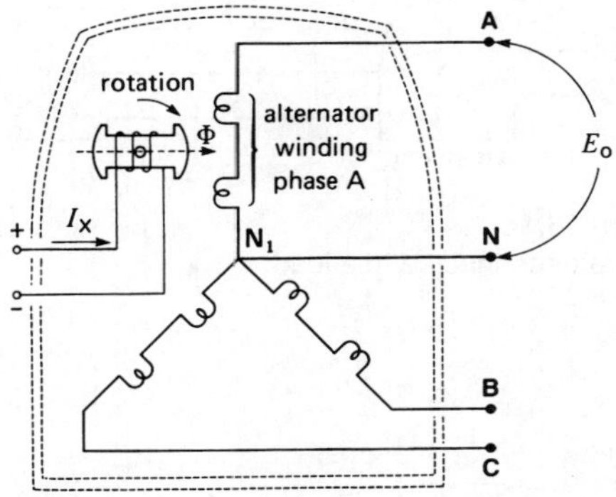

Figure 16.13c
Electric circuit representing the generator of Fig. 16.13a.

is an alternating-current machine, the inductance manifests itself as a reactance X_s, given by

$$X_s = 2\pi f L$$

where

X_s = synchronous reactance, per phase [Ω]
f = generator frequency [Hz]
L = apparent inductance of the stator winding, per phase [H]

The *synchronous reactance* of a generator is an internal impedance, just like its internal resistance R. The impedance is there, but it can neither be seen nor touched. The value of X_s is typically 10 to 100 times greater than R; consequently, we can always neglect the resistance, unless we are interested in efficiency or heating effects.

We can simplify the schematic diagram of Fig. 16.16 by showing only one phase of the stator. In effect, the two other phases are identical, except that their respective voltages (and currents) are out of phase by 120°. Furthermore, if we neglect the resistance of the windings, we obtain the very simple circuit of Fig. 16.17. A synchronous generator can therefore be represented by an equivalent circuit composed of an induced voltage E_o in series with a reactance X_s.

In this circuit the exciting current I_x produces the flux Φ which induces the internal voltage E_o. For a

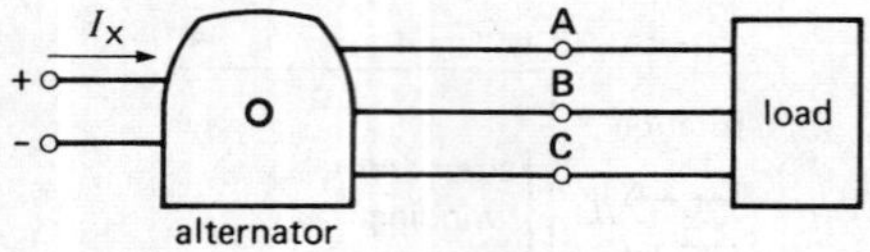

Figure 16.14
Generator connected to a load.

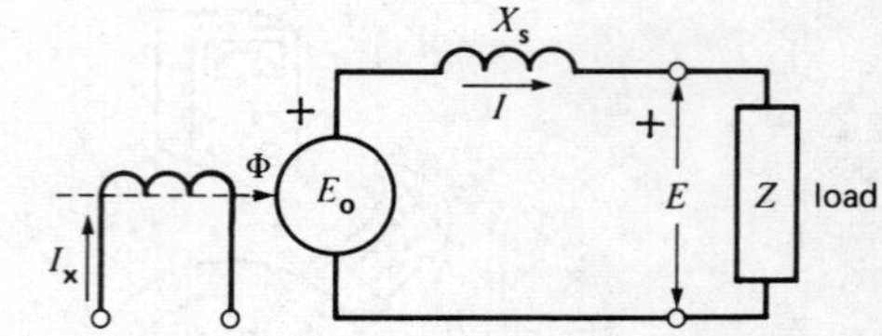

Figure 16.17
Equivalent circuit of a 3-phase generator, showing only one phase.

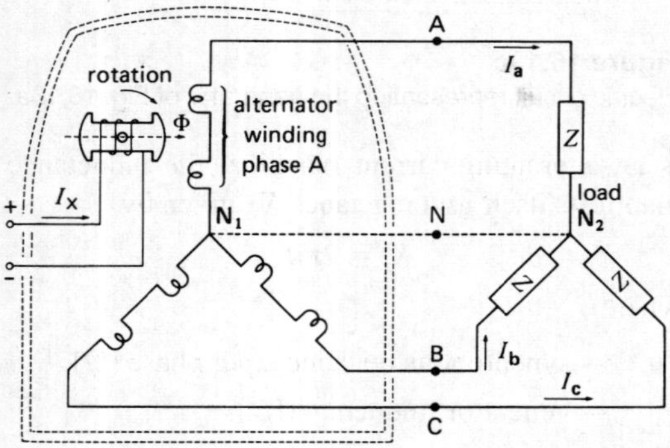

Figure 16.15
Electric circuit representing the installation of Fig. 16.14.

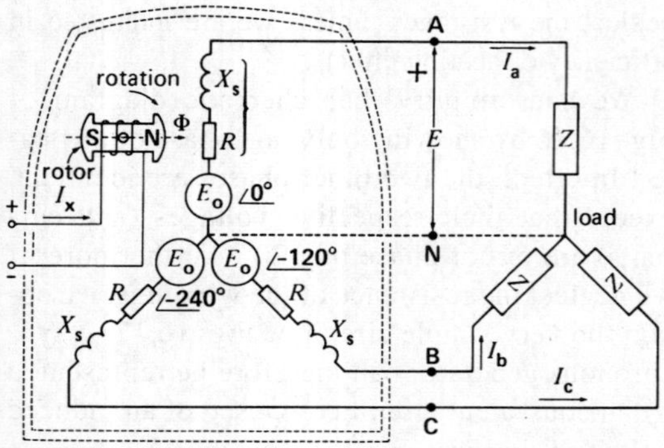

Figure 16.16
Voltages and impedances in a 3-phase generator and its connected load.

given synchronous reactance, the voltage E at the terminals of the generator depends upon E_o and the load Z. Note that E_o and E are line-to-neutral voltages and I is the line current.

16.10 Determining the value of X_s

We can determine the unsaturated value of X_s by the following open-circuit and short-circuit test.

During the open-circuit test the generator is driven at rated speed and the exciting current is raised until the rated line-to-line voltage is attained. The corresponding exciting current I_{xn} and line-to-neutral voltage E_n are recorded.

The excitation is then reduced to zero and the three stator terminals are short-circuited together. With the generator again running at rated speed, the exciting current is gradually raised to its original value I_{xn}.

The resulting short-circuit current I_{sc} in the stator windings is measured and X_s is calculated by using the expression

$$X_s = E_n/I_{sc} \tag{16.2}$$

where

X_s = synchronous reactance, per phase [Ω]*
E_n = rated open-circuit line-to-neutral voltage [V]

* This value of X_s corresponds to the direct-axis synchronous reactance. It is widely used to describe synchronous machine behavior.

I_{sc} = short-circuit current, per phase, using the same exciting current I_{xn} that was required to produce E_n [A]

The synchronous reactance is not constant, but varies with the degree of saturation. When the iron is heavily saturated, the value of X_s may be only half its unsaturated value. Despite this broad range we usually take the unsaturated value for X_s because it yields sufficient accuracy in most cases of interest.

Example 16-2

A 3-phase synchronous generator produces an open-circuit line voltage of 6928 V when the dc exciting current is 50 A. The ac terminals are then short-circuited, and the three line currents are found to be 800 A.

a. Calculate the synchronous reactance per phase.
b. Calculate the terminal voltage if three 12 Ω resistors are connected in wye across the terminals.

Solution

a. The line-to-neutral induced voltage is

$$E_o = E_L/\sqrt{3} \quad (8.4)$$
$$= 6928/\sqrt{3}$$
$$= 4000 \text{ V}$$

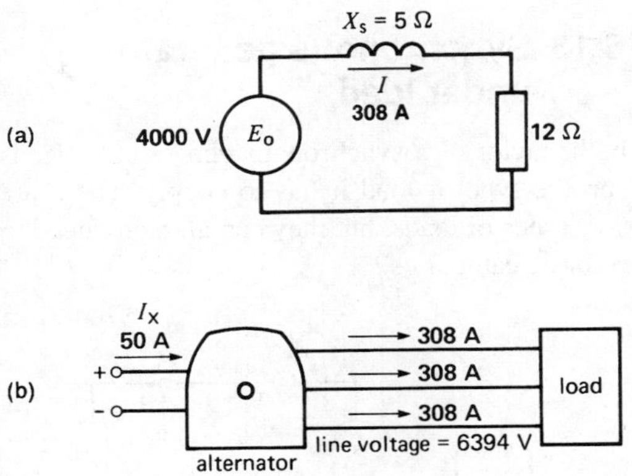

Figure 16.18
See Example 16-2.
Actual line voltages and currents.

When the terminals are short-circuited, the only impedance limiting the current flow is that due to the synchronous reactance. Consequently,

$$X_s = E_o/I = 4000/800$$
$$= 5 \ \Omega$$

The synchronous reactance per phase is therefore 5 Ω.

b. The equivalent circuit per phase is shown in Fig. 16.18a.
The impedance of the circuit is

$$Z = \sqrt{R^2 + X_s^2} \quad (2.12)$$
$$= \sqrt{12^2 + 5^2}$$
$$= 13 \ \Omega$$

The current is

$$I = E_o/Z = 4000/13 = 308 \text{ A}$$

The voltage across the load resistor is

$$E = IR = 308 \times 12 = 3696 \text{ V}$$

The line voltage under load is

$$E_L = \sqrt{3}\, E$$
$$= \sqrt{3} \times 3696$$
$$= 6402 \text{ V}$$

The schematic diagram of Fig. 16.18b helps us visualize what is happening in the actual circuit.

16.11 Base impedance, per-unit X_s

We recall that when using the per-unit system we first select a base voltage and a base power. In the case of a synchronous generator, we use the rated line-to-neutral voltage as the base voltage E_B and the rated power *per phase* as the base power.* It follows that the base impedance Z_B is given by

$$Z_B = \frac{E_B^{\,2}}{S_B} \quad (16.3)$$

* In many power studies the base power is selected to be equal to the rated power of the generator and the base voltage is the line-to-line voltage. This yields the same value Z_B for the base impedance.

where

Z_B = base impedance (line-to-neutral) of the generator [Ω]

E_B = base voltage (line-to-neutral) [V]

S_B = base power per phase [VA]

The base impedance is used as a basis of comparison for other impedances that the generator possesses. Thus, the synchronous reactance may be expressed as a per-unit value of Z_B. In general, X_s(pu) lies between 0.8 and 2, depending upon the design of the machine.

Example 16-3

A 30 MVA, 15 kV, 60 Hz ac generator has a synchronous reactance of 1.2 pu and a resistance of 0.02 pu.

Calculate

a. The base voltage, base power and base impedance of the generator
b. The actual value of the synchronous reactance
c. The actual winding resistance, per phase
d. The total full-load copper losses

Solution

a. The base voltage is

$$E_B = E_L/\sqrt{3} = 15\,000/\sqrt{3} = 8660 \text{ V}$$

The base power is

$$S_B = 30 \text{ MVA}/3 = 10 \text{ MVA} = 10^7 \text{ VA}$$

The base impedance is

$$Z_B = E_B{}^2/S_B \quad (16.3)$$
$$= 8660^2/10^7$$
$$= 7.5\ \Omega$$

b. The synchronous reactance is

$$X_s = X_s(\text{pu}) \times Z_B = 1.2\, Z_B = 1.2 \times 7.5 = 9\ \Omega$$

c. The resistance per phase is

$$R = R(\text{pu}) \times Z_B = 0.02\, Z_B = 0.02 \times 7.5 = 0.15\ \Omega$$

Note that all impedance values are from line to neutral.

d. The per-unit copper losses at full-load are

$$P(\text{pu}) = I^2(\text{pu})\, R(\text{pu}) = 1^2 \times 0.02 = 0.02$$

Note that at full-load the per-unit value of I is equal to 1.
The copper losses for all 3 phases are

$$P = 0.02\, S_B = 0.02 \times 30 = 0.6 \text{ MW} = 600 \text{ kW}$$

16.12 Short-circuit ratio

Instead of expressing the synchronous reactance as a per-unit value of Z_B, the *short-circuit ratio* is sometimes used. It is the ratio of the field current I_{x1} needed to generate rated open-circuit armature voltage E_B to the field current I_{x2} needed to produce rated current I_B, on a sustained short-circuit. The short-circuit ratio (I_{x1}/I_{x2}) is exactly equal to the reciprocal of the per-unit value of X_s as defined in Eq. 16.2. Thus, if the per-unit value of X_s is 1.2, the short-circuit ratio is 1/1.2 or 0.833.

16.13 Synchronous generator under load

The behavior of a synchronous generator depends upon the type of load it has to supply. There are many types of loads, but they can all be reduced to two basic categories:

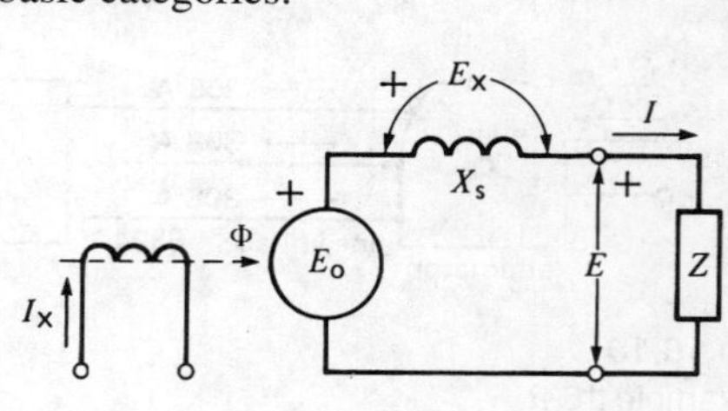

Figure 16.19
Equivalent circuit of a generator under load.

1. Isolated loads, supplied by a single generator
2. The infinite bus

We begin our study with isolated loads, leaving the discussion of the infinite bus to Section 16.16.

Consider a 3-phase generator that supplies power to a load having a lagging power factor. Fig. 16.19 represents the equivalent circuit for one phase. In order to construct the phasor diagram for this circuit, we list the following facts:

1. Current I lags behind terminal voltage E by an angle θ.
2. Cosine θ = power factor of the load.
3. Voltage E_x across the synchronous reactance leads current I by 90°. It is given by the expression $E_x = jIX_s$.
4. Voltage E_o generated by the flux Φ is equal to the phasor sum of E plus E_x.
5. Both E_o and E_x are voltages that exist inside the synchronous generator windings and cannot be measured directly.
6. Flux Φ is that produced by the dc exciting current I_x.

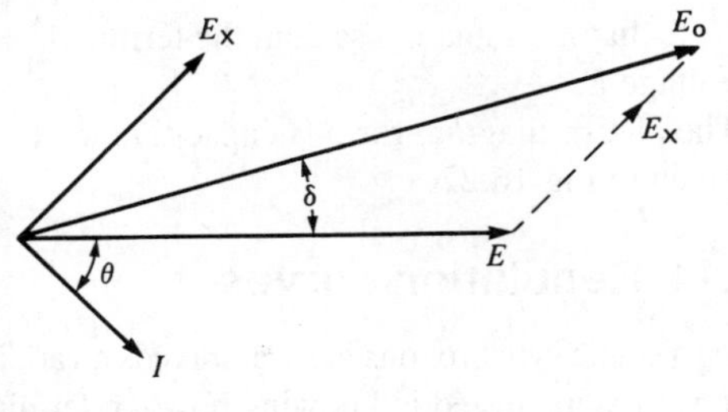

Figure 16.20
Phasor diagram for a lagging power factor load.

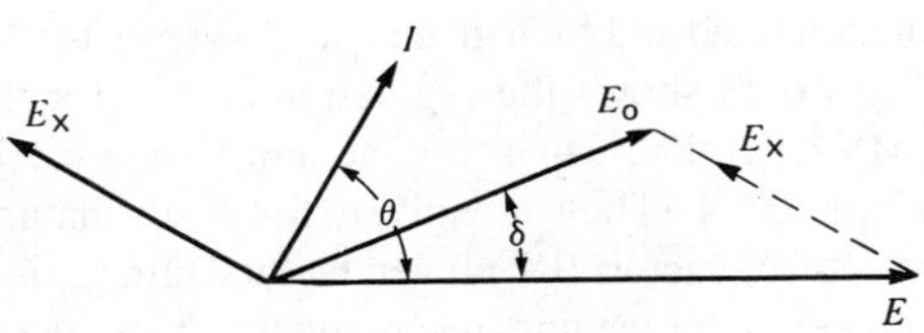

Figure 16.21
Phasor diagram for a leading power factor load.

The resulting phasor diagram is given in Fig. 16.20. Note that E_o leads E by δ degrees. Furthermore, the internally-generated voltage E_o is greater than the terminal voltage, as we would expect.

In some cases the load is somewhat capacitive, so that current I leads the terminal voltage by an angle θ. What effect does this have on the phasor diagram? The answer is found in Fig. 16.21. The voltage E_x across the synchronous reactance is still 90° ahead of the current. Furthermore, E_o is again equal to the phasor sum of E and E_x. However, the terminal voltage is now *greater* than the induced voltage E_o, which is a very surprising result. In effect, the inductive reactance X_s enters into partial resonance with the capacitive reactance of the load. Although it may appear we are getting something for nothing, the higher terminal voltage does not yield any more power.

If the load is entirely capacitive, a very high terminal voltage can be produced with a small exciting current. However, in later chapters, we will see that such under-excitation is undesirable.

Example 16-4

A 36 MVA, 20.8 kV, 3-phase alternator has a synchronous reactance of 9 Ω and a nominal current of 1 kA. The no-load saturation curve giving the relationship between E_o and I_x is given in Fig. 16.13b. If the excitation is adjusted so that the terminal voltage remains fixed at 21 kV, calculate the exciting current required and draw the phasor diagram for the following conditions:

a. No-load
b. Resistive load of 36 MW
c. Capacitive load of 12 Mvar

Solution

We shall immediately simplify the circuit to show only one phase. The line-to-neutral terminal voltage for all cases is fixed at

$$E = 20.8/\sqrt{3} = 12 \text{ kV}$$

a. At no-load there is no voltage drop in the synchronous reactance; consequently,

$$E_o = E = 12 \text{ kV}$$

Figure 16.22a
Phasor diagram at no-load.

The exciting current is

$$I_x = 100 \qquad \text{(see Fig. 16.13b)}$$

The phasor diagram is given in Fig. 16.22a.

With a resistive load of 36 MW:

b. The power per phase is

$$P = 36/3 = 12 \text{ MW}$$

The full-load line current is

$$I = P/E = 12 \times 10^6/12\,000 = 1000 \text{ A}$$

The current is in phase with the terminal voltage. The voltage across X_s is

$$E_x = jIX_s = j1000 \times 9 = 9 \text{ kV}\angle 90°$$

This voltage is 90° ahead of I.
The voltage E_o generated by I_x is equal to the phasor sum of E and E_x. Referring to the phasor diagram, its value is given by

$$E_o = \sqrt{E^2 + E_x^2} = \sqrt{12^2 + 9^2} = 15 \text{ kV}$$

The required exciting current is

$$I_x = 200 \text{ A} \qquad \text{(see Fig. 16.13b)}$$

The phasor diagram is given in Fig. 16.22b.

With a capacitive load of 12 Mvar:

c. The reactive power per phase is

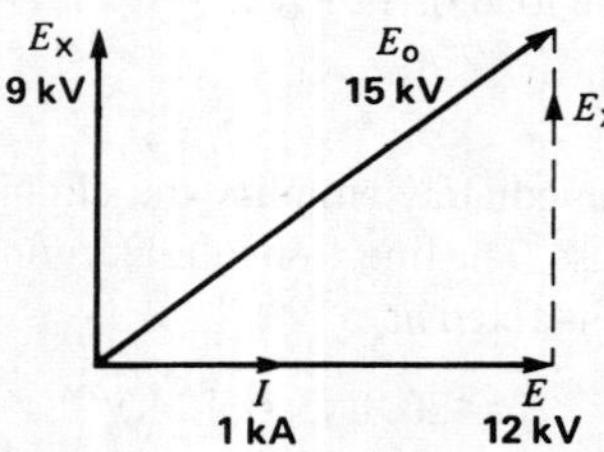

Figure 16.22b
Phasor diagram with a unity power factor load.

$$Q = 12/3 = 4 \text{ Mvar}$$

The line current is

$$I = Q/E = 4 \times 10^6/12\,000$$
$$= 333 \text{ A}$$

The voltage across X_s is

$$E_x = jIX_s = j333 \times 9 = 3 \text{ kV}\angle 90°$$

As before, E_x leads I by 90° (Fig. 16.22c).

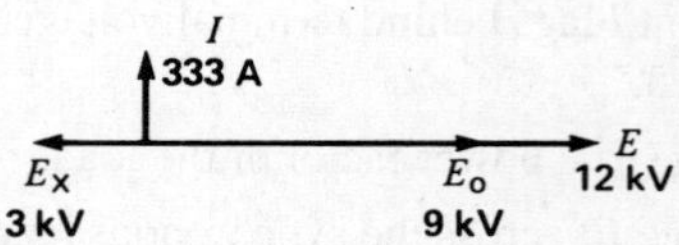

Figure 16.22c
Phasor diagram with a capacitive load.

The voltage E_o generated by I_x is equal to the phasor sum of E and E_x.

$$E_o = E + E_x = 12 + (-3)$$
$$= 9 \text{ kV}$$

The corresponding exciting current is

$$I_x = 70 \text{ A} \qquad \text{(see Fig. 16.13b)}$$

Note that E_o is again less than the terminal voltage E.
The phasor diagram for this capacitive load is given in Fig. 16.22c.

16.14 Regulation curves

When a single synchronous generator feeds a variable load, we are interested in knowing how the terminal voltage E changes as a function of the load current I. The relationship between E and I is called the *regulation curve.* Regulation curves are plotted with the field excitation fixed and for a given load power factor.

Fig. 16.23 shows the regulation curves for the 36 MVA, 21 kV, 3-phase generator discussed in Example 16-4. They are given for loads having unity power factor, 0.9 power factor lagging, and 0.9 power factor leading, respectively. These curves were derived using the method of Example 16-4,

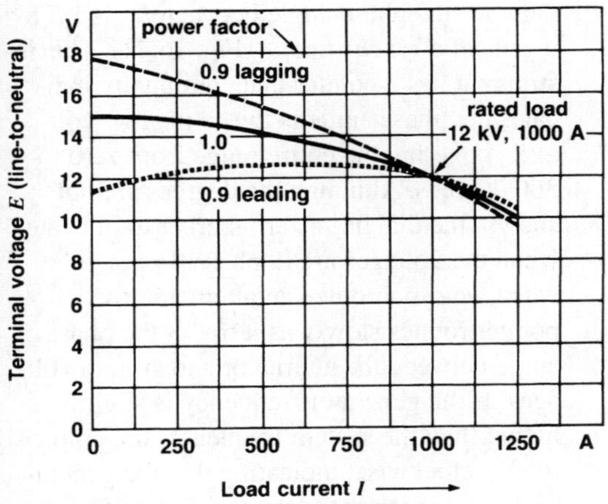

Figure 16.23
Regulation curves of a synchronous generator at three different load power factors.

except that E_o was kept fixed instead of E. In each of the three cases, the value of E_o was set so that the starting point for all the curves was the rated line-to-neutral terminal voltage (12 kV) at rated line current (1000 A).

The change in voltage between no-load and full-load is expressed as a percent of the rated terminal voltage. The percent regulation is given by the equation

$$\% \text{ regulation} = \frac{E_{NL} - E_B}{E_B} \times 100$$

where

$$E_{NL} = \text{no-load voltage [V]}$$
$$E_B = \text{rated voltage [V]}$$

Example 16-5
Calculate the percent regulation corresponding to the unity power factor curve in Fig. 16.23.

Solution
The rated line-to-neutral voltage at full-load is

$$E_B = 12 \text{ kV}$$

The no-load terminal voltage is

$$E_{NL} = 15 \text{ kV}$$

The percent regulation is

$$\% \text{ regulation} = \frac{E_{NL} - E_B}{E_B} \times 100$$
$$= \frac{(15 - 12)}{12} \times 100 = 25\%$$

We note that the percent regulation of a synchronous generator is much greater than that of a dc generator. The reason is the high impedance of the synchronous reactance.

16.15 Synchronization of a generator

We often have to connect two or more generators in parallel to supply a common load. For example, as the power requirements of a large utility system build up during the day, generators are successively connected to the system to provide the extra power. Later, when the power demand falls, selected generators are temporarily disconnected from the system until power again builds up the following day. Synchronous generators are therefore regularly being connected and disconnected from a large power grid in response to customer demand. Such a grid is said to be an *infinite bus* because it contains so many generators essentially connected in parallel that neither the voltage nor the frequency of the grid can be altered.

Before connecting a generator to an infinite bus (or in parallel with another generator), it must be *synchronized.* A generator is said to be synchronized when it meets all the following conditions:

1. The generator frequency is equal to the system frequency.
2. The generator voltage is equal to the system voltage.
3. The generator voltage is in phase with the system voltage.
4. The phase sequence of the generator is the same as that of the system.

To synchronize an alternator, we proceed as follows:

1. Adjust the speed regulator of the turbine so that the generator frequency is close to the system frequency.
2. Adjust the excitation so that the generator voltage E_o is equal to the system voltage E.

Figure 16.24
Synchroscope.
(Courtesy of Lab-Volt)

3. Observe the phase angle between E_o and E by means of a *synchroscope* (Fig. 16.24). This instrument has a pointer that continually indicates the phase angle between the two voltages, covering the entire range from zero to 360 degrees. Although the degrees are not shown, the dial has a zero marker to indicate when the voltages are in phase. In practice, when we synchronize an alternator, the pointer rotates slowly as it tracks the phase angle between the alternator and system voltages. If the generator frequency is slightly higher than the system frequency, the pointer rotates clockwise, indicating that the generator has a tendency to lead the system frequency. Conversely, if the generator frequency is slightly low, the pointer rotates counterclockwise. The turbine speed regulator is fine-tuned accordingly, so that the pointer barely creeps across the dial. A final check is made to see that the alternator voltage is still equal to the system voltage. Then, at the moment the pointer crosses the zero marker . . .

Figure 16.25
This floating oil derrick provides its own energy needs. Four diesel-driven generators rated 1200 kVA, 440 V, 900 r/min, 60 Hz supply all the electrical energy. Although ac power is generated and distributed, all the motors on board are thyristor-controlled dc motors.
(Courtesy of Siemens)

4. The line circuit breaker is closed, connecting the generator to the system.

In modern generating stations, synchronization is usually done automatically.

16.16 Synchronous generator on an infinite bus

We seldom have to connect only two generators in parallel except in isolated locations (Fig. 16.25). As mentioned previously, it is much more common to connect a generator to a large power system (infinite bus) that already has many alternators connected to it.

An infinite bus is a system so powerful that it imposes its own voltage and frequency upon any apparatus connected to its terminals. Once connected to a large system (infinite bus), a synchronous generator becomes part of a network comprising hundreds of other generators that deliver power to thousands of loads. It is impossible, therefore, to specify the nature of the load (large or small, resistive or capacitive) connected to the terminals of this particular generator. What, then, determines the power the machine delivers? To answer this question, we must remember that both the value and the frequency of the terminal voltage across the generator are fixed. Consequently, we can vary only two machine parameters:

1. The exciting current I_x
2. The mechanical torque exerted by the turbine

Let us see how a change in these parameters affects the performance of the machine.

16.17 Infinite bus—effect of varying the exciting current

Immediately after we synchronize a generator and connect it to an infinite bus, the induced voltage E_o is equal to, and in phase with, the terminal voltage E of the system (Fig. 16.26a). There is no difference of potential across the synchronous reactance and, consequently, the load current I is zero. Although the generator is connected to the system, it delivers no power; it is said to *float* on the line.

If we now increase the exciting current, the voltage E_o will increase and the synchronous reactance X_s will experience a difference of potential E_x given by

$$E_x = E_o - E$$

A current I will therefore circulate in the circuit given by

$$I = (E_o - E)/X_s$$

Because the synchronous reactance is inductive, the current lags 90° behind E_x (Fig. 16.26b). The current is therefore 90° behind E, which means that the generator sees the system as if it were an inductive reactance. Consequently, when we over-excite a synchronous generator, it supplies reactive power to the infinite bus. The reactive power increases as we raise the dc exciting current. Contrary to what we might expect, it is impossible to make a generator deliver active power by raising its excitation.

Let us now decrease the exciting current so that E_o becomes smaller than E. As a result, phasor $E_x = E_o - E$ becomes negative and therefore points to the left (Fig. 16.26c). As always, current $I = E_x/X_s$ lags 90° behind E_x. However, this puts I 90° ahead of E, which means that the alternator sees the system as if it were a capacitor. Consequently, when we under-excite an alternator, it draws reactive power from the system. This reactive power produces part of the magnetic field required by the machine; the remainder is supplied by exciting current I_x.

16.18 Infinite bus—effect of varying the mechanical torque

Let us return to the situation with the synchronous generator floating on the line, E_o and E being equal and in phase. If we open the steam valve of the turbine driving the generator, the immediate result is an increase in mechanical torque (Fig. 16.27a). The rotor will accelerate and, consequently, E_o will attain its maximum value a little sooner than before. Phasor E_o will slip ahead of phasor E, leading it by a phase angle δ. Although both voltages have the same value, the phase angle produces a difference

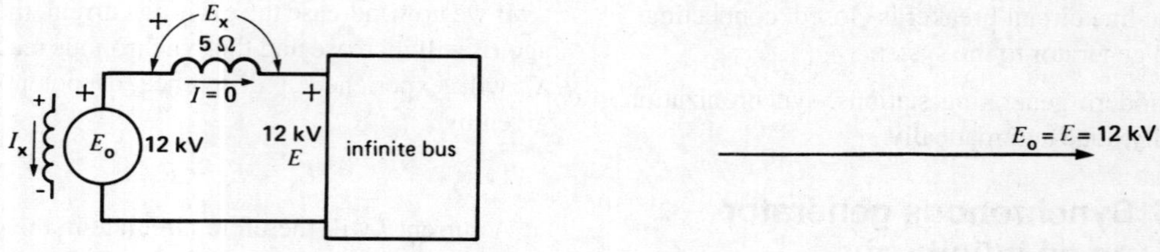

Figure 16.26a
Generator *floating* on an infinite bus.

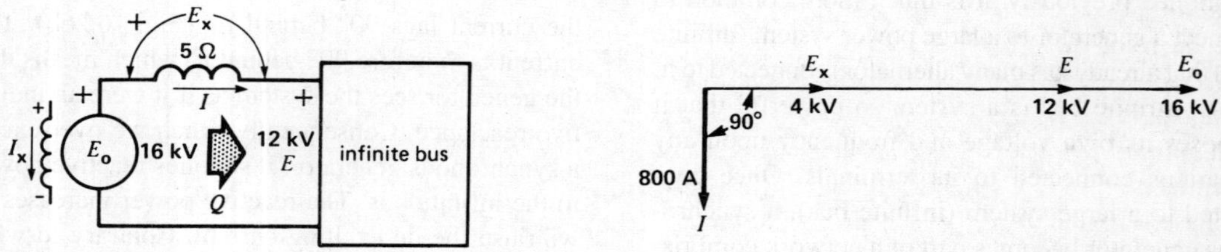

Figure 16.26b
Over-excited generator on an infinite bus.

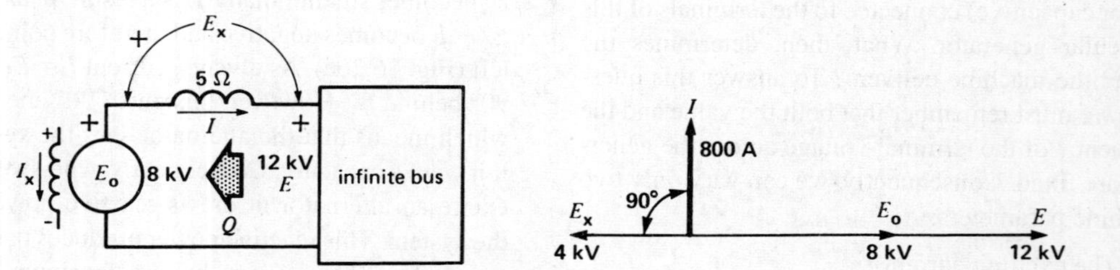

Figure 16.26c
Under-excited generator on an infinite bus.

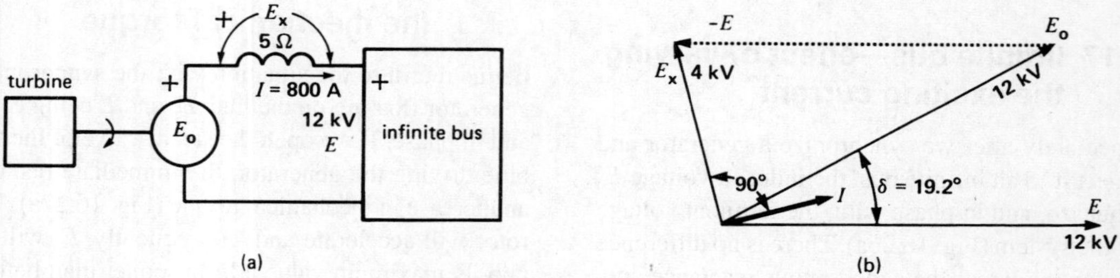

Figure 16.27
a. Turbine driving the generator.
b. Phasor diagram showing the torque angle δ.

of potential $E_x = E_o - E$ across the synchronous reactance (Fig. 16.27b).

A current I will flow (again lagging 90° behind E_x), but this time it is almost in phase with E. It follows that the generator feeds active power into the system. Under the driving force of the turbine, the rotor will continue to accelerate, the angle δ will continue to diverge, and the electrical power delivered to the system will gradually build up. However, as soon as the electrical power delivered to the system is equal to the mechanical power supplied by the turbine, the rotor will cease to accelerate. The generator will again run at synchronous speed, and the *torque angle* δ between E_o and E will remain constant.

It is important to understand that a difference of potential is created when two equal voltages are out of phase. Thus, in Fig. 16.27, a potential difference of 4 kV exists between E_o and E, although both voltages have a value of 12 kV.

16.19 Physical interpretation of alternator behavior

The phasor diagram of Fig. 16.27b shows that when the phase angle between E_o and E increases, the value of E_x increases and, hence, the value of I increases. But a larger current means that the active power delivered by the generator also increases. To understand the physical meaning of the diagram, let us examine the currents, fluxes, and position of the poles inside the machine.

Whenever 3-phase currents flow in the stator of a generator, they produce a rotating magnetic field identical to that in an induction motor. In a synchronous generator this field rotates at the same speed and in the same direction as the rotor. Furthermore, it has the same number of poles. The respective fields produced by the rotor and stator are, therefore, stationary with respect to each other. Depending on the relative position of the stator poles on the one hand and the rotor poles on the other hand, powerful forces of attraction and repulsion may be set up between them. When the generator floats on the line, the stator current I is zero and so no forces are developed. The only flux is that created by the rotor, and it induces the voltage E_o (Fig. 16.28a).

If a mechanical torque is applied to the generator (by admitting more steam to the turbine), the rotor accelerates and gradually advances by a mechanical angle α, compared to its original position (Fig. 16.28b). Stator currents immediately begin to flow, owing to the electrical phase angle δ between induced voltage E_o and terminal voltage E. The

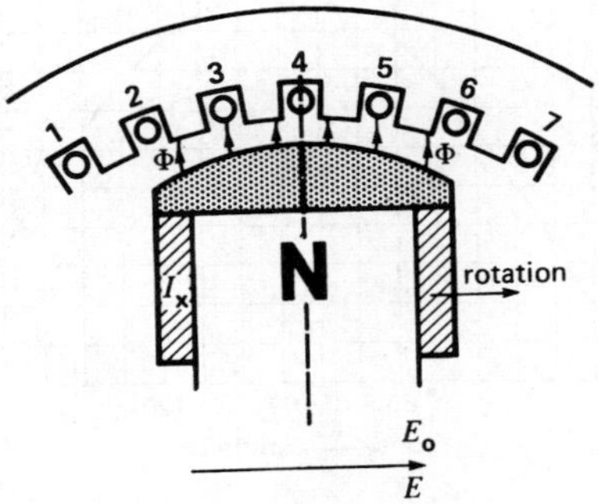

Figure 16.28a
The N poles of the rotor are lined up with the S poles of the stator.

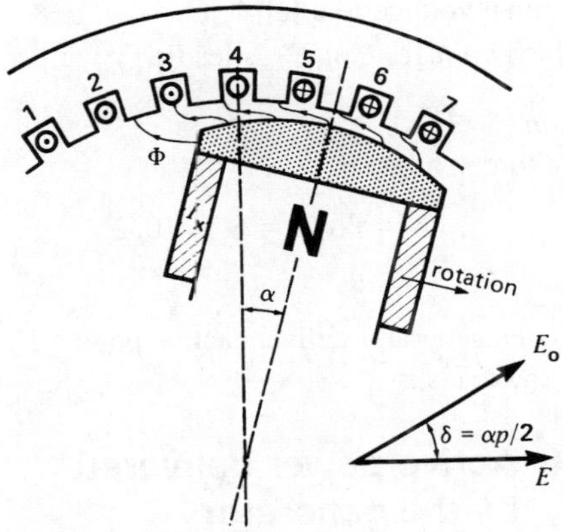

Figure 16.28b
The N poles of the rotor are ahead of the S poles of the stator.

stator currents create a revolving field and a corresponding set of N and S poles. Forces of attraction and repulsion are developed between the stator poles and rotor poles, and these magnetic forces produce a torque that opposes the mechanical torque exerted by the turbine. When the electromagnetic torque is equal to the mechanical torque, the mechanical angle will no longer increase but will remain at a constant value α.

There is a direct relationship between the mechanical angle α and the torque angle δ, given by

$$\delta = p\alpha/2 \tag{16.4}$$

where

δ = torque angle between the terminal voltage E and the excitation voltage E_o [electrical degrees]
p = number of poles on the generator
α = mechanical angle between the centers of the stator and rotor poles [mechanical degrees]

Example 16-6

The rotor poles of an 8-pole synchronous generator shift by 10 mechanical degrees from no-load to full-load.

a. Calculate the torque angle between E_o and the terminal voltage E at full-load.
b. Which voltage, E or E_o, is leading?

Solution

a. The torque angle is:

$$\delta = p\alpha/2 = 8 \times 10/2 = 40°$$

b. When a generator delivers active power, E_o *always* leads E.

16.20 Active power delivered by the generator

We can prove (see Section 16.23) that the active power delivered by a synchronous generator is given by the equation

$$P = \frac{E_oE}{X_s} \sin \delta \tag{16.5}$$

where

P = active power, per phase [W]
E_o = induced voltage, per phase [V]
E = terminal voltage, per phase [V]
X_s = synchronous reactance per phase [Ω]
δ = torque angle between E_o and E [°]

This equation can be used under all load conditions, including the case when the generator is connected to an infinite bus.

To understand its meaning, suppose a generator is connected to an infinite bus having a voltage E. Furthermore, suppose that the dc excitation of the generator is kept constant so that E_o is constant. The term E_oE/X_s is then fixed, and the active power which the alternator delivers to the bus will vary directly with sin Δ, the sine of the torque angle. Thus, as we admit more steam, δ will increase and so, too, will the active power output. The relationship between the two is shown graphically in Fig. 16.29. Note that between zero and 30° the power increases almost linearly with the torque angle. Rated power is typically attained at an angle of 30°.

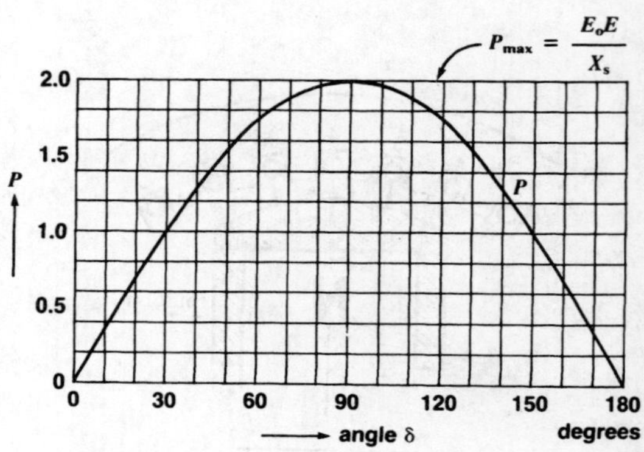

Figure 16.29
Graph showing the relationship between the active power delivered by a synchronous generator and the torque angle.

However, there is an upper limit to the active power the generator can deliver. This limit is reached when δ is 90°. The peak power output is then $P_{max} = E_oE/X_s$. If we try to exceed this limit (such as by admitting more steam to the turbine), the rotor will accelerate and lose synchronism with the infinite bus. The rotor will turn faster than the rotating field of the stator, and large, pulsating currents will flow in the stator. In practice, this condition is never reached because the circuit breakers trip as soon as synchronism is lost. We then have to resynchronize the generator before it can again deliver power to the grid.

Example 16-7

A 36 MVA, 21 kV, 1800 r/min, 3-phase generator connected to a power grid has a synchronous reactance of 9 Ω per phase. If the exciting voltage is 12 kV (line-to-neutral), and the system voltage is 17.3 kV (line-to-line), calculate the following:

a. The active power which the machine delivers when the torque angle δ is 30° (electrical)
b. The peak power that the generator can deliver before it falls out of step (loses synchronism)

Solution

a. We have

$$E_o = 12 \text{ kV}$$
$$E = 17.3 \text{ kV}/\sqrt{3} = 10 \text{ kV}$$
$$\delta = 30°$$

The active power delivered to the power grid is

$$P = (E_oE/X_s) \sin \delta$$
$$= (12 \times 10/9) \times 0.5$$
$$= 6.67 \text{ MW}$$

The total power delivered by all three phases is

$$(3 \times 6.67) = 20 \text{ MW}$$

b. The maximum power, per phase, is attained when δ = 90°.

$$P = (E_oE/X_s) \sin 90$$
$$= (12 \times 10/9) \times 1$$
$$= 13.3 \text{ MW}$$

The peak power output of the alternator is, therefore,

$$(3 \times 13.3) = 40 \text{ MW}$$

16.21 Control of active power

When a synchronous generator is connected to a system, its speed is kept constant by an extremely sensitive governor. This device can detect speed changes as small as 0.01%. An automatic control system sensitive to such small speed changes immediately modifies the valve (or gate) opening of the turbine so as to maintain a constant speed and constant power output.

On a big utility network, the power delivered by each generator depends upon a program established in advance between the various generating stations. The station operators communicate with each other to modify the power delivered by each station so that the generation and transmission of energy is done as efficiently as possible. In more elaborate systems the entire network is under the control of a computer.

In addition, individual overspeed detectors are always ready to respond to a large speed change, particularly if a generator, for one reason or another, should suddenly become disconnected from the system. Because the steam valves are still wide open, the generator will rapidly accelerate and may attain a speed 50 percent above normal in 4 to 5 seconds. The centrifugal forces at synchronous speed are already close to the limit the materials can withstand, so any excess speed can quickly create a very dangerous situation. Consequently, steam valves must immediately be closed off during such emergencies. At the same time, the pressure build-up in the steam boilers must be relieved and the fuel burners must be shut off.

16.22 Transient reactance

A synchronous generator connected to a system is subject to unpredictable load changes that sometimes occur very quickly. In such cases the simple

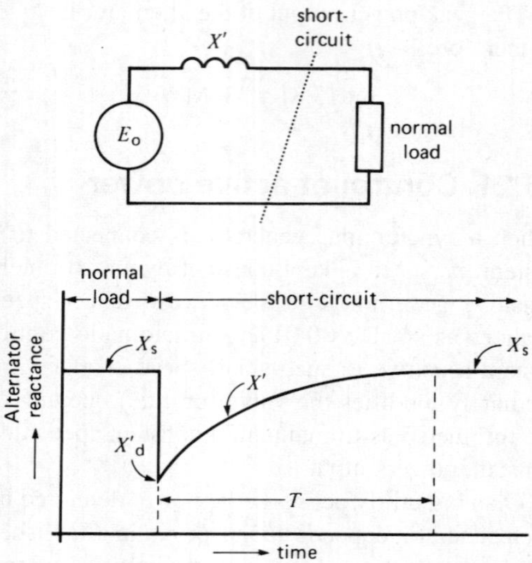

Figure 16.30
Variation of generator reactance following a short-circuit.

equivalent circuit shown in Fig. 16.17 does not reflect the behavior of the machine. This circuit is only valid under steady-state conditions or when the load changes gradually.

For *sudden* load current changes, the synchronous reactance X_s must be replaced by another reactance X' whose value varies as a function of time. Fig. 16.30 shows how X' varies when a generator is suddenly short-circuited. Prior to the short-circuit, the synchronous reactance is simply X_s. However, at the instant of short-circuit, the reactance immediately falls to a much lower value X'_d. It then increases gradually until it is again equal to X_s after a time interval T. The duration of the interval depends upon the size of the generator. For machines below 100 kVA it only lasts a fraction of a second, but for machines in the 1000 MVA range it may last as long as 10 seconds.

The reactance X'_d is called the *transient reactance* of the alternator. It may be as low as 15 percent of the synchronous reactance. Consequently, the initial short-circuit current is much higher than that corresponding to the synchronous reactance X_s.

This has a direct bearing on the capacity of the circuit breakers at the generator output. In effect, because they must interrupt a short-circuit in three to six *cycles,* it follows that they have to interrupt a very high current.

On the other hand, the low transient reactance simplifies the voltage regulation problem when the load on the generator increases rapidly. First the internal voltage drop due to X'_d is smaller than it would be if the synchronous reactance X_s were acting. Second, X' stays at a value far below X_s for a sufficiently long time to quickly raise the exciting current I_x. Raising the excitation increases E_o, which helps to stabilize the terminal voltage.

Example 16-8

A 250 MVA, 25 kV, 3-phase, steam-turbine generator has a synchronous reactance of 1.6 pu and a transient reactance X'_d of 0.23 pu. It delivers its rated output at a power factor of 100%. A short-circuit suddenly occurs on the line, close to the generating station.

Calculate

a. The induced voltage E_o prior to the short-circuit
b. The initial value of the short-circuit current
c. The final value of the short-circuit current if the circuit breakers should fail to open

Solution

a. The base impedance of the generator is

$$Z_B = E_B{}^2/S_B$$
$$= 25\,000^2/(250 \times 10^6)$$
$$= 2.5\ \Omega$$

The synchronous reactance is

$$X_s = X_s(\text{pu})\ Z_B$$
$$= 1.6 \times 2.5$$
$$= 4\ \Omega$$

The rated line-to-neutral voltage per phase is

$$E = 25/\sqrt{3} = 14.4\ \text{kV}$$

The rated load current per phase is

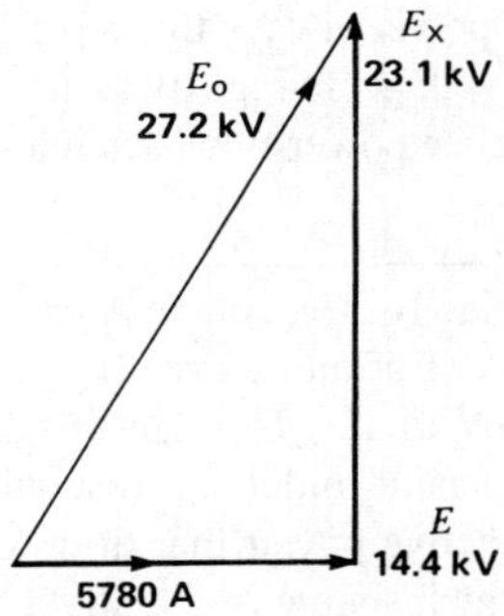

Figure 16.31
Example 16-8.

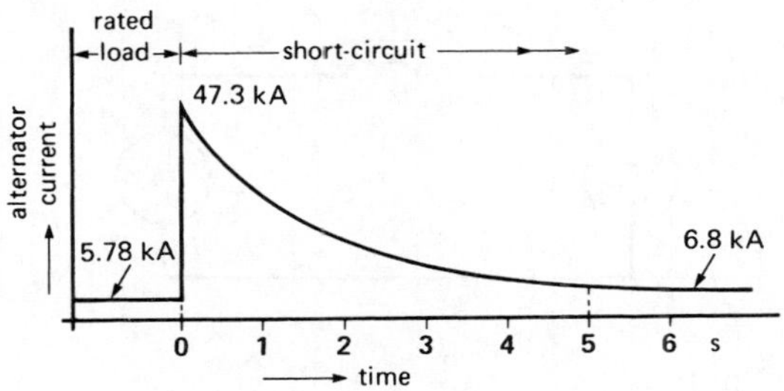

Figure 16.32
Change in current when a short-circuit occurs across the terminals of a generator. See Example 16-8.

$$I = S/\sqrt{3}\,E$$
$$= 250 \times 10^6/(1.73 \times 25\,000)$$
$$= 5774 \text{ A}$$

The internal voltage drop E_x is

$$E_x = IX_s = 5774 \times 4$$
$$= 23.1 \text{ kV}$$

The current is in phase with E because the power factor of the load is unity. Thus, referring to the phasor diagram (Fig. 16.31), E_o is

$$E_o = \sqrt{E^2 + E_X^2}$$
$$= \sqrt{14.4^2 + 23.1^2}$$
$$= 27.2 \text{ kV}$$

b. The transient reactance is

$$X'_d = X'_d(\text{pu})\, Z_B$$
$$= 0.23 \times 2.5$$
$$= 0.575\ \Omega$$

The initial short-circuit current is

$$I_{sc} = E_o/X'_d$$
$$= 27.2/0.575$$
$$= 47.3 \text{ kA}$$

which is 8.2 times rated current.

c. If the short-circuit is sustained and the excitation is unchanged, the current will eventually level off at a steady-state value:

$$I = E_o/X_s = 27.2/4$$
$$= 6.8 \text{ kA}$$

which is only 1.2 times rated current.

Fig. 16.32 shows the generator current prior to, and during the short-circuit. We assume a time interval T of 5 seconds. Note that in practice the circuit breakers would certainly trip within 0.1 s after the short-circuit occurs. Consequently, they have to interrupt a current of about 47 kA.

16.23 Power transfer between two sources

The circuit of Fig. 16.33a is particularly important because it is encountered in the study of generators, synchronous motors, and transmission lines. In such circuits we are often interested in the active power transmitted from a source A to a source B or vice versa. The magnitude of voltages E_1 and E_2, as well as the phase angle between them, are quite arbitrary. Applying Kirchhoff's voltage law to this circuit, we obtain the equation

$$E_1 = E_2 + jIX$$

If we assume that I lags behind E_2 by an arbitrary angle θ and E_1 leads E_2 by an angle δ, we obtain the phasor diagram shown (Fig. 16.33b). Phasor IX leads I by 90°. The active power absorbed by B is

$$P = E_2 I \cos\theta \qquad (16.6)$$

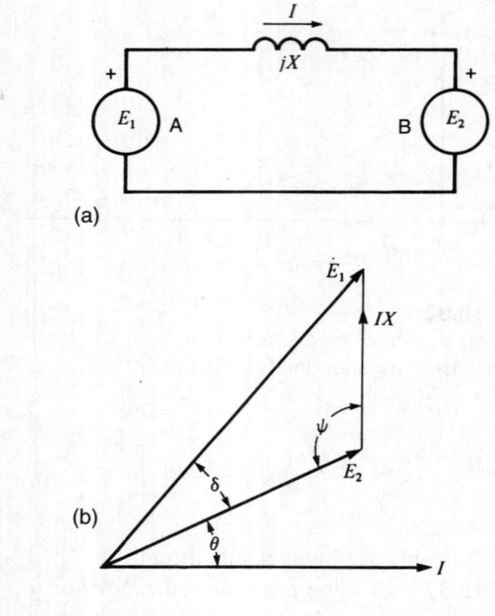

Figure 16.33
Power flow between two voltage sources.

From the sine law for triangles, we have

$$IX/\sin\delta = E_1/\sin\psi$$
$$= E_1/\sin(90+\theta)$$
$$= E_1/\cos\theta$$

Consequently, $I\cos\theta = E_1 \sin\delta/X$ (16.7)
Substituting (16.7) in Eq. 16.6, we find

$$P = \frac{E_1E_2}{X}\sin\delta \tag{16.8}$$

where

P = active power transmitted [W]
E_1 = voltage of source 1 [V]
E_2 = voltage of source 2 [V]
X = reactance connecting the sources [Ω]
δ = phase angle between E_1 and E_2 [°]

The active power P received by B is equal to that delivered by A, because the reactance consumes no active power. The magnitude of P is determined by the phase angle between E_1 and E_2; the angle θ between E_2 and I does not have to be specified.

The active power always flows from the leading to the lagging voltage. In Fig. 16.33, it is obvious that E_1 leads E_2; hence power flows from left to right.

Example 16-9

Referring to Fig. 16.33a, source A generates a voltage $E_1 = 20\text{ kV}\angle 5°$ and source B generates a voltage $E_2 = 15\text{ kV}\angle 42°$. The transmission line connecting them has an inductive reactance of 14 Ω. Calculate the active power that flows over the line and specify which source is actually a load.

Solution

The phase angle between the two sources is 42° − 5° = 37°. The voltage of source B leads that of source A because its phase angle is more positive. Consequently, power flows from B to A and so A is actually a load. The active power is given by

$$P = \frac{E_1E_2}{X}\sin\delta \tag{16.8}$$

$$= \frac{20\text{ kV}\times 15\text{ kV}}{14}\sin 37°$$

$$= \frac{20\,000\times 15\,000}{14}\,0.602 = 12.9\times 10^6$$

$$= 12.9\text{ MW}$$

Note that, strange as it may seem, power flows from the source having the lower voltage (15 kV) to the one having the higher voltage (20 kV).

16.24 Efficiency, power, and size of electrical machines

The physical size of an electrical machine has a profound effect upon its efficiency, power output, relative cost, and temperature rise. The following analysis reveals why these characteristics are intimately related.

Let us consider a small ac generator having the following characteristics:

power output	1 kW
rated voltage	120 V, 3-phase
rated current	4.8 A
rated speed	1800 r/min

efficiency	73%
input torque	7.27 N·m
moment of inertia	0.0075 kg·m^2
external diameter	0.180 m
external length	0.15 m
mass	20 kg
power output/mass	50 W/kg

Using this information, we can calculate the losses of the machine:

$$\eta = \frac{P_o}{P_i} \times 100 \quad (3.6)$$

$$73 = \frac{1 \text{ kW}}{P_i} \times 100$$

input power $P_i = 1.37$ kW

$$\text{losses} = 1.37 \text{ kW} - 1.0 \text{ kW} = 0.37 \text{ kW}$$

The losses comprise the I^2R losses in the windings, the hysteresis and eddy-current losses in the iron and the windage and friction losses.

Let us increase the size of the machine in such a way that its linear dimensions are raised in exactly the same proportion, while keeping the same materials throughout. Thus, if a particular type of iron lamination was used in the stator, the same type is used in the larger machine. The same type of insulation is also used, thereby duplicating and magnifying everything, including the bearings, nuts, and bolts.

In this larger generator we will keep the same current densities (A/m^2) as in the original machine. We will also maintain the same flux densities (teslas) in the various parts of the magnetic circuit (core, air gap, stator teeth, etc.).

As a result, the I^2R losses per cm^3 and the iron losses per cm^3 will be the same everywhere as in the original machine. It follows that the copper losses and iron losses will increase in proportion to its volume. Let's assume that the windage and friction losses also increase the same way.

We further assume that the number of slots, conductors, and interconnections remain the same as before and that the speed of rotation (1800 r/min) is left unchanged.

Under these conditions, we can predict the properties of the generator as its size is increased.

For example, suppose that all the linear dimensions are *tripled.* The volume will therefore increase by a factor of $3^3 = 27$. Consequently, the mass will increase by a factor of 27 and so, too, will the losses. The mass of the bigger machine will therefore be 27×20 kg = 540 kg. The losses will rise to 27×0.37 kW = 10 kW.

The slots are 3 times wider and 3 times deeper. As a result, the cross section of the conductors is 9 times greater which means they can carry 9 times more current. The larger machine can therefore deliver a current of 9×4.8 A = 43.2 A.

As regards the generated voltage per conductor, it is determined by Eq. 2.25, $E = Blv$. We recall that B is the flux density, l is the length of the conductor, and v is the speed at which the flux cuts across it.

The flux density in the larger machine is the same as before. However, the length l has tripled. Furthermore, the peripheral speed v has increased 3 times because the diameter of the rotor has tripled. As a result, the voltage generated per conductor also increases by a factor of 9. Because the larger generator has the same number of conductors as before and because they are connected the same way, the generator will produce a voltage of 9×120 V = 1080 V.

Thus, by tripling the linear dimensions, the voltage and current both increase by a factor of 9. This means that the power output increases $9 \times 9 = 81$ times. The power output of the new generator is therefore 81×1 kW = 81 kW.

The power input needed to drive the ac generator is P_i = 81 kW + losses = 81 kW + 10 kW = 91 kW. The new efficiency is therefore

$$\eta = \frac{P_o}{P_i} \times 100 \quad (3.6)$$

$$= \frac{81 \text{ kW}}{91 \text{ kW}} \times 100$$

$$= 0.89 = 89\%$$

The efficiency has increased from 73% to 89% which is a dramatic improvement. The reason is that the power output has increased 81 times, while the losses increased only 27 times. Consequently, the efficiency of the machine was *bound* to increase with size.

The original machine produced an output of 50 W/kg. The larger machine has a mass of 540 kg and produces 81 kW. Consequently, it produces 81 kW/540 kg = 150 W/kg which is 3 times greater than before.

The larger generator is therefore relatively lighter and cheaper than the smaller machine. As proof, if eighty-one 1 kW generators were used to produce 81 kW, their combined mass would be 81·20 kg = 1620 kg. This generating center would obviously be more costly and take up more floor space than the single 81 kW generator.

As another matter of interest, we recall that the moment of inertia J of a rotor is proportional to its mass and the square of its radius (see Table 3A). Hence, when linear dimensions are tripled, J will increase by a factor of $J = mr^2 = 27 \cdot 3^2 = 3^5 = 243$. The moment of inertia of the larger machine is therefore $243 \cdot 0.0075 \text{ kg·m}^2 = 1.8 \text{ kg·m}^2$.

The characteristics of the larger generator are summarized below. They are in striking contrast to the original 1 kW machine.

power output	81 kW
rated voltage	1080 V, 3-phase
rated current	43.2 A
rated speed	1800 r/min
efficiency	89%
input torque	483 N·m
moment of inertia	1.8 kg·m^2
external diameter	0.54 m
external length	0.45 m
mass	540 kg
power output/mass	150 W/kg

The one big problem is temperature rise. When linear dimensions are tripled, the heat-dissipating surface area of the machine increases 9 times but the losses increase 27 times. Hence, the power dissipated per square meter increases by a factor of 3. Consequently, unless better cooling means are used, the larger machine is *bound* to be hotter. To prevent damage to the insulating materials, the temperature rise has to be limited to a maximum of about 200°C. Consequently, the cooling of large machines is a very important matter.

In conclusion, the general principles covered here regarding physical size, power output, efficiency, temperature rise, and so forth, apply to all machines, including ac and dc motors and transformers.

Questions and Problems

Practical level

16-1 What are the advantages of using a stationary armature in large synchronous generators? Why is the stator always connected in wye?

16-2 State the main differences between steam-turbine generators and salient-pole generators. For a given power output, which of these machines is the larger?

16-3 In analyzing a hydropower site, it is found that the turbines should turn at close to 350 r/min. If the directly coupled generators must generate a frequency of 60 Hz, calculate the following:

a. The number of poles on the rotor
b. The exact turbine speed

16-4 An isolated 3-phase generator produces a no-load line voltage of 13.2 kV. If a load having a lagging power factor of 0.8 is connected to the machine, must the excitation be increased or decreased in order to maintain the same line voltage?

16-5 What conditions must be met before a generator can be connected to a 3-phase system?

16-6 Calculate the number of poles on the generator in Fig. 16.12 using the information given.

16-7 Calculate the number of poles on the aircraft generator shown in Fig. 16.11.

16-8 A 3-phase generator turning at 1200 r/min generates a no-load voltage of 9 kV, 60 Hz. How will the terminal voltage be affected if the following loads are connected to its terminals?

a. Resistive load
b. Inductive load
c. Capacitive load

16-9 In Problem 16-8, if the field current is kept constant, calculate the no-load voltage and frequency if the speed is

a. 1000 r/min
b. 5 r/min

Intermediate level

16-10 What is meant by the synchronous reactance of a 3-phase generator? Draw the equivalent circuit of a generator and explain the meaning of all the parameters.

16-11 State the advantages of brushless excitation systems over conventional systems. Using a schematic circuit diagram, show how the rotor in Fig. 16.7 is excited.

16-12 Referring to Fig. 16.13, calculate the exciting current needed to generate a no-load *line* voltage of
a. 24.2 kV
b. 12.1 kV

16-13 A 3-phase generator possesses a synchronous reactance of 6 Ω and the excitation voltage E_o is 3 kV per phase (ref. Fig. 16.19). Calculate the line-to-neutral voltage E for a resistive load of 8 Ω and draw the phasor diagram.

16-14 **a.** In Problem 16-13, draw the curve of E versus I for the following resistive loads: infinity, 24, 12, 6, 3, 0 ohms.
b. Calculate the active power P per phase in each case.
c. Draw the curve of E versus P. For what value of load resistance is the power output a maximum?

16-15 Referring to Fig. 16.2, calculate the length of one pole-pitch measured along the internal circumference of the stator.

16-16 The 3-phase generator shown in Fig. 16.16 has the following characteristics:

$$E_o = 2440 \text{ V}$$
$$X_s = 144 \ \Omega$$
$$R = 17 \ \Omega$$

load impedance $Z = 175 \ \Omega$ (resistive)

Calculate

a. The synchronous impedance Z_s per phase
b. The total resistance of the circuit, per phase
c. The total reactance of the circuit, per phase
d. The line current
e. The line-to-neutral voltage across the load
f. The line voltage across the load
g. The power of the turbine driving the alternator
h. The phase angle between E_o and the voltage across the load

16-17 A 3-phase generator rated 3000 KVA, 20 kV, 900 r/min, 60 Hz delivers power to a 2400 KVA, 16 kV load having a lagging power factor of 0.8. If the synchronous reactance is 100 Ω, calculate the value of E_o, per phase.

16-18 The generator in Fig. 16.2 has a synchronous reactance of 0.4 Ω, per phase. It is connected to an infinite bus having a line voltage of 14 kV, and the excitation voltage is adjusted to 1.14 pu.

Calculate

a. The torque angle δ when the generator delivers 420 MW
b. The mechanical displacement angle α
c. The linear pole shift (measured along the inside stator circumference) corresponding to this displacement angle [in]

16-19 A test taken on the 500 MVA alternator of Fig. 16.2 yields the following results:

1. Open-circuit line voltage is 15 kV for a dc exciting current of 1400 A.
2. Using the same dc current, with the armature short-circuited the resulting ac line current is 21 000 A.

Calculate

a. The base impedance of the generator, per phase
b. The value of the synchronous reactance

c. The per-unit value of X_s
d. The short-circuit ratio

Advanced level

16-20 The synchronous generator in Fig. 16.2 has an efficiency of 98.4% when it delivers an output of 500 MW. Knowing that the dc exciting current is 2400 A at a dc voltage of 300 V, calculate the following:
a. The total losses in the machine
b. The copper losses in the rotor
c. The torque developed by the turbine
d. The average difference in temperature between the cool incoming air and warm outgoing air, if the air flow is 280 m^3/s

16-21 Referring to Fig. 16.4, each coil on the rotor has 21.5 turns, and carries a dc current of 500 A. Knowing that the air gap length is 1.3 inches, calculate the flux density in the air gap at no-load. Neglect the mmf required for the iron portion of the magnetic circuit. (See Section 2.17).

16-22 Referring to Fig. 16.17, the following information is given about a generator:

$$E_o = 12 \text{ kV}$$
$$E = 14 \text{ kV}$$
$$X_s = 2\ \Omega$$

E_o leads E by 30°

a. Calculate the total active power output of the generator.
b. Draw the phasor diagram for one phase.
c. Calculate the power factor of the load.

16-23 The steam-turbine generator shown in Fig. 16.3 has a synchronous reactance of 1.3 pu. The excitation voltage E_o is adjusted to 1.2 pu and the machine is connected to an infinite bus of 19 kV. If the torque angle δ is 20°, calculate the following:
a. The active power output
b. The line current
c. Draw the phasor diagram, for one phase

16-24 In Problem 16-23, calculate the active power output of the generator if the steam valves are closed. Does the alternator receive or deliver reactive power and how much?

16-25 The generator in Problem 16-20 is driven by a hydraulic turbine whose moment of inertia is 54×10^6 lb·ft^2. The rotor has a J of 4.14×10^6 kg·m^2.
a. If the line circuit breakers suddenly trip, calculate the speed of the generating unit (turbine and alternator) 1 second later, assuming that the wicket gates remain wide open.
b. By how many mechanical degrees do the poles advance (with respect to their normal position) during the 1-second interval? By how many electrical degrees?

16-26 A 400 Hz alternator has a 2-hour rating of 75 kVA, 1200 r/min, 3-phase, 450 V, 80 percent power factor (Fig. 16.34a). The stator possesses 180 slots and has an internal diameter of 22 inches and an axial length of 9.5 in. The rotor is designated for a field current of 31 A at 115 V.

Calculate

a. The number of poles on the rotor
b. The number of coils on the stator
c. The number of coils per phase group on the stator
d. The length of one pole-pitch, measured along the circumference of the stator
e. The resistance of the dc winding on the rotor and the power needed to excite it

Industrial application

16-27 A 33.8 kVA, 480 V, 3-phase, 60 Hz, diesel-driven emergency alternator is designed to operate at a power factor of 80 percent. The following additional information is given:

Efficiency: 83.4%

Weight: 730 lb

Wk^2 (moment of inertia): 15.7 lb·ft^2

Insulation: class B

Calculate

a. The minimum horsepower rating of the diesel engine to drive the generator
b. The maximum allowable temperature of the windings, using the resistance method

16-28 A 220 MVA, 500 r/min, 13.8 kV, 50 Hz, 0.9 power factor, water-turbine synchronous generator, manufactured by Siemens, has the following properties:

Insulation class: F

Moment of inertia: 525 t·m^2

Total mass of stator: 158 t

(t = metric ton)

Total mass of rotor: 270 t

Efficiency at full-load, unity power factor: 98.95%

Unsaturated synchronous reactance: 1.27 pu

Transient reactance: 0.37 pu

Runaway speed in generator mode: 890 r/min

Static excitation is used and the excitation current is 2980 A under an excitation voltage of 258 V.

Figure 16.34a
Rotor (left) and stator (right) of a 75 kVA, 1200 r/min, 3-phase, 450 V, 400 Hz alternator for shipboard use. The alternator is driven by a 100 hp, 1200 r/min synchronous motor.

Figure 16.34b
Rotor (left) and stator (right) of the 100 hp, 1200 r/min, 60 Hz synchronous motor. The stator is mounted on a bedplate that also serves as a base for the alternator. The rotor is equipped with a squirrel-cage winding to permit starting as an induction motor.
(Courtesy of Electro-Mécanik)

The generator is also designed to operate as a motor, driving the turbine as a pump. Under these conditions, the motor develops an output of 145 MW.

Both the stator and rotor are water-cooled by passing the water through the hollow current-carrying conductors. The water is treated so that its conductivity is less than 5 μS/cm. The pure water flows through the stator at a rate of 8.9 liters per second and through the rotor at 5.9 liters per second. Given the above information, make the following calculations:

a. The rated active power output, in MW at unity power factor and at 0.9 lagging power factor

b. The rated reactive power output, in Mvar

c. The short-circuit ratio

d. The value of the line-to-neutral synchronous reactance, per phase

e. The total losses of the generator at full-load and unity power factor

16-29 In industry application Problem 16-28, calculate the following:

a. The horsepower rating of the generator when it runs as a pump motor

b. The kinetic energy of the rotor when it runs at rated speed

c. The kinetic energy of the rotor when it reaches its maximum allowable runaway speed

d. The time to reach the runaway speed in the event that a short-circuit occurs when the generator is delivering its rated load, and assuming that the water continues to flow unchecked through the turbine (gates wide open)

16-30 In Problem 16-28, calculate the power dissipated in the rotor windings and the power loss per pole. Knowing the rate of water flow and that the inlet temperature is 26°C, calculate the temperature of the water flowing out of the rotor windings. What is the minimum resistivity (Ω·m) of the circulating water?

Chapter 17
Synchronous Motors

17.0 Introduction

The synchronous generators described in the previous chapter can operate either as generators or as motors. When operating as motors (by connecting them to a 3-phase source), they are called *synchronous motors*. As the name implies, synchronous motors run in synchronism with the revolving field. The speed of rotation is therefore tied to the frequency of the source. Because the frequency is fixed, the motor speed stays constant, irrespective of the load or voltage of the 3-phase line. However, synchronous motors are used not so much because they run at constant speed but because they possess other unique electrical properties. We will study these features in this chapter.

Most synchronous motors are rated between 150 kW (200 hp) and 15 MW (20 000 hp) and turn at speeds ranging from 150 to 1800 r/min. Consequently, these machines are mainly used in heavy

Figure 17.1
Three-phase, unity power factor synchronous motor rated 3000 hp (2200 kW), 327 r/min, 4000 V, 60 Hz driving a compressor used in a pumping station on the Trans-Canada pipeline. Brushless excitation is provided by a 21 kW, 250 V alternator/rectifier, which is mounted on the shaft between the bearing pedestal and the main rotor. *(Courtesy of General Electric)*

industry (Fig. 17.1). At the other end of the power spectrum, we find tiny single-phase synchronous motors used in control devices and electric clocks. They are discussed in Chapter 18.

17.1 Construction

Synchronous motors are identical in construction to salient-pole ac generators. The *stator* is composed of a slotted magnetic core, which carries a 3-phase lap winding. Consequently, the winding is also identical to that of a 3-phase induction motor.

The *rotor* has a set of salient poles that are excited by a dc current (Fig. 17.2). The exciting coils are connected in series to two slip-rings, and the dc current is fed into the winding from an external exciter. Slots are also punched out along the circumference of the salient poles. They carry a squirrel-cage winding similar to that in a 3-phase induction motor. This *damper winding* serves to start the motor.

Modern synchronous motors often employ brushless excitation, similar to that used in synchronous generators. Referring to Fig. 17.3, a relatively small 3-phase generator, called an *exciter,* and a 3-phase rectifier are mounted at one end of the motor shaft. The dc current I_x from the rectifier is fed directly into the salient-pole windings, without going through brushes and slip-rings. The current can be varied by controlling the small exciting current I_c that flows in the stationary field winding of the exciter. Fig. 17.4

Figure 17.2
Rotor of a 50 Hz to 16 2/3 Hz frequency converter used to power an electric railway. The 4-pole rotor at the left is associated with a single-phase alternator rated 7000 kVA, 16 2/3 Hz, PF 85%. The rotor on the right is for a 6900 kVA, 50 Hz, 3-phase, 90% PF synchronous motor which drives the single-phase alternator. Both rotors are equipped with squirrel-cage windings. Today, these machines are replaced by solid-state frequency converters. (See Section 29.6.) *(Courtesy of ABB)*

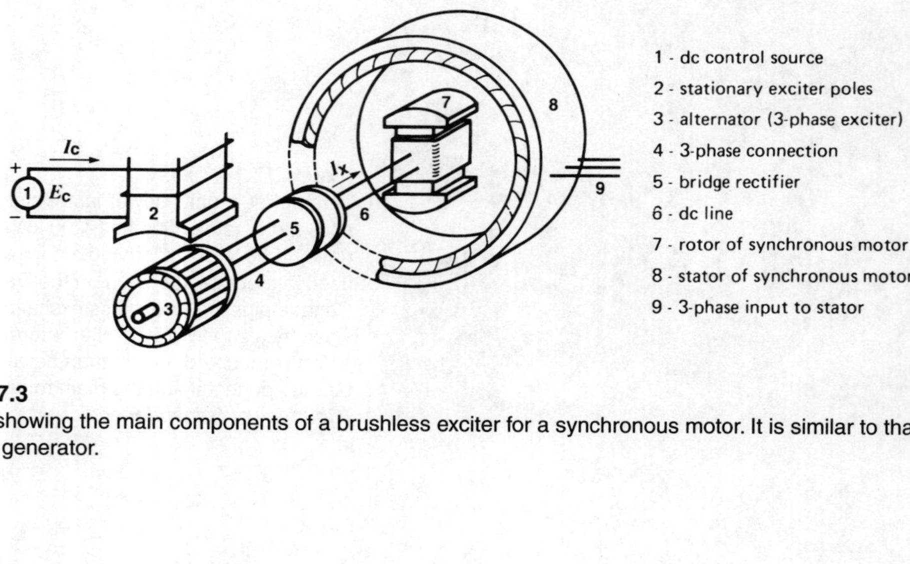

Figure 17.3
Diagram showing the main components of a brushless exciter for a synchronous motor. It is similar to that of a synchronous generator.

shows how the exciter, rectifier, and salient poles are mounted in a 3000 kW synchronous motor.

The rotor and stator always have the same number of poles. As in the case of an induction motor, the number of poles determines the synchronous speed of the motor:

$$n_s = 120\frac{f}{p} \tag{17.1}$$

where

n_s = motor speed [r/min]
f = frequency of the source [Hz]
p = number of poles

Example 17-1

Calculate the number of salient poles on the rotor of the synchronous motor shown in Fig. 17.4a.

Solution

The motor operates at 60 Hz and runs at 200 r/min; consequently,

$$n_s = 120 f/p$$
$$200 = (120 \times 60)/p$$
$$p = 36 \text{ poles}$$

The rotor possesses 18 north poles and 18 south poles.

Figure 17.4a
Synchronous motor rated 4000 hp (3000 kW), 200 r/min, 6.9 kV, 60 Hz, 80% power factor designed to drive an ore crusher. The brushless exciter (alternator/rectifier) is mounted on the overhung shaft and is rated 50 kW, 250 V. *(Courtesy of General Electric)*

Figure 17.4b
Close-up of the 50 kW exciter, showing the armature winding and 5 of the 6 diodes used to rectify the ac current. *(Courtesy of General Electric)*

17.2 Starting a synchronous motor

A synchronous motor cannot start by itself; consequently, the rotor is usually equipped with a squirrel-cage winding so that it can start up as an induction motor. When the stator is connected to the 3-phase line, the motor accelerates until it reaches a speed slightly below synchronous speed. The dc excitation is suppressed during this starting period.

While the rotor accelerates, the rotating flux created by the stator sweeps across the slower moving salient poles. Because the coils on the rotor possess a relatively large number of turns, a high voltage is induced in the rotor winding when it turns at low speeds. This voltage appears between the slip-rings and it decreases as the rotor accelerates, eventually becoming negligible when the rotor approaches synchronous speed. To limit the voltage, and to improve the starting torque, we either short-circuit the slip-rings or connect them to an auxiliary resistor during the starting period.

If the power capacity of the supply line is limited, we sometimes have to apply reduced voltage to the stator. As in the case of induction motors, we use either autotransformers or series reactors to limit the starting current (see Chapter 20). Very large synchronous motors (20 MW and more) are sometimes brought up to speed by an auxiliary motor, called a *pony motor.* Finally, in some big installations the motor may be brought up to speed by a variable-frequency electronic source.

17.3 Pull-in torque

As soon as the motor is running at close to synchronous speed, the rotor is excited with dc current. This produces alternate N and S poles around the circumference of the rotor (Fig. 17.5). If the poles at this moment happen to be facing poles of *opposite* polarity on the stator, a strong magnetic attraction is set up between them. The mutual attraction locks the rotor and stator poles together, and the rotor is literally yanked into step with the revolving field. The torque developed at this moment is appropriately called the *pull-in torque.*

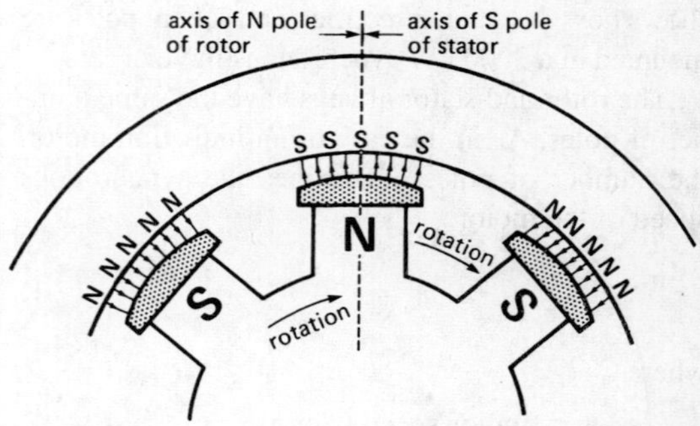

Figure 17.5
The poles of the rotor are attracted to the opposite poles on the stator. At no-load the axes of the poles coincide.

The pull-in torque of a synchronous motor is powerful, but the dc current must be applied at the right moment. For example, if it should happen that the emerging N, S poles of the rotor are opposite the N, S poles of the stator, the resulting magnetic repulsion produces a violent mechanical shock. The motor will immediately slow down and the circuit breakers will trip. In practice, starters for synchronous motors are designed to detect the precise moment when excitation should be applied. The motor then pulls automatically and smoothly into step with the revolving field.

Once the motor turns at synchronous speed, no voltage is induced in the squirrel-cage winding and so it carries no current. Consequently, the behavior of a synchronous motor is entirely different from that of an induction motor. Basically, a synchronous motor rotates because of the magnetic attraction between the poles of the rotor and the opposite poles of the stator.

To reverse the direction of rotation, we simply interchange any two lines connected to the stator.

17.4 Motor under load—general description

When a synchronous motor runs at no-load, the rotor poles are directly opposite the stator poles and their axes coincide (Fig. 17.5). However, if we apply a mechanical load, the rotor poles fall

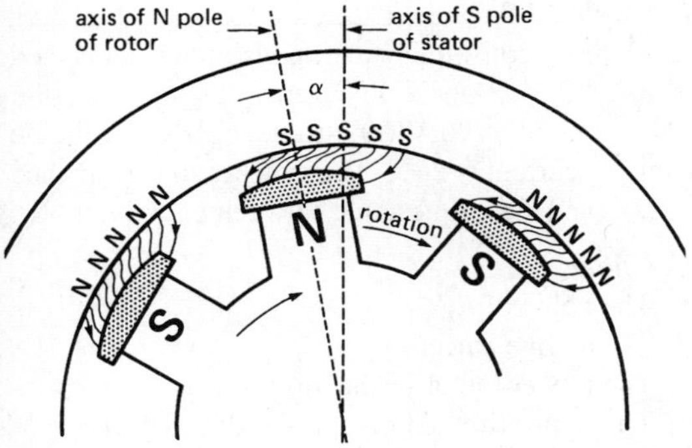

Figure 17.6
The rotor poles are displaced with respect to the axes of the stator poles when the motor delivers mechanical power.

slightly behind the stator poles, but the rotor continues to turn at synchronous speed. The mechanical angle α between the poles increases progressively as we increase the load (Fig. 17.6). Nevertheless, the magnetic attraction keeps the rotor locked to the revolving field, and the motor develops an ever more powerful torque as the angle increases.

But there is a limit. If the mechanical load exceeds the *pull-out torque* of the motor, the rotor poles suddenly pull away from the stator poles and the motor comes to a halt. A motor that pulls out of step creates a major disturbance on the line, and the circuit breakers immediately trip. This protects the motor because both the squirrel-cage and stator windings overheat rapidly when the machine ceases to run at synchronous speed.

The pull-out torque depends upon the magnetomotive force developed by the rotor and the stator poles. The mmf of the rotor poles depends upon the dc excitation I_x, while that of the stator depends upon the ac current flowing in the windings. The pull-out torque is usually 1.5 to 2.5 times the nominal full-load torque.

The mechanical angle α between the rotor and stator poles has a direct bearing on the stator current. As the angle increases, the current increases. This is to be expected because a larger angle corresponds to a bigger mechanical load, and the increased power can only come from the 3-phase ac source.

17.5 Motor under load—simple calculations

We can get a better understanding of the operation of a synchronous motor by referring to the equivalent circuit shown in Fig. 17.7a. It represents one phase of a wye-connected motor. It is identical to the equivalent circuit of an ac generator, because both machines are built the same way. Thus, the flux Φ created by the rotor induces a voltage E_o in the stator. This flux depends on the dc exciting current I_x. Consequently, E_o varies with the excitation.

As already mentioned, the rotor and stator poles are lined up at no-load. Under these conditions, induced voltage E_o is in phase with the line-to-neutral voltage E (Fig. 17.7b). If, in addition, we adjust the excitation so that $E_o = E$, the motor "floats" on the line and the line current I is practically zero. In effect, the only current needed is to supply the small windage and friction losses in the motor, and so it is negligible.

What happens if we apply a mechanical load to the shaft? The motor will begin to slow down, causing the rotor poles to fall behind the stator poles by an angle α. Due to this mechanical shift, E_o reaches its maximum value a little later than before. Thus, referring to Fig. 17.7c, E_o is now δ electrical degrees behind E. The mechanical displacement α produces an *electrical* phase shift δ between E_o and E.

The phase shift produces a difference of potential E_x across the synchronous reactance X_s given by

$$E_x = E - E_o$$

Consequently, a current I must flow in the circuit, given by

$$jIX_s = E_x$$

from which

$$I = -jE_x/X_s$$
$$= -j(E - E_o)/X_s$$

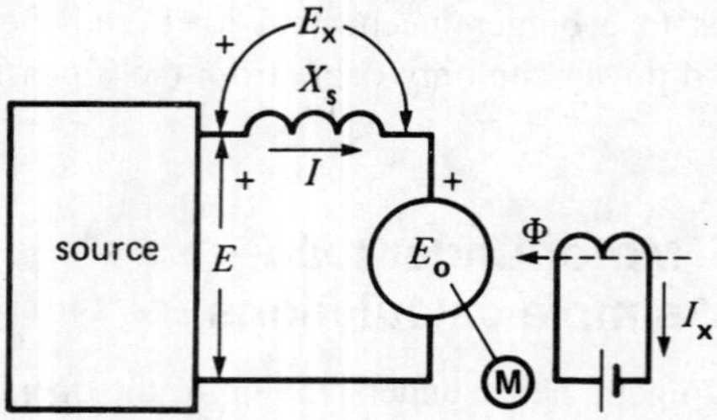

Figure 17.7a
Equivalent circuit of a synchronous motor, showing one phase.

Figure 17.7b
Motor at no-load, with E_o adjusted to equal E.

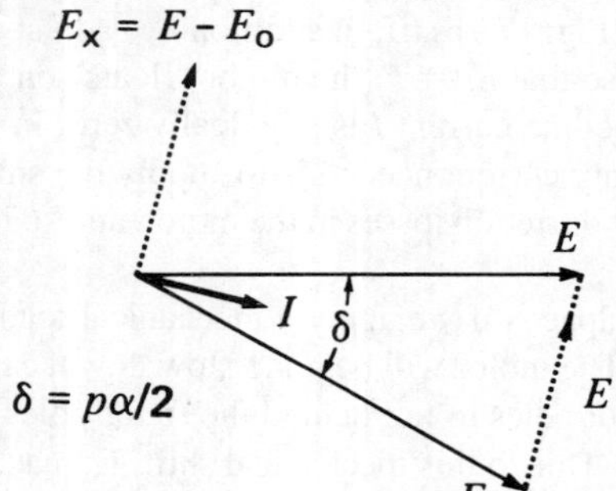

Figure 17.7c
Motor under load E_o has the same value as in Fig. 17.7b, but it lags behind E.

The current lags 90° behind E_x because X_s is inductive. The phasor diagram under load is shown in Fig. 17.7c. Because I is nearly in phase with E, the motor absorbs active power. This power is entirely transformed into mechanical power, except for the relatively small copper and iron losses in the stator.

In practice, the excitation voltage E_o is adjusted to be greater or less than the supply voltage E. Its value depends upon the power output of the motor and the desired power factor.

Example 17-2a

A 500 hp, 720 r/min synchronous motor connected to a 3980 V, 3-phase line generates an excitation voltage E_o of 1790 V (line-to-neutral) when the dc exciting current is 25 A. The synchronous reactance is 22 Ω and the torque angle between E_o and E is 30°.

Calculate

a. The value of E_x
b. The ac line current
c. The power factor of the motor
d. The approximate horsepower developed by the motor
e. The approximate torque developed at the shaft

Solution

This problem can best be solved by using vector notation.

a. The voltage E (line-to-neutral) applied to the motor has a value

$$E = E_L/\sqrt{3} = 3980/\sqrt{3}$$
$$= 2300 \text{ V}$$

Let us select E as the reference phasor, whose angle with respect to the horizontal axis is assumed to be zero. Thus,

$$E = 2300 \angle 0°$$

It follows that E_o is given by the phasor

$$E_o = 1790 \angle -30°$$

The equivalent circuit per phase is given in Fig. 17.8a.
Moving clockwise around the circuit and applying Kirchhoff's voltage law we can write

$$-E + E_x + E_o = 0$$
$$E_x = E - E_o$$
$$= 2300\angle 0° - 1790\angle -30°$$
$$= 2300\,(\cos 0° + j \sin 0°) - 1790\,(\cos -30° + j \sin -30°)$$
$$= 2300 - 1550 + j\,895$$
$$= 750 + j\,895$$
$$= 1168\angle 50°$$

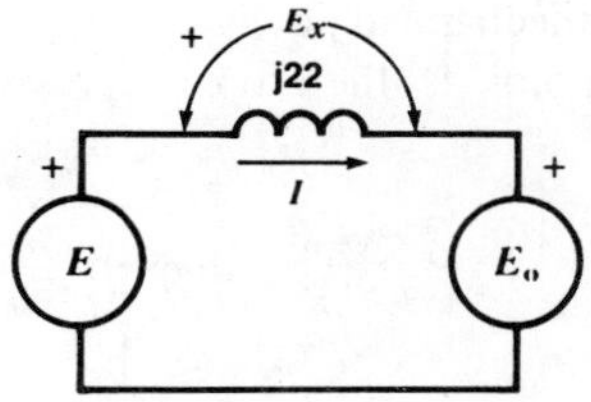

Figure 17.8a
Equivalent circuit of a synchronous motor connected to a source *E*.

Thus, phasor E_x has a value of 1168 V and it leads phasor *E* by 50°.

b. The line current *I* is given by

$$j\,22\,I = E_x$$

$$I = \frac{1168 \angle 50°}{22 \angle 90°}$$

$$= 53 \angle -40°$$

Thus, phasor *I* has a value of 53 A and it lags 40° behind phasor *E*.

c. The power factor of the motor is given by the cosine of the angle between the line-to-neutral voltage *E* across the motor terminals and the current *I*. Hence,

$$\text{power factor} = \cos\theta = \cos 40°$$

$$= 0.766, \text{ or } 76.6\%$$

The power factor is lagging because the current lags behind the voltage.
The complete phasor diagram is shown in Fig. 17.8b.

d. Total active power input to the stator

$$P_i = 3 \times E_{LN} I_L \cos\theta$$

$$= 3 \times 2300 \times 53 \times \cos 40°$$

$$= 280\,142 \text{ W} = 280.1 \text{ kW}$$

Neglecting the I^2R losses and iron losses in the stator, the electrical power transmitted across the airgap to the rotor is 280.1 kW.
Approximate horsepower developed

$$P = 280.1 \times 10^3/746 = 375 \text{ hp}$$

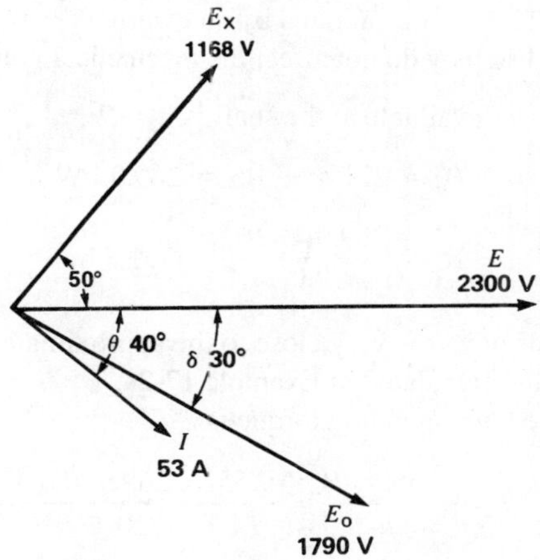

Figure 17.8b
See Example 17-2.

e. Approximate torque

$$T = \frac{9.55 \times P}{n} = \frac{9.55 \times 280.1 \times 10^3}{720}$$

$$= 3715 \text{ N·m}$$

Example 17-2b

The motor in Example 17-2a has a stator resistance of 0.64 Ω per phase and possesses the following losses:

I_2R losses in the rotor:	3.2 kW
Stator core loss:	3.3 kW
Windage and friction loss:	1.5 kW

Calculate

a. The actual horsepower developed
b. The actual torque developed at the shaft
c. The efficiency of the motor

Solution

a. Power input to the stator is 280.1 kW

Stator I^2R losses $= 3 \times 53^2 \times 0.64\ \Omega = 5.4$ kW
Total stator losses $= 5.4 + 3.3 = 8.7$ kW
Power transmitted to the rotor $= 280.1 - 8.7$ $= 271.4$ kW

The power at the shaft is the power to the rotor minus the windage and friction losses. The rotor

I^2R losses are supplied by an external dc source and so they do not affect the mechanical power.

Power available at the shaft is

$$P_o = 271.4 - 1.5 = 269.9 \text{ kW}$$

$$= \frac{269.9 \times 10^3}{746} = 361.8 \text{ hp}$$

This power is very close to the approximate value calculated in Example 17-2a.

b. The corresponding torque is

$$T = \frac{9.55 \times P}{n} = \frac{9.55 \times 269.9 \times 10^3}{720}$$

$$= 3580 \text{ N·m}$$

c. Total losses = 5.4 + 3.3 + 3.2 + 1.5 = 13.4 kW

Total power input = 280.1 + 3.2 = 283.3 kW
Total power output = 269.9 kW
Efficiency = 269.9/283.3 = 0.9527 = 95.3%

Note that the stator resistance of 0.64 Ω is very small compared to the reactance of 22 Ω. Consequently, the true phasor diagram is very close to the phasor diagram of Fig. 17.8b.

17.6 Power and torque

When a synchronous motor operates under load, it draws active power from the line. The power is given by the same equation we previously used for the synchronous generator in Chapter 16:

$$P = (E_o E/X_s) \sin \delta \quad (16.5)$$

As in the case of a generator, the active power absorbed by the motor depends upon the supply voltage E, the excitation voltage E_o, and the phase angle δ between them. If we neglect the relatively small I^2R and iron losses in the stator, all the power is transmitted across the air gap to the rotor. This is analogous to the power P_r transmitted across the air gap of an induction motor (Section 13.13). However, in a synchronous motor, the rotor I^2R losses are entirely supplied by the dc source. Consequently, all the power transmitted across the air gap is available in the form of mechanical power. The mechanical power developed by a synchronous motor is therefore expressed by the equation

$$P = \frac{E_o E}{X_s} \sin \delta \quad (17.2)$$

where

P = mechanical power of the motor, per phase [W]
E_o = line-to-neutral voltage induced by I_x [V]
E = line-to-neutral voltage of the source [V]
X_s = synchronous reactance per phase [Ω]
δ = torque angle between E_o and E [electrical degrees]

This equation shows that the mechanical power increases with the torque angle, and its maximum value is reached when δ is 90°. The poles of the rotor are then midway between the N and S poles of the stator. The peak power P_{max} (per phase) is given by

$$P_{max} = \frac{E_o E}{X_s} \quad (17.3)$$

As far as torque is concerned, it is directly proportional to the mechanical power because the rotor speed is fixed. The torque is derived from Eq. 3.5:

$$T = \frac{9.55\,P}{n_s} \quad (17.4)$$

where

T = torque, per phase [N·m]
P = mechanical power, per phase [W]
n_s = synchronous speed [r/min]
9.55 = a constant [exact value = $60/2\pi$]

The maximum torque the motor can develop is called the pull-out torque, mentioned previously. It occurs when δ = 90° (Fig. 17.9).*

* The remarks in this section apply to motors having smooth rotors. Most synchronous motors have salient poles; in this case the pull-out torque occurs at an angle of about 70°.

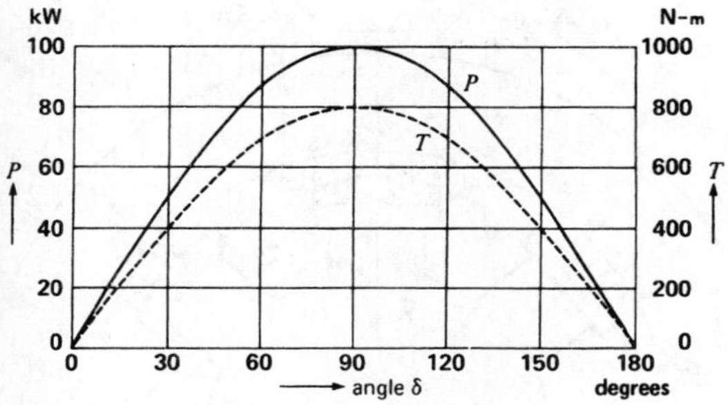

Figure 17.9
Power and torque per phase as a function of the torque angle δ. Synchronous motor rated 150 kW (200 hp), 1200 r/min, 3-phase, 60 Hz. See Example 17-3.

Example 17-3

A 150 kW, 1200 r/min, 460 V, 3-phase synchronous motor has a synchronous reactance of 0.8 Ω, per phase. If the excitation voltage E_o is fixed at 300 V, per phase, determine the following:

a. The power versus δ curve
b. The torque versus δ curve
c. The pull-out torque of the motor

Solution

a. The line-to-neutral voltage is

$$E = E_L/\sqrt{3} = 460/\sqrt{3} = 266 \text{ V}$$

The mechanical power per phase is

$$P = (E_oE/X_s) \sin \delta \quad (17.2)$$
$$= (266 \times 300/0.8) \sin \delta$$
$$= 99\,750 \sin \delta \text{ [W]}$$
$$= 100 \sin \delta \text{ [kW]}$$

By selecting different values for δ, we can calculate the corresponding values of *P* and *T*, per phase.

δ [°]	*P* [kW]	*T* [N•m]
0	0	0
30	50	400
60	86.6	693
90	100	800
120	86.6	693
150	50	400
180	0	0

These values are plotted in Fig. 17.9.

b. The torque curve can be found by applying Eq. 17.4:

$$T = 9.55\, P/n_s = 9.55\, P/1200 = P/125$$

c. The pull-out torque T_{max} coincides with the maximum power output:

$$T_{max} = 800 \text{ N·m}$$

The actual pull-out torque is 3 times as great (2400 N·m) because this is a 3-phase machine. Similarly, the power and torque values given in Fig. 17.9 must also be multiplied by 3. Consequently, this 150 kW motor can develop a maximum output of 300 kW, or about 400 hp.

17.7 Mechanical and electrical angles

As in the case of synchronous generators, there is a precise relationship between the mechanical angle α, the torque angle δ and the number of poles *p*. It is given by

$$\delta = p\alpha/2 \quad (17.5)$$

Example 17-4

A 3-phase, 6000 kW, 4 kV, 180 r/min, 60 Hz motor has a synchronous reactance of 1.2 Ω. At full-load the rotor poles are displaced by a *mechanical* angle of 1° from their no-load position. If the line-to-neutral excitation E_o = 2.4 kV, calculate the mechanical power developed.

Solution

The number of poles is

$$p = 120\, f/n_s = 120 \times 60/180 = 40$$

The electrical torque angle is

$$\delta = p\alpha/2 = (40 \times 1)/2 = 20°$$

Assuming a wye connection, the voltage E applied to the motor is

$$E = E_L/\sqrt{3} = 4\text{ kV}/\sqrt{3}$$
$$= 2.3\text{ kV}$$
$$= 2309\text{ V}$$

and the excitation voltage is

$$E_o = 2400\text{ V}$$

The mechanical power developed per phase is

$$P = (E_oE/X_s)\sin\delta \qquad (17.2)$$
$$= (2400 \times 2309/1.2)\sin 20°$$
$$= 1\,573\,300$$
$$= 1573\text{ kW}$$

$$\text{Total power} = 3 \times 1573$$
$$= 4719\text{ kW } (\sim 6300\text{ hp})$$

17.8 Reluctance torque

If we gradually reduce the excitation of a synchronous motor when it is running at no-load, we find that the motor continues to run at synchronous speed even when the exciting current is zero. The reason is that the flux produced by the stator prefers to cross the short gap between the salient poles and the stator rather than the much longer air gap between the poles. In other words, because the reluctance of the magnetic circuit is less in the axis of the salient poles, the flux is concentrated as shown in Fig. 17.10a. On account of this phenomenon, the motor develops a *reluctance torque.*

If a mechanical load is applied to the shaft, the rotor poles will fall behind the stator poles, and the stator flux will have the shape shown in Fig. 17.10b. Thus, a considerable reluctance torque can be developed without any dc excitation at all.

The reluctance torque becomes zero when the rotor poles are midway between the stator poles. The reason is that the N and S poles on the stator attract

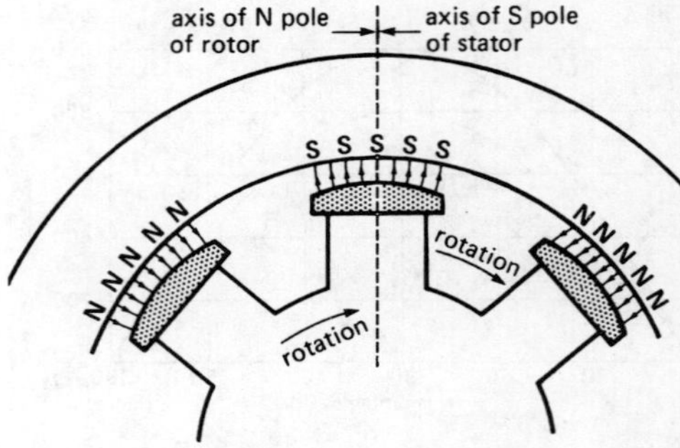

Figure 17.10a
The flux produced by the stator flows across the air gap through the salient poles.

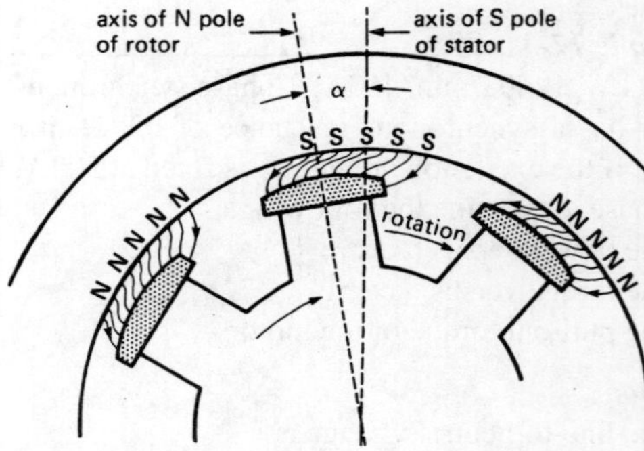

Figure 17.10b
The salient poles are attracted to the stator poles, thus producing a reluctance torque.

the salient poles in opposite directions (Fig. 17.10c). Consequently, the reluctance torque is zero precisely at that angle where the regular torque T attains its maximum value, namely at $\delta = 90°$.

Fig. 17.11 shows the reluctance torque as a function of the angle δ. The torque reaches a maximum positive value at $\delta = 45°$. For larger angles it attains a maximum *negative* value at $\delta = 135°$. Obviously, to run as a reluctance-torque motor, the angle must lie between zero and 45°. Although a positive torque is still developed between 45° and 90°, this is an unstable region of operation. The reason is that as the angle increases the power decreases.

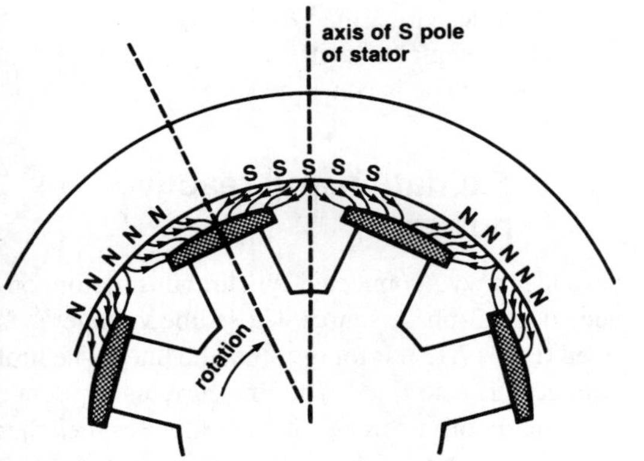

Figure 17.10c
The reluctance torque is zero when the salient poles are midway between the stator poles.

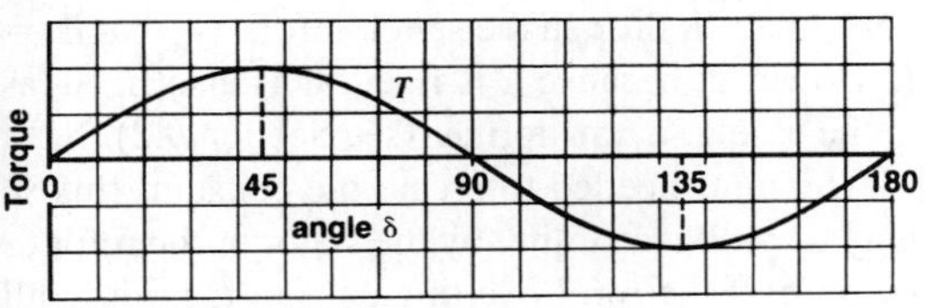

Figure 17.11
Reluctance torque versus the torque angle.

As in the case of a conventional synchronous motor, the mechanical power curve has exactly the same shape as the torque curve. Thus, in the absence of dc excitation, the mechanical power reaches a peak at $\delta = 45°$.

Does the saliency of the poles modify the power and torque curves shown in Fig. 17.9? The answer is yes. In effect, the curves shown in Fig. 17.9 are those of a smooth-rotor synchronous motor. The torque of a salient-pole motor is equal to the sum of the smooth-rotor component and the reluctance-torque component of Fig. 17.11. Thus, the true torque curve of a synchronous motor has the shape (3) given in Fig. 17.12.

The peak reluctance torque is about 25 percent of the peak *smooth-rotor torque.* As a result, the peak torque of a salient-pole motor is about 8 percent greater than that of a smooth-rotor motor, as

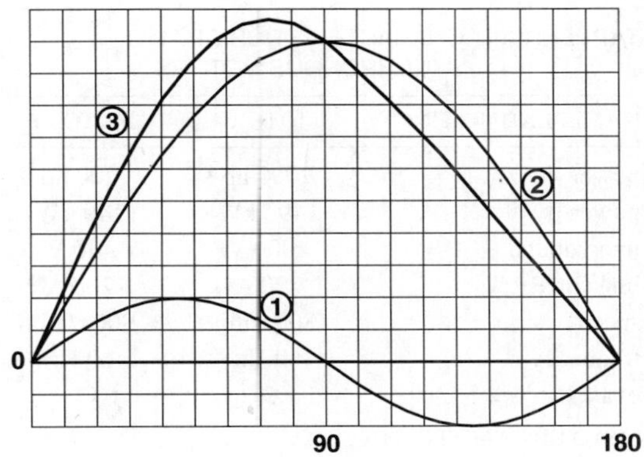

Figure 17.12
In a synchronous motor the reluctance torque (1) plus the smooth-rotor torque (2) produce the resultant torque (3). Torque (2) is due to the dc excitation of the rotor.

can be seen in Fig. 17.12. However, the difference is not very great, and for this reason we shall continue to use Eqs. 17.2 and 17.5 to describe synchronous motor behavior.

17.9 Losses and efficiency of a synchronous motor

In order to give the reader a sense of the order of magnitude of the pull-out torque, resistance, reactance, and losses of a synchronous motor, we have drawn up Table 17A. It shows the characteristics of a 2000 hp and a 200 hp synchronous motor, respectively labeled Motor A and Motor B.

The following points should be noted:

1. The torque angle at full-load ranges between 27° and 37°. It corresponds to the electrical angle δ mentioned previously.
2. The power needed to excite the 2000 hp motor (4.2 kW) is only about twice that needed for the 200 hp motor (2.1 kW). In general, the larger the synchronous motor, the smaller the per-unit power needed to excite it.
3. The total losses of Motor A (38 kW) are only four times those of Motor B (9.5 kW) despite

TABLE 17A CHARACTERISTICS OF TWO SYNCHRONOUS MOTORS

NAMEPLATE RATING	MOTOR A	MOTOR B
power [hp]	2000 hp	200 hp
power [kW]	1492 kW	149 kW
line voltage	4000 V	440 V
line current	220 A	208 A
speed	1800 r/min	900 r/min
frequency	60 Hz	60 Hz
phases	3	3
LOAD CHARACTERISTICS		
power factor	1.0	1.0
pull-out torque (pu)	1.4	2.2
torque angle at full-load	36.7°	27°
connection	wye	wye
dc exciter power	4.2 kW	2.1 kW
dc exciter voltage	125 V	125 V
air gap	10 mm	6 mm
LOSSES		
windage and friction	8.5 kW	1 kW
stator core loss	11 kW	2 kW
stray losses	4 kW	1 kW
stator I^2R	10.3 kW	3.5 kW
rotor I^2R	4.2 kW	2 kW
total losses	38 kW	9.5 kW
efficiency	97.5%	94.0%
IMPEDANCES AND VOLTAGES (line-to-neutral values)		
stator X_s	7.77 Ω	0.62 Ω
stator resistance R_s	0.0638 Ω	0.0262 Ω
ratio X_s/R_s	122	23
phase voltage E	2309 V	254 V
phase voltage E_o	2873 V	285 V

the fact that Motor A is ten times as powerful. This is another property of large motors: the more horsepower they develop, the smaller the relative losses are. As a result, the efficiencies improve with increase in power. Compare the efficiencies of the two motors: 97.5% versus 94.0%.

4. The synchronous reactance X_s per phase is much larger than the resistance of the stator winding. Note that for the 2000 hp motor X_s is 122 times larger than R_s. As a result, we can always neglect the effect of R_s as far as motor performance is concerned.

17.10 Excitation and reactive power

Consider a wye-connected synchronous motor connected to a 3-phase source whose line voltage E_L is fixed (Fig. 17.13). It follows that the line-to-neutral voltage E is also fixed. The line currents I produce a magnetomotive force U_a in the stator. On the other hand, the rotor produces a dc magnetomotive force U_r. The total flux Φ is therefore created by the combined action of U_a and U_r.

Pursuing our reasoning, flux Φ induces a line-to-neutral voltage E_a in the stator. If we neglect the very small IR drop in the stator, it follows that $E_a = E$. However, because E is fixed, Φ is also fixed, as in the case of a transformer (see Section 9.2).

The mmf needed to create the constant flux Φ may be produced either by the stator or the rotor or by both. If the rotor exciting current I_x is zero, all

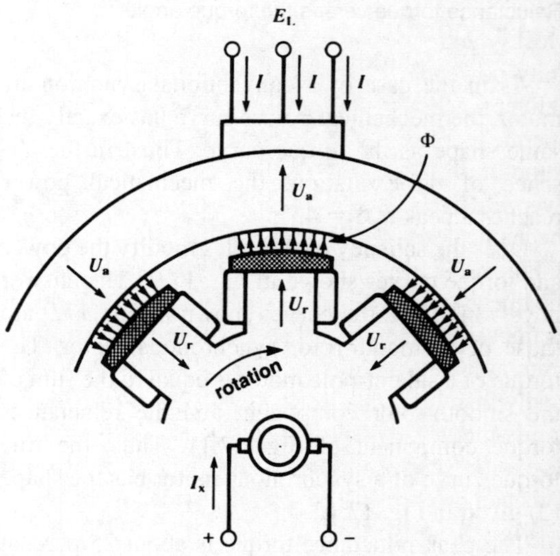

Figure 17.13
The total flux Φ is due to the mmf produced by the rotor (U_r) plus the mmf produced by the stator (U_a). For a given E_L, the flux Φ is essentially fixed.

the flux has to be produced by the stator. The stator must then absorb considerable reactive power from the 3-phase line (see Section 7.9). But if we excite the rotor with a dc current I_x, the rotor mmf helps produce part of the flux Φ. Consequently, less reactive power is drawn from the ac line. If we gradually raise the excitation, the rotor will eventually produce all the required flux by itself. The stator then draws no more reactive power, with the result that the power factor of the motor becomes unity (1.0).

What happens if we excite the motor above this critical level? The stator, instead of absorbing reactive power, actually *delivers* reactive power to the 3-phase line. The motor then behaves like a source of reactive power, just as if it were a capacitor. Thus, by varying the dc excitation we can cause the motor to either absorb or deliver reactive power. Because of this important property, synchronous motors are sometimes used to correct the power factor of a plant at the same time as they furnish mechanical power to the load they are driving.

17.11 Power factor rating

Most synchronous motors are designed to operate at unity power factor. However, if they also have to deliver reactive power, they are usually designed to operate at a full-load power factor of 0.8 (leading). A motor designed for a power factor of 0.8 can deliver reactive power equal to 75 percent of its rated mechanical load. Thus, the 3000 kW motor shown in Fig. 17.4 can supply $75\% \times 3000 = 2250$ kvar to the line at the same time as it develops its rated mechanical output of 3000 kW. Motors designed to operate at leading power factors are bigger and more costly than unity power factor motors are. The reason is that for a given horsepower rating, both the dc exciting current and the stator current are higher. This can be explained as follows.

Fig. 17.14 is the schematic diagram of a unity power factor motor operating at full-load. The line-to-neutral voltage is E_{ab} and the line current is I_p. The active power absorbed per phase is, therefore,

$$P = E_{ab}I_p \tag{17.6}$$

The active power absorbed is equal to the mechanical power of the motor.

Figure 17.14
Unity power factor synchronous motor and phasor diagram at full-load.

Fig. 17.15 shows an 80% power factor motor also operating at full-load. It develops the same mechanical power as the motor in Fig. 17.14. The line current I_s leads E_{ab} by arcos 0.8 = 36.87°. This current can be broken up into two components I_p and I_q, and it is clear that

$$I_p = 0.8\, I_s \tag{17.7}$$

$$I_q = 0.6\, I_s \tag{17.8}$$

The active power P is given by

$$P = E_{ab}I_p = 0.8\, E_{ab}I_s \tag{17.9}$$

The reactive power delivered by the motor is

$$Q = E_{ab}I_q = 0.6\, E_{ab}I_s \tag{17.10}$$

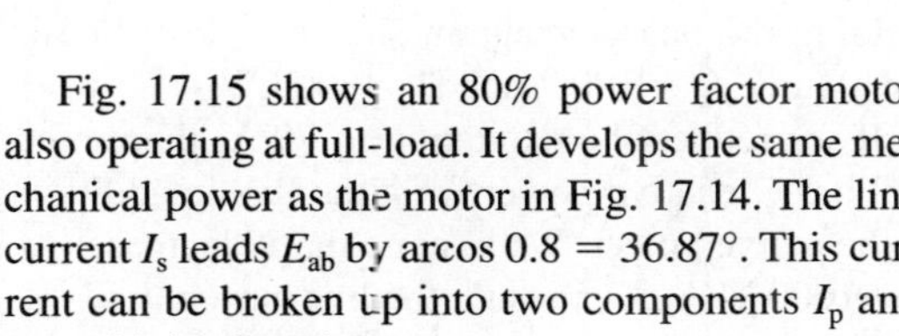

Figure 17.15
80 percent power factor synchronous motor and phasor diagram at full-load.

It follows from Eqs. 17.9 and 17.10 that

$$\begin{aligned} Q &= 0.75\, P \\ &= 75\% \text{ of rated mechanical output} \end{aligned}$$

as was stated previously.

If we compare I_p with I_s, we find that $I_s = 1.25\, I_p$. Thus, for the same mechanical power output, a motor designed for a leading power factor of 80% has to carry a line current that is 25% greater than one that operates at unity power factor.

17.12 V-curves

Suppose a synchronous motor is operating at its rated mechanical load. We wish to examine its behavior as the excitation is varied. Because a change in excitation does not affect the speed, the mechanical power remains fixed. Let us begin by adjusting the excitation I_x so that the power factor is unity, thus yielding the phasor diagram shown in Fig. 17.16. We assume $I_x = 100$ A and $P = 800$ kW.

If we reduce the excitation to 70 A, the motor will draw reactive power from the line in addition to the active power. We assume that S increases to $S = 1000$ kVA. As a result, the line current will in-

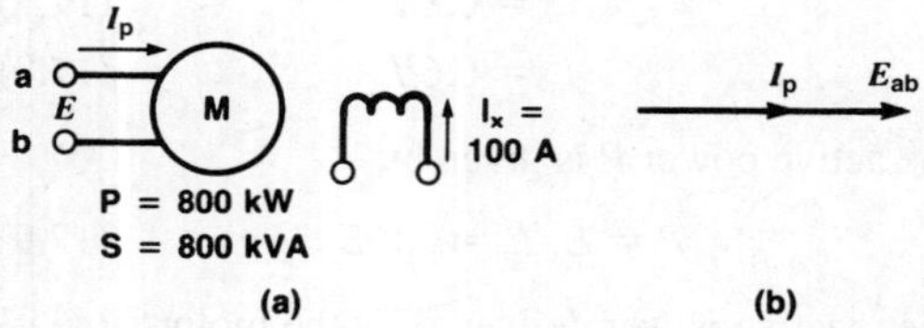

Figure 17.16
a. Synchronous motor operating at unity power factor with a mechanical load of 800 kW. Field excitation is 100 A.
b. Phasor diagram shows current in phase with the voltage.

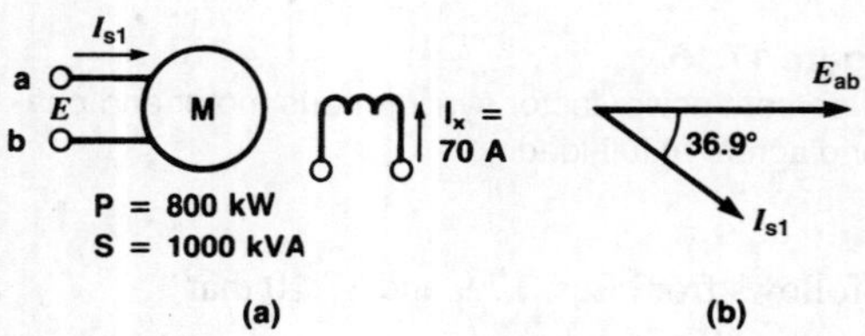

Figure 17.17
a. Field excitation reduced to 70 A but with same mechanical load. Motor absorbs reactive power from the line.
b. Phasor diagram shows current lagging behind the voltage.

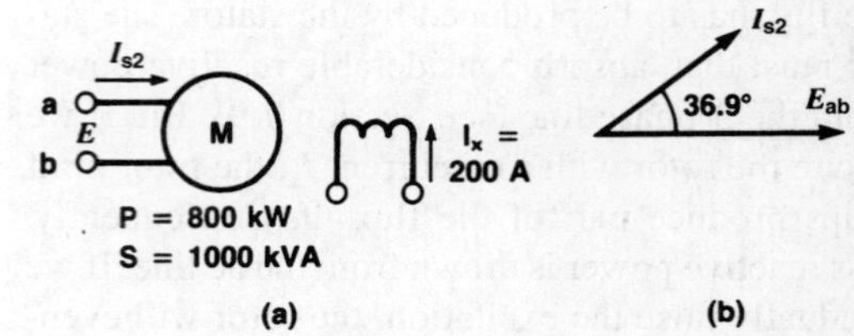

Figure 17.18
a. Field excitation raised to 200 A but with same mechanical load. Motor delivers reactive power to the line.
b. Phasor diagram shows current leading the voltage.

crease from I_p to I_{s1} (Fig. 17.17). Note that the component of I_{s1} in phase with E_{ab} is the same as before because the motor is still developing the same mechanical power.

Current I_{s1} lags behind E_{ab}, and so the power factor of the motor is lagging. The field current I_x in the rotor is smaller than before, but the apparent power S absorbed by the stator is greater.

If we increase the excitation to $I_x = 200$ A, the motor *delivers* reactive power to the line to which it is connected (Fig. 17.18). The apparent power is again greater than in the unity power factor case. We assume $S = 1000$ kVA. The line current becomes I_{s2} and it leads E_{ab}. However, the in-phase component of I_{s2} is still equal to I_p because the mechanical power is the same.

By varying the excitation this way, we can plot the apparent power of the synchronous motor as a function of the dc exciting current. This yields a V-shaped curve (Fig. 17.19). The V-curve is always displayed for a fixed mechanical load. In our case, the V-curve corresponds to full-load. The no-load V-curve is also shown, to illustrate the large reactive power that can be absorbed or delivered by simply changing the excitation.

Example 17-5

A 4000 hp (3000 kW), 6600 V, 60 Hz, 200 r/min synchronous motor operates at full-load at a leading power factor of 0.8. If the synchronous reactance is 11 Ω, calculate the following:

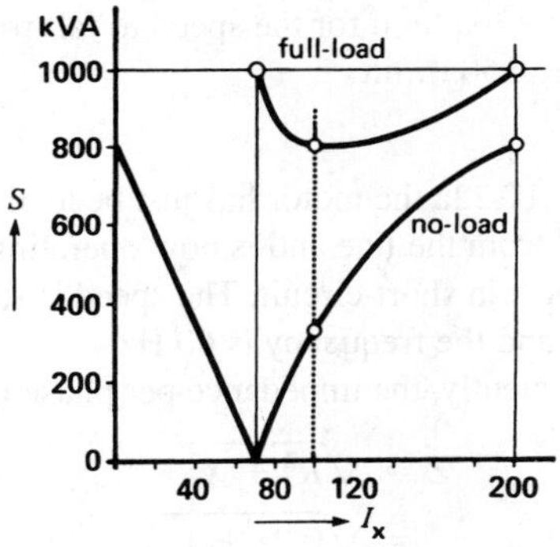

Figure 17.19
No-load and full-load V-curves of a 1000 hp synchronous motor.

a. The apparent power of the motor, per phase
b. The ac line current
c. The value and phase of E_o
d. Draw the phasor diagram
e. Determine the torque angle δ

Solution
We shall immediately change the given values to correspond to one phase of a wye-connected motor.

a. The active power per phase is

$$P = 3000/3 = 1000 \text{ kW}$$

The apparent power per phase is

$$S = P/\cos\theta = 1000/0.8 \quad (8.11)$$
$$= 1250 \text{ kVA}$$

b. The line-to-neutral voltage is

$$E = E_L/\sqrt{3} = 6600/\sqrt{3} = 3811 \text{ V}$$

The line current is

$$I = S/E = 1250 \times 1000/3811$$
$$= 328 \text{ A}$$

I leads E by an angle of arcos 0.8 = 36.9°.

c. To determine the value and phase of the excitation voltage E_o, we draw the equivalent circuit of one phase (Fig. 17.20). This will enable us to write the circuit equations. Furthermore, we select E as the reference phasor and so

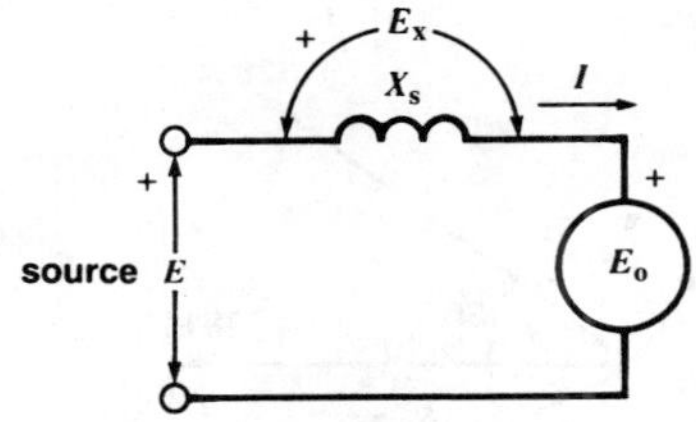

Figure 17.20
Circuit of a synchronous motor connected to a source E. Note the arbitrary (+) polarity marks and arbitrary direction of current flow. See Example 17-5.

$$E = 3815\angle 0°$$

It follows that I is given by

$$I = 328\angle 36.9°$$

Writing the equation for the circuit we find

$$-E + jIX_s + E_o = 0$$

thus

$$\begin{aligned} E_o &= E - jIX_s \\ &= 3811\angle 0° - j(328\angle 36.9°)11 \\ &= 3811\angle 0° - 3608\angle(36.9° + 90°) \\ &= 3811(\cos 0° + j\sin 0°) - \\ &\quad 3608(\cos 126.9° + j\sin 126.9°) \\ &= 3811 + 2166 - j\,2885 \\ &= 5977 - j\,2885 \\ &= 6637\angle -26° \end{aligned}$$

d. Consequently, E_c lags 26° behind E, and the complete phasor diagram is shown in Fig. 17.21.
e. The torque angle δ is 26°.

17.13 Stopping synchronous motors

Owing to the inertia of the rotor and its load, a large synchronous motor may take several hours to stop after being disconnected from the line. To reduce the time, we use the following braking methods:

1. Maintain full dc excitation with the armature in short-circuit.

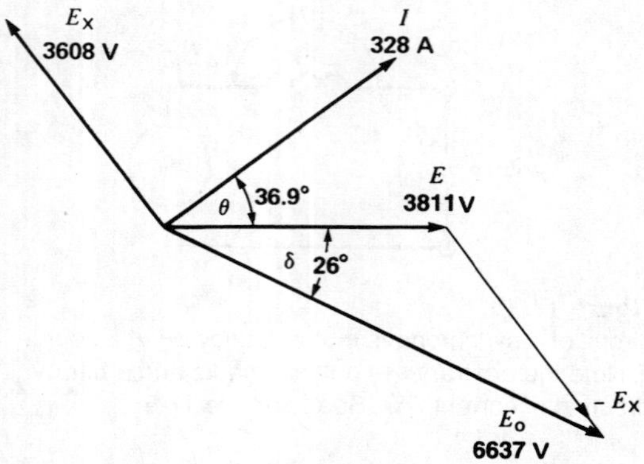

Figure 17.21
See Example 17-5.

2. Maintain full dc excitation with the armature connected to three external resistors.
3. Apply mechanical braking.

In methods 1 and 2, the motor slows down because it functions as a generator, dissipating its energy in the resistive elements of the circuit. Mechanical braking is usually applied only after the motor has reached half-speed or less. A lower speed prevents undue wear of the brake shoes.

Example 17-6

A 1500 kW, 4600 V, 600 r/min, 60 Hz synchronous motor possesses a synchronous reactance of 16 Ω and a stator resistance of 0.2 Ω, per phase. The excitation voltage E_o is 2400 V, and the moment of inertia of the motor and its load is 275 kg·m². We wish to stop the motor by short-circuiting the armature while keeping the dc rotor current fixed.

Calculate

a. The power dissipated in the armature at 600 r/min
b. The power dissipated in the armature at 150 r/min
c. The kinetic energy at 600 r/min
d. The kinetic energy at 150 r/min
e. The time required for the speed to fall from 600 r/min to 150 r/min

Solution

a. In Fig. 17.22a the motor has just been disconnected from the line and is now operating as a generator in short-circuit. The speed is still 600 r/min, and the frequency is 60 Hz. Consequently, the impedance per phase is

$$Z = \sqrt{R^2 + X_L^2} \quad (2.12)$$
$$= \sqrt{0.2^2 + 16^2}$$
$$= 16\ \Omega$$

The current per phase is

$$I = E_o/Z = 2400/16$$
$$= 150\ \text{A}$$

The power dissipated in the 3 phases at 600 r/min is

$$P = 3I^2R = 3 \times 150^2 \times 0.2$$
$$= 13.5\ \text{kW}$$

b. Because the exciting current is fixed, the induced voltage E_o is proportional to the speed. Consequently, when the speed has dropped to 150 r/min,

$$E_o = 2400 \times (150/600) = 600\ \text{V}$$

The frequency is also proportional to the speed, and so

$$f = 60 \times (15/60) = 15\ \text{Hz}$$

The synchronous reactance is proportional to the frequency; consequently,

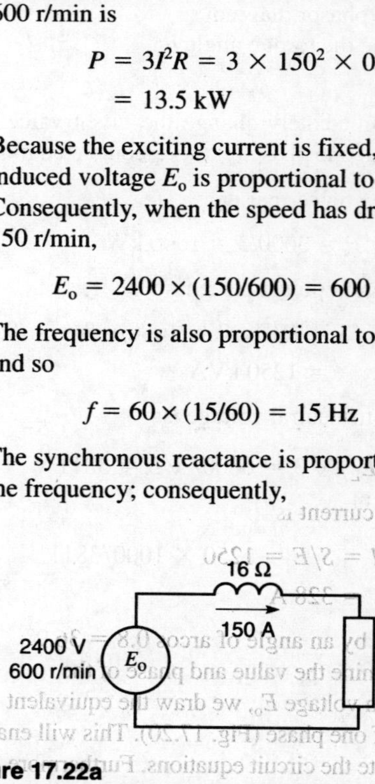

Figure 17.22a
Motor turning at 600 r/min (Example 17-6).

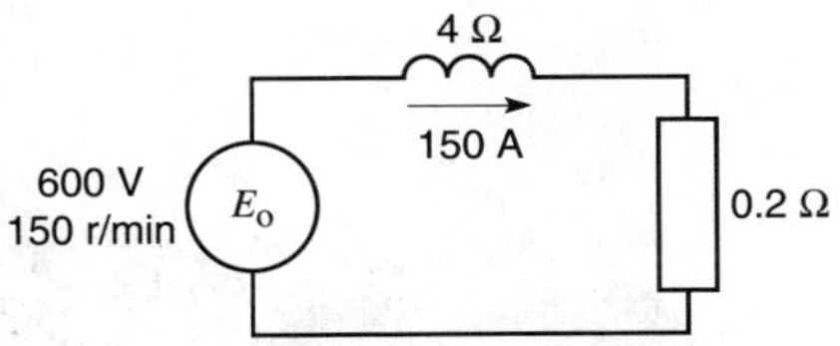

Figure 17.22b
Motor turning at 150 r/min (Example 17-6).

$$X_s = 16 \times (15/60) = 4\ \Omega$$

Referring to Fig. 17.22b the new impedance per phase at 150 r/min is

$$Z = \sqrt{0.2^2 + 4^2} = 4\ \Omega$$

The current phase is

$$I = E_o/Z = 600/4 = 150\ \text{A}$$

Thus, the short-circuit current remains unchanged as the motor decelerates from 600 r/min to 150 r/min. The power dissipated in the 3 phases is therefore the same as before:

$$P = 13.5\ \text{kW}$$

c. The kinetic energy at 600 r/min is

$$E_{k1} = 5.48 \times 10^{-3}\ Jn^2 \qquad (3.8)$$
$$= 5.48 \times 10^{-3} \times 275 \times 600^2$$
$$= 542.5\ \text{kJ}$$

d. The kinetic energy at 150 r/min is

$$E_{k2} = 5.48 \times 10^{-3} \times 275 \times 150^2$$
$$= 33.9\ \text{kJ}$$

e. The loss in kinetic energy in decelerating from 600 r/min to 150 r/min is

$$W = E_{k1} - E_{k2}$$
$$= 542.5 - 33.9$$
$$= 508.6\ \text{kJ}$$

This energy is lost as heat in the armature resistance. The time for the speed to drop from 600 r/min to 150 r/min is given by

$$P = W/t \qquad (3.4)$$
$$13.5 = 508.6/t$$
$$\text{whence } t = 37.7\ \text{s}$$

Note that the motor would stop much sooner if external resistors were connected across the stator terminals.

17.14 The synchronous motor versus the induction motor

We have already seen that induction motors have excellent properties for speeds above 600 r/min. But at lower speeds they become heavy, costly, and have relatively low power factors and efficiencies.

Synchronous motors are particularly attractive for low-speed drives because the power factor can always be adjusted to 1.0 and the efficiency is high. Although more complex to build, their weight and cost are often less than those of induction motors of equal power and speed. This is particularly true for speeds below 300 r/min.

A synchronous motor can improve the power factor of a plant while carrying its rated load. Furthermore, its starting torque can be made considerably greater than that of an induction motor. The reason is that the resistance of the squirrel-cage winding can be high without affecting the speed or efficiency at synchronous speed. Fig. 17.23 compares the properties of a squirrel-cage induction motor and a synchronous motor having the same nominal rating. The biggest difference is in the starting torque.

High-power electronic converters generating very low frequencies enable us to run synchronous motors at ultra-low speeds. Thus, huge motors in the 10 MW range drive crushers, rotary kilns, and variable-speed ball mills.

17.15 Synchronous capacitor

A synchronous capacitor is essentially a synchronous motor running at no-load. Its only purpose is to absorb or deliver reactive power on a 3-phase system, in order to stabilize the voltage (see Chapter 25). The machine acts as an enormous 3-phase capacitor (or

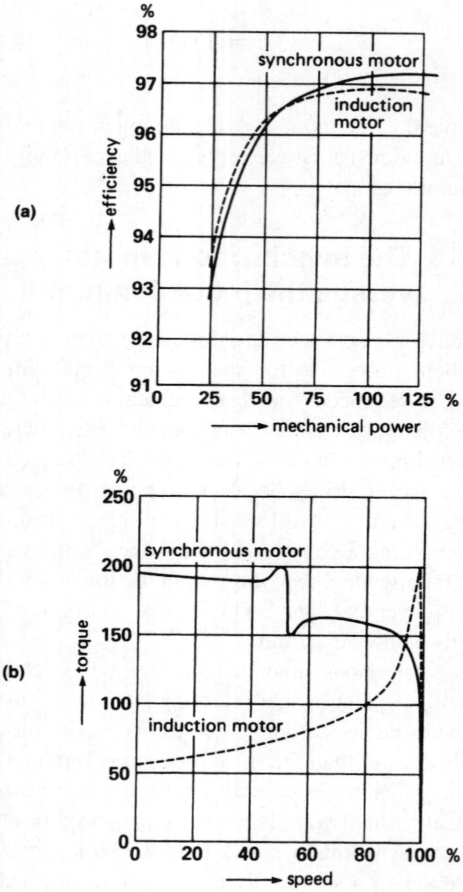

Figure 17.23
Comparison between the efficiency (a) and starting torque (b) of a squirrel-cage induction motor and a synchronous motor, both rated at 4000 hp, 1800 r/min, 6.9 kV, 60 Hz.

Figure 17.24a
Three-phase, 16 kV, 900 r/min synchronous capacitor rated −200 Mvar (supplying reactive power) to +300 Mvar (absorbing reactive power). It is used to regulate the voltage of a 735 kV transmission line. Other characteristics: mass of rotor: 143 t; rotor diameter: 2670 mm; axial length of stator iron: 3200 mm; air gap length: 39.7 mm.

Figure 17.24b
Synchronous capacitor enclosed in its steel housing containing hydrogen under pressure (300 kPa, or about 44 lbf/in^2).
(Courtesy of Hydro-Québec)

inductor) whose reactive power can be varied by changing the dc excitation.

Most synchronous capacitors have ratings that range from 20 Mvar to 200 Mvar and many are hydrogen-cooled (Fig. 17.24). They are started up like synchronous motors. However, if the system cannot furnish the required starting power, a pony motor is used to bring them up to synchronous speed. For example, in one installation, a 160 Mvar synchronous capacitor is started and brought up to speed by means of a 1270 kW wound-rotor motor.

Example 17-7

A synchronous capacitor is rated at 160 Mvar, 16 kV, 1200 r/min, 60 Hz. It has a synchronous reactance of 0.8 pu and is connected to a 16 kV line. Calculate the value of E_o so that the machine

a. Absorbs 160 Mvar
b. Delivers 120 Mvar

Solution

a. The nominal impedance of the machine is

$$Z_n = E_n^2/S_n \quad (16.3)$$
$$= 16\,000^2/(160 \times 10^6)$$
$$= 1.6\ \Omega$$

The synchronous reactance per phase is

$$X_s = X_S(\text{pu})\, Z_n = 0.8 \times 1.6$$
$$= 1.28\ \Omega$$

The line current for a reactive load of 160 Mvar is

$$I_n = S_n/(\sqrt{3}\, E_n)$$
$$= (160 \times 10^6)/(1.73 \times 16\,000)$$
$$= 5780\ \text{A}$$

The drop across the synchronous reactance is

$$E_x = IX_s = 5780 \times 1.28$$
$$= 7400\ \text{V}$$

The line-to-neutral voltage is

$$E = E_L/\sqrt{3} = 16\,000/1.73$$
$$= 9250\ \text{V}$$

Selecting E as the reference phasor, we have

$$E = 9250\angle 0°$$

The current I lags 90° behind E because the machine is absorbing reactive power; consequently,

$$I = 5780\angle -90°$$

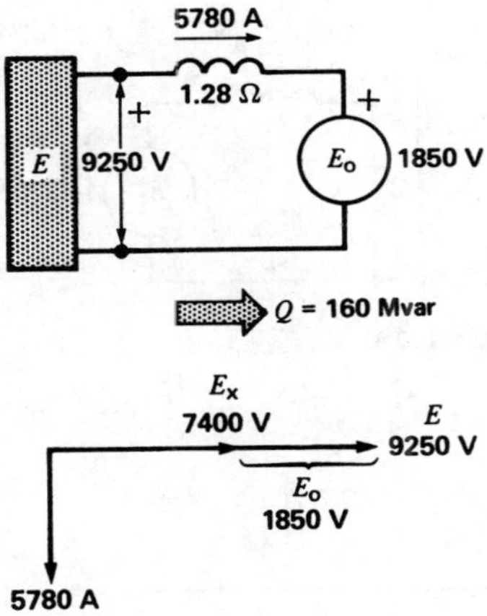

Figure 17.25a
Under-excited synchronous capacitor absorbs reactive power (Example 17-7).

From Fig. 17.25a we can write

$$-E + jIX_s + E_o = 0$$

hence

$$E_o = E - jIX_s$$
$$= 9250\angle 0° - 5780 \times 1.28\angle(90° - 90°)$$
$$= 1850\angle 0°$$

Note that the excitation voltage (1850 V) is much less than the line voltage (9250 V).

b. The load current when the machine is delivering 120 Mvar is

$$I_n = Q/(\sqrt{3}\, E_n)$$
$$= (120 \times 10^6)/(1.73 \times 16\,000)$$
$$= 4335\ \text{A}$$

This time I leads E by 90° and so

$$I = 4335\angle 90°$$

From Fig. 17.25b we can write

$$E_o = E - jIX_s$$
$$= 9250\angle 0° - 4335 \times 1.28\angle 180°$$
$$= (9250 + 5550)\angle 0°$$
$$= 14\,800\angle 0°$$

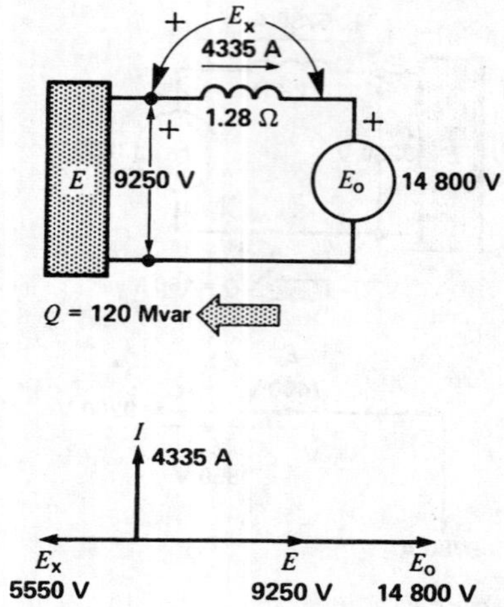

Figure 17.25b
Over-excited synchronous capacitor delivers reactive power (Example 17-7).

The excitation voltage (14 800 V) is now considerably greater than the line voltage (9250 V).

Questions and Problems

Practical level

17-1 Compare the construction of a synchronous generator, a synchronous motor, and a squirrel-cage induction motor.

17-2 Explain how a synchronous motor starts up. When should the dc excitation be applied?

17-3 Why does the speed of a synchronous motor remain constant even under variable load?

17-4 Name some of the advantages of a synchronous motor compared to a squirrel-cage induction motor.

17-5 What is meant by a *synchronous capacitor* and what is it used for?

17-6 **a.** What is meant by an *under-excited synchronous motor?*
b. If we over-excite a synchronous motor, does its mechanical power output increase?

17-7 A synchronous motor draws 2000 kVA at a power factor of 90% leading. Calculate the approximate power developed by the motor [hp] knowing it has an efficiency of 95%.

17-8 A synchronous motor driving a pump operates at a power factor of 100%. What happens if the dc excitation is increased?

17-9 A 3-phase, 225 r/min synchronous motor connected to a 4 kV, 60 Hz line draws a current of 320 A and absorbs 2000 kW.

Calculate

a. The apparent power supplied to the motor
b. The power factor
c. The reactive power absorbed
d. The number of poles on the rotor

17-10 A synchronous motor draws 150 A from a 3-phase line. If the exciting current is raised, the current drops to 140 A. Was the motor over- or under-excited before the excitation was changed?

Intermediate level

17-11 **a.** Calculate the approximate full-load current of the 3000 hp motor in Fig. 17.1, if it has an efficiency of 97%.
b. What is the value of the field resistance?

17-12 Referring to Fig. 17.2, at what speed must the rotor turn to generate the indicated frequencies?

17-13 A 3-phase synchronous motor rated 800 hp, 2.4 kV, 60 Hz operates at unity power factor. The line voltage suddenly drops to 1.8 kV, but the exciting current remains unchanged. Explain how the following quantities are affected:

a. Motor speed and mechanical power output
b. Torque angle δ
c. Position of the rotor poles
d. Power factor
e. Stator current

17-14 A synchronous motor has the following parameters, per phase (Fig. 17.7a):

$$E = 2.4 \text{ kV}; E_o = 3 \text{ kV}$$
$$X_s = 2\ \Omega$$
$$I = 900 \text{ A}$$

Draw the phasor diagram and determine:

- **a.** Torque angle δ
- **b.** Active power, per phase
- **c.** Power factor of the motor
- **d.** Reactive power absorbed (or delivered), per phase

17-15 **a.** In Problem 17-14 calculate the line current and the new torque angle δ if the mechanical load is suddenly removed.
b. Calculate the new reactive power absorbed (or delivered) by the motor, per phase.

17-16 A 500 hp synchronous motor drives a compressor and its excitation is adjusted so that the power factor is unity. If the excitation is increased without making any other change, what is the effect upon the following:

- **a.** The active power absorbed by the motor
- **b.** The line current
- **c.** The reactive power absorbed (or delivered) by the motor
- **d.** The torque angle

Advanced level

17-17 The 4000 hp, 6.9 kV motor shown in Fig. 17.4 possesses a synchronous reactance of 10 Ω, per phase. The stator is connected in wye, and the motor operates at full-load (4000 hp) with a leading power factor of 0.89. If the efficiency is 97%, calculate the following:

- **a.** The apparent power
- **b.** The line current
- **c.** The value of E_o, per phase
- **d.** The mechanical displacement of the poles from their no-load position
- **e.** The total reactive power supplied to the electrical system
- **f.** The approximate maximum power the motor can develop, without pulling out of step [hp]

17-18 In Problem 17-17 we wish to adjust the power factor to unity.

Calculate

- **a.** The exciting voltage E_o required, per phase
- **b.** The new torque angle

17-19 A 3-phase, unity power factor synchronous motor rated 400 hp, 2300 V, 450 r/min, 80 A, 60 Hz, drives a compressor. The stator has a synchronous reactance of 0.88 pu, and the excitation E_o is adjusted to 1.2 pu.

Calculate

- **a.** The value of X_s and of E_o, per phase
- **b.** The pull-out torque [ft·lbf]
- **c.** The line current when the motor is about to pull out of synchronism

17-20 The synchronous capacitor in Fig. 17.24 possesses a synchronous reactance of 0.6 Ω, per phase. The resistance per phase is 0.007 Ω. If the machine coasts to a stop, it will run for about 3 h. In order to shorten the stopping time, the stator is connected to three large 0.6 Ω braking resistors connected in wye. The dc excitation is fixed at 250 A so that the initial line voltage across the resistors is one-tenth of its rated value, or 1600 V, at 900 r/min.

Calculate

- **a.** The total braking power and braking torque at 900 r/min
- **b.** The braking power and braking torque at 450 r/min
- **c.** The average braking torque between 900 r/min and 450 r/min
- **d.** The time for the speed to fall from 900 r/min to 450 r/min, knowing that the moment of inertia of the rotor is 1.7×10^6 lb·ft²

Industrial application

17-21 A 500 hp, 3-phase, 2200 V, unity power factor synchronous motor has a rated current of 103 A. It can deliver its rated output so long as the air inlet temperature is 40°C or less. The manufacturer states that the output of the motor must be decreased by 1 percent for each degree Celsius above 40°C. If the air inlet temperature is 46°C, calculate the maximum allowable motor current.

17-22 An 8800 kW, 6.0 kV, 1500 r/min, 3-phase, 50 Hz, 0.9 power factor synchronous motor manufactured by Siemens has the following properties:

1. Rated current: 962 A
2. Rated torque: 56.0 kN·m
3. Pull-out torque: 1.45 pu
4. Locked-rotor current: 4.9 pu
5. Excitation voltage: 160 V
6. Excitation current: 387 A
7. Full-load efficiency, excluding excitation system losses: 97.8%
8. Moment of inertia of rotor: 520 kg·m^2
9. Temperature rise of cooling water: 25°C to 32°C
10. Flow of cooling water: 465 L/min
11. Maximum permissible external moment of inertia: 1370 kg·m^2
12. Mass of rotor: 6.10 t (t = metric ton)
13. Mass of stator: 7.50 t
14. Mass of enclosure: 3.97 t

Using the above information, calculate the following:

a. The total mass of the motor including its enclosure, in metric tons

b. The flow of cooling water in gallons (U.S.) per minute

c. The maximum total moment of inertia (in lb·ft^2), which the motor can pull into synchronism

d. The total losses of the motor at full-load

e. The total efficiency of the motor at full-load

f. The reactive power delivered by the motor at full-load

g. If the iron losses are equal to the stator copper losses, calculate the approximate resistance between two terminals of the stator

h. Calculate the resistance of the field circuit

CHAPTER 18
Single-Phase Motors

18.0 Introduction

Single-phase motors are the most familiar of all electric motors because they are used in home appliances and portable machine tools. In general, they are employed when 3-phase power is not available.

There are many kinds of single-phase motors on the market, each designed to meet a specific application. However, we will limit our study to a few basic types, with particular emphasis on the widely used split-phase induction motor.

18.1 Construction of a single-phase induction motor

Single-phase induction motors are very similar to 3-phase induction motors. They are composed of a squirrel-cage rotor (identical to that in a 3-phase motor) and a stator (Fig. 18.1). The stator carries a *main winding*, which creates a set of N, S poles. It also carries a smaller *auxiliary winding* that only operates during the brief period when the motor starts up. The auxiliary winding has the same number of poles as the main winding has.

Fig. 18.2 shows the progressive steps in winding a 4-pole, 36-slot stator. Starting with the laminated iron stator, paper insulators—called *slot liners*—are first inserted in the slots. The main winding is then

Figure 18.1
Cutaway view of a 5 hp, 1725 r/min, 60 Hz single-phase capacitor-start motor.
(Courtesy of Gould)

Figure 18.2a
Bare, laminated stator of a 1/4 hp (187 W), single-phase motor. The 36 slots are insulated with a paper liner. The squirrel-cage rotor is identical to that of a 3-phase motor.

Figure 18.2b
Four poles of the main winding are inserted in the slots.

Figure 18.2c
Four poles of the auxiliary winding straddle the main winding.
(Courtesy of Lab-Volt)

laid in the slots (Figs. 18.2a, 18.2b). Next, the auxiliary winding is embedded so that its poles straddle those of the main winding (Fig. 18.2c). The reason for this arrangement will be explained shortly.

Each pole of the main winding consists of a group of four concentric coils, connected in series (Fig. 18.3a). Adjacent poles are connected so as to produce alternate N, S polarities. The empty slot in the center of each pole (shown as a vertical dash

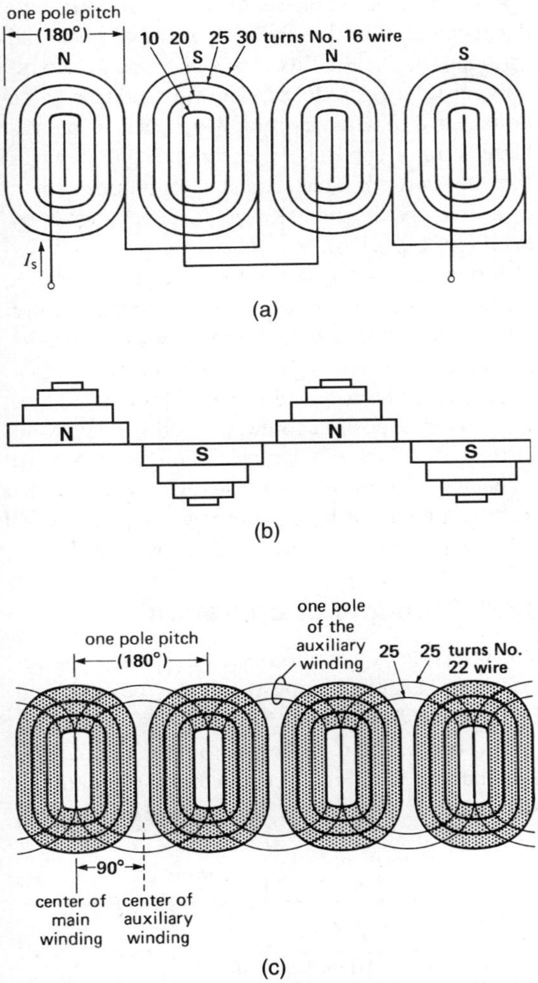

Figure 18.3
a. Main winding of a 4-pole, 36-slot motor laid out flat, showing the number of turns per coil.
b. Mmfs produced by the main winding.
c. Position of the auxiliary winding with respect to the main winding.

line) and the partially filled slots on either side of it are used to lodge the auxiliary winding. The latter has only two concentric coils per pole (Fig. 18.3c).

Fig. 18.4 shows a 2-pole stator; the large main winding and the smaller auxiliary winding are displaced at right angles to each other.

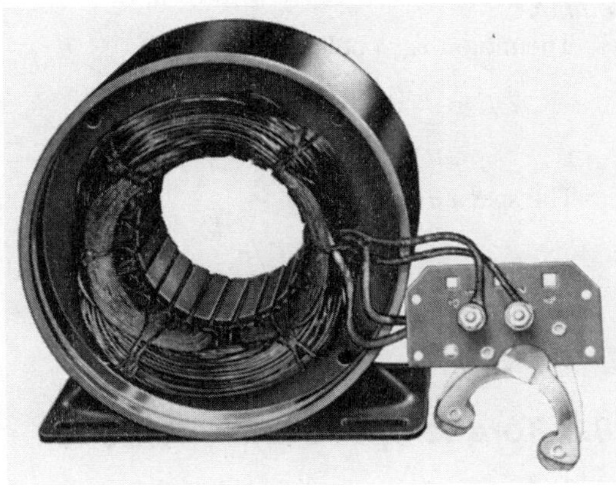

Figure 18.4
Main and auxiliary windings in a 2-pole, single-phase motor. The stationary contact in series with the auxiliary winding opens when the centrifugal switch, mounted on the shaft, reaches 75 percent of synchronous speed.

18.2 Synchronous speed

As in the case of 3-phase motors, the synchronous speed of all single-phase induction motors is given by the equation

$$n_s = \frac{120 f}{p} \tag{17.1}$$

where

n_s = synchronous speed [r/min]
f = frequency of the source [Hz]
p = number of poles

The rotor turns at slightly less than synchronous speed, and the full-load slip is typically 3 percent to 5 percent for fractional horsepower motors.

Example 18-1

Calculate the speed of the 4-pole, single-phase motor shown in Fig. 18.1 if the slip at full-load is 3.4 percent. The line frequency is 60 Hz.

Solution

The motor has 4 poles, consequently,

$$n_s = 120f/p = (120 \times 60)/4$$
$$= 1800 \text{ r/min}$$

The speed n is given by

$$s = (n_s - n)/n_s \qquad (17.2)$$
$$0.034 = (1800 - n)/1800$$
$$n = 1739 \text{ r/min}$$

18.3 Torque-speed characteristic

Fig. 18.5 is a schematic diagram of the rotor and main winding of a 2-pole, single-phase induction motor. Suppose the rotor is locked. If an ac voltage is applied to the stator. the resulting current I_s produces an ac flux Φ_s. The flux pulsates back and forth but, unlike the flux in a 3-phase stator, no revolving field is produced. The flux induces an ac voltage in the stationary rotor which, in turn, creates large ac rotor currents. In effect, the rotor behaves like the short-circuited secondary of a transformer; consequently, the motor has no tendency to start by itself (see Fig. 18.6).

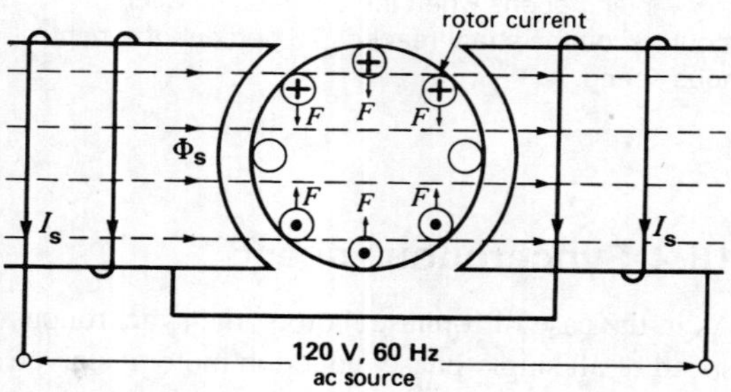

Figure 18.5
Currents in the rotor bars when the rotor is locked. The resulting forces cancel each other and no torque is produced.

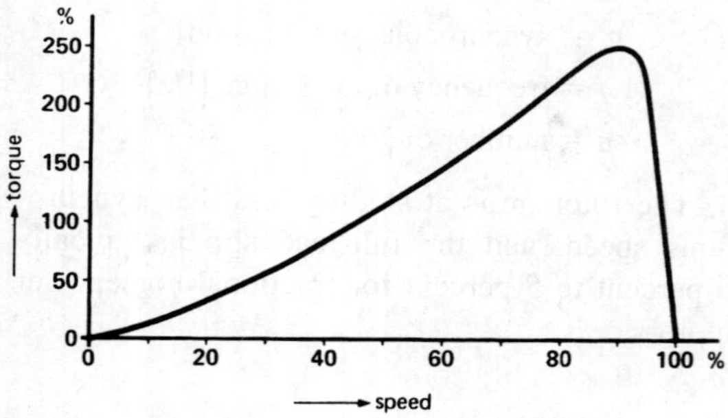

Figure 18.6
Typical torque-speed curve of a single-phase motor.

However, if we spin the rotor in one direction or the other, it will continue to rotate in the direction of spin. As a matter of fact, the rotor quickly accelerates until it reaches a speed slightly below synchronous speed. The acceleration indicates that the motor develops a positive torque as soon as it begins to turn. Fig. 18.6 shows the typical torque-speed curve when the main winding is excited. Although the starting torque is zero, the motor develops a powerful torque as it approaches synchronous speed.

18.4 Principle of operation

The principle of operation of a single-phase induction motor is quite complex, and may be explained by the **cross-field theory**.*

As soon as the rotor begins to turn, a *speed emf* E is induced in the rotor conductors as they cut the stator flux Φ_s (Fig. 18.7). This voltage increases as

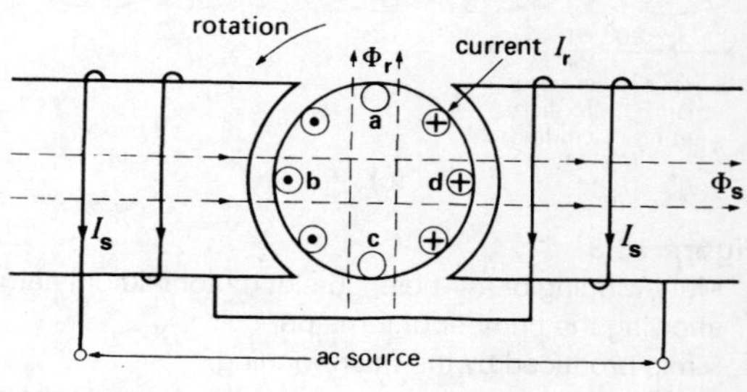

Figure 18.7
Currents induced in the rotor bars due to rotation. They produce a flux Φ_r that acts at right angles to the stator flux Φ_s.

* The double revolving field theory (discussed in Section 18.18) is also used to explain the behavior of the single-phase motor.

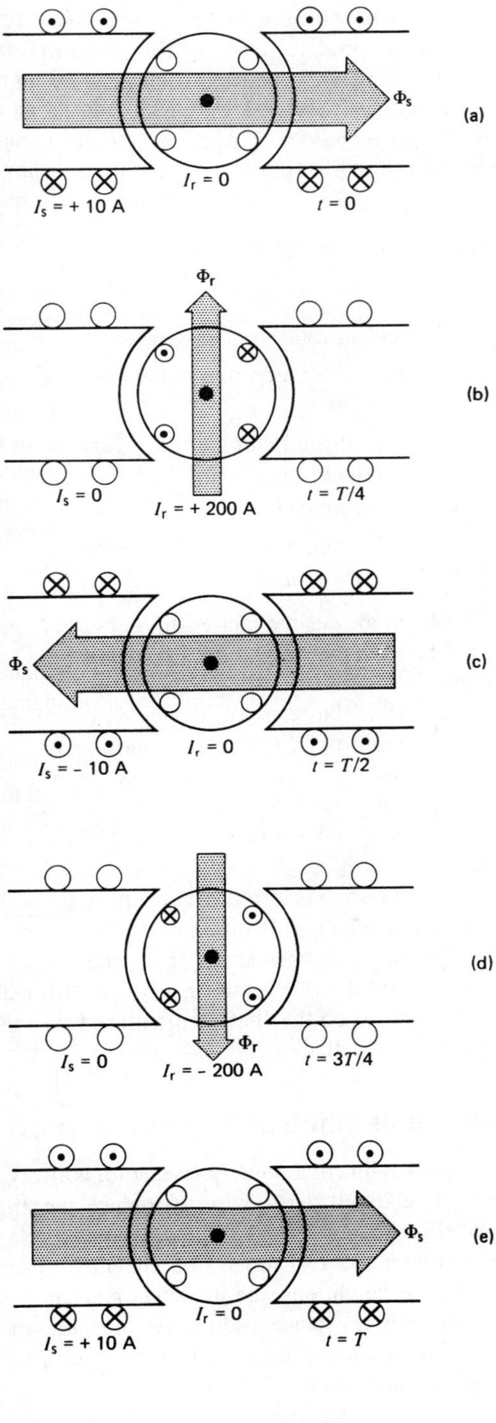

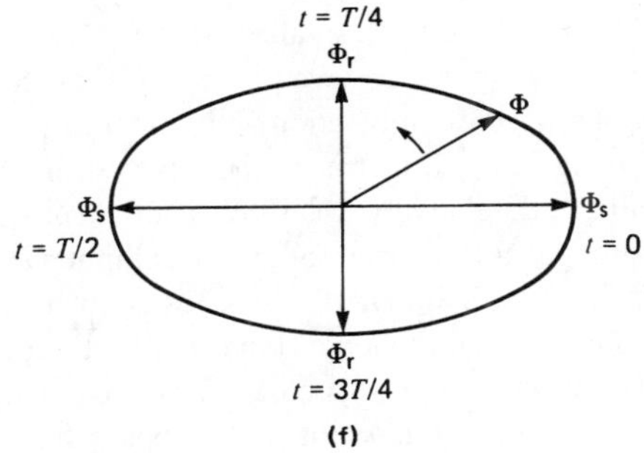

Figure 18.8
Instantaneous currents and flux in a single-phase motor with the main winding excited. The duration of one cycle is T seconds, and conditions are shown at successive quarter-cycle intervals.

a. Stator current I_s is maximum, rotor current I_r is zero.
b. Stator current is zero, rotor current is maximum; however, Φ_r is smaller than Φ_s.
c. Stator current is maximum, but negative.
d. Rotor current is maximum, but negative.
e. After one complete cycle ($t = T$) the conditions repeat.
f. Resulting flux Φ in the air gap rotates ccw at synchronous speed. Its amplitude varies from a maximum of Φ_s to a minimum Φ_r.

the rotor speed increases. It causes currents I_r to flow in the rotor bars facing the stator poles. These currents produce an ac flux Φ_r which acts at right angles to the stator flux Φ_s. Equally important is the fact that Φ_r does not reach its maximum value at the same time as Φ_s does. In effect, Φ_r lags almost 90° behind Φ_s, due to the inductance of the rotor.

The combined action of Φ_s and Φ_r produces a revolving magnetic field, similar to that in a 3-phase motor. The value of Φ_r increases with increasing speed, becoming almost equal to Φ_s at synchronous speed. This explains in part why the torque increases as the motor speeds up.

We can understand how the revolving field is produced by referring to Fig. 18.8. It gives a snapshot of the currents and fluxes created respectively by the rotor and stator, at successive intervals of time. We assume that the motor is running far below synchronous speed, and so Φ_r is much smaller than Φ_s. By observing the flux in the successive pictures of Fig. 18.8, it is obvious that the combination of Φ_s and Φ_r produces a revolving field. Furthermore, the flux is strong horizontally and relatively weak vertically. Thus, the field strength at low speed follows the elliptic pattern shown in Fig. 18.8f. The flux rotates counterclockwise in the same direction as the rotor. Furthermore, it rotates at synchronous speed, irrespective of the actual speed of the rotor. As the motor approaches synchronous speed, Φ_r becomes almost equal to Φ_s and a nearly perfect revolving field is produced.

18.5 Locked-rotor torque

To produce a starting torque in a single-phase motor, we must somehow create a revolving field. This is done by adding an auxiliary winding, as shown in Fig. 18.9. When the main and auxiliary windings are connected to an ac source, the main winding produces a flux Φ_s, while the auxiliary winding produces a flux Φ_a. If the two fluxes are out of phase, so that Φ_a either lags or leads Φ_s, a rotating field is set up. The 2-phase revolving field is created in a manner similar to the revolving field of a 3-phase motor (see Section 13.3).

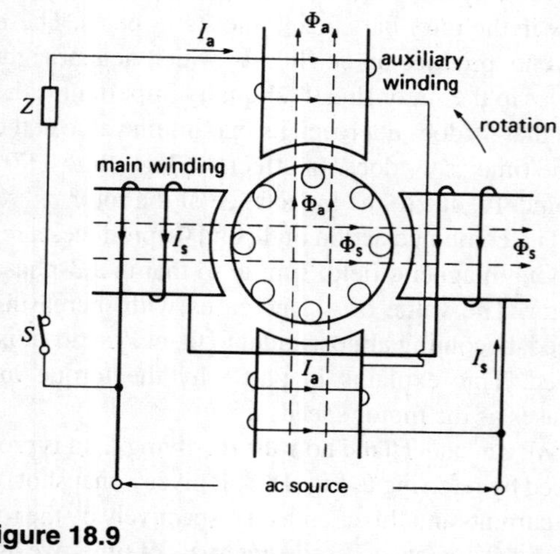

Figure 18.9
Currents and fluxes at standstill when the main and auxiliary windings are energized. An elliptical revolving field is produced.

The reader will immediately see that the auxiliary winding produces a strong flux Φ_a during the acceleration period when the rotor flux Φ_r (mentioned previously) is weak. As a result, Φ_a strengthens Φ_r, thereby producing a powerful torque both at standstill and at low speeds. The locked-rotor torque is given by

$$T = kI_aI_s \sin \alpha \tag{18.1}$$

where

T = locked-rotor torque [N·m]
I_a = locked-rotor current in the auxiliary winding [A]
I_s = locked-rotor current in the main winding [A]
α = phase angle between I_s and I_a [°]
k = a constant, depending on the design of the motor

To obtain the desired phase shift between I_s and I_a (and hence between Φ_s and Φ_a), we add an impedance Z in series with the auxiliary winding. The impedance may be resistive, inductive, or capacitive, depending upon the desired starting torque. The choice of impedance gives rise to various types of *split-phase motors*. In many cases the desired impedance is incorporated in the auxiliary winding itself, as explained below.

A special switch is also connected in series with the auxiliary winding. It disconnects the winding when the motor reaches about 75 percent of synchronous speed. A speed-sensitive centrifugal switch mounted on the shaft is often used for this purpose (Fig. 18.10).

18.6 Resistance split-phase motor

The main winding of a single-phase motor is always made of relatively large wire, to reduce the I^2R losses (Fig. 18.11a). The winding also has a relatively large number of turns. Consequently, under locked-rotor conditions, the inductive reactance is high and the resistance is low. As a result, the locked-rotor current I_s lags considerably behind the applied voltage E (Fig. 18.11b).

(a) (b)

Figure 18.10

a. Centrifugal switch in the closed, or stopped, position. The stationary contact is closed.
b. Centrifugal switch in the open, or running, position. Due to centrifugal force, the rectangular weights have swung out against the restraining tension of the springs. This has caused the plastic collar to move to the left along the shaft, thus opening the stationary contact in series with the auxiliary winding.

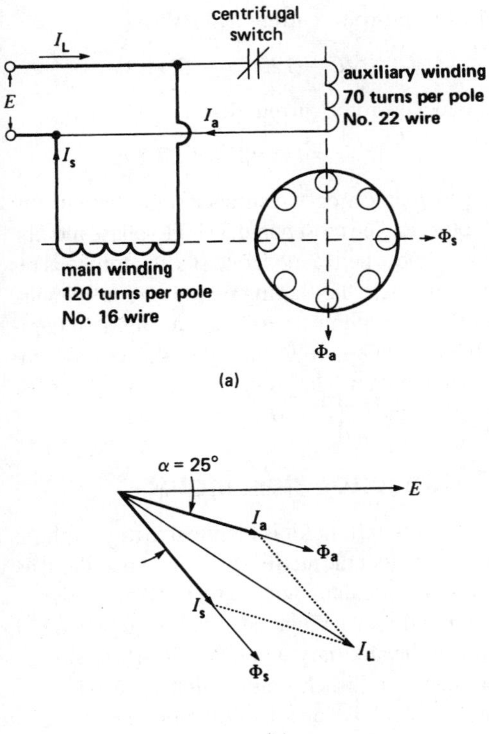

(b)

Figure 18.11

a. Resistance split-phase motor (1/4 hp, 115 V, 1725 r/min, 60 Hz) at standstill.
b. Corresponding phasor diagram. The current in the auxiliary winding leads the current in the main winding by 25°.

In a *resistance split-phase motor* (often simply called *split-phase motor*), the auxiliary winding has a relatively small number of turns of fine wire. Its resistance is higher and its reactance lower than that of the main winding, with the result that the locked-rotor current I_a is more nearly in phase with E. The resulting phase angle α between I_a and I_s produces the starting torque.

The line current I_L is equal to the phasor sum of I_s and I_a. At start-up, it is usually 6 to 7 times the nominal current of the motor.

Owing to the small wire used on the auxiliary winding, the current density is high and the winding heats up very quickly. If the starting period lasts for more than 5 seconds, the winding begins to smoke and may burn out, unless the motor is protected by a built-in thermal relay. This type of split-phase motor is well suited for infrequent starting of low-inertia loads.

Example 18-2

A resistance split-phase motor is rated at 1/4 hp (187 W), 1725 r/min, 115 V, 60 Hz. When the rotor is locked, a test at reduced voltage on the main and auxiliary windings yields the following results:

	main winding	**auxiliary winding**
applied voltage	$E = 23$ V	$E = 23$ V
current	$I_s = 4$ A	$I_a = 1.5$ A
active power	$P_s = 60$ W	$P_a = 30$ W

Calculate

a. The phase angle between I_a and I_s

b. The locked-rotor current drawn from the line at 115 V

Solution

We first calculate the phase angle Φ_s between I_s and E of the main winding.

a. The apparent power is

$$S_s = EI_s = 23 \times 4 = 92 \text{ VA}$$

The power factor is

$$\cos \phi_s = P_s/S_s = 60/92 = 0.65$$

thus,

$$\phi_s = 49.6°$$

I_s lags 49.6° behind the voltage E.

We now calculate the phase angle Φ_a between I_a and E of the auxiliary winding.

The apparent power is

$$S_a = EI_a = 23 \times 1.5 = 34.5 \text{ VA}$$

The power factor is

$$\cos \phi_a = P_a/S_a = 30/34.5 = 0.87$$

thus,

$$\phi_a = 29.6°$$

I_a lags 29.6° behind the voltage.

The phase angle between I_s and I_a is

$$\alpha = \phi_s - \phi_a = 49.6° - 29.6°$$
$$= 20.0°$$

b. To determine the total line current, we first calculate the total value of P and Q drawn by both windings and then deduce the total apparent power S.

The total active power absorbed is

$$P = P_s + P_a$$
$$= 60 + 30 = 90 \text{ W}$$

The reactive powers Q_s and Q_a of the main and auxiliary windings are

$$Q_s = \sqrt{S_s^2 - P_s^2}$$
$$= \sqrt{92^2 - 60^2} = 69.7 \text{ var}$$
$$Q_a = \sqrt{S_a^2 - P_a^2}$$
$$= \sqrt{34.5^2 - 30^2} = 17.0 \text{ var}$$

The total reactive power absorbed by the motor is

$$Q = Q_s + Q_a$$
$$= 69.7 + 17.0 = 86.7 \text{ var}$$

The total apparent power absorbed is

$$S = \sqrt{P^2 + Q^2}$$
$$= \sqrt{90^2 + 86.7^2} = 125 \text{ VA}$$

The locked-rotor current at 23 V is

$$I_1 = S/E = 125/23 = 5.44 \text{ A}$$

The locked-rotor current drawn at 115 V is

$$I_L = 5.44 \times (115/23) = 27.2 \text{ A}$$

Due to their low cost, resistance split-phase induction motors are the most popular single-phase motors. They are used where a moderate starting torque is required and where the starting periods are infrequent. They drive fans, pumps, washing machines, oil burners, small machine tools, and other devices too numerous to mention. The power rating usually lies between 60 W and 250 W (1/12 hp to 1/3 hp).

18.7 Capacitor-start motor

The capacitor-start motor is identical to a split-phase motor, except that the auxiliary winding has about as many turns as the main winding has. Furthermore, a capacitor and a centrifugal switch are connected in series with the auxiliary winding (Fig. 18.12a).

The capacitor is chosen so that I_a leads I_s by about 80°, which is considerably more than the 25° found in a split-phase motor. Consequently, for equal starting torques, the current in the auxiliary winding is only about half that in a split-phase motor. It follows that during the starting period the auxiliary winding of a capacitor motor heats up less quickly. Furthermore, the locked-rotor line current

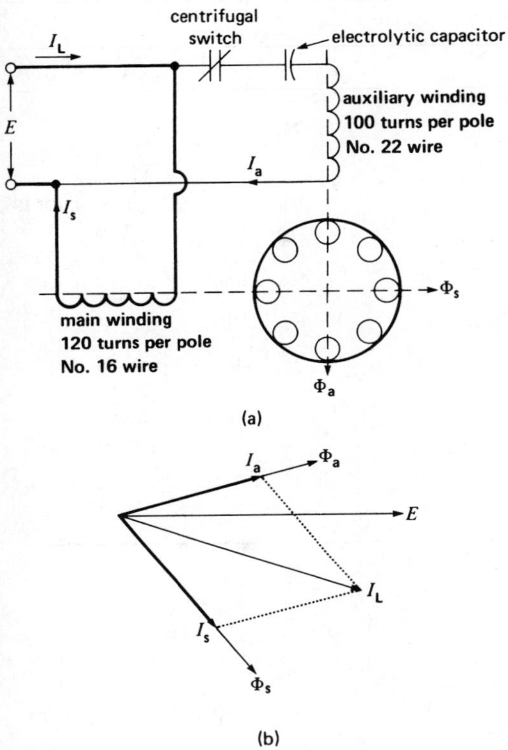

Figure 18.12
a. Capacitor-start motor.
b. Corresponding phasor diagram.

I_L is smaller, being typically 4 to 5 times the rated full-load current.

Owing to the high starting torque and the relatively low value of I_a the capacitor-start motor is well suited to applications involving either frequent or prolonged starting periods. Although the *starting* characteristics of this motor are better than those of a split-phase motor, both machines possess the same characteristics under load. The reason is that the main windings are identical and the auxiliary winding is no longer in the circuit when the motor has come up to speed.

The wide use of capacitor-start motors is a direct result of the availability of small, reliable, low-cost electrolytic capacitors. For given capacitance and voltage, electrolytic capacitors are much smaller and cheaper than paper capacitors. However, electrolytic capacitors can only be used for short periods in ac circuits whereas paper capacitors can operate on ac indefinitely. Prior to the development of electrolytic capacitors, repulsion-induction motors had to be used whenever a high starting torque was required. Repulsion-induction motors possess a special commutator and brushes that require considerable maintenance. Most motor manufacturers have stopped making them.

Capacitor-start motors are used when a high starting torque is required. They are built in sizes ranging from 120 W to 7.5 kW (~1/6 hp to 10 hp). Typical loads are compressors, large fans, pumps, and high-inertia loads.

Table 18A gives the properties of a capacitor-start motor having a rating of 250 W (1/3 hp), 1760 r/min, 115 V, 60 Hz. Fig. 18.13 shows the torque-speed curve for the same machine. Note that during the acceleration phase (0 to 1370 r/min) the main and auxiliary windings together produce a very high starting torque. When the rotor reaches 1370 r/min, the centrifugal switch snaps open, causing the motor to operate along the torque-speed curve of the main winding. The torque suddenly drops from 9.5 N·m to 2.8 N·m, but the motor continues to accelerate until it reaches 1760 r/min, the rated full-load speed.

18.8 Efficiency and power factor of single-phase induction motors

The efficiency and power factor of fractional horsepower single-phase motors are usually low. Thus, at full-load a 186 W motor (1/4 hp) has an efficiency and power factor of about 60 percent. The low power factor is mainly due to the large magnetizing current, which ranges between 70 percent and 90 percent of full-load current. Consequently, even at no-load these motors have substantial temperature rises.

The relatively low efficiency and power factor of these motors is a consequence of their fractional horsepower ratings. Integral horsepower single-phase motors can have efficiencies and power factors above 80 percent.

TABLE 18A CHARACTERISTICS OF A CAPACITOR-START MOTOR

Rating: 250 W, 1760 r/min, 115 V, 60 Hz, Insulation Class 105°C

Full-load			No-load		
voltage	–	115 V	voltage	–	115 V
power	–	250 W	current	–	4.0 A
current	–	5.3 A	losses	–	105 W
P.F.		64%			
efficiency	–	63.9%	**Locked rotor**		
speed	–	1760 r/min	voltage	–	115 V
torque	–	1.35 N·m	current I_s	–	23 A
Breakdown			current I_a	–	19 A
			current I_L	–	29 A
torque	–	3.4 N·m	torque	–	6 N·m
speed	–	1600 r/min	capacitor	–	320 μF
current	–	13 A			

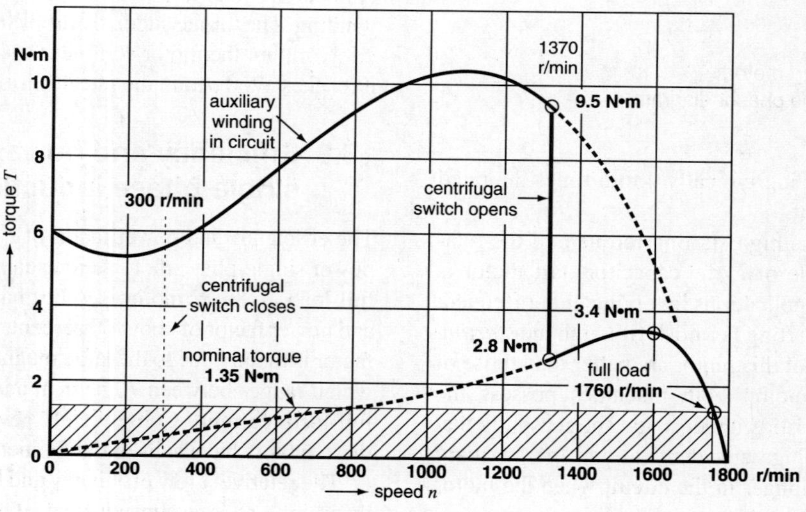

Figure 18.13
Torque-speed curves of a capacitor-start motor, rated 1/3 hp (250 W), 1760 r/min, 115 V, 60 Hz, class A insulation.

18.9 Vibration of single-phase motors

If we touch the stator of a single-phase motor, we note that it vibrates rapidly, whether it operates at full-load or no-load. These vibrations do not exist in 2-phase or 3-phase motors; consequently, single-phase motors are more noisy.

What causes this vibration? It is due to the fact that a single-phase motor always receives *pulsating* electric power whereas it delivers *constant* mechanical power. Consider the 250 W motor having the properties given in Table 18A. The full-load current is 5.3 A and it lags 50° behind the line voltage. If we draw the waveshapes of voltage and current, we can plot the instantaneous power P supplied to the motor (Fig. 18.14). We find that P oscillates between +1000 W and −218 W. When the power is positive the motor receives energy from the line. Conversely, when it is negative the motor returns energy to the line. However, whether the instantaneous electric power is positive, negative, or zero, the mechanical power delivered is a steady 250 W.

The motor will slow down during the brief periods when the electric power it receives is less than 250 W. On the other hand, it will accelerate whenever the electric power exceeds the mechanical output plus the losses. The acceleration intervals coincide with the positive peaks of the power curve. Similarly, the deceleration intervals coincide with the negative peaks. Consequently, the acceleration/deceleration intervals occur twice per cycle, or 120 times per second on a 60 Hz system. As a result, both the stator and rotor vibrate at twice the line frequency.

The stator vibrations are transmitted to the mounting base which, in turn, generates additional vibration and noise. To eliminate the problem, the motor is often cradled in a resilient mounting (Fig. 18.15). It consists of two soft rubber rings placed between the end-bells and a supporting metal bracket. Because the rotor also vibrates, a tubular rubber isolator is sometimes

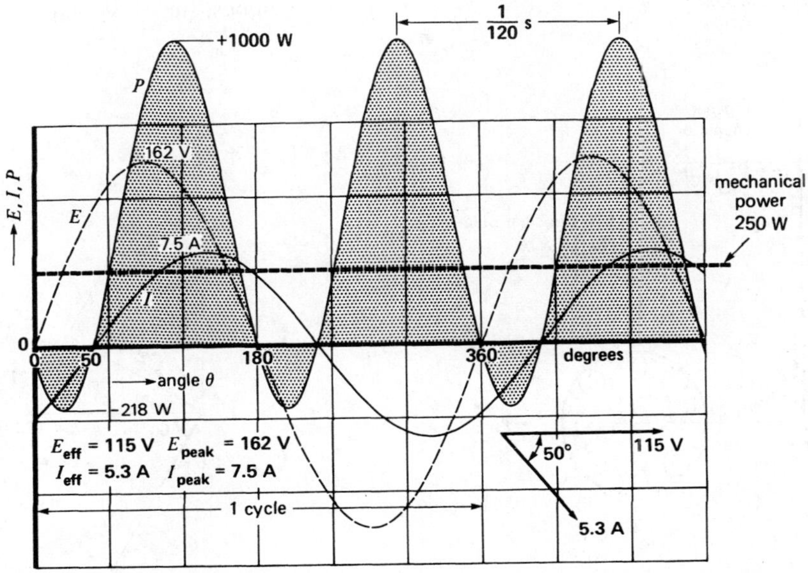

Figure 18.14
The instantaneous power absorbed by a single-phase motor varies between +1000 W and −218 W. The power output is constant at 250 W; consequently, vibrations are produced.

Figure 18.15
Single-phase capacitor-start motor supported in a resilient-mount cradle to reduce the vibration and noise transmitted to the mounting surface. Motor rated at 1/3 hp, 1725 r/min, 230 V, 60 Hz has a full-load current of 3.0 A, efficiency of 60 percent, and power factor of 60 percent. Other characteristics: no-load current: 2.6 A; locked-rotor current: 13 A; locked-rotor torque: 3.6 pu; breakdown torque: 3.0 pu; service factor: 1.35; total weight: 10 kg; overall length including shaft: 278 mm; overall height: 232 mm.
(Courtesy of Baldor Electric Company)

placed between the shaft and the mechanical load, particularly when the load is a fan.

Two-phase and 3-phase motors do not vibrate because the total instantaneous power they receive from *all* the phases is constant (see Section 8.7).

18.10 Capacitor-run motor

The capacitor-run motor is essentially a 2-phase motor that receives its power from a single-phase source. It has two windings, one of which is directly connected to the source. The other winding is also connected to the source, but in series with a paper capacitor (Fig. 18.16). The capacitor-fed winding has a large number of turns of relatively small wire, compared to the directly connected winding.

This particularly quiet motor is used to drive fixed loads in hospitals, studios, and other places where silence is important. It has a high power factor on account of the capacitor and no centrifugal switch is required. However, the starting torque is low.

The motor acts as a true 2-phase motor only when it operates at full-load (Fig. 18.16b). Under these conditions, fluxes Φ_a and Φ_s created by the

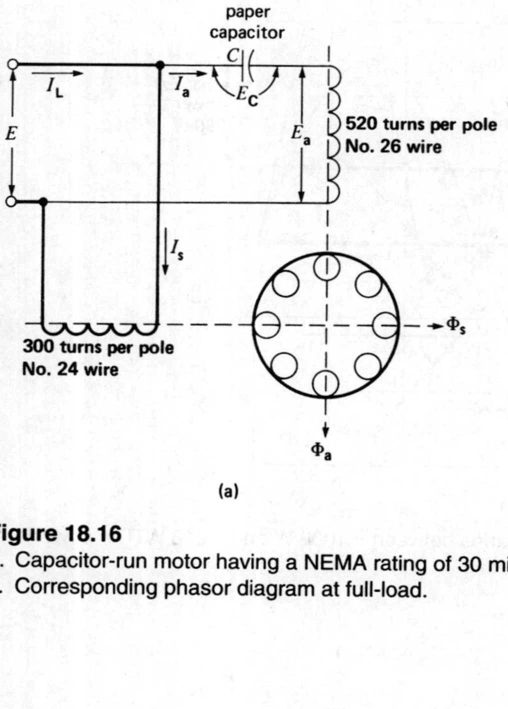

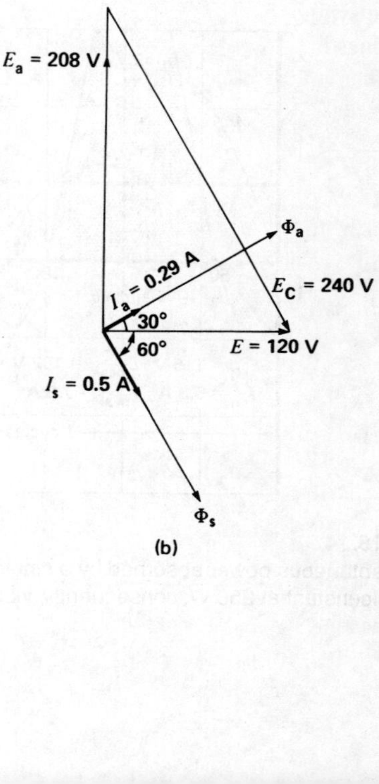

Figure 18.16
a. Capacitor-run motor having a NEMA rating of 30 millihorsepower.
b. Corresponding phasor diagram at full-load.

two windings are equal and out of phase by 90°. The motor is then essentially vibration-free. Capacitor-run motors are usually rated below 500 W.

18.11 Reversing the direction of rotation

In order to reverse the direction of rotation of the motors we have discussed so far, we have to interchange the leads of either the auxiliary winding or the main winding.

However, if a single-phase motor is equipped with a centrifugal switch, its rotation cannot be reversed while the motor is running. If the main winding leads are interchanged, the motor will continue to turn in the same direction.

In the case of a capacitor-run motor (Fig. 18.16) the direction of rotation *can* be changed while the motor is running because both windings are in the circuit at all times. In the case of very small motors, the rotation can be reversed by using a double-throw switch as shown in Fig. 18.17. In such a motor, the main and auxiliary windings are identical. When the switch is in position 1, winding A is directly across the line, while winding B is in series with the capacitor. With this connection the motor turns clockwise. When the switch is thrown to position 2, the role of the windings is reversed and the motor will come to a halt and then run up to speed in the opposite direction.

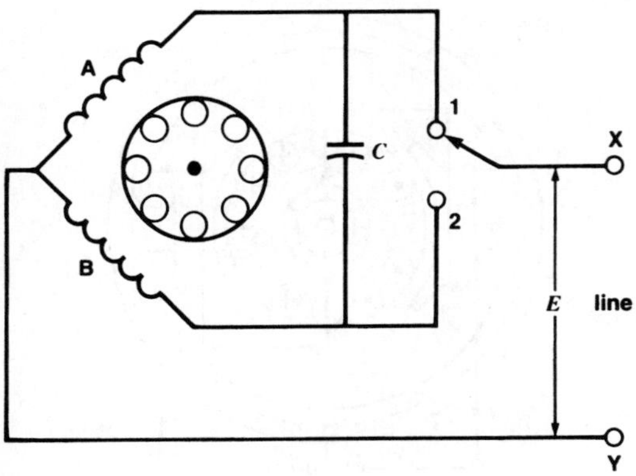

Figure 18.17
Reversible single-phase motor using a 2-pole switch and capacitor.

18.12 Shaded-pole motor

The shaded-pole motor is very popular for ratings below 0.05 hp (~40 W) because of its extremely simple construction (Fig. 18.18). It is basically a small squirrel-cage motor in which the auxiliary winding is composed of a copper ring surrounding a portion of each pole.

The main winding is a simple coil connected to the ac source. The coil produces a total flux Φ that may be considered to be made up of three components Φ_1, Φ_2, and Φ_3, all in phase. Flux Φ_1 links the short-circuited ring on the left-hand pole, inducing a rather large current I_a. This current produces a flux Φ_a that lags behind Φ_1. Consequently, Φ_a also lags behind Φ_2 and Φ_3. The combined action of $(\Phi_2 + \Phi_3)$ and Φ_a produces a weak revolving field, which starts the motor. The direction of rotation is from the unshaded side to the shaded (ring) side of the pole. A similar torque is set up by the pole on the right. Flux Φ_2 induces a current I_b in the ring, and the resulting flux Φ_b lags behind Φ_2. As before, the combined action of $(\Phi_1 + \Phi_3)$ and Φ_b produces a weak revolving field that drives the rotor clockwise.

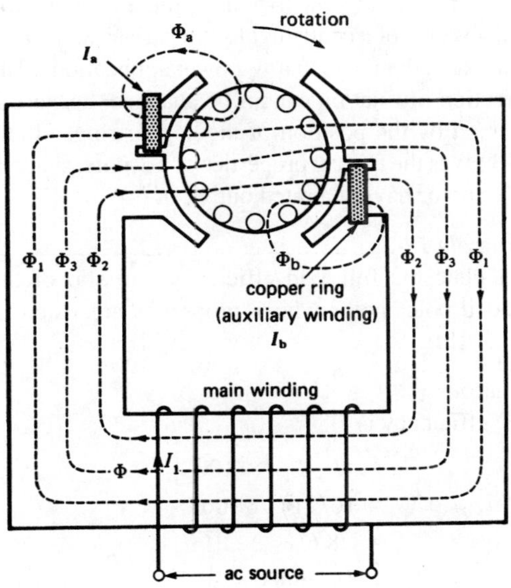

Figure 18.18a
Fluxes in a shaded-pole motor.

Figure 18.18b
Shaded-pole motor rated at 5 millihorsepower, 115 V, 60 Hz, 2900 r/min.
(Courtesy of Gould)

TABLE 18B

Properties of a Shaded-Pole Motor, Having 2 poles, Rated 6 W, 115 V, 60 Hz.

No-load	
current	0.26 A
input power	15 W
speed	3550 r/min
Locked rotor	
current	0.35 A
input power	24 W
torque	10 mN·m
Full-load	
current	0.33 A
input power	21 W
speed	2900 r/min
torque	19 mN·m
mechanical power	6 W
breakdown speed	2600 r/min
breakdown torque	21 mN·m

Although the starting torque, efficiency, and power factor are very low, the simple construction and absence of a centrifugal switch gives this motor a marked advantage in low-power applications. The direction of rotation cannot be changed, because it is fixed by the position of the copper rings. Table 18B gives the typical properties of a 2-pole, shaded-pole motor having a rated output of 6 W.

Example 18-3

Calculate the full-load efficiency and slip of the shaded-pole motor whose properties are listed in Table 18B.

Solution

The efficiency is

$$\eta = (P_o/P_i) \times 100 \quad (3.6)$$
$$= (6/21) \times 100$$
$$= 28.6\%$$
$$s = (n_s - n)/n_s$$
$$= (3600 - 2900)/3600$$
$$= 0.194 = 19.4\%$$

18.13 Universal motor

The single-phase universal motor is very similar to a dc series motor (Section 5.8). The basic construction of a small universal motor is shown in Fig. 18.19. The entire magnetic circuit is laminated to reduce

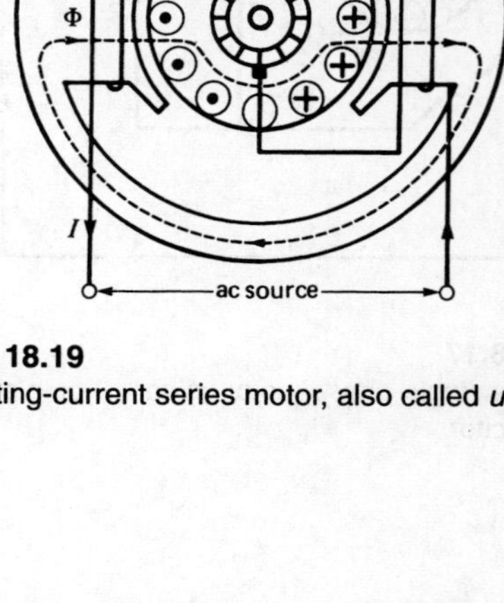

Figure 18.19
Alternating-current series motor, also called *universal motor.*

eddy-current losses. Such a motor can operate on either ac or dc, and the resulting torque-speed is about the same in each case. That is why it is called a *universal motor*.

When the motor is connected to an ac source, the ac current flows through the armature and the series field. The field produces an ac flux Φ that reacts with the current flowing in the armature to produce a torque. Because the armature current and the flux reverse simultaneously, the torque always acts in the same direction. No revolving field is produced in this type of machine; the principle of operation is the same as that of a dc series motor and it possesses the same basic characteristics.

The main advantage of fractional horsepower universal motors is their high speed and high starting torque. They can therefore be used to drive high-speed centrifugal blowers in vacuum cleaners. The high speed and corresponding small size for a given power output is also an advantage in driving portable tools, such as electric saws and drills. No-load speeds as high as 5000 to 15 000 r/min are possible but, as in any series motor, the speed drops rapidly with increasing load.

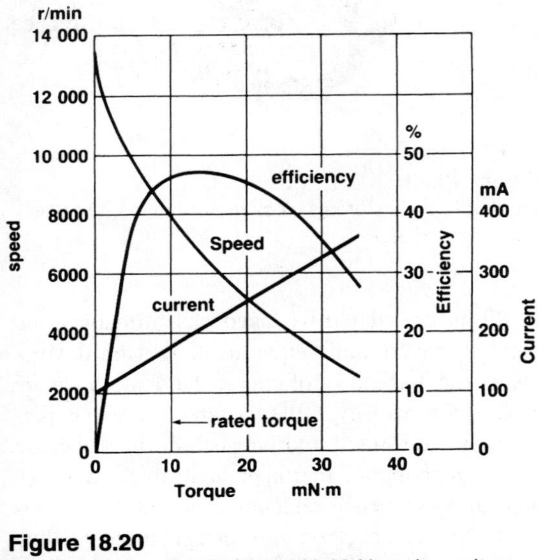

Figure 18.20
Characteristics of a small 115 V, 60 Hz universal motor having a full-load rating of 1/100 hp at 8000 r/min.

Series motors are built in many different sizes, starting from small toy motors to very large traction motors formerly used in some electric locomotives.

Fig. 18.20 gives the ac performance curves of a 115 V, 8000 r/min, universal motor rated at 1/100 hp. The full-load current is 175 mA.

18.14 Hysteresis motor

To understand the operating principle of a hysteresis motor, let us first consider Fig. 18.21. It shows a stationary rotor surrounded by a pair of N, S poles that can be rotated mechanically in a clockwise direction. The rotor is composed of a ceramic material of high coercive force. Thus, it is a permanent magnet material whose resistivity approaches that of an insulator. Consequently, it is impossible to set up eddy currents in such a rotor.

As the N, S field rotates, it magnetizes the rotor; consequently, poles of opposite polarity are continuously produced under the moving N, S poles. In effect, the revolving field is continuously reorienting the magnetic domains in the rotor. Clearly, the individual domains go through a complete cycle (or hysteresis loop) every time the field makes one complete revolution. Hysteresis losses are therefore produced in the rotor, proportional to the area of the hysteresis loop (Section 2.26). These losses are dissipated as heat in the rotor.

Let us assume that the hysteresis loss per revolution is E_h joules and that the field rotates at

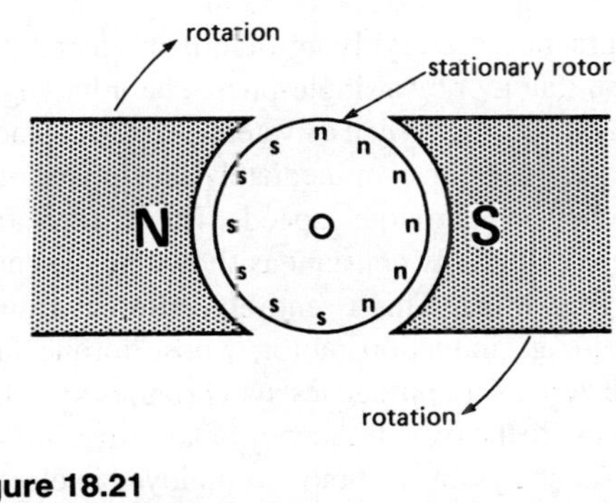

Figure 18.21
Permanent magnet rotor and a mechanically driven revolving field.

n revolutions per minute. The energy dissipated in the rotor per minute is

$$W = nE_h$$

The corresponding power (dissipated as heat) is

$$P_h = W/t \tag{3.4}$$
$$= nE_h/60 \text{ [W]}$$

However, the power dissipated in the rotor can only come from the mechanical power used to drive the N, S poles. This power is given by

$$P = nT/9.55 \tag{3.5}$$

Because $P = P_h$, we have

$$nT/9.55 = nE_h/60$$

whence

$$T = E_h/6.28 \tag{18.2}$$

where

T = torque exerted on the rotor [N·m]
E_h = hysteresis energy dissipated in the rotor, per turn [J/r]
6.28 = constant [exact value = 2π]

Eq. 18.2 brings out the remarkable feature that the torque needed to drive the magnets (Fig. 18.21) is constant, irrespective of the speed of rotation. In other words, whether the poles just barely creep around the rotor or whether they move at high speed, the torque exerted on the rotor is always the same. It is this basic property that distinguishes hysteresis motors from all other motors.

In practice, the revolving field is produced by a 3-phase stator, or by a single-phase stator having an auxiliary winding. When a hysteresis rotor is placed inside such a stator, it immediately accelerates until it reaches synchronous speed. The accelerating torque is essentially constant as shown by the curve (a) in Fig. 18.22. This is entirely different from a squirrel-cage induction motor, whose torque falls toward zero as it approaches synchronous speed.

Thanks to the fixed frequency of large distribution systems, the hysteresis motor is employed in electric clocks, and other precise timing devices (Fig. 18.23).

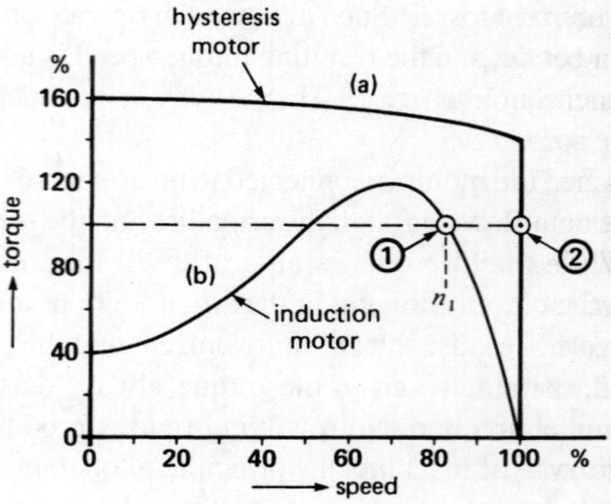

Figure 18.22
Typical torque-speed curves of two capacitor-run motors:
a. Hysteresis motor
b. Induction motor

Figure 18.23
Single-phase hysteresis clock motor having 32 poles and a ferrite rotor.

It is also used to drive tapedecks, turntables, and other precision audio equipment. In such devices the constant speed is, of course, the feature we are looking for. However, the hysteresis motor is particularly well suited to drive such devices because of their high inertia. Inertia prevents many synchronous motors (such as reluctance motors) from coming up to speed because to reach synchronism, they have to *suddenly* lock in with the revolving field.

No such abrupt transition occurs in the hysteresis motor because it develops a constant torque right up to synchronous speed.

In some turntable audio equipment these features are further enhanced by designing the motor to function as a vibration-free capacitor-run motor.

While the motor is accelerating, its full torque is available to carry the mechanical load and to overcome inertia. Once it reaches synchronous speed, the rotor poles are still magnetized and so the motor runs like an ordinary permanent-magnet sychronous motor. The rotor poles will lag behind the stator poles by a certain angle, whose magnitude depends upon the mechanical torque exerted by the load.

Example 18-4

A small 60 Hz hysteresis clock motor possesses 32 poles. In making one complete turn with respect to the revolving field, the hysteresis loss in the rotor amounts to 0.8 J.

Calculate

a. The pull-in and pull-out torques
b. The maximum power output before the motor stalls
c. The rotor losses when the motor is stalled
d. The rotor losses when the motor runs at synchronous speed

Solution

a. The pull-in and pull-out torques are about equal in a hysteresis motor:

$$T = E_h/6.28 = 0.8/6.28 \qquad (18.2)$$
$$= 0.127 \text{ N·m}$$

b. The synchronous speed is

$$n_s = 120 f/p = 120 \times 60/32$$
$$= 225 \text{ r/min}$$

The maximum power is

$$P = nT/9.55 = (225 \times 0.127)/9.55$$
$$= 3\text{W (or } 3/746 = 1/250 \text{ hp)}$$

c. When the motor stalls, the rotating field moves at 225 r/min with respect to the rotor. The energy loss per minute is, therefore,

$$W = 225 \times 0.8 = 180 \text{ J}$$

The power dissipated in the rotor is

$$P = W/t = 180/60 = 3 \text{ W}$$

d. There is no energy loss in the rotor when the motor runs at synchronous speed because the magnetic domains no longer reverse.

18.15 Synchronous reluctance motor

We can build a synchronous motor by milling out a standard squirrel-cage rotor so as to create a number of salient poles. The number of poles must be equal to the number of poles on the stator. Fig. 18.24 shows a rotor milled out to create four salient poles.

Such a *reluctance motor* starts up as a standard squirrel-cage motor but, when it approaches synchronous speed, the salient poles lock with the revolving field, and so the motor runs at synchronous speed. Both the pull-in and pull-out torques are weak, compared to those of a hysteresis motor of equal size. Furthermore, reluctance motors cannot accelerate high-inertia loads to synchronous speed. The reason can be seen by referring to Fig. 18.22. Suppose the motor has reached a speed n_1 corresponding to full-load torque (operating point 1).

The stator poles are slipping past the rotor poles at a rate that corresponds to the slip. If the

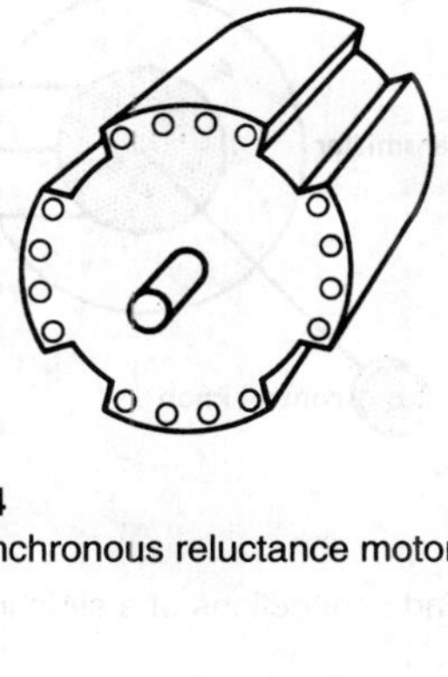

Figure 18.24
Rotor of a synchronous reluctance motor.

rotor is to lock with the revolving field, it must do so in the time it takes for one stator pole to sweep past a rotor pole. If pull-in is not achieved during this interval (Δt), it will never be achieved. The problem is that in going from speed n_1 to synchronous speed n_s, the kinetic energy of the revolving parts must increase by an amount given by Eq. 3.8:

$$\Delta E_k = 5.48 \times 10^{-3} J(n_s^2 - n_1^2) \quad (18.3)$$

where J is the moment of inertia.
Furthermore, the time interval is given by

$$\Delta t = 60/(n_s - n_1)p \quad (18.4)$$

Consequently, to reach synchronous speed, the motor must develop an accelerating power P_a of at least

$$P_a = \Delta E_k/\Delta t \quad (18.5)$$
$$= 1.8 \times 10^{-4} n_s(n_s - n_1)^2 Jp \text{ (approx.)}$$

Furthermore, the motor must continue to supply the power P_L demanded by the load. If the sum of $P_a + P_L$ exceeds the power capacity of the motor, it will never pull into step. In essence, a reluctance motor can only synchronize when the slip speed is small and the moment of inertia J is low.

Despite this drawback, the reluctance motor is cheaper than any other type of synchronous motor. It is particularly well adapted to variable-frequency electronic speed control. Inertia is then no problem because the speed of the revolving field always tracks with the speed of the rotor. Three-phase reluctance motors of several hundred horsepower have been built, using this approach.

18.16 Synchro drive

In some remote-control systems we may have to move the position of a small rheostat that is one or two meters away. This problem is easily solved by using a flexible shaft. But if the rheostat is 100 m away, the flexible-shaft solution becomes impractical. We then employ an electrical shaft to tie the knob and rheostat together. How does such a shaft work?

Consider two conventional wound-rotor induction motors whose 3-phase stators are connected in parallel (Fig. 18.25). Two phases of the respective rotors are also connected in parallel and energized from a *single-phase* source. The remarkable feature about this arrangement is that the rotor on one machine will automatically track with the rotor on the other. Thus, if we slowly turn rotor A clockwise through 17°, rotor B will move clockwise through 17°. Obviously, such a system enables us to control a rheostat from a remote location.

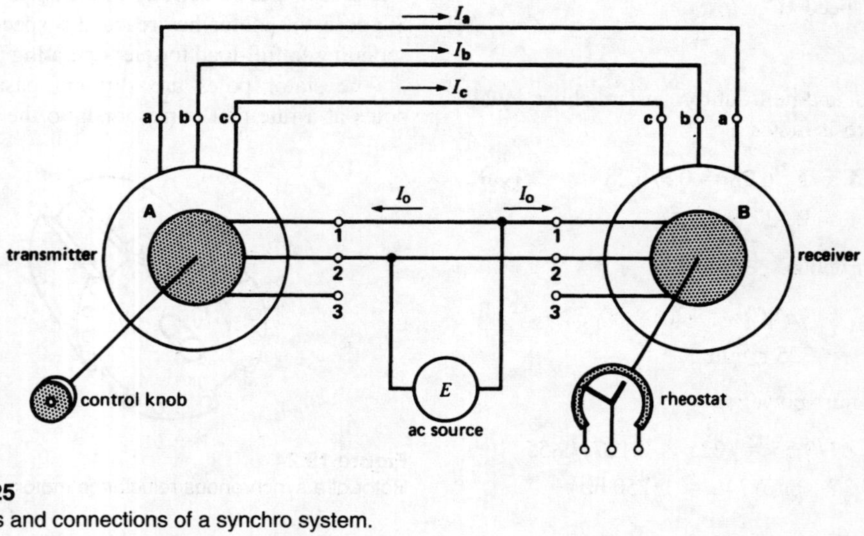

Figure 18.25
Components and connections of a synchro system.

Two miniature wound-rotor motors are required. One (the transmitter) is coupled to a control knob, and the other (the receiver) is coupled to the rheostat. The 5-conductor cable (conductors a-b-c-1-2) linking the transmitter and receiver constitutes the flexible electrical shaft.

The behavior of this *selsyn* or *synchro* control system is explained as follows. Assume that the transmitter and receiver are identical and the rotors are in identical positions. When the rotors are excited, they behave like the primaries of two transformers, inducing voltages in the respective stator windings. The voltages induced in the three stator windings of the transmitter are always unequal because the windings are displaced from each other by 120°. The same is true for the voltages induced in the stator of the receiver.

Nevertheless, no matter what the respective stator voltages of the transmitter and receiver may be, they are identical in both synchros (phase by phase) when the rotors occupy the same position. The stator voltages then balance each other and, consequently, no current flows in the lines connecting the stators. The rotors, however, carry a small exciting current I_o.

Now if we turn the rotor of the transmitter, its three stator voltages will change. They will no longer balance the stator voltages of the receiver; consequently, currents I_a, I_b, I_c will flow in the lines connecting the two devices. These currents produce a torque on both rotors, tending to line them up. Since the rotor of the receiver is free to move, it will line up with the transmitter. As soon as the rotors are aligned, the stator voltages are again in balance (phase by phase), and the torque-producing currents disappear.

Synchros are often employed to indicate the position of an antenna, a valve, a gun turret, and so on, with the result that the torque requirements are small. Such transmitters and receivers are built with watch-like precision to ensure that they will track with as little error as possible.

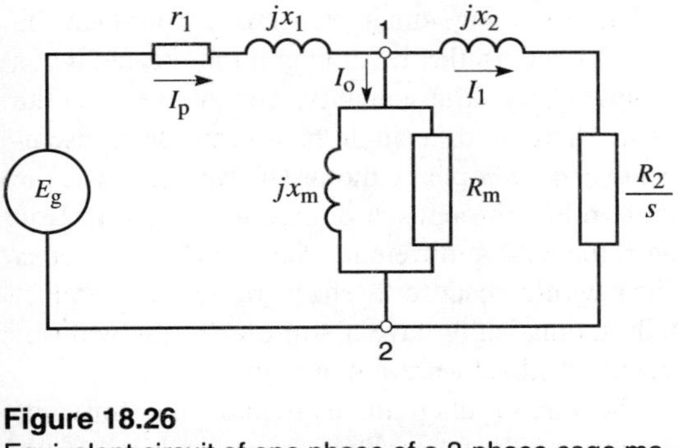

Figure 18.26
Equivalent circuit of one phase of a 3-phase cage motor referred to the primary (stator) side.

EQUIVALENT CIRCUIT OF A SINGLE-PHASE MOTOR

In Chapter 15 we developed the equivalent circuit (Fig. 15.6) for one phase of a 3-phase induction motor. This circuit is reproduced in Fig. 18.26, with the exception that the magnetizing branch has been moved to the technically correct position between points 1 and 2. The reason for the change is that most single-phase motors are fractional horsepower machines for which the exact circuit diagram is needed to get reasonably accurate results. Using this model, we now develop a similar equivalent circuit for a single-phase motor.

18.17 Magnetomotive force distribution

In order to optimize the starting torque, efficiency, power factor, and noise level of a single-phase motor, the magnetomotive force produced by each stator pole must be distributed sinusoidally across the pole face. That is the reason for using the special number of turns (10, 20, 25, and 30) on the four concentric coils shown in Fig. 18.3a.

Let us examine the mmf created by one of the four poles when the concentric coils carry a peak current of, say, 2 amperes. Table 18C shows the distribution of the mmf, using the slot numbers as a measure of distance along the pole. For example, the 25-turn coil lodged in slots 2 and 8 (Fig. 18.27), produces between these slots an mmf of $25 \times 2 = 50$ amperes (or ampere-turns). Similarly, the 10-turn coil in slots 4 and 6 produces between these slots an mmf of 20 A.

The distribution of these mmfs is illustrated in Fig. 18.27. The total mmf produced in the middle of the pole is $60 + 50 + 40 + 20 = 170$ A and it drops

TABLE 18C

Coil pitch	Turns	Mmf
slot 1–9	30	2 × 30 = 60 A
slot 2–8	25	2 × 25 = 50 A
slot 3–7	20	2 × 20 = 40 A
slot 4–6	10	2 × 10 = 20 A
	85 turns	170 ampere-turns

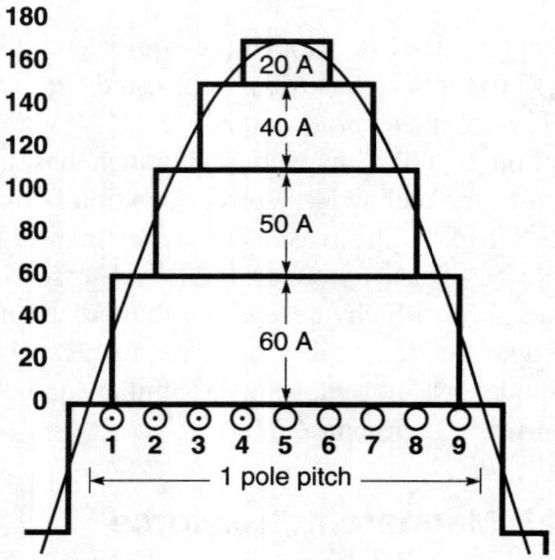

Figure 18.27
Distribution of the magnetomotive force across one pole when current is 2 A.

off in steps on either side of center. Adjacent poles have the same mmf distribution but with opposite magnetic polarities.

We have superimposed upon this figure a smooth mmf having a perfectly sinusoidal distribution. It reveals that the stepped mmf produced by the four concentric coils tracks the sine wave very closely. Indeed, we could replace the stepped mmf by a sinusoidal mmf without introducing a significant error.

The current flowing in the four coils alternates sinusoidally (in time) at the line frequency of 60 Hz. Consequently, as the current varies, the mmf varies in proportion. For example, when the current is momentarily 0.4 A, the mmf distribution remains sinusoidal, but the mmf in the center of the pole will be only 0.4 A × 85 turns = 34 A. Subsequently, when the current reverses and is equal to, say, −1.2 A, the mmf will also reverse. However, the mmf will still be distributed sinusoidally but with a peak value in the center of −1.2 A × 85 turns = −102 A.

We conclude that the ac current produces a pulsating mmf, which is distributed sinusoidally across each pole and whose amplitude varies sinusoidally in time. Thus, unlike the mmf produced by a 3-phase stator, the mmf of a single-phase stator does not rotate but remains fixed in place.

18.18 Revolving mmfs in a single-phase motor

It can be proved mathematically that a stationary pulsating mmf having a peak amplitude M can be replaced by two mmfs having a *fixed* amplitude $M/2$ revolving in opposite directions at synchronous speed. Referring to our previous example, a 4-pole pulsating mmf that reaches positive and negative peaks of 170 A at a frequency of 60 Hz can be replaced by two 4-pole mmfs having a constant amplitude of 85 A rotating in opposite directions at 1800 r/min. The revolving mmfs are also distributed sinusoidally in space. As the oppositely moving mmfs take up successive positions, the sum of their magnitudes at any point in space is equal to the pulsating mmf at that point. This can be seen by referring to Fig. 18.28, which shows a portion of the forward and backward revolving fields (mmf_F and mmf_B), sweeping past the stationary but pulsating mmf.

The revolving mmfs respectively produce the same effect as the revolving mmf created by a 3-phase stator. Consequently, we would expect the circuit diagram of a single-phasor motor to resemble that of a 3-phase motor. However, since the mmfs rotate in opposite directions, their effect on the rotor will be different. Thus, if the rotor has a slip s with respect to the forward-moving mmf, it will automatically have a slip of $(2 - s)$ with respect to the backward-moving mmf.

The circuit diagram as regards the forward-moving mmf having a slip s is shown in Fig. 18.29a.

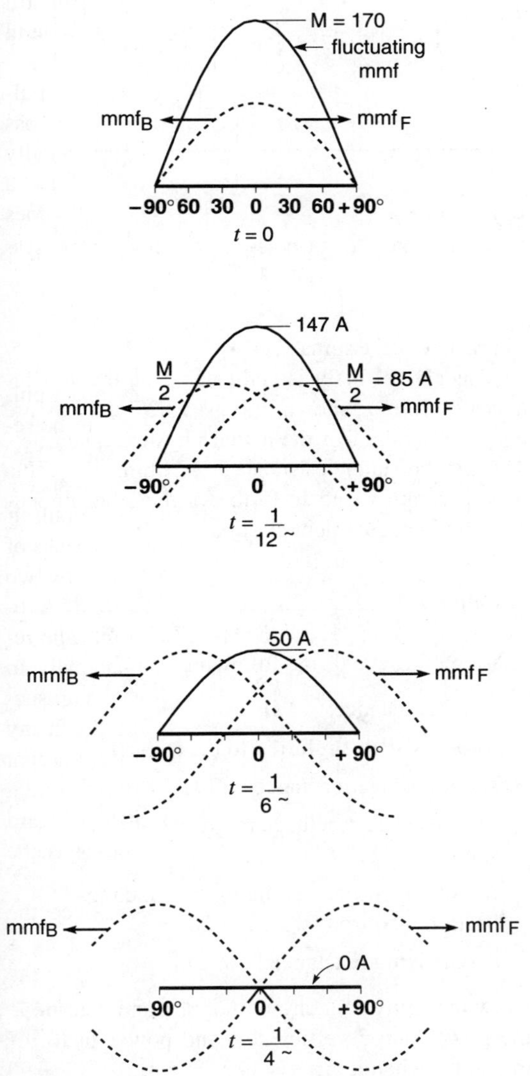

Figure 18.28
The pulsating mmf having a peak amplitude of 170 A can be represented by a forward and backward revolving mmf having a fixed amplitude of 85 A. Shown are successive positions of mmf_F and mmf_B and the corresponding amplitude of the stationary, pulsating mmf.

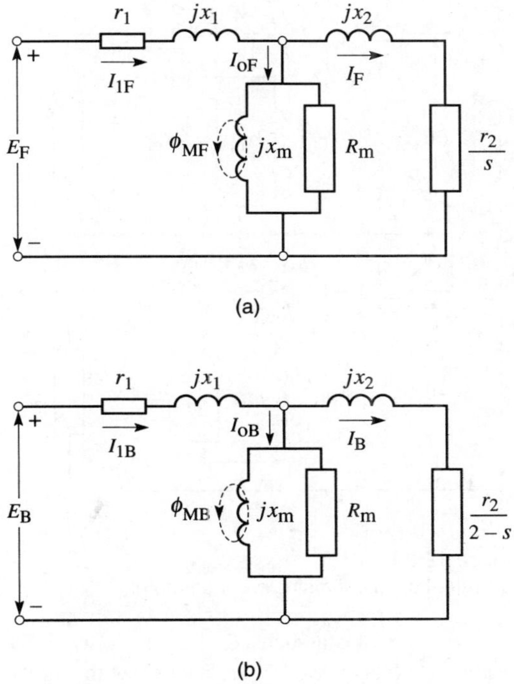

Figure 18.29
a. Equivalent circuit as regards the forward-moving mmf.
b. Equivalent circuit as regards the backward-moving mmf.

Similarly, the circuit diagram for the backward-revolving mmf having a slip $(2 - s)$ is shown in Fig. 18.29b. For the moment we will not define the physical meaning of r_1, r_2, x_1, x_2, etc., except to say that they are related to the stator and rotor resistances and reactances. How should we merge these two diagrams into a single diagram to represent the single-phase motor?

18.19 Deducing the circuit diagram of a single-phase motor

First, we know that the oppositely rotating mmfs have the same magnitude. Consequently, the stator currents I_{1F} and I_{1B} are identical, which means that the two circuits can be connected in series. Second, the *forward*

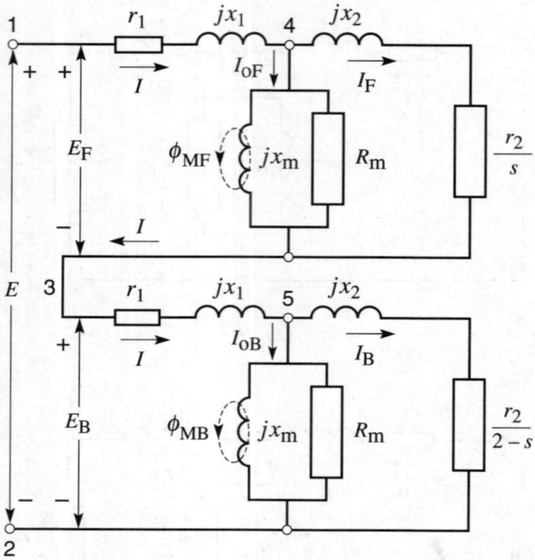

Figure 18.30
Equivalent circuit of a single-phase motor.

stator voltage E_F is associated with mmf_F, while the *backward* voltage E_B is associated with mmf_B. Because the circuits are in series, the sum of these voltages must be equal to the voltage E applied to the stator. It follows that the equivalent circuit of the single-phase motor can be represented by Fig. 18.30.

To interpret the meaning of the circuit parameters r_1, r_2, x_1, x_2, etc., suppose the motor is stationary, in which case the slip $s = 1$. Under these conditions, the forward and backward circuits are identical. The circuit of Fig. 18.30 therefore reduces to that shown in Fig. 18.31. In essence, the motor behaves like a simple transformer in which the secondary winding (the rotor) is in short-circuit. It reveals that the parameters r_1, x_1, etc., represent the following physical elements:

$2r_1$ = stator resistance

$2r_2$ = rotor resistance referred to the stator

$2jx_1$ = stator leakage reactance

$2jx_2$ = rotor leakage reactance referred to the stator

$2R_m$ = resistance corresponding to the windage, friction, and iron losses

$2jX_m$ = magnetizing reactance

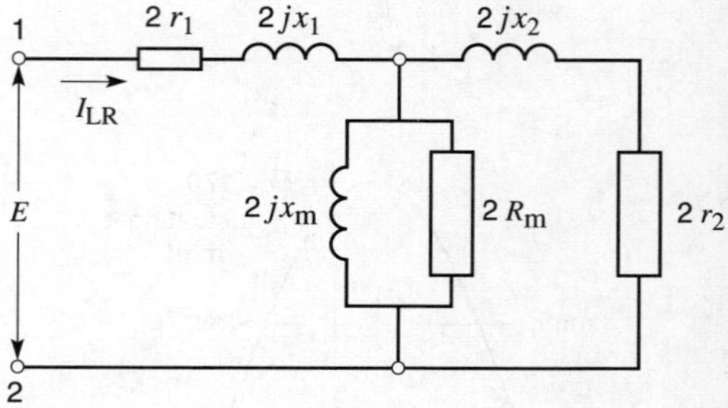

Figure 18.31
Equivalent circuit of a single-phase motor at standstill.

In practice we assume $x_1 = x_2$.

The above analysis indicates that the impedances r_1, x_1, etc., shown in Figs. 18.29 to 18.31 are equal to one-half of the actual physical quantities. Thus, if the stator resistance is 10 ohms, the value of r_1 is 5 ohms, and so forth, for the other impedances in the equivalent circuit.

Example 18-5

A test on a 1/4 hp, 120 V, 60 Hz, 1725 r/min, single-phase motor reveals the following results:

stator resistance: 2 Ω

rotor resistance referred to the stator: 4 Ω

stator leakage reactance: 3 Ω

rotor leakage reactance referred to the stator: 3 Ω

resistance corresponding to the windage, friction, and iron losses: 600 Ω

magnetizing reactance: 60 Ω

Draw the equivalent circuit diagram and determine the power output, efficiency, and power factor of the motor when it turns at 1725 r/min.

Solution

The equivalent circuit diagram (Fig. 18.32) shows the values of the listed impedances divided by two. The slip is $s = (1800 - 1725)/1800 = 0.0417$.

We first determine the impedance of the forward circuit between points **1, 3:**

$$Z_F = 1 + j\,1.5 + \cfrac{1}{\cfrac{1}{j\,30} + \cfrac{1}{300} + \cfrac{1}{48 + j\,1.5}}$$

$$= 1 + j\,1.5 + 13.89 + j\,19.53$$

$$= 14.89 + j\,21.03$$

The impedance of the backward circuit between points **3, 2** is

$$Z_B = 1 + j\,1.5 + \cfrac{1}{\cfrac{1}{j\,30} + \cfrac{1}{300} + \cfrac{1}{1.02 + j\,1.5}}$$

$$= 1 + j\,1.5 + 0.93 + j\,1.45$$

$$= 1.93 + j\,2.95$$

The current in the stator is

$$I = E/(Z_F + Z_B) = 120/(16.82 + j\,23.98)$$

$$= 120/(29.29\angle 54.95)$$

$$\therefore I = 4.097\angle -54.95$$

The forward voltage between points **1, 3** is

$$E_B = I\,Z_F = 4.097\angle -54.95 \times (14.89 + j\,21.03)$$

$$= 4.097\angle -54.95 \times 25.77\angle 54.7$$

$$= 105.6\angle -0.25$$

The backward voltage between points **3, 2** is

$$E_B = I\,Z_B = 4.097\angle -54.95 \times (1.93 + j\,2.95)$$

$$= 4.097\angle -54.95 \times 3.52\angle 56.8$$

$$= 14.42\angle 1.85$$

Forward rotor current

$$I_F = I\frac{\cfrac{1}{\cfrac{1}{j\,30} + \cfrac{1}{300} + \cfrac{1}{48 + j\,1.5}}}{48 + j\,1.5}$$

$$= \frac{4.097\angle -54.95(13.89 + j\,19.53)}{48.02\angle 1.79}$$

$$= \frac{4.097\angle -54.95 \times 23.96\angle 54.58}{48.02\angle 1.79}$$

$$= 2.044\angle -2.16$$

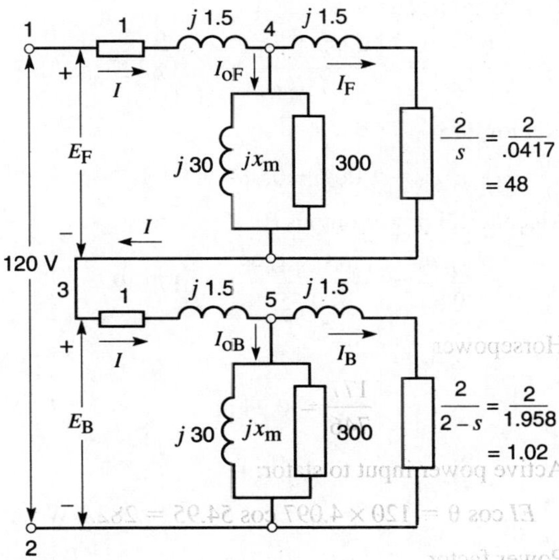

Figure 18.32
See Example 18-5.

Backward rotor current

$$I_B = I\frac{\cfrac{1}{\cfrac{1}{j\,30} + \cfrac{1}{300} + \cfrac{1}{1.02 + j\,1.5}}}{1.02 + j\,1.5}$$

$$= \frac{4.097\angle -54.95\,(0.93 + j\,1.45)}{1.81\angle 55.78}$$

$$= \frac{4.097\angle -54.95 \times 1.72\angle 57.32}{1.81\angle 55.78}$$

$$= 3.89\angle -53.4$$

Forward power to rotor

$$P_F = I_F^2 \times 48 = 2.044^2 \times 48 = 200.5\ \text{W}$$

Forward torque T_F:

$$\frac{9.55\,P_F}{n_s} = \frac{9.55 \times 200.5}{1800} = 1.064\ \text{N·m}$$

Backward power to rotor P_B

$$I_B^2 \times 1.02 = 3.89^2 \times 1.02 = 15.4\ \text{W}$$

Backward torque T_B

$$\frac{9.55\ P_B}{n_s} = \frac{9.55 \times 15.4}{1800} = 0.082 \text{ N·m}$$

Net torque

$$T_F - T_B = 1.064 - 0.082 = 0.982 \text{ N·m}$$

Mechanical power output P

$$\frac{nT}{9.55} = \frac{1725 \times 0.982}{9.55} = 177 \text{ W}$$

Horsepower

$$\frac{177}{746} = 0.24 \text{ hp}$$

Active power input to stator:

$$EI \cos \theta = 120 \times 4.097 \cos 54.95 = 282.3 \text{ W}$$

Power factor

$$\cos 54.95 = 0.57 = 57\%$$

Efficiency

$$\frac{177}{282} = 0.627 = 62.7\%$$

Questions and Problems

Practical level

18-1 A 6-pole, single-phase motor is connected to a 60 Hz source. What is its synchronous speed?

18-2 What is the purpose of the auxiliary winding in a single-phase induction motor? How can we change the rotation of such a motor?

18-3 State the main difference between a split-phase motor and a capacitor-start motor. What are their relative advantages?

18-4 Explain briefly how a shaded-pole motor operates.

18-5 List some of the properties and advantages of a universal motor.

18-6 Why are some single-phase motors equipped with a resilient mounting? Is such a mounting necessary on 3-phase motors?

18-7 What is the main advantage of a capacitor-run motor?

18-8 Which of the motors discussed in this chapter is best suited to drive the following loads:

a. A small portable drill
b. A 3/4 hp air compressor
c. A vacuum cleaner
d. A 1/100 hp blower
e. A 1/3 hp centrifugal pump
f. A 1/4 hp fan for use in a hospital ward
g. An electric timer
h. A hi-fi turntable

Intermediate level

18-9 Referring to Fig. 18.11, the effective impedance of the main and auxiliary windings under locked-rotor conditions are given as follows:

	Effective resistance	Effective reactance
Main winding	4 Ω	7.5 Ω
Auxiliary winding	7.5 Ω	4 Ω

If the line voltage is 119 V, calculate the following:

a. The magnitude of I_a and I_s
b. The phase angle between I_a and I_s
c. The line current I_L
d. The power factor under locked-rotor conditions

18-10 The palm of the human hand can just barely tolerate a temperature of 130°F. If the full-load temperature of the frame of a 1/4 hp motor is 64°C in an ambient temperature of 76°F,

a. Can a person keep his hand on the frame?
b. Is the motor running too hot?

18-11 Referring to Fig. 18.13, if the motor is connected to a load whose torque is constant at 4 N·m, explain the resulting behavior of the motor when it is switched on the line.

18-12 **a.** A single-phase motor vibrates at a frequency of 100 Hz. What is the frequency of the power line?
b. A capacitor-run motor does not have to be set in a resilient mounting. Why?
c. A 4-pole, 60 Hz, single-phase hysteresis motor develops a torque of 6 in·lb when running at 1600 r/min. Calculate the hysteresis loss per revolution [J].

18-13 Referring to the 6 W, shaded-pole motor in Table 18B, calculate the following:
a. The rated power output in millihorsepower
b. The full-load power factor
c. The slip at the breakdown torque
d. The per unit no-load current and locked-rotor current

18-14 Referring again to Fig. 18.13, calculate the following:
a. The locked-rotor torque [ft·lbf]
b. The per-unit value of the LR torque
c. The starting torque when only the main winding is excited
d. The per-unit breakdown torque
e. How are the torque-speed curves affected if the line voltage falls from 115 V to 100 V?

Advanced level

18-15 In Table 18A, calculate the following:
a. The voltage across the capacitor under locked-rotor conditions
b. The corresponding phase angle between I_s and I_a

18-16 Referring to Fig. 18.16, if the capacitor-run motor operates at full-load, calculate the following:
a. The line current I_L
b. The power factor of the motor
c. The active power absorbed by each winding
d. The efficiency of the motor

18-17 The motor described in Table 18A has an LR power factor of 0.9 lagging. It is installed in a workshop situated 600 ft from a home, where the main service entrance is located. The line is composed of a 2-conductor cable made of No. 12 gauge copper. The ambient temperature is 25°C and the service entrance voltage is 122 V. Using Table AX3 in the Appendix, calculate the following:
a. The resistance of the transmission line
b. The starting current and the voltage at the motor terminals
c. The starting torque [N·m]

Industrial application

18-18 A 3 hp, 1725 r/min, 230 V, totally enclosed, fan-cooled, capacitor-start, capacitor-run, single-phase motor manufactured by Baldor Electric Company has the following properties:

no-load current: 5 A

locked-rotor current: 90 A

full-load current: 15 A

locked-rotor torque: 30 lbf·ft

full-load efficiency: 79%

breakdown torque: 20 lbf·ft

full-load power factor: 87%

service factor: 1.15

full-load torque: 9 lbf·ft

mass: 97 lb

Using the above information, calculate the following:
a. The per-unit values of locked-rotor torque, locked-rotor current, and breakdown torque
b. The full-load torque expressed in newton-meters
c. The capacitor that could be added across the stator so that the full-load power factor rises from 87% to 90%

18-19 A 3/4 hp, 1725 r/min, 230 V, totally enclosed, fan-cooled, capacitor-start, single-phase motor manufactured by

Baldor Electric Company has the following properties:

no-load current: 4.4 A

locked-rotor current: 30 A

full-load current: 5.3 A

locked-rotor torque: 9.5 lbf·ft

locked-rotor power factor: 58%

full-load efficiency: 66%

breakdown torque: 6.1 lbf·ft

full-load power factor: 68%

service factor: 1.25

full-load torque: 2.25 lbf·ft

mass: 29 lb

The motor is fed by a 2-conductor No. 12 copper cable that has a National Electrical Code rating of 20 A. The cable is 240 feet long and is fed from the service entrance where the voltage is 230 V ±5%.

Using the above information, determine the following:

a. The lowest starting torque (newton-meters), assuming a cable temperature of 25°C

b. We wish to raise the power factor of the motor to 90% at full-load by installing a capacitor across its terminals. Calculate the approximate value of the capacitance, in microfarads.

CHAPTER 19

Stepper Motors

19.0 Introduction

Stepper motors are special motors that are used when motion and position have to be precisely controlled. As their name implies, stepper motors rotate in discrete steps, each step corresponding to a pulse that is supplied to one of its stator windings. Depending on its design, a stepper motor can advance by 90°, 45°, 18°, or by as little as a fraction of a degree per pulse. By varying the pulse rate, the motor can be made to advance very slowly, one step at a time, or to rotate stepwise at speeds as high as 4000 r/min.

Stepper motors can turn clockwise or counterclockwise, depending upon the sequence of the pulses that are applied to the windings.

The behavior of a stepper motor depends greatly upon the power supply that drives it. The power supply generates the pulses, which in turn are usually initiated by a microprocessor. The pulses are counted and stored, clockwise (cw) pulses being (+) while counterclockwise (ccw) pulses are (−). As a result, the net number of steps is known *exactly* at all times. It follows that the number of revolutions is always precisely known to an accuracy of one step. This permits the motor to be used as a precise positioning device in machine tools, X-Y plotters, typewriters, tapedecks, valves, and printers.

In this chapter we will cover the operating principle of the more common stepper motors, together with their properties and limitations. We will also discuss the types of drives used to actuate these machines.

19.1 Elementary stepper motor

A very simple stepper motor is shown in Fig. 19.1. It consists of a stator having three salient poles and a 2-pole rotor made of soft iron. The windings can be successively connected to a dc power supply by means of three switches A, B, C.

When the switches are open, the rotor can take up any position. However, if switch A is closed, the resulting magnetic field created by pole 1 will attract the rotor and so it will line up as shown. If we now open switch A and simultaneously close switch B, the rotor will line up with pole 2. In so doing, it will rotate ccw by 60°. Next, if we open switch B and simultaneously close switch C, the rotor will turn ccw by an additional 60°, this time lining up with pole 3.

Clearly, we can make the rotor advance ccw in 60° steps by closing and opening the switches in the sequence A, B, C, A, B, C, ... Furthermore, we

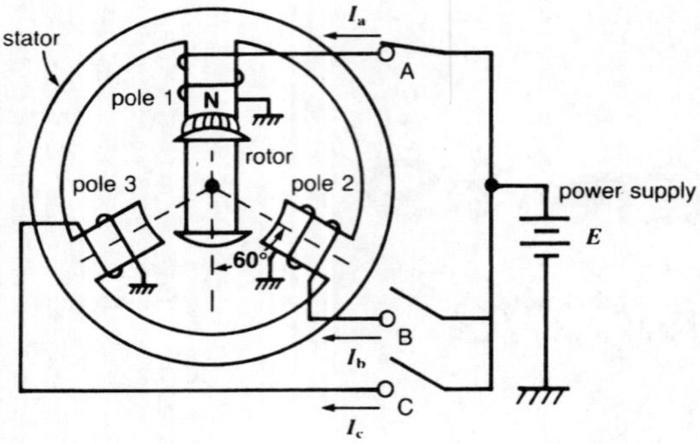

Figure 19.1
Simple stepper motor in which each step moves the rotor by 60°.

can reverse the rotation by operating the switches in the reverse sequence A, C, B, A, C, B. . . . In order to fix the final position of the rotor, the last switch that was closed in a switching sequence must remain closed. This holds the rotor in its last position and prevents it from moving under the influence of external torques. In this stationary state the motor will remain locked provided the external torque does not exceed the *holding torque* of the motor.

In moving from one position to the next, the motion of the rotor will be influenced by the inertia and the frictional forces that come into play. We now examine the nature of these forces.

19.2 Effect of inertia

Suppose the motor operates at no-load and that the rotor has a low inertia and a small amount of bearing friction. It is initially facing pole 1. Let this correspond to the zero degree (0°) angular position. At the moment switch A opens and switch B closes, the rotor will start accelerating ccw toward pole 2. It rapidly picks up speed and soon reaches the center line of pole 2, where it should come to rest. However, the rotor is now moving with considerable speed and it will overshoot the center line. As it does so, the magnetic field of pole 2 will pull it in the opposite direction, thereby braking the rotor. The rotor will come to a halt and start moving in the opposite (cw) direction. Picking up speed, it will again overshoot the center line of pole 2, whereupon the magnetic field will exert a pull in the ccw direction.

The rotor will therefore oscillate like a pendulum around the center line of pole 2. The oscillations will gradually die out because of bearing friction. Fig. 19.2 shows the angular position of the rotor as a function of time. The rotor starts at 0° (center of pole 1) and reaches 60° (center line of pole 2) after 2 ms. It overshoots the center line by 30° before coming to a halt (at 3 ms). The rotor now moves in reverse and again crosses the center line at $t = 4$ ms.

The oscillations continue this way, gradually diminishing in amplitude until the rotor comes to rest at $t > 10$ ms.

The reader will note that in Fig. 19.2 we have also drawn the instantaneous speed of the rotor as a function of time. The speed can be given in revolutions per second, but for stepper motors it is more meaningful to speak of degrees per second. The speed is momentarily zero at $t = 3$ ms, 5 ms, 7 ms, and becomes permanently zero at $t > 10$ ms. The speed is greatest whenever the rotor crosses the center line of pole 2. Clearly, the oscillations last a relatively long time before the rotor settles down.

Without making any other changes, suppose we increase the inertia of the rotor by mounting a flywheel on the shaft. We discover that both the period and the amplitude of the oscillations increase when the inertia increases. In Fig. 19.3, for example, the time to reach the 60° position has increased from 2 ms to 4 ms. Furthermore, the amplitude of the oscillations has increased. The rotor also takes a longer time to settle down (20 ms instead of 10 ms).

The oscillations can be damped by increasing the friction. For example, if the bearing friction is raised sufficiently, the oscillations shown in Fig. 19.3 can be suppressed so as to give only a single overshoot, shown in Fig. 19.4. In practice, the damping is accomplished by using an eddy-current brake or a viscous damper. A viscous damper uses a fluid such as oil or air to brake the rotor whenever it is

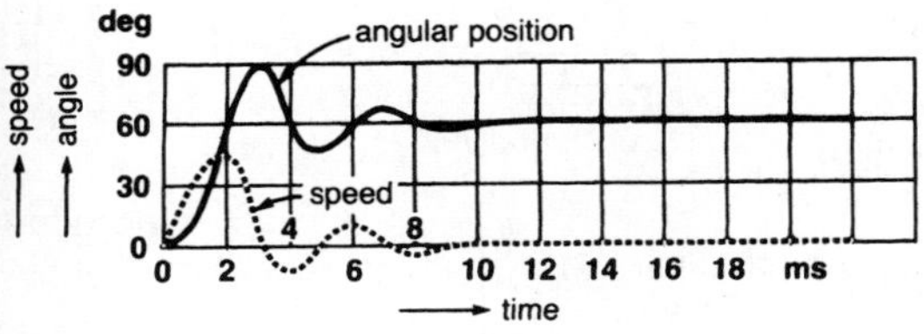

Figure 19.2
In moving from pole 1 to pole 2, the rotor oscillates around its 60° position before coming to rest. The speed is zero whenever the rotor reaches the limit of its overshoot.

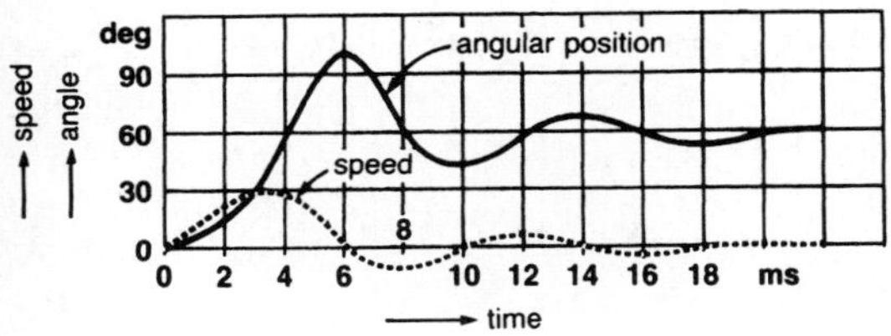

Figure 19.3
Same conditions as in Fig. 19.2, except that the inertia is greater. The overshoot is greater and the rotor takes longer to settle down.

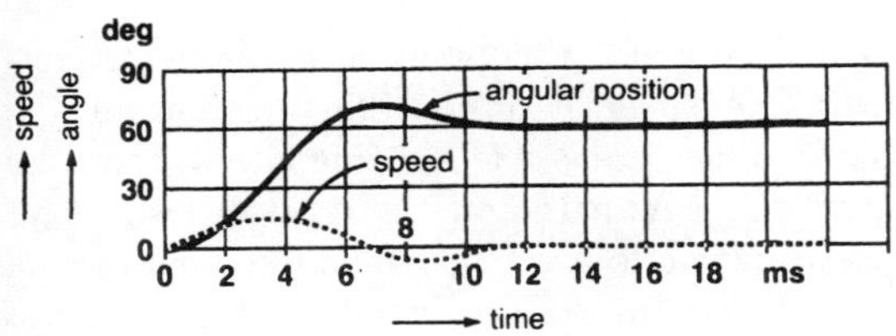

Figure 19.4
Same conditions as in Fig. 19.3, except that viscous damping has been added.

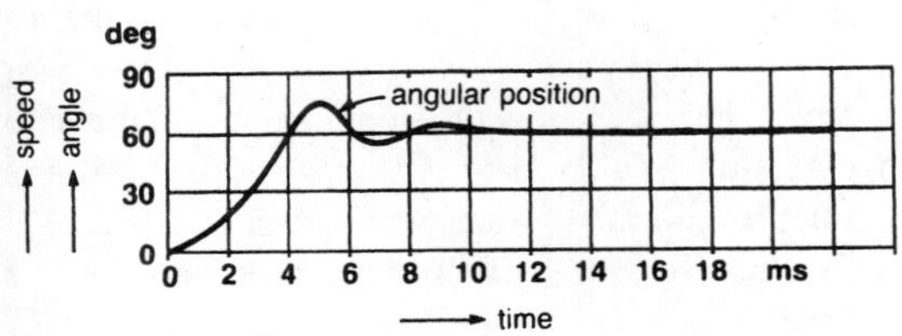

Figure 19.5
Same conditions as in Fig. 19.2, except that the rotor is coupled to a mechanical load.

moving. Viscous damping means that the braking effect is proportional to speed; it is therefore zero when the rotor is at rest.

19.3 Effect of a mechanical load

Let us return to the condition shown in Fig. 19.2, where the rotor has low inertia and a small amount of viscous damping due to bearing friction. If the rotor is coupled to a mechanical load while it is moving, the effect is shown in Fig. 19.5. As we would expect, it takes longer for the motor to attain the 60° position (compare 2 ms in Fig. 19.2 with 4 ms in Fig. 19.5). Furthermore, the overshoot is smaller and the oscillations are damped more quickly.

In summary, both the mechanical load and the inertia increase the stepping time. The oscillations also prolong the time before the rotor settles down. Therefore, in order to obtain fast stepping response, the inertia of the rotor (and its load) should be as small as possible and the oscillations should be suppressed by using a viscous damper.

The time to move from one position to the next can also be reduced by increasing the current in the winding. However, thermal limitations due to I^2R losses dictate the maximum current that can be used.

Returning to Fig. 19.1, let us excite the windings in succession so that the motor rotates. Fig. 19.6 shows the current pulses I_a, I_b, I_c and the instantaneous position of the rotor (as well as its speed) when the motor makes one-half revolution. We assume that the stepper motor has some inertia and that it is driving a mechanical load. Note that the speed of the rotor is zero at the beginning and at the end of each pulse. In this figure the pulses have a duration of 8 ms. Consequently, the stepping rate is 1000/8 = 125 steps per second. One revolution requires 6 steps, and so it takes 6 ÷ 125 = 0.048 s to complete one turn. The *average* speed is, therefore, 60/0.048 = 1250 revolutions per minute. However, the stepper motor rotates in start-stop jumps and not as smoothly as an ordinary motor would.

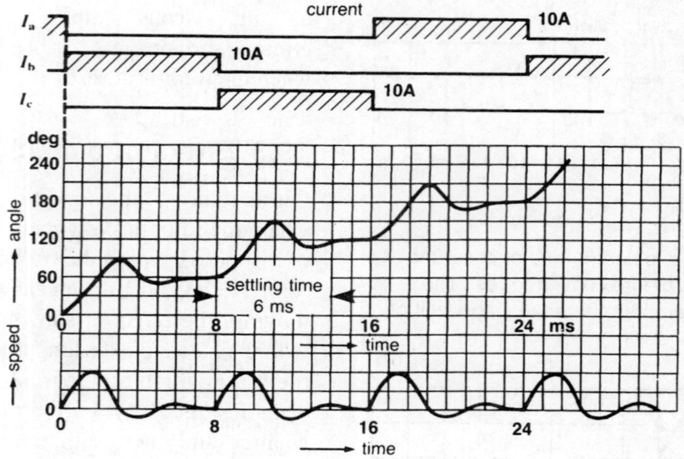

Figure 19.6
Graph of current pulses, angular position, and instantaneous speed of rotor during the first four steps. Three steps (24 ms) produce one half-revolution.

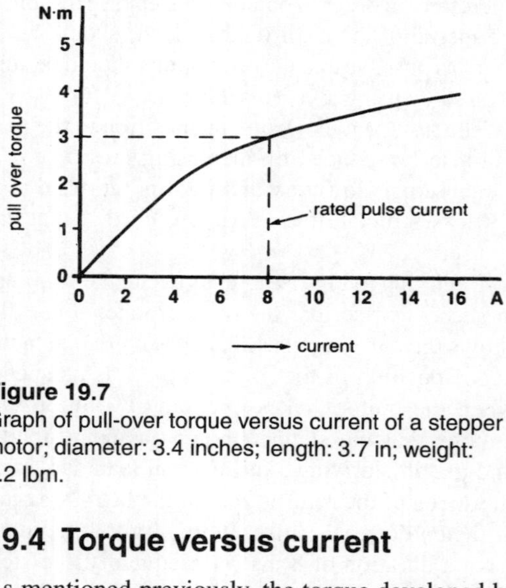

Figure 19.7
Graph of pull-over torque versus current of a stepper motor; diameter: 3.4 inches; length: 3.7 in; weight: 5.2 lbm.

19.4 Torque versus current

As mentioned previously, the torque developed by a stepper motor depends upon the current. Fig. 19.7 shows the relationship between the two for a typical stepper motor. When the current is 8 A, the motor develops a torque of 3 N·m. This is the torque that the motor can exert while moving from one position to the next, so it is called the *pull-over* torque.

When the motor is at rest, a holding current must continue to flow in the last winding that was excited so that the rotor remains locked in place.

19.5 Start-stop stepping rate

When the stepping motor inches along in the start-stop fashion shown in Fig. 19.6, there is an upper limit to the permissible stepping rate. If the pulse rate of the current in the windings is too fast, the rotor is unable to accurately follow the pulses, and steps will be lost. This defeats the whole purpose of the motor, which is to correlate its instantaneous position (steps) with the number of net (+ and −) pulses. In order to maintain synchronism, the rotor must settle down before advancing to the next position. Referring to Fig. 19.6, this means that the interval between successive steps must be at least 6 ms, which means that the stepping rate is limited to a maximum of 1000/6 = 167 steps per second (sps).

Bearing in mind what was said in Section 19.2, it is clear that the maximum number of steps per second depends upon the load torque and the inertia of the system. The higher the load and the greater the inertia, the lower will be the allowable number of steps per second.

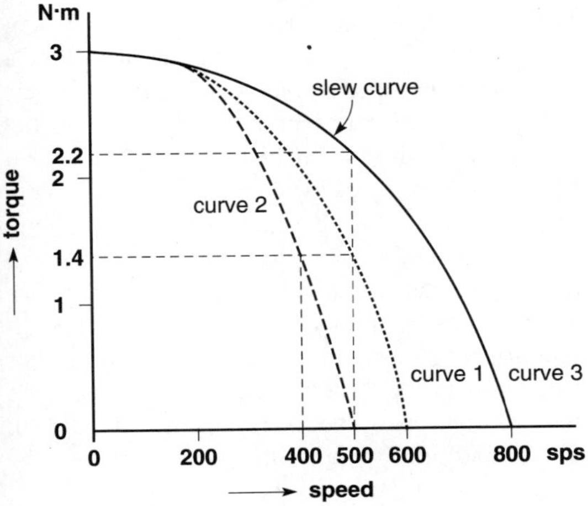

Figure 19.8
Start-stop and slewing characteristic of a typical stepper motor. Each step corresponds to an advance of 1.8 degrees.
Curve 1: start-stop curve with only stepper motor inertia
Curve 2: same conditions as curve 1, but with an additional load inertia of 2 kg·cm^2
Curve 3: slewing curve

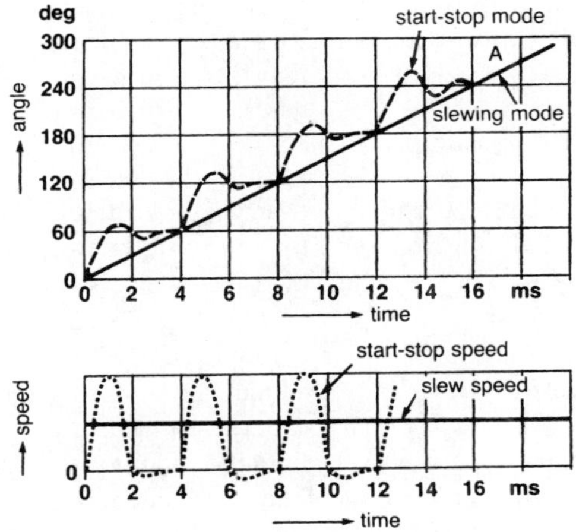

Figure 19.9
a. Angular position versus time curve when the stepper motor operates in the start-stop mode and the slewing mode. Stepping rate is the same in both cases.
b. Instantaneous speed versus time curve when the stepper motor operates in the start-stop and the slewing mode.

The start-stop stepping mode is sometimes referred to as the *start-without-error* mode. A start-without-error characteristic is shown by curve 1 in Fig. 19.8. It shows that if the stepper motor runs alone, under a load torque of, say, 1.4 N·m, the maximum possible stepping rate, without losing count, is 500 steps per second.

But if the motor drives a device having some inertia, the permissible start-stop rate drops to about 400 steps per second for the same load torque (curve 2).

19.6 Slew speed

A stepper motor can be made to run at uniform speed without starting and stopping at every step. When the motor runs this way it is said to be *slewing*. Because the motor runs essentially at uniform speed, the inertia effect is absent. Consequently, for a given stepping rate, the motor can carry a greater load torque when it is slewing. Curve 3 in Fig. 19.8 shows the relationship between the load torque and the steps per second when the motor is slewing. For example, the motor can develop a torque of 2.2 N·m when it slews at 500 steps per second. However, if the load torque should exceed 2.2 N·m when the pulse rate is 500 sps, the motor will fall out of step and the position (steps) of the rotor will no longer correspond to the net number of pulses provided to its windings.

Fig. 19.9 shows the difference between the start-stop mode and slewing. Suppose the motor is turning at an average speed of 250 steps per second in both cases. The motor will therefore cover the same number of steps per second, namely 1 step every 4 ms. However, the angle (position) increases smoothly with time when the motor is slewing, and this is shown by the uniform slope of line 0A (Fig. 19.9a). The corresponding slew speed is constant (Fig. 19.9b).

On the other hand, in the start-stop mode, the angle increases stepwise. Consequently, the speed continually oscillates between a maximum and zero and its *average* value is equal to the slew speed (Fig. 19.9b).

19.7 Ramping

When a stepper motor is carrying a load, it cannot suddenly go from zero to a stepping rate of, say, 5000 sps. In the same way, a motor that is slewing at 5000 sps cannot be brought to a dead stop in one step. Thus, to bring a motor up to speed, it must be accelerated gradually. Similarly, to stop a motor that is running at high speed, it must be decelerated gradually—always subject to the condition that the instantaneous position of the rotor must correspond to the number of pulses. The process whereby a motor is accelerated and decelerated is called *ramping.* During the acceleration phase, ramping consists of a progressive increase in the number of driving pulses per second.

The ramping phase is usually completed in a fraction of a second. The ramp is generated by the power supply that drives the stepper motor. Furthermore, it is programmed to retain precise position control over the motor and its load.

19.8 Types of stepper motors

There are 3 main types of stepper motors:

- variable reluctance stepper motors
- permanent magnet stepper motors
- hybrid stepper motors

Variable reluctance stepper motors are based upon the principle illustrated in Fig. 19.1. However, to obtain small angular steps, of the order of 1.8° (instead of the 60° jumps shown in the figure), the structure of the stator and rotor has to be modified to create many more poles. This is done by using a circular rotor and milling out slots around its periphery. The teeth created thereby constitute the salient poles of the rotor, of which there may be as many as 100.

As to the stator, it often has four, five, or eight main poles, instead of the three shown. However, the pole-faces are also slotted so as to create a number of teeth. These teeth are the real salient poles on the stator. The typical construction of a toothed 8-pole stator is shown in the circular insert of Fig. 19.13. For a given drive system, it is the number of teeth (salient poles) on the rotor and stator that determines the angular motion per step. Steps of 18°, 15°, 7.5°, 5°, and 1.8° are common.

Permanent magnet stepper motors are similar to variable reluctance motors, except that the rotor has permanent N and S poles. Fig. 19.10 shows a permanent magnet motor having 4 stator poles and 6 rotor poles, the latter being permanent magnets. Due to the permanent magnets, the rotor remains lined up with the last pair of stator poles that were excited by the driver. In effect, the motor develops a *detent torque* which keeps the rotor in place even when no current flows in the stator windings.

Coils A1, A2 are connected in series, as are coils B1, B2. Starting from the position shown, if coils B are excited, the rotor will move through an angle of 30°. However, the direction of rotation depends upon the direction of current flow. Thus, if the cur-

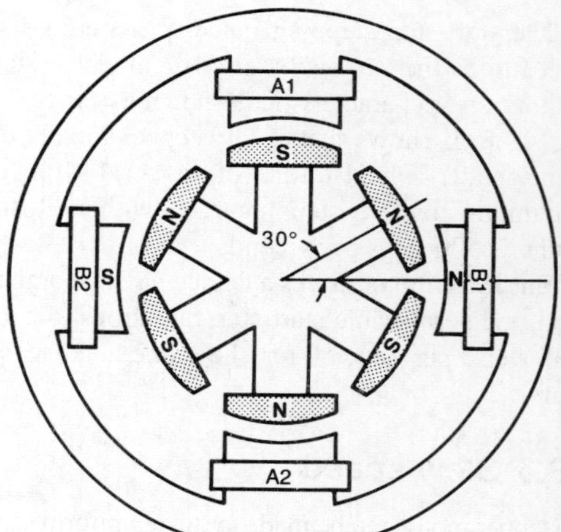

Figure 19.10
Permanent magnet stepper motor that advances 30° per step.

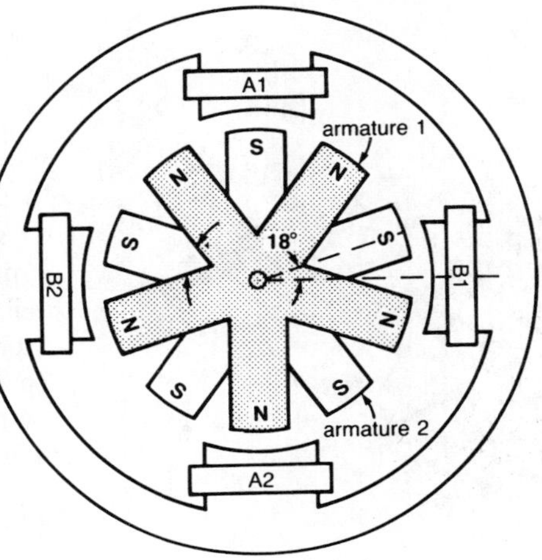

(a)

Figure 19.11a
Hybrid motor having a 4-pole stator and two 5-pole armatures mounted on the same shaft. The salient poles on the first armature are all N poles, while those on the second armature are all S poles. Each step produces an advance of 18°.

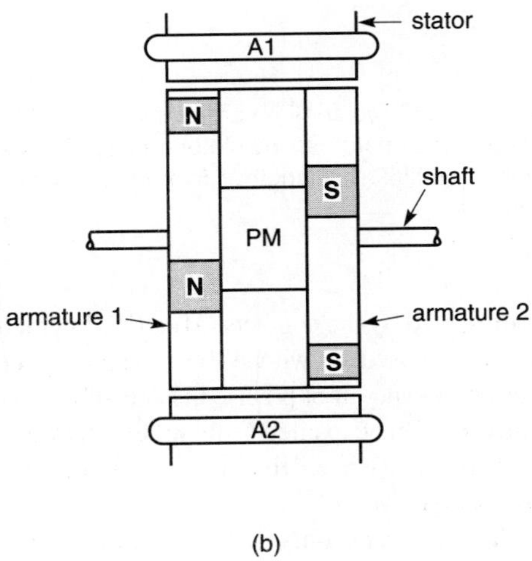

(b)

Figure 19.11b
Side view of the rotor, showing the permanent magnet PM sandwiched between the two armatures. The 4-pole stator is common to both armatures.

rent in coils B produces N and S poles as shown in Fig. 19.10, the rotor will turn ccw. Stepper motors that have to develop considerable power are usually equipped with permanent magnets.

Hybrid stepper motors have two identical soft-iron armatures mounted on the same shaft. The armatures are indexed so that the salient poles interlap. Fig. 19.11a shows two 5-pole armatures that are driven by a 4-pole stator. This arrangement makes the motor look like a variable reluctance motor. However, a permanent magnet PM is sandwiched between the armatures (Fig. 19.11b). It produces a unidirectional axial magnetic field, with the result that all the poles on armature 1 are N poles, while those on armature 2 are S poles.

Stator coils A1, A2 are connected in series, and so are stator coils B1, B2. The motor develops a small detent torque because of the permanent magnet, and the rotor will remain in the position shown in Fig. 19.11a. If we now excite coils B, the rotor will rotate by 18°, thereby lining up with stator poles B. The direction of rotation will again depend upon the direction of current flow in coils B.

Fig. 19.12 shows an exploded view of a hybrid stepping motor. Fig. 19.13 shows the special construction of a stator in which permanent magnets are embedded in the stator slots, in addition to the permanent magnet on the rotor.

Fig. 19.14a shows another type of hybrid motor and Fig. 19.14b is a cross-section view of its construction. Figs. 19.14c and 19.14d, respectively show the specifications and torque-speed characteristics of this motor. Note that the pull-out characteristic corresponds to the slewing curve while the pull-in characteristic corresponds to the start-without-error curve.

It should be noted that the number of poles on the stator of a stepper motor is never equal to the number of poles on the rotor. This feature is totally different from that in any other type of motor we have studied so far. Indeed, it is the difference in the number of poles that enables the motors to step as they do.

Figure 19.12
Exploded view of a standard hybrid stepping motor. The rotor is composed of two soft-iron armatures having 50 salient poles each. A short permanent magnet is sandwiched between the armatures. The stator has 8 poles, each of which has 5 salient poles in the pole face. Outside diameter of motor: 2.2 in; axial length: 1.5 in; weight: 0.8 lb. *(Courtesy of Pacific Scientific, Motor and Control Division, Rockford, IL)*

19.9 Motor windings and associated drives

Stepper motors use either a *bipolar* or a *unipolar* winding on the stator.

Bipolar Winding. In a 4-pole stator, the bipolar winding consists of the two coil sets A1, A2 and B1, B2 such as shown in Fig. 19.11. They are represented schematically in Fig. 19.15. The current I_a in coil set A reverses periodically, and the same is true for current I_b in coil set B. The coils are excited by a common dc source, and because the current pulses I_a, I_b must alternate, a switching means is required. The switches are represented by the contacts Q1 to Q8. In practice, transistors are used as switches because they can turn the current on and off at precise instants of time.

The coils can be excited sequentially in three different ways: (1) wave drive, (2) normal drive, and (3) half-step drive.

In the *wave drive* only one set of coils is excited at a time. The switching sequence for cw rotation is given in Table 19A and the resulting current pulses I_a, I_b are shown in Fig. 19.16. Note that the flux produced by I_a and I_b rotates by 90° per step.

In the *normal drive,* both sets of coils are excited at a time. The switching sequence for cw rotation is given

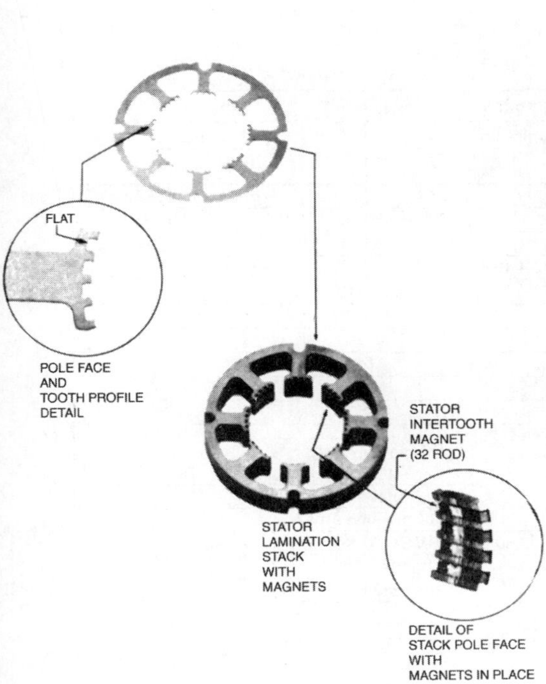

Figure 19.13
Stator lamination details and construction of an enhanced motor stator lamination stack assembly. Rare earth permanent magnets are fitted into the stator slots in addition to the permanent magnet of the hybrid rotor.
(Courtesy of Pacific Scientific, Motor and Control Division, Rockford, IL)

Figure 19.14a
External view of a hybrid stepper motor. It is equipped with bipolar windings rated to operate at 5 V. External diameter of motor: 1.65 in; axial length: 0.86 in; weight: 5.1 oz.
(Courtesy of AIRPAX © Corporate)

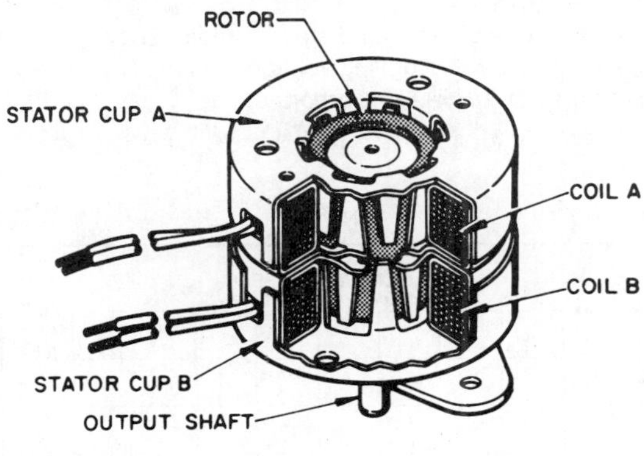

Figure 19.14b
Cross-section view of the hybrid stepper motor shown in Fig. 19.14a.
(Courtesy of AIRPAX © Corporate)

in Table 19B, and the resulting current pulses I_a, I_b are shown in Fig. 19.17. Note that the flux is oriented midway between the poles at each step. However, it still rotates by 90° per step. The normal drive develops a slightly greater torque than the wave drive.

The *half-step drive* is obtained by combining the wave drive and the normal drive. The switching sequence for cw rotation is given in Table 19C, and the resulting current pulses I_a, I_b are shown in Fig. 19.18. The flux now rotates only 45° per step. The main advantage of the half-step drive is that it improves the resolution of position and it tends to reduce the problem of resonance.

Unipolar Winding. The unipolar winding consists of two coils per pole instead of only one (Fig. 19.19a). *Unipolar* means that the current in a winding always flows in the same direction. The coil set A1, A2 produces flux in the opposite direction to coil set 1A, 2A. Consequently, when they are operated in sequence, an alternating flux is produced. The advantage of the unipolar winding is that the number of switching transistors drops from 8 to 4, and the transient response is slightly faster. Fig. 19.19b shows the schematic diagram of the windings and the switching sequence for a wave drive. The flux rotates in exactly the same way as shown in Fig. 19.16.

Specifications

Ordering Part No. (Add Suffix)	L82401 Unipolar		L82402 Bipolar	
Suffix Designation	**– P1**	**– P2**	**– P1**	**– P2**
DC Operating Voltage	5	12	5	12
Res. per Winding Ω	9.1	52.4	9.1	52.4
Ind. per Winding mH	7.5	46.8	14.3	77.9
Holding Torque mNm/oz-in*	73.4/10.4		87.5/12.4	
Rotor Moment of Inertia g · m²	12.5×10^{-4}			
Detent Torque mNm/oz-in	9.2/1.3			
Step Angle	7.5°			
Step Angle Tolerance*	.5°			
Steps per Rev.	48			
Max Operating Temp	100°C			
Ambient Temp Range **Operating** **Storage**	 – 20°C to 70°C – 40°C to 85°C			
Bearing Type	Bronze sleeve			
Insulation Res. at 500Vdc	100 megohms max			
Dielectric Withstanding Voltage	650 ± 50 VRMS 60 Hz for 1 to 2 seconds			
Weight g/oz	144/5.1			
Lead Wires	26 AWG			

*Measured with 2 phases energized.

Figure 19.14c
Specifications of the hybrid stepper motor shown in Fig. 19.14a. The motor can be built for either unipolar or bipolar operation at a rated driving voltage of either 5 V or 12 V.
(Courtesy of AIRPAX © Corporate)

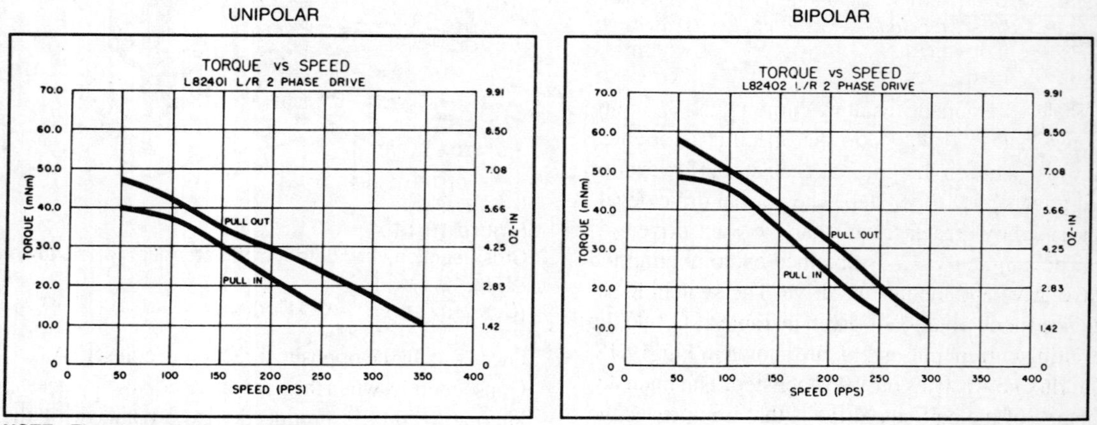

NOTE: The above curves are typical.

Figure 19.14d
Typical torque-speed characteristics of the hybrid stepper motor shown in Fig. 19.14a. The pull-out curve corresponds to the slewing characteristics; the pull-in curve corresponds to the start-without-error characteristic.
(Courtesy of AIRPAX © Corporate)

19.10 High-speed operation

So far, we have assumed that the current pulse in a winding rises immediately to its rated value I at the beginning of the pulse and drops immediately to zero at the end of the pulse interval T_p (Fig. 19.20a). In practice, this does not happen because of the inductance of the windings. If a winding has an inductance of L henrys and a resistance of R ohms, its time constant T_o is equal to L/R seconds.

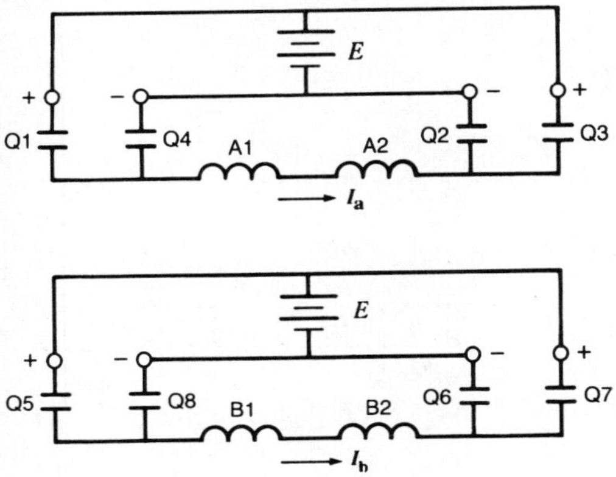

Figure 19.15
Schematic diagram showing how the stator coils A1, A2 and B1, B2 are connected to the common dc source by means of switches Q1 to Q8. The dc source is shown twice to simplify the connection diagram.

TABLE 19A WAVE SWITCHING SEQUENCE FOR CW ROTATION

Step	1	2	3	4	1
Q1 Q2	on	—	—	—	on
Q3 Q4	—	—	on	—	—
Q5 Q6	—	on	—	—	—
Q7 Q8	—	—	—	on	—

Let the coil be connected to a dc source of E volts by means of a transistor (Fig. 19.20b). A diode (D) is connected across the windings to prevent the high induced voltage from destroying the switching transistor at the moment it interrupts the current flow. The resulting current has the shape given in Fig. 19.20d.

How can we explain this pulse shape? When the transistor is switched on, the transient current i_1 only reaches its rated value $I = E/R$ after about 3 time constants, namely 3 T_o seconds. Then, when the transistor turns the line current off, the transient current i_2 continues to flow in the coil for about 3 T_o seconds (Fig. 19.20c). If this current pulse is compared with the ideal current pulse shown in Fig. 19.20a, we observe two important facts:

1. Because the current does not immediately rise to its final value when the transistor is turned on, the initial torque developed by the stepping motor is smaller than normal. As a result, the rotor does not move as quickly as we would expect.
2. When the transistor is turned off, current i_2 continues to circulate in the coil/diode loop.

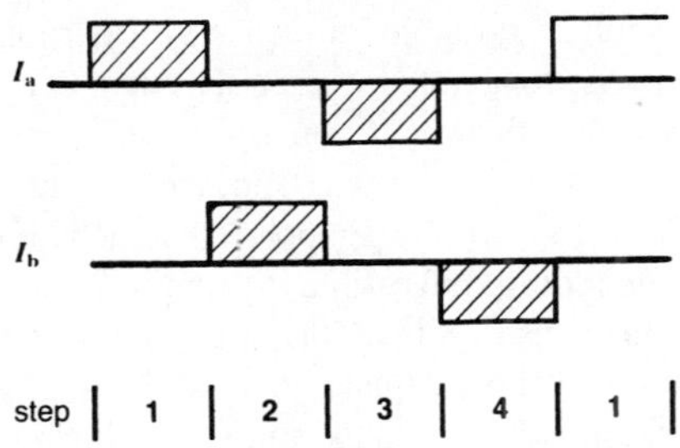

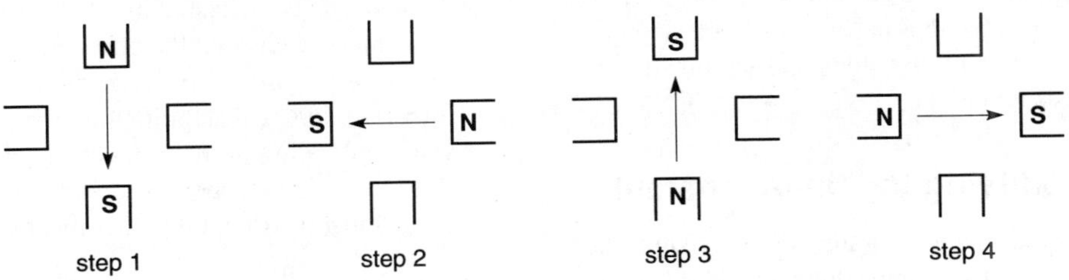

Figure 19.16
Current pulses in a wave drive and the resulting flux positions at each step. See Table 19A for switching sequence.

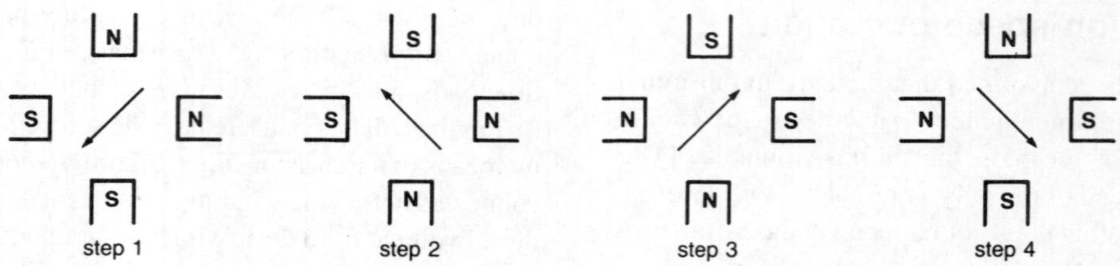

Figure 19.17
Current pulses in a normal drive and resulting flux positions at each step. See Table 19B for switching sequence.

TABLE 19B NORMAL SWITCHING SEQUENCE FOR CW ROTATION

Step		1	2	3	4	1
Q1	Q2	on	—	—	on	on
Q3	Q4	—	on	on	—	—
Q5	Q6	on	on	—	—	on
Q7	Q8	—	—	on	on	—

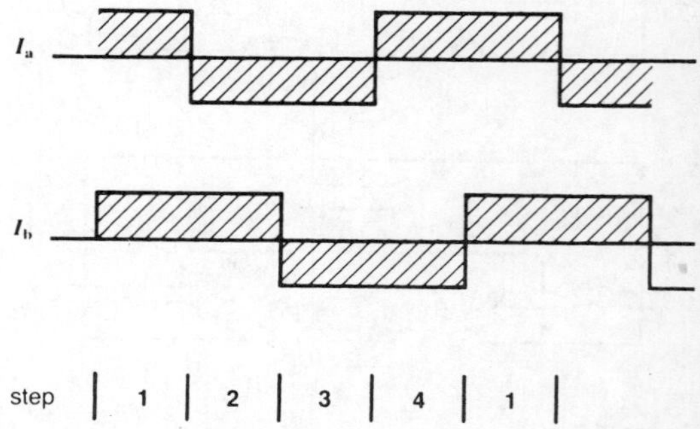

As a result, the effective duration of the pulse is $T_p + 3\ T_o$ instead of T_p. The pulse being thus prolonged by the component $3\ T_o$ means that we cannot switch from one coil to the next as quickly as we would have thought.

The shortest possible pulse that still permits the current to rise to its rated value I has a length of $6\ T_o$ seconds (Fig. 19.20e). It consists of $3\ T_o$ (current rises to its rated value) plus another $3\ T_o$ (current drops from I to zero). It so happens that the windings of stepper motors have time constants T_o ranging from about 1 ms to 8 ms. Thus, the duration of one step can be no shorter than about 6×1 ms $= 6$ ms. This corresponds to a maximum stepping rate of about $1000/6 = 166$ steps per second. Such stepping rates are considered to be slow, and various means are used to speed them up.

19.11 Modifying the time constant

One way to quicken the stepping rate is to reduce the time constant T_o. This can be done by adding an external resistance to the motor windings and raising the dc voltage so that the same rated current I will flow. Such an arrangement is shown in Fig. 19.21.

The external resistor has a value 4 times that of the coil resistance R, and the dc voltage is raised from E to $5\ E$ volts. As a result, the time constant drops by a factor of 5 (L/R to $L/5\ R$). This means that the maximum stepping rate can be increased by the same factor. Thus, stepping rates of the order of 1000 per second become feasible.

The only drawbacks to this solution are the following:

1. The power supply is more expensive because it has to deliver 5 times as much power (the voltage is $5\ E$ instead of E).
2. A lot of power is wasted in the external resistor, which means that the efficiency of the system is very low. Low efficiency is not too important in small stepping motors that develop only a few watts of mechanical power. But fast-acting stepper motors in the 100 W range must be driven by other means.

19.12 Bilevel drive

Bilevel drives enable us to obtain fast rise and fall times of current without using external resistors. The

TABLE 19C HALF-STEP SWITCHING SEQUENCE FOR CW ROTATION

Step		1	2	3	4	5	6	7	8	1
Q1	Q2	on	on	—	—	—	—	—	on	on
Q3	Q4	—	—	—	on	on	on	—	—	—
Q5	Q6	—	on	on	on	—	—	—	—	—
Q7	Q8	—	—	—	—	—	on	on	on	—

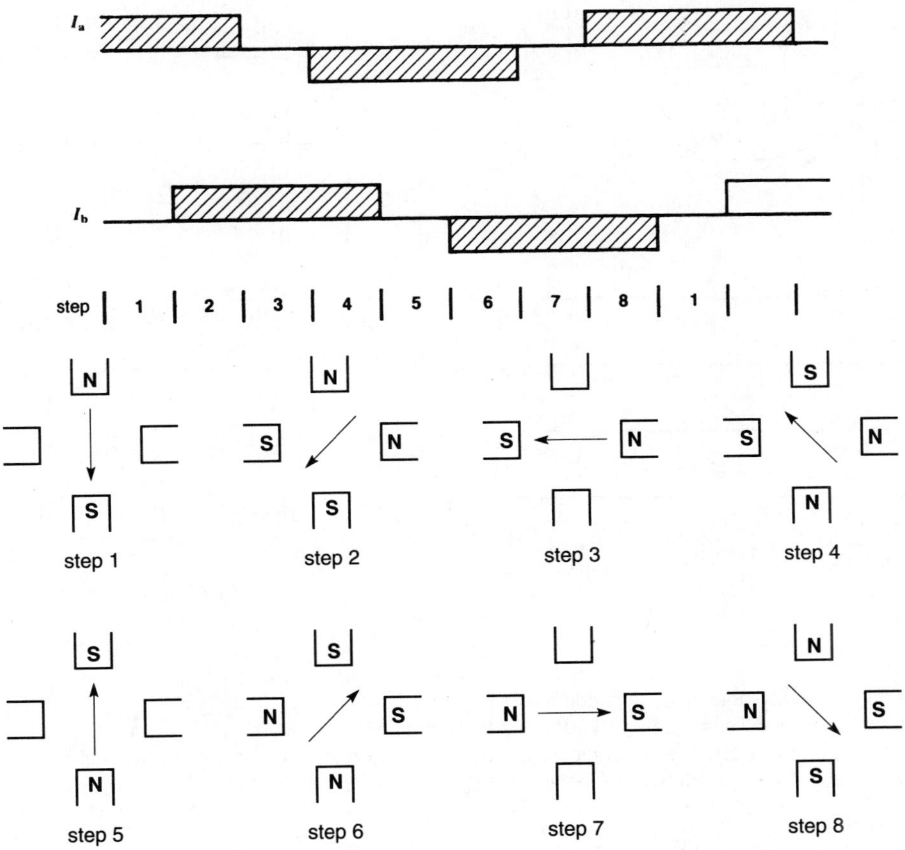

Figure 19.18
Current pulses in a half-step drive and resulting flux positions at each step. See Table 19C for switching sequence.

principle of a **bilevel drive** can be understood by referring to Fig. 19.22a. Switches Q1 and Q2 represent transistors that open and close the circuit in the manner explained below. Numerical values will be used to explain how the circuit behaves. Thus, the winding is assumed to have a resistance of 0.3 Ω, an inductance of 2.4 mH, and a rated current of 10 A. The power supply is 60 V with a tap at 3 V. Thus, if the

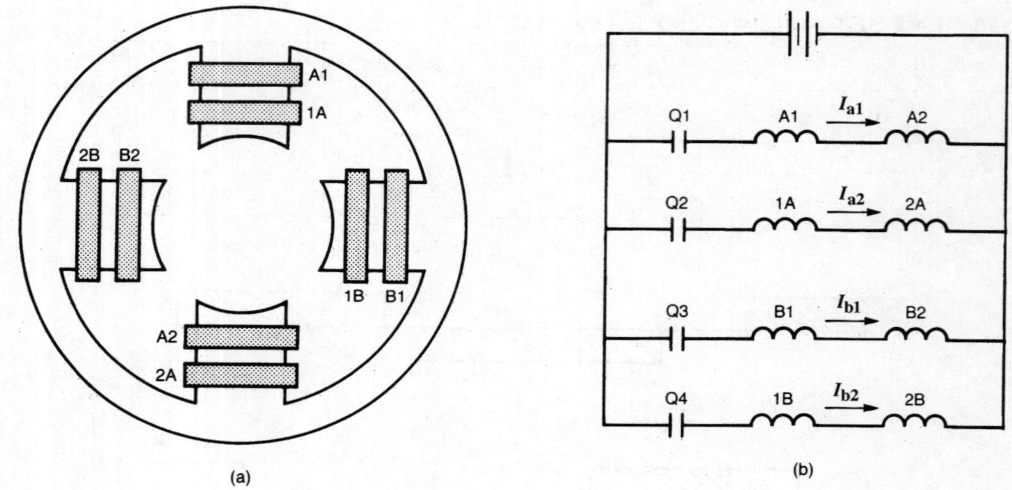

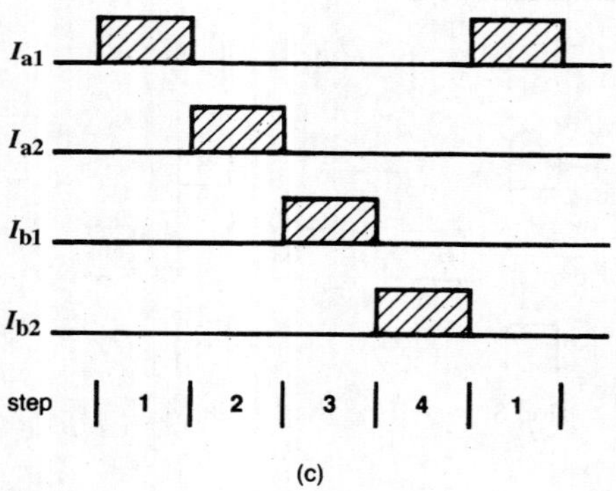

TABLE 19D WAVE SWITCHING SEQUENCE FOR CW ROTATION

Step	1	2	3	4	1
Q1	on	—	—	—	on
Q2	—	—	on	—	—
Q3	—	on	—	—	—
Q4	—	—	—	on	—

Figure 19.19
a. Coil arrangement in a 4-pole unipolar winding.
b. Schematic diagram of coils, switches, and power supply in a unipolar drive.
c. Current pulses in a wave drive using a unipolar winding. The flux rotates in the same way as in a bipolar winding. See Table 19D for switching sequence.

voltage were applied permanently, the resulting current in the winding would be 60 V/0.3 Ω = 200 A. This is much greater than the rated current of 10 A.

Switch Q1 is initially closed. The current pulse is initiated by closing Q2. Current then starts flowing as shown in Fig. 19.22b.

The time constant of this electronic circuit is T_o = 2.4 mH/0.3 Ω = 8 ms. The initial rate of rise of current corresponds to a straight line OP that reaches 200 A in 8 ms. Thus, the current in the coil rises at a rate of 200 A/8 ms = 25 000 A/s. The time to reach 10 A is, therefore, 10/25 000 = 0.4 ms (Fig. 19.22c).

As soon as the current reaches this rated value, switch Q1 opens, which forces the current to follow the new path shown in Fig. 19.22d. The current is

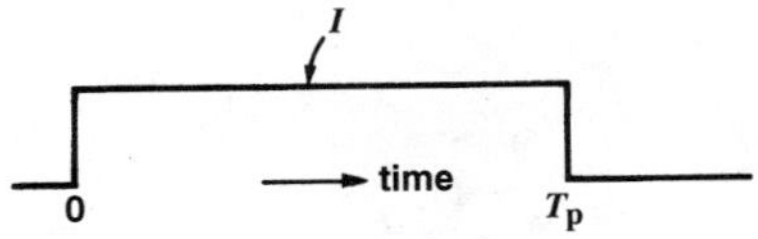

Figure 19.20a
Ideal current pulse in a winding.

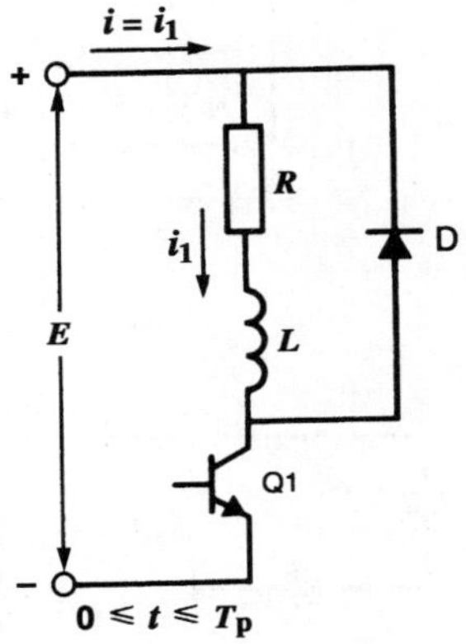

Figure 19.20b
Typical circuit of a switching transistor and coil connected to a dc source. The diode protects the transistor against overvoltage.

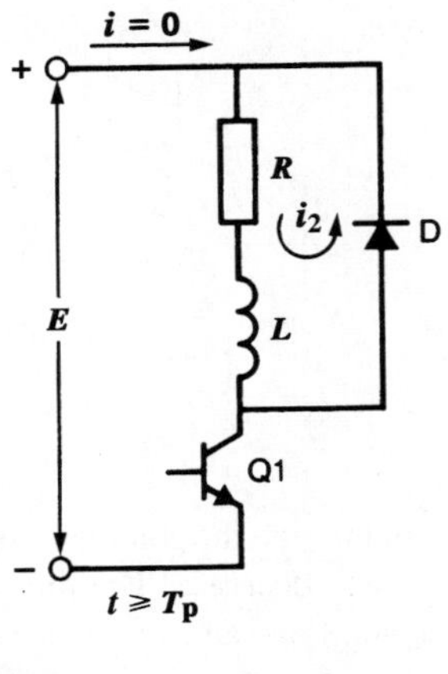

Figure 19.20c
Transient current in coil and diode when transistor is switched off.

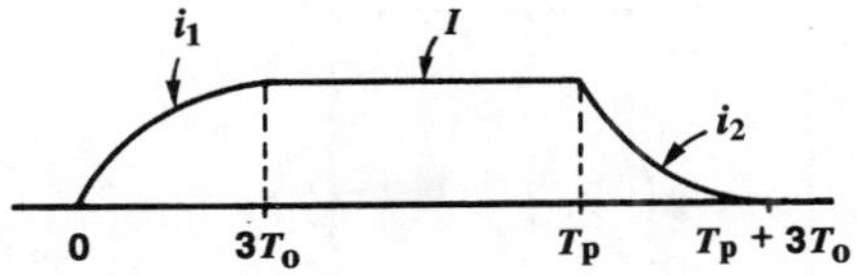

Figure 19.20d
Real current pulse.

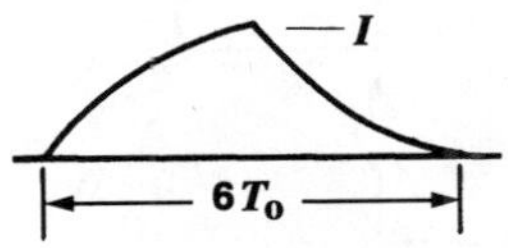

Figure 19.20e
Shortest possible current pulse that still attains the rated current *I*.

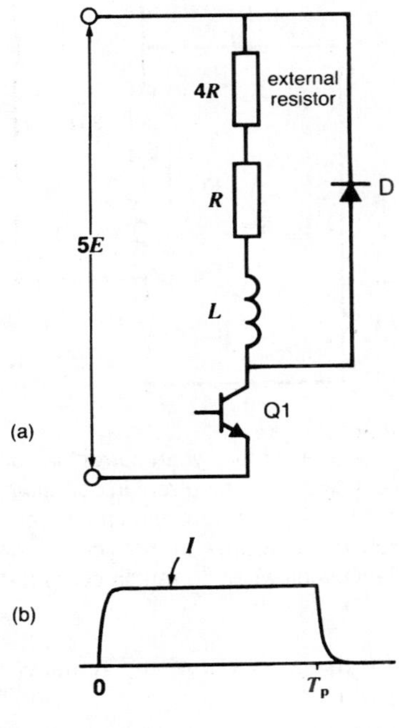

Figure 19.21
a. Circuit to increase the rate of growth and decay of current in the coil.
b. Resulting current pulse. Compare with Fig. 19.20d.

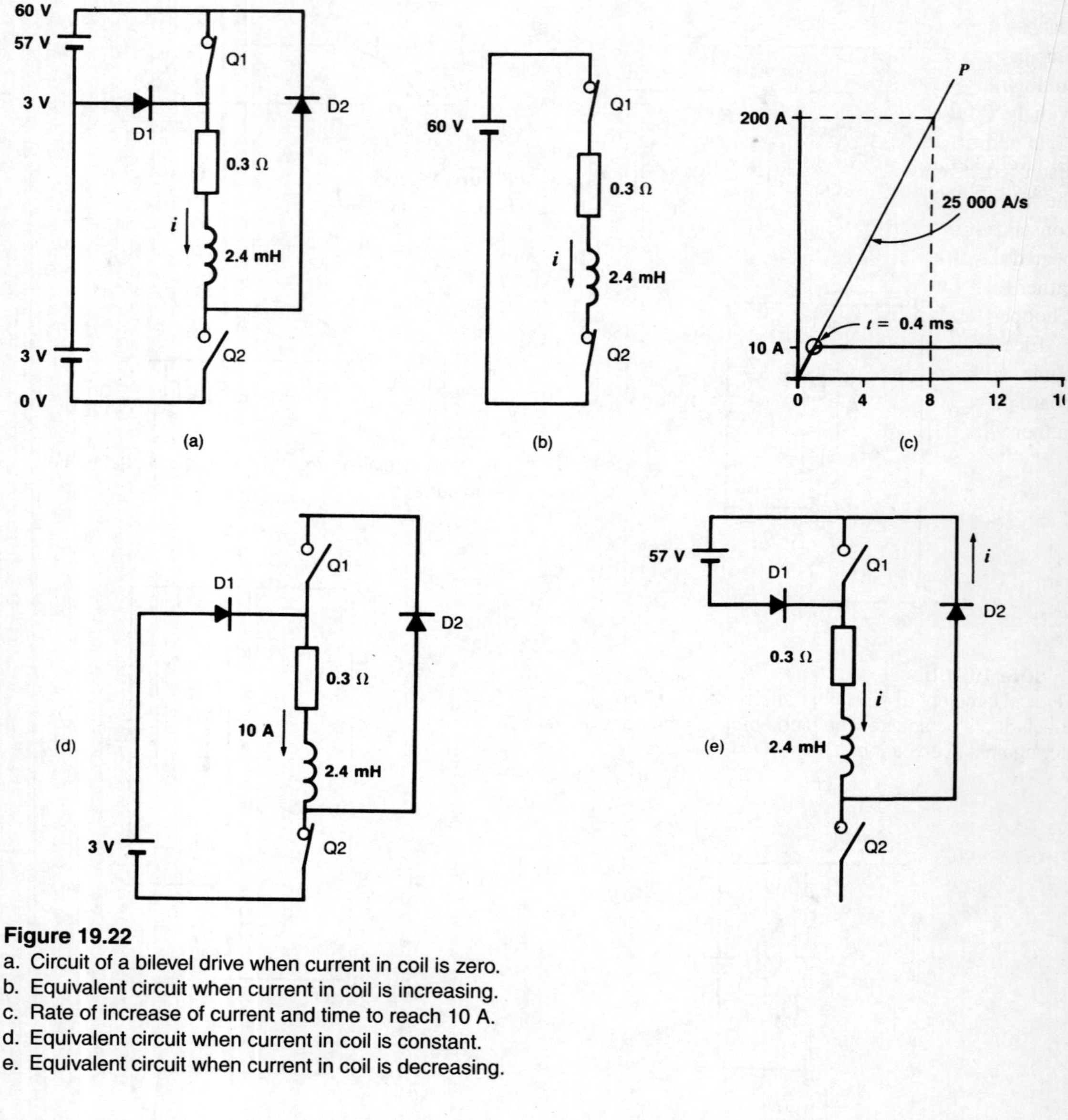

Figure 19.22
a. Circuit of a bilevel drive when current in coil is zero.
b. Equivalent circuit when current in coil is increasing.
c. Rate of increase of current and time to reach 10 A.
d. Equivalent circuit when current in coil is constant.
e. Equivalent circuit when current in coil is decreasing.

now fed by the 3 V source and remains fixed at 3 V/0.3 Ω = 10 A.

The current will stay at this value until we want to end the pulse, say after 5 ms. To terminate the pulse we open Q2, which forces the current to follow the path shown in Fig. 19.22e. The 57 V source now tries to drive a current through the coil that is opposite to *i*. Consequently, *i* will decrease. The time constant of the circuit is again 8 ms, and so the current will decrease at a rate of 57/60 × 25 000 = 23 750 A/s. It will therefore become zero after a time interval of 10/23 750 = 0.42 ms. The moment the current reaches zero, Q1 closes. This forces the current to remain zero until the next pulse is initiated. The resulting pulse shape is shown in Fig. 19.22f, together with the Q1, Q2 switching sequence that produces it.

In addition to bilevel drives, *chopper drives* are also used. Their principle of operation is similar to the bilevel method, except that the current is kept constant during the flat portion of the pulse by repeated on-off switching of the high voltage (60 V) rather than by using a low fixed dc voltage (3 V). Choppers are described in Chapter 21.

Electronic drives for stepper motors have become very sophisticated. Some of these circuit-board drives are shown in Figs. 19.23 and 19.24, together with the motors they control.

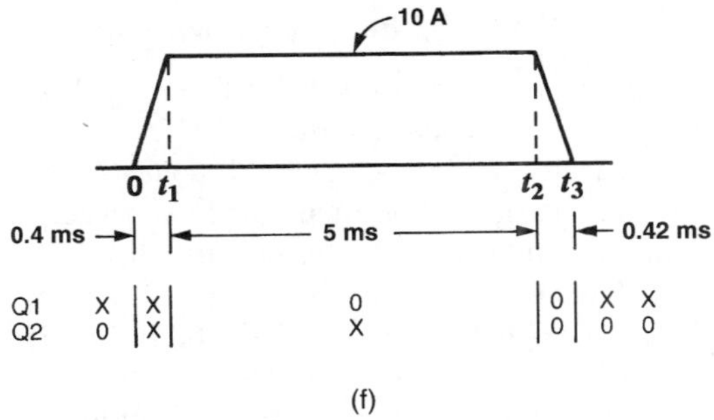

Figure 19.22f
Pulse waveshape using a bilevel drive. Note the switching sequence of Q1 and Q2 that creates it (x = closed, o = open).

Figure 19.23
Typical electronic drives and the stepper motors they control.
(Courtesy of Pacific Scientific, Motor and Control Division, Rockford, IL)

19.13 Instability and resonance

When a stepper motor is operating at certain slewing speeds, it may become unstable. The rotor may turn erratically or simply chatter without rotating any more. This instability, often called resonance, is due to the natural vibration of the stepper motor, which manifests itself at one or more range of speeds. For example, the range of instability may lie between 2000 sps and 8000 sps. Nevertheless, it is possible to ramp through this range without losing step and thereby attain stable slewing speeds between 8000 and 15 000 sps.

19.14 Stepper motors and linear drives

Most stepper motors are coupled to a lead screw of some kind which permits the rotary motion to be converted to a linear displacement. Suppose, for example, that a stepper motor having 200 steps per revolution is coupled to a lead screw having a pitch of 5 threads per inch. The motor has to make $200 \times 5 = 1000$ steps to produce a linear motion of 1 inch. Consequently, each step produces a displacement of 0.001 in. By counting the pulses precisely, we can position a machine tool, X-Y arm, and so on, to a precision of one-thousandth of an inch over the full length of the desired movement.

This great precision without feedback is the reason why stepper motors are so useful in control systems.

Questions and Problems

Practical Level

19-1 What is the main use of stepper motors?

19-2 What is the difference between a reluctance and a permanent magnet stepper motor?

19-3 Describe the construction of a hybrid stepper motor.

19-4 A stepper motor advances 2.5° per step. How many pulses are needed to complete 8 revolutions?

19-5 Explain what is meant by *normal drive, wave drive,* and *half-step drive.*

Intermediate Level

19-6 The 2-pole rotor in Fig. 19.1 is replaced by a 4-pole rotor. Calculate the new angular motion per pulse.

19-7 Why is viscous damping employed in stepper motors?

19-8 When a stepper motor is ramping or slewing properly, every pulse corresponds to a precise angle of rotation. True or false?

19-9 The stepper motor in Fig. 19.10 is driven by a series of pulses having a duration of 20 ms. How long will it take for the rotor to make one complete revolution?

19-10 A stepper motor rotates 1.8° per step. It drives a lead screw having a pitch of 20 threads per inch. The lead screw, in turn, produces a linear motion of a cutting tool. If the motor is pulsed 7 times, by how much does the cutting tool move?

19-11 A stepper motor advances 7.5° per pulse. If its torque-speed characteristic is given by Fig. 19.8, calculate the power [watts] it develops when it is slewing

a. At 500 steps per second
b. At 200 steps per second

19-12 A stepper motor similar to that shown in Fig. 19.14 has a unipolar winding. It operates in the start-stop mode at a pulse rate of 150 per second, (see Fig. 19.14d).

a. What is the maximum torque it can develop?
b. How much mechanical power (millihorsepower) does it develop?
c. How much mechanical energy [J] does it produce in 3 seconds?

19-13 For a given load torque, the stepping rate can be increased by increasing the rate of rise and rate of fall of the current in the windings. Name two ways this can be accomplished.

19-14 Referring to Fig. 19.14d, what is the maximum slew speed of the unipolar motor, expressed in revolutions per minute?

Advanced Level

19-15 **a.** Referring to the stepper motor properties listed in Fig. 19.14c, calculate the time constant of a bipolar winding rated at 12 V.
b. If the 12 V are applied to the winding, approximately how long will it take for the current to reach its final value?
c. What is the final value of the current in the winding?

19-16 The two armatures on a hybrid stepper motor each have 50 salient poles (teeth). Calculate the following:
a. The angle between two successive teeth on an armature
b. The angle between one tooth on one armature and the next tooth on the other armature
c. The angle of advance per pulse

19-17 Why can a stepper motor develop a larger torque when it is slewing than when it is operating in the stop-start mode?

19-18 A powerful permanent magnet stepper motor used for positioning a valve has the following specifications:

winding: bipolar
current: 13 A
winding resistance: 60 mΩ
winding inductance: 0.77 mH
detent torque: 0.16 N·m
holding torque: 9.5 N·m
torque at 50 sps: 8 N·m
steps per revolution: 200
rotor inertia: 0.7×10^{-3} kg·m^2

Motor diameter: 4.2 in
Motor axial length: 7.0 in
Motor weight: 9 kg

The motor is chopper-driven at 65 V and it develops a torque of 2.2 N·m at 10 000 sps. Calculate the following:
a. The speed [r/min] and power [hp] of the motor when it is running at 10 000 sps
b. The time constant of the windings [ms]
c. The time to reach 13 A when 65 V is applied to the winding [μS]

Industrial application

19-19 The holding torque of a stepper motor is the maximum static torque it can exert when it is excited. The detent torque is the maximum torque that a nonexcited stepper motor can exert when it is equipped with a permanent magnet. A stepper motor is known to have a holding torque of 74 oz·in and a detent torque of 11 oz·in. Express these values in SI units (N·m).

19-20 The windings of a stepper motor possess a resistance of 26 Ω and an inductance of 33 mH. What value of resistance should be connected in series with each winding so that the time constant becomes 400 microseconds?

19-21 A unipolar stepper motor is designed to operate between 0°C and 100°C. The time constant at 25°C is 1.32 ms. Calculate the time constant at 100°C.

19-22 It is proposed to use the 12 V stepper motor L82402, whose characteristics are shown in Fig. 19.14c, to drive a metal disc having a moment of inertia of 80×10^{-6} g·m^2. The desired speed is 250 r/min. The disc rubs against a stationary member, which exerts a constant friction torque T_F.
a. How many pulses are required per second to produce a speed of 250 r/min?
b. We want the motor to operate in the start-stop mode using the pulse rate calculated in (a). How much pull-in torque does it develop under these conditions?

c. What torque is needed to accelerate the metal disc from zero to 250 r/min?

d. What is the largest admissible friction torque T_F?

19-23 A stepper motor advances 1.8° per impulse, and its slew rate is limited to 1200 pulses per second. We wish to drive a machine tool at a speed of 500 r/min. Can this objective be achieved by coupling the device directly to the motor? If not, can you suggest a solution?

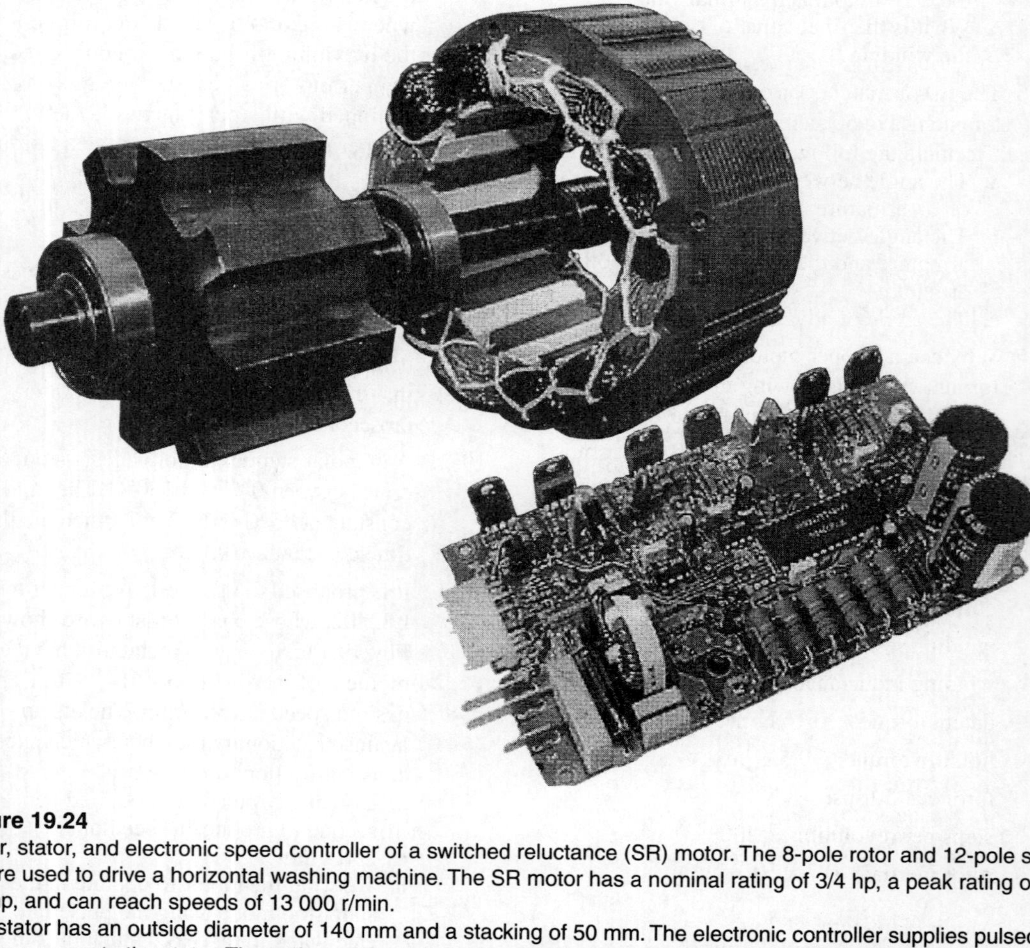

Figure 19.24
Rotor, stator, and electronic speed controller of a switched reluctance (SR) motor. The 8-pole rotor and 12-pole stator are used to drive a horizontal washing machine. The SR motor has a nominal rating of 3/4 hp, a peak rating of 1.5 hp, and can reach speeds of 13 000 r/min.
The stator has an outside diameter of 140 mm and a stacking of 50 mm. The electronic controller supplies pulsed 3-phase power to the stator. The entire unit is designed to operate from a 120 V, 60 Hz, single-phase source. Switched reluctance motors operate on the same principle as stepper motors.
(Courtesy of Emerson Electric)

PART THREE

Electrical and Electronic Drives

CHAPTER 20

Basics of Industrial Motor Control

20.0 Introduction

Industrial control, in its broadest sense, encompasses all the methods used to control the performance of an electrical system. When applied to machinery, it involves the starting, acceleration, reversal, deceleration, and stopping of a motor and its load. In this chapter we will study the electrical (but not electronic) control of 3-phase alternating-current motors. Our study is limited to elementary circuits because industrial circuits are usually too intricate to explain briefly. However, the basic principles covered here apply to any system of control, no matter how complex it may appear to be.

20.1 Control devices

Every control circuit is composed of a number of basic components connected together to achieve the desired performance. The size of the components varies with the power of the motor, but the principle of operation remains the same. Using only a dozen basic components, it is possible to design control systems that are very complex. The basic components are the following:

1. Disconnecting switches
2. Manual circuit breakers
3. Cam switches
4. Pushbuttons
5. Relays
6. Magnetic contactors
7. Thermal relays and fuses
8. Pilot lights
9. Limit switches and other special switches
10. Resistors, reactors, transformers, and capacitors

The ensuing list of Basic Components for Control Circuits illustrates these devices, and states their main purpose and application. Fuses are not included here because they are protective devices rather than control devices. They are discussed in Chapter 26. The symbols for these and other devices are given in Table 20A.

BASIC COMPONENTS FOR CONTROL CIRCUITS

Disconnecting switches

A *disconnecting switch* isolates the motor from the power source. It consists of 3 knife-switches and 3 line fuses enclosed in a metallic box. The knife-switches can be opened and closed simultaneously by means of an external handle. An interlocking mechanism prevents the hinged cover from opening when the switch is closed. Disconnecting switches (and their fuses) are selected to carry the nominal full-load current of the motor, and to withstand short-circuit currents for brief intervals.

Figure 20.1
Three-phase, fused disconnecting switch rated 600 V, 30 A.
(Courtesy of Square D)

Manual circuit breakers

A *manual circuit breaker* opens and closes a circuit, like a toggle switch. It trips (opens) automatically when the current exceeds a predetermined limit. After tripping, it can be reset manually. Manual circuit breakers are often used instead of disconnecting switches because no fuses have to be replaced.

Figure 20.2
Three-phase circuit breaker, 600 V, 100 A.
(Courtesy of Square D)

Cam switches

A *cam switch* has a group of fixed contacts and an equal number of moveable contacts. The contacts can be made to open and close in a preset sequence by rotating a handle or knob. Cam switches are used to control the motion and position of hoists, callenders, machine tools, and so on.

Figure 20.3
Three-phase, surface-mounted cam switch, 230 V, 2 kW.
(Courtesy of Klockner-Moeller)

Pushbuttons

A *pushbutton* is a switch activated by finger pressure. Two or more contacts open or close when the button is depressed. Pushbuttons are usually spring loaded so as to return to their normal position when pressure is removed.

Figure 20.4
Mechanical-interlocked pushbuttons with NO (normally open) and NC (normally closed) contacts; rated to interrupt an ac current of 6 A one million times.
(Courtesy of Siemens)

Control relays

A *control relay* is an electromagnetic switch that opens and closes a set of contacts when the *relay coil* is energized. The relay coil produces a strong magnetic field which attracts a movable armature bearing the contacts. Control relays are mainly used in low-power circuits. They include time-delay relays whose contacts open or close after a definite time interval. Thus, a time-delay *closing* relay actuates its contacts after the relay coil has been energized. On the other hand, a time-delay *opening* relay actuates its contacts some time after the relay coil has been de-energized.

Figure 20.5
Single-phase relays: 25 A, 115/230 V and 5 A, 115 V.
(Courtesy of Potter and Brumfield)

Thermal relays

A *thermal relay* (or *overload relay*) is a temperature-sensitive device whose contacts open or close when the motor current exceeds a preset limit. The current flows through a small, calibrated heating element which raises the temperature of the relay. Thermal relays are inherent time-delay devices because the temperature cannot follow the instantaneous changes in current.

Figure 20.6
Three-phase thermal relay with variable current setting, 6 A to 10 A.
(Courtesy of Klockner-Moeller)

(continued)

Magnetic contactors

A *magnetic contactor* is basically a large control relay designed to open and close a power circuit. It possesses a relay coil and a magnetic plunger, which carries a set of movable contacts. When the relay coil is energized, it attracts the magnetic plunger, causing it to rise quickly against the force of gravity. The movable contacts come in contact with a set of fixed contacts, thereby closing the power circuit. In addition to the power contacts, one or more normally open or normally closed auxiliary contacts are usually available, for control purposes. When the relay coil is de-energized, the plunger falls, thereby opening and closing the respective contacts. Magnetic contactors are used to control motors ranging from 0.5 hp to several hundred horsepower. The size, dimensions, and performance of contactors are standardized.

Figure 20.7
Three-phase magnetic contactor rated 50 hp, 575 V, 60 Hz. Width: 158 mm; height: 155 mm; depth: 107 mm; weight: 3.5 kg.
(Courtesy of Siemens)

Pilot lights

A *pilot light* indicates the on/off state of a remote component in a control system.

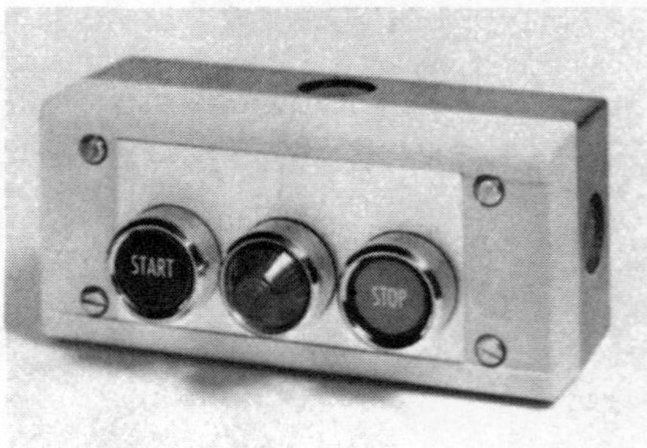

Figure 20.8
Pilot light, 120 V, 3 W mounted in a start-stop push-button station.
(Courtesy of Siemens)

Limit switches and special switches

A *limit switch* is a low-power snap-action device that opens or closes a contact, depending upon the position of a mechanical part. Other limit switches are sensitive to pressure, temperature, liquid level, direction of rotation, and so on.

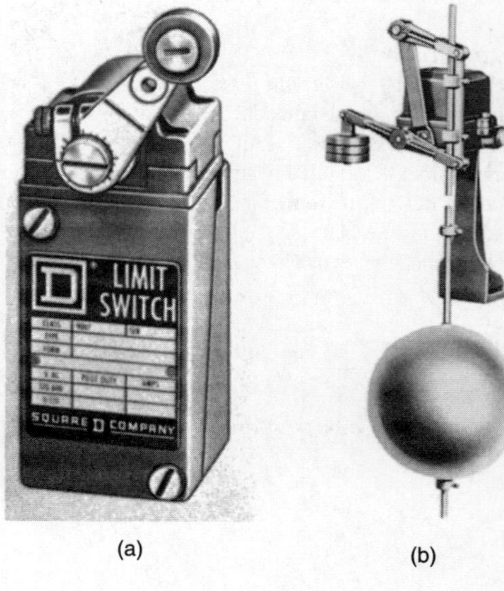

(a) (b)

Figure 20.9a
Limit switch with one NC contact; rated for ten million operations; position accuracy: 0.5 mm.
(Courtesy of Square D)

Figure 20.9b
Liquid level switch.
(Courtesy of Square D)

Proximity detectors
Proximity detectors are sealed devices that can detect objects without coming in direct contact with them. Their service life is independent of the number of operations. They are wired to an external dc source and generate an alternating magnetic field by means of an internal oscillator. When a metal object comes within a few millimeters of the detector, the magnetic field decreases, which in turn causes a dc control current to flow. This current can be used to activate another control device, such as a relay or a programmable logic controller. Capacitive proximity detectors, based on a similar principle but generating an ac electric field, are able to detect nonmetallic objects, including liquids.

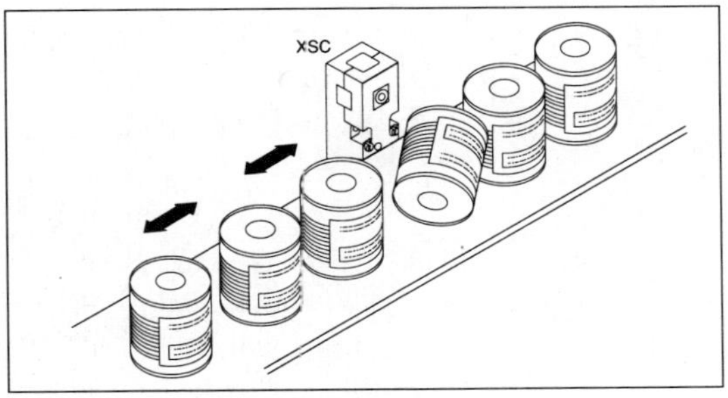

Figure 20.10
Proximity detector to monitor the loading of a conveyor belt. *(Courtesy of Telemecanique, Groupe Schneider)*

In order to understand the sections that follow, the legends in Table 20A should be read before proceeding further.

20.2 Normally open and normally closed contacts

Control circuit diagrams always show components in a state of rest, that is, when they are not energized (electrically) or activated (mechanically). In this state, some electrical contacts are open while others are closed. They are respectively called *normally open contacts* (NO) and *normally closed contacts* (NC) and are designated by the following symbols:

normally open contact (NO) 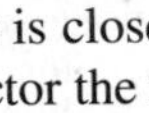

normally closed contact (NC) 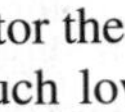

20.3 Relay coil exciting current

When a magnetic contactor is in its de-energized or open position, the magnetic circuit has a very long air gap, compared to when the contactor is closed. Consequently, in the case of an ac contactor the inductive reactance of the relay coil is much lower when the contactor is open than when it is closed. Because the coil is excited by a fixed ac voltage, the magnetizing current is much higher in the open than in the closed contactor position. In other words, a considerable inrush current is drawn by the relay coil at the moment it is excited. This places a heavier than expected duty on auxiliary contacts that energize the coil.

Example 20-1

A 3-phase NEMA size 5 magnetic contactor rated at 270 A, 460 V possesses a 120 V, 60 Hz relay coil. The coil absorbs an apparent power of 2970 VA and 212 VA, respectively, in the open and closed contactor position. Calculate the following:

a. The inrush exciting current
b. The normal, sealed exciting current
c. The control power needed to actuate the relay coil compared to the power handled by the contactor

Solution

a. The inrush current in the relay coil is

$$I = S/E = 2970/120 = 24.75 \text{ A}$$

b. The normal relay coil current when the contactor is sealed (closed) is

$$I = S/E = 212/120 = 1.77 \text{ A}$$

c. The steady-state apparent control power needed to actuate the relay coil is 212 VA. The apparent power that the contactor can handle is

$$S = EI\sqrt{3} = 460 \times 270\sqrt{3}$$
$$= 215\ 120 \text{ VA}$$

TABLE 20A GRAPHIC SYMBOLS FOR ELECTRICAL DIAGRAMS

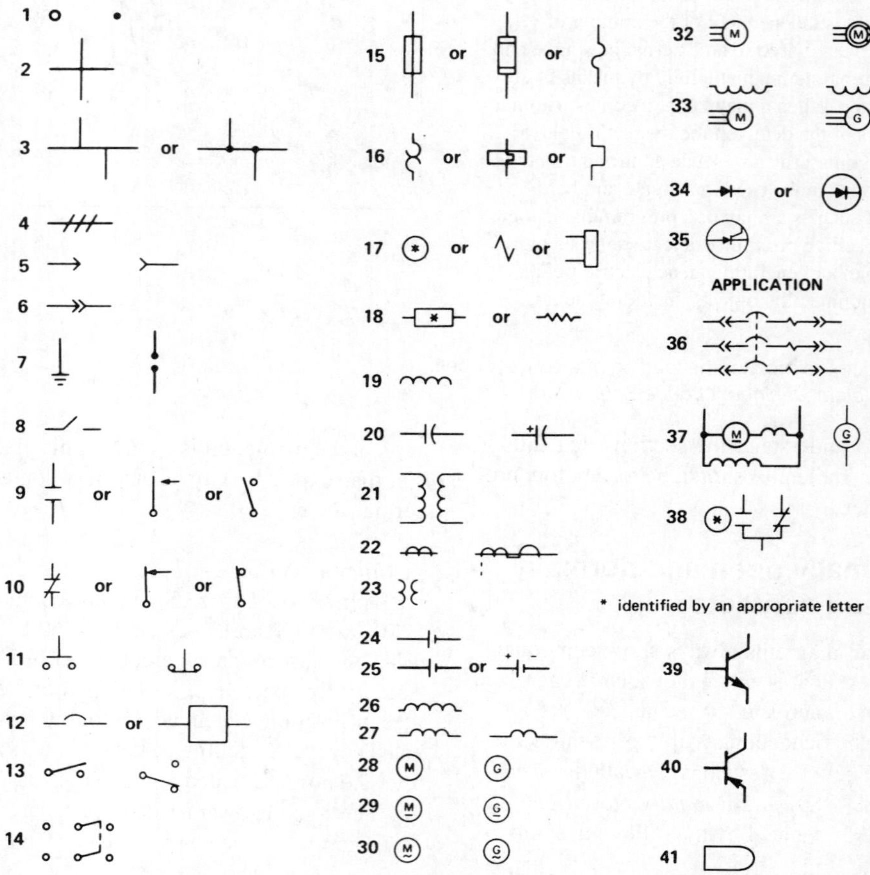

1. terminal; connection 2. conductors crossing 3. conductors connected 4. three conductors 5. plug; receptacle 6. separable connector 7. ground connection; arrester 8. disconnecting switch 9. normally open contact (NO) 10. normally closed contact (NC) 11. pushbutton NO; NC 12. circuit-breaker 13. single-pole switch; three-way switch 14. double pole double throw switch 15. fuse 16. thermal overload element 17. relay coil 18. resistor 19. winding, inductor or reactor 20. capacitor; electrolytic capacitor 21. transformer 22. current transformer; bushing type 23. potential transformer 24. dc source (general) 25. cell 26. shunt winding 27. series winding; commutating pole or compensating winding 28. motor; generator (general symbols) 29. dc motor; dc generator (general symbols) 30. ac motor; ac generator (general symbols) 32. 3-phase squirrel-cage induction motor; 3-phase wound-rotor motor 33. synchronous motor; 3-phase alternator 34. diode 35. thyristor or SCR 36. 3-pole circuit breaker with magnetic overload device, drawout type 37. dc shunt motor with commutating winding; permanent magnet dc generator 38. magnetic relay with one NO and one NC contact. 39. NPN transistor 40. PNP transistor 41. pilot light

For a complete list of graphic symbols and references see *"IEEE Standard and American National Standard Graphic Symbols for Electrical and Electronics Diagrams"* (ANSI Y32.2/IEEE No. 315) published by the Institute of Electrical and Electronics Engineers, Inc., New York, NY 10017. Essentially the same symbols are used in Canada and several other countries.

Thus, the small control power (212 VA) can control a load whose power is 215 120/212 = 1015 times greater.

20.4 Control diagrams

A control system can be represented by four types of circuit diagrams. They are listed as follows, in order of increasing detail and completeness:

- block diagram
- one-line diagram*
- wiring diagram
- schematic diagram

* Also called single-line diagram.

A *block diagram* is composed of a set of rectangles, each representing a control device, together with a brief description of its function. The rectangles are connected by arrows that indicate the direction of power or signal flow (Fig. 20.11).

A *one-line diagram* is similar to a block diagram, except that the components are shown by their symbols rather than by rectangles. The symbols give us an idea of the nature of the components; consequently, one-line diagrams yield more information. A list of typical symbols is displayed in Table 20A. The lines connecting the various components represent two or more conductors (Fig. 20.12).

A *wiring diagram* shows the connections between the components, taking into account the physical location of the terminals and even the color

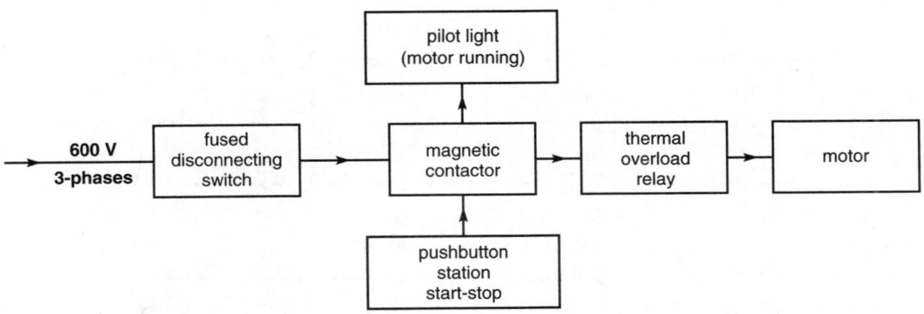

Figure 20.11
Block diagram of a combination starter.

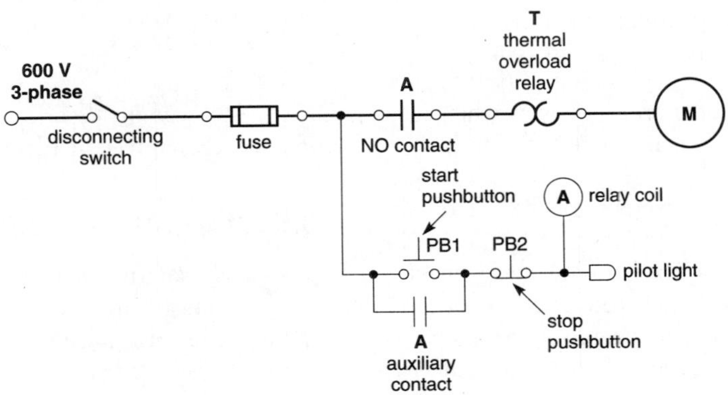

Figure 20.12
One-line diagram of a combination starter.

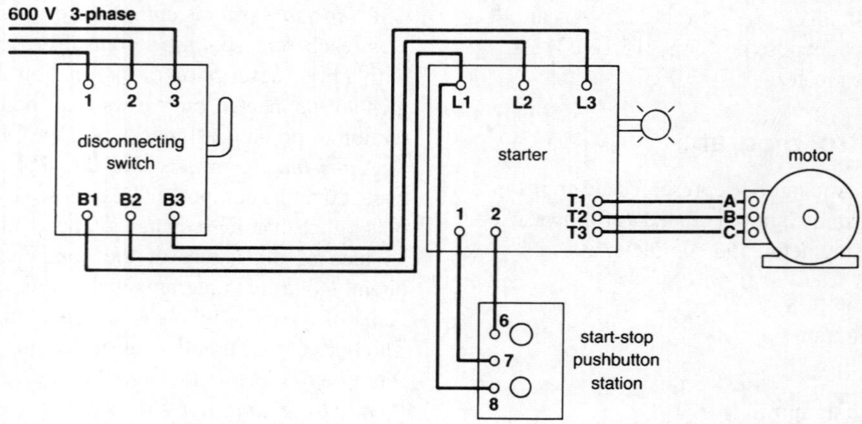

Figure 20.13
Wiring diagram of a combination starter.

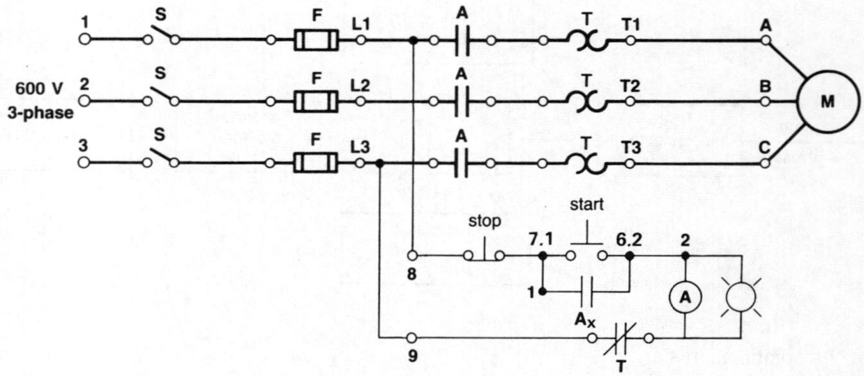

Figure 20.14
Schematic diagram of a combination starter.

of wire. These diagrams are employed when installing equipment or when troubleshooting a circuit (Fig. 20.13).

A *schematic diagram* shows all the electrical connections between components, without regard to their physical location or terminal arrangement. This type of diagram is indispensable when troubleshooting a circuit or analyzing its mode of operation (Fig. 20.14). In the sections that follow, this is the kind of diagram we will be using.

The reader should note that the four diagrams in Figs. 20.11 to 20.14 all relate to the same control circuit. The symbols used to designate the various components are given in Table 20B.

20.5 Starting methods

Three-phase, squirrel-cage motors are started either by connecting them directly across the line or by applying reduced voltage to the stator. The starting method depends upon the power capacity of the supply line and the type of load.

Across-the-line starting is simple and inexpensive. The main disadvantage is the high starting current, which is 5 to 6 times the rated full-load current. It can produce a significant line voltage drop, which may affect other customers connected to the same line. Voltage-sensitive devices such as incandescent lamps, television sets, and high-precision machine tools respond badly to such voltage dips.

Mechanical shock is another problem that should not be overlooked. Equipment can be seriously damaged if full-voltage starting produces a hammerblow torque. Conveyor belts are another example where sudden starting may not be acceptable.

In large industrial installations we can sometimes tolerate across-the-line starting even for motors rated up to 10 000 hp. Obviously, the fuses and circuit breakers must be designed to carry the starting current during the acceleration period.

A motor control circuit contains two basic components: a disconnecting switch and a starter. The disconnecting switch is always placed between the supply line and the starter. The switch and starter are sometimes mounted in the same enclosure to make a *combination starter.* The fuses in the disconnecting switch are rated at about 3.5 times full-load current; consequently, they do not protect the motor against sustained overloads. Their primary function is to protect the motor and supply line against catastrophic currents resulting from a short-circuit in the motor or starter or a failure to start up. Under normal start-up conditions, the fuses do not have time to blow, even though the initial current is 6 to 7 times full-load current. The fuse rating, in amperes, must comply with the requirements of the National Electric Code.

In some cases the disconnecting switch and its fuses are replaced by a manual circuit breaker.

20.6 Manual across-the-line starters

Manual 3-phase starters are composed of a circuit breaker and either two or three thermal relays, all mounted in an appropriate enclosure. Such starters are used for small motors (10 hp or less) at voltages ranging from 120 V to 600 V. The thermal relays trip the circuit breaker whenever the current in one of the phases exceeds the rated value for a significant length of time.

Figure 20.15
Manual starters for single-phase motors rated 1 hp (0.75 kW); left: surface mounted; center: flush mounted; right: waterproof enclosure.
(Courtesy of Siemens)

Single-phase manual starters (Fig. 20.15) are built along the same principles but they contain only one thermal relay. The thermal relays are selected for the particular motor that is connected to the starter.

20.7 Magnetic across-the-line starters

Magnetic across-the-line starters are employed whenever a motor has to be controlled from a remote location. They are also used whenever the power rating exceeds 10 kW.

Fig. 20.16 shows a typical magnetic starter and its associated schematic diagram. The disconnecting switch is external to the starter. The starter has three main components: a magnetic contactor, a thermal relay, and a control station. We now describe these components.

1. The *magnetic contactor* A possesses three heavy contacts A and one small auxiliary contact A_x. As can be seen, these contacts are normally open. Contacts A must be big enough to carry the starting current and the nominal full-load current without overheating. Contact A_x is much smaller because it only carries the current of relay coil A.

   The relay coil is represented by the same symbol (A) as the contacts it controls. Contacts A and A_x remain closed as long as the coil is energized.

2. The *thermal relay* T protects the motor against sustained overloads.* The relay comprises three individual heating elements, respectively connected in series with the three

* The thermal relay is often designated by the letters *OL* (overload).

Figure 20.16a
Three-phase, across-the-line magnetic starter, 30 hp, 600 V, 60 Hz.
(Courtesy of Klockner-Moeller)

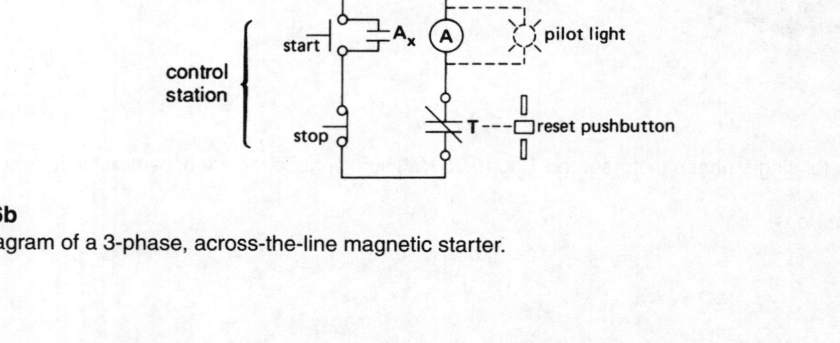

Figure 20.16b
Schematic diagram of a 3-phase, across-the-line magnetic starter.

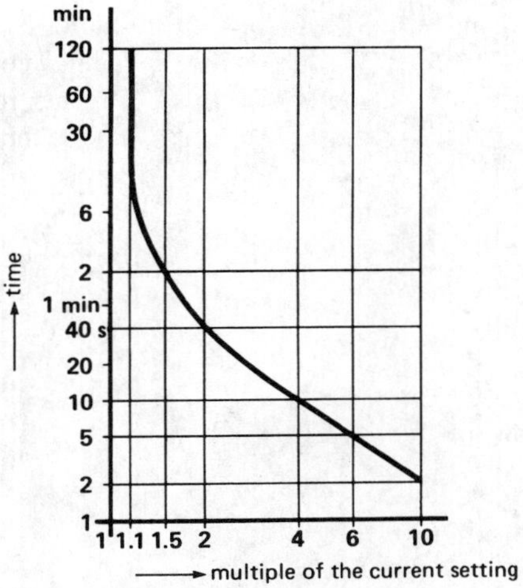

Figure 20.17
Typical curve of a thermal overload relay, showing tripping time versus line current. The tripping time is measured from cold-start conditions. If the motor has been operating at full-load for one hour or more, the tripping time is reduced about 30 percent.

phases. A small, normally closed contact T forms part of the relay assembly. It opens when the thermal relay gets too hot and stays open until the relay is manually reset.

The current rating of the thermal relay is chosen to protect the motor against sustained overloads. Contact T opens after a period of time that depends upon the magnitude of the overload current. Thus, Fig. 20.17 shows the tripping time as a multiple of the rated relay current. At rated current (multiple 1), the relay never trips, but at twice rated current, it trips after an interval of 40 s. The thermal relay is equipped with a reset button enabling us to reclose contact T following an overload. It is preferable to wait a few minutes before pushing the button to allow the relay to cool down.

3. The *control station,* composed of start-stop pushbuttons, may be located either close to, or far away from the starter. The pilot light is optional.

Figure 20.18
Three-phase, across-the-line combination starter, 150 hp, 575 V, 60 Hz. The protruding knob controls the disconnecting switch; the pushbutton station is set in the transparent polycarbonate cover.
(Courtesy of Klockner-Moeller)

Referring to Fig. 20.16b, to start the motor we first close the disconnecting switch and then depress the *start* button. Coil A is immediately energized causing contacts A and A_x to close. The full line voltage appears across the motor and the pilot light is on. When the pushbutton is released it returns to its normal position, but the relay coil remains excited because auxiliary contact A_x is now closed. Contact A_x is said to be a *self-sealing* contact.

To stop the motor, we simply push the *stop* button, which opens the circuit to the coil. In case of a sustained overload, the opening of contact T produces the same effect.

It sometimes happens that a thermal relay will trip for no apparent reason. This condition can occur when the ambient temperature around the starter is too high. We can remedy the situation by changing the location of the starter or by replacing the relay by another one having a higher current rating. Care must be taken before making such a change, because if the ambient temperature around the motor is also too high, the occasional tripping may actually serve as a warning.

Fig. 20.18 shows a typical combination starter. Fig. 20.19 shows another combination starter

Figure 20.19
Three-phase, across-the-line combination starter rated 100 hp, 575 V, 60 Hz. The isolating circuit breaker is controlled by an external handle. The magnetic contactor is mounted in the bottom left-hand corner of the waterproof enclosure. The small 600 V/120 V transformer in the lower right-hand corner supplies low-voltage power for the control circuit.
(Courtesy of Square D)

Figure 20.20
Three-phase, 5 kV starter for a 2500 hp cage motor. The medium- and low-voltage circuits are completely isolated from each other to ensure safety. The compartment is 2286 mm high, 610 mm wide, and 813 mm deep. The entire starter weighs 499 kg.
(Courtesy of Square D, Groupe Schneider)

equipped with a small step-down transformer to excite the control circuit. Such transformers are always used on high-voltage starters (above 600 V) because they permit the use of standard control components, such as pushbuttons and pilot lights while reducing the shock hazard to operating personnel.

Fig. 20.20 shows a medium-voltage across-the-line starter for a 2500 hp, 4160 V, 3-phase, 60 Hz, squirrel-cage motor. The metal compartment houses three fuses and a 3-phase vacuum contactor. The contactor can perform 250 000 operations at full-load before maintenance is required. The 120 V holding coil draws 21.7 A during pull-in, and the current drops to 0.4 A during normal operation. Closing and opening times of the main contactor are respectively 65 ms and 130 ms.

Fig. 20.21 shows a special combination starter that can be reset remotely following a short-circuit. Its distinguishing feature is that it is programmable and requires no fuses. The sophisticated contactor is designed to interrupt short-circuit currents in less than 3 ms, which is comparable to that offered by HRC fuses. The contactor acts also as a disconnecting switch and consequently the overall size is much smaller than more conventional combination starters.

20.8 Inching and jogging

In some mechanical systems, we have to adjust the position of a motorized part very precisely. To accomplish this, we energize the motor in short spurts so that it barely starts before it again comes to a halt. A double-contact pushbutton J is added to the usual start/stop circuit, as shown in Fig. 20.22. This arrangement permits conventional start-stop control as well as *jogging,* or *inching.* The following description shows how the control circuit operates.

If the jog button J is in its normal position (not depressed) relay coil A is excited as soon as the start but-

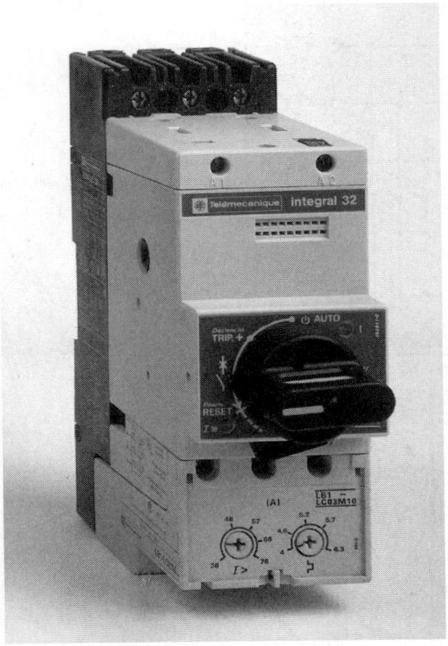

Figure 20.21
Special self-protected starter rated at 40 hp, 460 V, 60 Hz. In addition to a short-circuit capability of 42 kA at 460 V, it features adjustable thermal and magnetic trip settings. Overall dimensions: 243 mm high, 90 mm wide, 179 mm deep.
(Courtesy of Telemecanique, Groupe Schneider)

ton is depressed. Sealing contact A_x in the main contactor closes and so the motor will continue to turn after the start button is released. Thus, the control circuit operates in the same way as in Fig. 20.16b.

Suppose now that the motor is stopped and we depress the jog button. This closes contacts 3, 4 and relay coil A is excited. Contact A_x closes, but contacts 1, 2 are now open and the closure of A_x has no effect. The motor will pick up speed so long as the jog button is depressed. However, when it is released, coil A will become de-energized and contactor A will drop out, causing A_x to open. Thus, when contacts 1, 2 are again bridged, the motor will come to a halt. Thus, by momentarily depressing the jog button we can briefly apply power to the motor.

Jogging imposes severe duty on the main power contacts A because they continually make *and break* currents that are 6 times greater than normal.

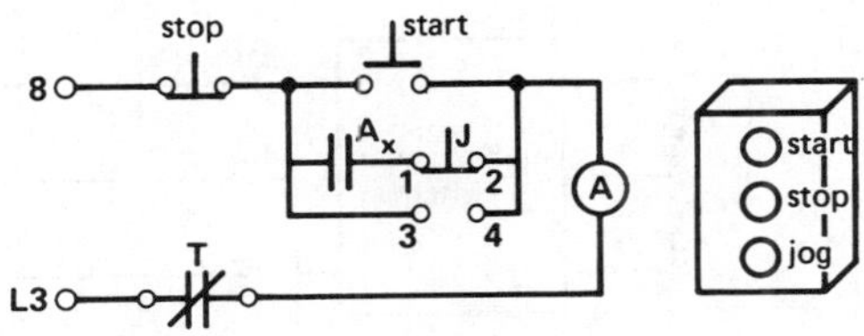

Figure 20.22
Control circuit and pushbutton station for start-stop job operation. Terminals 8, L3 correspond to terminals 8, L3 in Fig. 20.13.

It is estimated that each impulse corresponds to 30 normal start-stop operations. Thus, a contactor that can normally start and stop a motor 3 million times, can only jog the motor 100 000 times, because the contacts have to be replaced.* Furthermore, jogging should not be repeated too quickly, because the intense heat of the breaking arc may cause the main contacts to weld together. Repeated jogging will also overheat the motor. When jogging is required, the contactor is usually selected to be one NEMA size larger than that for normal duty.

20.9 Reversing the direction of rotation

We can reverse the direction of rotation of a 3-phase motor by interchanging any two lines. This can be done by using two magnetic contactors A and B and a manual 3-position cam switch as shown in Fig. 20.23. When contactor A is closed, lines L1, L2, and L3 are connected to terminals A, B, C of the motor. But when contactor B is closed, the same lines are connected to motor terminals C, B, A.

In the forward direction, the cam switch engages contact 1, which energizes relay coil A, causing contactor A to close.**

---

* A magnetic contact has an estimated mechanical life of about 20 million open/close cycles, but the electrical contacts should be replaced after 3 million normal cycles.

** The contacts and relay coils may be designated by any appropriate letters. Thus, the letters *F* and *R* are often used to designate *forward* and *reverse* operating components. In this book we have adopted the letters *A* and *B* mainly for reasons of continuity from one circuit to the next.

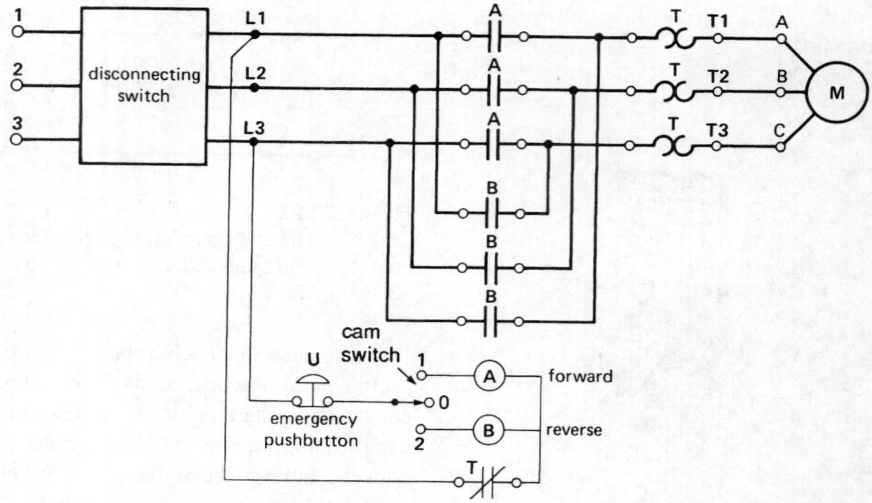

Figure 20.23a
Simplified schematic diagram of a reversible magnetic starter.

Figure 20.23b
Three-position cam switch in Fig. 20.23a.
(Courtesy of Siemens)

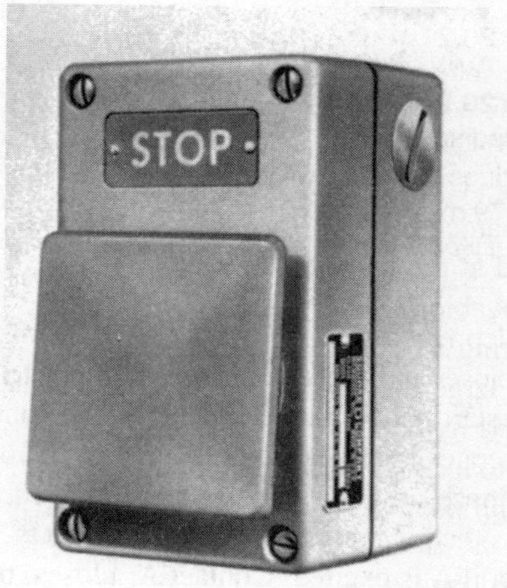

Figure 20.23c
Emergency stop pushbutton in Fig. 20.23a.
(Courtesy of Square D)

To reverse the rotation, we move the cam switch to position 2. However, in doing so, we have to move past the off position (0). Consequently, it is impossible to energize coils A and B simultaneously. Occasionally, however, a mechanical defect may prevent a contactor from dropping out, even after its relay coil is de-energized. This is a serious situation, because when the *other* contactor closes, a short-circuit results across the line. The short-circuit current could easily be 50 to 500 times greater than normal, and both contactors could be severely damaged. To eliminate this danger, the contactors are mounted side by side and mechanically interlocked, so as to make it physically impossible for both to be closed

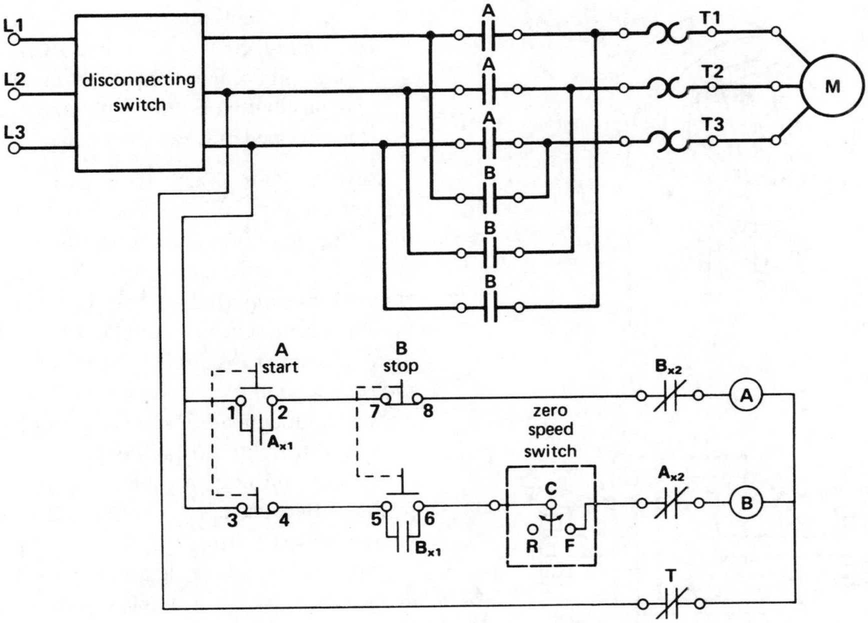

Figure 20.24a
Simplified schematic diagram of a starter with plugging control.

at the same time. The interlock is a simple steel bar, pivoted at the center, whose extremities are tied to the movable armature of each contactor.

During an emergency, pushbutton U, equipped with a large red bull's-eye, can be used to stop the motor (Fig. 20.23c). In practice, operators find it easier to hit a large button than to turn a cam switch to the *off* position.

20.10 Plugging

We have already seen that an induction motor can be brought to a rapid stop by reversing two of the lines (Section 14.8). However, to prevent the motor from running in reverse, a zero-speed switch must open the line as soon as the machine has come to rest. The circuit of Fig. 20.24a shows the basic elements of such a plugging circuit. The circuit operates as follows:

1. Contactor A is used to start the motor. In addition to its 3 main contacts A, it has 2 small auxiliary contacts A_{x1} and A_{x2}.
2. The start pushbutton has one NO contact 1, 2 and one NC contact 3, 4 which operate together. Thus, contact 3, 4 opens before contact 1, 2 closes.
3. Contactor B is used to stop the motor. It is identical to contactor A, having 2 auxiliary contacts B_{x1} and B_{x2} in addition to the 3 main contacts B.
4. The stop pushbutton is identical to the start pushbutton. Thus, when it is depressed contact 7, 8 opens before contact 5, 6 closes.
5. Contact F-C of the zero-speed switch is normally open, but it closes as soon as the motor turns in the forward direction. This prepares the plugging circuit for the eventual operation of coil B.
6. Contacts A_{x1} and B_{x1} are sealing contacts so that pushbuttons A and B have only to be pressed momentarily to start or stop the motor.
7. Contacts A_{x2} and B_{x2} are electrical interlocks to prevent the relay coils A and B from being

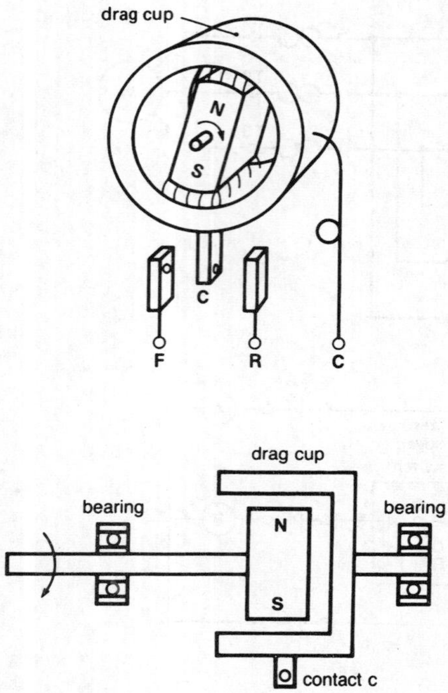

Figure 20.24b
Typical zero-speed switch for use in Fig. 20.24a.

Figure 20.24c
Zero-speed switch, centrifugal type.
(Courtesy of Hubbel)

excited at the same time. Thus, when the motor is running, contact A_{x2} is open. Consequently, relay coil B cannot become excited by depressing pushbutton B until such time as contactor A has dropped out, causing contact A_{x2} to reclose.

Several types of zero-speed switches are on the market and Fig. 20.24b shows one that operates on the principle of an induction motor. It consists of a small permanent magnet rotor N, S and a bronze ring or cup supported on bearings, which is free to pivot between stationary contacts F and R. The permanent magnet is coupled to the shaft of the main motor. As soon as the motor turns clockwise, the permanent magnet drags the ring along in the same direction, thereby closing contacts F-C. When the motor stops turning, the brass ring returns to the *off* position. Because of its function and shape, the ring is often called a *drag cup.*

Fig. 20.24c shows another zero-speed switch that operates on the principle of centrifugal force.

20.11 Reduced-voltage starting

Some industrial loads have to be started very gradually. Examples are coil winders, printing presses, conveyor belts, and machines that process fragile products. In other industrial applications, a motor cannot be directly connected to the line because the starting current is too high. In all these cases we have to reduce the voltage applied to the motor either by connecting resistors (or reactors) in series with the line or by employing an autotransformer. In reducing the voltage, we recall the following:

1. The locked-rotor current is proportional to the voltage: Reducing the voltage by half reduces the current by half.
2. The locked-rotor torque is proportional to the *square* of the voltage: Reducing the voltage by half reduces the torque by a factor of four.

20.12 Primary resistance starting

Primary resistance starting consists of placing three resistors in series with the motor during the start-up period (Fig. 20.25a). Contactor A closes first and

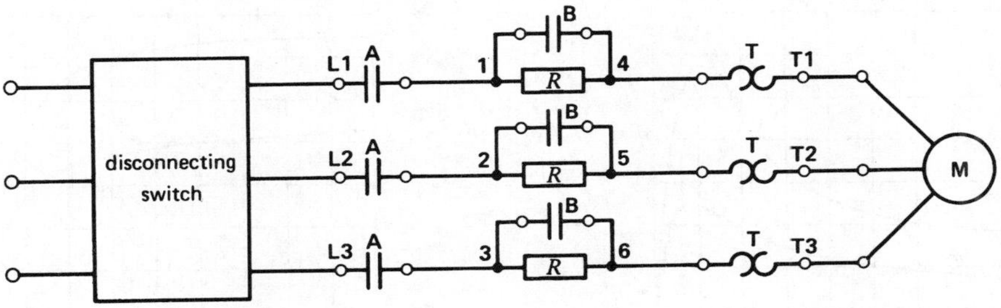

Figure 20.25a
Simplified schematic diagram of the power section of a reduced-voltage primary resistor stator.

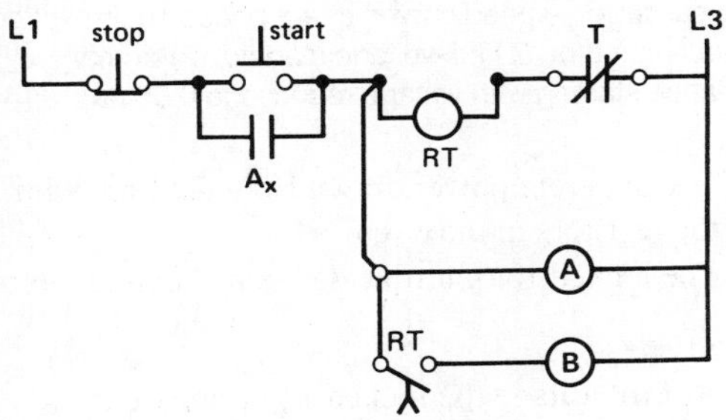

Figure 20.25b
Control circuit of Fig. 20.25a.

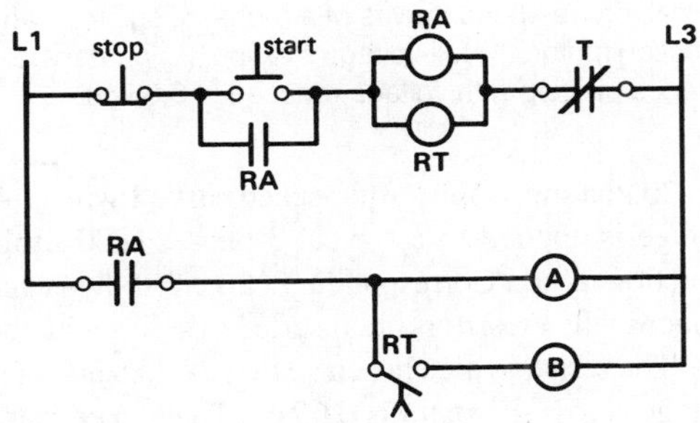

Figure 20.25c
Control circuit of Fig. 20.25a using an auxiliary relay RA.

when the motor has nearly reached synchronous speed, a second contact B short-circuits the resistors. This method gives a very smooth start with complete absence of mechanical shock. The voltage drop across the resistors is high at first, but gradually diminishes as the motor picks up speed and the current falls. Consequently, the voltage across the motor terminals increases with speed, and so the electrical and mechanical shock is negligible when full voltage is finally applied (closure of contactor B). The resistors are short-circuited after a delay that depends upon the setting of a time-delay relay.

The schematic control diagram (Fig. 20.25b) reveals the following circuit elements:

A, B: magnetic contactor relay coils

A_x: auxiliary contact associated with A

RT: time-delay relay that closes the circuit of coil B after a preset interval of time

As soon as the start pushbutton is depressed, relay coils A and RT are excited. This causes the contacts A and A_x to close immediately. However, the contact RT only closes after a certain time delay and so the relay coil of contactor B is only excited a few seconds later.

If the magnetic contactors A, B are particularly large, the inrush exciting currents could damage the start pushbutton contacts if they are connected as shown in Fig. 20.25b. In such cases, it is better to add an auxiliary relay having more robust contacts. Thus, in Fig. 20.25c, the purpose of auxiliary relay RA is to carry the exciting currents of relay coils A and B. Note that the start pushbutton contacts carry only the exciting current of relay coils RA and RT. Other circuit components are straightforward, and the reader should have no difficulty in analyzing the operation of the circuit.

How are the starting characteristics affected when resistors are inserted in series with the stator?

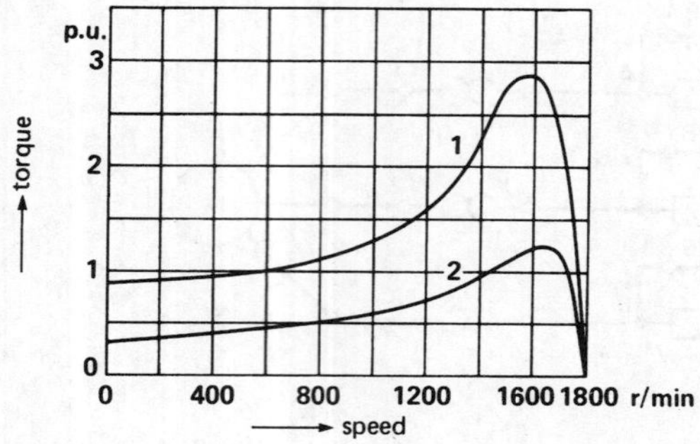

Figure 20.26a
Typical torque-speed curves of a 3-phase, squirrel-cage induction motor: (1) full-voltage starting; (2) primary resistance starting with voltage reduced to 0.65 pu.

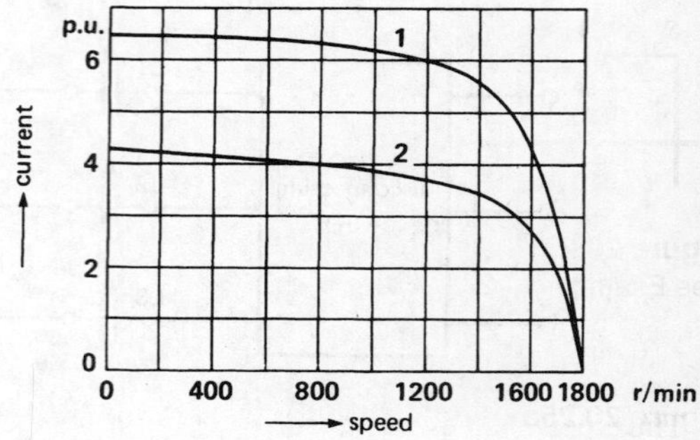

Figure 20.26b
Typical current-speed curves of a 3-phase squirrel-cage induction motor: (1) full-voltage starting; (2) primary resistance starting with voltage reduced to 0.65 pu.

Fig. 20.26a shows the torque-speed curve 1 when full voltage is applied to a typical 3-phase, 1800 r/min induction motor. Corresponding curve 2 shows what happens when resistors are inserted in series with the line. The resistors are chosen so that the locked-rotor voltage across the stator is 0.65 pu. The locked-rotor torque is, therefore, $(0.65)^2 = 0.42$ pu or only 42 percent of full-load torque. This means that the motor must be started at light load.

Fig. 20.26b shows the current versus speed curve 1 when full voltage is applied to the stator. Curve 2 shows the current when the resistors are in the circuit. When the speed reaches about 1700 r/min, the resistors are short-circuited. The current jumps from about 1.8 pu to 2.5 pu, which is a very moderate jump.

Example 20-2

A 150 kW (200 hp), 460 V, 3-phase, 3520 r/min, 60 Hz induction motor has a locked-rotor torque of 600 N·m and a locked-rotor current of 1400 A. Three resistors are connected in series with the line so as to reduce the voltage across the motor to 0.65 pu.

Calculate

a. The apparent power absorbed by the motor under full-voltage, locked-rotor conditions
b. The apparent power absorbed by the motor when the resistors are in the circuit
c. The apparent power drawn from the line, with the resistors in the circuit
d. The locked-rotor torque developed by the motor

Solution

a. At full voltage the locked-rotor apparent power is

$$S = \sqrt{3}\,EI \tag{8.9}$$
$$= \sqrt{3} \times 460 \times 1400$$
$$= 1114 \text{ kVA}$$

b. The voltage across the motor at 0.65 pu is

$$E = 0.65 \times 460 = 299 \text{ V}$$

The current drawn by the motor decreases in proportion to the voltage:

$$I = 0.65 \times 1400 = 910 \text{ A}$$

The apparent power drawn by the motor is

$$S_m = \sqrt{3}\,EI$$
$$= \sqrt{3} \times 299 \times 910$$
$$= 471 \text{ kVA}$$

c. The apparent power drawn from the line is

$$S_L = \sqrt{3}\,EI$$
$$= \sqrt{3} \times 460 \times 910$$
$$= 724 \text{ kVA}$$

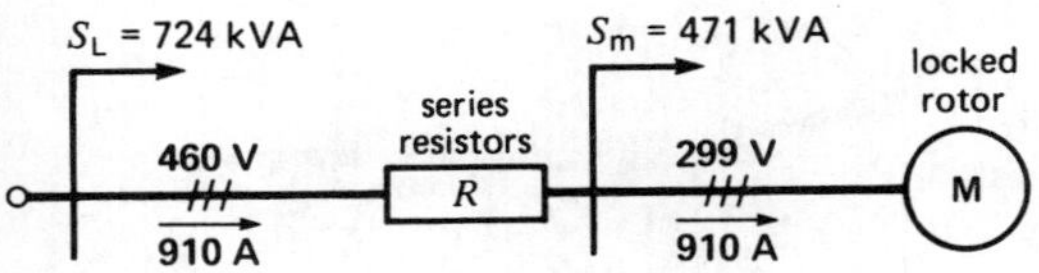

Figure 20.27
See Example 20-2.

Thus, percentagewise, the apparent power is only 724 kVA/1114 kVA = 65% of the apparent power under full-voltage conditions.

d. The torque varies as the square of the voltage:

$$T = 0.65^2 \times 600$$
$$= 0.42 \times 600$$
$$= 252 \text{ N·m } (\sim 186 \text{ ft·lbf})$$

The results of these calculations are summarized in Fig. 20.27.

Example 20-3

In Example 20-2, if the locked-rotor power factor of the motor alone is 0.35, calculate the value of the series resistors and the power they dissipate.

Solution

We will solve this problem by considering active and reactive powers and using the power triangle method. The apparent power drawn by the motor at reduced voltage is

$$S_m = 471 \text{ kVA (from Example 20-2)}$$

The corresponding apparent power drawn by the line is

$$S_L = 724 \text{ kVA (from Example 20-2)}$$

The active power drawn by the motor is

$$P_m = S_m \cos\theta = 471 \times 0.35$$
$$= 165 \text{ kW}$$

The reactive power absorbed by the motor is

$$Q_m = \sqrt{S_m^2 - P_m^2} = \sqrt{471^2 - 165^2}$$
$$= 441 \text{ kvar}$$

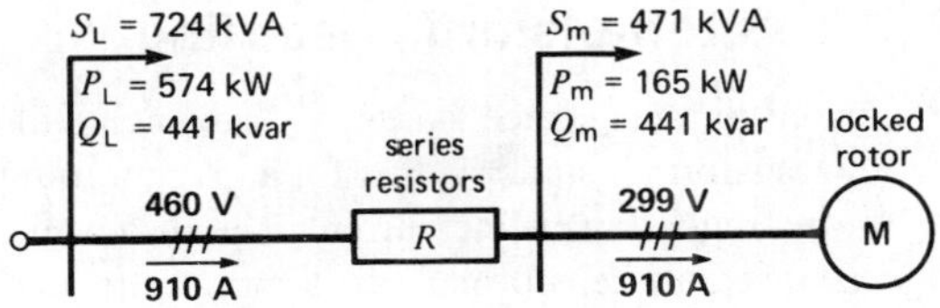

Figure 20.28
See Example 20-3.

The resistors can only absorb active power in the circuit. Consequently, the reactive power supplied by the line *must* be equal to that absorbed by the motor:

$$Q_L = 441 \text{ kvar}$$

The active power supplied by the line is

$$P_L = \sqrt{S_L^2 - Q_L^2} = \sqrt{724^2 - 441^2}$$
$$= 574 \text{ kW}$$

The active power absorbed by the three resistors is

$$P_R = P_L - P_m$$
$$= 574 - 165$$
$$= 409 \text{ kW}$$

The active power per resistor is

$$P = P_R/3 = 409/3 = 136 \text{ kW}$$

The current in each resistor is

$$I = 910 \text{ A (from Example 20-2)}$$

The value of each resistor is

$$P = I^2R$$
$$136\,000 = 910^2 R$$
$$R = 0.164 \ \Omega$$

The three resistors must therefore each have a resistance of 0.164 Ω and a short-term rating of 136 kW. The physical size of these resistors is much smaller than if they were designed for continuous duty.

This is an interesting example of the usefulness of the power triangle method in solving a relatively difficult problem. The results are summarized in Fig. 20.28.

20.13 Autotransformer starting

Compared to a resistance starter, the advantage of an autotransformer starter is that for a given torque it draws a much lower line current. The disadvantage is that autotransformers cost more, and the transition from reduced-voltage to full-voltage is not quite as smooth.

Autotransformers usually have taps to give output voltages of 0.8, 0.65, and 0.5 pu. The corresponding starting torques are respectively 0.64, 0.42, and 0.25 of the full-voltage starting torque. Furthermore, the starting currents on the *line* side are also reduced to 0.64, 0.42, and 0.25 of the full-voltage locked-rotor current.

Fig. 20.29 shows a starter using two autotransformers connected in open delta. A simplified circuit diagram of such a starter is given in Fig. 20.30. It has two contactors A and B. Contactor A has five NO contacts A and one small NO contact A_x. This contactor is in operation only during the brief period when the motor is starting up.

Figure 20.29
Reduced-voltage autotransformer starter, 100 hp, 575 V, 60 Hz.
(Courtesy of Square D)

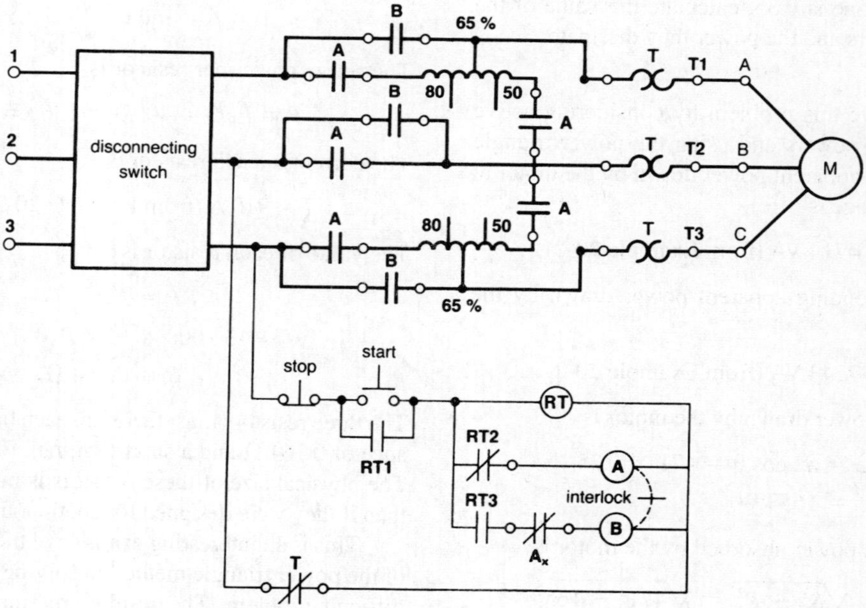

Figure 20.30
Simplified schematic diagram of an autotransformer starter.

Contactor B has 3 NO contacts B. It is in service while the motor is running.

The autotransformers are set on the 65 percent tap. The time-delay relay RT possesses three contacts RT1, RT2, RT3. The contact RT1 in parallel with the start button closes as soon as coil RT is energized. The other two contacts RT2, RT3 operate after a delay that depends upon the RT relay setting. Contactors A and B are mechanically interlocked to prevent them from closing simultaneously.

Contactor A closes as soon as the start button is depressed. This excites the autotransformer and reduced voltage appears across the motor terminals. A few seconds later, contact RT2 in series with coil A opens, causing contactor A to open. At the same time, contact RT3 causes contactor B to close. Thus, contactor A drops out, followed almost immediately by the closure of contactor B. This action applies full voltage to the motor and simultaneously disconnects the autotransformer from the line.

In transferring from contactor A to contactor B, the motor is disconnected from the line for a fraction of a second. This creates a problem because when contactor B closes, a large transient current is drawn from the line. This transient surge is hard on the contacts and also produces a mechanical shock. For this reason, we sometimes employ more elaborate circuits in which the motor is never completely disconnected from the line.

Figs. 20.31a and 20.31b compare the torque and line current when autotransformer starting (3) and resistance starting (2) is used. The locked-rotor voltage in each case is 0.65 pu. The reader will note that the locked-rotor torques are identical, but the locked-rotor line current is much lower using an autotransformer (2.7 versus 4.2 pu).

However, when the motor reaches about 90 percent of synchronous speed, resistance starting produces a higher torque because the terminal voltage is slightly higher than the 65 percent value that existed at the moment of start-up. On the other hand, the line current at all speeds is smaller when using an autotransformer.

Because the autotransformers operate for very short periods, they can be wound with much smaller wire than continuously rated devices. This enables us to drastically reduce the size, weight, and cost of these components.

Example 20-4

A 200 hp (150 kW), 460 V, 3-phase, 3520 r/min, 60 Hz induction motor has a locked-rotor torque of 600 N·m and a locked-rotor current of 1400 A (same motor as in Example 20-2). Two autotransformers, connected in open delta, and having a 65-percent tap, are employed to provide reduced-voltage starting.

Calculate

a. The apparent power absorbed by the motor
b. The apparent power supplied by the 460 V line

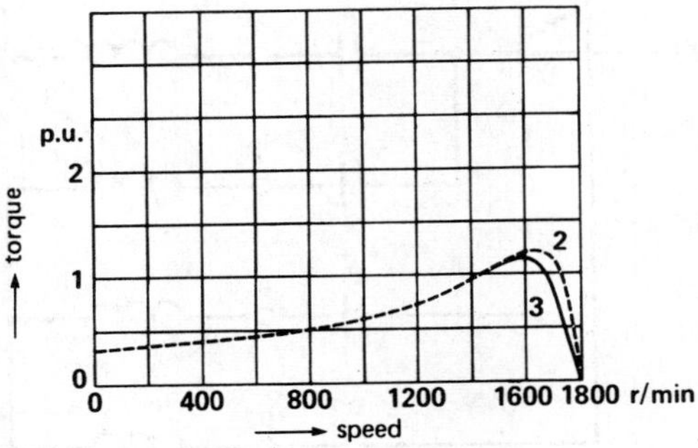

Figure 20.31a
Typical reduced-voltage (0.65 pu) torque-speed curves of a 3-phase, squirrel-cage induction motor: (2) primary resistance starting; (3) autotransformer starting.

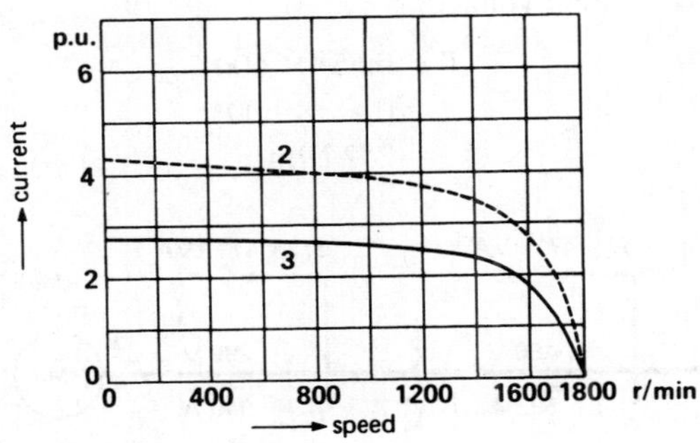

Figure 20.31b
Typical reduced-voltage (0.65 pu) current-speed curves of a 3-phase, squirrel-cage induction motor: (2) primary resistance starting; (3) autotransformer starting.

c. The current supplied by the 460 V line
d. The locked-rotor torque

Solution

a. The voltage across the motor is

$$E = 0.65 \times 460 = 299 \text{ V}$$

The current drawn by the motor is

$$I = 0.65 \times 1400 = 910 \text{ A}$$

The apparent power drawn by the motor is

$$\begin{aligned} S_m &= \sqrt{3}\,EI \\ &= \sqrt{3} \times 299 \times 910 \\ &= 471 \text{ kVA} \end{aligned}$$

b. The apparent power supplied by the line is equal to that absorbed by the motor because the active and reactive power consumed by the autotransformers is negligible (Section 12.1). Consequently,

$$S_L = S_m = 471 \text{ kVA}$$

c. The current drawn from the line is

$$\begin{aligned} I &= S_L/(\sqrt{3}\,E) \qquad (8.9) \\ &= 471\,000/(1.73 \times 460) \\ &= 592 \text{ A} \end{aligned}$$

Note that this current is considerably smaller than the line current (910 A) with resistance starting.

d. The locked-rotor torque varies as the square of the motor voltage:

$$\begin{aligned} T &= 0.65^2 \times 600 \\ &= 0.42 \times 600 \\ &= 252 \text{ N·m} \end{aligned}$$

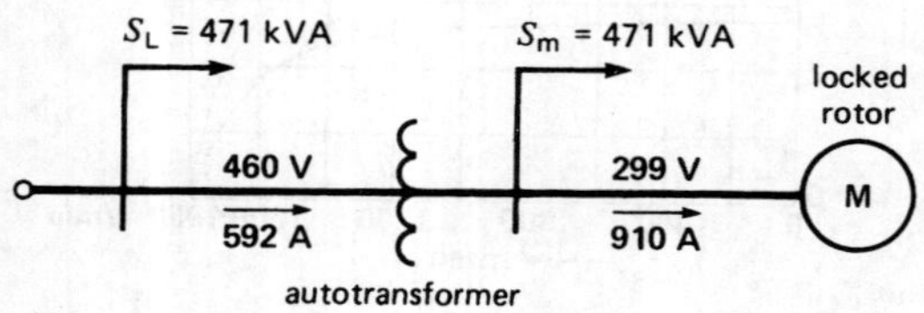

Figure 20.32
See Example 20-4.

The results of these calculations are summarized in Fig. 20.32. It is worthwhile comparing them with the results in Fig. 20.27.

20.14 Other starting methods

In addition to resistors and autotransformers, several other methods are employed to limit the current and torque when starting induction motors. Some only require a change in the stator winding connections. The *part-winding* starting method can be used when the induction motor has two identical 3-phase windings that operate in parallel when the motor is running. During the starting phase, only one of these 3-phase windings is used. As a result, the impedance is higher than if the two windings were connected in parallel. After the motor has picked up speed, the second 3-phase winding is brought into service so that the two windings operate in parallel. Fig. 20.33 shows how two 3-pole contactors A and B can be arranged for part-winding starting. Contactor A closes first, thus energizing windings 1, 2, 3. Shortly after, contactor B closes, bringing windings 7, 8, 9 in parallel with windings 1, 2, 3.

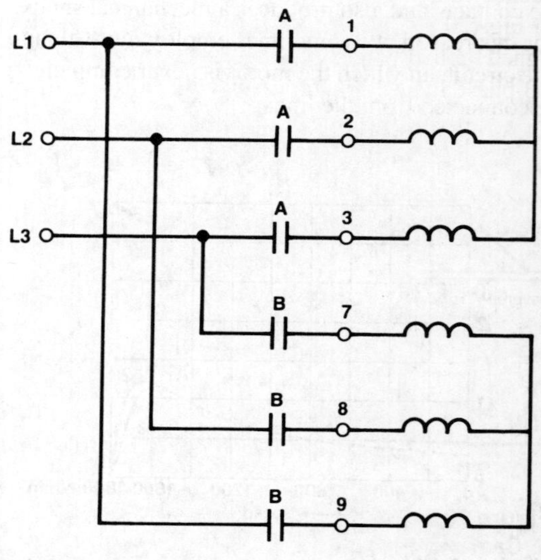

Figure 20.33
Part-winding starting of an induction motor.

There are many different types of part-winding connections and some larger motors have specially designed windings so that the starting performance is optimized.

In *wye-delta* starting, all six stator leads are brought out to the terminal box. The windings are connected in wye during start-up, and in delta during normal running conditions. This starting method gives the same results as an autotransformer starter having a 58-percent tap. The reason is that the voltage across each wye-connected winding is only $1/\sqrt{3}$ (= 0.58) of its rated value.

Finally, to start wound-rotor motors, we progressively short-circuit the external *rotor* resistors in one, two, or more steps. The number of steps depends upon the size of the machine and the nature of the load (see Fig. 13.19).

20.15 Cam switches

Some industrial operations have to be under the continuous control of an operator. In hoists, for example, an operator has to vary the lifting and lowering rate, and the load has to be carefully set down at the proper place. Such a supervised control sequence can be done with cam switches.

Fig. 20.34 shows a 3-position cam switch designed for the *forward, reverse,* and *stop* operation of a 3-phase induction motor. For each position of the knob, some contacts are closed while others are open. This information is given in a table, usually glued to the side of the switch. A cross (**X**) designates a closed contact, while a blank space is an open contact. In the forward position, for example, contacts 2, 4, and 5 are closed and contacts 1 and 3 are open. When the knob is turned to the stop position, all contacts are open. Fig. 20.34b shows the shape of the cam that controls the opening and closing of contact 1.

The schematic diagram (Fig. 20.35) shows how to connect the cam switch to a 3-phase motor. The state of the contacts (open or closed) is shown directly on the diagram for each position of the knob.

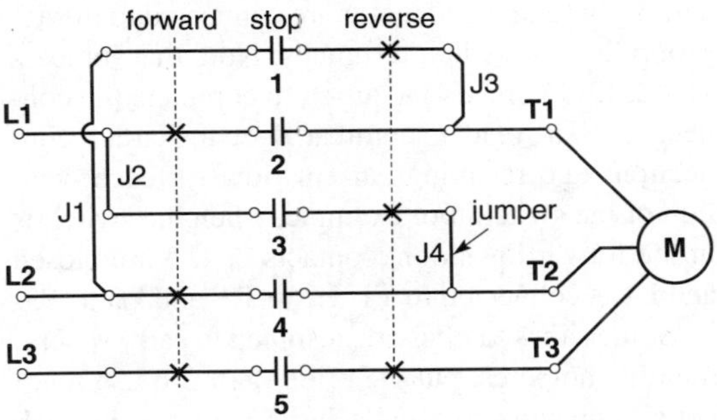

Figure 20.35
Schematic diagram of a cam switch permitting forward-reverse and stop operation of a 3-phase motor.

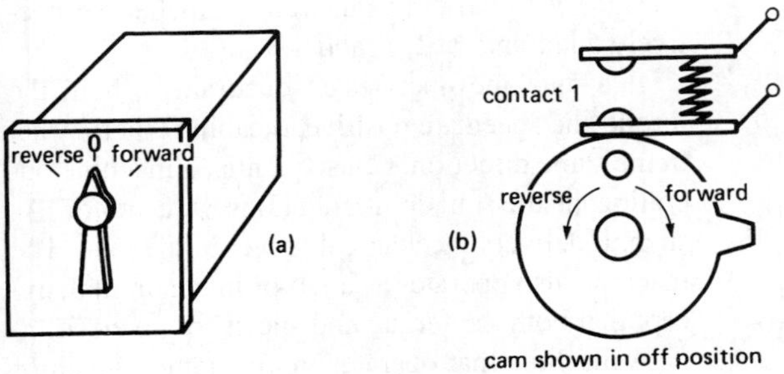

(c)

contact	forward	stop	reverse
1			X
2	X		
3			X
4	X		
5	X		X

Figure 20.34
a. Cam switch external appearance.
b. Detail of the cam controlling contact 1 in the *stop* position.
c. Table listing the on-off state of the five contacts.

The 3-phase line and motor are connected to the appropriate cam-switch terminals. Note that jumpers J1, J2, J3, J4 are also required to complete the connections. The reader should analyze the circuit connections and resulting current flow for each position of the switch. For example, when the switch is in the forward position, contacts 2, 4, 5 are closed and L1 is connected to T1, L2 to T2, and L3 to T3.

Some cam switches are designed to carry several hundred amperes, but we often prefer to use magnetic contactors to handle large currents. In such cases a small cam switch is employed to control the relay coils of the contactors. Very elaborate control schemes can be designed with multicontact cam switches.

20.16 Computers and controls

The control devices we have covered in this chapter are used throughout the industry. However, with the advent of computers, it is now possible to *simulate* the behavior of many relay coils and relay contacts. Furthermore, the connections between these devices can also be simulated. As a result, it is possible to make very complex control circuits by simply using a keyboard, a monitor, and a computer. Thus, instead of using real relays, contacts, and time-delay dashpots, we simply *program* these devices (and their wiring) on a computer. The computers used for this purpose are called Programmable Logic Controllers (PLCs). Their construction and basic principle of operation are covered in Chapter 31.

ELECTRIC DRIVES

20.17 Fundamentals of electric drives*

In this chapter we have seen the basic control equipment that is used to start and stop induction motors.

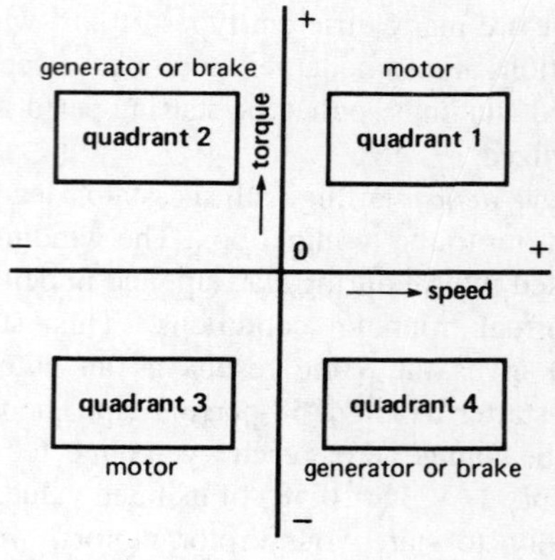

Figure 20.36
Electric drives can operate in four distinct quadrants.

However, some industrial drives require a motor to function at various torques and speeds, both in forward and reverse. In addition to operating as a motor, the machine often has to function for brief periods as a generator or brake. In electric locomotives, for example, the motor may run clockwise or counterclockwise, and the torque may act either with or against the direction of rotation. In other words, the speed and torque may be positive or negative.

In describing industrial drives, the various operating modes can best be shown in graphical form. The positive and negative speeds are plotted on a horizontal axis, and the positive and negative torques on a vertical axis (Fig. 20.36). This gives rise to four operating quadrants, labelled respectively quadrants 1, 2, 3, and 4.

If a machine operates in quadrant 1, both the torque and speed are positive, meaning that they act in the same direction. Consequently, a machine operating in this quadrant functions as a motor. As such, it delivers mechanical power to the load. The machine also operates as a motor in quadrant 3, except that both the torque and speed are reversed.

A machine that operates in quadrant 2 develops a positive torque but its speed is negative. In other words, the torque acts clockwise while the machine turns counterclockwise. In this quadrant, the machine *absorbs* mechanical power from the load;

* An electric drive is a system consisting of one or several electric motors and of the entire electric control equipment designed to govern the performance of these motors. (*IEEE Standard Dictionary of Electrical and Electronics Terms*)

consequently, it functions basically as a generator. The mechanical power is converted into electric power and the latter is usually fed back into the line. However, the electric power may be dissipated in an external resistor, such as in dynamic braking.

Depending on the way it is connected, a machine may also function as a *brake* when operating in quadrant 2. The mechanical power absorbed is again converted to electric power, but the latter is immediately and unavoidably converted into heat. In effect, when a machine functions as a brake, it absorbs electric power from the supply line at the same time as it absorbs mechanical power from the shaft. Both power inputs are dissipated as heat—often inside the machine itself. For example, whenever a machine is plugged, it operates as a brake. In larger power drives we seldom favor the brake mode of operation because it is very inefficient. Consequently, the circuit is usually arranged so that the machine functions as a generator when operating in quadrant 2.

Quadrant 4 is identical to quadrant 2, except that the torque and speed are reversed; consequently, the same remarks apply.

20.18 Typical torque-speed curves

The torque-speed curve of a 3-phase induction motor is an excellent example of the motor-generator-brake behavior of an electrical machine. We first examined it in Chapter 14, Section 14.16. The reader is encouraged to take a few moments to review this section, with particular attention to Fig. 14.16.

Referring now to the solid curve in Fig. 20.37, the machine acts as a motor in quadrant 1, as a brake in quadrant 2, and as a generator in quadrant 4 (Section 14.16). If the stator leads are reversed, another torque-speed curve is obtained. This dashed-line curve shows that the machine now operates as a motor in quadrant 3, as a generator in quadrant 2, and as a brake in quadrant 4. Note that the machine can function either as a generator or brake in quadrants 2 and 4. On the other hand, it always runs as a motor in quadrants 1 and 3.

To give another example, Fig. 20.38 shows the complete torque-speed curve of a dc shunt motor

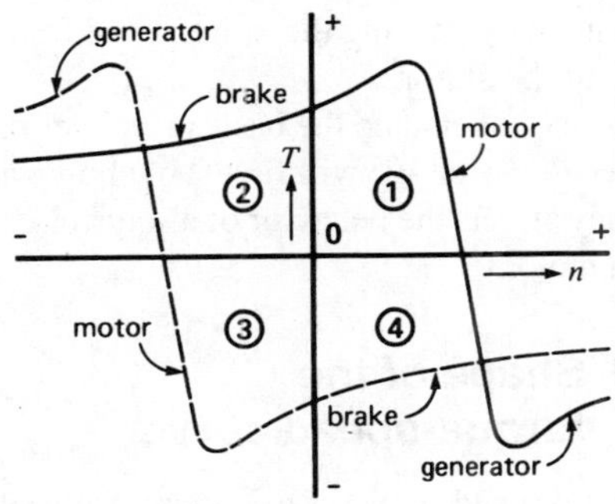

Figure 20.37
Typical torque-speed curve of a squirrel-cage induction motor operating at fixed voltage and frequency.

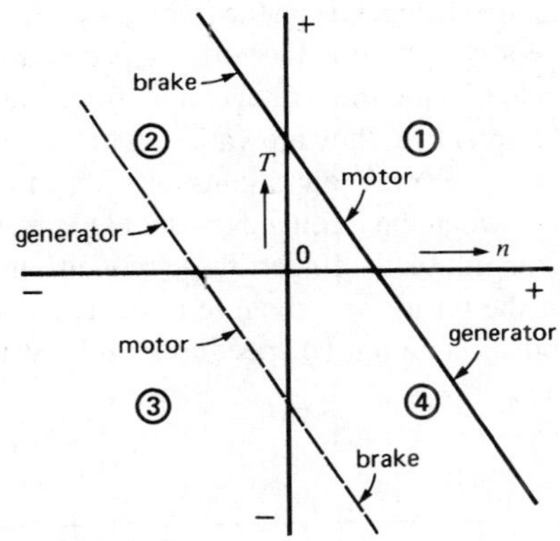

Figure 20.38
Typical torque-speed curve of a dc motor.

when the armature voltage is fixed. The motor-generator-brake modes are again apparent. If the armature leads are reversed, we obtain the dashed torque-speed curve.

In designing variable-speed electric drives, we try to vary the speed and torque in a smooth, continuous way to satisfy the load requirements. This is usually done by shifting the entire torque-speed characteristic back and forth along the horizontal axis. For example, the torque-speed curve of the dc motor (Fig. 20.38) may be shifted back and forth by varying the armature voltage. Similarly, we can shift the curve of an induction motor by simultaneously varying the voltage and frequency applied to the stator.

To better understand the basic principles of variable speed control, we will first show how variable frequency affects the behavior of a squirrel-cage induction motor.

20.19 Shape of the torque-speed curve

The torque-speed curve of a 3-phase, squirrel-cage induction motor depends upon the voltage and frequency applied to the stator. We already know that if the frequency is fixed, the torque varies as the square of the applied voltage. We also know that the synchronous speed depends on the frequency. The question now arises, how is the torque-speed curve affected when both the voltage and frequency are varied? In practice, they are varied in the same proportion so as to maintain a constant flux in the air gap. Thus, when the frequency is doubled, the stator voltage is doubled. Under these conditions, the shape of the torque-speed curve remains the same, but its position along the speed axis shifts with the frequency.

Varying the voltage and frequency in the same proportion has given rise to the "volts per hertz rule" of motor operation. By keeping the volts per hertz at the same level while the frequency is varied, we ensure that the flux in the motor is always close to its rated value. However, at frequencies below about 20% of rated frequency, the volts per hertz ratio has to be progressively increased to compensate for the IR drop in the stator.

Fig. 20.39 shows the torque-speed curve of a 15 hp, (11 kW) 3-phase, 460 V, 60 Hz, squirrel-cage induction motor. The full-load speed and torque are respectively 1725 r/min and 60 N·m, the breakdown torque is 160 N·m, and the locked-rotor torque is 80 N·m.

If we reduce both the voltage and frequency to one-fourth their original value (115 V and 15 Hz), the new torque-speed curve is shifted toward the left. The curve retains the same shape, but crosses the axis at a synchronous speed of 1800/4 = 450 r/min (Fig. 20.40). Similarly, if we raise the voltage and frequency by 50 percent (690 V, 90 Hz), the curve is shifted to the right and the new synchronous speed is 2700 r/min.

Even if we bring the frequency down to zero (dc), the torque-speed curve retains essentially the same

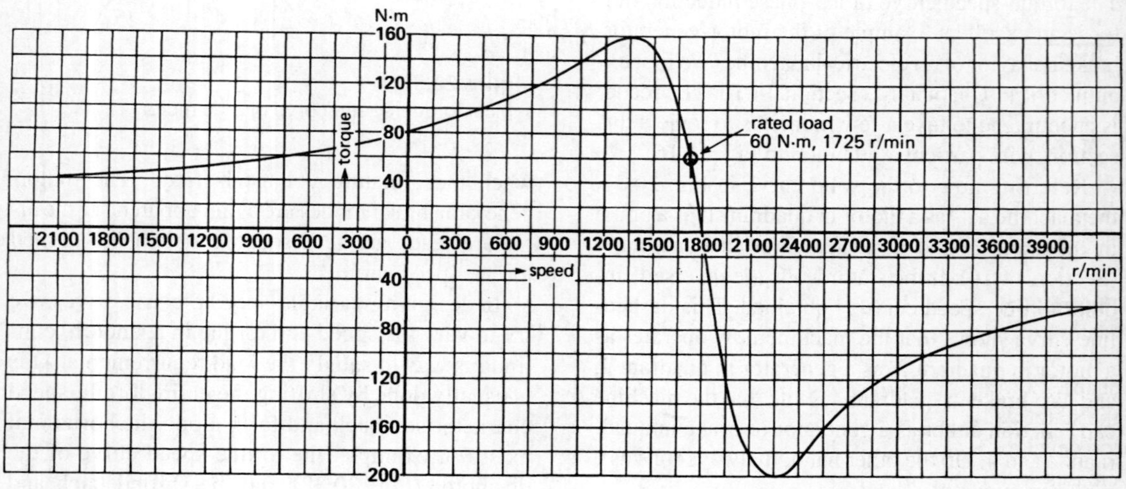

Figure 20.39
Torque-speed curve of a 15 hp, 460 V, 60 Hz, 3-phase, squirrel-cage induction motor.

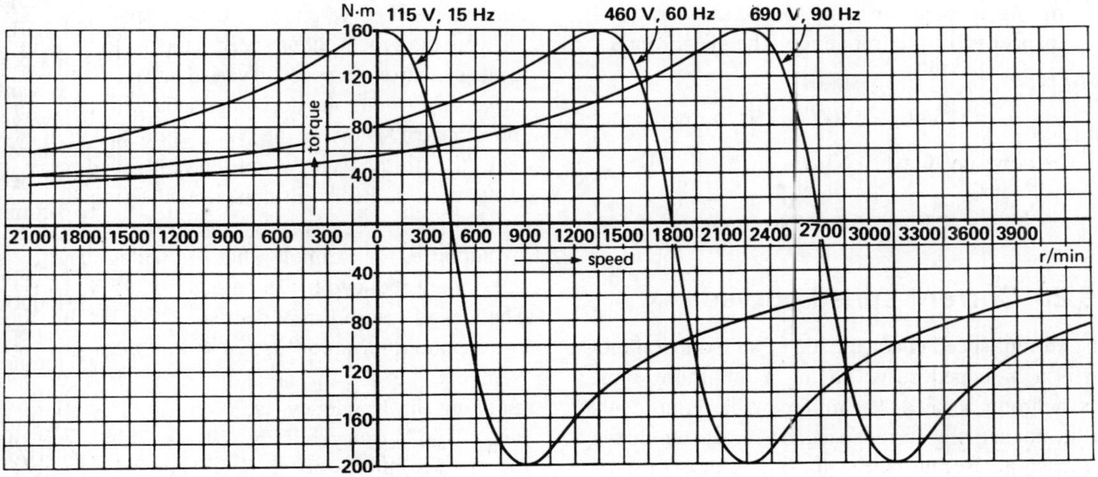

Figure 20.40
Torque-speed curve at three different frequencies and voltages.

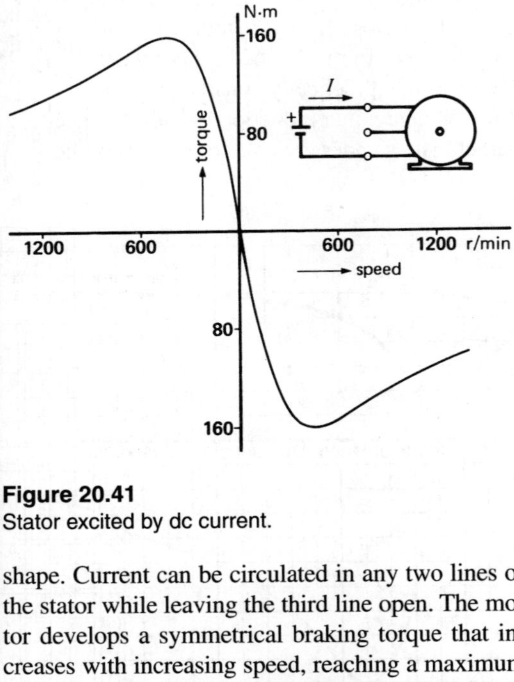

Figure 20.41
Stator excited by dc current.

shape. Current can be circulated in any two lines of the stator while leaving the third line open. The motor develops a symmetrical braking torque that increases with increasing speed, reaching a maximum in both directions, as shown in Fig. 20.41. In this figure, the dc current in the windings is adjusted to produce the rated breakdown torque.

Because the shape of the torque-speed curve is the same at all frequencies, it follows that the torque developed by an induction motor is the same whenever the slip speed (in r/min) is the same.

Example 20-5

A standard 3-phase, 10 hp, 575 V, 1750 r/min, 60 Hz, NEMA class D squirrel-cage induction motor develops a torque of 110 N·m at a speed of 1440 r/min. If the motor is excited at a frequency of 25 Hz, calculate the following:

a. The required voltage to maintain the same flux in the machine
b. The new speed at a torque of 110 N·m

Solution

a. To keep the same flux, the voltage must be reduced in proportion to the frequency:

$$E = (25/60) \times 575 = 240 \text{ V}$$

b. The synchronous speed of the 4-pole, 60 Hz motor is obviously 1800 r/min. Consequently, the slip speed at a torque of 110 N·m is

$$\begin{aligned} n_1 &= n_s - n \\ &= 1800 - 1440 = 360 \text{ r/min} \end{aligned}$$

The slip speed is the same for the same torque, irrespective of the frequency. The synchronous speed at 25 Hz is

$$n_s = (25/60) \times 1800 = 750 \text{ r/min}$$

The new speed at 110 N·m is

$$n = 750 - 360 = 390 \text{ r/min}$$

20.20 Current-speed curves

The current-speed characteristic of an induction motor is a V-shaped curve having a minimum value at synchronous speed. The minimum current is equal to the magnetizing current needed to create the flux in the machine. Because the stator flux is kept constant, the magnetizing current is the same at all speeds.

Fig. 20.42 shows the current-speed curve of the 15 hp, 460 V, 60 Hz, squirrel-cage induction motor mentioned previously. We have plotted the *effective* values of current for all speeds; consequently, the current is always positive. The locked-rotor current is 120 A and the corresponding torque is 80 N·m.

As in the case of the torque-speed curve, it can be shown that if the stator flux is held constant, the current-speed curve retains the same shape, no matter what the synchronous speed happens to be. Thus, as the synchronous speed is varied, the current-speed curve shifts along the horizontal axis with the minimum current following the synchronous speed. In effect, the torque-speed and current-speed curves move back and forth in unison as the frequency is varied.

Suppose, for example, that the voltage and frequency are reduced by 75 percent to 115 V, 15 Hz. The locked-rotor current decreases to 80 A, but the corresponding torque (Fig. 20.40) *increases* to 160 N·m, equal to the full breakdown torque. Thus, by reducing the frequency, we obtain a larger torque with a smaller current (Fig. 20.43). This is one of the big advantages of frequency control. In effect, we can gradually accelerate a motor and its load by progressively increasing the voltage and frequency. During the start-up period, the voltage and frequency can be varied automatically so that the motor develops close to its breakdown torque all the way from zero to rated speed. This ensures a rapid acceleration at practically constant current.

In conclusion, an induction motor has excellent characteristics under variable frequency conditions.

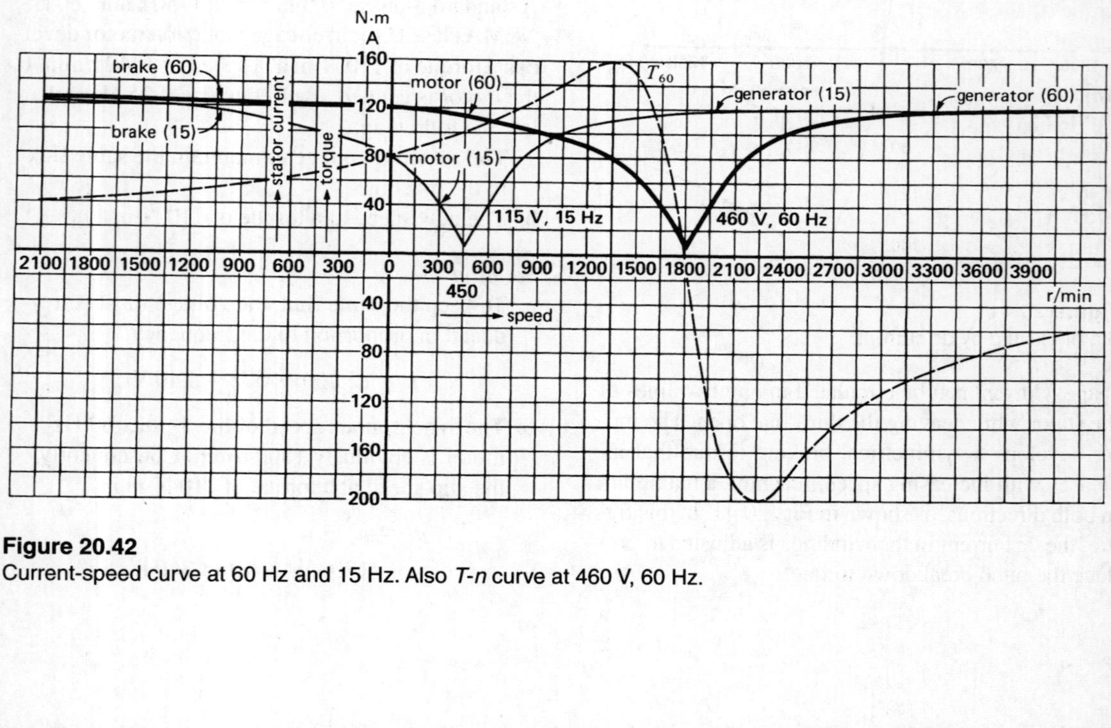

Figure 20.42
Current-speed curve at 60 Hz and 15 Hz. Also *T-n* curve at 460 V, 60 Hz.

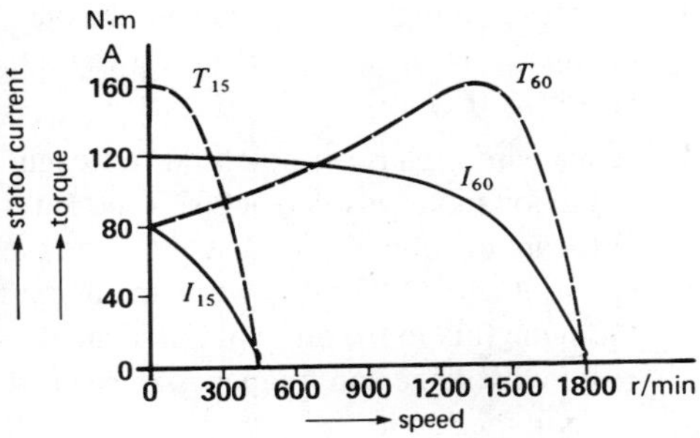

Figure 20.43
The starting torque increases and the current decreases with decreasing frequency.

For a given frequency the speed changes very little with increasing load. In many ways, the torque-speed characteristic resembles that of a dc shunt motor with variable armature-voltage control.

Example 20-6

Using the information revealed by the 60 Hz torque-speed and current-speed curves of Fig. 20.42, calculate the voltage and frequency required so that the machine will run at 3200 r/min while developing a torque of 100 N·m. What is the corresponding stator current?

Solution

We first have to find the slip speed corresponding to a torque of 100 N·m.

According to Fig. 20.42, when the motor operates at 60 Hz and a torque of 100 N·m, the speed is 1650 r/min. Consequently, the slip speed is

$$n_1 = n_s - n$$
$$= 1800 - 1650 = 150 \text{ r/min}$$

The slip speed is the same when the motor develops 100 N·m at 3200 r/min. Consequently, the synchronous speed must be

$$n_s = 3200 + 150 = 3350 \text{ r/min}$$

The corresponding frequency is, therefore,

$$f = (3350/1800) \times 60 = 111.7 \text{ Hz}$$

The corresponding stator voltage is

$$E = (111.7/60) \times 460 = 856 \text{ V}$$

The 60 Hz current-speed and torque-speed curves (Fig. 20.42) show that the stator current is 40 A when the torque is 100 N·m. Because the current-speed curve shifts along with the torque-speed curve, the current is again 40 A at 3200 r/min and 100 N·m.

20.21 Regenerative braking

A further advantage of frequency control is that it permits regenerative braking. Referring to Fig. 20.44, suppose the motor is connected to a 460 V, 60 Hz line. It is running at 1650 r/min, driving a load of constant torque $T_L = 100$ N·m (operating point **1**). If we suddenly reduce the frequency and voltage by 50 percent, the motor will immediately operate along the 30 Hz, 230 V, torque-speed curve. Because the speed cannot change instantaneously (due to inertia), we suddenly find ourselves at operating point **2** on the new torque-speed curve. The motor torque is negative; consequently, the speed will drop very quickly, following the 50-percent curve until we reach torque T_L (operating point **4**) The interesting feature is that

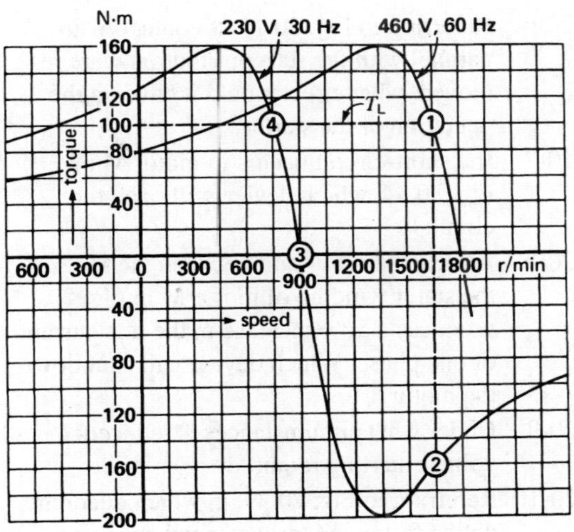

Figure 20.44
Effect of suddenly changing the stator frequency.

in moving along the curve from point **2** to point **3,** energy is returned to the ac line, because the motor acts as an asynchronous generator during this interval.

The ability to develop a high torque from zero to full speed, together with the economy of regenerative braking, is the main reason why frequency-controlled induction motor drives are becoming so popular. These electronically controlled drives are covered in Chapter 23.

Questions and Problems

Practical level

20-1 Name four types of circuit diagrams and describe the purpose of each.

20-2 Without referring to the text, describe the operation of the starter shown in Fig. 20.16b, and state the use of each component.

20-3 Give the symbols for a NO and a NC contact, and for a thermal relay.

20-4 Identify all the components shown in Fig. 20.23a using the equipment list given in Table 20A. Where are contact T and coil A situated physically?

20-5 If the start and stop pushbuttons in Fig. 20.24a are pushed simultaneously, what will happen?

20-6 Referring to Fig. 20.14, if contact A_x in parallel with the start pushbutton were removed, what effect would it have on the operation of the starter?

20-7 If a short-circuit occurs in motor M of Fig. 20.14, which device will open the circuit?

20-8 A partial short-circuit between the turns of the stator winding of motor M in Fig. 20.14 produces a 50% increase in the line current of one phase. Which device will shut down the motor?

20-9 Under what circumstances is reduced-voltage starting required?

20-10 Referring to Fig. 20.39, in which quadrants do the following torque-speed operating points occur?

a. +1650 r/min, + 100 N·m

b. +3150 r/min, − 100 N·m

20-11 Referring to Fig. 20.39, calculate the mechanical power [hp] of the motor when it runs at 450 r/min.

20-12 A standard 3-phase, 4-pole, squirrel-cage induction motor is rated at 208 V, 60 Hz. We want the motor to turn at a no-load speed of about 225 r/min while maintaining the same flux in the air gap. Calculate the required voltage and frequency to be applied to the stator.

20-13 Referring to Fig. 20.42, what is the current in the stator under the following conditions, knowing that the stator is energized at 460 V, 60 Hz?

a. Machine running as a motor at 1650 r/min and developing a torque of 100 N·m

b. Machine running as a brake at 300 r/min

c. Machine driven as an asynchronous generator at a torque of 120 N·m

20-14 State in which quadrants a machine operates

a. As a brake

b. As a motor

c. As a generator

20-15 A machine is turning clockwise in quadrant 3. Does it develop a clockwise or counterclockwise torque?

Intermediate level

20-16 A thermal relay having the tripping curve given in Fig. 20.17 has to protect a 40 hp, 575 V, 3-phase, 720 r/min induction motor having a nominal current rating of 40 A. If the relay is set to 40 A, how long will it take to trip if the motor current is

a. 60 A?

b. 240 A?

20-17 **a.** If the control circuit of Fig. 20.22 is used in place of that shown in Fig. 20.14, show that the motor will start and continue to run if we momentarily press the start button.

b. Show that if we press the jog button, the motor only runs for as long as the button is depressed.

20-18 A magnetic contactor can make 3 million normal circuit interruptions before its contacts need to be replaced. If an operator jogs the motor so that it starts and stops once per minute, after approximately how many working days will the contacts have to be replaced, assuming the operator works an 8-hour day?

20-19 **a.** Referring to Fig. 20.24a and assuming that the motor is initially at rest, explain the operation of the circuit when the start button is momentarily depressed.
b. If the motor is running normally, what happens if we momentarily press the stop button?

20-20 **a.** Explain the sequence of events that takes place when the start button in Fig. 20.25c is momentarily depressed, knowing that relay RT is adjusted for a delay of 10 s.
b. With the motor running, explain what happens when the stop button is depressed.

20-21 Referring to Fig. 20.30, describe the sequence of events that takes place when the start button is momentarily depressed, knowing that relay RT is set for a delay of 5 s. Draw the actual circuit connections, in sequence, until the motor reaches its final speed.

20-22 A 100 hp, 460 V, 3-phase induction motor possesses the characteristics given by curve 1 in Figs. 20.26a and 20.26b. The full-load current is 120 A, and the thermal relays are set to this value. If the relay tripping curve is given by Fig. 20.17, calculate the approximate tripping time if the load current suddenly rises to 240 A. (Assume that the motor had been running for several hours at full-load.)

20-23 Referring to Fig. 20.39 and neglecting windage and friction losses, calculate the power P_r supplied to the rotor when the machine runs
a. As a motor at 1650 r/min
b. As a brake at 750 r/min
c. As a generator at 2550 r/min

20-24 In Problem 20-23, calculate the value of the rotor I^2R losses in each case.

20-25 Referring to Fig. 20.39, calculate the voltage and frequency that must be applied to the machine so that it runs as a relatively high-efficiency motor
a. At a speed of 1200 r/min, developing a torque of 100 N·m
b. At a speed of 2400 r/min, developing a torque of 60 N·m

20-26 Referring to Fig. 20.42, calculate the voltage and frequency to be applied to the stator so that the locked-rotor torque is 100 N·m at a current of 40 A.

20-27 **a.** It is impossible for a machine to instantaneously change from a point in quadrant 1 to point in quadrant 2. Why?
b. Can it move instantaneously from quadrant 1 to a quadrant 4?

20-28 A 4-pole, shunt-wound dc motor has an armature circuit resistance of 4 Ω. It is connected to a 240 V dc source, and the no-load speed is 1800 r/min; the corresponding armature current is negligible. Assuming constant field excitation and assuming that armature reaction effects can be neglected, calculate the following:
a. The armature current at 900 r/min
b. The mechanical power output [hp] at 1200 r/min
c. The torque [N·m] at 300 r/min
d. The starting torque [ft·lbf]
e. Draw the torque-speed curve that passes through quadrants 1, 2, and 4 (see Fig. 20.38)

20-29 **a.** In Problem 20-28 draw the torque-speed curve if 60 V is applied to the armature, while maintaining the same field excitation.
b. What is the frequency of the current in the armature coils at a speed of 300 r/min?

Advanced level

20-30 **a.** The curves in Fig. 20.26 relate to a 100 hp, 460 V, 1765 r/min, 3-phase,

60 Hz induction motor, whose full-load current is 120 A. Calculate the breakdown torque for curves 1 and 2 [ft·lbf].

b. Calculate the torque developed when the resistors are in the circuit and the line current is 480 A [ft·lbf].

20-31 The motor having the *T-n* characteristic given in Fig. 20.39 is running at a no-load speed of 1800 r/min. The total moment of inertia of the rotor and its load is 90 lb·ft^2. The speed has to be reduced to a no-load value of 1200 r/min by suddenly changing the voltage and frequency applied to the stator.

Calculate

a. The voltage and frequency required
b. The initial kinetic energy stored in the moving parts
c. The final kinetic energy in the moving parts
d. Is all the lost kinetic energy returned to the 3-phase line? Explain.

20-32 A 15 hp, 460 V, 3-phase, 60 Hz induction motor has the torque-speed characteristic given in Fig. 20.39.

a. What is the new shape of the curve if we apply 230 V, 60 Hz to the stator?
b. Calculate the new breakdown torque [ft·lbf].

20-33 In Problem 20-32 calculate the stator voltage needed to reduce the breakdown torque to 60 N·m.

Industrial application

20-34 A 30 hp, 1780 r/min, 200 V, 3-phase cage motor driving a compressor is protected by a thermal relay having the time/current characteristic shown in Fig. 20.45. Curve 3 relates to normal 3-phase operation, and curve 2 applies when the motor runs single-phase.

The plant electrician set the relay at 82 A, which corresponds to the rated full-load current of the motor. Under normal operating conditions, a hook-on ammeter indicated that the motor draws a current of 71 A from the 200 V line.

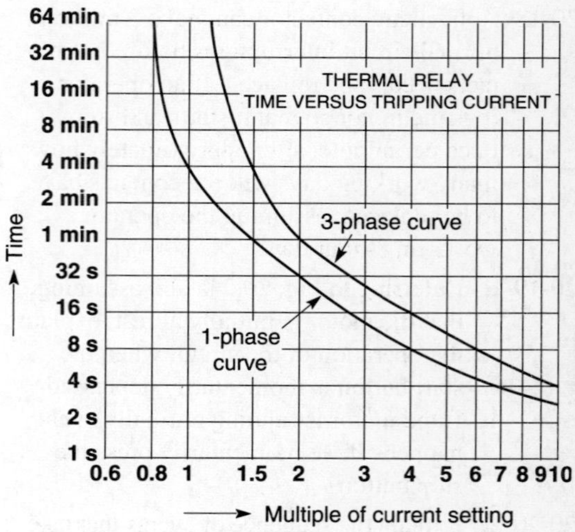

Figure 20.45
See Problem 20-34.

Due to a fault on another circuit, the fuse in the distribution panel associated with phase C of the compressor motor suddenly blew, causing it to run as a single-phase motor. As a result, the current in phases A and B rose to 135 A.

What is the maximum possible time it took for the thermal relay to trip the contactor? (The thermal characteristic corresponds to cold start conditions.)

20-35 According to the manufacturer's specifications, it is known that the motor in Problem 20-34 draws a locked-rotor current of 465 A at 200 V, 3-phase. The per-unit starting torque is 2.20.

The motor is started during a particularly low voltage-sag in the electric utility system. This sag, combined with the line voltage drop caused by the large starting current, causes the voltage across the motor terminals to fall to 155 V. In turn, the reduced torque causes the motor to accelerate very slowly and it doesn't reach full speed before the thermal relay trips out.

a. What is the per-unit starting current and per-unit starting torque under these abnormal conditions?

b. Estimate the time it took for the relay to trip.

20-36 The stator winding of the motor in Problem 20-34 has a line-to-neutral resistance of 23 mΩ.

a. Calculate the stator copper losses when the motor runs normally on the 3-phase line, driving the compressor.

b. Calculate the stator copper losses when the motor runs as a single-phase motor.

Does single-phasing tend to overheat the motor?

20-37 The holding coil of a 13 kW, 230 V, 3-phase 60 Hz contactor has a rating of 120 V. According to the manufacturer's catalog, when the contactor is in the open position, the coil draws 100 VA at a power factor of 0.75. In the holding position, the coil absorbs 3 W and 11.5 VA.

We want to excite the coil directly off the 230 V line. To achieve this result, calculate the resistance and power rating of the resistor that should be connected in series with the coil a) when the contactor is open and b) when the contactor is closed.

CHAPTER 21

Fundamental Elements of Power Electronics

21.0 Introduction

Electronic systems and controls have gained wide acceptance in power technology; consequently, it has become almost indispensable to know something about power electronics. Naturally, we cannot cover all aspects of this broad subject in a single chapter. Nevertheless, we can explain in simple terms the behavior of a large number of electronic power circuits, including those most commonly used today.

As far as electronic devices are concerned, we will first cover diodes and thyristors. They are found in all electronic systems that involve the conversion of ac power to dc power and vice versa. We then go on to discuss the application of more recent devices such as gate turn-off thyristors (GTOs), bipolar junction transistors (BJTs), metal oxide semiconductor field effect transistors (power MOSFETs), and insulated gate bipolar transistors (IGBTs). Their action on a circuit is basically no different from that of a thyristor and its associated switching circuitry. In power electronics all these devices act basically as high-speed switches; so much so, that much of power electronics can be explained by the opening and closing of circuits at precise instants of time. However, we should not conclude that circuits containing these components and devices are simple—they are not—but their behavior can be understood without having an extensive background in semiconductor theory.

21.1 Potential level

In Chapter 2, Sections 2.4 and 2.5, we described two ways of representing voltages in a circuit. We now introduce a third method that is particularly useful in circuits dealing with power electronics. The method is based upon the concept of potential levels.

To understand the operation of electronic circuits, it is useful to imagine that individual terminals have a potential level with respect to a reference terminal. The reference terminal is any convenient point chosen in a circuit; it is assumed to have zero electric potential. The potential level of all other points is then measured with respect to this zero reference terminal. In graphs, the reference level is shown as a horizontal line having a potential of 0 V.

Consider, for example, the circuit of Fig. 21.1, composed of an 80 V battery connected in series with an ac source *E* having a peak voltage of 100 V. Of the three possible terminals, let us choose terminal 1 as the reference point. The potential level of

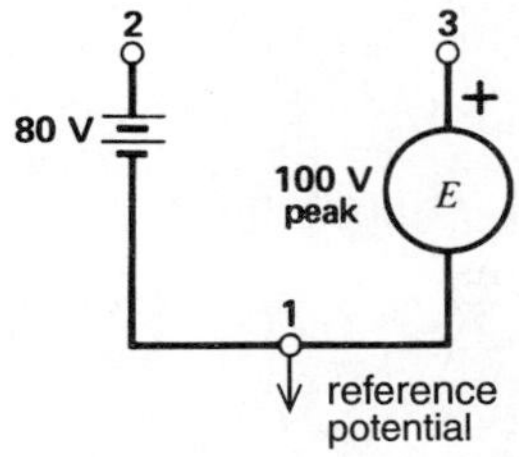

Figure 21.1
Potential level method of representing voltages.

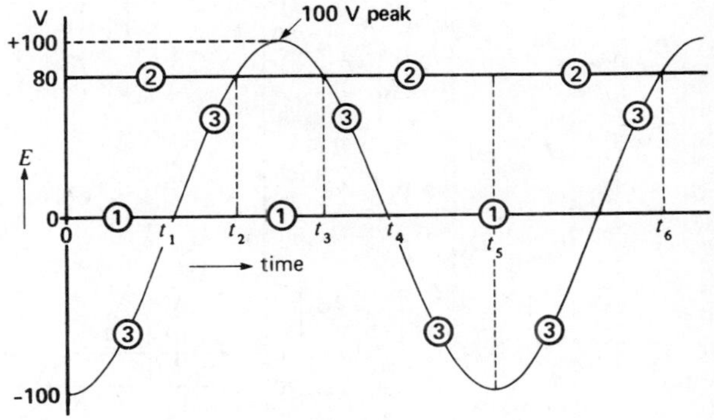

Figure 21.2
Potential levels of terminals 1, 2, and 3.

this terminal is therefore shown by a horizontal line, designated **1** in Fig. 21.2.

Consider now the potential level of terminal 2. The difference of potential between terminals 1 and 2 is always 80 V, and terminal 2 is positive with respect to terminal 1. The level of this terminal is therefore indicated by a second horizontal line **2** placed 80 V above line **1.**

Now consider terminal 3. Voltage E between terminals 1 and 3 is alternating and we assume that its initial value is 100 V, with terminal 3 negative with respect to terminal 1. Because E is alternating, the potential of terminal 3 is first negative, then positive, with respect to terminal 1. The changing level is shown by curve **3.** Thus, during the interval from 0 to t_1, the level of point **3** is below the level of point **1,** which indicates that terminal 3 is negative with respect to terminal 1. During the interval t_1 to t_4, the polarity reverses, and so the level of curve **3** is now above line **1.** Terminal 1 is therefore negative with respect to terminal 3, because line **1** is below curve **3.**

This potential-level method now enables us to determine the instantaneous voltages between any two terminals in a circuit, as well as their relative polarities. For example, during the interval from t_2 to t_3, terminal 3 is positive with respect to terminal 2, because curve **3** is above line **2.** The voltage between these terminals reaches a maximum of 20 V during this interval. Then, from t_3 to t_6, terminal 3 is negative with respect to terminal 2 and the voltage between them reaches a maximum value of 180 V at instant t_5.

We could have chosen another terminal as a reference terminal. Thus, in Fig. 21.3 we chose terminal 3 and, as before, we represent the zero potential of this reference terminal by a horizontal line **3** (Fig. 21.4). Knowing that E is an alternating voltage and that terminal 3 is initially 100 V negative with respect to terminal 1 (as in Fig. 21.2), we can draw curve **1.**

To determine the level of terminal 2, we know that it is always 80 V positive with respect to terminal 1. Consequently, we draw curve **2** so that it is always 80 V above curve **1.** By so doing, we automatically establish the level of terminal 2 with respect to terminal 3.

Figs. 21.2 and 21.4 do not have the same appearance; however, at every instant, the relative polarities and potential differences between terminals are identical. From an electrical point of view, the two figures are identical. We invite the reader to check by comparing the voltages and their relative polarities at various instants in the two figures.

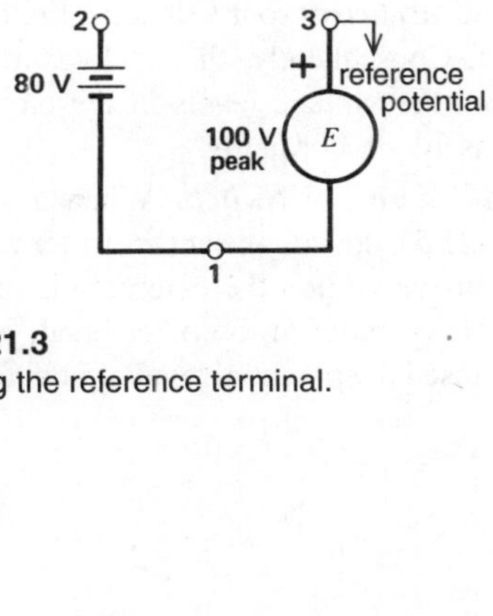

Figure 21.3
Changing the reference terminal.

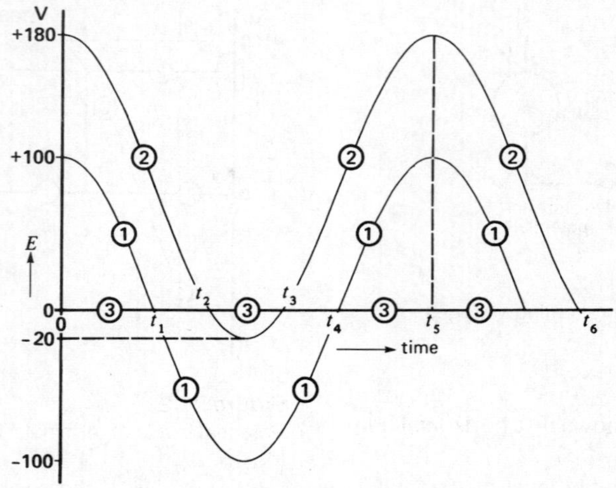

Figure 21.4
The relative potential levels are the same as in Fig. 21.2.

In analyzing electronic circuits the reference terminal may be selected anywhere; however, it should be selected so that it is easy to observe the waveshapes of the voltages we are interested in.

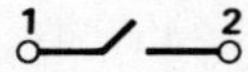

Figure 21.5
Potential across a switch.

21.2 Voltage across some circuit elements

Let us first look at the voltage levels that appear across some active and passive circuit elements commonly found in electronic circuits. Specifically, we examine sources, switches, resistors, coils, and capacitors.

1. Sources. By definition, ideal ac and dc voltage sources have zero internal impedance. Consequently, they impose rigid potential levels; nothing that happens in a circuit can modify these levels. On the other hand, ac and dc *current* sources have infinite internal impedance. Consequently, they deliver a constant current, and the voltage levels in the circuit must adapt themselves accordingly.

2. Potential across a Switch. When a switch is open (Fig. 21.5), the voltage across its terminals depends exclusively upon the external elements that make up the circuit. On the other hand, when the switch is closed the potential level of both terminals must be the same. Thus, if we happen to know the level of terminal 2, then the level of terminal 1 is also known. This simple rule also applies to *idealized* thyristors and diodes, because they behave like perfect (albeit one-way) switches.

3. Potential across a Resistor. If no current flows in a resistor, its terminals 3, 4 must be at the same potential, because the *IR* drop is zero (Fig. 21.6). Consequently, if we happen to know the potential level of one of the terminals, the level of the other is also known. On the other hand, if the resistor carries a current *I*, the *IR* drop produces a corresponding potential difference between the terminals. For example, if current actually flows in the direction shown

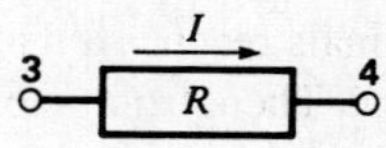

Figure 21.6
Potential across a resistor.

in Fig. 21.6, the potential of terminal 3 is above that of terminal 4, by an amount equal to *IR*.

*4. **Potential across a Coil or Inductance.*** The terminals of a coil are at the same potential only during those moments when the current is not changing. If the current varies, the potential difference is given by

$$E = L\,(\Delta I/\Delta t) \qquad (2.27)$$

Thus, if the current in Fig. 21.7 is *increasing* while flowing in the direction shown, the potential level of terminal 5 is *above* that of terminal 6 by an amount equal to $L\,\Delta I/\Delta t$. Conversely, if I is *decreasing* while flowing in the direction shown, the potential of terminal 5 is *below* that of terminal 6.

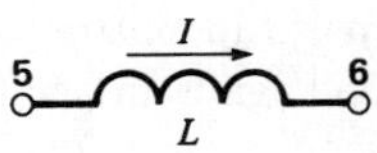

Figure 21.7
Potential across an inductor.

*5. **Potential across a Capacitor.*** The terminals of a capacitor are at the same potential only when the capacitor is completely discharged. Furthermore, the potential difference between the terminals remains unchanged during those intervals when the current I is zero (Fig. 21.8).

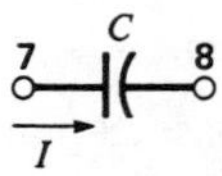

Figure 21.8
Potential across a capacitor.

*6. **Initial Potential Level.*** A final rule regarding potential levels is worth remembering. Unless we know otherwise, we assume the following initial conditions:

a. All currents in the circuit are zero and none are in the process of changing.
b. All capacitors are discharged.

These assumed starting conditions enable us to analyze the behavior of any circuit from the moment power is applied.

THE DIODE AND DIODE CIRCUITS

21.3 The diode

A diode is an electronic device possessing two terminals, respectively called anode (A) and cathode (K) (Fig. 21.9). Although it has no moving parts, a diode acts like a high-speed switch whose contacts open and close according to the following rules:

Rule 1. When no voltage is applied across a diode, it acts like an open switch. The circuit is therefore open between terminals A and K (Fig. 21.9a).

Rule 2. If we apply an *inverse voltage* E_2 across the diode so that the anode is *negative* with respect to the cathode, the diode continues to act as an open switch (Fig. 21.9b). We say that the diode is reverse biased.

Rule 3. If a momentary *forward voltage* E_1 of 0.7 V or more is applied across the terminals so that anode A is slightly *positive* with respect to the cathode, the terminals become short-circuited. The diode acts like a closed switch and a current I immediately begins to flow from anode to cathode (Fig. 21.9c). We say that the diode is forward biased.

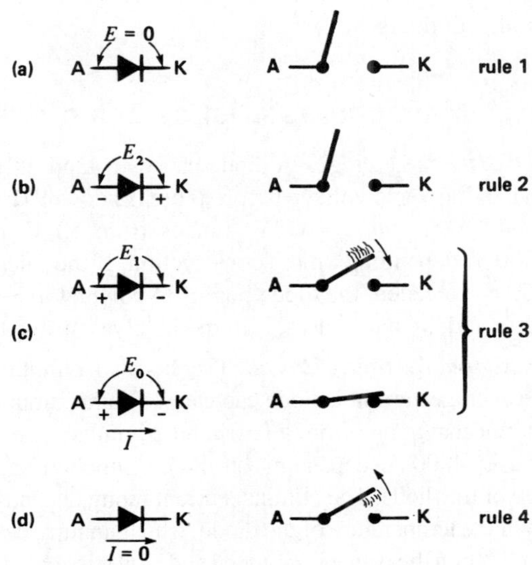

Figure 21.9
Basic rules governing diode behavior.

In practice, while the diode conducts, a small voltage drop appears across its terminals. However, the voltage drop has an upper value of about 1.5 V, so it can be neglected in most electronic circuits. It is precisely because the voltage drop is small with respect to other circuit voltages that we can assume the diode is essentially a closed switch when it conducts.

Rule 4. As long as current flows, the diode acts like a closed switch. However, if it stops flowing for even as little as 10 μs, the ideal diode immediately returns to its original open state (Fig. 21.9d). Conduction will only resume when the anode again becomes slightly positive with respect to the cathode (Rule 3).

In conclusion, a perfect diode behaves like a normally open switch whose contacts close as soon as the anode *voltage* becomes slightly positive with respect to the cathode. Its contacts only reopen when the *current* (not the voltage) has fallen to zero. This simple rule is crucially important to an understanding of circuits involving diodes and thyristors.

Symbol for a Diode. The symbol for a diode (Fig. 21.9) bears an arrow that indicates the direction of conventional current flow when the diode conducts.

21.4 Main characteristics of a diode

Peak Inverse Voltage. A diode can withstand only so much inverse voltage before it breaks down. The *peak inverse voltage* (PIV) ranges from 50 V to 4000 V, depending on the construction. If the rated PIV is exceeded, the diode begins to conduct in reverse and, in many cases, is immediately destroyed.

Maximum Average Current. There is also a limit to the average current a diode can carry. The maximum current may range from a few hundred milliamperes to over 4000 A, depending on the construction and size of the diode. The nominal current rating depends upon the temperature of the diode, which, in turn, depends upon the way it is mounted and how it is cooled.

Maximum Temperature. The voltage across a diode times the current it carries is equal to a power loss which is entirely converted into heat. The resulting temperature rise of the diode must never exceed the permissible limits, otherwise the diode will be destroyed. Most silicon diodes can operate satisfactorily provided their internal temperature lies between −50°C and +200°C. The temperature of a diode can change very quickly, due to its small size and small mass. To improve heat transfer, diodes are usually mounted on thick metallic supports, called *heat sinks.* Furthermore, in large installations, the diodes may be cooled by fans, by oil, or by a continuous flow of deionized water. Table 21A gives the specifications of some typical diodes. Fig. 21.10 shows a range of low-power to very-high-power diodes.

Diodes have many applications, some of which are found again and again, in one form or another, in electronic power circuits. In the sections that follow, we will analyze a few circuits that involve only diodes. They will illustrate the methodology of power circuit analysis while revealing some basic principles common to many industrial applications. Sections 21.5 to 21.14 cover the following topics:

21.5	Battery charger with series resistor
21.6	Battery charger with series inductor
21.7	Single-phase bridge rectifier
21.8	Filters
21.9	Three-phase, 3-pulse diode rectifier
21.10	Three-phase, 6-pulse diode rectifier
21.11	Effective line current; fundamental line current
21.12	Distortion power factor
21.13	Displacement power factor
21.14	Harmonic content

21.5 Battery charger with series resistor

The circuit of Fig. 21.11a represents a simplified battery charger. Transformer T, connected to a 120 V ac supply, furnishes a sinusoidal secondary voltage

TABLE 21A PROPERTIES OF SOME TYPICAL DIODES

Relative power	I_0 [A]	E_0 [V]	I_{cr} [A]	E_2 [V]	I_2 [mA]	T_J [°C]	d [mm]	l [mm]
low	1	0.8	30	1000	0.05	175	3.8	4.6
medium	12	0.6	240	1000	0.6	200	11	32
high	100	0.6	1 600	1000	4.5	200	25	54
very high	1000	1.1	10 000	2000	50	200	47	26

I_0 – average dc current
E_0 – voltage drop corresponding to I_0
I_{cr} – peak value of surge current for one cycle
E_2 – peak inverse voltage
I_2 – reverse leakage current corresponding to E_2
T_J – maximum junction temperature (inside the diode)
d – diameter
l – length

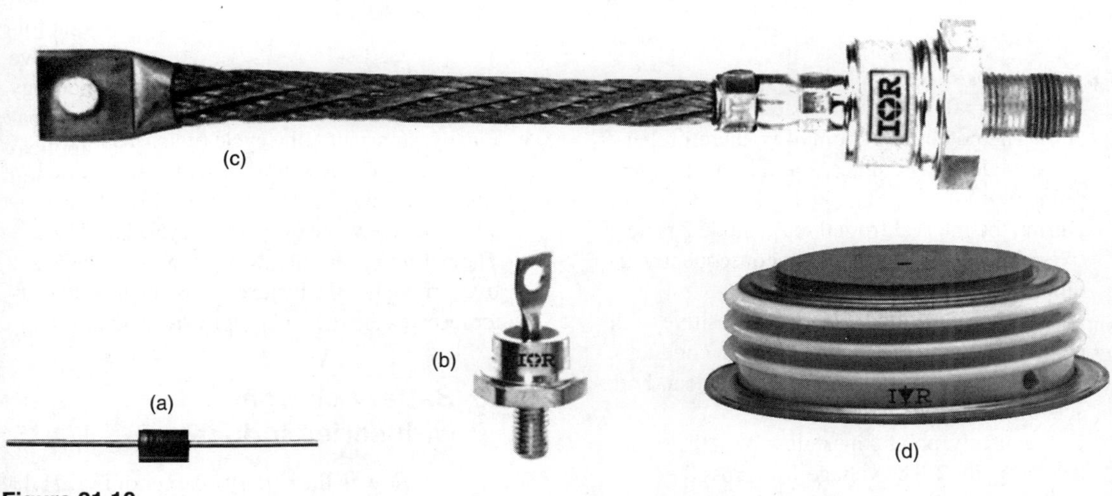

Figure 21.10
a. Average current: 4 A; PIV: 400 V; body length: 10 mm; diameter: 5.6 mm.
b. Average current: 15 A; PIV: 500 V; stud type; length less thread: 25 mm; diameter: 17 mm.
c. Average current: 500 A; PIV: 2000 V; length less thread: 244 mm; diameter: 40 mm.
d. Average current: 2600 A; PIV: 2500 V; Hockey Puk; distance between pole-faces: 35 mm; diameter: 98 mm.
(Photos courtesy of International Rectifier)

having a peak of 100 V. A 60 V battery, a 1 Ω resistor, and an ideal diode D are connected in series across the secondary.

To explain the operation of the circuit, let us choose point **1** as the reference terminal. The potential of this terminal is, therefore, a straight horizontal line. The potential of terminal 2 swings sinusoidally above and below point **1,** according to whether 2 is positive or negative with respect to 1. The level of terminal 3 is always 60 V above terminal 1, because the battery voltage is constant. The potential levels are shown in Fig. 21.11b.

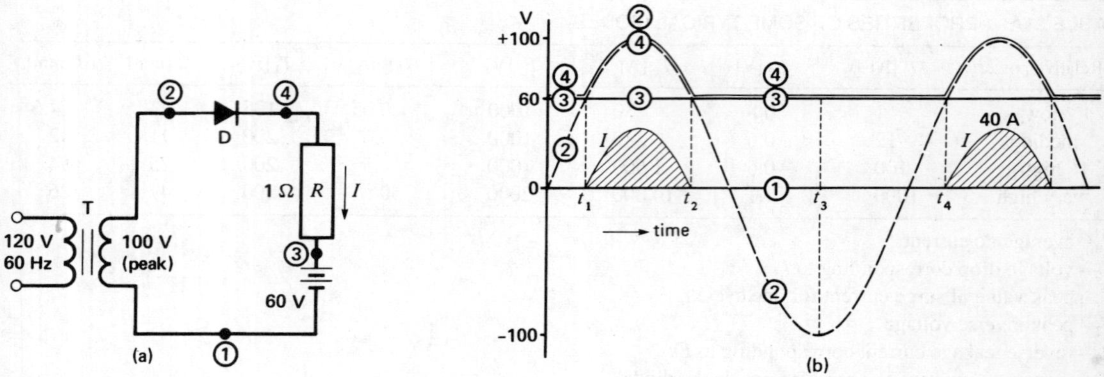

Figure 21.11
a. Simple battery charger circuit.
b. Corresponding voltage and current waveforms.

Circuit analysis

a. Prior to $t = 0$, we assume that all currents are zero. The potential of point **4** is, therefore, at the same level as point **3,** and **2** is at the level of point **1.**
b. During the interval from 0 to t_1, anode 2 is negative with respect to cathode 4; consequently, the diode cannot conduct (Rule 2).
c. At instant t_1, terminal 2 becomes positive with respect to 4, and the diode begins to conduct (Rule 3). From this moment on, the ideal diode acts like a closed switch.
Consequently, point **4** must now be at the same level as point **2.** The voltage E_{43} across the resistor gradually builds up, reaching a maximum of 40 V before it falls to zero at instant t_2.
d. From t_1 to t_2 the current in the circuit is given by

$$I = E_{43}/1\ \Omega$$

The current reaches a peak of 40 A when $E_{43} = +40$ V. As long as current flows, the diode behaves like a closed switch.
e. At instant t_2 the current is zero, and the diode immediately opens the circuit (Rule 4). From this moment on, point **4** must follow point **3.**
f. From t_2 to t_4, point **2** is negative with respect to point **3.** Because point **4** follows point **3** (no *IR* drop in the resistor), the PIV across the diode reaches a maximum of 160 V at instant t_3.
g. Finally, at instant t_4 the cycle (items a to f) repeats itself. The resulting current is a truncated sine wave having a peak value of 40 A. Its calculated average value during one cycle is 7.75 A. The pulsating current always flows into the positive terminal of the battery. Consequently, the latter receives energy and progressively charges up.

21.6 Battery charger with series inductor

The current flow in the battery charger of Fig. 21.11 is limited by resistor *R*. Unfortunately, this produces I^2R losses and a corresponding poor efficiency. We can get around the problem by replacing the resistor by an inductor, as shown in Fig. 21.12a. Let us analyze the operation of this circuit, bearing in mind the behavior of an inductor, previously explained in Section 2.31.

a. As in the example of Fig. 21.11, the ideal diode begins to conduct at instant t_1 when anode 2 becomes positive with respect to cathode 4. From this moment on, point **4** follows point **2,** and voltage E_{43} appears across the inductor

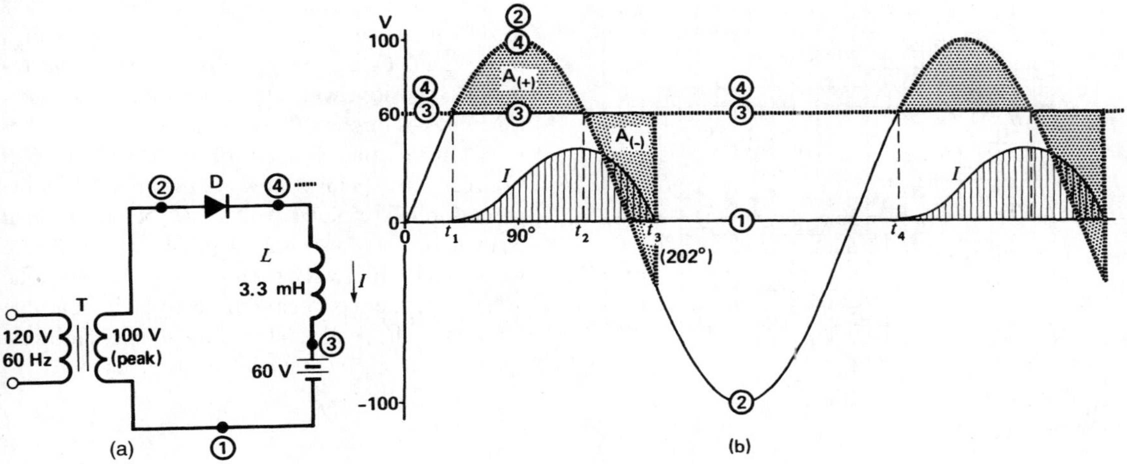

Figure 21.12
a. Battery charger using a series inductor.
b. Corresponding voltage and current waveforms.

(Fig. 21.12b). The latter begins to accumulate volt-seconds, and the current increases gradually until it reaches a maximum given by

$$I_{max} = A_{(+)}/L \qquad (2.28)$$

where

$A_{(+)}$ = dotted area between t_1 and t_2 [V·s]
L = inductance [H]

Note that the current reaches its peak at instant t_2, whereas it was zero at this moment when a resistor was used. This is consistent with the fact that current through an inductor is no longer changing (has reached a maximum) because the voltage E_{43} across it is zero.

b. After t_2 the voltage E_{43} across the inductor becomes negative and so the inductor discharges volt-seconds. Consequently, the current decreases between t_2 and t_3, becoming zero at t_3 when dotted area $A_{(-)}$ is equal to dotted area $A_{(+)}$.
c. As soon as the current is zero, the diode opens the circuit, whereupon point **4** must jump from the level of point **2** to the level of point **3.** It stays at this level until instant t_4, whereupon the whole cycle repeats.

This is an interesting example of the use of an inductor to store and release electrical energy. During the interval from t_1 to t_2, the inductor stores energy and, from t_2 to t_3, it returns it again to the circuit (see Section 2.13).

Example 21-1

The coil in Fig. 21.12 has an inductance of 3.3 mH and the battery voltage is 60 V. Calculate the peak current if the line frequency is 60 Hz.

Solution

a. To calculate the peak current, we must find the value of area $A_{(+)}$. This can be done by integral calculus, but we will employ a much simpler graphical method. Thus, referring to Fig. 21.12c, we have redrawn the voltage levels using graph paper. The 60 Hz voltage cycle is divided into 24 equal parts, each representing time interval Δt equal to

$$\Delta t = (1/24) \times (1/60) = 1/1440 \text{ s}$$

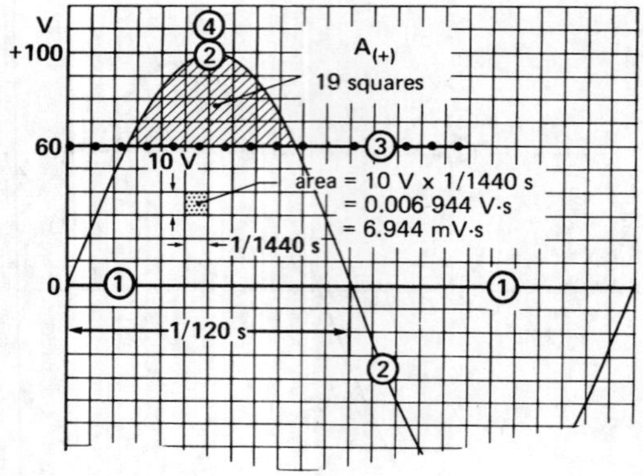

Figure 21.12c
See Example 21-1.

Similarly, the ordinates are scaled off in 10 V intervals. Consequently, each small square represents an area of (1/1440 s) × 10 V = 0.006944 V·s = 6.944 mV·s.

b. By counting squares, we find that $A_{(+)}$ contains approximately 19 squares; consequently, its area corresponds to

$$A_{(+)} = 19 \times 6.944 = 132 \text{ mV·s} = 0.132 \text{ V·s}$$

The peak current is, therefore,

$$I_{max} = A_{(+)}/L = 0.132/0.0033 = 40 \text{ A}$$

Thus, the current reaches the same peak with an inductor of 3.3 mH as it did with a resistor of 1 Ω. However, the big advantage of the inductor is that it has essentially no losses. The conversion of ac power to dc power is therefore much more efficient.

21.7 Single-phase bridge rectifier

The circuit of Fig. 21.13a enables us to rectify both the positive and negative half-cycles of an ac source, to supply dc power to a load *R*. The four diodes together make up what is called a *single-phase bridge rectifier.* It is commercially available in a single package.

The circuit operates as follows: When source voltage E_{12} is positive, terminal 1 is positive with respect to terminal 2 and current i_a flows through *R* by way of diodes A1 and A2. Consequently, point **3** follows point **1,** and point **4** follows point **2** during this conduction interval. Conduction ceases when i_a falls to zero at instant t_1 (Fig. 21.13b). The polarity then reverses and E_{21} becomes positive, meaning that terminal 2 is positive with respect to terminal 1. Current i_b now flows through *R* in the same direction as before, but this time by way of diodes B1 and B2. Consequently, point **3** now follows point **2** while point **4** follows point **1.** Voltage E_{34} across the load is, therefore, composed of a series of half-cycle sine waves that are always positive (Fig. 21.13c). The voltage pulsates between zero and a maximum value E_m equal to the peak voltage of the source. The average value of this rectified voltage is given by

$$E_d = 0.90\,E \tag{21.1}$$

where

E_d = dc voltage of a single-phase bridge rectifier [V]

E = effective value of the ac line voltage [V]

0.90 = constant [exact value = $(2\sqrt{2})/\pi$]

Referring to Fig. 21.13b, in addition to drawing the curve E_{12} for the source voltage, we have also drawn curve E_{21}. This enables us to use the potential levels of either terminals 1 or 2 as zero reference potentials. Thus, we can select as reference level terminal 2 during the first half-cycle, terminal 1 during the second half-cycle, terminal 2 during the third half-cycle, and so forth, on alternate half-cycles. By using this technique, terminal 4 always remains at zero potential while terminal 3 follows the positive portion of the sine waves. It then becomes evident that E_{34} across the load is a pulsating dc voltage. Figure 21.13c shows the rectified voltage and current of the load.

In addition to its dc value, load voltage E_{34} contains an ac component whose fundamental frequency is twice the line frequency. In effect, the voltage across the load pulsates between zero and $+E_m$, twice per cycle. Consequently, the peak-to-peak *ripple* is equal to E_m.

In the case of a resistive load, the current has the same waveshape as the voltage; its average, or dc value, is given by

$$I_d = E_d/R$$

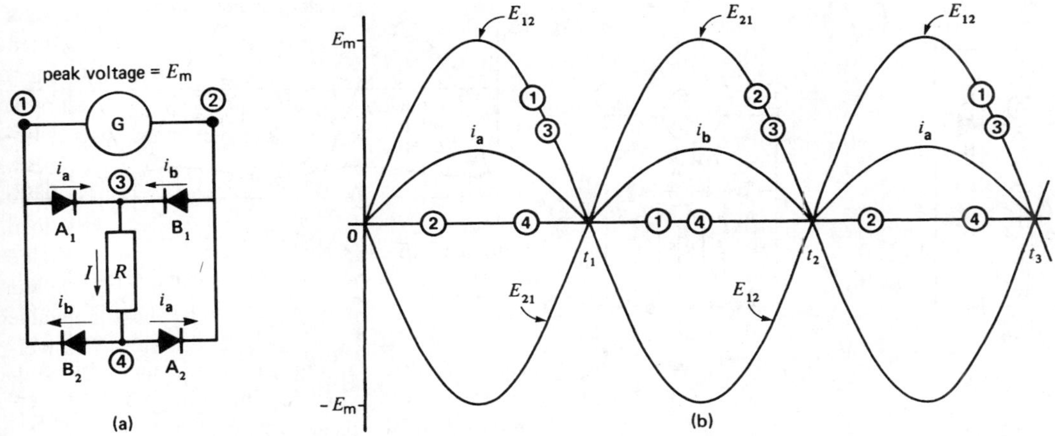

Figure 21.13
a. Single-phase bridge rectifier.
b. Voltage levels.

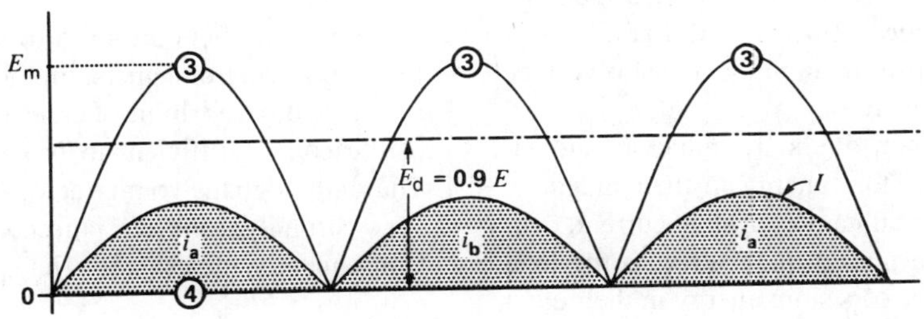

Figure 21.13c
Voltage and current waveforms in load *R*.

Example 21-2

The ac source in Fig. 21.13a has an effective voltage of 120 V, 60 Hz. The load draws a dc current of 20 A.

Calculate

a. The dc voltage across the load
b. The average dc current in each diode

Solution

a. The dc voltage across the load is given by Eq. 21.1:

$$\begin{aligned} E_d &= 0.90\ E \\ &= 0.90 \times 120 \\ &= 108\ \text{V} \end{aligned}$$

b. The dc current in the load is known to be 20 A, but the diodes only carry the current on alternate half-cycles. Consequently, the average dc current in each diode is

$$I = I_d/2 = 20/2 = 10\ \text{A}$$

21.8 Filters

The rectifier circuits we have studied so far produce pulsating voltages and currents. In some types of loads, we cannot tolerate such pulsations, and *filters* must be used to smooth out the valleys and peaks. The basic purpose of a dc filter is to produce a smooth power flow into a load. Consequently, a

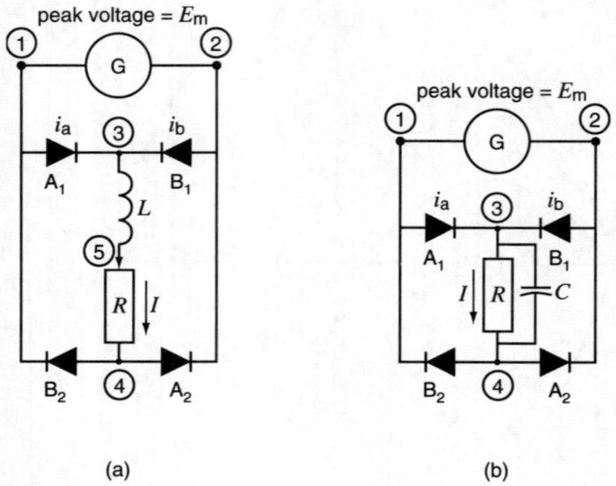

Figure 21.14
a. Rectifier with inductive filter.
b. Rectifier with capacitive filter.

filter must absorb energy whenever the dc voltage or current tends to rise, and it must release energy whenever the voltage or current tends to fall. In this way the filter tends to maintain a constant voltage and current in the load.

The most common filters are inductors and capacitors. Inductors store energy in their magnetic field. They tend to maintain a constant current; consequently, they are placed *in series* with the load (Fig. 21.14a). Capacitors store energy in their electric field. They tend to maintain a constant voltage; consequently, they are placed *in parallel* with the load (Fig. 21.14b).

The greater the amount of energy stored in the filter, the better is the filtering action. In the case of a bridge rectifier using an inductor, the peak-to-peak ripple in percent is given by

$$\text{ripple} = 5.5\,\frac{P}{fW_L} \tag{21.2}$$

where

ripple = peak-to-peak current as a percent of the dc current [%]
W_L = dc energy stored in the smoothing inductor [J]
P = dc power drawn by the load [W]
f = frequency of the source [Hz]
5.5 = coefficient to take care of units

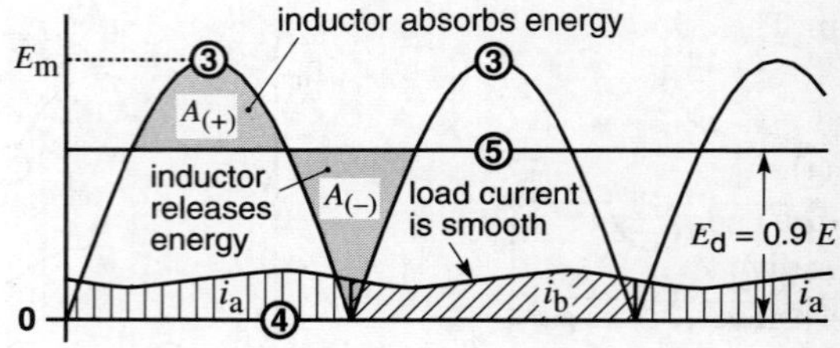

Figure 21.15
Current and voltage waveforms with inductive filter.

The load current in Fig. 21.14a is much more constant than in Fig. 21.13a. The voltage between terminals 3 and 4 pulsates between zero and E_m as before, but the voltage E_{54} across the load is very smooth (Fig. 21.15). The dc voltage across the load is still given by Eq. 21.1. This is to be expected because the dc *IR* drop across the inductor is negligibly small.

Bridge rectifiers are used to provide dc current for relays, electromagnets, motors, and many other magnetic devices. In most cases the self-inductance of the coil is sufficient to provide good filtering. Thus, although the voltage across a coil may pulsate very strongly, the dc current can be smooth. Consequently, the magnetic field pulsates very little.

Example 21-3

We wish to build a 135 V, 20 A dc power supply using a single-phase bridge rectifier and an inductive filter. The peak-to-peak current ripple should be about 10%. If a 60 Hz ac source is available, calculate the following:

a. The effective value of the ac supply voltage
b. The energy stored in the inductor
c. The inductance of the inductor
d. The peak-to-peak current ripple

Solution

a. The effective ac voltage E can be derived from Eq. 21.1:

$$E_d = 0.9\,E$$
$$135 = 0.9\,E$$
$$E = 150\text{ V}$$

b. The dc power output of the rectifier is

$$P = E_d I_d$$
$$= 135 \times 20 = 2700 \text{ W}$$

The energy to be stored in the inductor or "choke" is given by

$$W_L = \frac{5.5\, P}{f \times \text{ripple}} \quad (21.2)$$
$$= \frac{5.5 \times 2700}{60 \times 10}$$
$$= 24.75 \text{ J}$$

Consequently, to obtain a peak-to-peak current ripple of 10 percent, the inductor must store 24.75 J in its magnetic field.

c. The inductance of the choke can be calculated from

$$W_L = \frac{1}{2} L I_d^2 \quad (2.8)$$
$$24.75 = \frac{1}{2} L(20)^2$$
$$L = 0.124 \text{ H}$$

d. The peak-to-peak ripple is about 10 percent of the dc current:

$$I_{\text{peak-to-peak}} = 0.1 \times 20 = 2 \text{ A}$$

The dc output current therefore pulsates between 19 A and 21 A.

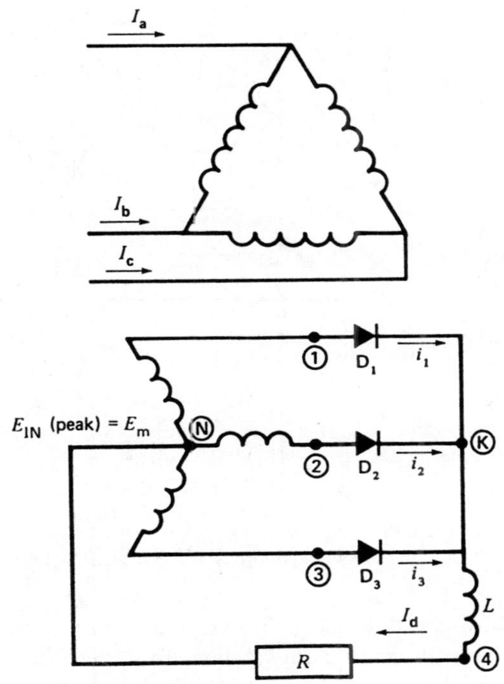

Figure 21.16
Three-phase, 3-pulse rectifier with inductive filter fed by a 3-phase transformer.

21.9 Three-phase, 3-pulse diode rectifier

The simplest 3-phase rectifier is composed of three diodes connected in series with the secondary windings of a 3-phase, delta-wye transformer (Fig. 21.16). The line-to-neutral voltage has a peak value E_m. A large filter inductance L is connected in series with the load, so that current I_d remains essentially ripple-free. Although the load is represented by a resistance R, in reality it is always a useful energy-consuming device and not a heat-dissipating resistor. Thus, the load may be a dc motor, a large magnet, or an electroplating bath. This simple rectifier has some serious drawbacks, but it provides a good introduction to 3-phase rectifiers in general. We now analyze its behavior.

1. Voltage across the Load. By choosing the transformer neutral as the zero potential reference point, the secondary terminals follow the voltage levels 1, 2, 3 shown in Fig. 21.17. These potential levels are rigidly fixed by the ac source and they successively reach a peak value E_m.

Before the transformer is energized, points **K, 4,** and **N** are at the same level because I_d is zero. However, the moment we apply power, voltages E_{1N}, E_{2N}, E_{3N} appear. Consequently, at $t = 0$ the potential of point **1** suddenly becomes positive with respect to **K.** This immediately initiates conduction in diode D1 (Section 21.3, Rule 3). Current i_1 increases rapidly, attaining a final value I which depends upon load R. During this interval **K** is at the same level as point **1** because the diode is conducting.

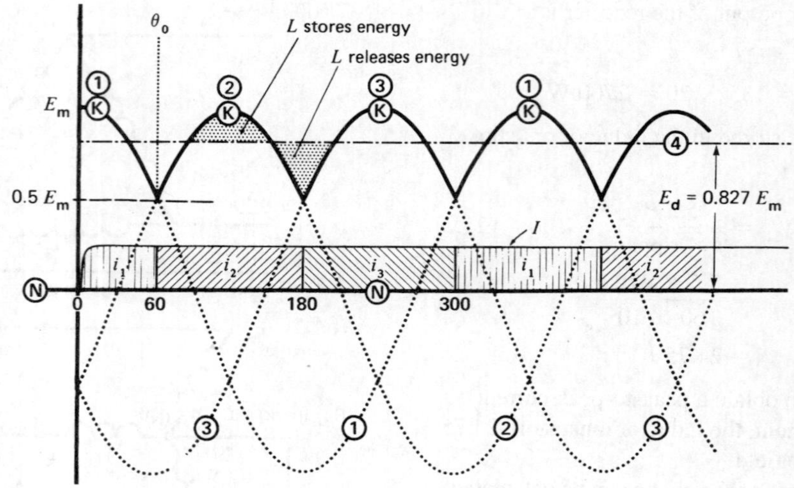

Figure 21.17
Voltage and current waveforms in a 3-phase, 3-pulse rectifier.

As points **K** and **1** move together in time, they eventually reach a critical moment, corresponding to an angle θ_0 of 60° (Fig. 21.17). The moment is critical because immediately later, terminal 2 becomes positive with respect to **K** and **1.** According to Rule 3, this initiates conduction in diode D2, and so *it* begins to carry current *I*. At the same time that conduction starts in diode D2, it ceases in diode D1. Consequently, beyond 60°, point **K** follows the level of point **2.**

The sudden switchover from one diode to another is called *commutation.* When the switchover takes place automatically (as it does in our example), it is called *natural commutation,* or *line commutation.* In this book we prefer the term *line commutation,* because it is the line voltage that forces the transfer of current from one diode to the next.

Commutation from one diode to another does not really take place instantaneously, as we have indicated. Owing to transformer leakage reactance, the current gradually increases in diode D2 while it decreases in diode D1. This gradual transition continues until all the load current is carried by diode D2. However, the commutation period is very short (typically less than 2 ms on a 60 Hz system) and, for our purposes, we will assume it occurs instantaneously.

The next critical moment occurs at 180°, because terminal 3 then becomes positive with respect to point **2** (and point **K**). Commutation again takes place as the load current switches from diode D2 to diode D3. Point **K** therefore follows the positive peaks of waves 1, 2, and 3, and each diode carries the full-load current for equal intervals of time (120°). The diode currents i_1, i_2, i_3 have rectangular waveshapes composed of positive current intervals of 120° followed by zero current intervals of 240°.

Voltage E_{KN} across the load and inductor in Fig. 21.17 pulsates between 0.5 E_m and E_m. The ripple voltage is therefore smaller than that produced by a single-phase bridge rectifier (Fig. 21.15). Moreover, the fundamental ripple frequency is three times the supply frequency, which makes it easier to achieve good filtering. The dc voltage across the load is given by

$$E_d = 0.675\,E \tag{21.3}$$

where

E_d = average or dc voltage of a 3-pulse rectifier [V]

E = effective ac line voltage [V]

0.675 = a constant [exact value = $3/(\pi\sqrt{2})$]

Note that if we reverse the diodes in Fig. 21.16, the rectifier operates the same way, except that the load current reverses. Voltage E_{KN} becomes negative and point **K** follows the negative peaks of waves 1, 2, and 3.

2. Line Currents. Currents i_1, i_2, i_3 that flow in the diodes also flow in the secondary windings of the transformer. As we have seen, these currents have a chopped rectangular waveshape which is quite different from the sinusoidal currents we are familiar with. Furthermore, the currents flow for only one-third of the time in a given winding. Due to this intermittent flow, the maximum possible dc output power is less than the nominal rating of the transformer. For example, if the transformer in Fig. 21.16 has a rating of 100 kVA, we can show that it can only deliver 74 kW of dc power without overheating.

The chopped secondary currents are reflected into the primary windings, with the result that the line currents feeding the transformer also change very abruptly. The sudden jumps in currents I_a, I_b, and I_c produce rapid fluctuations in the magnetic field surrounding the feeder. These fluctuations can induce substantial voltages and noise in nearby telephone lines.

Because of these drawbacks, we try to design rectifiers so that the transformer windings carry current for more than one-third of the time. This is achieved by using 3-phase, 6-pulse rectifier.

21.10 Three-phase, 6-pulse rectifier*

Consider the circuit of Fig. 21.18 in which a transformer T (identical to the one shown in Fig. 21.16), supplies power to 6 diodes and their associated dc loads R_1 and R_2. The upper set of diodes together with inductor L_1 and load R_1 are identical to the 3-phase, 3-pulse rectifier we have just studied. Thus, load current I_{d1} flows in the neutral line, as shown. The lower set of diodes, together with R_2 and L_2, also constitute a 3-phase, 3-pulse rectifier but with the polarity reversed. The corresponding load current I_{d2} flows in the neutral, as shown. The two 3-phase rectifiers operate quite independently of each other, **K** following the positive peaks of points **1, 2, 3** while A follows the negative peaks. All diodes conduct during 120° intervals.

If we make $R_1 = R_2$, then $I_{d1} = I_{d2}$ and the dc current in the neutral becomes zero. Consequently, we can remove the neutral conductor, yielding the circuit of Fig. 21.19. The two loads and the two inductors are simply combined into one, shown as R and L, respectively. The 6 diodes constitute what is called a 3-phase, 6-pulse rectifier. It is called *6-pulse* because the currents flowing in the 6 diodes start at 6 different moments during each cycle of the line frequency. However, each diode still conducts for only 120°.

* Also called a 3-phase bridge rectifier.

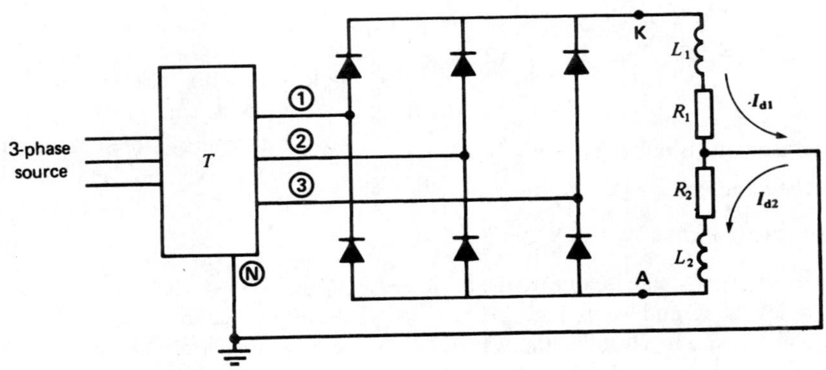

Figure 21.18
Dual 3-phase, 3-pulse rectifier.

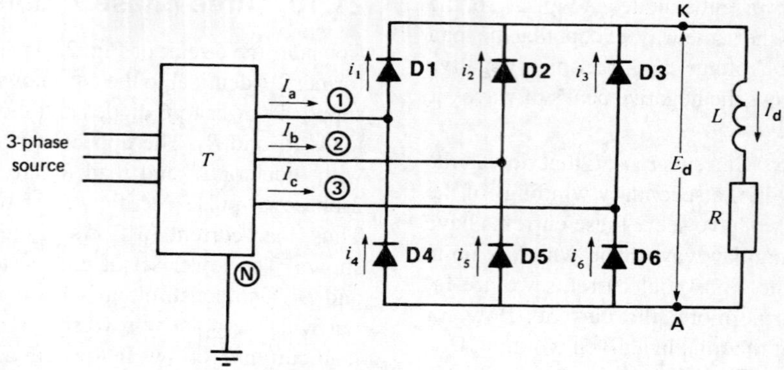

Figure 21.19
Three-phase, 6-pulse rectifier with inductive filter.

The line currents I_a, I_b, I_c supplied by the transformer are given by Kirchhoff's law:

$$I_a = i_1 - i_4$$
$$I_b = i_2 - i_5$$
$$I_c = i_3 - i_6$$

They consist of three identical rectangular waves that are out of phase by 120° (Fig. 21.20). The currents now flow for two-thirds of the time in the secondary windings. As a result, it can be shown that a 100 kVA transformer can deliver 95 kW of dc power without overheating.

Figs. 21.18 and 21.19 reveal that the average dc output voltage is twice that of a 3-phase, 3-pulse rectifier. Its value is given by

$$E_d = 1.35\,E \qquad (21.4)$$

where

E_d = dc voltage of a 6-pulse rectifier [V]
E = effective line voltage [V]
1.35 = a constant [exact value $= 3\sqrt{2}/\pi$]

The instantaneous output voltage is equal to the intercept between levels K and A in Fig. 21.20. However, it is much easier to visualize the waveshape of E_{KA} by using terminal A as a reference point. Thus, in Fig. 21.21, we show the line voltages, E_{12}, E_{23}, E_{31} (and E_{21}, E_{32}, E_{13}) rather than the line-to-neutral voltages used in Fig. 21.20. The level of K follows the tops of the successive sine waves while A remains at zero potential. The output voltage fluctuates between 1.414 E and 1.225 E, where E is the effective value of the line voltage. The average value of E_{KA} is 1.35 E, as given by Eq. 21.4.

The peak-to-peak ripple is only (1.414 − 1.225) E = 0.189 E and the fundamental ripple frequency is six times the line frequency. Consequently, the ripple is much easier to filter. The approximate peak-to-peak current ripple in percent is given by

$$\text{ripple} = 0.17\frac{P}{fW_L} \qquad (21.5)$$

where

ripple = peak-to-peak current as a percent of the dc current [%]
W_L = dc energy stored in the inductor [J]
P = dc power drawn by the load [W]
f = frequency of the 3-phase, 6-pulse source [Hz]

Fig. 21.21 shows that the inductor stores energy whenever the rectifier voltage exceeds the average value E_d. This energy is then released during the brief interval when the rectifier voltage is less than E_d.

The peak inverse voltage across each diode is equal to the peak value of the line voltage, or $\sqrt{2}\,E$.

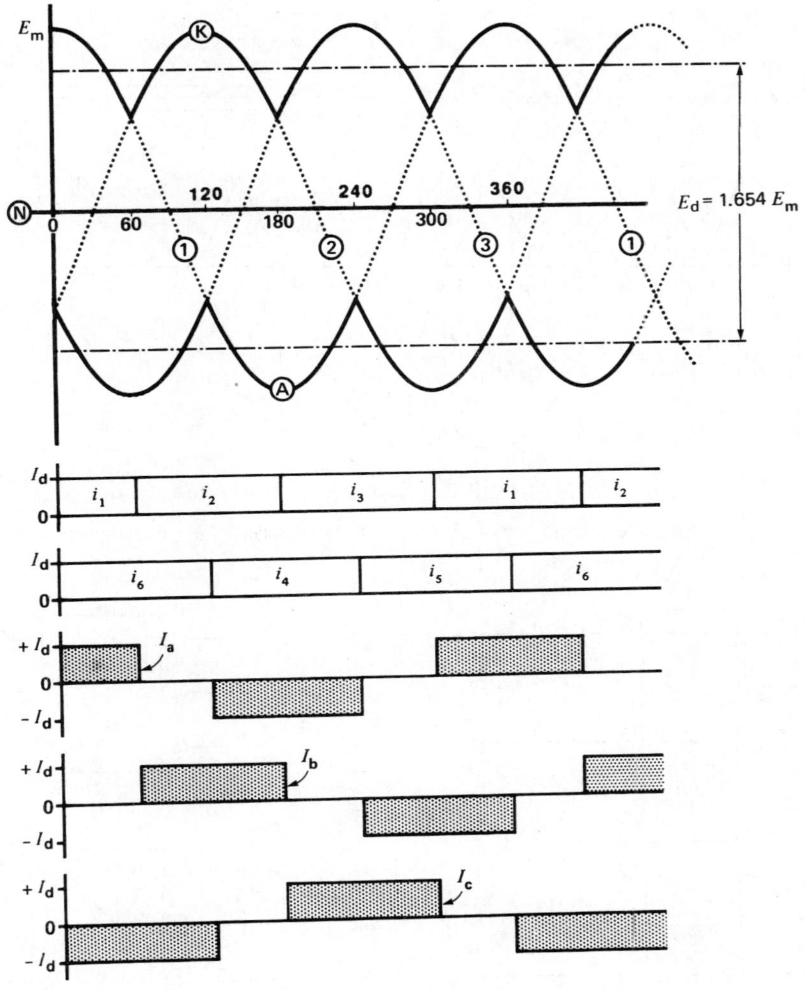

Figure 21.20
Voltage and current waveforms in Fig. 21.19.

The 3-phase, 6-pulse rectifier is a big improvement over the 3-phase, 3-pulse rectifier. It constitutes the basic building block of most large rectifier installations.

Another way of looking at the 3-phase bridge rectifier is to imagine the diodes to be in a box (Fig. 21.22). The box is fed by three ac lines and it has two output terminals K and A. The diodes act like automatic switches that successively connect these terminals to the ac lines. The connections can be made in six distinct ways, as shown in Fig. 21.22. It follows that the output voltage E_{KA} is composed of segments of the ac line voltages. That is why we draw line voltages in Fig. 21.21 instead of line-to-neutral voltages.

Each dotted connection in Fig. 21.22 represents a diode that is conducting. The successive 60-degree intervals correspond to those in Fig. 21.20.

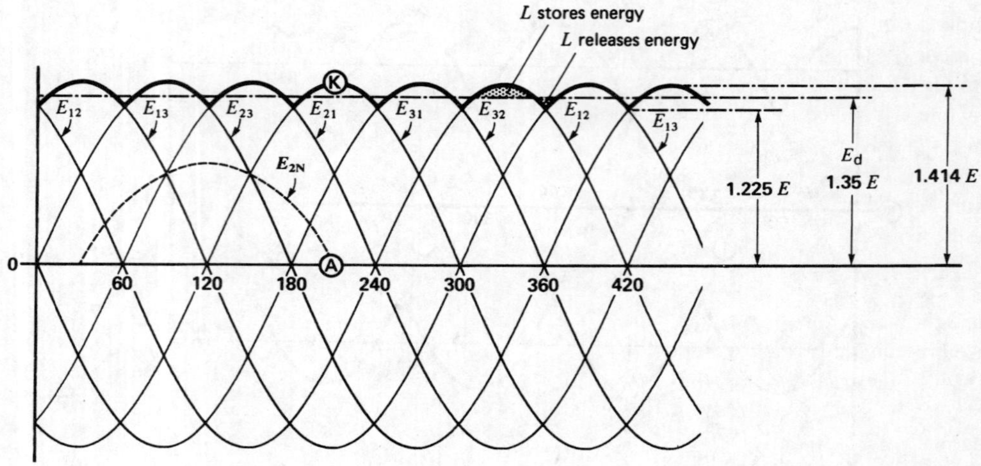

Figure 21.21
Another way of showing E_{KA} using line voltage potentials. Note also the position of E_{2N} with respect to the line voltages.

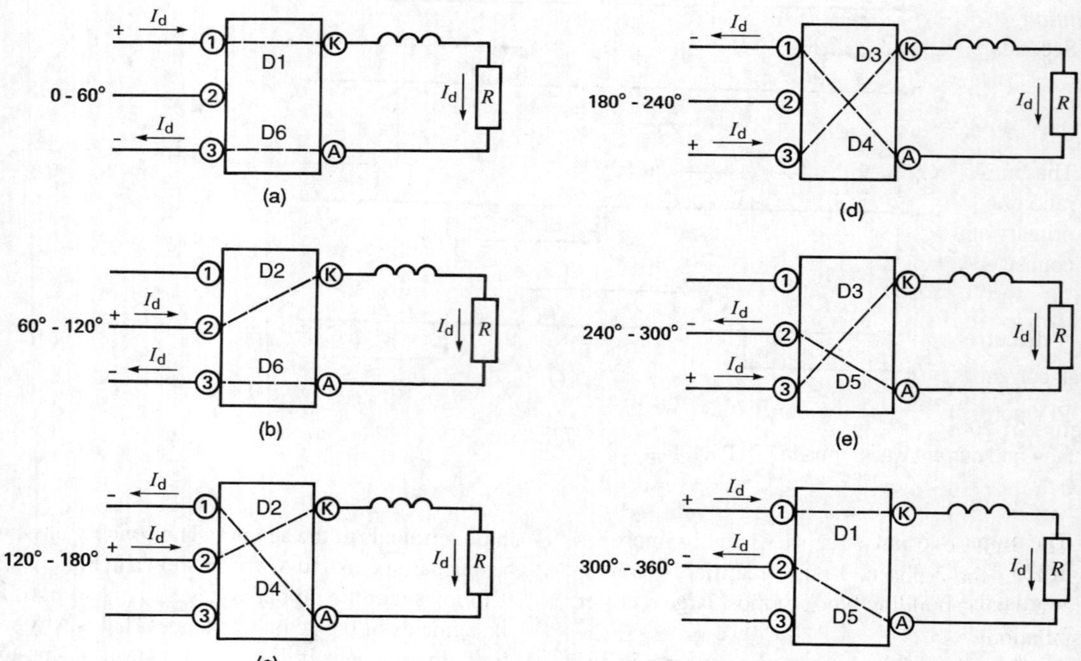

Figure 21.22
Successive diode connections between the 3-phase input and dc output terminals of a 3-phase, 6-pulse rectifier.

For example, from 300° to 360°, because i_1 and i_5 are flowing, diodes D1 and D5 are conducting. It follows from Fig. 21.19 that K is effectively connected to line 1 while A is effectively connected to line 2.

Because the diode voltage drop is small, we can assume that each dotted line represents a loss-free connection. The dc power absorbed by the load must therefore be equal to the active power drawn from the 3-phase source.

Example 21-4

A 3-phase bridge rectifier has to supply power to a 360 kW, 240 V dc load. If a 600 V, 3-phase, 60 Hz feeder is available, calculate the following:

a. Voltage rating of the 3-phase transformer
b. DC current per diode
c. PIV across each diode
d. Peak-to-peak ripple in the output voltage and its frequency

Solution

a. Secondary line voltage is

$$E = E_d/1.35 = 240/1.35$$
$$= 177 \text{ V}$$

Thus, a 3-phase transformer having a line voltage ratio of 600 V/177 V would be satisfactory. The primary and secondary windings may be connected either in wye or in delta.

b. dc load current $I_d = 360 \text{ kW}/240 = 1500 \text{ A}$

dc current per diode = 1500/3 = 500 A

peak current in each diode = 1500 A

c. PIV across each diode

$$= \sqrt{2}\,E = 1.414 \times 177$$
$$= 250 \text{ V}$$

d. The output voltage E_{KA} fluctuates between 1.225 E and 1.414 E (Fig. 21.21). In other words, the voltage fluctuates between

$$E_{min} = 1.225 \times 177 = 217 \text{ V and}$$
$$E_{max} = 1.414 \times 177 = 250 \text{ V}$$

The peak-to-peak ripple is, therefore,

$$E_{peak\text{-}to\text{-}peak} = 250 - 217 = 33 \text{ V}$$

Fundamental ripple frequency

$$= 6 \times 60 \text{ Hz} = 360 \text{ Hz}$$

Example 21-5

a. Calculate the inductance of the smoothing choke required in Example 21-4, if the peak-to-peak ripple in the current is not to exceed 5 percent.
b. Does the presence of the choke modify the peak-to-peak ripple in the output voltage E_{KA}?

Solution

a. Using Eq. 21.5, we have

$$\text{ripple} = \frac{0.17\,P}{f\,W_L}$$
$$5 = \frac{0.17 \times 360\,000}{60 \times W_L}$$
$$W_L = 204 \text{ J}$$

Consequently, the inductor must store 204 J in its magnetic field. The inductance is found from

$$W_L = \frac{1}{2}LI_d^2$$
$$204 = \frac{1}{2}L\,(1500)^2$$
$$L = 1.8 \times 10^{-4}$$
$$= 0.18 \text{ mH}$$

b. The presence of the choke does not affect the voltage ripple between K and A. It remains at 33 V peak-to-peak.

21.11 Effective line current, fundamental line current

We saw in Fig. 21.20 that the ac line currents consist of 120-degree rectangular waves having an amplitude I_d, where I_d is the dc current flowing in the load. Let us direct our attention to the current I_b flowing in line 2 and to the corresponding line-to-neutral voltage E_{2N}. They are shown in Fig. 21.23 and it can be seen that the rectangular current wave is symmetrically located with respect to the sinusoidal voltage maximum. In other words, the center of the positive current pulse coincides with the peak of the positive voltage wave. Thus, I_b can be considered to be "in phase" with E_{2N}.

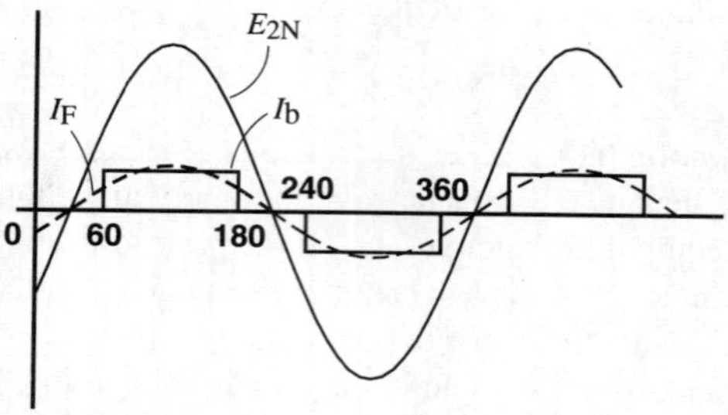

Figure 21.23
Line-to-neutral voltage and line current in phase 2 of Fig. 21.20.

The effective value I of the rectangular line current can be deduced from the relationship

$$I^2 \times 180° = I_d^2 \times 120°$$

therefore

$$I = \sqrt{120/180}\, I_d$$
$$= 0.816\, I_d \qquad (21.6)$$

This effective current is composed of a *fundamental* rms component I_F plus all the harmonic components. As we have seen, I_F is in phase with the line-to-neutral voltage.

What is the value of I_F? To calculate it we reason as follows:

The dc power to the load is

$$P_d = E_d I_d$$

The active ac power supplied to the rectifier (and its load) is

$$P_{ac} = \sqrt{3}\, E I_F \qquad (8.9)$$

Because no power is lost or stored in our ideal rectifier, it follows that $P_{ac} = P_d$. We can therefore write

$$P_{ac} = P_d$$
$$\sqrt{3}\, E I_F = E_d I_d$$
$$= 1.35\, E I_d$$

and so

$$I_F = 0.78\, I_d \qquad (21.7)$$

Combining Eqs. 21.6 and 21.7 we find

$$I_F = 0.955\, I \qquad (21.8)$$

Thus, owing to the presence of harmonics,* the fundamental component I_F is slightly less than the effective value of the line current I.

21.12 Distortion power factor

We have just seen that the fundamental component I_F is in phase with the corresponding line-to-neutral voltage (Fig. 21.23). Consequently, we would be inclined to say that the power factor of the 3-phase, 6-pulse rectifier is 100 percent. However, by definition, power factor is given by the expression

$$\text{power factor} = \frac{\text{active power}}{\text{apparent power}}$$
$$= \frac{\text{active power}}{\text{effective voltage} \times \text{effective current} \times \sqrt{3}}$$
$$= \frac{P_{ac}}{EI\sqrt{3}} = \frac{EI_F\sqrt{3}}{EI\sqrt{3}} = \frac{I_F}{I}$$

But according to Eq. 21.8, $I_F = 0.955\, I$. As a result,

$$\text{power factor} = 0.955$$

Thus, the actual power factor is not 100% but only 95.5%. The reason is that the line current is rectangular and not sinusoidal. Thus, the power factor of 95.5% is due to distortion in the current.

Although the power factor of our rectifier is less than 100%, the fundamental component of current is nevertheless in phase with the line-to-neutral voltage. Consequently, this ideal rectifier absorbs no reactive power from the line.

21.13 Displacement power factor, total power factor

In Fig. 21.23, the fundamental component of current is in phase with the line-to-neutral voltage. However, in later circuits we will discover that the rectangular current wave can shift so that it lags behind the line-to-neutral voltage. This causes the fundamental component I_F to shift along with it.

---

* Harmonics are discussed in detail in Chapter 30.

This angular shift of the fundamental component of current with respect to the line-to-neutral voltage is called *displacement,* and the cosine of the angle is called *displacement power factor.* The displacement power factor in Fig. 21.23 is unity. The *total power factor* of a load or electrical installation is given by the expression:

$$\text{Total power factor} = \frac{P}{EI_L} \qquad (21.9a)$$

The displacement power factor is given by

$$\text{Displacement power factor} = \frac{P}{EI_F} \qquad (21.9b)$$

In these equations,

P = active power per phase [W]

E = effective value of voltage per phase [V]

I_L = effective value of line current including the fundamental and harmonics [A]

I_F = effective value of fundamental component of line current [A]

21.14 Harmonic content and THD

The rectangular current wave of Fig. 21.23 occurs very frequently in power electronics. It is therefore worthwhile to examine it more closely, particularly as regards its harmonic content. First, any periodic current in a line can be expressed by the equation

$$I_2 = I_F^2 + I_H^2 \qquad (21.10)$$

in which

I = rms value of the line current

I_F = rms value of the fundamental component of line current

I_H = rms value of all the harmonic components combined

It can also be shown that the total harmonic content I_H^2 is equal to the sum of the squares of the individual harmonics. Thus, we can write

$$I_H^2 = I_{HA}^2 + I_{HB}^2 + I_{HC}^2 + I_{HD}^2 + \ldots \qquad (21.11a)$$

in which I_{HA}, I_{HB}, I_{HC}, etc., are the rms values of the harmonic components in the line current.

The rectangular wave in Fig. 21.23 contains the 5th, 7th, 11th, 13th, 17th, harmonics, and so forth; in other words, all odd harmonics that are not multiples of 3. The remarkable feature of these harmonic components is that their respective amplitudes are equal to the amplitude of the fundamental I_F divided by the order of the harmonic. For example, if the fundamental component has an rms value of 1500 A, the 17th harmonic has an rms value of 1500/17 = 88 A.

The degree of distortion of an ac voltage or current is defined as the ratio of the rms value of all the harmonics divided by the rms value of the fundamental component. This *total harmonic distortion* (THD) is given by the formula

$$\text{THD} = \frac{I_H}{I_F} \qquad (21.11b)$$

where I_F and I_H are defined as before.

For more information on harmonics, the reader should refer to Chapter 30.

Example 21-6

The 3-phase, 6-pulse rectifier in Fig. 21.19 furnishes a dc current of 400 A to the load. Estimate, for line 1

a. The effective value of the line current measured by an rms hook-on ammeter
b. The effective value of the fundamental component of line current
c. The peak value of the 7th harmonic
d. The rms value of the 7th and 11th harmonics combined

Solution

a. The effective or rms value of the line current is

$$I = 0.816\, I_d = 0.816 \times 400 = 326 \text{ A} \qquad (21.6)$$

b. The rms value of the fundamental is

$$I_F = 0.955\, I = 0.955 \times 326 = 311 \text{ A}$$

c. The rms value of the 7th harmonic is

$$I_{H7} = I_F/7 = 311/7 = 44 \text{ A}$$

The peak value of the $I_{H7} = 44\sqrt{2} = 62$ A

d. The rms value of the 11th harmonic = $I_F/11$ = 311/11 = 28 A

The rms value of the 7th and 11th harmonics combined is given by

$$I^2_{(H7 + H11)} = I^2_{H7} + I^2_{H11}$$
$$= 44^2 + 28^2 = 2720$$

$$\text{consequently, } I_{(H7 + H11)} = \sqrt{2720} = 52 \text{ A}$$

THE THYRISTOR AND THYRISTOR CIRCUITS

21.15 The thyristor*

A thyristor is an electronic switch, similar to a diode, but wherein the instant of conduction can be controlled. Like a diode, a thyristor possesses an anode and a cathode, plus a third terminal called a gate (Fig. 21.24). If the gate is connected to the cathode, the thyristor will not conduct, even if the anode is positive.† The thyristor is said to be *blocked* (Fig. 21.25a). To initiate conduction, two conditions have to be met:

a. The anode must be positive.
b. A current I_g must flow into the gate for at least a few microseconds. In practice, the current is injected by applying a short, positive voltage pulse E_g to the gate (Fig. 21.25b). In some applications, it is useful to prolong the pulse for several milliseconds.

As soon as conduction starts, the gate loses all further control. Conduction will only stop when anode current I falls to zero, after which the gate again exerts control.

Basically, a thyristor behaves the same way a diode does except that the gate enables us to initiate conduction precisely when we want to. This seemingly slight advantage is of profound importance. It enables us not only to convert ac power into dc power, but also to do the reverse, convert dc power into ac power. Thanks to the development of reliable SCRs we have witnessed a fundamental change in the control of large blocks of power. Table 21B lists some of the properties of typical thyristors. See also Figure 21.26.

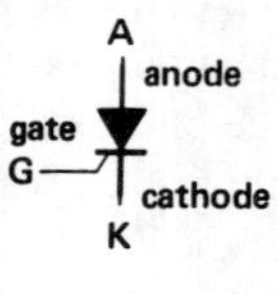

Figure 21.24
Symbol of a thyristor, or SCR.

* *Thyristor* is a generic term that applies to all 4-layer controllable semiconductor devices. However, we use it in this book to refer specifically to the reverse-blocking triode thyristor, commonly called SCR (semiconductor controlled rectifier). This is in response to a general trend in the literature to use the terms SCR and thyristor interchangeably.

† To simplify the wording, we adopt the following terms:
1. When the anode is positive with respect to the cathode, we simply say the anode is positive.
2. When the gate is positive with respect to the cathode, we simply say the gate is positive.

21.16 Principles of gate firing

Consider Fig. 21.27a in which a thyristor and a resistor are connected in series across an ac source. A number of short positive pulses E_g is applied to the gate, of sufficient amplitude to initiate conduction, provided the anode is positive. These pulses may be generated by a manual switch or an electronic control circuit.

Referring to Fig. 21.27b, the gate pulses occur at angles θ_1, θ_2, θ_3, θ_4, and θ_5. Table 21C explains how the circuit reacts to these pulses. The reader should follow the explanations carefully.

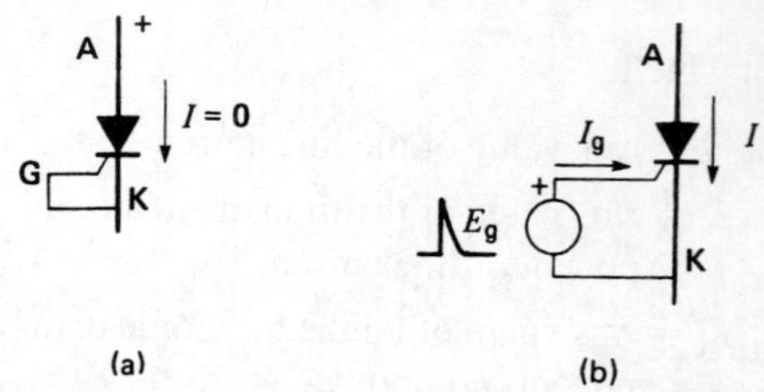

Figure 21.25
a. A thyristor does not conduct when the gate is connected to the cathode.
b. A thyristor conducts when the anode is positive and a current pulse is injected into the gate.

TABLE 21B PROPERTIES OF SOME TYPICAL THYRISTORS

Relative power	I_1 [A]	I_{cr} [A]	E_2 [V]	E_p [V]	I_G [mA]	E_G [V]	T_J [°C]	d [mm]	l [mm]
medium	8	60	500	−10	50	2.5	105	11	33
high	110	1 500	1200	−5	50	1.25	125	27	62
very high	1200	10 000	1200	−20	50	1.5	125	58	27

I_1 – maximum effective current during conduction
I_{cr} – peak value of surge current for one cycle
E_2 – peak inverse anode voltage
E_p – peak inverse gate voltage
E_G – positive gate voltage to initiate conduction
I_G – gate current corresponding to E_G
T_J – maximum junction temperature
d – diameter
l – length

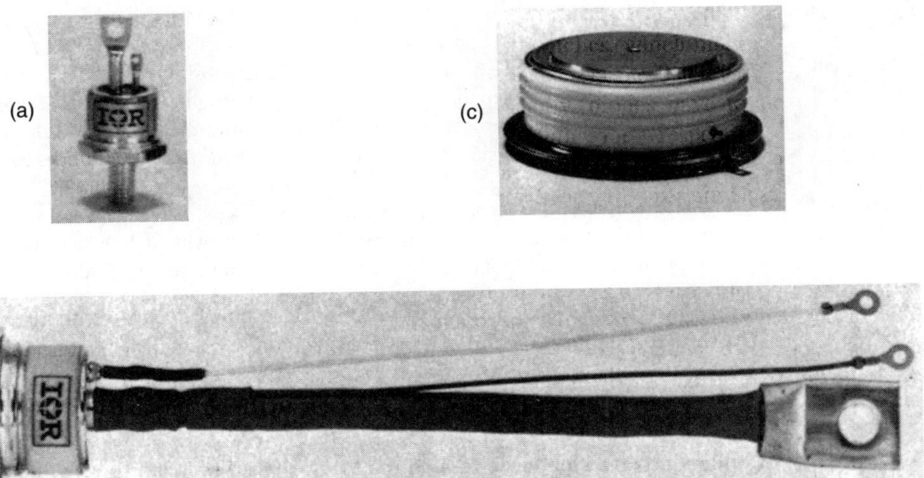

Figure 21.26
Range of SCRs from medium to very high power capacity.
a. Average current: 50 A; voltage: 400 V; length less thread: 31mm; diameter: 17 mm.
b. Average current: 285 A; voltage: 1200 V; length less thread: 244 mm; diameter: 37 mm.
c. Average current: 1000 A; voltage: 1200 V; distance between pole-faces: 27 mm; overall diameter: 73 mm.
(Photos courtesy of International Rectifier)

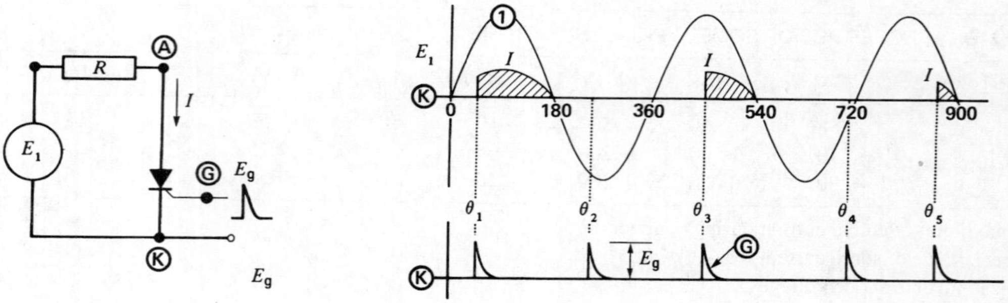

(a) (b)

Figure 21.27
a. Thyristor and resistor connected to an ac source.
b. Thyristor behavior depends on the timing of the gate pulses.

TABLE 21C DESCRIPTION OF THYRISTOR BEHAVIOR (SEE FIG. 21.27)

Angle or time interval	Explanation of circuit operation
zero to θ_1	Although the anode is positive, conduction is impossible because the gate voltage is zero. The thyristor behaves like an open switch.
angle θ_1	Conduction starts because both the anode and gate are positive.
θ_1 to 180°	Conduction continues even though the gate voltage has fallen to zero. Gate pulses have no further effect once the thyristor conducts. The anode to cathode voltage drop is less than 1.5 V; consequently, we can consider that the anode and cathode are shorted. The thyristor behaves like a closed switch.
angle 180°	The thyristor current is zero, conduction ceases, and the gate regains control.
180° to 360°	Conduction is impossible because the anode is negative. Although the gate is triggered at angle θ_2, it produces no effect. The thyristor experiences an inverse voltage during this half-cycle.
360° to 540°	Conduction starts at θ_3 and ceases again as soon as the current is zero. The gate pulse is delayed more than during the first positive half-cycle. Consequently, the anode current flows for a shorter time.
720° to 900°	Conduction starts at angle θ_5, but the resulting anode current is very small because of the long delay in firing the gate.

To summarize Table 21C, we can control the current in an ac circuit by delaying the gate pulses with respect to the start of each positive half-cycle. If the pulses occur at the very beginning of each half-cycle, conduction lasts for 180°, and the thyristor behaves like an ordinary diode. On the other hand, with a resistive load—if the pulses are delayed, say, by 150°—current only flows during the remaining 30° of each half-cycle.

21.17 Power gain of a thyristor

When a voltage pulse is applied to the gate, a certain gate current flows. Because the pulses last only a few microseconds, the average power supplied to the gate is very small, in comparison to the average power supplied to the load. The ratio of the two powers, called power gain, may exceed one million. Thus, an average gate input of only 1 W may control a load of 1000 kW.

An SCR does not, of course, have the magical property of turning one watt into a million watts. The large power actually comes from an appropriate power source, and the SCR gate only serves to *control* the power flow. Thus, in the same way that a small power input to the accelerator of an automobile produces a tremendous increase in motive power, so does a small input to the gate of an SCR produce a tremendous increase in electrical power.

21.18 Current interruption and forced commutation

A thyristor ceases to conduct and the gate regains control only after the anode current falls to zero. The current may cease flowing quite naturally (as it did at the end of each cycle in Fig. 21.27) or we can force it to zero artificially. Such *forced commutation* is required in some circuits where the anode current has to be interrupted at a specific instant.

Consider Fig. 21.28a in which a thyristor and a load resistor R are connected in series across a dc source E. If we apply a single positive pulse to the gate, the resulting dc load current I_1 will flow indefinitely thereafter. However, we can stop conduction in the SCR in one of three ways:

1. Momentarily reduce the dc supply voltage E to zero.
2. Open the load circuit by means of a switch.
3. Force the anode current to zero for a brief period.

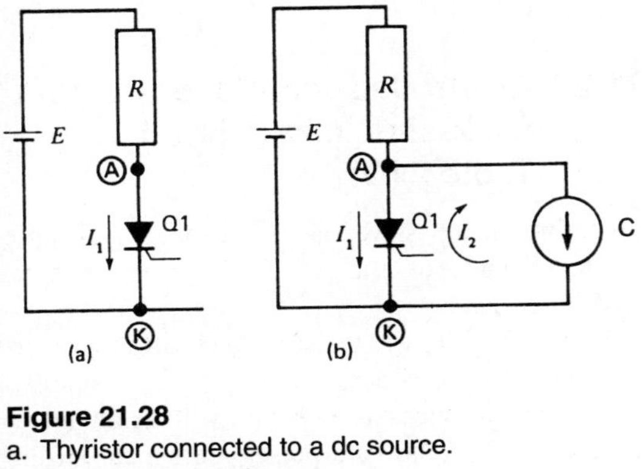

Figure 21.28
a. Thyristor connected to a dc source.
b. Forced commutation.

The first two solutions are trivial, so let us examine the third method. In Fig. 21.28b, a variable current source C delivering a current I_2 is connected in parallel with thyristor Q1. As we gradually increase I_2, the net current ($I_1 - I_2$) flowing in the thyristor decreases. However, so long as the net current is not zero, the thyristor continues to conduct, with the result that the current flowing in the resistor is unchanged. But if we increase I_2 until it is equal to I_1, the thyristor stops conducting, and the gate regains control. In practice, I_2 can be a brief current pulse, usually supplied by triggering a second thyristor. For example, in Fig. 21.29a, a load R can be switched on and off by alternately firing thyristors Q1 and Q2.

To understand how the circuit operates, suppose Q1 is conducting and Q2 is not. We assume that the circuit has been in operation long enough so that the voltages and currents have reached their steady-state values. It follows that capacitor C is charged to the supply voltage E, with polarities as shown in Fig. 21.29a. Neglecting the voltage drop across Q1, full voltage appears across load R. Thus, $I_1 = E/R$ and $I_2 = 0$.

To stop conduction in Q1, we trigger thyristor Q2 (Fig. 21.29b). This causes the capacitor to discharge in the circuit formed by C, Q1, and Q2. The discharge current I_C forces Q1 to stop conducting and produces the condition shown in Fig. 21.29c. The level of point **1** drops to E volts below the level of point **K,** with the result that I_1 reaches a momentary peak of $I_1 = 2\ E/R$. Current I_1 will quickly charge the capacitor in the opposite way and so point **1** will eventually reach the level of point **3.** When the transients have subsided, the circuit appears as shown in Fig. 21.29d, but with $I_1 = 0$. Current I_2 can be made much smaller than load current I_1 by using a relatively high resistance R_0.

To restart conduction in the load, we fire Q1, producing the condition shown in Fig. 21.29e. Discharge current I_C now causes the extinction of Q2, and the capacitor charges up with the opposite polarity as shown in Fig. 21.29f. When conditions become stable, the circuit reverts to the one we started with, namely Fig. 21.29a.

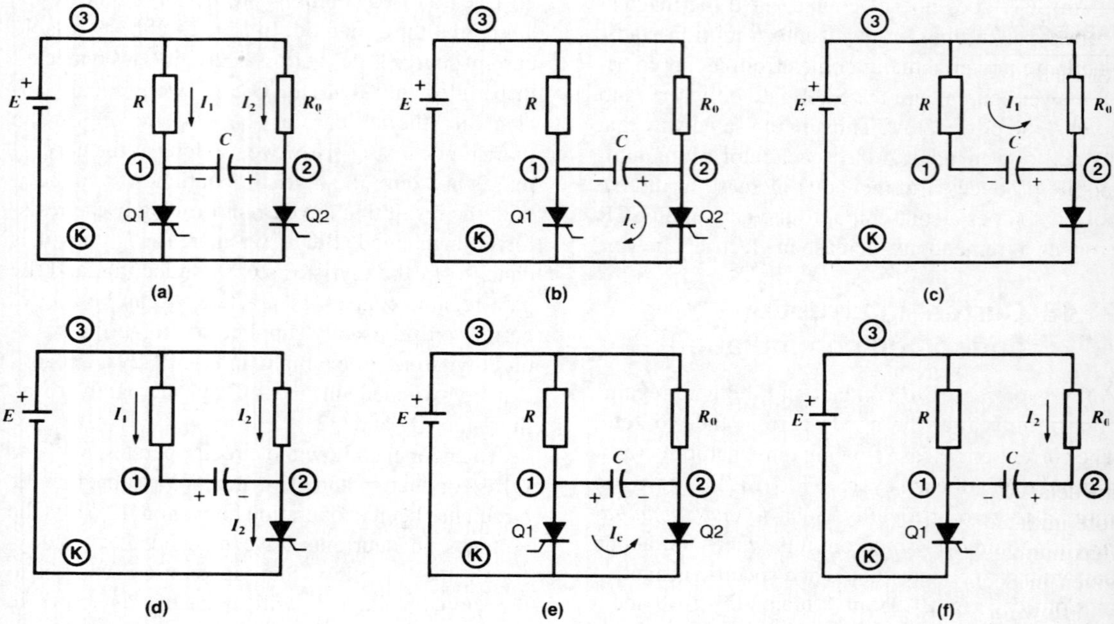

Figure 21.29
A discharging capacitor C and an auxiliary thyristor Q2 can force-commutate the main thyristor Q1. Thus, the current in load R can be switched on and off by triggering Q1 and Q2 in succession.

This type of forced commutation, using a commutating capacitor, is employed in some converters* that generate their own frequency. However, the availability of GTOs, MOSFETs, and IGBTs has largely eliminated the need to use thyristors in such force-commutated applications. For this reason, in the following discussion of thyristor power circuits, we consider only those involving line commutation.

21.19 Basic thyristor power circuits

Thyristors are used in many different ways. However, in power electronics, six basic circuits cover about 90 percent of all industrial applications. These circuits, and some of their applications, are listed in Table 21D. They are labeled circuit 1, circuit 2, circuit 3, . . . circuit 6.

To explain the principle of operation of these basic circuits, we will use single-phase sources. In practice, 3-phase sources are mainly used, but single-phase examples are less complex, and they enable us to focus attention on the essential principles involved.

21.20 Controlled rectifier supplying a passive load (Circuit 1, Table 21D)

By definition, a passive load is one that contains no inherent source of energy. The simplest passive load is a resistor.

Fig. 21.30a shows a resistive load and a thyristor connected in series across a single-phase source. The source produces a sinusoidal voltage having a peak value E_m. The gate pulses are synchronized with the line frequency and, in our example, they

* A converter is any device that converts power of one frequency into power of another frequency, including zero frequency (dc). A converter may be a rectifier, inverter, or even a rotating machine.

TABLE 21D SOME BASIC THYRISTOR POWER CIRCUITS

Circuit No.	Thyristor circuit	Typical applications
1	Controlled rectifier supplying a passive load	Electroplating, dc arc welding, electrolysis
2	Controlled rectifier supplying an active load	Battery charger, dc motor control, dc transmission line
3	Line-commutated inverter supplying an active ac load	AC motor control, wound-rotor motor speed control, dc transmission line
4	AC static switch	Spot welding, lighting control, ac motor speed control, ac starter
5	Cycloconverter	Low-speed synchronous motor control, electroslag refining of metals
6	Three-phase converter	High-voltage dc transmission, synchronous motor drive

are delayed by an angle of 90°. Conduction is therefore initiated every time the ac voltage reaches its maximum positive value. Based upon explanations given in Section 21.16, it is obvious that current will flow for 90°.

In Fig. 21.30b, it is seen that the current lags behind the voltage because it only flows during the final 90 degrees. This lag produces the same effect as an inductive load. Consequently, the ac source has to supply reactive power Q in addition to the active power P (see Section 7.13). The displacement power factor decreases as we delay the triggering pulse. On the other hand, if the SCR is triggered at zero degrees (the start of the cycle), no reactive power is absorbed by the rectifier.

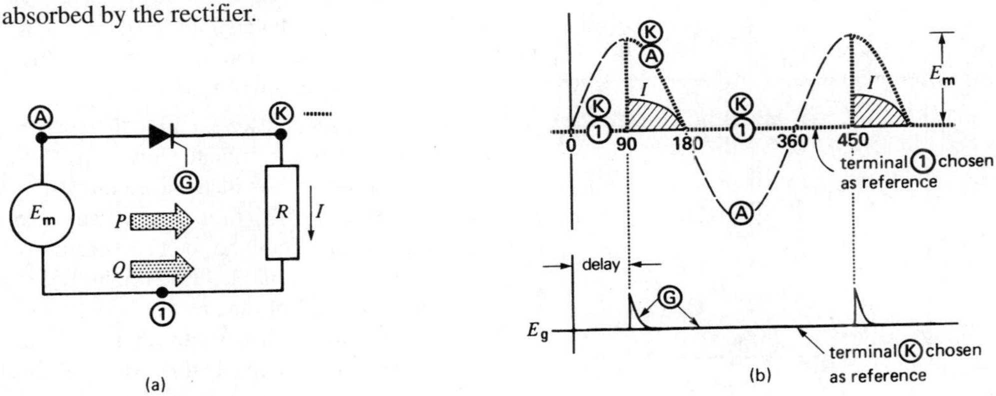

Figure 21.30
a. SCR supplying a passive load.
b. Voltage and current waveforms.

21.21 Controlled rectifier supplying an active load (Circuit 2, Table 21D)

Fig. 21.31 shows an ac source E_m and a dc load E_d connected by an SCR in series with an inductor. The load (represented by a battery) receives energy because when the thyristor conducts, current I enters the positive terminal. Smoothing inductor L limits the peak current to a value within the SCR rating. Gate pulses E_g initiate conduction at an angle θ_1 (Fig. 21.31b).

Using terminal 1 as a zero reference potential, it follows that the potential of terminal 2 lies E_d volts above it. Furthermore, the potential of terminal A oscillates sinusoidally above and below the level of terminal 1.

If the SCR were replaced by a diode, conduction would begin at angle θ_0 because this is the instant when the anode becomes positive. However, in our example, conduction only begins when the gate is fired at θ_1 degrees. As soon as conduction starts, point **K** jumps from level **2** to the level of point **A,** and voltage E_{A2} appears across the inductor. The latter begins storing volt-seconds, and current I increases accordingly. The volt-seconds reach a maximum at **2**, where area $A_{(+)}$ is maximum. The corresponding peak current is given by

$$I_{max} = A_{(+)}/L \qquad (2.28)$$

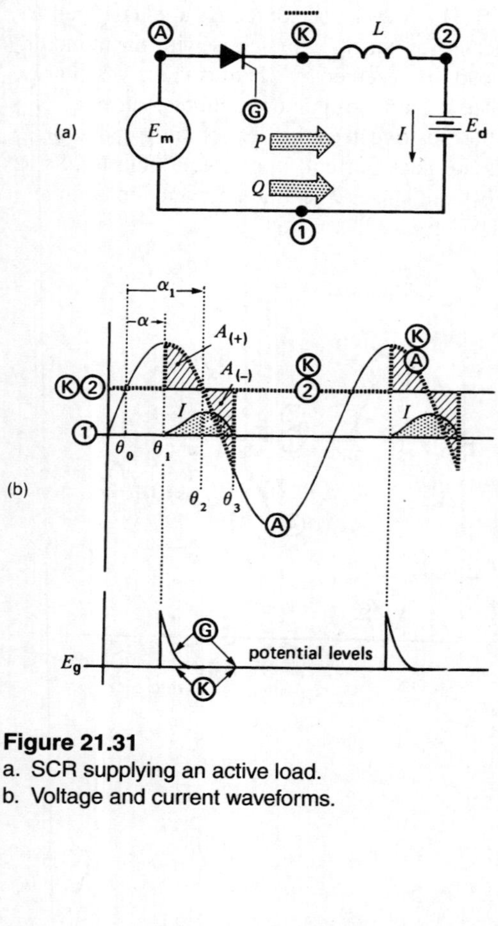

Figure 21.31
a. SCR supplying an active load.
b. Voltage and current waveforms.

The current then gradually decreases and becomes zero at angle θ_3, where $A_{(-)}$ is equal to $A_{(+)}$. As soon as conduction stops, point **K** jumps from level **A** to the level of point **2** and stays there until the next gate pulse. The level of **K** is shown by the dotted line. As in circuit 1 (Fig. 21.30), the load current lags (is displaced) behind voltage E_m; consequently, the source again has to supply reactive power Q as well as active power P. If we reduce the *firing angle* α, area $A_{(+)}$ increases, and so does current I. We can therefore vary the active power supplied to the load from zero ($\alpha = \alpha_1$) to a maximum ($\alpha = 0$), where α is measured starting from θ_0.

From a practical point of view, the circuit could be used as a variable battery charger. Another application is to control the speed and torque of a dc motor. In this case, E_d represents the counter-emf of the armature, and L the armature inductance.

21.22 Line-commutated inverter (Circuit 3, Table 21D)

An *inverter,* by definition, changes dc power into ac power. It performs the reverse operation of a rectifier, which converts ac power into dc power. There are two main types of inverters:

1. Self-commutated inverters (also called *force-commutated inverters*) in which the commutation means are included within the power inverter
2. Line-commutated inverters, wherein commutation is effected by virtue of the line voltages on the ac side of the inverter

In this section we examine the operating principle of a line-commutated inverter. The circuit of such an inverter is identical to that of a controlled rectifier, except that the battery terminals are reversed (Fig. 21.32a). Thus, the potential of terminal 2 lies below that of terminal 1 (Fig. 21.32b). Because current can only flow from anode to cathode, the dc source E_d *delivers* power whenever the thyristor conducts.

On the other hand, this power P must be absorbed by the ac terminals because we assume no losses in the inductor or the thyristor. Consequently, the circuit of Fig. 21.32a is potentially able to convert dc power into ac power.

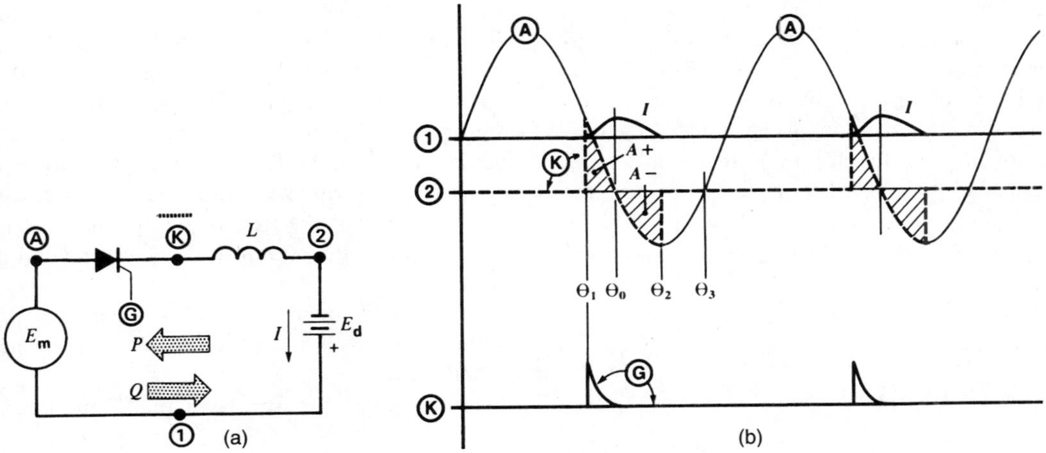

Figure 21.32
a. Line-commutated inverter.
b. Voltage and current waveforms.

The power converter consists therefore of a simple thyristor and inductor that connect the dc source to the ac load. However, it is important to note that the ac side must be an existing ac system that generates its own ac voltage, whether or not the inverter is in operation. For example, the ac system could be that of an electric utility company composed of hundreds of generators and thousands of loads that are easily able to absorb the additional power *P* delivered by the inverter.

To achieve power conversion, the peak ac voltage has to be greater than the dc voltage, and the thyristor has to be triggered within a precisely defined range. First, to initiate conduction, anode **A** must be positive with respect to **K.** Since **K** is initially at the level of terminal 2, the triggering pulse must be applied either prior to θ_0 or after θ_3 (Fig. 21.32b). For reasons that will soon become clear, the gate must be triggered *prior* to θ_0.

Suppose the SCR is triggered at θ_1 degrees. Point **K** immediately jumps from level **2** to level **A** and the inductor accumulates volt-seconds until angle θ_0 is reached. Thus, the resulting current reaches a peak at θ_0, equal to area $A_{(+)}/L$. The current then gradually falls as the negative volt-seconds begin to build up. Conduction stops at θ_2, when $A_{(-)} = A_{(+)}$.

To increase the current and hence the active power flow, we simply advance the firing angle θ_1. This causes $A_{(+)}$ to increase. However, this process cannot be carried too far. In order for conduction to cease, $A_{(-)}$ must equal $A_{(+)}$. However, the maximum area that $A_{(-)}$ can have is that bounded by the trough of the sine wave between θ_0 and θ_3, and the horizontal line of point **2** (Fig. 21.32b). As the firing angle is advanced, $A_{(+)}$ becomes larger and larger; but if it should exceed the maximum available value of $A_{(-)}$, conduction will never stop. In essence, current *I* will not be zero when angle θ_3 is reached. The dc current will then build up with each cycle, until the circuit breakers trip. For the same reason, conduction must never be initiated after angle θ_3.

Under normal inverter conditions, the current peaks lag behind the positive voltage peaks, and so the ac source still has to supply reactive power *Q* to the inverter. Consequently, *P* and *Q* flow in opposite directions in an inverter. In our example, $P = E_d I_d$ where I_d is the average value of current *I*.

The current pulses flowing into the ac terminals are far from sinusoidal and a stiff (low-impedance) ac system is needed so as not to distort the sinusoidal voltage. However, the pulses do contain a fundamental component that is in phase with the sinusoidal voltage E_{1A}. The effective value of this component is given by $I_p = E_d I_d / E$, where E is the effective value of the ac voltage. In practice, appropriate filters are added to ensure that the current flowing into the ac line is reasonably sinusoidal. We should also bear in mind that line-commutated inverters always involve 3-phase systems and not the simple single-phase circuit of Fig. 21.32.

21.23 AC static switch (Circuit 4, Table 21D)

An ac static switch is composed of two thyristors connected in antiparallel (back-to-back), so that current can flow in both directions (Fig. 21.33). The ac current flowing in the load resistor R can be precisely controlled by varying the phase angle α of gates g1 and g2. Thus, if the gate pulses are synchronized with the line frequency, a greater or lesser ac current will flow in the load. However, such delayed firing will draw reactive power from the line, even if the load is purely resistive. The reason is that the current is displaced behind the voltage.

The well-known triac used in domestic light-dimming controls is an example of such an electronic switch.

If the gates are fired at 0° and 180° respectively, the static switch is in the fully *closed* position. On the other hand, if neither gate is fired, the switch is in the *open* position. Thus, a static switch can be used to replace a magnetic contactor. In contrast to magnetic contactors, an electronic contactor is absolutely silent and its contacts never wear out.

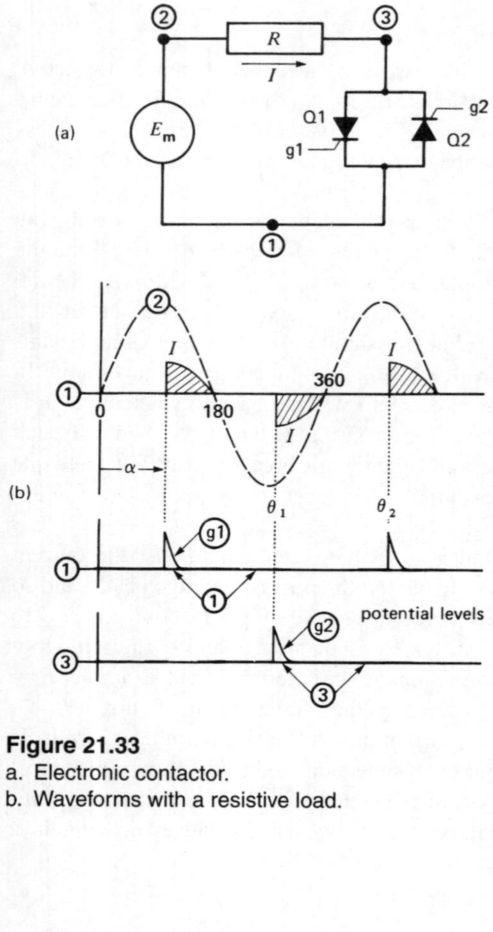

Figure 21.33
a. Electronic contactor.
b. Waveforms with a resistive load.

Figure 21.33c
Single-phase, water-cooled contactor composed of two Hockey Puk thyristors. Continuous current rating: 1200 A (RMS) at 2000 V; cooling water requirements: 4.5 L/min at 35° max. For intermittent (10% duty) spot welding applications, this unit can handle 2140 A for 20 cycles. Width: 175 mm; length: 278 mm; depth: 114 mm.
(Photo Courtesy of International Rectifier)

21.24 Cycloconverter (Circuit 5, Table 21D)

A cycloconverter produces low-frequency ac power directly from a higher-frequency ac source. A simple cycloconverter is shown in Fig. 21.34. It consists of three groups of thyristors, mounted back-to-back and connected to a 3-phase source. They jointly supply single-phase power to a resistive load *R*.

To understand the operation of the circuit, suppose all thyristors are initially blocked (nonconducting). Then, for an interval *T*, the gates of thyristors Q1, Q2, and Q3 are triggered by 4 successive pulses g1, g2, g3, g1, in such a way that the thyristors function as if they were ordinary diodes. As a result, the circuit behaves like a 3-pulse rectifier and terminal 4 is positive with respect to N (Fig. 21.35). The waveshape of E_{4N} is identical to that of Fig. 21.17.

During the next interval *T*, thyristors Q4, Q5, Q6, are fired by 4 similar pulses g4, g5, g6, g4. This makes terminal 4 *negative* with respect to N. The firing process is then repeated for the Q1, Q2, Q3

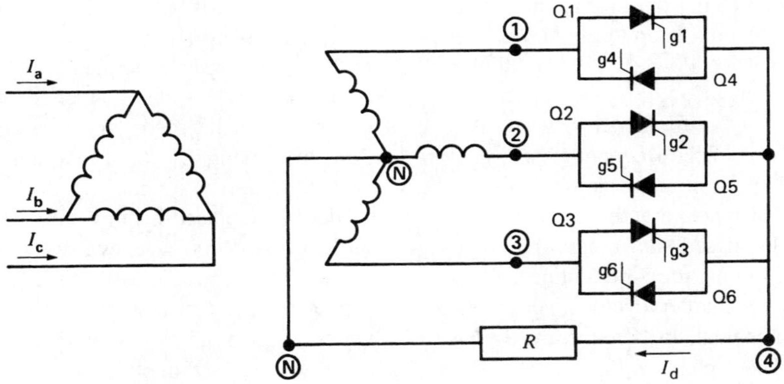

Figure 21.34
Elementary cycloconverter.

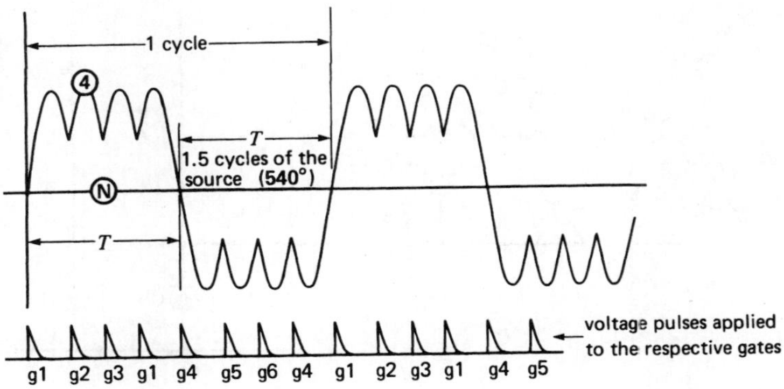

Figure 21.35
Typical voltage output of a cycloconverter.

thyristors, and so on, with the result that a low-frequency ac voltage appears across the load. The duration of 1 cycle is 2 T seconds. Compared to a sine wave, the low-frequency waveshape is rather poor. It is flat-topped and contains a large 180 Hz ripple when the 3-phase frequency is 60 Hz. However, this is of secondary importance because means are available to improve it.

Returning to Fig. 21.35 and assuming a 60 Hz source, we can show that each half-cycle corresponds to 540°, on a 60 Hz base. The duration of T is, therefore, $(540/360) \times (1/60) = 0.025$ s, which corresponds to a frequency of $1/(2 \times 0.025) = 20$ Hz.

Obviously, by repeating the firing sequence g1, g2, g3, g1, . . . , we could keep terminal 4 positive for as long as we wish, followed by an equally long negative period, when g4, g5, g6, g4 . . . are fired. In this way we can generate frequencies as low as we please. The high end of the frequency spectrum is limited to about 40 percent of the supply frequency. The reader should also note that this cycloconverter can supply a single-phase load from a 3-phase system, without unbalancing the 3-phase lines.

Later, we will encounter cycloconverters that can produce a sinusoidal, low-frequency, 3-phase output from a 60 Hz, 3-phase input.

21.25 3-phase, 6-pulse controllable converter (Circuit 6, Table 21D)

The 3-phase, 6-pulse thyristor converter is one of the most widely used rectifier/inverter units in power electronics. Due to its practical importance, we will explain how it operates in some detail. As in all 3-phase converters, the waveforms become rather complex, although not particularly difficult to understand. Even the simplest circuits yield chopped voltages and currents that pile on top of each other, and it taxes the mind to keep track of everything that is going on. Consequently, we will keep the waveforms as simple as possible, so as to highlight the basic principle of operation.

Three-phase, 6-pulse converters have 6 thyristors connected to the secondary winding of a 3-phase transformer (Fig. 21.36). The arrangement is identical to the rectifier circuit of Fig. 21.19, except that the diodes are replaced by thyristors. Because we can initiate conduction whenever we please, the thyristors enable us to vary the dc output voltage when the converter operates in the rectifier mode. The converter can also function as an inverter, provided that a dc source is used in place of the load resistor R.

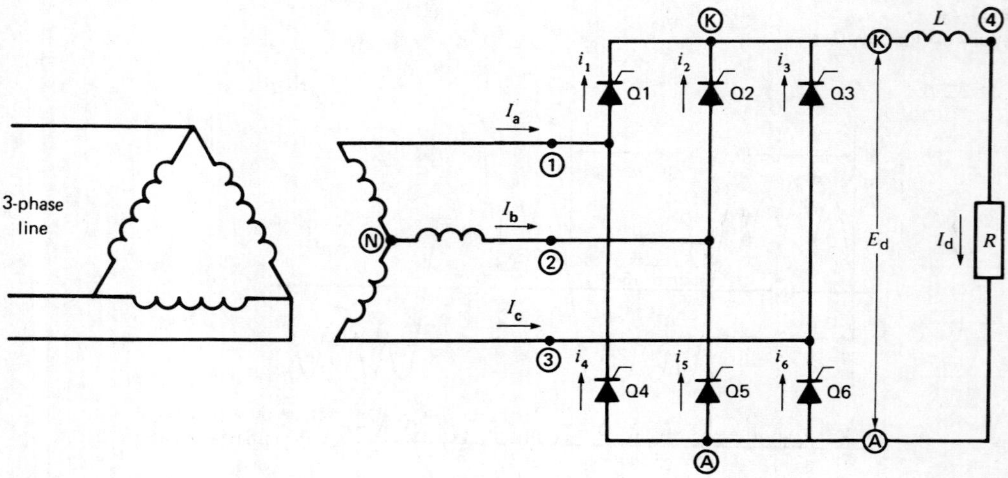

Figure 21.36
Three-phase, 6-pulse thyristor converter.

21.26 Basic principle of operation

We can gain a basic understanding of how the converter works in the rectifier mode by referring to Fig. 21.37. In this figure, the six SCRs are assumed to be enclosed in a box, where they successively switch the output terminals K, A to the ac supply lines 1, 2, 3. The load is represented by a resistor in series with an inductor *L*. The inductor is assumed to have a very large inductance, so that the load current I_d remains constant. In Fig. 21.37a, the two thyristors Q1, Q5 located between terminals K-1 and A-2 are conducting. A moment later, the thyristors Q2, Q4 between K-2 and A-1 conduct (Fig. 21.37b). The other thyristors are similarly switched, in sequence. When these steps have been completed, the entire switching cycle repeats. The reader will note that the dc current I_d flows in the ac lines. However, Fig. 21.37 shows that the current in each line reverses periodically, and so it is a true ac current of amplitude I_d. It is also evident that the current in one of the three lines is zero for brief intervals. For example, in Fig. 21.37, there is momentarily no current in line 3.

The switching sequence we have just described is similar to that of the diode bridge rectifier of Fig. 21.22. There is, however, an important difference. The thyristors can be made to conduct at precise moments on the ac voltage cycle. Thus, conduction can be initiated when the instantaneous voltage between the ac lines is either high or low. If the voltage is low, the dc output voltage will also be low. Conversely, if the thyristors conduct when the ac line voltage is momentarily near its peak, the dc output voltage will be high. In effect, the output voltage E_{KA} is composed of short 60-degree segments of the ac line voltage. The average value of E_{KA} becomes the dc output voltage E_d.

In examining Fig. 21.37, it can be seen that the line current always flows out of a line that is momentarily positive. This must be so because the line delivers active power to the load. For example, in Fig. 21.37a, e_{12} is positive when I_d flows in the direction shown.

Knowing how the thyristor converter behaves as a rectifier, the question arises: How can it be made to operate as an inverter? Three basic conditions have to be met.

First, we must have a source of dc current I_d. Such a current source can be provided if a voltage source E_0 is connected in series with a large inductance (Figs. 21.38a and 21.38b).

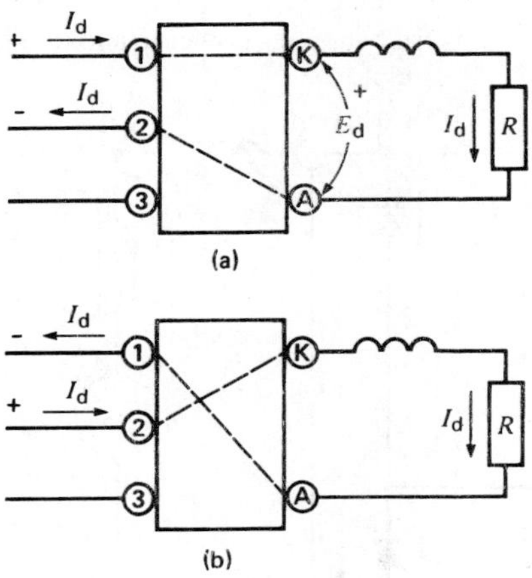

Figure 21.37
Rectifier mode (see Fig. 21.36)
a. Q1 and Q5 conducting.
b. Q2 and Q4 conducting.

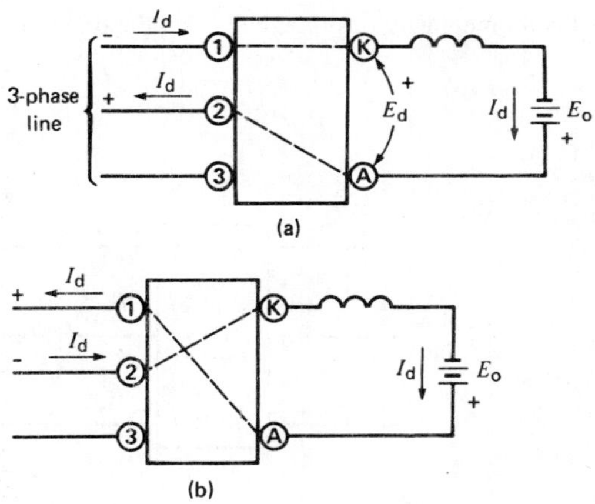

Figure 21.38
Inverter mode (see Fig. 21.36)
a. Q1 and Q5 conducting.
b. Q2 and Q4 conducting.

Second, the converter must be connected to a 3-phase line that can maintain an undistorted sinusoidal voltage, even when the line current is nonsinusoidal. The voltage may be taken from a power utility, or generated by a local alternator.

Third, to force power into the line, the thyristors must be switched so that current I_d flows into an ac line that is momentarily positive. The gate firing must therefore be precisely synchronized with the line frequency.

The inverter operation can best be understood by referring to Fig. 21.38. The SCRs enclosed in the box are arranged the same way as in Fig. 21.37. In other words, the converters in the two figures are absolutely identical. Looking first at the dc side, the dc current I_d must flow in the same direction as before because SCRs cannot conduct in reverse. On the other hand, because we want the dc source E_0 to deliver power, I_d must flow out of the positive terminal, as shown. In other words, the positive side of E_0 must be connected to terminal A. On the ac side, the 3-phase line is simply connected to terminals 1, 2, 3.

We are now ready to fire the thyristors. However, the firing must be properly timed so that the ac line receives power. This is consistently done in Fig. 21.38, because current I_d always flows into an ac terminal that is momentarily positive. Note that the line voltage polarities in the inverter mode are consistently opposite to those in the rectifier mode.

The reader can see that the line current alternates as before, and it has a peak value equal to I_d. Indeed, the waveshape of the ac line currents is the same in Figs. 21.37 and 21.38; it is only the instantaneous line voltages that differ.

If the dc supply voltage E_0 is low, the thyristors must be fired when the instantaneous ac voltage is low. Conversely, if the dc voltage is high, the thyristors must be triggered when the ac line voltage is near its peak.

We wish to make one final important observation. The voltage that appears between terminals K and A is composed of 60-degree segments of the ac line voltages. Consequently, E_{KA} is a fluctuating voltage whose average value is E_d. This average voltage must be equal to E_0 because the dc voltage drop across the inductor is negligible. In addition to keeping current I_d constant and almost ripple free, the inductor serves as a buffer between the fluctuating voltage E_{KA} and the constant voltage E_0.

21.27 Three-phase, 6-pulse rectifier feeding an active load

Consider the circuit of Fig. 21.39 in which a 3-phase, 6-pulse converter supplies power to a load. The load

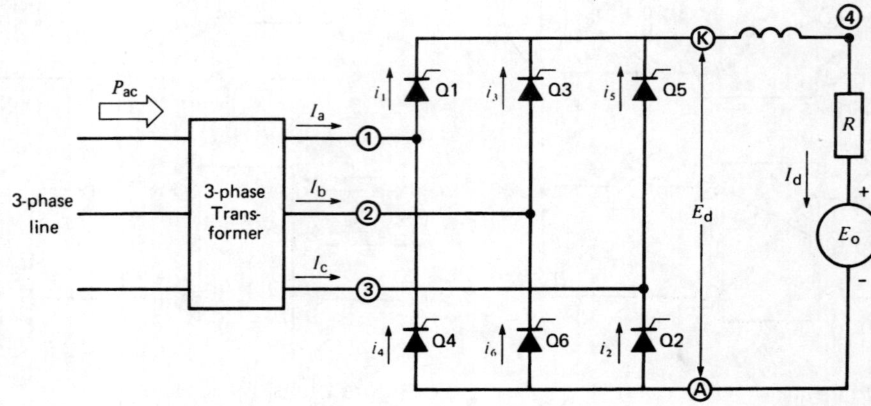

Figure 21.39
Three-phase, 6-pulse rectifier.

is composed of a dc voltage E_0 and a resistor R in series with a smoothing inductor. The converter is fed from a 3-phase transformer. The gates of thyristors Q1 to Q6 are triggered in succession at 60-degree intervals. We assume that the converter has been in operation for some time, so that conditions are stable. Initially, suppose thyristors Q5 and Q6 are conducting, carrying load current I_d (Fig. 21.40a). Then, at the 0° point (θ_0), thyristor Q1 is triggered by gate pulse g1. Commutation occurs and Q1 starts conducting, taking over from Q5.

At 60° thyristor Q2 is fired and the resulting commutation transfers the load current from Q6 to Q2. This switching process continues indefinitely and, as in Fig. 21.21, point **K** follows the peaks of the successive waves. The thyristors are labelled so as to indicate the sequence in which they are fired. Two SCRs conduct at a time; the conduction pairs are, therefore, Q1-Q2, Q2-Q3, Q3-Q4, and so on. Thus, by referring to Fig. 21.39, we can tell at a glance which thyristors are conducting at any given time.

The converter acts as a rectifier and the average or dc voltage between **K** and **A** is $E_d = 1.35\ E$. Because there is no appreciable dc voltage drop in an inductor, the dc voltage between points **4** and **A** is also 1.35 E. Consequently, the dc current I_d is given by

$$I_d = (E_d - E_0)/R \qquad (21.12)$$

The triggering time has to be fairly precise to obtain the rectified voltage shown in Fig. 21.40a. Thus, if g1 fires slightly ahead of θ_0, conduction cannot start because anode 1 is then negative. On the other hand, if g1 fires after θ_0, Q5 (along with Q6) will continue to conduct until g1 *is* fired. In practice, the triggering pulses are made wide enough to ensure that commutation occurs at the desired instant.

21.28 Delayed triggering—rectifier mode

Let us now delay all triggering pulses by an angle α of 15° (Fig. 21.40b). Current I_d, instead of switching over to Q1 at θ_0, will continue to flow in Q5 until gate pulse g1 triggers Q1. Commutation occurs, and the potential of point **K** jumps from line 3 to line 1. A similar switching action takes place (but at later times) for the other thyristors. The resulting choppy waveshape between terminals K and A is shown in Fig. 21.40b.

Note that the triggering delay does not shorten the conduction period; each thyristor still conducts for a full 120° and each voltage segment has a duration of 60 degrees. Furthermore, the current remains constant and ripple-free, due to the presence

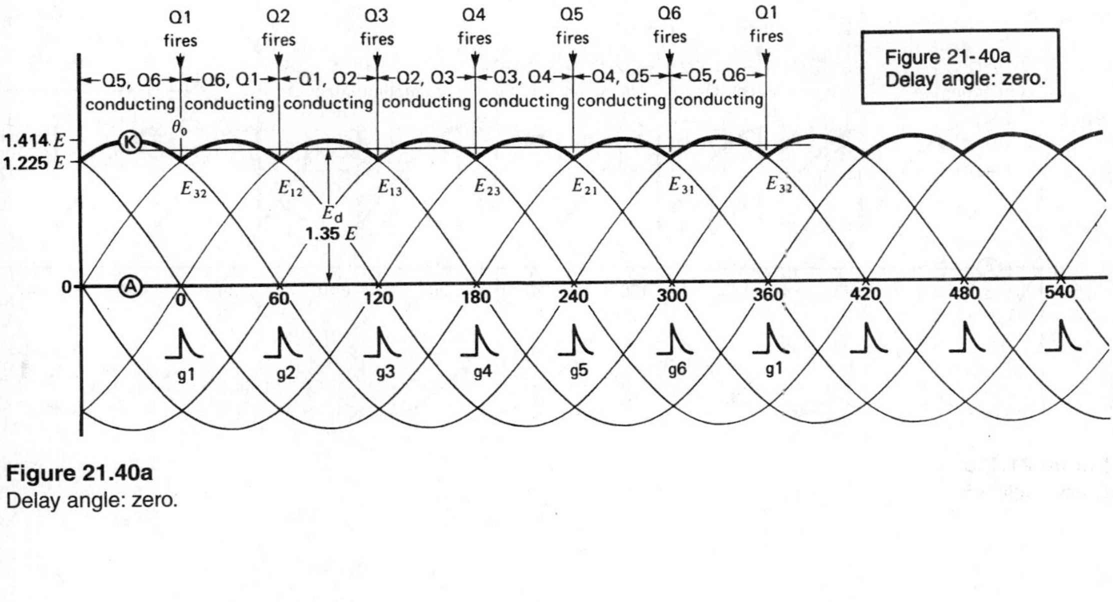

Figure 21.40a
Delay angle: zero.

of the big inductor. The level of point **K** follows the tops of the individual sine waves, but the average voltage E_d, between **K** and **A,** is obviously smaller than before. We can prove that it is given by

$$E_d = 1.35\, E \cos \alpha \qquad (21.13)$$

where

E_d = dc voltage produced by the 3-phase, 6-pulse converter [V]

E = effective value of the ac line-to-line voltage [V]

α = firing angle [°]

According to Eq. 21.13, E_d becomes smaller and smaller as α increases. However, if E_d becomes equal to or less than E_0, the load current flows intermittently. Ordinarily, the current would reverse when E_d is smaller than E_0. However, this is impossible, because the SCRs can only conduct in the for-

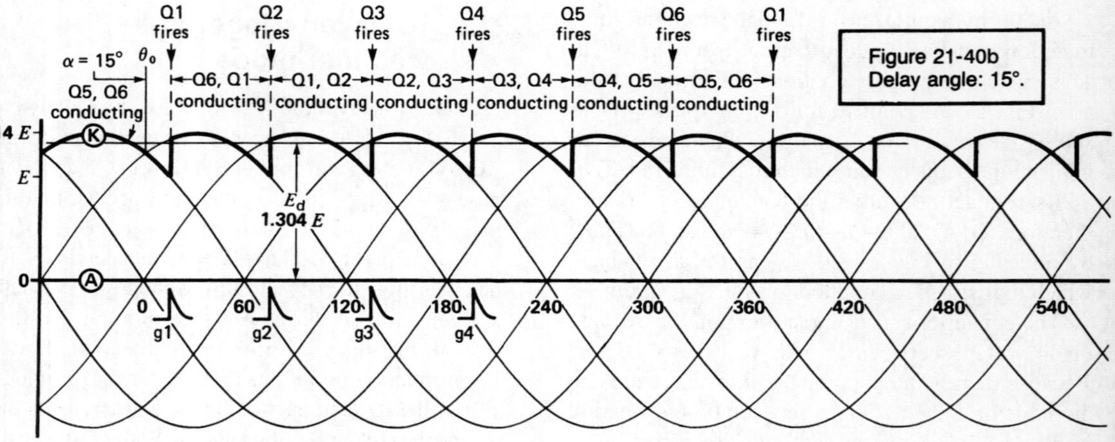

Figure 21.40b
Delay angle: 15°.

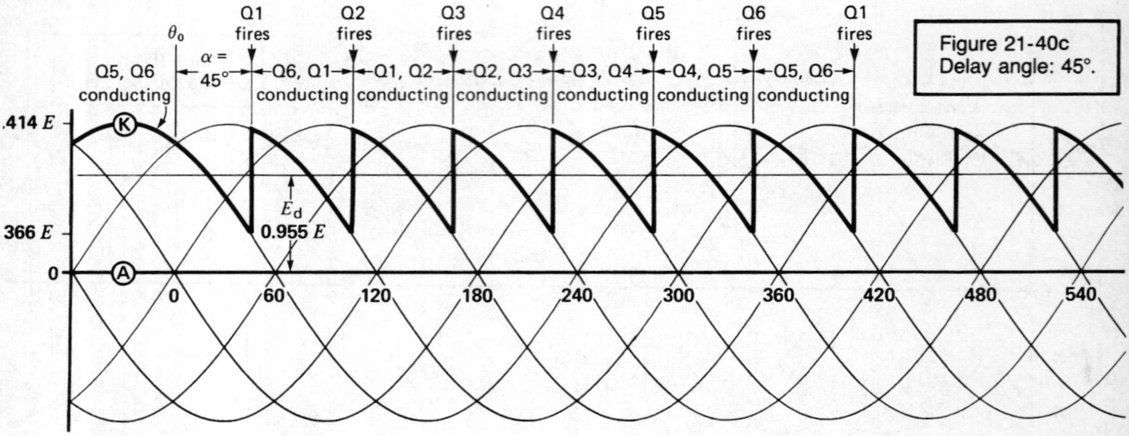

Figure 21.40c
Delay angle: 45°.

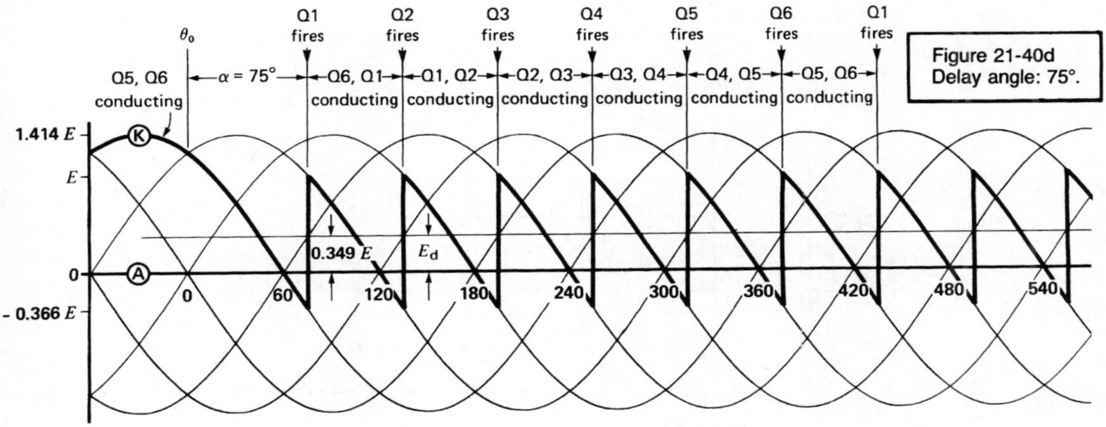

Figure 21.40d
Delay angle: 75°.

ward direction. We will not study the condition of intermittent current flow.

Figs. 21.40c and 21.40d show the waveform between **K** and **A** for $\alpha = 45°$ and $75°$, respectively. Note that when $\alpha = 75°$ the ac component in E_{KA} is very large, compared to the dc component.

Example 21-7

The 3-phase converter of Fig. 21.39 is connected to a 3-phase, 480 V, 60 Hz source. The load consists of a 500 V dc source having an internal resistance of 2 Ω. Calculate the power supplied to the load for triggering delays of (a) 15° and (b) 75°.

Solution

a. The dc output voltage of the converter is

$$E_d = 1.35\, E \cos \alpha$$
$$= 1.35 \times 480 \cos 15°$$
$$= 626 \text{ V}$$

Because the dc voltage drop across the inductor is negligible, the IR drop across the 2 Ω internal resistance is

$$E = E_d - E_0$$
$$= 626 - 500 = 126 \text{ V}$$

The dc load current is therefore

$$I_d = E/R = 126/2 = 63 \text{ A}$$

The power supplied to the load is

$$P = E_d I_d$$
$$= 626 \times 63 = 39.4 \text{ kW}$$

b. With a phase angle delay of 75°, the converter voltage is

$$E_d = 1.35\, E \cos \alpha$$
$$= 1.35 \times 480 \times \cos 75°$$
$$= 167.7 \text{ V}$$

Because E_d is less than E_0, the current tends to flow in reverse. This is impossible and, consequently, the current is simply zero and so, too, is the power.

21.29 Delayed triggering—inverter mode

If triggering is delayed by more than 90°, the voltage E_d developed by the converter becomes negative, according to Eq. 21.13. This does not produce a negative current because, as we said, SCRs

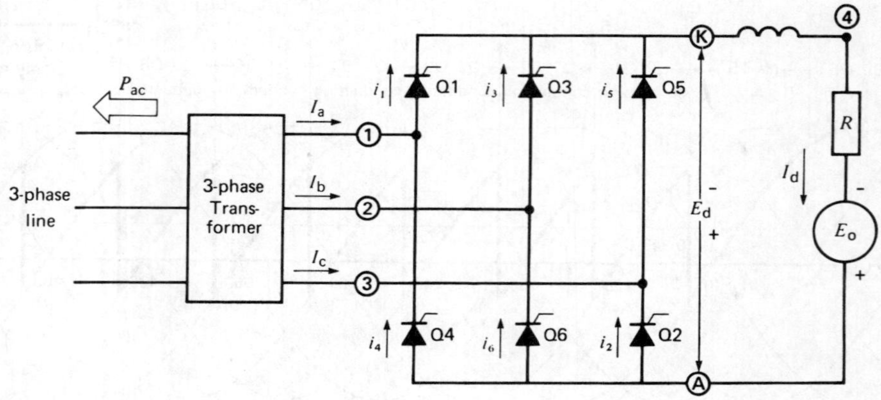

Figure 21.41
Three-phase, 6-pulse converter in the inverter mode.

conduct in only one direction. Consequently, the load current is simply zero. However, we can *force* a current to flow by connecting a dc voltage of proper magnitude and polarity across the converter terminals. This external voltage E_0 must be slightly greater than E_d in order for current to flow (Fig. 21.41). The load current is given by

$$I = (E_0 - E_d)/R$$

Because current flows out of the positive terminal of E_0, the load is actually a source, delivering a power output $P = E_0 I_d$. Part of this power is dissipated as heat in the circuit resistance R and the remainder is delivered to the secondaries of the 3-phase transformer. If we subtract the small transformer losses and the virtually negligible SCR losses, we are left with a net active power P_{ac} that is delivered to the 3-phase line.

The original rectifier has now become an *inverter*, converting dc power into ac power. The transition from rectifier to inverter is smooth, and requires no change in the converter connections. In the rectifier mode, the firing angle lies between 0° and 90°, and the load may be active or passive. In the inverter mode, the firing angle lies between 90° and 180°, and a dc source of proper polarity *must* be provided.

Fig. 21.42 shows the waveshapes at firing angles of 105°, 135°, and 165°. The dc voltage E_d generated by the inverter is still given by Eq. 21.13. It reaches a maximum value of $E_d = -1.35\ E$ at a firing angle of 180°.

21.30 Triggering range

The triggering angle of a given thyristor is usually kept between 15° and 165°. The thyristor acts as a rectifier between 15° and 90° and as an inverter between 90° and 165°. Under these conditions, the dc voltage developed reaches its maximum value at 15° and 165°; it is zero at 90°.

The triggering angle is seldom less than 8° in the rectifier mode. The reason is that sudden line voltage changes might cause a thyristor to misfire, thus producing a discontinuity in the dc output current.

In the inverter mode we seldom permit the firing angle to exceed 165°. If we go beyond this point, the inverter may lose its ability to switch from one thyristor to the next. As a result, the currents build up very quickly until the circuit breakers trip. In some cases, the firing angle is not allowed to exceed 150°, to ensure an adequate safety margin.

Fig. 21.43 shows the allowed and forbidden gate firing zones for a particular thyristor in a 3-phase,

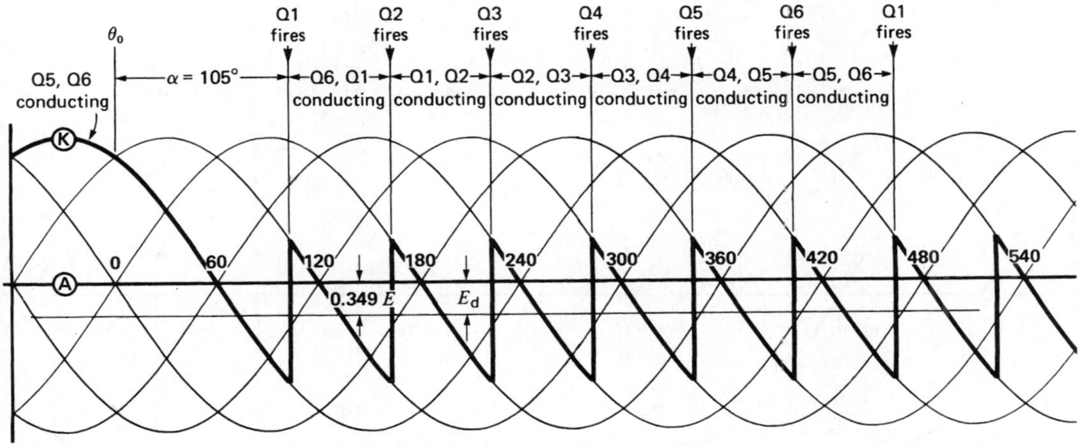

Figure 21.42a
Triggering sequence and waveforms with a delay angle of 105°.

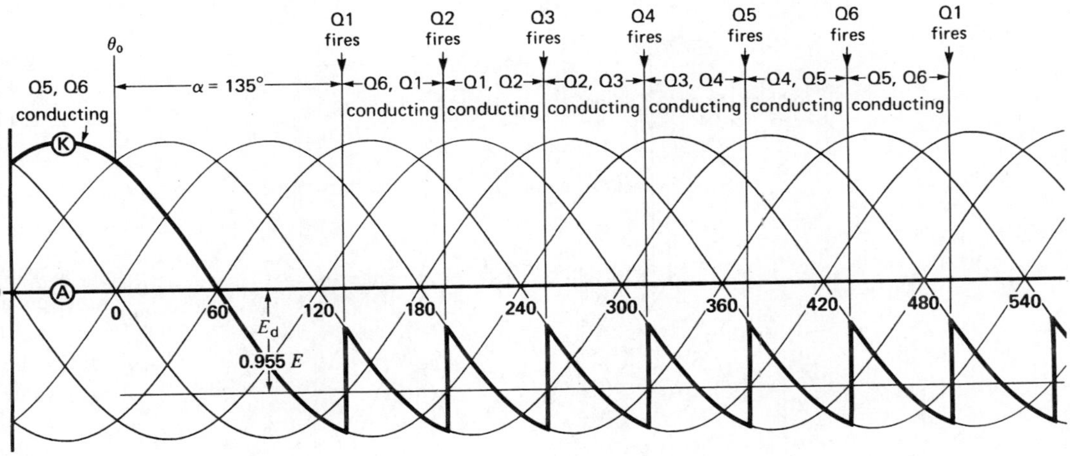

Figure 21.42b
Triggering sequence and waveforms with a delay angle of 135°.

6-pulse converter. Specifically, it refers to Q1 in Fig. 21.39. The other thyristors have similar firing zones, but they occur at different times.

21.31 Equivalent circuit of a converter

We may think of a converter as being a static ac/dc motor-generator set whose dc output voltage E_d changes both in magnitude and polarity, depending upon the gate pulse delay. However, the dc generator has some special properties:

1. It can carry current in only one direction.
2. It produces an increasingly large ac ripple voltage as the dc voltage decreases.

The analogy may be represented by the circuit of Fig. 21.44, in which

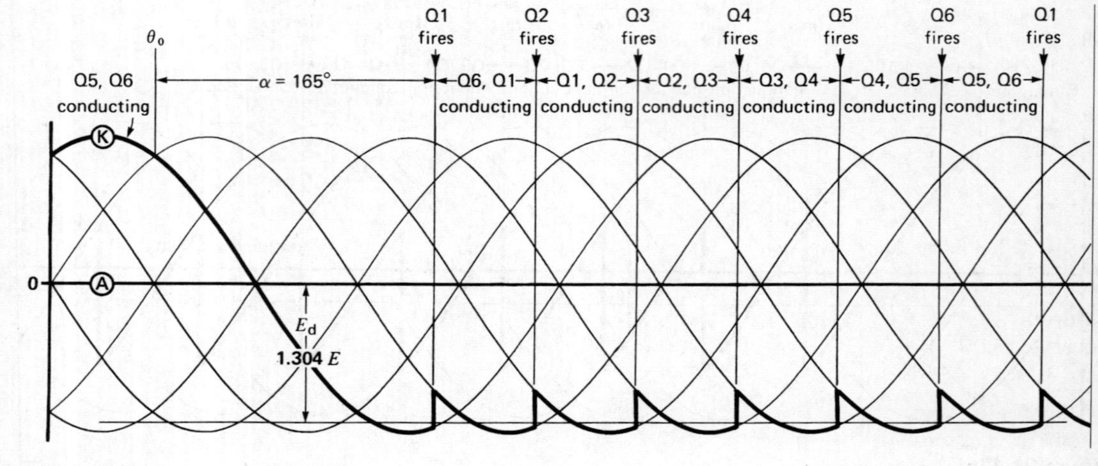

Figure 21.42c
Triggering sequence and waveforms with a delay angle of 165°.

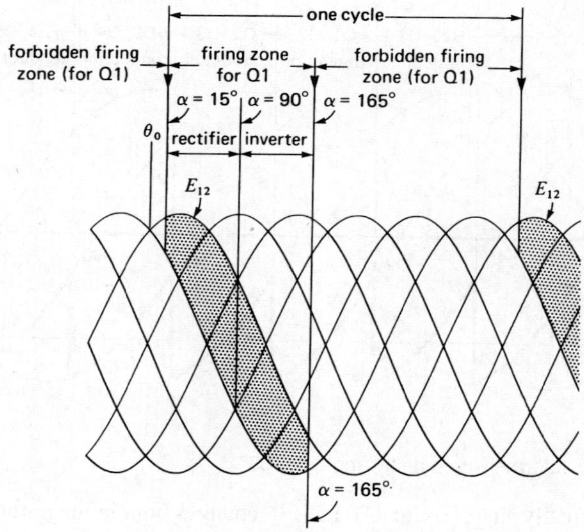

Figure 21.43
Permitted gate firing zones for thyristor Q1.

- E_{ac} represents the 3-phase line voltage.
- E_d is the dc voltage generated by the converter.
- e_c is the ac voltage generated by the converter on the dc side (mainly the 6th and 12th harmonics).
- D is a diode to remind us that current can flow in only one direction.
- The dotted line between E_{ac} and E_d indicates that active power can flow in either direction between the ac and dc systems.

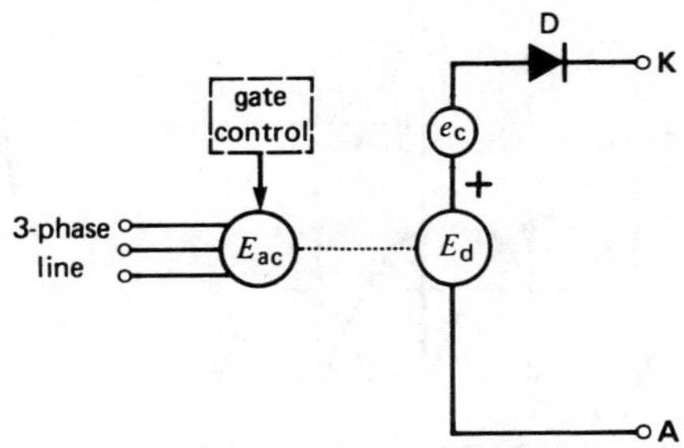

Figure 21.44
Equivalent circuit of a thyristor converter.

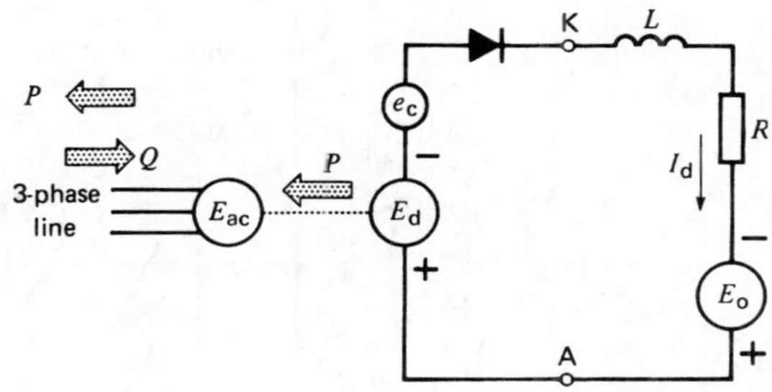

Figure 21.46
Equivalent circuit of a 3-phase thyristor converter in the inverter mode.

- Unlike a motor/generator set, the dc and ac systems are not electrically isolated from each other.

When the converter is operating as a rectifier, the equivalent circuit is shown in Fig. 21.45. When operating as an inverter, the circuit is given by Fig. 21.46. The ac voltage generated by the converter appears across inductor L. Its inductance is assumed to be sufficiently large to ensure an almost ripple-free dc current.

It will also be recognized that the currents flowing in the 3-phase lines are not sinusoidal. Thus, on the ac side, the converter generates harmonic currents, as we have already seen (Section 21.14).

21.32 Currents in a 3-phase, 6-pulse converter

Fig. 21.47 shows the voltage and current waveshapes when the converter functions as a rectifier

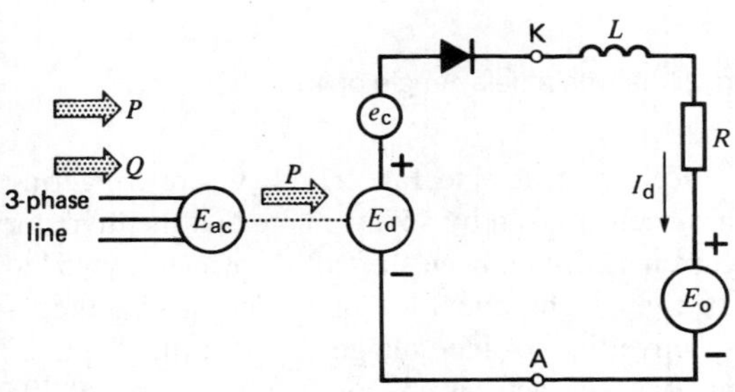

Figure 21.45
Equivalent circuit of a 3-phase converter in the rectifier mode.

at a firing angle of 45°. The currents i_1, i_2, i_3, i_4, i_5, i_6 in the thyristors flow for 120°, and their peak value is equal to the dc current I_d. This holds true for any firing angle between zero and 180°. Consequently, the currents in a thyristor converter are identical to those in a plain 3-phase diode rectifier (Fig. 21.20). The only difference is that they flow later in the cycle.

The waveshapes of the corresponding ac line currents are easily found because they are equal to the difference between the respective thyristor currents. Thus, referring to Fig. 21.39, line current $I_a = i_1 - i_4$. These line currents also have a peak value I_d, but they flow in positive and negative blocks of 120°.

The heating effect of the ac line currents is important because they usually flow in the windings of a converter transformer. The I^2R loss depends upon the effective value I of the current. From Eq. 21.6 we know that

$$I = 0.816\, I_d \tag{21.6}$$

The effective value of the ac line current is, therefore, directly related to the dc output current and is unaffected by the firing angle. Clearly, the same is true when the converter operates as an inverter.

21.33 Power factor

We recall that in the 3-phase, 3-pulse diode rectifier (Figs. 21.16 and 21.17), the currents in lines 1, 2, and 3 are symmetrical with respect to the line-to-neutral voltages. Thus, rectangular current i_2 is exactly in the middle of the positive E_{2N} wave.

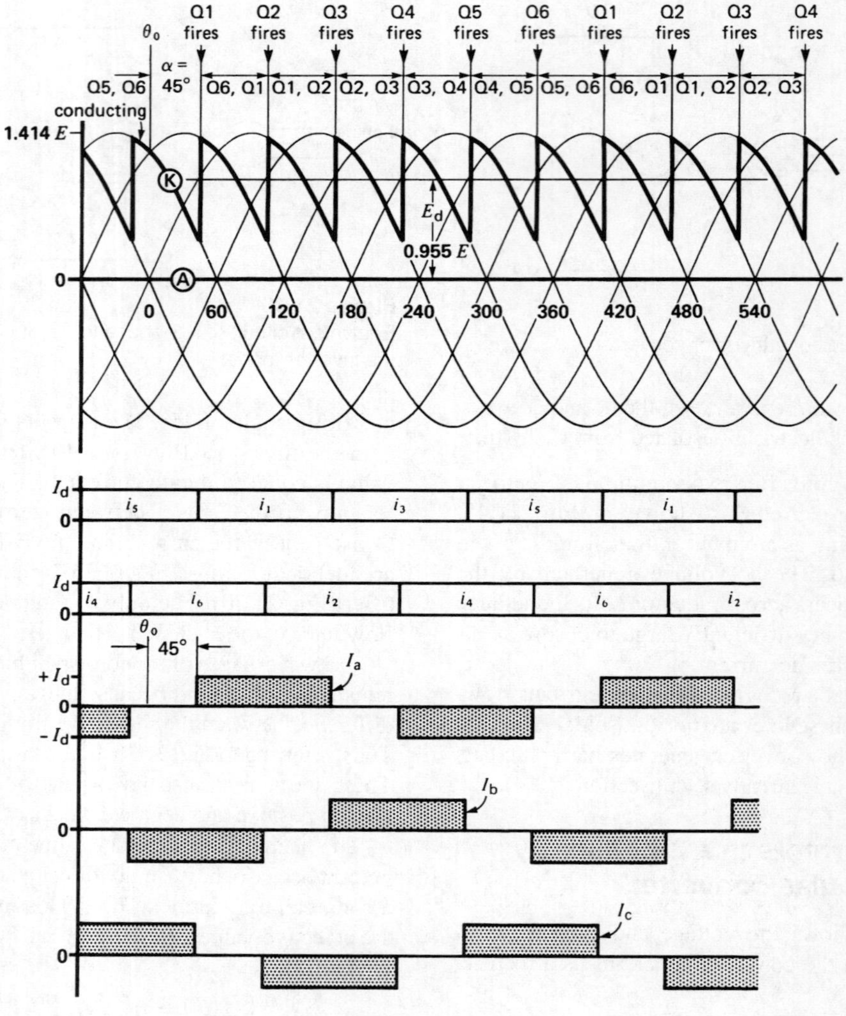

Figure 21.47
Voltage and current waveforms in the thyristor converter of Fig. 21.39 with a delay angle of 45°.

In essence (and in actual fact), i_2 is in phase with E_{2N}. This is also true for the currents in the other two lines, as regards their respective voltages. This condition is reflected back into the primary of the transformer, and from there to the 3-phase feeder. Because the currents are in phase with the voltages, the *displacement power factor* is 100%. As a result, the rectifier draws no reactive power from the line.

Referring now to Fig. 21.47, where triggering has been delayed by 45°, we note that the thyristor currents have all been shifted (displaced) by 45° to the right. Consequently, the line currents lag the respective line-to-line voltages by 45°; the displacement power factor is no longer unity but only 0.707 (cos 45° = 0.707). This means that a converter absorbs reactive power from the ac system to which it is connected. This is true whether the converter operates as a rectifier or inverter. The reactive power is given by

$$Q = P \tan \alpha \qquad (21.14)$$

where

Q = reactive power absorbed by the converter [var]

P = dc power of the converter (positive for a rectifier, negative for an inverter) [W]

α = triggering angle [°]

The reader will note that the waveshapes of the currents in Fig. 21.47 are the same as those in a conventional 6-pulse rectifier (Fig. 21.20).

Example 21-8

In Example 21-7, and for a triggering angle of 15°, calculate the following:

a. The displacement power factor
b. The reactive power absorbed by the converter
c. The total power factor

Solution

a. The displacement between the fundamental line current and the line-to-neutral voltage is $\alpha = 15°$. The displacement power factor is

$$\cos \alpha = \cos 15° = 0.966, \text{ or } 96.6\%$$

b. The active power supplied to the converter is

$$P = E_d I_d = 39.4 \text{ kW}$$

Hence

$$Q = P \tan \alpha$$
$$= 39.4 \tan 15$$
$$= 10.6 \text{ kvar}$$

c. The total power factor = displacement power factor × distortion power factor

$$= 0.966 \times 0.955$$
$$= 0.923 = 92.3\%$$

Example 21-9

A 16 kV dc source having an internal resistance of 1 Ω supplies 900 A to a 12 kV, 3-phase, 6-pulse, 60 Hz inverter (Fig. 21.48).

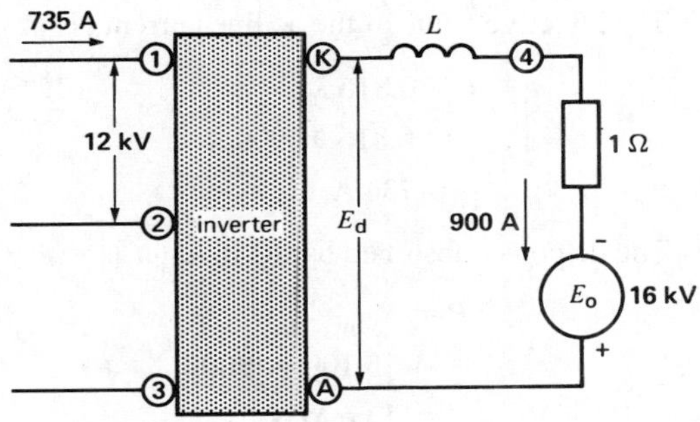

Figure 21.48
See Example 21-11.

Calculate

a. The dc current carried by each SCR
b. The dc voltage generated by the inverter
c. The required firing angle α
d. The effective value of the ac line currents
e. The reactive power absorbed by the inverter

Solution

a. Each SCR carries the load current for one-third of the time. The dc current is, therefore,

$$I = I_d/3 = 900/3$$
$$= 300 \text{ A}$$

b. The voltage E_d generated by the inverter is equal to E_0 less the IR drop. Thus,

$$E_d = E_0 - I_d R$$
$$= 16\,000 - 900 \times 1$$
$$= 15\,100 \text{ V}$$

c. Knowing that the effective ac line voltage is 12 000 V, the firing angle can be found from Eq. 21.13:

$$E_d = 1.35\, E \cos \alpha$$
$$15\,100 = 1.35 \times 12\,000 \cos \alpha$$
$$\cos \alpha = 0.932$$
$$\alpha = 21.2°$$

This is the firing angle that would be required if the converter operated as a rectifier. However, because it is in the inverter mode, the actual firing angle is

$$\alpha = 180 - 21.2 = 158.8°$$

d. The effective value of the ac line current is

$$I = 0.816\,I_d \quad (21.6)$$
$$= 0.816 \times 900$$
$$= 734 \text{ A}$$

e. The dc power absorbed by the inverter is

$$P = E_d I_d$$
$$= 15\,100 \times 900$$
$$= 13.6 \text{ MW}$$

P is actually negative because the inverter *absorbs* dc power; hence,

$$P = -13.6 \text{ MW}$$

The reactive power absorbed by the inverter is

$$Q = P \tan \alpha \quad (21.14)$$
$$= -13.6 \tan 158.8$$
$$= 5.27 \text{ Mvar}$$

In practice, the actual reactive power is higher than the calculated value, due to commutation overlap.

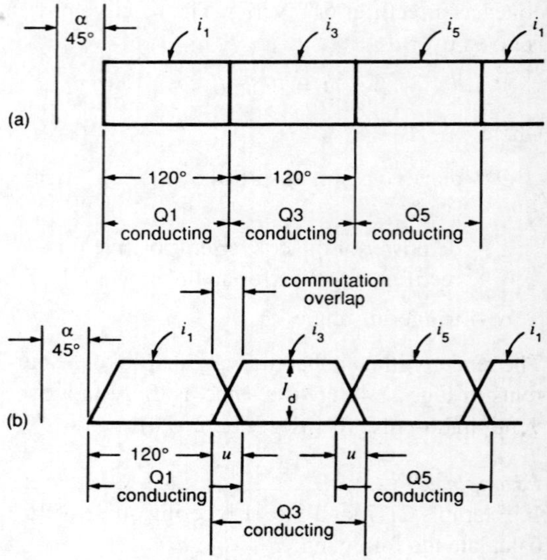

Figure 21.49

a. Instantaneous commutation in a rectifier when α = 45° (see Fig. 21.58).

b. Same conditions with commutation overlap of 30°, showing current waveshapes in Q1, Q3, Q5.

21.34 Commutation overlap

We mentioned in Section 21.9, that the current in a three-phase rectifier cannot switch instantaneously from one diode to the next. The commutation process takes time and this is also true for thyristors. Thus, in a six-pulse converter, the commutation from Q1 to Q3 followed by Q3 to Q5 is not instantaneous (as assumed in Fig. 21.47), but is more like that shown in Fig. 21.49b.

The transfer of I_d from one thyristor to the next is effected during the so-called *commutation overlap* period, defined by angle u. The amount of overlap varies with the current I_d. At full-load, u lies typically between 20° and 30°. At light load it can be as small as 5°. On account of commutation overlap, the current in each thyristor flows for a period of 120 + u degrees instead of 120°, as we have assumed so far. The commutation overlap modifies the waveshape of E_{AK}, but we will not examine this aspect of converter behavior.

The commutation overlap delays the current build-up by angle u. It also delays the current cutoff by the same angle. Owing to these delays, the effective firing angle is somewhat greater than the triggering angle α. This reduces the power factor of the converter in both the rectifier and inverter modes. It also reduces the average dc voltage E_{dc}.

21.35 Extinction angle

We have seen that when a converter operates in the inverter mode, it is very important that conduction be initiated prior to α = 180°. Because the current in an ideal inverter flows for 120°, the conduction must also cease before the angle of (180 + 120) = 300° is reached. The interval between the end of commutation and 300° is called the *extinction angle* γ (Fig. 21.50). The extinction angle permits thyristor Q1 to recover its blocking ability before its anode (1) again becomes positive with respect to the cathode K. The value of γ lies typically between 15° and 20°.

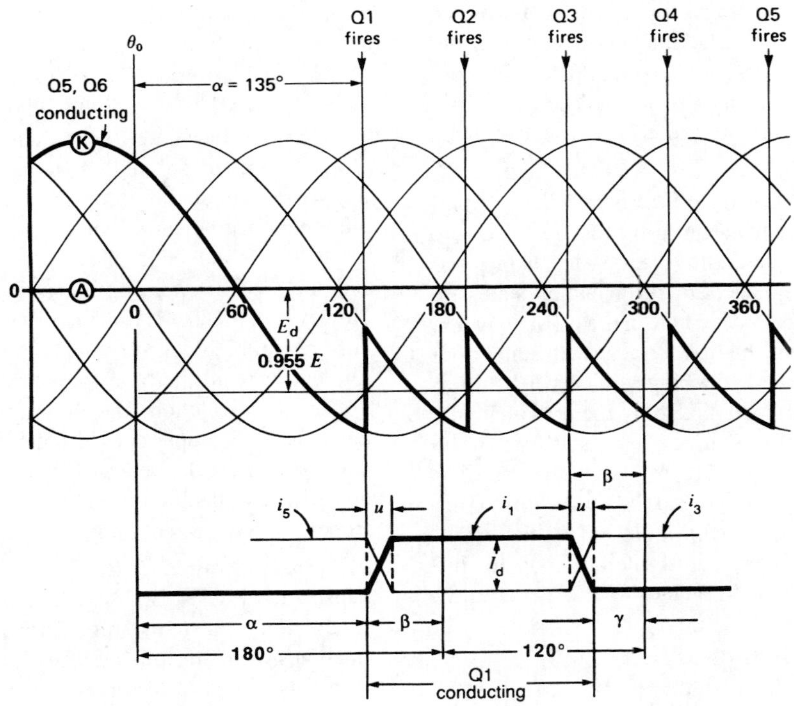

Figure 21.50
Waveshape of i_1 in thyristor Q1 for a delay angle α. The extinction angle γ permits Q1 to establish its blocking ability before the critical angle of 300° is reached. At 300° the anode of Q1 becomes positive with respect to its cathode. The figure also shows the relationship between angles α, β, γ, and *u*.

In the case of an inverter, we often define the firing instant by the *angle of advance* β, rather than by the angle of delay α. From Fig. 21.50 it can be shown that the following relationships exist between the commutation angle *u*, the delay angle α, the angle of advance β, and the extinction angle γ:

$$\beta = 180 - \alpha \qquad (21.15)$$

$$\beta = u + \gamma \qquad (21.16)$$

DC-TO-DC SWITCHING CONVERTERS

21.36 Semiconductor switches

So far we have studied circuits in which the electronic switching is accomplished by thyristors. We saw that one of its shortcomings was that conduction only stopped when the anode current dropped naturally to zero. Although it is possible to force the anode current to zero by special techniques, such as mentioned in Section 21.18, the additional circuit components make this solution cumbersome and expensive. Another problem is that thyristor switching is limited to a maximum of about 2 kHz.

To overcome this problem, special semiconductor switches have been developed whereby conduction can be initiated or blocked by controlling the gate current or gate voltage. These devices are constantly being improved upon, but we will limit our attention to those that are most frequently used. As mentioned in the introduction to this chapter, they are GTOs, bipolar transistors, power MOSFETs, and IGBTs. These controllable on/off switching devices enable us to design dc-to-dc and dc-to-ac converters of extraordinary versatility. The basic principles of these switch-type converters are explained in the ensuing sections.

Thyristor and GTO Basic Characteristics. Apart from their important gate turn-off feature, GTOs are very similar to ordinary thyristors. The characteristics of both these devices in the on and off states are illustrated in Fig. 21.51. Thus, in the off state, when the current is zero the thyristor can withstand both forward and reverse blocking voltages E_{AK}, up to the maximum limits bounded by the cross-hatched bands (Fig. 21.51a). During the on state, when the thyristor conducts, the figure shows that the E_{AK} voltage drop is about 2 V, and the upper limit of the anode current I_{AK} is again indicated by the cross-hatched band. These bands merely indicate the broad-brush maximum values that are currently available. Most thyristors are designed to operate far within the limits shown.

Fig. 21.51b shows that GTOs are able to withstand forward voltages but not reverse blocking voltages. Furthermore, the voltage drop is about 3 V compared to 2 V for thyristors. As in the case of a thyristor, conduction in a GTO is initiated by injecting a positive current pulse into the gate. In order to keep conducting, the anode current must not fall below the *holding current* of the GTO. However, the GTO is a device in which the anode current can be blocked by injecting a strong negative current into the base for a few microseconds. To ensure extinction, the amplitude of the gate pulse has to be about one third the value of the anode current. GTOs are high-power switches, some of which can handle currents of several thousand amperes at voltages of up to 4000 V.

BJT Basic Characteristics. The bipolar junction transistor, or BJT, is designated bipolar because conduction is due to the migration of both electrons and holes within the device. The transistor has three terminals named collector C, emitter E, and base B (Fig. 21.52). The collector current I_C that flows from collector to emitter is initiated and maintained by causing a sustained current I_B to flow into the base. When operated as a switch, the base current must be large enough to drive the BJT into *saturation.* Under these conditions, the voltage E_{CE} between the collector and emitter is about 2 to 3 volts, at rated collector current. Conduction ceases as soon as the base current is suppressed. The characteristics

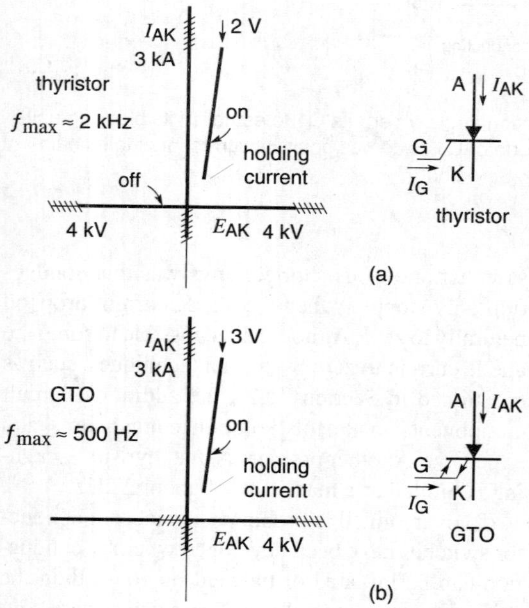

Figure 21.51
Typical properties and approximate limits of GTOs and thyristors in the on and off states.

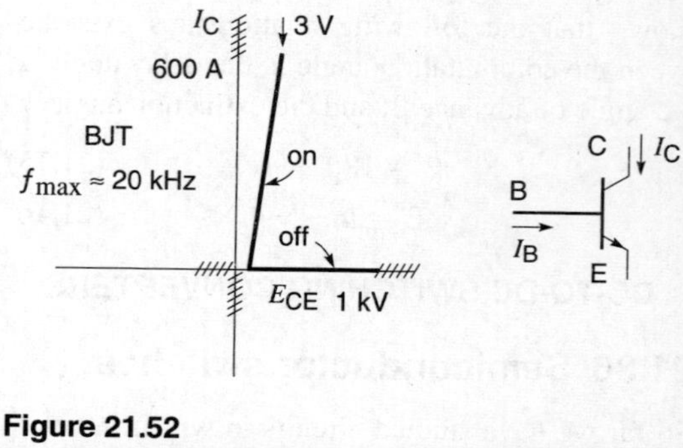

Figure 21.52
Typical properties and approximate limits of BJTs.

of the BJT in the on and off states are shown in Fig. 21.52, together with the approximate limits of the collector-emitter voltage E_{CE} and collector current I_C. Note that the transistor cannot tolerate negative values of E_{CE}. Power transistors can carry currents of several hundred amperes and withstand E_{CE} voltages of about 1 kV. To establish collector currents of 100 A, the corresponding base current is typically about 1 A.

MOSFET Basic Characteristics. The power MOSFET is a voltage-controlled three-terminal device having an anode and cathode, respectively called drain D, source S, and gate G (Fig. 21.53). The drain current I_D is initiated by applying and maintaining a voltage E_{GS} of about 12 V between the gate and the source. Conduction stops whenever E_{GS} falls below a threshold limit (about 1 V). The gate currents are extremely small; consequently, very little power is needed to drive this electronic switch. The characteristics in the on and off states are shown in Fig. 21.53, together with typical maximum limits of drain voltage E_{DS} and drain current I_D. The MOSFET cannot tolerate negative values of E_{DS}. To meet this requirement, it has incorporated within it a reverse-biased diode, as shown in the symbol for the device. Power MOSFETs can carry drain currents of about a hundred amperes and withstand E_{CE} voltages of about 500 V. At rated current, when driven into saturation, the E_{DS} voltage drop ranges from about 2 V to 5 V.

IGBT Basic Characteristics. The IGBT is also a voltage-controlled switch whose terminals are identified the same way as those in a transistor, namely collector, emitter, and base. The characteristics in the on and off states are shown in Fig. 21.54, together with the limiting voltages and current. The collector current in an IGBT is much higher than in a MOSFET. Consequently, the IGBT can handle more power.

Compared to GTOs, an important feature of BJTs, MOSFETs, and IGBTs is their fast turn-on and turn-off times. This enables these switches to be used at much higher frequencies. As a result, the associated transformers, inductors, and capacitors are smaller and cheaper. Typical maximum frequencies are shown in Figs. 21.51 to 21.54. Another advantage of high-speed switching is that the semiconductor switches can generate lower-frequency voltages and currents whose waveshapes and phase can be tailored to meet almost any requirement.

21.37 DC-to-DC switching converter

In some power systems there is a need to transform dc power from one dc voltage level to either a higher or lower dc level. For example, in a public transportation system, a 4000 V dc overhead line may be the source to drive a 300 V dc motor in a bus. In other cases, a 12 V battery may have to power a device rated at 120 V dc. In alternating-current systems the voltage step-up or step-down can easily be done with a transformer. But in dc

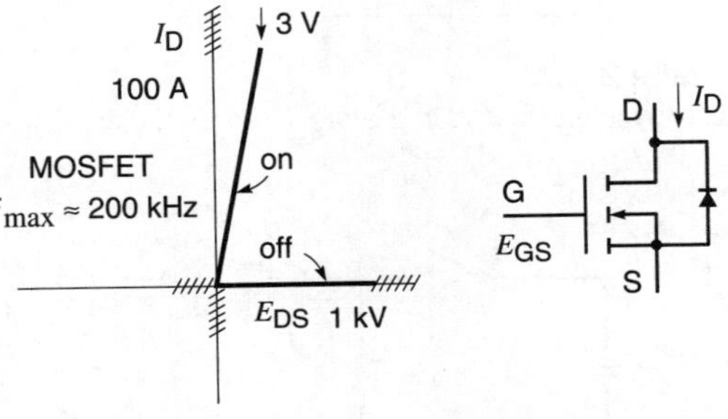

Figure 21.53
Typical properties and approximate limits of MOSFETs.

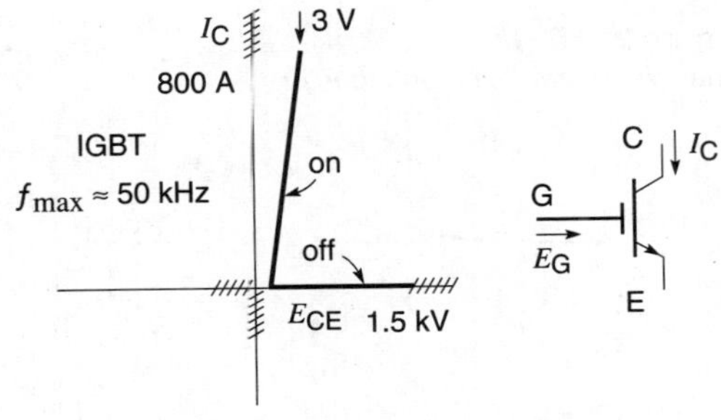

Figure 21.54
Typical properties and approximate limits of IGBTs.

systems, an entirely different approach is required. It involves the use of a dc-to-dc switching converter, sometimes called a *chopper.*

Suppose that power has to be transferred from a high-voltage dc source E_S to a lower-voltage dc load E_0. One solution is to connect an inductor between the source and the load and to open and close the circuit periodically with a switch (Fig. 21.55). In order to follow the transfer of energy, assume the switch closes for a time T_1. During this interval, the voltage across the inductor is $E_S - E_0$, with polarities as shown in Fig. 21.56. The inductor accumulates volt-seconds, and the resulting current i increases at a constant rate given by

$$i = \frac{(E_S - E_0)\,t}{L}$$

After a time T_1 (when i has reached a value I_a, say, and the switch is about to open), the current is

$$I_a = (E_S - E_0)\,T_1/L \qquad (21.17)$$

The corresponding magnetic energy stored in the inductor is

$$W = \frac{1}{2}LI_a^2 \qquad (2.8)$$

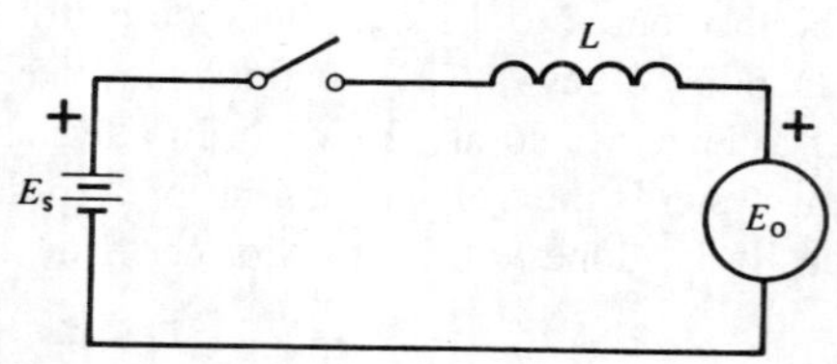

Figure 21.55
Energy transfer using an inductor.

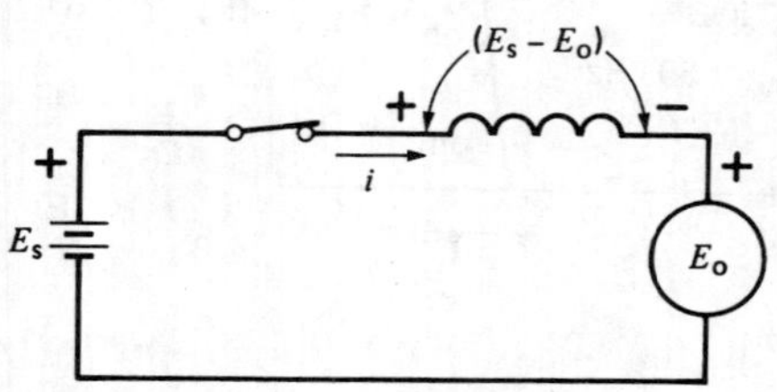

Figure 21.56
Energy is stored in the inductor.

When the switch opens (Fig. 21.57) the current collapses and all the stored energy is dissipated in the arc across the switch. At the same time, a high voltage e_L is induced across the inductor because the current is collapsing so quickly. The polarity of this voltage is *opposite* to what it was when the current was increasing (compare Figs. 21.56 and 21.57). The high negative voltage indicates that the inductor is rapidly discharging the volt-seconds it had previously accumulated. As a result, the current decreases very quickly.

Although some energy is transferred from the source E_S to the load E_0 while the switch is closed, there is a great loss of energy every time the switch opens. The efficiency is therefore poor.

We can prevent this energy loss by adding a diode to the circuit as shown in Fig. 21.58. When the switch closes, the current rises to I_a as before. The diode has no effect because its cathode is positive with respect to the anode and so the diode does not conduct. When the switch opens, current i again begins to fall, inducing a voltage e_L. However, e_L cannot jump to the high value it reached before because as soon as it exceeds E_0, the anode of the diode becomes positive and so the diode begins to conduct. Assuming the

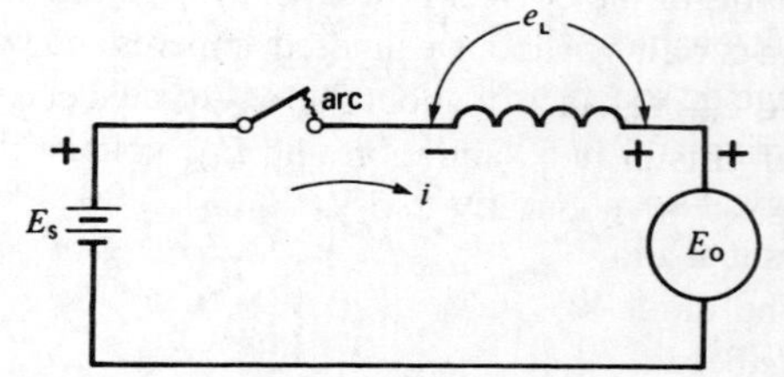

Figure 21.57
Energy is dissipated in the arc. Note the polarity of e_L.

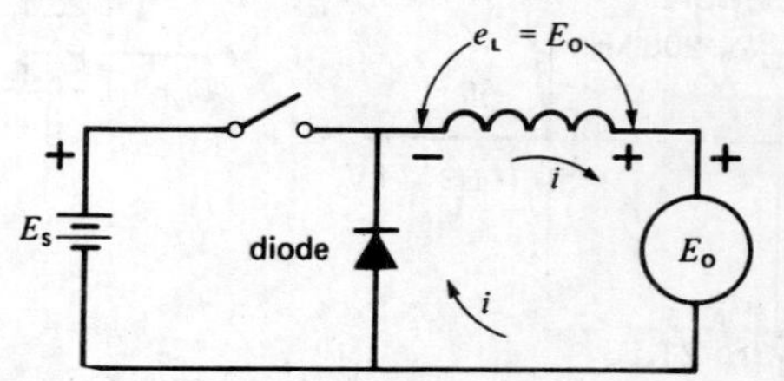

Figure 21.58
Energy transferred without loss.

diode voltage drop is negligible, it follows that $e_L = E_0$. Because E_0 is constant, the voltage across the inductor is also constant. Starting from I_a, current i therefore falls at a uniform rate given by

$$i = I_a - \frac{E_0 t}{L} \tag{2.28}$$

The current eventually becomes zero after a time T_2. We can calculate T_2 because the volt-seconds accumulated during the charging period T_1 must equal the volt-seconds released during the discharge interval T_2. Referring to Fig. 21.59, we have

V·s during charge period = V·s during discharge period

$$A_{(+)} = A_{(-)}$$

$$(E_S - E_0)\,T_1 = E_0 T_2$$

Consequently,

$$T_2 = \frac{(E_S - E_0)\,T_1}{E_0} \tag{21.18}$$

When the current is zero, the inductor will have delivered all its stored energy to load E_0. Simultaneously, the diode will cease to conduct. We can therefore reclose the switch for another interval T_1 and repeat the cycle indefinitely. Consequently, this circuit enables us to transfer energy from a high-voltage dc source to a lower-voltage dc load without incurring any losses. In effect, the inductor absorbs energy at a relatively high voltage $(E_S - E_0)$ and delivers it at a lower voltage E_0.

The diode is sometimes called a *freewheeling diode* because it automatically starts conducting as soon as the switch opens and stops conducting when the switch closes.

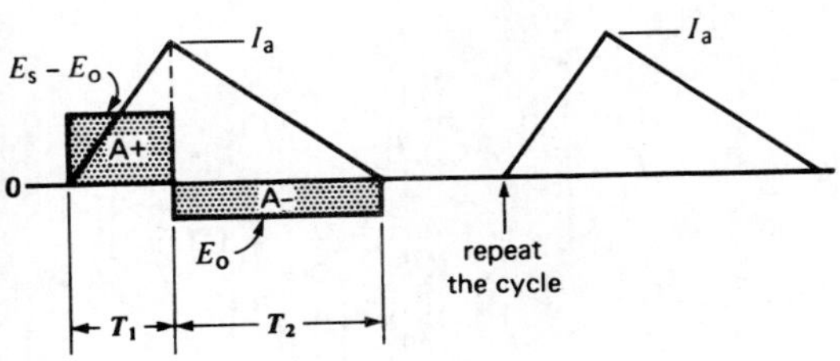

Figure 21.59
E and *I* in the inductor of Fig. 21.58.

The switch is actually a GTO, MOSFET, or IGBT, whose on/off state is controlled by a signal applied to the gate. The combination of the electronic switch, inductor, and diode constitutes what is known as a step-down dc-to-dc converter, or *buck chopper.*

21.38 Rapid switching

Instead of letting the load current swing between zero and I_a, we can close the switch for a short period T_1 (as in Fig. 21.59) until the current reaches the desired value I_a. We then open and close the switch rapidly so that the current increases and decreases by small increments. Referring to Fig. 21.60a, the switch is closed for an interval T_a and open during an interval T_b. When the switch is open, the load current falls from its peak value I_a to a lower value I_b. During this interval, current flows in the inductor, the load, and the freewheeling diode. The current decreases at the same rate as it did in Fig. 21.59.

When the current has fallen to a value I_b, the switch recloses. Because the cathode of the diode is now (+), the current in the diode immediately stops flowing, and the source now supplies current I_b. The current then builds up and when it reaches the value I_a (after a time T_a), the switch reopens. The freewheeling diode again comes into play and the cycle repeats. The current supplied to the load fluctuates therefore between I_a and the slightly lower value I_b (Fig. 21.60b). Its average or dc value I_0 is nearly equal to I_a, but the exact value is given by

$$I_0 = (I_a + I_b)/2 \tag{21.19}$$

Whereas the current in the load is essentially constant, having only a small ripple (Fig. 21.60b), the current supplied by the source is composed of a series of sharp pulses, as shown in Fig. 21.60c. What is the average value of these pulses? It is found by noting that the average current during each *pulse* (duration T_a) is $(I_a + I_b)/2 = I_0$. Consequently, the average current I_S during one *cycle* (time T) is

$$I_S = I_0\,(T_a/T)$$

that is

$$I_S = I_0\,D \tag{21.20}$$

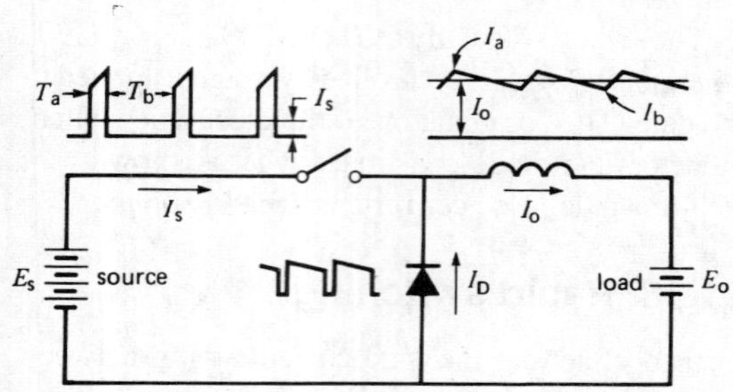

Figure 21.60a
Currents in a chopper circuit.

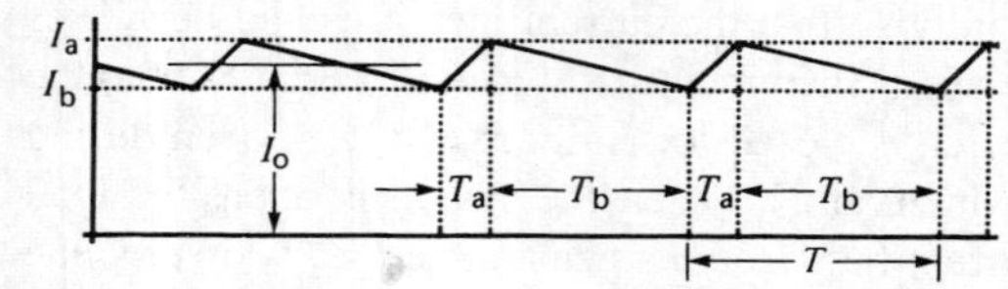

Figure 21.60b
Current in the load.

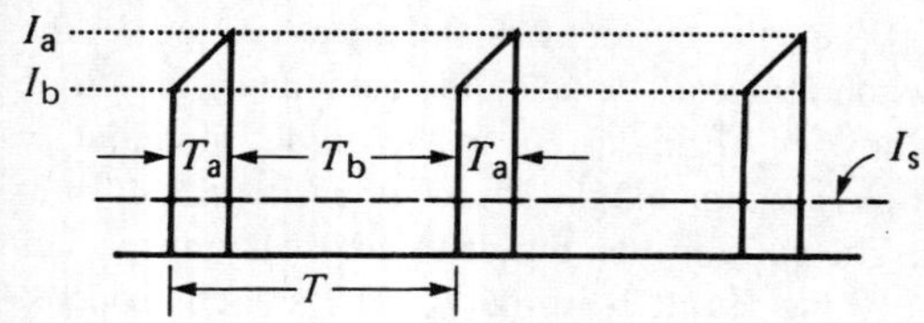

Figure 21.60c
Current pulses provided by the source.

where

I_S = dc current drawn from the source [A]
I_0 = dc current absorbed by the load [A]
T_a = *on* time of the switch [s]
T = period of one cycle [s]
D = duty cycle = T_a/T

The circuit of Fig. 21.60a shows the current waveshapes in the source, the load, and the diode. Although the waveshapes are choppy and discontinuous, they still obey Kirchhoff's current law, instant by instant.

Turning our attention to the power aspects, the dc power drawn from the source must equal the dc power absorbed by the load because, ideally, there is no power loss in the switch, the inductor, or the freewheeling diode. We can, therefore, write

$$E_S I_S = E_0 I_0$$

If we substitute Eq. 21.20 in the above equation, we obtain

$$E_0 = E_S \frac{I_S}{I_0} = E_S \frac{T_a}{T}$$

which gives the important relationship

$$E_0 = DE_S \tag{21.21}$$

where

E_0 = dc output voltage of the converter [V]
E_S = dc voltage of the source [V]
D = duty cycle

Eq. 21.21 signifies that the dc output voltage E_0 can be controlled simply by varying the duty cycle D. Thus, the converter behaves like a highly efficient dc transformer in which the "turns ratio" is D. For a given switching frequency, this ratio can be changed as needed by varying the *on* time T_a of the switch.

In practice, the mechanical switch is replaced by an electronic switch, such as an IGBT. It can be turned on and off at a frequency that may be as high as 50 kHz. If more power is required, a GTO is used, wherein the frequency could be of the order of 300 Hz.

Example 21-10

The switch in Fig. 21.60a opens and closes at a frequency of 20 Hz and remains closed for 3 ms per cycle. A dc ammeter connected in series with the load E_0 indicates a current of 70 A.

a. If a dc ammeter is connected in series with the source, what current will it indicate?
b. What is the average current per pulse?

Solution

a. Using Eq. 21.20, we have

$$\text{period } T = \frac{1}{20} = 50 \text{ ms}$$

$$\text{duty cycle} = \frac{T_a}{T} = \frac{3}{50} = 0.06$$

$$I_S = I_0 D$$
$$= 70 \times 0.06$$
$$= 4.2 \text{ A}$$

b. The average current during each *pulse* (duration T_a) is 70 A. Considering that the average current is only 4.2 A, the source has to be specially designed to supply such a high 70 A pulse. In most cases a large capacitor is connected across the terminals of the source. It can readily furnish the high current pulses as it discharges.

Example 21-11

We wish to charge a 120 V battery from a 600 V dc source using a dc chopper. The average battery current should be 20 A, with a peak-to-peak ripple of 2 A. If the chopper frequency is 200 Hz, calculate the following:

a. The dc current drawn from the source
b. The dc current in the diode
c. The duty cycle
d. The inductance of the inductor

Solution

The circuit diagram is shown in Fig. 21.61a and the desired battery current is given in Fig. 21.61b. It fluctuates between 19 A and 21 A, thus yielding an average of 20 A with a peak-to-peak ripple of 2 A.

a. The power supplied to the battery is

$$P = 120 \text{ V} \times 20 \text{ A} = 2400 \text{ W}$$

The power supplied by the source is, therefore, 2400 W.
The dc current from the source is

$$I_S = P/E_S = 2400/600 = 4 \text{ A}$$

b. To calculate the average current in the diode, we refer to Fig. 21.61a. Current I_0 is 20 A and I_S was found to be 4 A. By applying Kirchhoff's current law to the diode/inductor junction, the average diode current I_D is

$$I_D = I_0 - I_S = 20 - 4 = 16 \text{ A}$$

c. The duty cycle is

$$D = E_0/E_S = 120/600 = 0.2$$
$$T = 1/f = 1/200 = 5 \text{ ms}$$

Consequently, the *on* time T_a is

$$T_a = DT = 0.2 \times 5 \text{ ms} = 1 \text{ ms}$$

The waveshapes of I_S and I_D are shown in Figs. 21.61c and 21.61d, respectively. Note the sharp pulses delivered by the source.

d. During interval T_a the average voltage across the inductor is $(600 - 120) = 480$ V.
The volt-seconds accumulated by the inductor during this interval is $A_{(+)} = 480 \text{ V} \times 1 \text{ ms} = 480 \text{ mV·s} = 0.48 \text{ V·s}$. The change in current during the interval is 2 A; consequently,

$$\Delta I = A_{(+)}/L \quad (2.28)$$
$$2 = 0.48/L$$
$$L = 0.24 \text{ H}$$

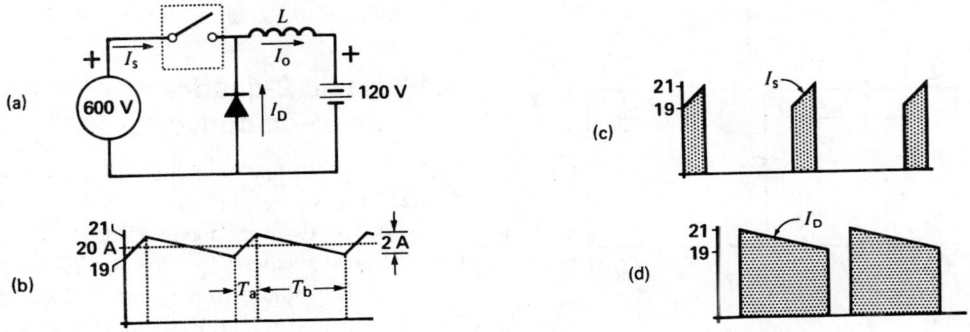

Figure 21.61
a. Circuit of Example 21-11.
b. Current in the load.
c. Current drawn from the source.
d. Current in the freewheeling diode.

Thus, the inductor should have an inductance of 0.24 H. If a larger inductance were used, the current ripple would be smaller, but the dc voltages and currents would remain the same.

21.39 Impedance transformation

So far, we have assumed that the converter feeds power to an active load E_0. However, it may also be used to connect a higher-voltage dc source E_S to a lower-voltage load resistor R_0 (Fig. 21.62). Eqs. 21.20 and 21.21 still apply, but we now have the additional relationship $E_0 = I_0R_0$. Furthermore, the apparent resistance R_S across the terminals of the source is given by

$$R_S = E_S/I_S$$

We can therefore write

$$R_S = E_S/I_S$$

$$= \frac{E_0/D}{I_0D}$$

$$= \frac{E_0}{I_0D^2}$$

$$\therefore R_S = \frac{R_0}{D^2} \qquad (21.22)$$

where

R_S = apparent resistance across the source [Ω]
R_0 = actual load resistance [Ω]
D = duty cycle

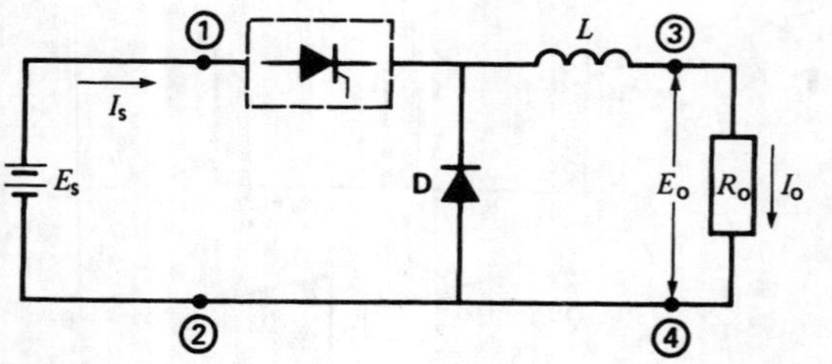

Figure 21.62
A chopper can make a fixed resistor R_o appear as a variable resistance between terminals 1-2.

The converter, therefore, has the ability to transform the resistance of a fixed resistor to a higher value whose magnitude depends upon the duty cycle. Thus, the chopper again behaves like a dc transformer in which the turns ratio is D.

Example 21-12

The chopper in Fig. 21.62 operates at a frequency of 4 kHz and the *on* time is 20 μs. Calculate the apparent resistance across the source, knowing that R_0 = 12 Ω.

Solution

The duty cycle is

$$D = T_a/T = T_af = 20 \times 10^{-6} \times 4000 = 0.08$$

Applying Eq. 21.22, we have

$$R_S = R_0/D^2$$

$$= 12/(0.08)^2$$

$$= 1875\ \Omega$$

This example shows that the actual value of a resistor can be increased many times by using a chopper. Although a chopper can be compared to a transformer, there is an important difference between the two. The reason is that a transformer permits power flow in both directions—from the high-voltage side to the low-voltage side or vice versa. The step-down chopper we have just studied can transfer power only from the high-voltage side to the low-voltage side. Because power flow in both directions is often required, we now examine a dc-to-dc converter that achieves this result.

21.40 Basic 2-quadrant dc-to-dc converter

Consider Fig. 21.63a in which two *mechanical* switches S1 to S2 are connected across a dc voltage source E_H. The switches open and close alternately in such a way that when S1 is closed, S2 is open and vice versa. The time of one cycle is T, and S1 is closed for a period T_a. It follows that the duty cycle of S1 is $D = T_a/T$, while that of S2 is $(1 - D)$. When S1 is closed, terminal 1 is at the level of point **3** and

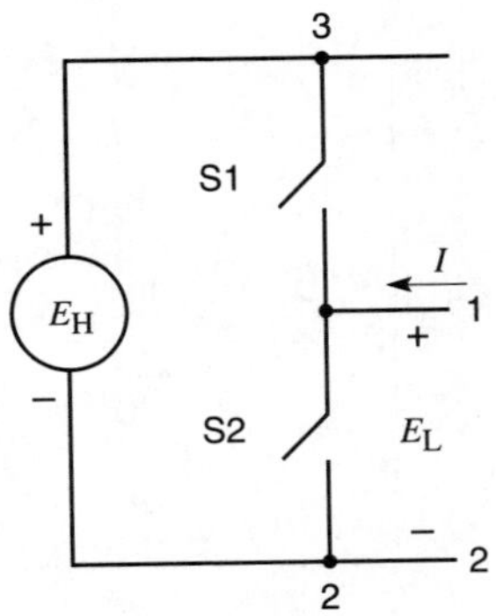

Figure 21.63a
Two-quadrant dc-to-dc converter.

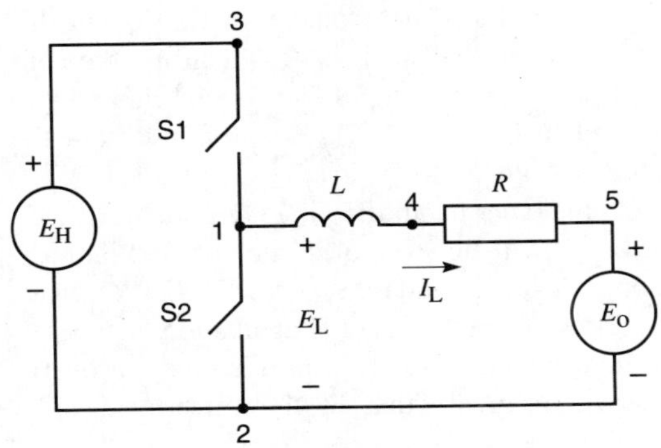

Figure 21.64
Power can flow from E_H to E_o and vice versa.

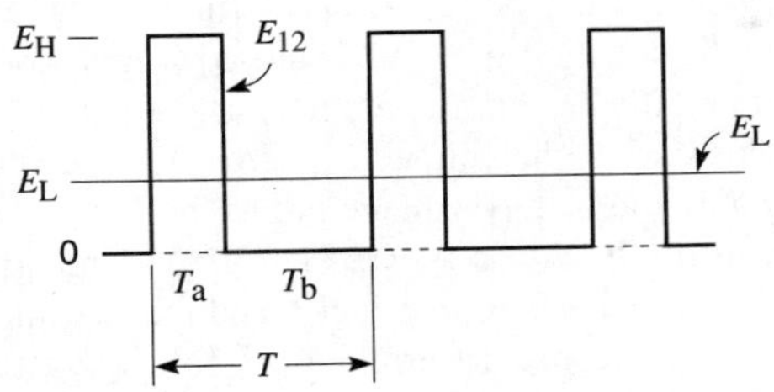

Figure 21.63b
Waveshape of E_{12} and average value E_L.

so the output voltage is $E_{12} = E_H$ for a period T_a. Then, when S1 is open, S2 is closed and so $E_{12} = 0$ for a period T_b. The output voltage oscillates, therefore, between E_H and zero (Fig. 21.63b) and its *average* dc value E_1 is given by Eq. 21.21

$$E_L = DE_H \tag{21.21}$$

By varying D from zero to 1, we can vary the magnitude of E_L from zero to E_H.

In examining Fig. 21.63a, it is apparent that the circuit on the left-hand side of terminals 1, 2 is never open. For example, if current I happens to flow into terminal 1, it can find its way back to terminal 2 either via S2 (if S2 is closed) or via S1 and source E_H if S2 is open. Because one of the switches is always closed, it is evident that current I can always circulate, no matter what its direction happens to be. This is a crucially important feature of the converter. It is called a *two-quadrant converter* because current I can flow in either direction, but the polarity of the dc voltage E_L remains fixed. In effect, owing to the polarity of E_H, terminal 1 is always (+) with respect to terminal 2.

Suppose we want to transfer dc power from terminals E_{12} to a load such as a battery, whose dc voltage E_{52} has a value E_0 (Fig. 21.64). Knowing that E_{12} is fluctuating while E_0 is constant, it is essential to place a buffer between the two, otherwise short-circuit currents will result. We could place a resistor between points **1** and **5,** but that would involve I^2R losses which would reduce the efficiency of the converter. The best solution is to use an inductance L as shown in Fig. 21.64. It has the advantage of opposing ac current flow while offering no opposition to dc. We assume that the load has a small internal resistance R.

Suppose that both the voltage source E_H and the duty cycle D are fixed. Consequently, the dc component E_L between points **1** and **2** is constant. If E_0 is exactly equal to E_L, no dc current will flow and no dc power exchange will take place. But if E_0 is less than E_L, a dc current I_L will flow from terminal 1 into terminal 5. Its magnitude is given by

$$I_L = (E_L - E_0)/R \tag{21.23}$$

Power equal to $E_L I_L$ will therefore flow from terminals 1, 2 toward the battery. This dc power can only come from the higher voltage source E_H. In this mode of operation, with E_0 less than E_L, the converter acts like the step-down (buck) chopper we covered in Section 21.37. Power flows from the higher voltage E_H to the lower voltage E_0.

On the other hand, if E_0 is *greater* than E_L, a dc current I_L will flow out of terminal 5 and into terminal 1. Its magnitude is $I_L = (E_0 - E_L)/R$. Power now flows from the low-voltage battery side E_0 to the higher voltage side E_H. In this mode of operation, with E_0 greater than E_L, the converter acts like a step-up (boost) chopper.

The mechanical switching system of Fig. 21.63a is therefore able to transfer dc power in both directions—from high-voltage side to low-voltage side or vice versa. Again, because the current can reverse while the polarity of E_L remains the same, this buck/boost converter operates in two quadrants.

Let us now examine the behavior of the converter more closely, by means of an example.

Example 21-13

The following data is given on a buck/boost converter (Fig. 21.65):

$$E_H = 100 \text{ V} \quad E_0 = 30 \text{ V} \quad R = 2\ \Omega \quad L = 10 \text{ mH}$$

switching frequency = 20 kHz with a duty cycle D of 0.2 for S1.

Determine the following:

a. The value and direction of the dc current I_L
b. The peak-to-peak ripple superposed on the dc current

Solution

Referring to Fig. 21.65, the value of $E_L = DE_H = 0.2 \times 100 \text{ V} = 20 \text{ V}$.

Because the battery voltage is greater than E_L, current I_L flows out of terminal 5 and into terminal 1. Its average value is

$$I_L = (30 \text{ V} - 20 \text{ V})/2\ \Omega = 5 \text{ A}$$

The duration of one cycle is

$$T = 1/f = 1/20\,000 = 50\ \mu\text{s}$$

Thus, S1 is closed for a time $T_a = 0.2 \times 50\ \mu\text{s} = 10\ \mu\text{s}$ and S2 is closed for 40 μs.

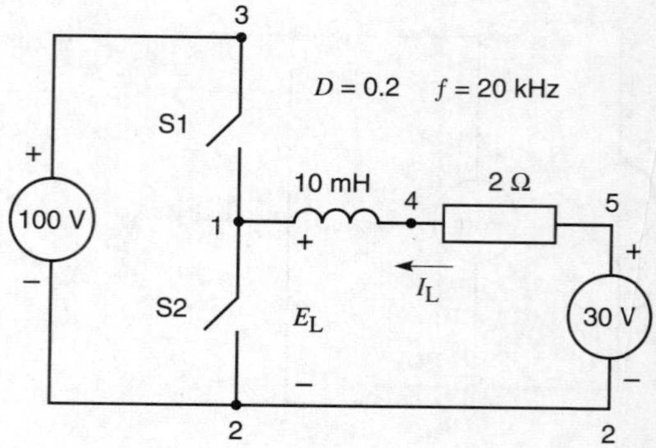

Figure 21.65
Circuit of Example 21-13.

To determine the peak-to-peak ripple, let us examine the situation when S2 is closed (Fig. 21.66). Assuming the current i is momentarily equal to its dc value of 5 A, the voltage E_{41} across the inductor is equal to the battery voltage minus the IR drop in the resistor: $30 \text{ V} - 5 \text{ A} \times 2\ \Omega = 20 \text{ V}$. Knowing that I_L is flowing into terminal 4 and that terminal 4 is (+) with respect to terminal 1, it follows that I_L must be increasing. The inductor accumulates volt-seconds and during the 40 μs that S2 is closed, the magnetic "charge" totals $20 \text{ V} \times 40\ \mu\text{s} = 800 \text{ V}\cdot\mu\text{s}$. Therefore the current increases by an amount $\Delta I = 800 \text{ V}\cdot\mu\text{s}/10 \text{ mH} = 0.08 \text{ A}$.

Let us now see what happens when S1 is closed and i is again momentarily 5 A (Fig. 21.67). The

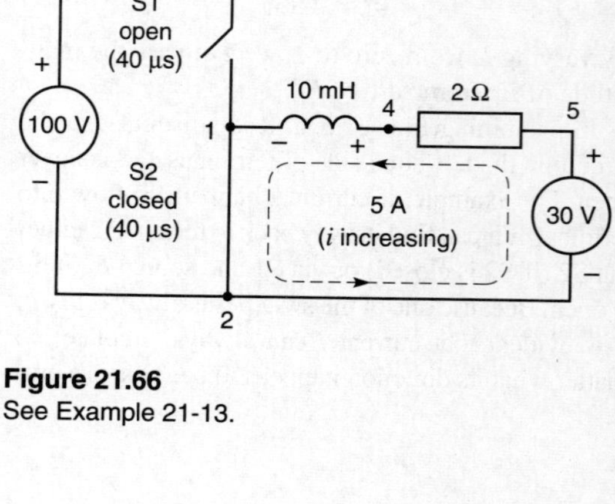

Figure 21.66
See Example 21-13.

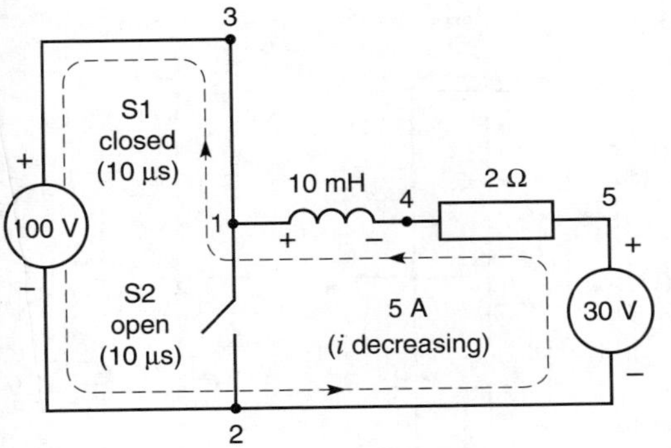

Figure 21.67
See Example 21-13.

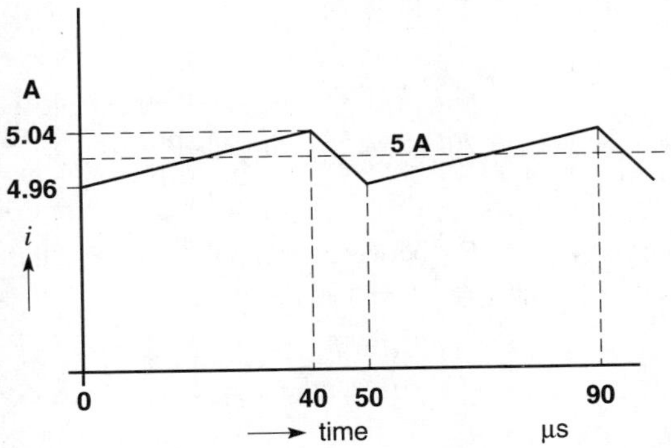

Figure 21.68
See Example 21-13.

voltage across the inductor is now 100 V − (30 − 10) V = 80 V, but terminal 4 is *negative* with respect to terminal 1. The current *i* is therefore decreasing. The volt-seconds discharged during the 10 μs interval is 80 V × 10 μs = 800 V·μs. The change in current is Δ*I* = 800 V·μs/10 mH = 0.08 A.

We observe that the decrease in current when S1 is closed is the same as the previous increase when S1 was open. Consequently, the peak-to-peak ripple is 0.08 A. The dc current fluctuates between 5.04 A and 4.96 A (Fig. 21.68). Direct-current power flows from the lower voltage battery toward the higher voltage source. The converter is said to function in the boost mode.

Note that if the duty cycle were raised to 0.45, the value of E_L would increase to 100 × 0.45 = 45 V. The current flowing into the battery would reverse and its value would become

$$(45\ \text{V} - 30\ \text{V})/2\ \Omega = 7.5\ \text{A}$$

Direct-current power now flows from the 100 V source toward the battery, causing the latter to charge up. Under these conditions, the converter is said to operate in the *buck* mode. Thus, the transition from boost to buck can be effected very smoothly by simply varying the duty cycle. Fig. 21.65 can be considered to be the mechanical equivalent of a buck/boost chopper.

21.41 Two-quadrant electronic converter

Figs. 21.66 and 21.67 show the direction of current flow in the case of a boost converter. If the converter operated in the buck mode, the currents would follow the same paths but in the opposite direction. With mechanical switches this creates no problem because they can carry current in either direction. But in the real world we have to deal with electronic switches, which inherently carry current in only one direction. Therefore, in order to get bidirectionality, diodes have to be placed in antiparallel with the respective semiconductor switches Q1 and Q2 (Fig. 21.69). The switch contacts are shown with an arrowhead to indicate the allowed direction of current flow. For example, when current flows into terminal 1, it can continue on to terminal 2 either by way of diode D1 and source E_H or by way of Q2, provided Q2 is closed.

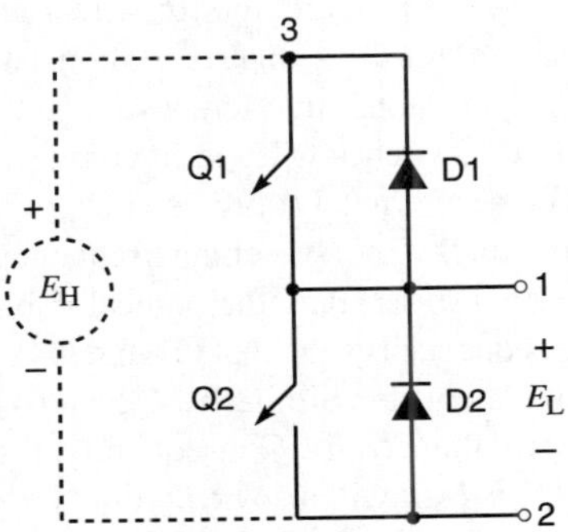

Figure 21.69
Two-quadrant electronic converter.

Similarly if current flows out of terminal 1, it can take the path through diode D2 or the path through Q1 and E_H, provided that Q1 is closed.

In this figure, Q1 and D1 together perform the same way as the mechanical switch S1. Similarly, Q2 and D2 together perform the same way as mechanical switch S2. Fig. 21.69 therefore represents the essence of a 2-quadrant electronic converter. If a dc voltage E_H is applied between terminals 3 and 2, the converter generates a dc voltage E_L between terminals 1 and 2 and the relationship is again $E_L = DE_H$, where D is the duty cycle of Q1.

It is important to note that Q1 and Q2 cannot be closed at the same time, otherwise a short-circuit will result across source E_H. Thus, for a very brief period, called *dead time,* both switches must be open. The current is carried by one of the two diodes during this instant.

Power can be made to flow from the higher voltage side to the lower voltage side or vice versa. The power transported in one direction or the other depends upon the respective voltages and the duty cycle. The 2-quadrant converter of Fig. 21.69 is the basic building block for most switch-mode converters.

21.42 Four-quadrant dc-to-dc converter

The 2-quadrant converter we have studied can only be used with a load whose voltage has a specific polarity. Thus, in Fig. 21.69, given the polarity of E_H, terminal 1 can only be (+) with respect to terminal 2. We can overcome this restriction by means of a *4-quadrant converter.* It consists of two identical 2-quadrant converters arranged as shown in Fig. 21.70. Switches Q1, Q2 in converter arm A open and close alternately, as do switches Q3, Q4 in converter arm B. The switching frequency f_c (assumed to be 100 kHz) is the same for both. The switching sequence is such that Q1 and Q4 open and close simultaneously. Similarly, Q2 and Q3 open and close simultaneously. Consequently, if the duty cycle for Q1 is *D,* it will also be *D* for Q4. It follows that the duty cycle for Q2 and Q3 is $(1 - D)$.

The dc voltage E_A appearing between terminals A, 2 is given by

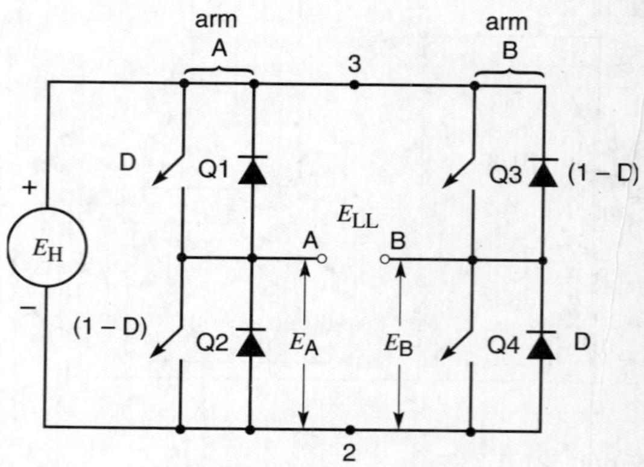

Figure 21.70
Four-quadrant dc-to-dc converter.

$$E_A = DE_H$$

The dc voltage E_B between terminals B, 2 is

$$E_B = (1 - D)E_H$$

The dc voltage E_{LL} between terminals A and B is the difference between E_A and E_B:

$$\begin{aligned} E_{LL} &= E_A - E_B \\ &= DE_H - (1 - D)E_H \end{aligned}$$

thus

$$E_{LL} = E_H\,(2\,D - 1) \tag{21.24}$$

Eq. 21.24 indicates that the dc voltage is zero when $D = 0.5$. Furthermore, the voltage changes linearly with *D,* becoming $+E_H$ when $D = 1$, and $-E_H$ when $D = 0$. The polarity of the output voltage can therefore be either positive or negative. Moreover, if a device is connected between terminals A, B, the direction of dc current flow can be either from A to B or from B to A. Consequently, the converter of Fig. 21.70 can function in all four quadrants.

The *instantaneous* voltages E_{A2} and E_{B2} oscillate rapidly between zero and $+E_H$. Fig. 21.71 shows the respective waveshapes when $D = 0.5$. Similarly, Fig. 21.72 shows the waveshapes when $D = 0.8$. Note that the instantaneous voltage E_{AB} between the output terminals A, B oscillates between $+E_H$ and $-E_H$. In practice, the high frequency alternating

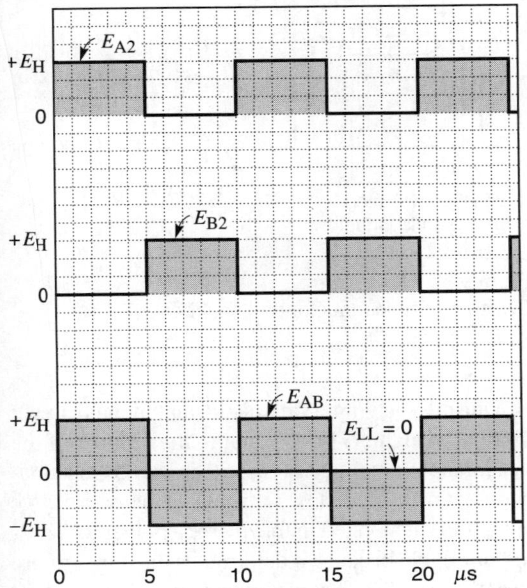

Figure 21.71
Voltage output when $D = 0.5$. The average voltage is zero. The period of one cycle is 10 microseconds.

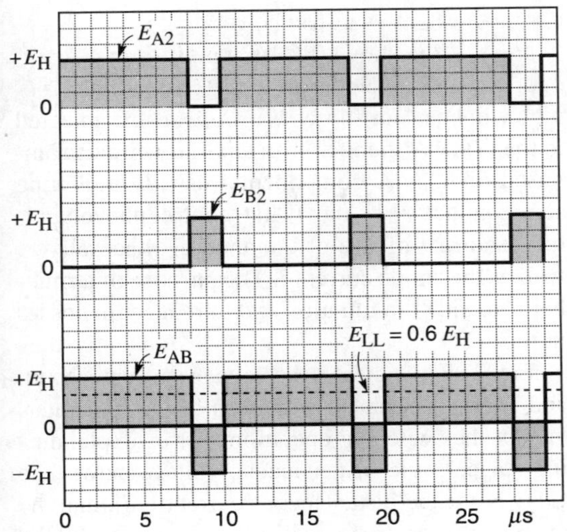

Figure 21.72
Voltage output when $D = 0.8$. The average voltage E_{LL} is 0.6 E_H.

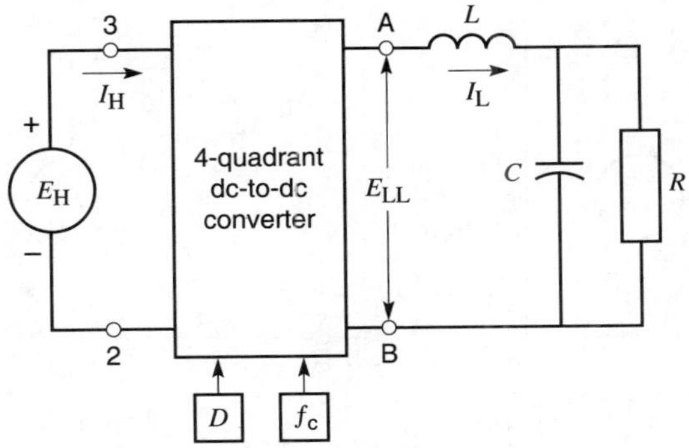

Figure 21.73
Four-quadrant dc-to-dc converter feeding a passive dc load *R*.

components that appear between terminals A, B are filtered out. Consequently, only the dc component E_{LL} remains as the active driving emf across the external device connected to terminals A, B.

Consider, for example, the block diagram of a converter feeding dc power to a passive load *R* (Fig. 21.73). The power is provided by source E_H. As we have seen, the magnitude and polarity of E_{LL} can be varied by changing the duty cycle *D*. The switching frequency f_c of several kilohertz is assumed to be constant. Inductor *L* and capacitor *C* act as filters so that the dc current flowing in the resistance has negligible ripple. Because the switching frequency is high, the inductance and capacitance can be small, thus making for inexpensive filter components.

The dc currents and voltages are related by the power-balance equation $E_H I_H = E_{LL} I_L$. We neglect the switching losses and the small control power associated with the *D* and f_c input signals.

Fig. 21.74 shows the converter connected to an active device E_0, which could be either a source or a load. If need be, the polarity of E_0 could be the reverse of that shown.

In all these applications we can force power to flow from E_H to E_0, or vice versa, by simply adjusting the duty cycle *D*. This 4-quadrant dc-to-dc converter is therefore an extremely versatile device.

The inductor *L* is a crucially important part of the converter. It alone is able to absorb energy at one

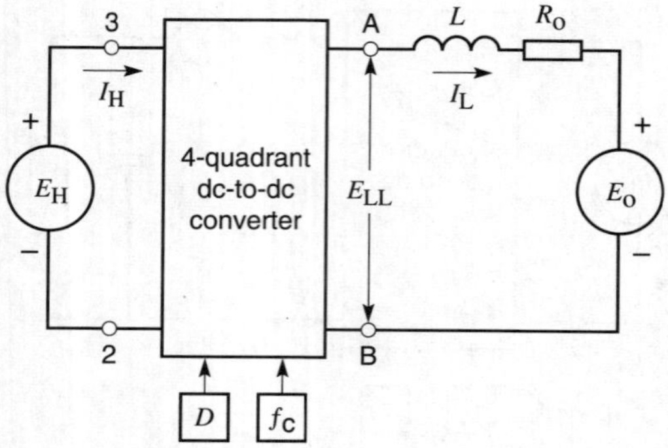

Figure 21.74
Four-quadrant dc-to-dc converter feeding an active dc source/sink E_o.

voltage level (high or low) and release it at another voltage level (low or high). And it performs this duty automatically, in response to the electronic switches and their duty cycle.

21.43 Switching losses

All semiconductor switches (or valves) such as GTOs, MOSFETs, and IGBTs have losses that affect their temperature rise and switching efficiency. The switches all function essentially the same way, but to focus our analysis we assume the switching device is a GTO. The switching operation involves four brief intervals:

1. *Turn-on time T_1:* The current in the GTO is rapidly increasing while the voltage across it is rapidly decreasing.
2. *On-state time T_2:* The current has reached a stable value I_T, and the voltage V_T across the GTO is about 2 to 3 volts.
3. *Turn-off time T_3:* The current in the GTO is rapidly falling while the voltage across it is rapidly increasing.
4. *Off-state time T_4:* The current in the GTO is zero while the forward voltage is relatively high.

The sum of $T_1 + T_2 + T_3 + T_4$ is equal to the period T of one cycle which, in turn, is equal to $1/f_c$ where f_c is the switching frequency.

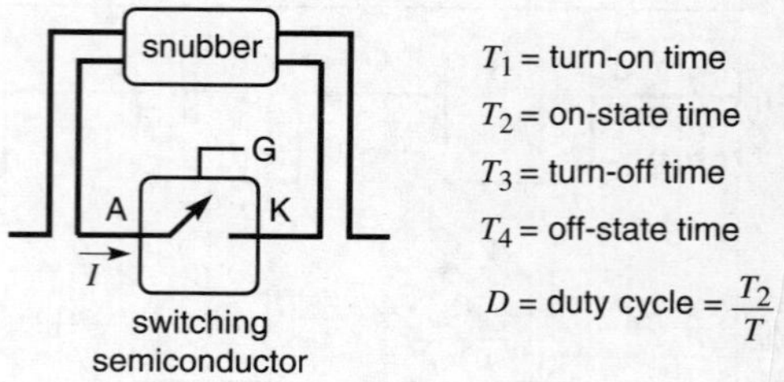

Figure 21.75a
Switching semiconductor and snubber.

During each interval the instantaneous power dissipated in the GTO is equal to the product of the instantaneous voltage across it times the instantaneous current that flows through it. However, we are mainly interested in the *average* power loss during one cycle because it determines the temperature rise of the GTO. The average power is equal to the energy dissipated in the GTO during one complete cycle, divided by T.

It so happens that the voltage across the GTO is substantial during the turn-on and turn-off periods, being far greater than the on-state voltage drop of 2 to 3 volts. As a result, the instantaneous power loss during these intervals can be very high.

Fig. 21.75a shows a GTO with its anode, cathode, and gate. In addition to the circuit that is being switched (not shown), a *snubber* is connected to the GTO. A snubber is an auxiliary circuit composed of *R, L, C* components (usually including semiconductor devices) that control the magnitude and rate of rise of the anode voltage E_{AK} as well as the anode current I. The purpose of a snubber is to aid commutation and to reduce the losses in the GTO.

Fig. 21.75b indicates the voltage, current, power, and energy associated with each of the four intervals of the switching operation. For example, during stage T_1 the instantaneous voltage across the GTO is V_1, the instantaneous current is I_1, and the average power dissipated is P_1. Consequently, the energy dissipated during this stage is P_1T_1 joules. On the other hand, the energy dissipated during interval T_4 is zero because the current is nil.

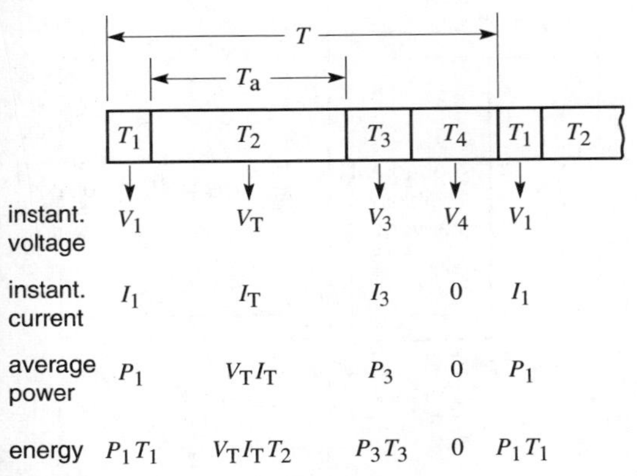

Figure 21.75b
Four stages of a GTO switching operation.

The total energy dissipated in the form of heat during one cycle is therefore given by

$$\text{energy} = P_1T_1 + V_TI_TT_2 + P_3T_3 \quad (21.25)$$

The on-time T_a, mentioned earlier, is equal to T_2. It is also related to T by the expression $T_a = DT$, where D is the duty cycle. We can, therefore, write

$$T_2 = DT$$

Substituting in Eq. 21.25, we obtain

$$\text{energy dissipated} = P_1T_1 + V_TI_TDT + P_3T_3 \quad (21.26)$$

The total power dissipated in the GTO is this energy divided by T

$$\text{power loss} = \frac{P_1T_1 + V_TI_T\,DT + P_3T_3}{T}$$

Recognizing that $T = 1/f_c$, we get

$$\text{power loss} = P_1T_1f_c + V_TI_TD + P_3T_3f_c \quad (21.27)$$

Eq. 21.27 reveals the factors that determine the power dissipated in the GTO and its consequent temperature rise. It can be seen that the dissipation increases with the switching frequency f_c and the duty cycle D. The equation also indicates that the dissipation can be reduced if the turn-on and turn-off times are shorter. That is one of the advantages offered by MOSFETs and IGBTs, whose brief turn-on and turn-off times (T_1 and T_3) permit them to operate at much higher switching frequencies than GTOs.

In addition to the anode-cathode losses, we must not overlook the losses (albeit much smaller) associated with the gate voltages and currents. They are not covered here.

DC-TO-AC SWITCHING CONVERTERS

We have studied the 2-quadrant and 4-quadrant dc-to-dc switching converters. In this section we will examine the same 4-quadrant converter as a dc-to-ac converter.

21.44 Dc-to-AC rectangular wave converter

Referring back to the 4-quadrant converter shown in Figs. 21.70 and 21.71, it is seen that when the duty cycle D has a value of 0.5, the dc output voltage E_{LL} is zero. However, the instantaneous value of E_{LL} oscillates symmetrically between $+E_H$ and $-E_H$ at a rate determined by the switching frequency. Consequently, when D is fixed at 0.5, the converter is able to transform the dc voltage E_H into a rectangular ac voltage. The rectangular wave can have any frequency, ranging from a few cycles per hour to several hundred kilohertz. If the dc supply voltage is 100 V, the output E_{LL} oscillates between +100 V and −100 V (Fig. 21.76a). The wave contains a fundamental sinusoidal component whose peak amplitude is 1.27 E_H. Consequently, the effective value of the fundamental is $1.27\ E_H/\sqrt{2} = 0.90\ E_H$. If an external device is connected to the output terminals A, B (Fig. 21.76b), power can flow from the dc side to the ac side and vice versa.

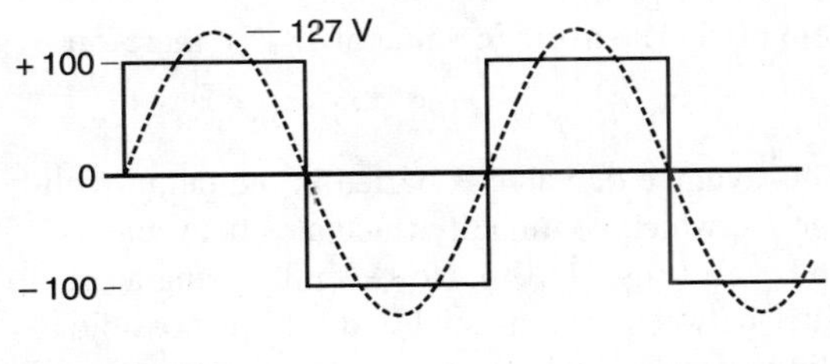

Figure 21.76a
The square wave contains a fundamental sinusiodal component.

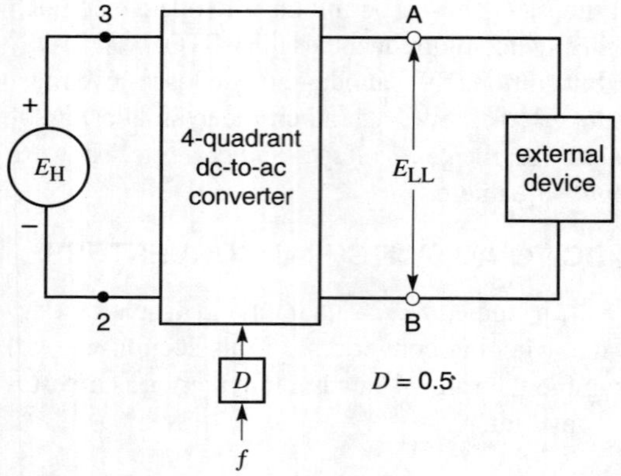

Figure 21.76b
Single-phase dc-to-ac switching converter in which $D = 0.5$ and f can be varied.

Although the frequency can be varied over a wide range, this rectangular-wave converter can only generate an output that fluctuates between $+E_H$ and $-E_H$. Furthermore, the wave contains rather large 3rd, 5th, and 7th harmonics which may be objectionable.

21.45 Dc-to-AC converter with pulse width modulation

When we studied the 4-quadrant dc-to-dc converter, we discovered that it produced an average output voltage given by

$$E_{LL} = E_H (2D - 1) \qquad (21.24)$$

Consider the 4-quadrant dc-to-dc converter of Fig. 21.77a, which is operating at a constant switching frequency f_c of several kilohertz. For reasons that will soon become apparent, it is called *carrier frequency.* Suppose that the duty cycle is set at 0.8. The average value of E_{LL} is, therefore,

$$E_{LL} = E_H (2 \times 0.8 - 1) = 0.6\, E_H$$

This average dc value is buried in the output voltage E_0, which continually fluctuates between $+E_H$ and $-E_H$ (Fig. 21.77b). However, by using a small filter between terminals L1 and L2 it is possible to eliminate the high frequency component f_c and thereby obtain the desired dc voltage across the output terminals. Note that the positive voltage pulses

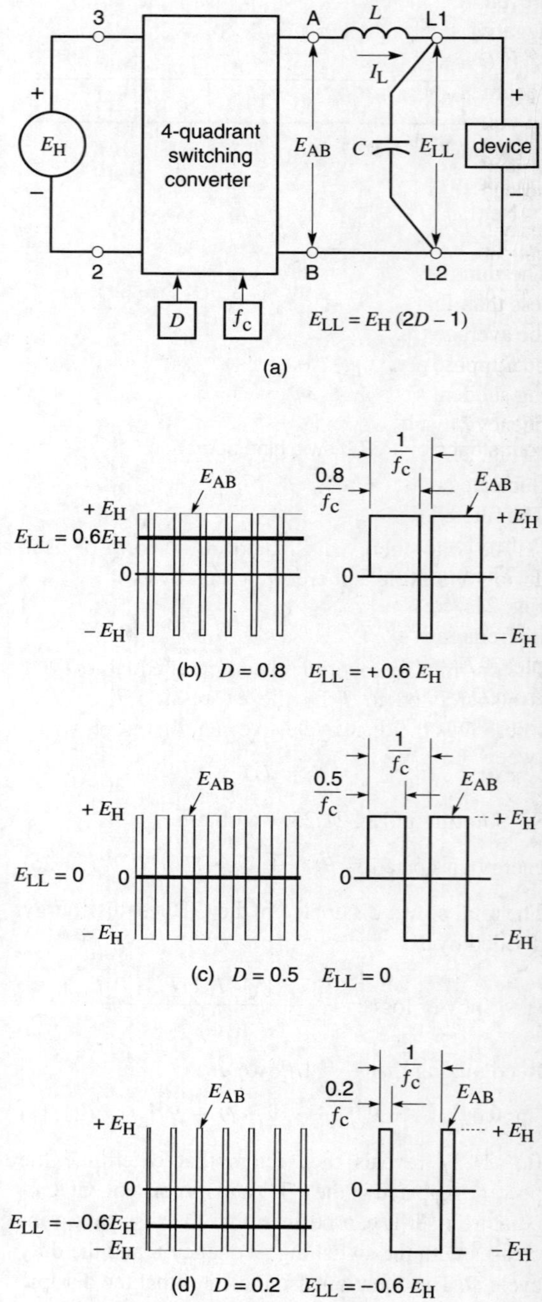

Figure 21.77
Four-quadrant dc-to-ac switching converter using carrier frequency f_c and three fixed values of D.

are on for a considerably longer period than the negative pulses.

If D is set to 0.5, the average output voltage E_{LL} becomes zero, buried again within the fluctuating ac voltage E_0 (Fig. 21.77c). Note that the duration of the positive voltage pulses is now equal to that of the negative pulses.

Next, if $D = 0.2$, we find that the average value of E_{LL} is $-0.6\ E_H$; this condition is seen in Fig. 21.77d. The duration of the positive voltage pulses is now less than that of the negative pulses and that is why the average (dc) output is negative.

Suppose now, that D is varied periodically, switching suddenly between $D = 0.8$ and $D = 0.2$ at a frequency f that is much lower than the carrier frequency f_c (Fig. 21.78). As a result, the output voltage E_{LL} will fluctuate continually between $+0.6\ E_H$ and $-0.6\ E_H$. The filtered output voltage between terminals L1, L2 is therefore a rectangular wave having a frequency f.

The big advantage over the rectangular wave of Fig. 21.76a is that the *magnitude* of E_{LL}, as well as its frequency f, can be controlled at will. For example, if $E_H = 100$ V and the duty cycle is switched from $D = 0.65$ to $D = 0.35$ at a frequency of 73 Hz, the resulting rectangular wave will fluctuate between $+30$ V and -30 V at a frequency of 73 Hz.

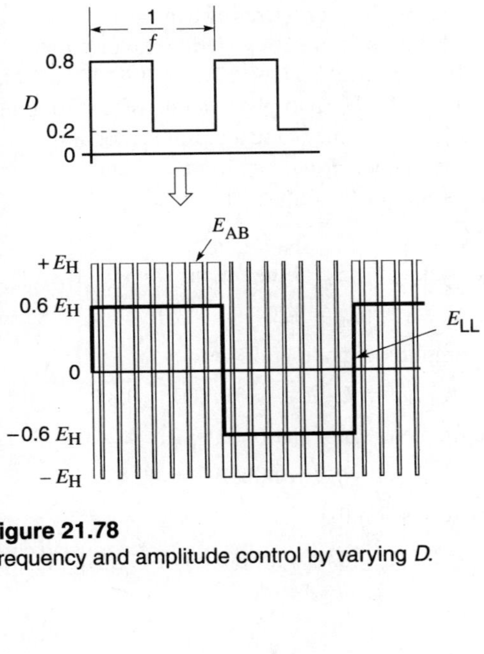

Figure 21.78
Frequency and amplitude control by varying D.

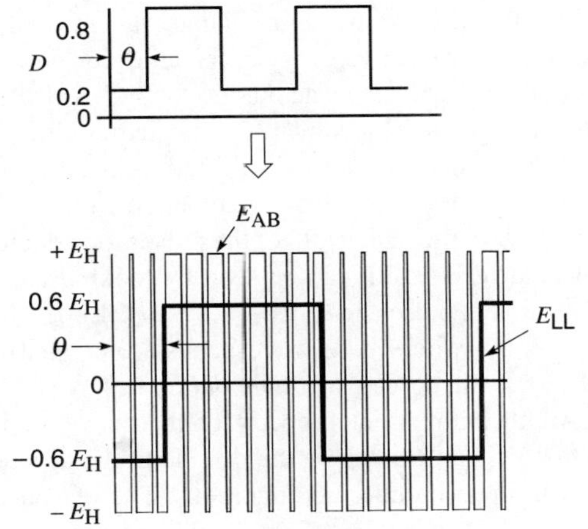

Figure 21.79
Frequency, amplitude, and phase control by varying D.

The only requirement is that the carrier frequency f_c be at least ten times the desired output frequency f.

Fig. 21.79 gives the same result as Fig. 21.78, except that the rectangular voltage has been shifted to the right by an angle of θ degrees. The phase-shift is achieved by simply delaying the duty cycle signal.

Next, consider Fig. 21.80 wherein the duty cycle is varied *gradually* between 0.8 and 0.2, following a triangular pattern. This causes the filtered output voltage E_{LL} to vary between $+0.6\ E_H$ and $-0.6\ E_H$,

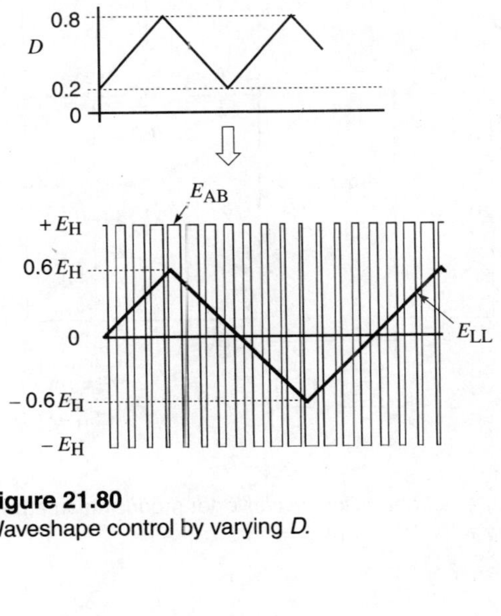

Figure 21.80
Waveshape control by varying D.

faithfully reproducing the triangular wave. Clearly, the 4-quadrant converter is a versatile device because it can generate an ac output voltage of almost any shape. The frequency, phase angle, amplitude, and waveshape can all be adjusted as needed by simply modifying the duty cycle pattern. The variation of D causes the width of the pulses to vary and this change in width can be seen by looking carefully at the pulses in Figs. 21.77 to 21.80. The process by which these waveshapes are created is therefore called *pulse width modulation* (PWM).

Another important property of the converter is that power can flow from the dc side to the ac side and vice versa, under all conditions. The reason is that no matter what the polarity of the output voltage happens to be, the current can always flow in one direction or the other. Furthermore, the ac output impedance is very low because the output terminals A, B are effectively connected to the dc supply E_H, which itself has a very low internal impedance.

21.46 Dc-to-AC sine wave converter

In order to determine the duty cycle pattern to generate a desired output voltage, consider Fig. 21.81 in which $E_{LL(t)}$ is a voltage having an arbitrary waveshape and frequency. Applying Eq. 21.24, we can write

$$E_{LL(t)} = E_H (2 D_{(t)} - 1)$$

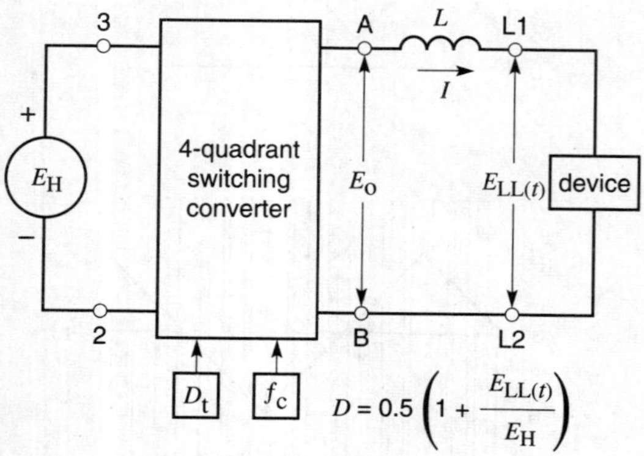

Figure 21.81
Four-quadrant switching converter producing an arbitrary waveshape $E_{LL(t)}$.

from which we immediately deduce

$$D_{(t)} = 0.5\left[1 + \frac{E_{LL(t)}}{E_H}\right] \quad (21.28)$$

Consequently, knowing E_H (whose value is fixed) and knowing the desired value of $E_{LL(t)}$ as a function of time, the pattern of $D_{(t)}$ as a function of time can be programmed. For example, suppose we want to generate an output voltage E given by

$$E = E_m \sin(360\,ft + \theta)$$

According to Eq. 21.28, $D_{(t)}$ is given by

$$D_{(t)} = 0.5\left[1 + \frac{E_m}{E_H}\sin(360\,ft + \theta)\right] \quad (21.29)$$

The ratio E_m/E_H is called *amplitude modulation ratio,* designated by the symbol m. Consequently, the duty cycle pattern to generate a sine wave can be expressed as

$$D_{(t)} = 0.5\,[1 + m \sin(360\,ft + \theta)] \quad (21.30)$$

In this equation, f is in hertz, t in seconds, and θ in degrees.

The ratio f_c/f is called *frequency modulation ratio,* designated by the symbol m_f.

Example 21-14

A 200 V dc source is connected to a 4-quadrant switching converter operating at a carrier frequency of 8 kHz. It is desired to generate a sinusoidal voltage having an effective value of 120 V at a frequency of 97 Hz and phase angle of 35° lagging. Calculate the value of the amplitude modulation ratio, the frequency modulation ratio, and derive an expression for the duty cycle.

Solution

The peak value E_m of the output voltage is

$$E_m = 120\sqrt{2} = 170 \text{ V}$$

The amplitude modulation ratio is

$$m = E_m/E_H = 170/200 = 0.85$$

The frequency modulation ratio is

$$m_f = f_c/f = 8000/97 = 82.47$$

The expression for D is

$$D_{(t)} = 0.5[1 + 0.85 \sin(360 \times 97\,t + 35)] \quad (21.31)$$

21.47 Generating a sine wave

To better understand the PWM switching process, let us determine the switching sequence to generate a sine wave between terminals A and B of Fig. 21.70. Here are the specifications:

Peak ac voltage required: 100 V

Frequency required: 83.33 Hz

Carrier frequency: 1000 Hz

DC supply voltage E_H: 200 V

Type of switching is standard: Q1, Q4 open and close simultaneously, as do Q2 and Q3 (see Fig. 21.70).

We reason as follows:

Duration of one cycle of the desired 83.33 Hz fundamental frequency

$$T = 1/f = 1/83.33 = 0.012 \text{ s} = 12\,000\ \mu\text{s}$$

This period corresponds to 360 electrical degrees.

Period of the carrier frequency

$$T_c = 1/f_c = 1/1000 \text{ s} = 1 \text{ ms} = 1000\ \mu\text{s}$$

Number of carrier cycles per fundamental cycle = 12 000 μs/1000 μs = 12.

Angular interval (at fundamental frequency) covered by one carrier period = 360°/12 = 30°. In one cycle of the fundamental voltage there are 12 such intervals.

Fig. 21.82 shows the positive half-cycle of the sine wave, with the 30° intervals labelled A to G. The average voltage for interval A is zero. The duty cycle during this interval is, therefore,

$$D = 0.5\left(1 + \frac{E_{LL(t)}}{E_H}\right) = 0.5\left(1 + \frac{0}{200}\right) = 0.5$$

The average voltage for interval B is 100 sin 30° = 50 V. The duty cycle during this interval is, therefore,

$$D = 0.5\left(1 + \frac{E_{LL(t)}}{E_H}\right) = 0.5\left(1 + \frac{50}{200}\right) = 0.625$$

The average voltage for interval C is 100 sin 60° = 86.6 V. The duty cycle during this interval is, therefore,

$$D = 0.5\left(1 + \frac{86.6}{200}\right) = 0.716.$$

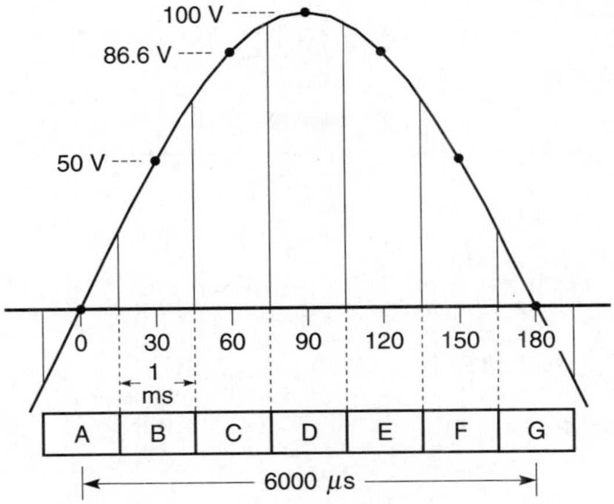

Figure 21.82
Positive half-cycle of the fundamental 83.33 Hz voltage comprises six carrier periods of 1 ms each.

Proceeding this way, we calculate the value of D until the end of the cycle (360°) is reached. Table 21E organizes the information and lists the items of interest. The intervals H to L cover the negative values of the 83.33 Hz since wave.

Knowing the duty cycle for each interval, the corresponding time that Q1, Q4 are on can be determined. For example, during interval B, they must be closed for 0.625 × 1000 μs = 625 μs. It follows

TABLE 21E GENERATING A SINE WAVE

angle [deg]	E_{AB} [V]	D	Q1, Q4 on [μs]	Q2, Q3 on [μs]	interval
0	0	0.5	500	500	A
30	50	0.625	625	375	B
60	86.6	0.716	716	284	C
90	100	0.75	750	250	D
120	86.6	0.716	716	284	E
150	50	0.625	625	375	F
180	0	0.5	500	500	G
210	−50	0.375	375	625	H
240	−86.6	0.284	284	716	I
270	−100	0.250	250	750	J
300	−86.6	0.284	284	716	K
330	−50	0.375	375	625	L
360	0	0.5	500	500	M

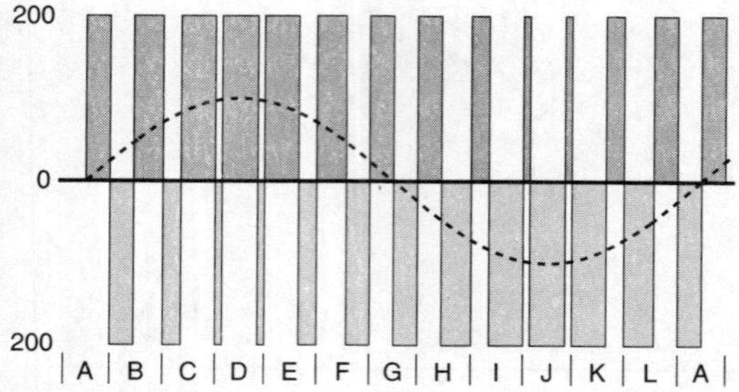

Figure 21.83
Alternative (+) and (−) pulses contain the sinusoidal component.

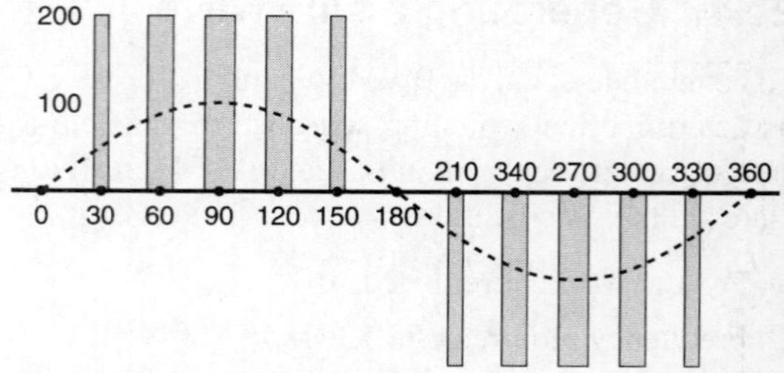

Figure 21.84
Sequential (+) and (−) pulses contain the sinusoidal components.

that Q2, Q3 must be closed for the remaining part of the interval, namely 1000 − 625 = 375 μs. Note that when Q1, Q4 are closed E_{AB} is momentarily positive, and when Q2,Q3 are closed E_{AB} is momentarily negative. Thus, during interval B, E_{AB} is +200 V for 625 μs and −200 V for 375 μs. Fig. 21.83 shows these (+) and (−) pulses.

It is seen that although the carrier period is fixed (= 1000 μs), the on/off pulse widths are changing continually. That is why this type of switching is called *pulse width modulation,* or PWM. The pulses in Fig. 21.83 constantly swing between positive and negative values. This type of switching is known as *bipolar* PWM.

It is worth noting that during each switching interval (A, B, C, etc.), the area of the 200 V positive pulse minus the area of the 200 V negative pulse is equal to the volt-second area of the sinusoidal segment during that interval. It follows that the area under the positive part of the sine wave, shown dotted in Fig. 21.83, is equal to the sum of the areas of the seven positive pulses less the areas of the six negative pulses. The same remarks apply to the negative half-cycle.

Fig. 21.84 shows another switching pattern that contains the same sinusoidal voltage. However, the pulses are all positive during the positive half-cycle and negative during the negative half-cycle. Again, in this case the sum of the areas of the five positive pulses included in the 180° interval is equal to the area of the dotted sine wave during that interval. This type of switching is known as *unipolar* PWM.

There are many other ways of programming the switching sequence, which will not be discussed here. In many cases the switching sequence is under computer control. In the simple method used above, the intention is to show the fundamental principle upon which pulse width modulation is based.

The sinusoidal voltage buried in the pulse train appears grossly distorted in both Figs. 21.83 and 21.84. However, once the 1000 Hz carrier frequency is filtered out, the resulting voltage will be very sinusoidal. Indeed, the lowest harmonics are clustered around 1000 Hz, which is 12 times the fundamental 83.33 Hz frequency.

A higher carrier frequency would yield a better waveshape because more points could be established along the sinusoidal curves and the filtering would be easier. But a higher frequency would increase the power losses in the IGBTs that are being switched.

21.48 Creating the PWM pulse train

We have seen that to convert a desired voltage waveshape into PWM form, the waveshape is chopped up into small intervals. The duration of each interval is equal to the period T of the carrier frequency. In the previous section we showed how that can be done by actual calculation. In practice, a very ingenious method is employed to create the PWM pulses.

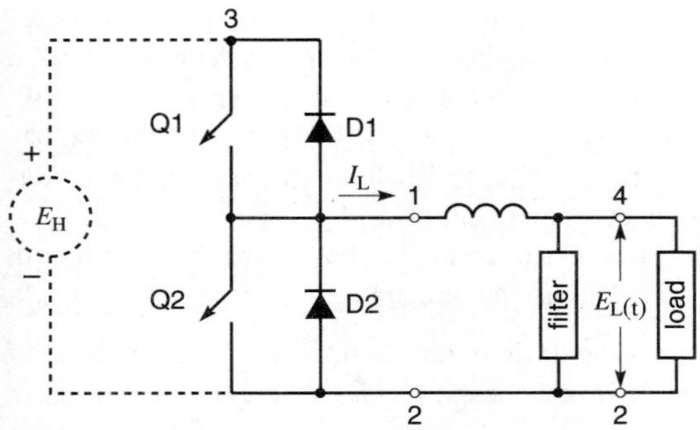

Figure 21.85
A two-quadrant PWM chopper and its load. The filter eliminates the unwanted carrier frequency component.

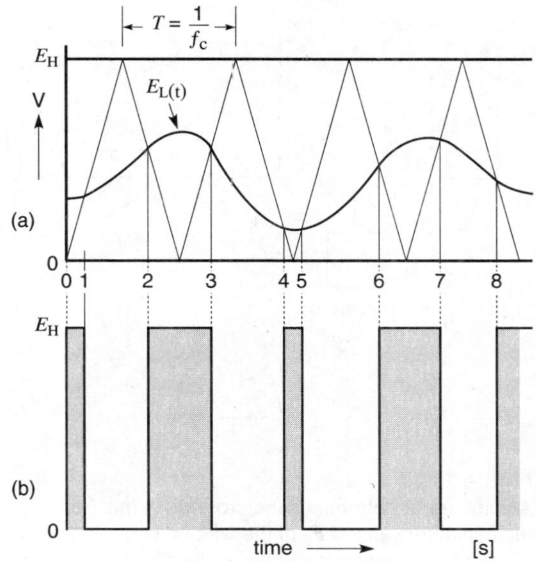

Figure 21.86
a. Transforming a desired voltage $E_{L(t)}$ into a series of PWM pulses using a two-quadrant chopper.
b. Pulse-width modulated form of the original $E_{L(t)}$ waveshape.

Consider one arm of a converter as illustrated in Fig. 21.85. Suppose the desired voltage $E_{L(t)}$ has the undulating shape shown in Fig. 21.86a and that E_H is the fixed dc voltage at the input to the converter.

We want to transform the continuous $E_{L(t)}$ waveshape into a series of pulses having a fixed amplitude E_H, a fixed period *T*, and an appropriate conduction period T_a for each pulse. To achieve this result, we first draw a series of isosceles triangles, each having a base *T* and a height E_H. It is clear that the sides of the triangles will intercept the waveshape $E_{L(t)}$ at various points (Fig. 21.86a).

The following simple rule is then applied: conduction T_a takes place whenever $E_{L(t)}$ lies above the triangular wave, and conduction ceases whenever $E_{L(t)}$ lies below. Thus, conduction occurs and the output voltage is $+E_H$ during the intervals 0-1, 2-3, 4-5, 6-7, and so forth. Conduction ceases, and the voltage is zero during the remaining intervals. The resulting pulse train, shown in gray (Fig. 21.86b), contains the original signal $E_{L(t)}$. If the carrier frequency is filtered out, the original smooth signal $E_{L(t)}$ will immediately appear across the load.

In practice, the period *T* is much shorter than that shown in Fig. 21.86a. A higher carrier frequency automatically improves the faithful reproduction of the original signal $E_{L(t)}$ that is buried in the PWM pulse train. A higher carrier frequency is also easier to filter out at a later stage.

The triangular method of establishing the successive pulse widths can be adapted in the following way. A signal E_s that is a duplicate but reduced value of the desired voltage $E_{L(t)}$ is applied to one side of a comparator (Fig. 21.87). A reduced triangular signal E_T is applied to the other side. The comparator detects the crossing points of the two signals and produces therefrom the required control signal $D_{(t)}$. This signal is applied to the gates of the two switches inside the converter, thus producing the chopped PWM voltage between terminals 1 and 2. As always, an inductance *L* is needed to ensure proper converter operation. A high-frequency *LC* filter is connected between terminals 4 and 2 to eliminate the carrier component. As a result, we obtain the desired output voltage $E_{L(t)}$ across the load.

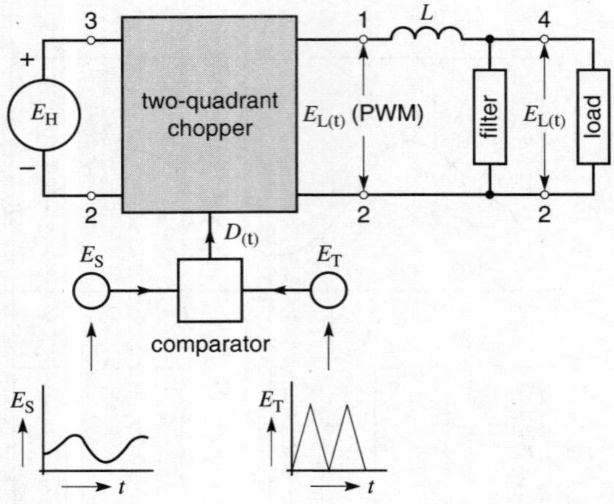

Figure 21.87
A comparator determines the crossing points between the miniature version E_S of the wanted waveshape $E_{L(t)}$ and a triangular waveshape, thereby producing the control signal $D_{(t)}$. The signal triggers the switches in the chopper to generate the PWM waveshape that contains the wanted output $E_{L(t)}$.

21.49 Dc-to-AC 3-phase converter

Several types of converters can be devised to transform dc power into 3-phase ac power. Fig. 21.88a shows a 3-phase PWM converter comprising three choppers connected to a dc source E_H.

The PWM voltages E_{AY}, E_{BY}, and E_{CY} between terminals A, B, C and the common point Y are mutually displaced by 120°. We now describe the programming and operation of this converter.

Suppose we wish to produce a 3-phase sinusoidal voltage E between terminals A, B, and C (Fig. 21.88a). It follows that the line-to-neutral voltages (E_{AN}, E_{BN}, E_{CN}) across the load have an effective value equal to $E/\sqrt{3}$. The peak value E_m of this line-to-neutral voltage is therefore $E_m = \sqrt{2}(E\sqrt{3}) = 0.8165\ E$. As we shall see, the value of E_m must not exceed $E_H/2$; otherwise, voltage distorsion will result.

The fundamental components of voltages E_{AN}, E_{BN}, and E_{CN} between terminals A, B, C and the neutral N are sinusoidal, as shown in Fig. 21.89. Also, we can prove that the fundamental components E_{AY}, E_{BY}, and E_{CY} are the same as the fundamental components E_{AN}, E_{BN}, and E_{CN}.

In order to create the PWM switching program, we again use a comparator and proceed as follows:

1. The desired line-to-neutral fundamental waveshapes of Fig. 21.89 are reproduced in

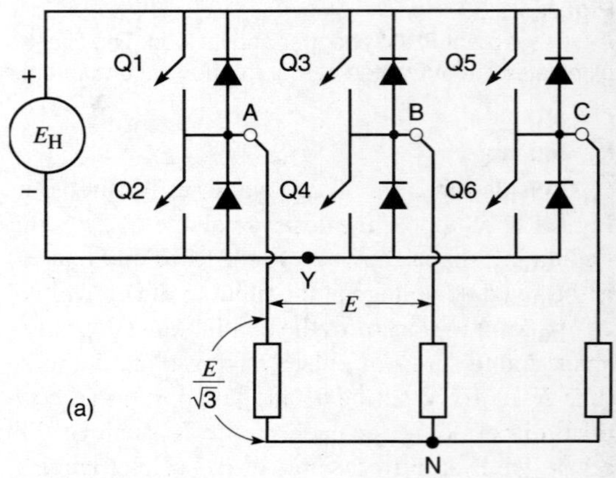

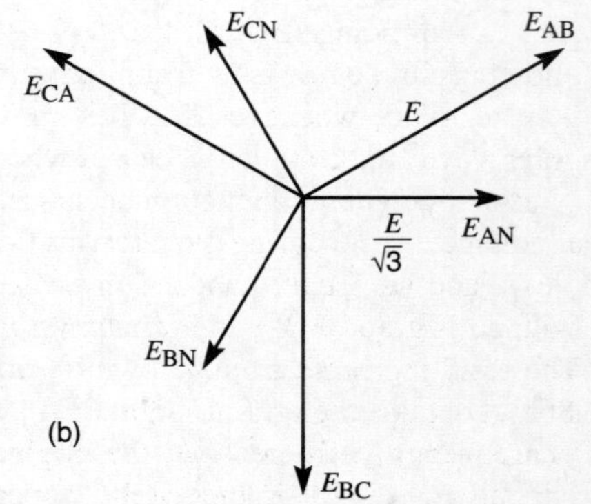

Figure 21.88
a. DC to 3-phase converter using three choppers.
b. Phasor diagram of the fundamental voltage components.

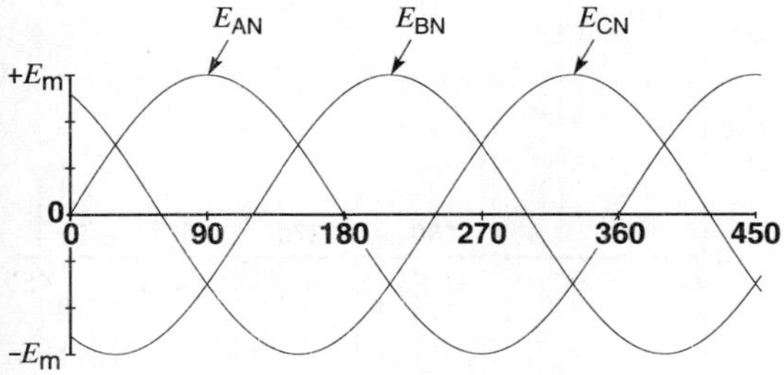

Figure 21.89
Fundamental components of the 3-phase line-to-neutral voltages.

Fig. 21.90 where they are made to oscillate around the median voltage $E_H/2$. We note that the amplitude E_m must not exceed $E_H/2$; otherwise, the sinusoidal peaks will be clipped off at the $+E_H$ and zero levels.

2. A triangular wave is superimposed upon the sinusoidal waveshapes. The triangles have a height E_H and a period T, as shown in Fig. 21.90.

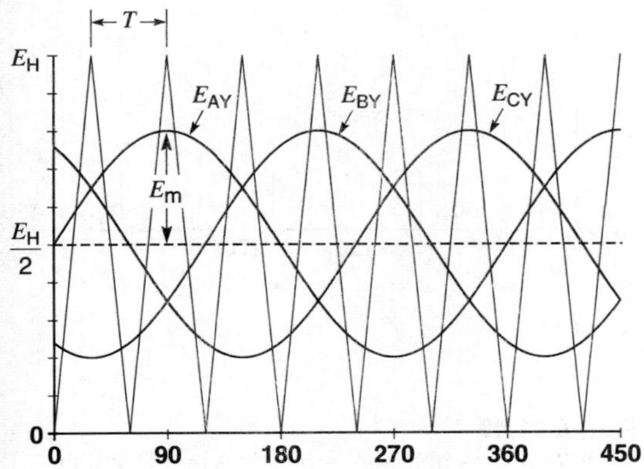

Figure 21.90
Graphical programming to generate the 3-phase PWM voltages. The sinusoidal voltages E_{AY}, E_{BY}, and E_{CY} are the sum of the respective fundamental components and the dc component $E_H/2$.

3. In order to transform the three sinusoidal voltages into three corresponding PWM voltages, we apply the following switching rules to Fig. 21.88:

   a. Q1 is closed whenever the level of E_{AY} is above the triangular wave.

   b. Q3 is closed whenever the level of E_{BY} is above the triangular wave.

   c. Q5 is closed whenever the level of E_{CY} is above the triangular wave.

As always, the two valves of each branch open and close alternatively. For example, when Q1 is closed, Q2 is open, and vice versa.

The three branches then generate identical PWM voltages, mutually displaced at 120°. For example, branches A and B respectively produce the pulse trains E_{AY} and E_{BY} (Figs. 21.91a and 21.91b). The pulse trains each contain a dc component equal to $E_H/2$, in addition to the respective sinusoidal line-to-neutral voltages whose amplitude is E_m.

The voltage between terminals A and B (Fig. 21.88) is given by $E_{AB} = E_{AY} + E_{YB} = E_{AY} - E_{BY}$. Thus, the line-to-line voltage E_{AB} is equal to the *difference* between the pulses shown in Figs. 21.91a and 21.91b. Consequently, the dc component cancels out and so the PWM voltage between lines A and B is strictly ac (Fig. 21.92a). The same remarks apply to the PWM voltage between terminals B and C (Fig. 21.92b).

The neutral N of the load is a floating neutral. We can show that the *instantaneous* voltages between the respective lines A, B, C and the neutral N are given by the expressions:

$$E_{AN} = \frac{1}{3}(E_{AB} + E_{AC}) \qquad (21.30a)$$

$$E_{BN} = \frac{1}{3}(E_{BA} + E_{BC}) \qquad (21.30b)$$

$$E_{CN} = \frac{1}{3}(E_{CA} + E_{CB}) \qquad (21.30c)$$

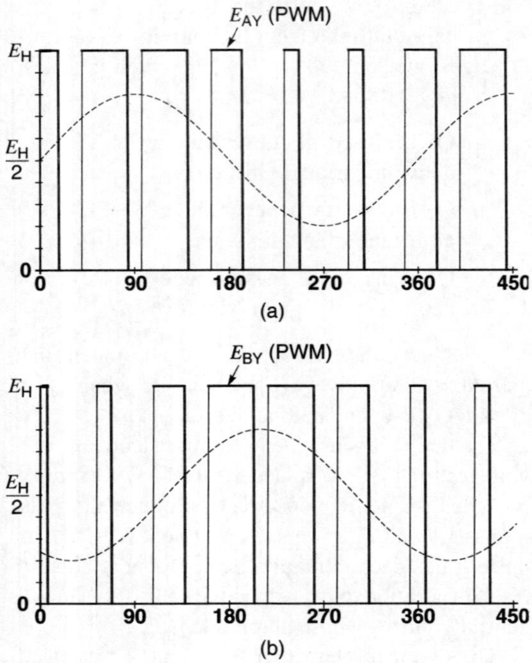

Figure 21.91

a. PWM pulses between terminals A and Y, and their sinusoidal E_{AY} component.
b. PWM pulses between terminals B and Y, and their sinusoidal E_{BY} component.

For example, by applying equation 21.30b to the waveshapes E_{AB} and E_{BC} of Fig. 21.92, we obtain the PWM waveshape between terminal B and the neutral N (Fig. 21.92c). We observe that the pulses E_{BN} are vastly different from those between terminal B and the common point Y (Fig. 21.91b). And yet, they contain exactly the same sinusoidal component. The odd-looking pulses of Fig. 21.92c illustrate how the addition or subtraction of simple pulses can generate surprising outputs.

Fig. 21.93 is a block diagram of the 3-phase converter and its load. The inductance L fills the same important role as in a conventional chopper, and the line-to-line filters (not shown) eliminate the unwanted carrier frequency voltages. The desired ac voltages appear between terminals L1, L2, and L3.

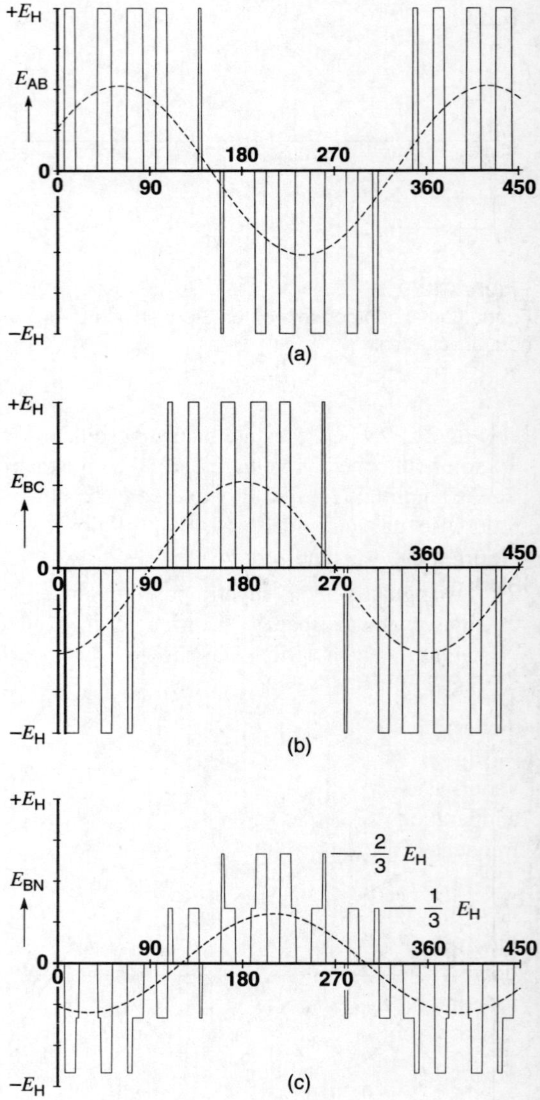

Figure 21.92

a. PWM pulses between terminals A and B and the fundamental E_{AB} component of the pulses.
b. PWM pulses between terminals B and C and the fundamental E_{BC} component of the pulses.
c. PWM pulses between terminal B and the neutral N of the load (Fig 21. 88a). The dotted sine wave is the fundamental component "buried" in the PWM pulses.

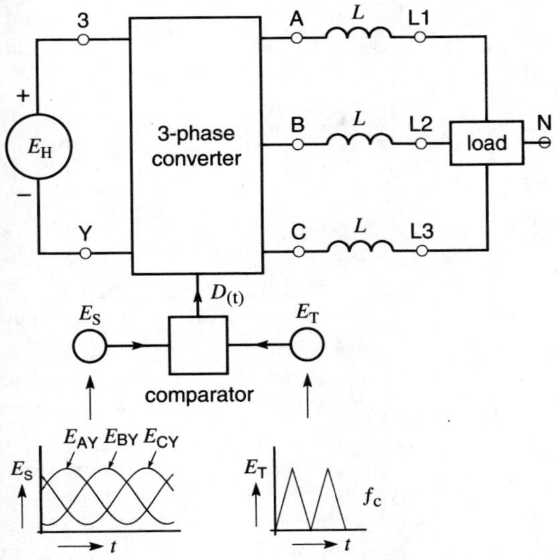

Figure 21.93
Block diagram of a 3-phase PWM converter.

The 3-phase converter contains the six switches and diodes shown in Fig. 21.88.

Fig. 21.94 is a more detailed version of the converter. The switches are represented by IGBTs in antiparallel with their respective diodes. The carrier frequency filters are represented by L_2, C_2, and R_2. The capacitors C_1 on the dc side of the converter establish a neutral point N. At the same time, they provide a path for the reactive currents that may be drawn by the ac load (not shown) that is connected to terminals L1, L2, and L3.

Example 21-15

We wish to generate a 3-phase, 245 V, 60 Hz source using the converter of Fig. 21.93. The dc supply voltage E_H is 500 V and the carrier frequency f_c is 540 Hz.

Determine

a. The peak value of the fundamental voltage between terminal L1 and the floating neutral N of the load
b. The period T of the triangular wave and the corresponding angular interval, in degrees
c. The PWM program
d. The waveshape of the PWM voltage between terminals A and Y during one cycle
e. The waveshapes of the PWM voltage between terminals A-Y, B-Y, and C-Y
f. The waveshapes of the PWM voltages between terminals A-B, B-C, and C-A

Solution

a. Effective line-to-neutral voltage

$$E_{LN} = 245/\sqrt{3} = 141.4 \text{ V}$$

Peak line-to-neutral voltage

$$E_m = E_{LN}\sqrt{2} = 141.4 \times \sqrt{2} = 200 \text{ V}$$

b. Because the desired carrier frequency is 540 Hz, the period of the triangular voltage is set at $T_c = 1/540 = 1852\ \mu s$. The angular

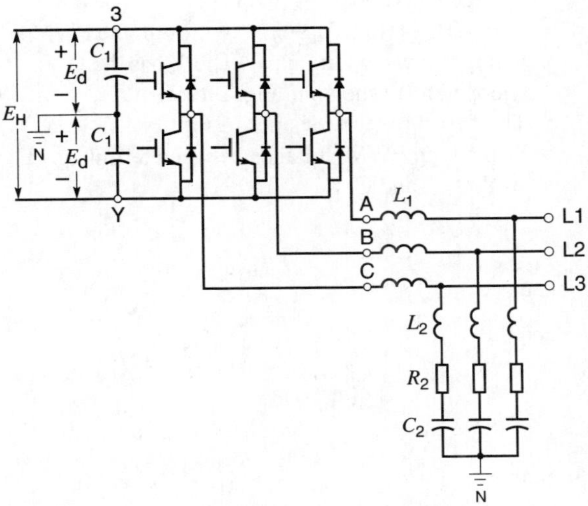

Figure 21.94
A more detailed diagram of a 3-phase PWM converter using IGBTs and a 3-phase *RLC* filter to suppress the carrier frequency components. The capacitors across the dc side provide a path for the reactive currents that are drawn by the 3-phase load.

interval of T with respect to the fundamental frequency is

$$360° \times 60\ \text{Hz}/540\ \text{Hz} = 40°$$

c. The graphical diagram that enables PWM programming is shown in Fig. 21.95. It contains the following information:

   (i) The dc source is 500 V.
   (ii) The median dc voltage is 500 V/2 = 250 V.
   (iii) The ac line-to-neutral voltage has a peak value of 200 V and it oscillates around the median dc voltage of 250 V. The period of one cycle is 360°.
   (iv) The peak-to-peak voltage of the triangular wave is the same as the dc voltage, namely 500 V.

d. We wish to transform the sinusoidal E_{AY} voltage (Fig. 21.95) into a PWM voltage whose pulses have a fixed amplitude of 500 V. We recall the rule: when E_{AY} (sinusoidal waveshape) lies above the triangular wave, Q1 is closed and voltage E_{AY} (PWM) = +500 V; otherwise E_{AY} (PWM) = 0 (Fig. 21.96a). As a result, the PWM voltage between terminals A and Y has the chopped form shown in Fig. 21.96b.

e. The first three waveshapes of Fig. 21.97 display the PWM voltages between terminals A-Y, B-Y, and C-Y.

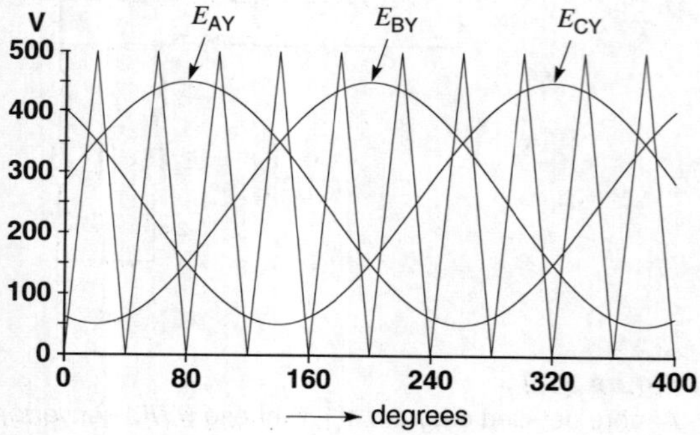

Figure 21.95
See Example 21-15.

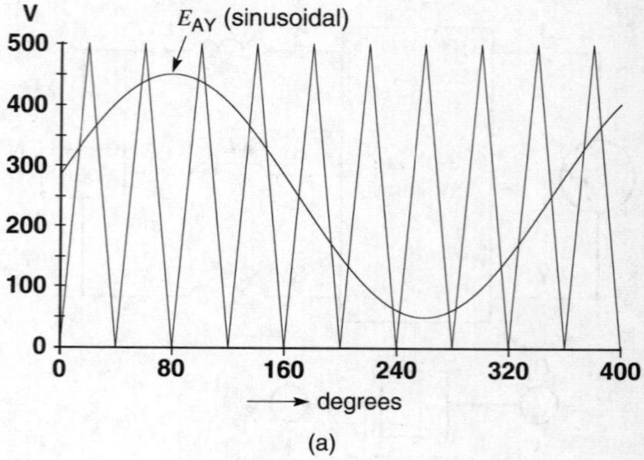

Figure 21.96a
See Example 21-15.

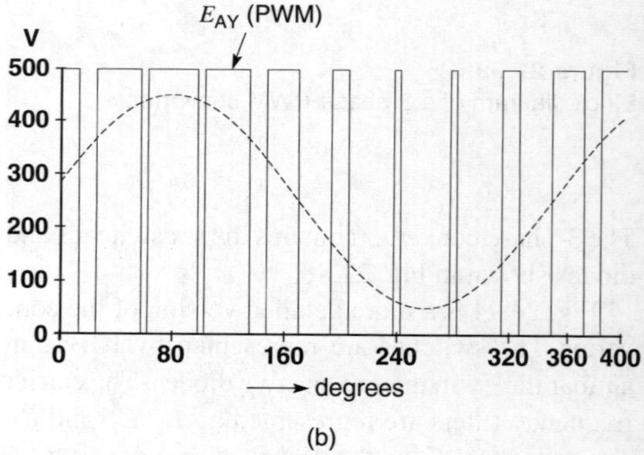

Figure 21.96b
See Example 21-15.

f. The next three waveshapes show the PWM voltages between lines A-B, B-C, and C-A. These line-to-line voltages are obtained by subtracting the respective *instantaneous* line-to-neutral voltages. Thus, $E_{AB} = E_{AY} - E_{BY}$. Owing to the presence of the carrier frequency filters (not shown) between terminals L1, L2, and L3 (Fig. 21.93), the 245 V, 3-phase, 60 Hz voltages across the load will be almost perfect sine waves.

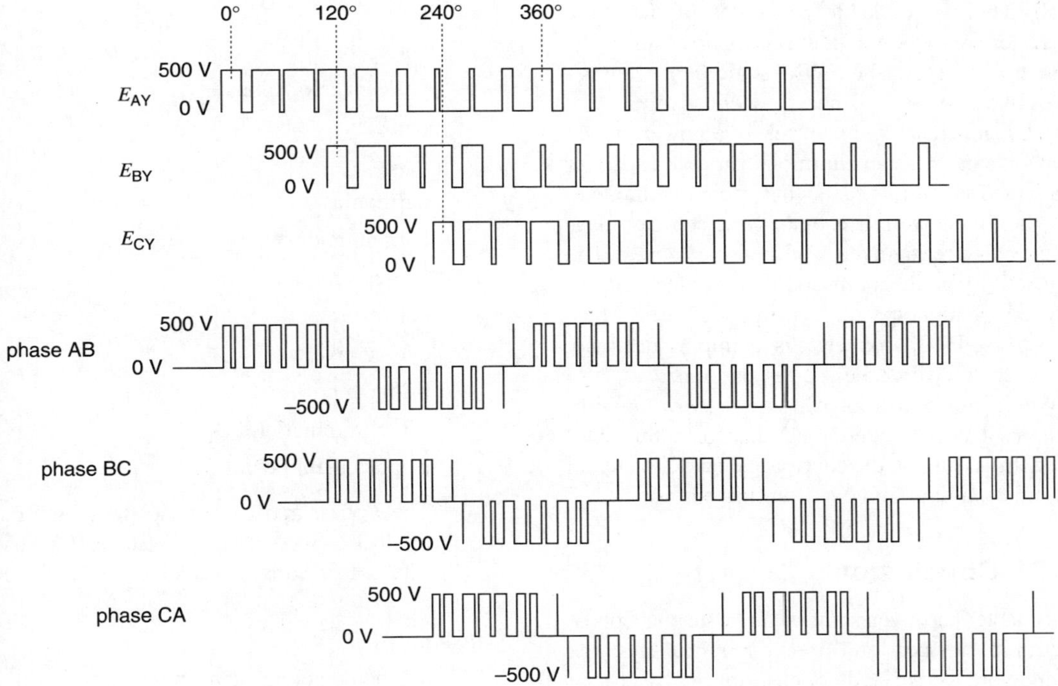

Figure 21.97
Three-phase PWM voltages produced by a dc-to-ac converter operating at a carrier frequency of 540 Hz with a 500 V dc input. Top: E_{AY}, E_{BY}, E_{CY} outputs, peak sinusoidal component = 200 V. Bottom: E_{AB}, E_{BC}, E_{CA} outputs, peak 60 Hz sinusoidal component = 346 V, RMS value = 245 V.

21.50 The converter as a universal generator

The 3-phase converter of Fig. 21.93 can deliver or absorb active power (watts) at the fundamental frequency. It can also deliver or absorb reactive power (vars) at the fundamental frequency. Thus, as far as the output terminals L1, L2, and L3 are concerned, the converter behaves exactly like a 3-phase synchronous generator that was covered in Chapter 16. Its synchronous reactance X_s is equal to $2\pi fL$, where f is the fundamental frequency and L is the inductance of the line reactors.

The load in Fig. 21.93 can be active or passive; hence, it can even be a 3-phase source of power. In the latter case, power is converted from ac to dc. The dc side E_H must be able to absorb the active power. Thus, E_H could be a battery, or it could be the input to another converter that drives, say, an ac motor.

The static converter can generate a sinusoidal voltage whose amplitude, frequency, phase angle, and phase sequence can be varied at will. The changes can be made in milliseconds—much faster than in the case of a synchronous generator. Furthermore, the impedance $X_s = 2\pi fL$ is relatively small. These remarkable properties of the static converter are exploited in many applications.

In a real sense, the PWM static converter behaves like a universal 3-phase generator. As such, it can also generate or absorb reactive power, which means it can act as an enormous variable capacitor or a huge inductor. It can switch from one mode to the other in a few milliseconds. No electric or magnetic fields are involved, and nothing moves! The only activity is the controlled flow of electricity as directed by high-speed electronic switches. Thus, the 3-phase PWM converter is as important as any machine we have studied so far, bar none.

We cannot overemphasize the *tremendous* impact this PWM converter has had on adjustable-speed drives and on the control of electric power on transmission lines and distribution systems.

21.51 Conclusion

This chapter has given some of the basic concepts of electronic devices and converters. It lays the groundwork for the study of electronic drives for dc and ac motors and the control of large blocks of power in electric utilities. In subsequent chapters we will see further applications of switching converters.

Questions and Problems

Practical level

21-1 State the basic properties of a diode.

21-2 State the basic properties of a thyristor.

21-3 What is the approximate voltage drop across a diode or SCR when it conducts?

21-4 What is the approximate maximum permissible operating temperature of a thyristor?

21-5 Explain the meaning of the following terms:

anode
cathode
gate
choke
filter
chopper
peak inverse voltage
rectifier
inverter
harmonic
commutation
line commutation
converter
cycloconverter
bridge rectifier
self commutation
displacement power factor

21-6 The 3-phase transformer shown in Fig. 21.16 produces a secondary line voltage of 2.4 kV. The dc load current I_d is 600 A.

Calculate

a. The dc voltage across the load
b. The average current carried by each diode
c. The maximum current carried by each diode

21-7 The 3-phase transformer shown in Fig. 21.19 produces a secondary line voltage of 2.4 kV. If the dc load current is 600 A, calculate the following:

a. The dc voltage across the load
b. The average current carried by each diode

21-8 An ac source having an effective voltage of 600 V, 60 Hz is connected to a single-phase bridge rectifier as shown in Fig. 21.14a. The load resistor has a value of 30 Ω.

Calculate

a. The dc voltage E_{34}
b. The dc voltage E_{54}
c. The dc load current I

d. The average current carried by each diode
e. The active power supplied by the ac source

21-9 The chopper shown in Fig. 21.62 is connected to a 3000 V dc source. The chopper frequency is 50 Hz and the on-time is 1 ms.

Calculate

a. The voltage across resistor R_0
b. The value of I_S if $R_0 = 2\ \Omega$

21-10 In Problem 21-9, if we double the on time, calculate the new power absorbed by the load.

Intermediate level

21-11 **a.** In Problem 21-7 calculate the power dissipated by the six diodes if the average voltage drop during the conduction period is 0.6 V.
b. What is the efficiency of the rectifier alone?

21-12 **a.** The current in Fig. 21.6 has a value of -6 A. What is the polarity of E_{34}?
b. The current in Fig. 21.7 has a value of $+6$ A and E_{65} is negative. Is the current increasing or decreasing?

21-13 The single-phase bridge rectifier shown in Fig. 21.14a is connected to a 120 V, 60 Hz source. If the load resistance is 3 Ω, calculate the following:
a. The dc load current
b. The PIV across the diodes
c. The energy that must be stored in the choke so that the peak-to-peak ripple is about 5 percent of the dc current
d. The inductance of the choke
e. The peak-to-peak ripple across the choke

21-14 The line voltage is 240 V, 60 Hz on the secondary side of the converter transformer in Fig. 21.19. The dc load draws a current of 750 A.

Calculate

a. The dc voltage produced by the rectifier
b. The active power supplied by the 3-phase source
c. The peak current in each diode
d. The duration of current flow in each diode [ms]
e. The effective value of the secondary line current
f. The reactive power absorbed by the converter
g. The peak-to-peak ripple across the inductor

21-15 The chopper shown in Fig. 21.62 is connected to a 2000 V dc source, and the load resistor R_0 has a value of 0.15 Ω. The on time is fixed at 100 μs and the dc voltage across the resistor is 60 V.

Calculate

a. The power supplied to the load
b. The power drawn from the source
c. The dc current drawn from the source
d. The peak value of I_S
e. The chopper frequency
f. The apparent resistance across the dc source
g. Draw the waveshapes of I_S, I_0, and I_D.

21-16 The 3-phase, 6-pulse converter shown in Fig. 21.36 is directly connected to a 3-phase, 208 V line.

Calculate

a. The dc output voltage for a firing angle of 90°
b. The firing angle needed to generate 60 V (rectifier mode)
c. The firing angle needed to generate 60 V (inverter mode)

21-17 The converter shown in Fig. 21.36 is connected to a transformer that produces a secondary line voltage of 40 kV, 60 Hz. The load draws a dc current of 450 A.

If the delay angle is 75°, calculate the following:

a. The dc output voltage
b. The active power drawn from the ac line
c. The effective value of the secondary line current
d. The reactive power absorbed by the converter

21-18 In Problem 21-17, calculate the following:

a. The peak positive value of E_{KA}
b. The peak negative value of E_{KA}
c. The peak-to-peak ripple across the inductor

21-19 The electronic contactor in Fig. 21.33 controls the power to a 15 Ω heater. The sinusoidal supply voltage has an effective value of 600 V at a frequency of 60 Hz. If the firing angle $\alpha = 0°$, calculate the following:

a. The effective current
b. The power supplied to the heater
c. The effective value of the harmonic currents
d. The displacement power factor
e. The reactive power furnished by the ac line

Advanced level

21-20 In Problem 21-19 the firing angle is increased to 120° and the effective current I is found to be 17.68 A. The rms value of the fundamental component is known to be $I_F = 12.34$ A.

Calculate

a. The rms value of all the harmonic currents
b. The power dissipated in the heater [W]
c. The distortion power factor
d. The apparent power supplied by the source
e. The total power factor
f. The displacement power factor
g. The reactive power supplied by the line [var]

21-21 The rectifier shown in Fig. 21.19 produces a dc output of 1000 A at 250 V. Inductor L reduces the current ripple, but an additional purpose is to limit the rapid build-up of dc current should load R become short-circuited. This enables the circuit breakers to trip before the dc current becomes too large. Assuming the initial current is 1000 A, calculate the minimum value of L so that the short-circuit current does not exceed 3000 A after 50 ms.

21-22 A diode having a PIV rating of 600 V is used in a battery charger similar to the one shown in Fig. 21.11a. The battery voltage is 120 V and $R = 10$ Ω.

a. Calculate the maximum effective secondary voltage of the transformer so that the diode will not break down.
b. For how many electrical degrees will the diode conduct if the rms secondary voltage is 300 V?
c. What is the peak current in the diode?

21-23 The cycloconverter in Fig. 21.34 is connected to a 60 Hz source. Calculate the time interval between the firing of gates g1 and g4 if we wish to generate an output frequency of 12 Hz. Draw the waveshape of the voltage across the load resistance.

21-24 **a.** Referring to Fig. 21.15, and recognizing that area $A_{(-)}$ is almost triangular, calculate the approximate value of $A_{(+)}$ if the effective voltage produced by the source is 2000 V, 60 Hz [V·s].
b. If the peak-to-peak current ripple must not exceed 7 A, calculate the inductance of choke L.

21-25 The chopper shown in Fig. 21.58 transfers power from a 400 V source to a 100 V load. The inductor has an inductance of 5 H. If the chopper is on for 2 s and off for 10 s, calculate the following:

a. The maximum current in the inductor
b. The energy transferred to the load, per cycle [J]

c. The average power delivered to the load [W]

d. Draw the waveshape of i as a function of time and compare it with that in Fig. 21.59.

21-26 In Problem 21-25, if the chopper is on for 2 s and off for 2 s, what is the value of the current

a. After 2 s?

b. After 4 s?

c. After 6 s?

d. After 8 s?

e. Will anything prevent the current from building up indefinitely?

21-27 A 3-phase, 6-pulse converter shown in Fig. 21.41 is to be used as an inverter. The dc side is connected to a 120 V battery and $R = 10\ \text{m}\Omega$. The ac side is connected to a 3-phase, 120 V, 60 Hz line. If the battery delivers a current of 500 A, calculate the following:

a. The firing angle required

b. The active power delivered to the ac line

c. The reactive power absorbed by the converter

Industrial application

21-28 A 24 V battery is connected in series with a 12 V (rms), 60 Hz generator to a 10 Ω resistor.

Calculate

a. The maximum and minimum voltage across the resistor

b. The effective value of the voltage across the resistor

c. The power dissipated in the resistor

21-29 A distorted 60 Hz current has an effective value of 547 A and a THD of 26 percent. Calculate the peak value of the fundamental component and the effective value of all the harmonics taken together.

21-30 One of the diodes in a bridge circuit similar to that in Fig. 21.13 fails and becomes open-circuited. The source voltage E_{12} has an effective value of 208 V and, before the diode failed, the resistor absorbed a power of 1400 W. Describe what happens after the failure and determine the new power absorbed by the resistor and the effective value of the voltage across it.

21-31 One of the thyristors (Q2) in Fig. 21.34 becomes short-circuited. Describe what will most likely happen in this unfused circuit.

21-32 A GTO operates under the following conditions:

1. Turn-on time: 2 ms
   Anode voltage: drops linearly from 1200 V to 3.2 V
   Anode current: rises linearly from zero to 260 A
2. On-state time: 250 ms
   On-state current: 420 A
   On-state voltage: 3.2 V
3. Turn-off time: 6 ms
   Anode voltage: rises linearly from 3.2 V to 550 V
   Anode current: falls linearly from 420 A to zero
4. Off-state time: 375 ms
   Off-state voltage: 1300 V
   Off-state reverse current: 6 mA

Calculate

a. The peak power dissipated in the GTO during the turn-on period

b. The peak power dissipated in the GTO during the on-state period

c. The approximate average power during the turn-on period

d. The approximate average power during the on-state period

e. The approximate energy dissipated in the GTO during the turn-on period

f. The approximate energy dissipated in the GTO during the on-state period

g. The approximate energy dissipated in the GTO during the turn-off period

h. The total power dissipated in the GTO, neglecting gate losses

i. The frequency and duty cycle of the switching operation

21-33 Referring to Fig. 21.63, the two-quadrant converter is connected to a 400 V dc source. The average dc output voltage is 70 V and the duration of one cycle is 60 μs. Calculate

a. The respective durations of T_a and T_b for switch S1

b. The switching frequency in kHz

21-34 A four-quadrant converter such as illustrated in Figure 21.70 is powered by a 600 V dc source and the switching frequency is 25 kHz. The duty cycle is set at a value of 0.35. Calculate

a. The average dc voltage between terminals A and 2. Is terminal A positive with respect to terminal 2?

b. The average dc voltage between terminals B and 2. Is terminal B positive with respect to terminal 2?

c. The average dc voltage between terminals A and B. What is the polarity of A with respect to B?

21-35 A four-quadrant converter such as illustrated in Figure 21.70 is powered by a 600 V dc source and the switching frequency is 25 kHz. The duty cycle is set at a value of 0.35. Calculate

a. The closing time and opening time of switch Q1

b. The closing time and opening time of switch Q3

c. Draw the waveshapes of E_{A2}, E_{B2}, and E_{AB}. Show that the average value of $E_{AB} = -180$ V

21-36 Referring to Figure 21.94, the 3-phase PWM converter is connected to a 4 kV dc source. The triggering modes of the IGBTs are set so that the 3-phase line voltage is sinusoidal with an effective value of 2100 V at 60 Hz. The ac load between terminals L1, L2, and L3 is 360 kVA at a power factor of 0.86 lagging. Calculate

a. The effective ac currents drawn by the 3-phase load

b. The dc current delivered by the 4 kV source

c. The maximum ac output voltage (rms) that the converter can deliver without clipping the sinusoidal peaks

CHAPTER 22

Electronic Control of Direct-Current Motors

22.0 Introduction

High-speed, reliable, and inexpensive semiconductor devices have produced a dramatic change in the control of dc motors. In this chapter we examine some of the basic principles of such electronic drives. The circuits involve rectifiers and inverters already covered in Chapter 21. The reader should, therefore, review this chapter before proceeding further. Sections 20.16 and 20.17 on electric drives should also be consulted.

In describing the various methods of control, we will only study the behavior of power circuits. Consequently, the many ingenious ways of shaping and controlling triggering pulses are not covered here. The reason is that they constitute, by themselves, a complex subject involving sophisticated electronics, logic circuits, integrated circuits, and microprocessors. Nevertheless, the omission of this important subject does not detract from the thrust of this chapter, which is to explain the fundamentals of electronic dc drives.

22.1 First quadrant speed control

We begin our study with a variable speed drive for a dc shunt motor. We assume that its operation is restricted to quadrant 1. The field excitation is fixed, and the speed is varied by changing the armature voltage. A 3-phase, 6-pulse converter is connected between the armature and a 3-phase source (Fig. 22.1). The field current I_f is provided by a single-phase bridge rectifier. External inductor L ensures a relatively smooth armature current. The armature inductance L_a is usually large enough, and so the external inductor can often be dispensed with. The armature is initially at rest and the disconnecting switch S is open.

A gate-triggering processor receives external inputs such as actual speed, actual current, actual torque, etc. These inputs are picked off the power circuit by means of suitable transducers. In addition, the processor can be set for any desired motor speed and torque. The actual values are compared with the desired values, and the processor automatically generates gate pulses to bring the two as close together as possible. Limit settings are also incorporated so that the motor never operates beyond acceptable values of current, voltage, and speed.

Gate pulses are initially delayed by an angle $\alpha = 90°$ so that converter output voltage E_d is zero. Switch S is then closed and α is gradually reduced so that E_d begins to build up. Armature current I_d

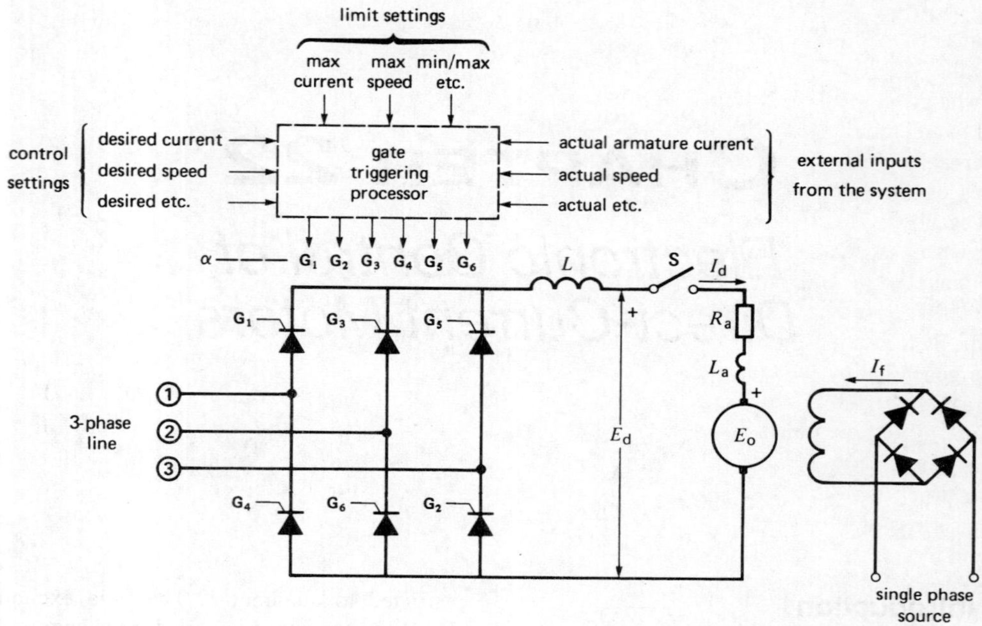

Figure 22.1
Armature torque and speed control of a dc motor using a thyristor converter.

starts flowing and the motor gradually accelerates. During the starting period, the current is monitored automatically. Furthermore, the gate-triggering processor is preset so that the pulses can never produce a current in excess of, say, 1.6 pu.

Four features deserve our attention as regards the start-up period:

1. No armature resistors are needed; consequently, there are no I^2R losses except those in the armature itself.
2. The power loss in the thyristors is small; consequently, all the active power drawn from the ac source is available to drive the load.
3. Even if an inexperienced operator tried to start the motor too quickly, the current-limit setting would override the manual command. In effect, the armature current can never exceed the allowable preset value.
4. The dc voltage E_d during start-up is much lower than rated voltage. Consequently, the converter absorbs a great deal of reactive power when the motor runs at low speed while developing its rated torque. Furthermore, the reactive power diminishes continually as the motor picks up speed. As a result, power-factor correction is difficult to apply during the start-up phase.

When the motor reaches full speed, the firing angle is usually between 15° and 20°. Converter voltage E_d is slightly greater than induced voltage E_0 by an amount equal to the armature circuit I_dR_a drop. The converter voltage is given by the basic equation

$$E_d = 1.35\, E \cos \alpha \qquad (21.17)$$

To reduce the speed, we increase the firing angle α so that E_d becomes less than E_0. In a Ward-Leonard system this would immediately cause the armature current to reverse (see Section 5.5).

Unfortunately, the current cannot reverse in Fig. 22.1 because the SCRs conduct in only one direction. As a result, when we increase α, the current is simply cut off and the motor *coasts* to the lower speed. During this interval, E_0 gradually falls and, when it eventually becomes less than the new setting of E_d, the armature current again starts to flow. The torque quickly builds up and, when it is equal to the load torque, the motor will continue to run at the lower speed.

The efficiency at the lower speed is still high because the SCR losses are small. However, the ripple voltage generated by the converter is greater than under rated full-load conditions because α is greater (Section 21.28). Consequently, the armature current is not as smooth as before, which tends to increase the armature copper losses and iron losses. An equally serious problem is the large reactive power absorbed by the converter as the firing angle is increased. For example, when the firing angle is 45°, the converter absorbs as much reactive power from the 3-phase line as it does active power.

To stop the motor, we delay the pulses by 90° so that $E_d = 0$ V. The motor will coast to a stop at a rate that depends on the mechanical load and the inertia of the revolving parts.

Example 22-1

A 750 hp, 250 V, 1200 r/min dc motor is connected to a 208 V, 3-phase, 60 Hz line using a 3-phase bridge converter (Fig. 22.2a). The full-load armature current is 2500 A and the armature resistance is 4 mΩ.

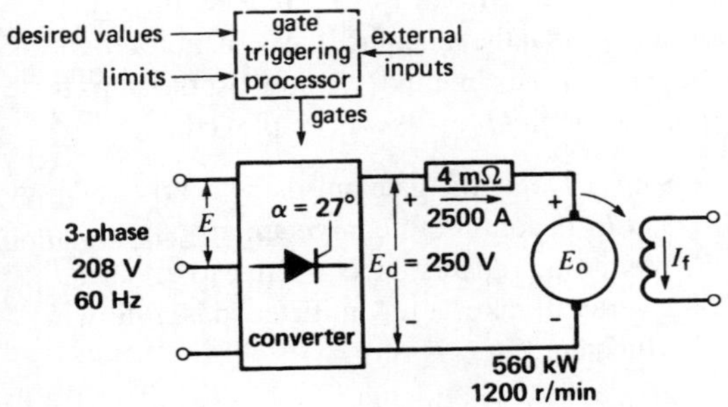

Figure 22.2a
See Example 22-1.

Calculate

a. The required firing angle α under rated full-load conditions
b. The firing angle required so that the motor develops its rated torque at 400 r/min

Solution

a. At full-load the converter must develop a dc output of 250 V:

$$E_d = 1.35\,E\cos\alpha \qquad (21.14)$$

$$250 = 1.35 \times 208\cos\alpha$$

$$\cos\alpha = 0.89$$

$$\alpha = 27°$$

Armature *IR* drop at rated current:

$$IR = 2500\text{ A} \times 0.004\ \Omega = 10\text{ V}$$

Counter-emf (cemf) at 1200 r/min

$$E_0 = 250 - 10 = 240\text{ V}$$

b. To develop rated torque at 400 r/min, the armature current must still be 2500 A. The cemf at 400 r/min is

$$E_0 = (400/1200) \times 240 = 80\text{ V}$$

Armature *IR* drop = 10 V
Armature terminal voltage is

$$E_d = 80 + 10 = 90\text{ V}$$

The converter must, therefore, generate 90 V. To determine the firing angle, we have

$$E_d = 1.35\,E\cos\alpha \qquad (21.14)$$

$$90 = 1.35 \times 208\cos\alpha$$

$$\alpha = 71° \text{ (see Fig. 22.2b)}$$

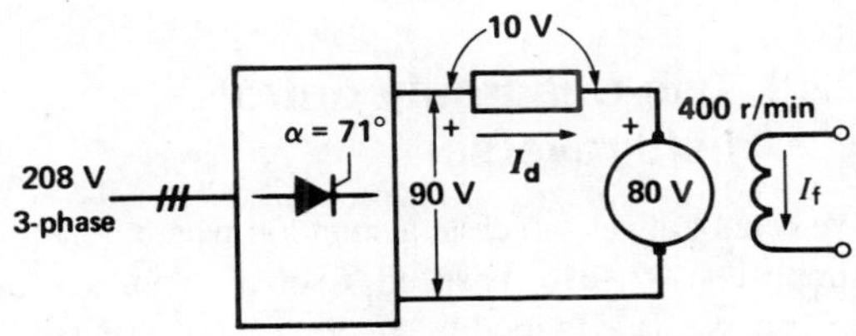

Figure 22.2b
Rated torque at 400 r/min.

Example 22-2

Referring to Example 22-1, calculate the reactive power absorbed by the converter when the motor develops full torque at 400 r/min.

Solution

The load condition is given in Fig. 22.2b. The dc power absorbed by the motor is

$$P = E_d I_d = 90 \times 2500 = 225 \text{ kW}$$

If we neglect the relatively small converter losses, the active power supplied by the ac source is also 225 kW.

The reactive power drawn from the ac source is given by

$$Q = P \tan \alpha$$
$$= 225 \tan 71°$$
$$= 653 \text{ kvar (compare this with the active power of 225 kW)}$$

This example shows that a large amount of reactive power is required as the firing angle is increased. It even exceeds the active power needed at full-load. Capacitors could be installed on the ac side of the converter to reduce the burden on the 3-phase feeder line. Alternatively, a variable-tap transformer could be placed between the 3-phase source and the converter. By reducing the ac voltage at the lower speeds, the reactive power can be reduced considerably. The reason is that the firing angle can then be kept between 15° and 20°. However, this may not be a feasible solution if the speed of the motor has to be continually varied. The tap-changing becomes too frequent to be practical. Later sections in this chapter (Sections 22.8 and 22.9) show other ways to reduce the reactive power demand.

22.2 Two-quadrant control—field reversal

We cannot always tolerate a situation where a motor simply coasts to a lower speed. To obtain a quicker response, we have to modify the circuit so that the motor acts temporarily as a generator. By controlling the generator output, we can make the speed fall as fast as we please. We often resort to dynamic braking, using a resistor connected across the armature. However, the converter can also be made to operate as an inverter, feeding power back into the 3-phase line. Such *regenerative braking* is preferred for large motors because the kinetic energy lost during the deceleration is converted to useful electrical energy. Furthermore, the generator output can be precisely controlled to obtain the desired rate of change in speed.

To make the converter act as an inverter, the polarity of E_d must be reversed, as shown in Fig. 22.3. This means we must also reverse the polarity of E_0. Finally, E_d must be adjusted to be slightly less than E_0, to obtain the desired braking current I_d (Fig. 22.3).

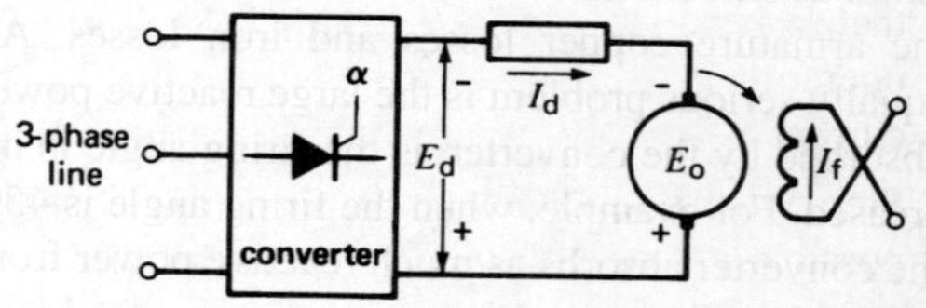

Figure 22.3
Motor control by field reversal.

These changes are not as simple as they first appear. The polarity of E_d can be changed almost instantaneously by delaying the gate pulses by more than 90°. However, to change the polarity of E_0, we must reverse either the field or the armature, and this requires additional equipment. Reversing the armature or field also takes a significant length of time. Furthermore, after the generator (braking) phase is over, we must again reverse the armature or field so that the machine runs as a motor. Bearing these conditions in mind, we now list the steps to be taken when *field reversal* is employed.

Step 1. Delay the gate pulses by nearly 180° so that E_d becomes quite large and negative. This operation prepares the converter to act as an inverter. It takes a few milliseconds, following which current I_d is zero.

Step 2. Reverse the field current as quickly as possible so as to reverse the polarity of E_0. The total reversing time may last from 1 to 5 seconds, owing to the high inductance of the shunt field. The armature current is still zero during this interval.

Step 3. Reduce α so that E_d becomes slightly less than E_0, enabling the desired armature current to flow. The motor now acts as a generator, feeding power back into the ac line by way of the inverter. Its speed drops rapidly toward the lower setting.

What do we do when the lower speed is reached? We quickly rearrange the circuit so the dc machine again runs as a motor. This involves the following steps:

Step 4. Delay the gate pulse by nearly 180° so that E_d becomes quite large and negative. This operation takes a few milliseconds, after which current I_d is again zero.

Step 5. Reverse the field current as quickly as possible so as to make E_0 positive. The reversing time again lasts from 1 to 2 seconds. During this interval, the armature current is zero.

Step 6. Reduce α so that E_d becomes positive and slightly *greater* than E_0, enabling the desired armature current to flow. The machine now acts as a motor, and the converter is back to the rectifier mode.

22.3 Two-quadrant control—armature reversal

In some industrial drives, the long delay associated with field reversal is unacceptable. In such cases we reverse the armature instead of the field. This requires a high-speed reversing switch designed to carry the full armature current. The control system is arranged so that switching occurs only when the armature current is zero. Although this reduces contact wear and arcing, the switch still has to be fairly large to carry a current, say, of several thousand amperes.

Due to its low inductance, the armature can be reversed in about 150 ms, which is at least 10 times faster than reversing the field. Fig. 22.4 is a simplified circuit showing a dc shunt motor connected to the converter by means of a reversing contactor. To

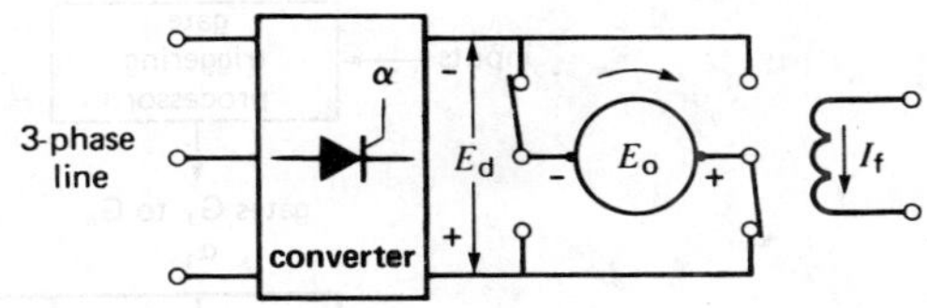

Figure 22.4
Motor control by armature reversal.

reduce speed, the same steps are followed as in the case of field reversal, except that the armature is reversed instead of the field.

22.4 Two-quadrant control—two converters

When speed control has to be even faster, we use two identical converters connected in reverse parallel. Both are connected to the armature, but only one operates at a given time, acting either as a rectifier or inverter (Fig. 22.5). The other converter is on standby, ready to take over whenever power to the armature has to be reversed. Consequently, there is no need to reverse the armature or field. The time to switch from one converter to the other is typically 10 ms. Reliability is considerably improved, and maintenance is reduced. Balanced against these advantages are the higher cost and increased complexity of the triggering source.

Because one converter is always ready to take over from the other, the respective converter voltages are close to the existing armature voltage, both in value and polarity. Thus, in Fig. 22.6a, converter 1 acts as a rectifier, supplying power to the motor at a voltage slightly higher than the cemf E_0. During this period, gate pulses are withheld from converter 2 so that it is inactive. Nevertheless, the control circuit continues to generate pulses having a delay α_2 so that E_{d2} *would* be equal to E_{d1} if the pulses were allowed to reach the gates (G7 to G12, Fig. 22.5).

To reduce the motor speed, gate pulses α_1 are delayed and, as soon as the armature current has fallen to zero, the control circuit withholds the pulses to converter 1 and simultaneously unblocks the pulses to converter 2. Converter 1 becomes inactive and

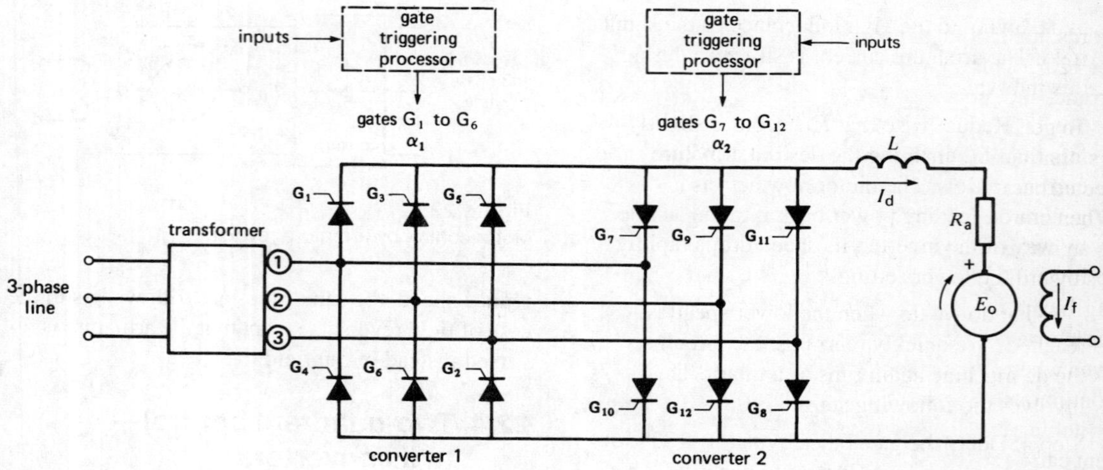

Figure 22.5
Two-quadrant control using two converters without circulating currents.

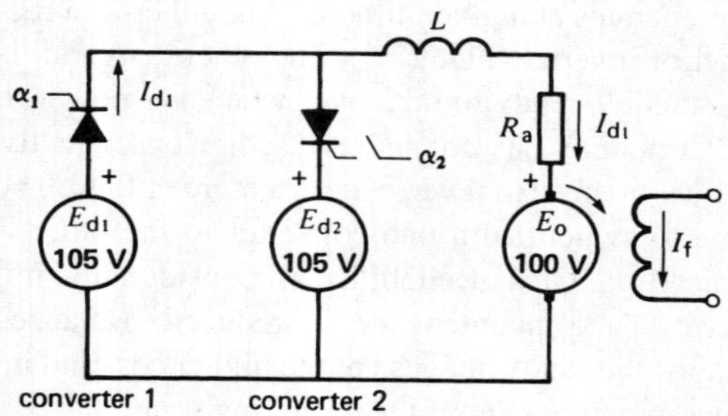

Figure 22.6a
Converter 1 in operation; converter 2 blocked.

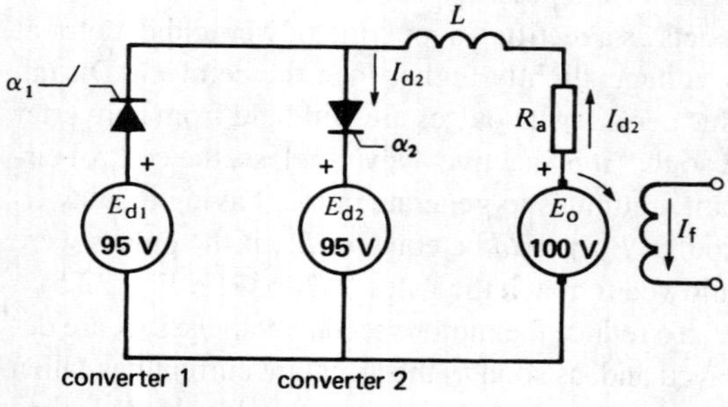

Figure 22.6b
Converter 2 in operation; converter 1 blocked.

the delay angle α_2 is then reduced so that E_{d2} becomes slightly less than E_0, thus permitting reverse current I_{d2} to flow (Fig. 22.6b).

This current reverses the torque, and the motor speed decreases rapidly. During the deceleration phase, α_2 is varied automatically so that E_{d2} follows the rapidly decreasing value of E_0. In some cases α_2 is varied to maintain a constant braking current. During this period the control circuit continues to generate gate pulses for converter 1, and the delay angle α_1 tracks α_2 so that E_{d1} would be equal to E_{d2} if the pulses were allowed to reach the gates (G1 to G6).

If the motor only operates in quadrants 1 and 4, the direction of rotation never reverses. Consequently, converters 1 and 2 always act respectively as rectifier and inverter.

22.5 Four-quadrant control—two converters with circulating current

Some industrial drives require precise speed and torque control right down to zero speed. This means that the torque may at times be much less than rated torque. Unfortunately, the converter current is discontinuous under these circumstances. In other words, the current in each thyristor no longer flows for 120°. Thus, at low torques the speed tends to be erratic, and precise control is difficult to achieve.

To get around this problem, we use two converters that function *simultaneously.* They are connected back-to-back across the armature (Fig. 22.8). When one functions as a rectifier the other functions as an inverter, and vice versa. The armature current I is the difference between currents I_{d1} and I_{d2} flowing in the two converters. With this arrangement, the currents in both converters flow during 120°, even when I is zero. Obviously, with two converters continuously in operation, there is no delay at all in switching from one to the other. The armature current can be reversed almost instantaneously; consequently, this represents the most sophisticated control system available. It is also the most expensive. The reason is that when converters operate simultaneously, each must be provided with a large series inductor (L_1, L_2) to limit the ac circulating currents. The converters may be fed from separate sources, such as the isolated secondary windings of a 3-phase transformer. A typical circuit composed of a delta-connected primary and two wye-connected secondaries is shown in Fig. 22.8. Other transformer circuits are sometimes used to optimize performance, to reduce cost, to enhance reliability, or to limit short-circuit currents.

Figure 22.7
Precise 4-quadrant electronic speed control is provided in a modern steel mill.
(Courtesy of Siemens)

Example 22-3

The dc motor in Fig. 22.8 has an armature voltage of 450 V while drawing a current of 1500 A. Converter 1 delivers a current I_{d1} of 1800 A, and converter 2 absorbs 300 A. If the ac line voltage for each converter is 360 V, calculate the following:

a. The dc power associated with converters 1 and 2
b. The active power drawn from the incoming 3-phase line
c. The firing angles for converters 1 and 2
d. The reactive power drawn from the incoming 3-phase line

Solution

a. The dc power delivered by converter 1 is

$$\begin{aligned} P_1 &= E_{d1}I_{d1} \\ &= 450 \times 1800 \\ &= 810 \text{ kW} \end{aligned}$$

The power absorbed by converter 2 (operating as an inverter) is

$$\begin{aligned} P_2 &= E_{d2}I_{d2} \\ &= 450 \times 300 \\ &= 135 \text{ kW} \end{aligned}$$

Note that the converter voltages E_{d1} and E_{d2} are essentially identical because the dc voltage drops in L_1 and L_2 are negligible. This means that the respective triggering of converters 1 and 2 cannot be voltage-controlled (by E_0, for example). In practice, the triggering is current-controlled and is made to depend on the desired converter currents I_{d1} and I_{d2}.

b. The active power drawn from the incoming ac line is

$$\begin{aligned} P &= P_1 - P_2 \\ &= 810 - 135 \\ &= 675 \text{ kW} \end{aligned}$$

Secondary winding 1, 2, 3 delivers 810 kW while secondary winding 7, 8, 9 receives 135 kW. It follows that the net active power drawn from the line (neglecting losses) is 675 kW.

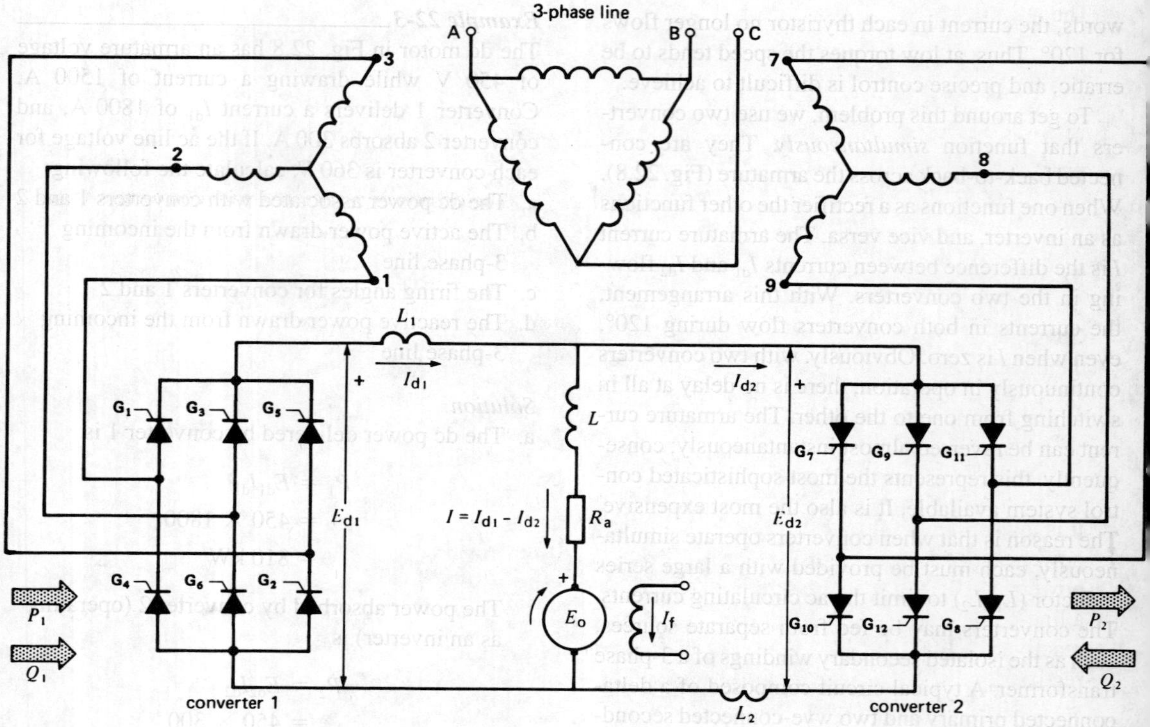

Figure 22.8
Two-quadrant control of a dc motor using two converters with circulating currents.

c. The approximate firing angle for converter 1 can be found from Eq. 21.13:

$$E_{d1} = 1.35\,E\cos\alpha_1$$
$$450 = 1.35 \times 360\cos\alpha_1$$
$$\cos\alpha_1 = 0.926$$
$$\alpha_1 = 22.2°$$

Because E_{d2} is nearly equal to E_{d1}, the firing angle for converter 2 is found to have the same approximate value. However, because it operates as an inverter, the angle is

$$\alpha_2 = 180 - \alpha_1$$
$$= 180 - 22.2$$
$$= 157.8°$$

Note that assuming I_{d2} is held constant, it would take a very small change in α_1 (and hence in E_{d1}) to make a big change in I_{d1}. The reason is that I_{d1} is equal to the *difference* between E_{d1} and E_o, divided by the very low armature resistance R_a. Such a big change in I_{d1} would produce a corresponding big change in the current I feeding the armature.

In the same way, a very small change in α_2 (with I_{d1} held constant) produces a big change in I_{d2} and, therefore, in the armature current. Thus, although the *approximate* values of α_1 and α_2 are mainly determined by the magnitude of the armature voltage E_o (which depends upon the speed), their precise values are set by the desired value of the armature current I. That is why I_{d1} and I_{d2} have to be current-controlled.

d. The reactive power drawn by converter 1 is

$$Q_1 = P_1 \tan \alpha_1$$
$$= 810 \tan 22.2°$$
$$= 331 \text{ kvar}$$

The reactive power drawn by converter 2 is

$$Q_2 = P_2 \tan \alpha_2$$
$$= -135 \tan 157.8°$$
$$= 55 \text{ kvar}$$

Consequently, the reactive power drawn from the incoming 3-phase line is

$$Q = Q_1 + Q_2$$
$$= 331 + 55$$
$$= 386 \text{ kvar}$$

It is interesting to note that whereas the active powers subtract ($P = P_1 - P_2$), the reactive powers add ($Q = Q_1 + Q_2$). The reason is that a line-commutated converter always absorbs reactive power, whether it functions as a rectifier or inverter.

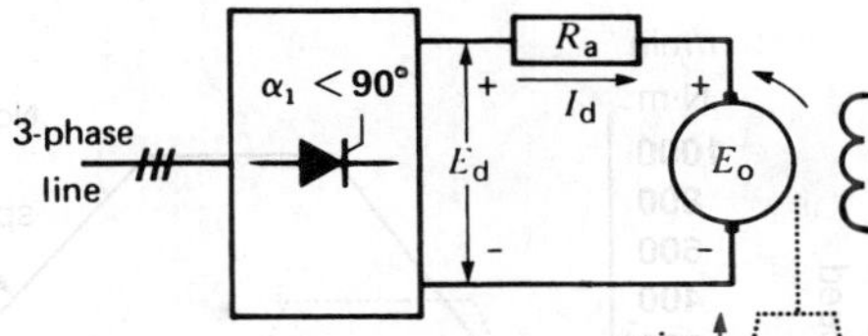

Figure 22.9
Hoist raising a load.

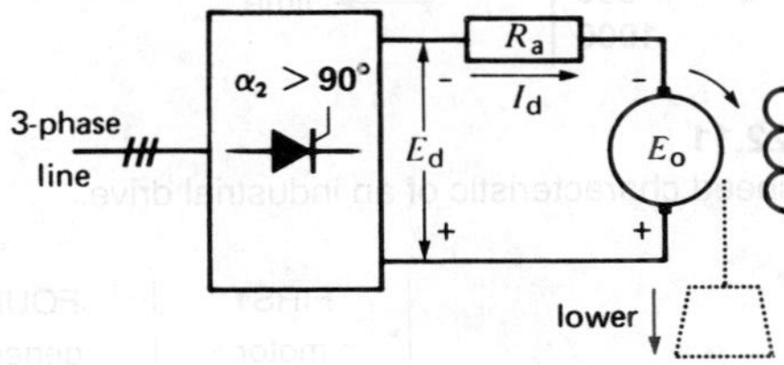

Figure 22.10
Hoist lowering a load.

22.6 Two-quadrant control with positive torque

So far, we have discussed various ways to obtain torque-speed control when the torque reverses. However, many industrial drives involve torques that always act in one direction, even when the speed reverses. Hoists and elevators fall into this category because gravity always acts downward whether the load moves up or down. Operation is therefore in quadrants 1 and 2.

Consider a hoist driven by a shunt motor having constant field excitation. The armature is connected to the output of a 3-phase, 6-pulse converter. When the load is being raised, the motor absorbs power from the converter. Consequently, the converter acts as a rectifier (Fig. 22.9). The lifting speed depends directly upon the converter voltage E_d. The armature current depends upon the weight of the load.

When the load is being lowered, the motor reverses, which changes the polarity of E_0. However, the descending weight delivers power to the motor, and so it becomes a generator. We can feed the resulting electric power into the ac line by making the converter act as an inverter. The gate pulses are simply delayed by more than 90°, and E_d is adjusted to obtain the desired current flow (Fig. 22.10).

Hoisting and lowering can, therefore, be done in a stepless manner and no field or armature reversal is required. However, the empty hook may not descend by itself. The downward motion must then be assisted by the motor, which means that either the field or armature has to be reversed.

22.7 Four-quadrant drive

We can readily achieve 4-quadrant drive of a dc machine by using a *single* converter combined with either field or armature reversal. However, a great deal of switching may be required. Four-quadrant control is possible without field or armature reversal by using two converters operating back-to-back. They may function either alternately or simultaneously, as previously described in Sections 22.4 and 22.5.

The following example illustrates 4-quadrant control of an industrial drive.

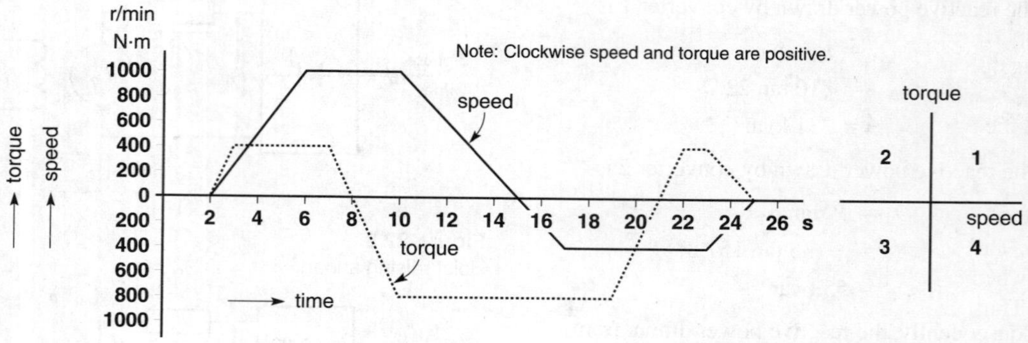

Figure 22.11
Torque-speed characteristic of an industrial drive.

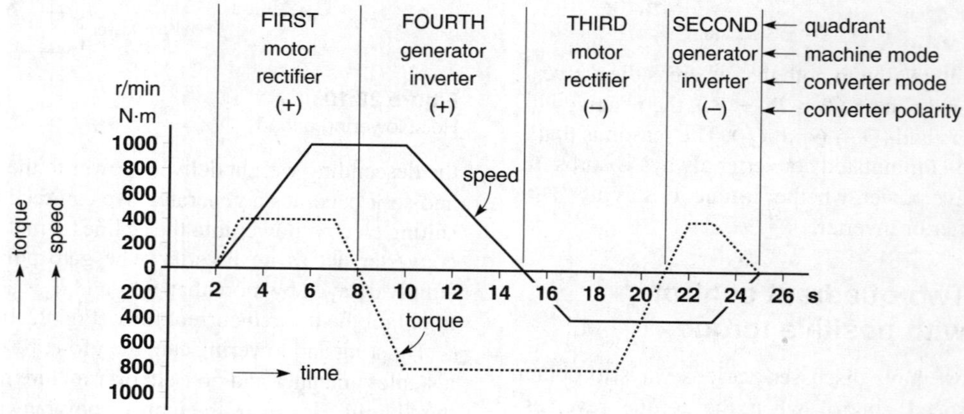

Figure 22.12
See Example 22-4.

Example 22-4

An industrial drive has to develop the torque-speed characteristic given in Fig. 22.11. A dc shunt motor is used, powered by two converters operating back-to-back. The converters function alternately (only one at a time) as explained in Section 22.4. Determine the state of each converter over the 26-second operating period, and indicate the polarity at the terminals of the dc machine. The speed and torque are considered positive when acting clockwise.

Solution

The analysis of such a drive is simplified by subdividing the torque-speed curves into the respective four quadrants. In doing so, we look for those moments when either the torque or speed pass through zero. These moments always coincide with the transition from one quadrant to another. Referring to Fig. 22.11, the speed or torque passes through zero at 2, 8, 15, 21, and 25 s.

We draw vertical lines through these points (Fig. 22.12). We then examine whether the torque and speed are positive or negative during each subdivided interval. Knowing the respective signs, we can immediately state in which quadrant the motor is operating. For example, during the interval from 2 s to 8 s, both the torque and speed are positive. Consequently, the machine is operating in quadrant 1.

On the other hand, in the interval from 21 s to 25 s, the speed is negative and the torque positive, indicating operation in quadrant 2.

Knowing the quadrant, we know whether the machine functions as a motor or generator. Finally, assuming that a positive (clockwise) speed corresponds to a positive armature voltage (Fig. 22.13a), we can deduce the required direction of current flow. This tells us which converter is in operation, and whether it acts as a rectifier or inverter.

Thus, taking the interval from 21 to 25 seconds, it is clear that the machine acts as a generator. Consequently, one of the two converters *must* function as an inverter. But which one? To answer the question, we first look at the polarity of the armature. Because the speed is negative, the armature polarity is negative, as shown in Fig. 22.13b. Current flows out of the positive terminal because the machine acts as a generator. Only converter 1 can carry this direction of current flow, and so it is the one in operation.

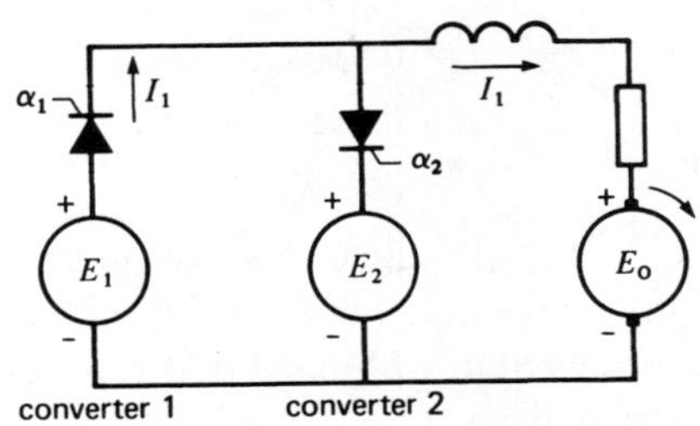

Figure 22.13a
Polarities when the speed is positive.

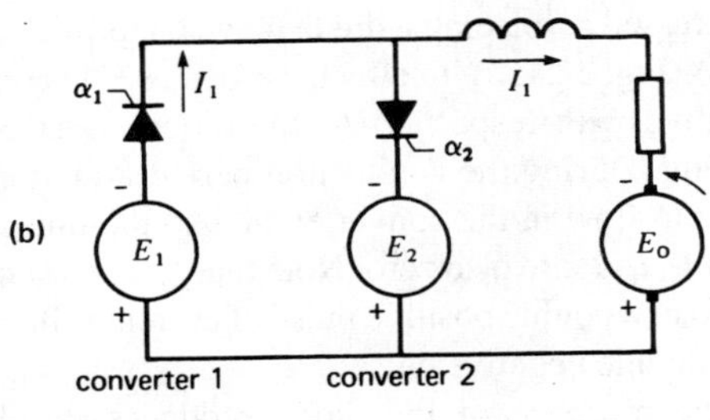

Figure 22.13b
Interval from 21 s to 25 s.

A similar line of reasoning enables us to determine the operating mode of each converter for the other intervals. The results are tabulated in Table 22A. We encourage the reader to verify them.

TABLE 22A

Time interval	Operating mode: Converter 1	Operating mode: Converter 2
2–8 s	rectifier	off
8–15 s	off	inverter
15–21 s	off	rectifier
21–25 s	inverter	off

22.8 Six-pulse converter with freewheeling diode

When a dc motor is started up, we can significantly reduce the reactive power absorbed by the converter by placing a diode across the converter output (Fig. 22.15). The usefulness of this freewheeling diode is best illustrated by a numerical example.

Suppose a dc motor has the following characteristics:

rated power: 100 hp

rated armature voltage: 240 V

rated armature current: 320 A

armature resistance: 25 mΩ

armature inductance: 1.7 mH

We begin our analysis using a conventional 6-pulse converter to drive the motor. The converter (rectifier) is fed by a 3-phase, 184 V, 60 Hz line. We will analyze the voltages and currents when the motor is at standstill with rated current flowing in the armature. As a result, the motor will develop rated torque. The circuit of the motor and converter is shown in Fig. 22.14a.

The motor is stalled and the value of E_d is only that needed to supply the armature *IR* drop.

$$E_d = IR = 320 \text{ A} \times 25 \text{ m}\Omega$$
$$= 8 \text{ V}$$

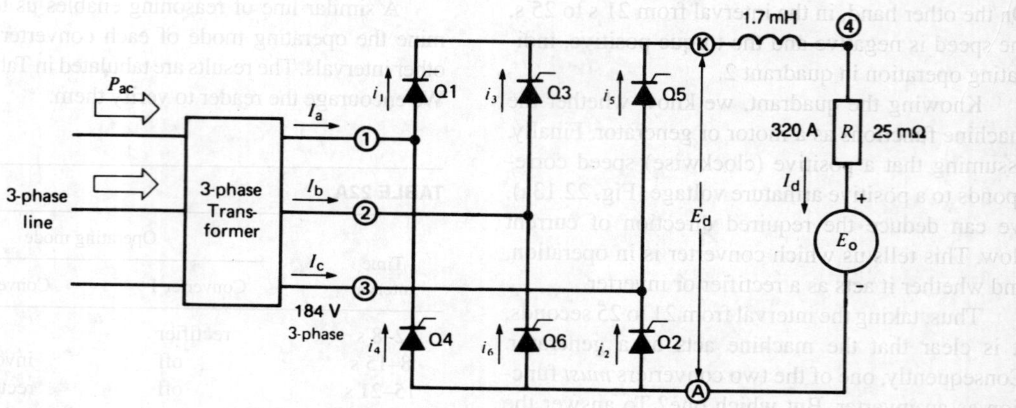

Figure 22.14a
Conventional rectifier supplying rated current to a stalled dc armature. Firing angle is 88.15°.

To develop this dc voltage, the required firing angle is given by

$$E_d = 1.35\, E \cos \alpha$$

$$8 = 1.35 \times 184 \cos \alpha$$

whence

$$\cos \alpha = 0.0322$$

and so

$$\alpha = 88.15°$$

The active ac power P supplied to the converter is necessarily equal to that absorbed by the armature. Thus,

$$P = E_d I_d = 8 \times 320 = 2560 \text{ W}$$

The reactive power Q absorbed by the converter is, therefore,

$$Q = P \tan \alpha = 2560 \tan 88.15°$$
$$= 79.25 \text{ kvar}$$

Note that the reactive power is 31 times greater than the active power.

The line-to-neutral voltage E_{1N} and the corresponding line current I_a are shown in Fig. 22.14b. Note that Q1 is triggered 88.15° after θ_o. As a result, the center of the positive current pulse lags 88.15° behind the positive voltage peak E_{1N}. Thus, I_a lags almost 90° behind E_{1N} and that is why the reactive power is so large. The same remarks apply to I_b, I_c, and their respective line-to-neutral voltages.

The effective value of the line current is

$$I = 0.816\, I_d \qquad (21.6)$$
$$= 0.816 \times 320$$
$$= 261 \text{ A}$$

Fig. 22.14b also shows that voltage E_{KA} across the armature is a sawtooth wave. The peak value oscillates between +137 V and −123 V, but the average value of the wave is only 8 V.

It would be useful if we could remove the negative voltages in E_{KA}. The reason is that for a given firing angle (such as 88.15°) the average voltage E_d will then increase. The negative voltages can be suppressed by placing a diode between terminals K and A (Fig. 22.15a). In effect, as soon as K becomes negative with respect to A, the diode starts conducting. During the conduction period all currents cease to flow in the converter, and so the line currents I_a, I_b, I_c are also zero. Note that I_a is now composed of a double positive pulse of current followed by a double negative pulse.

The presence of the diode produces the E_{KA} waveshape shown in Fig. 22.15a. The negative volt-

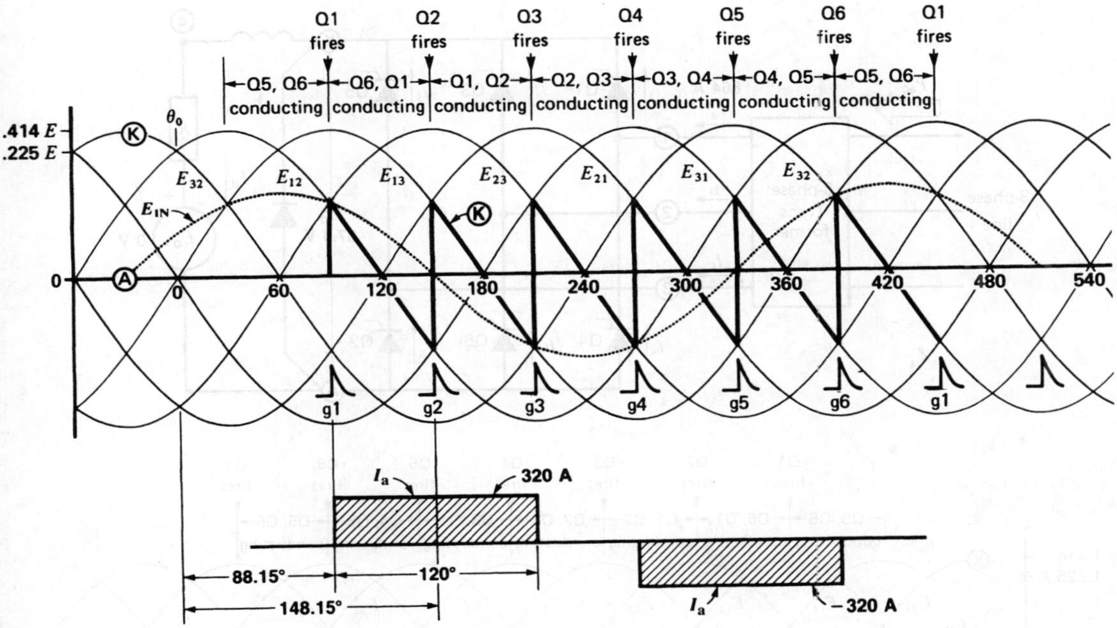

Figure 22.14b
Voltage and current waveshapes when armature is stalled while developing rated torque.

ages are clipped off, and so the dc voltage across the armature becomes much larger than 8 V. As a result, the armature current also becomes much greater than 320 A. In order to make $E_d = 8$ V, we must increase the firing angle α. It can be proved that the dc voltage of a 3-phase, 6-pulse converter equipped with such a freewheeling diode is given by

$$E_d = 1.35\,E(1 - \cos\,[120 - \alpha]) \qquad (22.1)$$

where

E_d = dc voltage [V]

E = effective value of line-to-line voltage [V]

α = firing angle (between 60° and 120°) [°]

1.35 = a constant that applies only when α lies between 60° and 120° [exact value $= 3\sqrt{2}/\pi$]

In our example, the dc voltage with a firing angle of 88.15° is

$$\begin{aligned}E_d &= 1.35\,E\,(1 - \cos\,[120 - \alpha])\\ &= 1.35 \times 184\,(1 - \cos\,[120 - 88.15])\\ &= 1.35 \times 184\,(1 - \cos 31.85°)\\ &= 37.4 \text{ V}\end{aligned}$$

The resulting armature current would, therefore, be

$$I = 37.4/0.025 = 1496 \text{ A}$$

This is nearly five times the rated current, which is clearly unacceptable.

In order to obtain the desired $E_d = 8$ V, we must increase the firing angle such that

$$E_d = 1.35\,E\,(1 - \cos\,[120 - \alpha]) \qquad (22.1)$$

$$8 = 1.35 \times 184\,(1 - \cos\,[120 - \alpha])$$

$$0.9678 = \cos\,(120 - \alpha)$$

therefore

$$120 - \alpha = \arccos 0.9678 = 14.6°$$

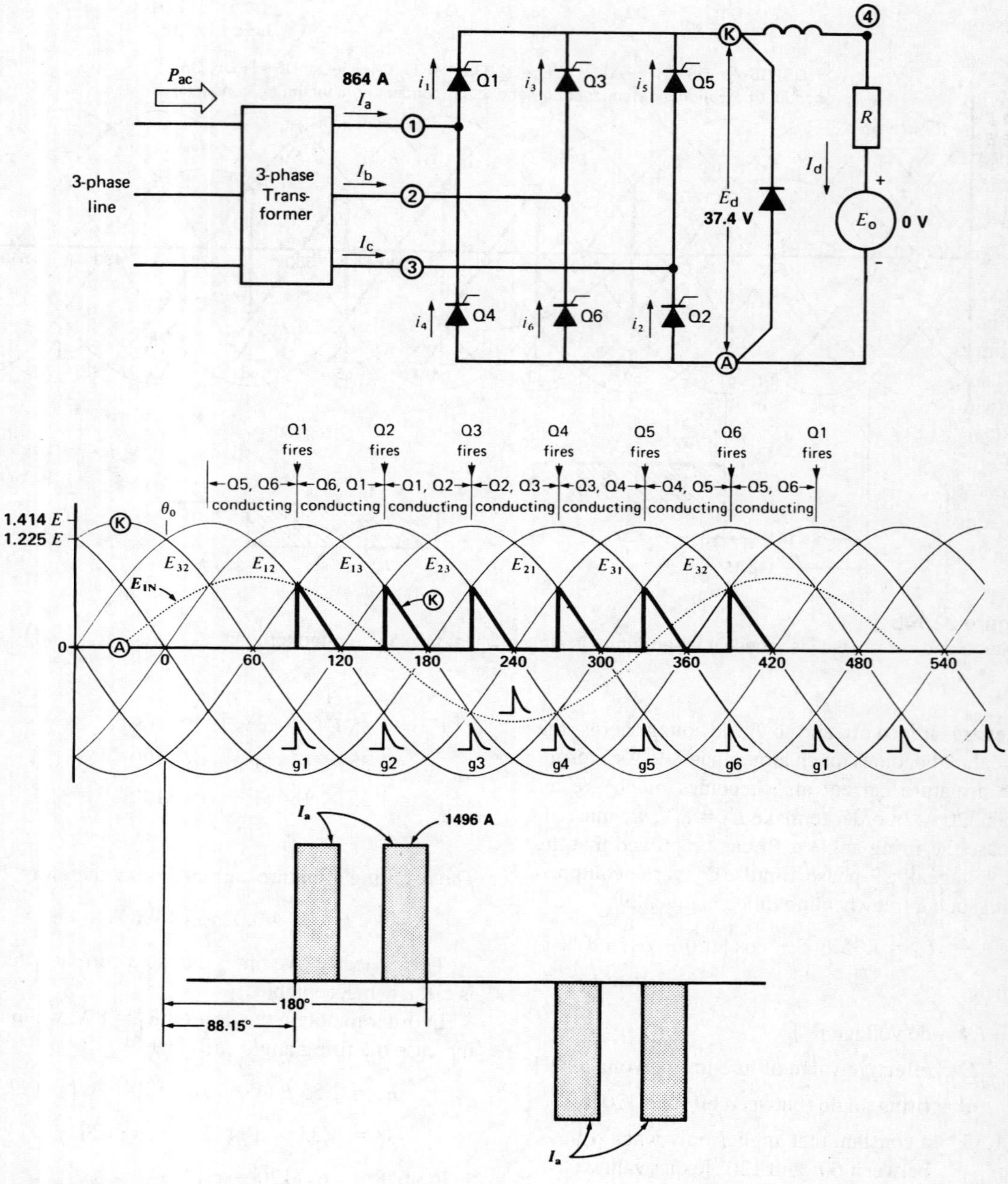

Figure 22.15a
Conventional rectifier and freewheeling diode supplying current to a stalled dc armature. Firing angle is 88.15°.

consequently,

$$\alpha = 120 - 14.6° = 105.4°$$

With this firing angle, the waveshapes of E_{KA} and I_a are as shown in Fig. 22.15b. The positive half-cycle of I_a is composed of two current pulses. Each has an amplitude of 320 A and a duration of (120° − 105.4°) = 14.6°. The effective value of I_a, therefore,

$$I_a(\text{eff}) = 320\sqrt{(4 \times 14.6)/360} = 128.9 \text{ A}$$

Thus, the 3-phase line currents are much lower than in Fig. 22.14a, even though the dc current in the armature is the same.

The positive half-cycle of current I_a is centered midway between 105.4° and 180° (see Fig. 22.15b). Thus, angle $\Phi_i = (105.4 + 180)/2 = 142.7°$. On the other hand, the positive peak of E_{IN} occurs at $\Phi_c = 60°$.

Consequently, the fundamental component of I_a lags by angle $\Phi_d = (142.7° - 60°) = 82.7°$ behind E_{IN}. The displacement angle is therefore 82.7° and the displacement power factor is

$$\text{PF (displacement)} = \cos 82.7° = 0.127$$

The active power P drawn from the 3-phase line is again 320 A × 8 V = 2.56 kW. The reactive power Q is

$$Q = P \tan(\text{displacement angle})$$
$$= 2.56 \tan 82.7°$$
$$= 20 \text{ kvar}$$

Thus, with the freewheeling diode the converter only draws 20 kvar from the line, compared to 79.26 kvar with no diode.

The reader should note that the freewheeling diode only begins to produce an effect when the firing angle lies between 60° and 120°. It is only then that E_{KA} starts to become negative, thus permitting the diode to exert its influence. The line current is

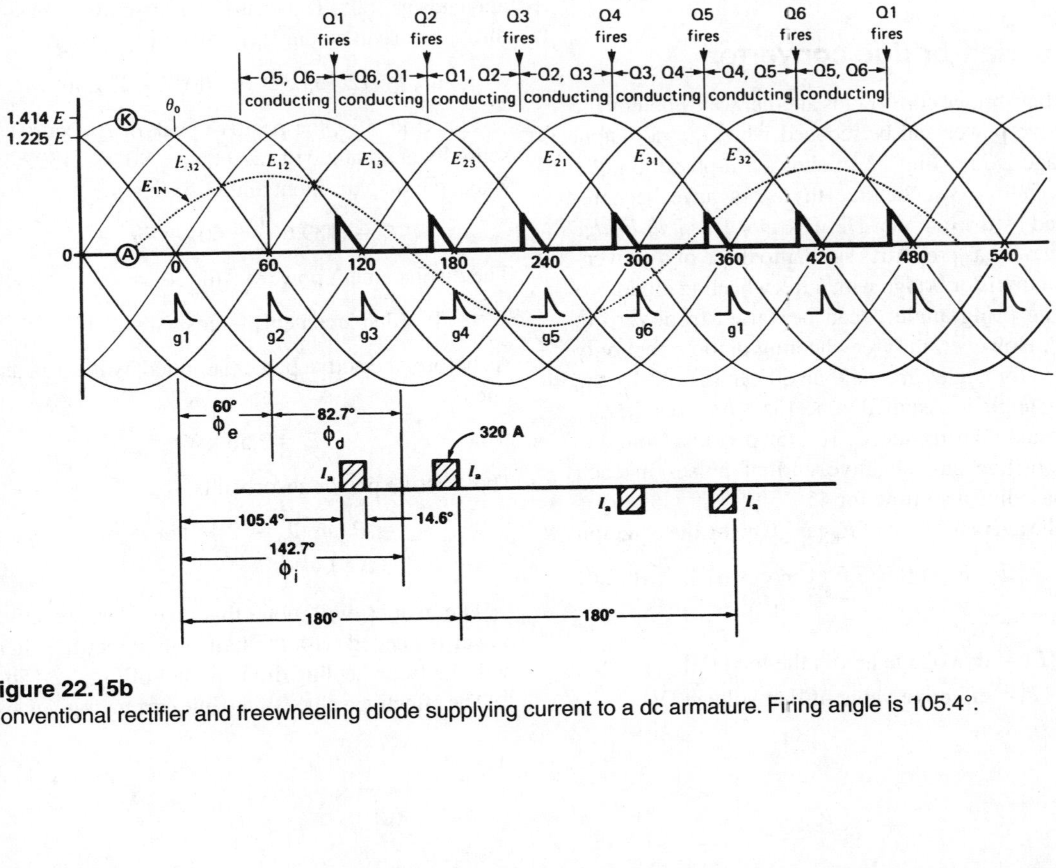

Figure 22.15b
Conventional rectifier and freewheeling diode supplying current to a dc armature. Firing angle is 105.4°.

not sinusoidal and possesses a strong harmonic content. It can be shown that the fundamental component of the line current lags behind the corresponding line-to-neutral voltage by an angle Φ_d given by

$$\Phi_d = 30° + \alpha/2 \tag{22.2}$$

where

Φ_d = displacement phase angle [°]
α = firing angle (must lie between 60° and 120°) [°]
30° = a constant for this type of converter

The effective value of the line current is given by

$$I = I_d\sqrt{(120 - \alpha)/90} \tag{22.3}$$

The displacement power factor is given by

$$\text{PF (displacement)} = \cos \Phi_d \tag{22.4}$$

The displacement angle Φ_d can be used to calculate the reactive power Q:

$$Q = P \tan \Phi_d \tag{22.5}$$

22.9 Half-bridge converter

The half-bridge converter is another way whereby the reactive power can be reduced when the dc output voltage is low. Fig. 22.16 shows a 3-phase, 6-pulse converter in which three thyristors have been replaced by three diodes D2, D4, D6. This *half-bridge converter* has properties similar to those of a conventional thyristor bridge with a freewheeling diode.

The firing angle α can be varied from zero to 180°. However, the freewheeling diode effect only begins for angles greater than 60°. In Fig. 22.16, the firing angle is assumed to be 135°. As a result, E_{KA} is positive during successive 45° periods. Note that the positive and negative current pulses in each 3-phase line also flow for 45°.

The average value of E_{KA} is given by the equation

$$E_d = 0.675\, E\, (1 + \cos \alpha) \tag{22.6}$$

in which

E_d = dc voltage across the load [V]
E = effective value of line voltage [V]
α = firing angle (must lie between 60° and 180°) [°]
0.675 = a constant that only applies for α between 60° and 180° [exact value is $(1.5\sqrt{2})/\pi$]

Using the same example as in Section 22.8, the firing angle needed to produce E_d = 8 V is given by

$$E_d = 0.675\, E\, (1 + \cos \alpha)$$
$$8 = 0.675 \times 184\, (1 + \cos \alpha)$$
$$-0.936 = \cos \alpha$$

whence

$$\alpha = 159.32°$$

The line-current pulses have an amplitude equal to the dc armature current, namely 320 A. The duration of the current pulses is (180° − 159.32°) = 20.68°. Based upon the example of Fig. 22.16, the positive current pulse starts at 159.32° and ends at 180°. The negative current pulse starts at 279.32° and ends at 300°. Thus, current I_a essentially passes through zero at an angle Φ_o given by

$$\Phi_o = 1/2(159.32° + 300°) = 229.66°$$

Consequently, the positive peak of I_a occurs essentially at an angle of (229.66° − 90°) = 139.66°. Thus, the displacement angle is

$$\Phi_d = (139.66° - 60) = 79.66°$$

The displacement power factor is

$$\text{PF (displacement)} = \cos \Phi_d = 0.179$$

As before, the active power supplied by the 3-phase line is

$$P = 2.56 \text{ kW}$$

The reactive power absorbed is

$$Q = P \tan \Phi_d = 2.56 \tan 79.66°$$
$$= 14 \text{ kvar}$$

The reader will note that even less reactive power is needed with the half-bridge rectifier than with the freewheeling diode circuit of Fig. 22.15b.

The effective value I of the line current is given by

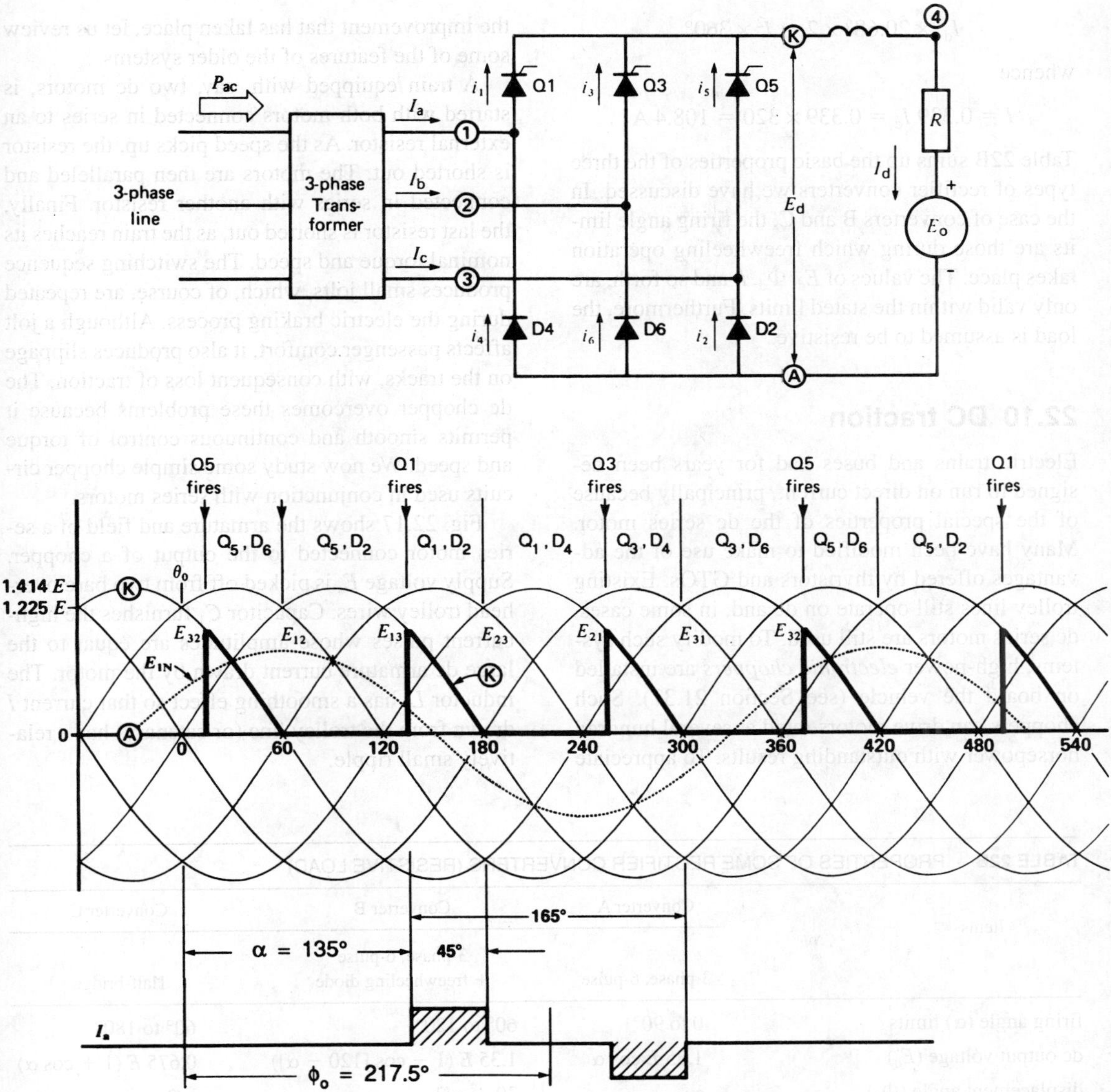

Figure 22.16
Half-bridge rectifier. Firing angle is 135°.

$$I_d^2 \times 20.68° \times 2 = I^2 \times 360°$$

whence

$$I = 0.339\ I_d = 0.339 \times 320 = 108.4\ \text{A}$$

Table 22B sums up the basic properties of the three types of rectifier converters we have discussed. In the case of converters B and C, the firing angle limits are those during which freewheeling operation takes place. The values of E_d, Φ_d, I, and so forth, are only valid within the stated limits. Furthermore, the load is assumed to be resistive.

22.10 DC traction

Electric trains and buses had for years been designed to run on direct current, principally because of the special properties of the dc series motor. Many have been modified to make use of the advantages offered by thyristors and GTOs. Existing trolley lines still operate on dc and, in some cases, dc series motors are still used. To modify such systems, high-power *electronic choppers* are installed on board the vehicle (see Section 21.37). Such choppers can drive motors rated at several hundred horsepower with outstanding results. To appreciate the improvement that has taken place, let us review some of the features of the older systems.

A train equipped with, say, two dc motors, is started with both motors connected in series to an external resistor. As the speed picks up, the resistor is shorted out. The motors are then paralleled and connected in series with another resistor. Finally, the last resistor is shorted out, as the train reaches its nominal torque and speed. The switching sequence produces small jolts, which, of course, are repeated during the electric braking process. Although a jolt affects passenger comfort, it also produces slippage on the tracks, with consequent loss of traction. The dc chopper overcomes these problems because it permits smooth and continuous control of torque and speed. We now study some simple chopper circuits used in conjunction with series motors.

Fig. 22.17 shows the armature and field of a series motor connected to the output of a chopper. Supply voltage E_s is picked off from two bare overhead trolley wires. Capacitor C_1 furnishes the high-current pulses whose amplitudes are equal to the large dc armature current drawn by the motor. The inductor L_1 has a smoothing effect so that current I drawn from the trolley line (or catenary) has a relatively small ripple.

TABLE 22B PROPERTIES OF SOME RECTIFIER CONVERTERS (RESISTIVE LOAD)

Items	Converter A 3-phase, 6-pulse	Converter B 3-phase, 6-pulse + freewheeling diode	Converter C Half-bridge
firing angle (α) limits	0 to 90°	60° to 120°	60° to 180°
dc output voltage (E_d)	$1.35\ E \cos \alpha$	$1.35\ E\ (1 - \cos\ [120 - \alpha])$	$0.675\ E\ (1 + \cos \alpha)$
displacement angle (Φ_d)	α	$30 + \alpha/2$	$\alpha/2$
PF (displacement) = $\cos \Phi_d$	$\cos \alpha$	$\cos\ (30 + \alpha/2)$	$\cos \alpha/2$
effective line current (I)	$0.816\ I_d$	$I_d \sqrt{(120 - \alpha) / 90}$	$I_d \sqrt{(180 - \alpha) / 180}$
Total apparent power (S)	$EI\sqrt{3}$	$EI\sqrt{3}$	$EI\sqrt{3}$
Total active power (P)	$E_d I_d$	$E_d I_d$	$E_d I_d$
Total reactive power (Q)	$P \tan \Phi_d$	$P \tan \Phi_d$	$P \tan \Phi_d$
PF (total)	P/S	P/S	P/S

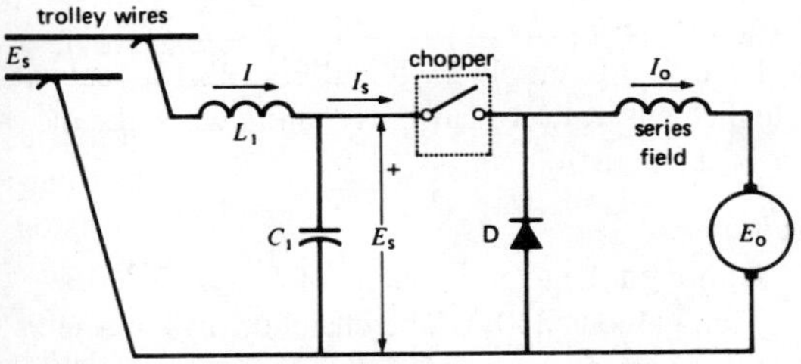

Figure 22.17
Direct-current series motor driven by a chopper. The chopper is not a switch as shown, but a force-commutated SCR.

As far as the motor is concerned, the total inductance of the armature and series field is large enough to store and release the energy needed during the chopper cycle. Consequently, no external inductor is required. When the motor starts up, a low chopper frequency is used, typically 50 Hz. The corresponding *on* time T_a is typically 500 μs. In some older systems, T_a is kept constant while the switching frequency varies. The top frequency (about 2000 Hz) is limited by the switching and turn-off time of the thyristors.

Most choppers function at constant frequency, but with a variable *on* time T_a. In still more sophisticated controls, both the frequency and T_a are varied. In such cases, T_a may range from 20 μs to 800 μs. Nevertheless, the basic chopper operation remains the same, no matter how the on-off switching times are varied. Thus, the chopper output voltage E_0 is related to the input voltage E_s by the equation

$$E_0 = E_s f T_a = DE_s \qquad (21.21)$$

where D is the duty cycle, f is the chopper frequency and T_a is the *on* time.

Example 22-5

A trolley-bus is driven by a 150 hp, 1500 r/min, 600 V series motor. The nominal full-load current is 200 A and the total resistance of the armature and field is 0.1 Ω. The bus is fed from a 700 V dc line.

A chopper controls the torque and speed. The chopper frequency varies from 50 Hz to 1600 Hz, but the *on* time T_a is fixed at 600 μs.

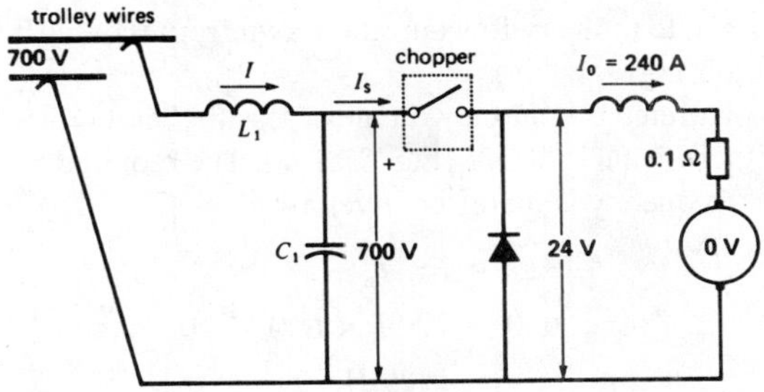

Figure 22.18a
See Example 22-5.

a. Calculate the chopper frequency and the current drawn from the line when the motor is at standstill and drawing a current of 240 A.
b. Calculate the chopper frequency when the motor delivers its rated output.

Solution

a. Referring to Fig. 22.18a, the armature *IR* drop is 240 A × 0.1 Ω = 24 V, and the cemf is zero because the motor is at standstill.

Consequently, E_0 = 24 V and E_s = 700 V. We can find the frequency from

$$E_0 = E_s f T_a \qquad (21.14)$$

$$24 = 700 f \times 600 \times 10^{-6}$$

$$f = 57.14 \text{ Hz}$$

$$T_a + T_b = 1/f = 1/57.14$$

$$= 17\,500 \text{ μs (Fig. 22.18b)}$$

The dc current drawn from the catenary is

$$I = I_s = P/E_s = 24 \times 240/700$$

$$= 8.23 \text{ A}$$

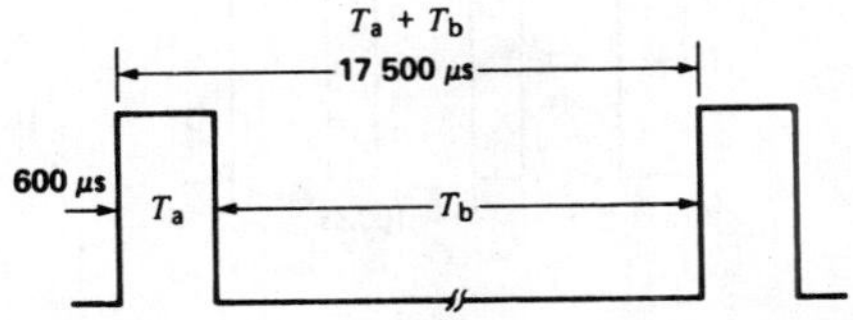

Figure 22.18b
Current pulses I_s drawn by the chopper from the 700 V source when the motor is stalled.

(Note the very low current drawn from the line during start-up.)

b. At rated output the voltage across the motor terminals is 600 V (Fig. 22.19a). The required frequency is therefore given by

$$E_0 = E_s f T_a$$
$$600 = 700 f \times 600 \times 10^{-6}$$
$$f = 1429 \text{ Hz}$$
$$T_a + T_b = 1/f = 1/1429$$
$$= 700 \ \mu\text{s (Fig. 22.19b)}$$

Line current I

$$I = I_s = P/E_s$$
$$= 600 \times 200/700$$
$$= 171 \text{ A}$$

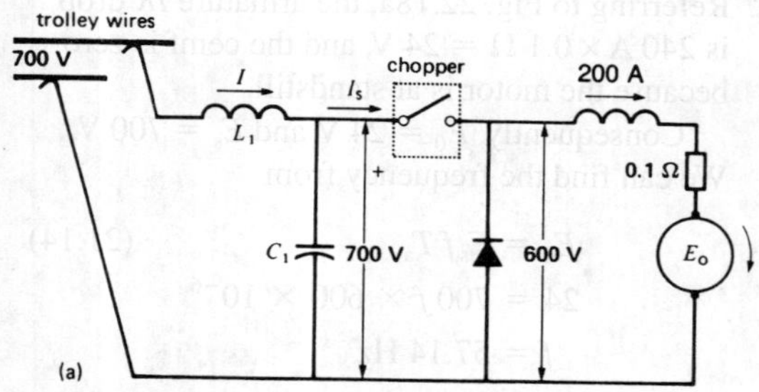

Figure 22.19a
Conditions when the motor is running at rated torque and speed.

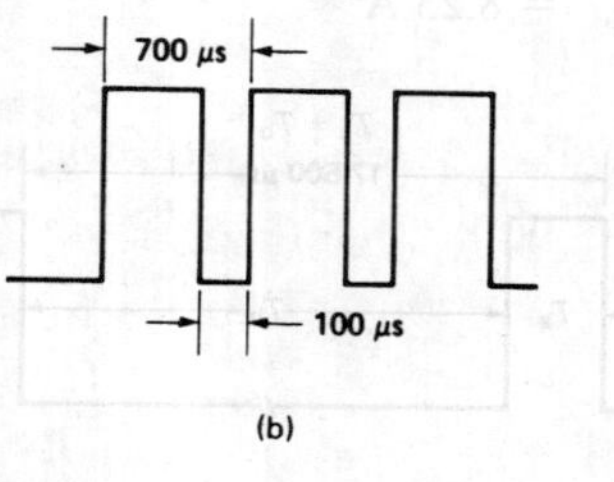

Figure 22.19b
Corresponding current pulses I_s drawn by the chopper from the 700 V source.

Example 22-6

Referring to Example 22-5 and Fig. 22.18a, calculate the peak value of currents I_s and I when the motor is at standstill.

Solution

a. Although the average value of I_s is 8.23 A, its peak value is 240 A. The current flows in a series of brief, sharp pulses. On the other hand, the armature current I_o is steady at 240 A.

b. The average value of line current I is 8.23 A. The voltage across the capacitor fluctuates and so current I will have a ripple because inductor L_1 does not have infinite inductance. Consequently, the peak value of I will be slightly greater than the average value.

22.11 Motor drive using a dc-to-dc switching converter

In Section 21.42 we studied the 4-quadrant dc-to-dc converter. It is eminently suited for dc motor drives. Consider Fig. 22.20 in which a 3-phase source is converted to dc by means of a 6-pulse uncontrolled rectifier. The dc output is applied to a 4-quadrant switching converter via a filter L_d, C. The converter is composed of IGBT switches Q1, Q2, Q3, Q4 and their associated diodes. Its output terminals A, B are connected to the armature of a dc motor. The armature is composed of the armature resistance R_a, armature inductance L_a, and the counter emf E_o. The shunt field is excited from a separate source (not shown).

Currents I_1, I_2, and I_a represent instantaneous values. Current I_d supplied by the rectifier is assumed to be constant and ripple-free. As we proceed, we will make distinctions between instantaneous and average, or dc values.

We could analyze the drive in terms of symbolic equations, but such an algebraic approach lacks the interest and impact of dealing with numerical values. Consequently, we will use two examples to illustrate the factors that come into play in a dc drive. The first examines the system when the motor operates at full-load. The second covers the behavior under dynamic braking conditions.

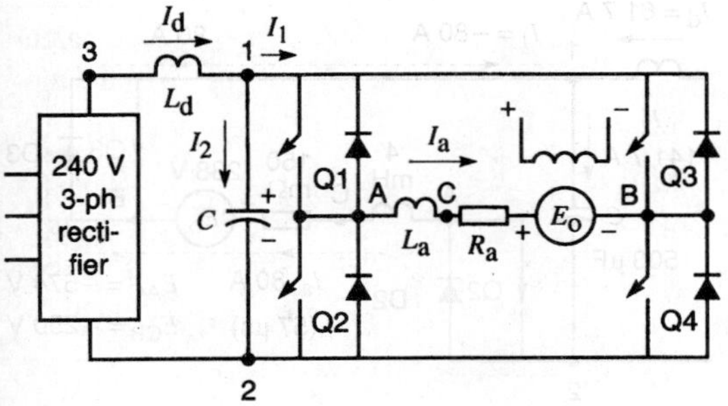

Figure 22.20
DC motor controlled by a 4-quadrant dc-to-dc converter.

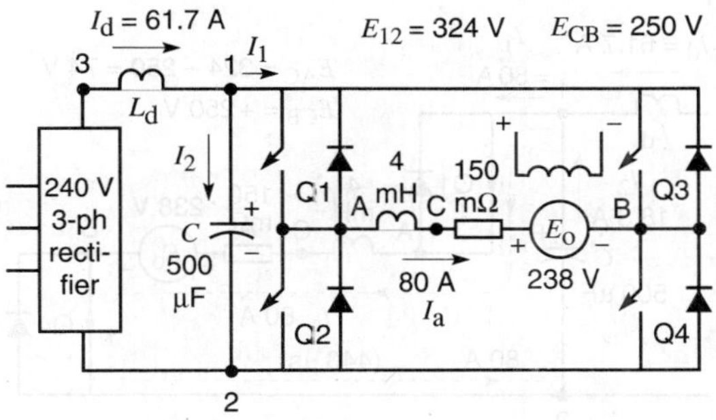

Figure 22.21a
See Example 22-7.

Example 22-7

A 25 hp, 250 V, 900 r/min dc motor is connected to a dc-to-dc converter that operates at a switching frequency of 2 kHz. The converter is fed by a 6-pulse rectifier connected to a 240 V, 3-phase, 60 Hz line (Fig. 22.21a). A 500 μF capacitor C and an inductor L_d act as filters. The armature resistance and inductance are respectively 150 mΩ and 4 mH. The rated dc armature current is 80 A. We wish to determine the following:

a. The required duty cycle when the motor develops its rated torque at rated speed
b. The waveshape of currents I_1, I_2, and I_a
c. The waveshape of voltages E_{12} and E_{AB}

Solution

The 3-phase rectifier produces a dc voltage E_d given by

$$E_d = 1.35\,E \qquad (21.4)$$
$$= 1.35 \times 240\text{ V} = 324\text{ V}$$

This voltage appears between the input terminals 1, 2 of the converter.

In order to produce the rated 250 V across the armature, the duty cycle of the converter has to be adjusted accordingly. The relationship is given by Eq. 21.24:

$$\text{output voltage} = \text{input voltage} \times (2\,D - 1)$$

$$E_{LL} = E_H\,(2\,D - 1) \qquad (21.24)$$

thus,

$$250 = 324\,(2\,D - 1)$$

and so,

$$D = 0.886$$

The 250 V appears between terminals A, B (Fig. 22.21a).

Because the motor develops rated torque, the armature draws its rated current, namely 80 A. The voltage drop in the armature resistance is

$$80\text{ A} \times 0.15\ \Omega = 12\text{ V}$$

The induced armature voltage, or counter emf, at 900 r/min is, therefore,

$$E_o = 250 - 12 = 238\text{ V}$$

The dc power input to the motor is

$$P = 250\text{ V} \times 80\text{ A} = 20\,000\text{ W}$$

Neglecting the losses in the converter, and recalling that the dc output of the rectifier is 324 V, it follows that current I_d is given by

$$324\,I_d = 20\,000$$
$$I_d = 61.7\text{ A}$$

The frequency of the converter is 2 kHz and so the period of one cycle is

$$T = 1/f = 1/2000 = 500\ \mu\text{s}$$

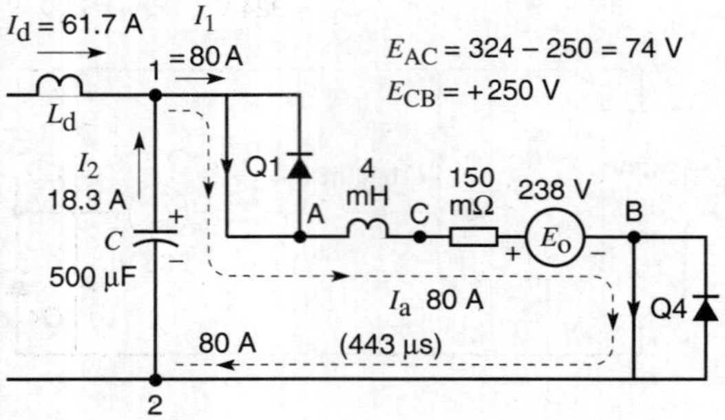

Figure 22.21b
Circuit when Q1 and Q4 are "on." Current I_a is increasing. $E_{CA} = -74$ V.

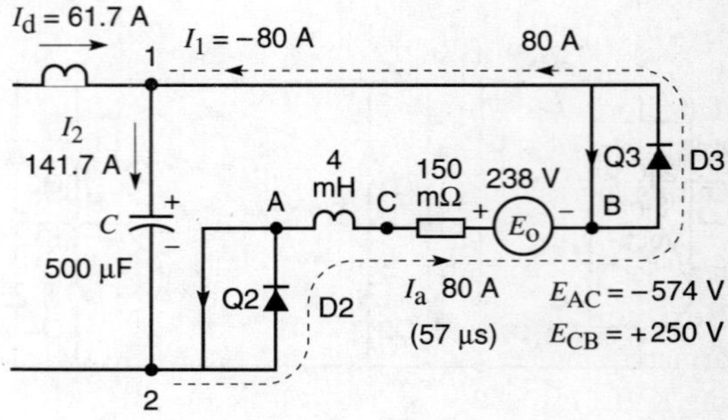

Figure 22.21c
Circuit when D2 and D3 are conducting. Current I_a is decreasing.

The *on* and *off* times of Q1 (and Q4) are, respectively,

$$T_a = DT = 0.886 \times 500 = 443 \ \mu s$$
$$T_b = 500 - 443 = 57 \ \mu s$$

It follows that the corresponding *on* and *off* times of Q2 (and Q3) are 57 μs and 443 μs.

We recall that Q1 and Q4 operate simultaneously, followed by Q2 and Q3, which also open and close simultaneously.

When Q1 and Q4 are conducting, the armature current follows the path shown in Fig. 22.21b. This lasts for 443 μs and during this time I_1 (= 80 A) flows in the positive direction. Note however, that the rectifier only furnishes 61.7 A, whereas the armature current is 80 A. It follows that the difference (80 − 61.7) = 18.3 A must come from the capacitor. The capacitor discharges, causing the voltage across it to drop by an amount ΔE given by

$$\Delta E = Q/C = 18.3 \text{ A} \times 443 \ \mu s/500 \ \mu F = 16 \text{ V}$$

Q1 and Q4 then open for 57 μs. During this interval Q2 and Q3 are closed (Fig. 22.21c), but they cannot carry the armature current because it is flowing opposite to the direction permitted by these IGBTs. However, the current *must* continue to flow because of the armature inductance. Fortunately, a path is offered by the diodes D2 and D3 associated with Q2 and Q3, as shown in the figure. Note that I_1 (= 80 A) now flows toward terminal 1, which is opposite to the direction it had in Fig. 22.21b.

Meanwhile, current I_d furnished by the rectifier continues to flow unchanged because of the presence of inductor L_d. As a result, by Kirchhoff's current law, the current I_2 must flow into the capacitor and its value is (80 + 61.7) = 141.7 A. This highlights the absolute necessity of having a capacitor in the circuit. Without it, the flow of armature current would be inhibited during this 57 μs interval. The capacitor charges up and the increase in voltage ΔE is given by

$$\Delta E = Q/C = 141.7 \text{ A} \times 57 \ \mu s/500 \ \mu F = 16 \text{ V}$$

Note that the increase in voltage across the capacitor during the 57 μs interval is exactly equal to the decrease during the 443 μs interval. The peak-to-peak ripple across the capacitor is, therefore, 16 V. Thus, the voltage between points **1** and **2** fluctuates between (324 + 8) = 332 V and (324 − 8) = 316 V. This 2.5 percent fluctuation does not affect the operation of the motor.

Let us now look more closely at the armature current, particularly as regards the ripple. In Fig. 22.21b the voltage across the armature inductance can be found by applying KVL:

$$E_{AC} + E_{CB} + E_{B2} + E_{21} + E_{1A} = 0$$
$$E_{AC} + 250 + 0 - 324 + 0 = 0$$

Hence

$$E_{AC} = 74 \text{ V}$$

Therefore, the volt seconds accumulated during this 443 μs interval is 74 × 443 = 32 782 μs·V. The resulting increase in armature current ΔI_a is

$$\Delta I_a = A/L_a = 32\,782 \times 10^{-6}/0.004 = 8 \text{ A} \quad (2.28)$$

Next, consider Fig. 22.21c. The voltage across the armature inductance can again be found by applying KVL:

$$E_{AC} + E_{CB} + E_{B1} + E_{12} + E_{2A} = 0$$
$$E_{AC} + 250 + 0 + 324 + 0 = 0$$

Hence, $E_{AC} = -574$ V. This negative voltage causes a very rapid decrease in the armature current. The decrease during the 57 μs interval is given by

$$\Delta I_a = 574 \times 57 \times 10^{-6}/0.004 = 8 \text{ A} \quad (2.28)$$

The 8 A decrease during the 57 μs interval is precisely equal to the increase during the previous 443 μs interval. The peak-to-peak ripple is, therefore, 8 A, which means that the armature current fluctuates between (80 + 4) = 84 A and (80 − 4) = 76 A. Fig. 22.21d shows the waveshapes of the various voltages and currents.

Example 22-8

We now consider the question of dynamic braking. The same motor is used as in Example 22-7, and we assume it is running at 900 r/min at the moment that braking is applied. We further assume that the inertia of the motor and its load is very large. As a result, the speed cannot change quickly. The connection between the converter and the 6-pulse rectifier is removed and a braking resistance of 20 Ω is connected between terminals 1 and 2, along with the 500 μF capacitor (Fig. 22.22). We assume that a braking torque equal to 75 percent of nominal torque is sufficient. Consequently, the required armature current is 0.75 × 80 A = 60 A. The switching frequency remains unchanged at 2 kHz. We wish to determine the following:

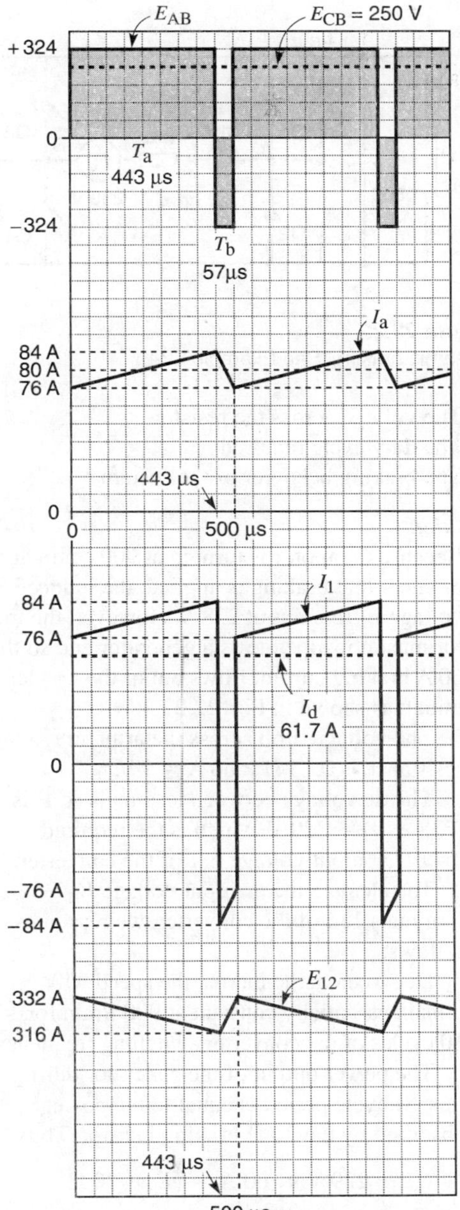

Figure 22.21d
Waveshapes of currents and voltages in Example 22-7.

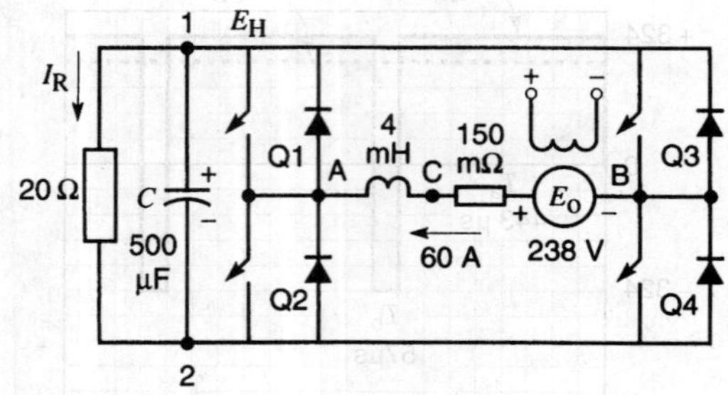

Figure 22.22
Dynamic braking. See Example 22-8.

a. The voltage across the resistor
b. The duty cycle required
c. The braking behavior of the system

Solution

a. Because the motor is turning at 900 r/min at the moment that braking is applied, the induced voltage E_0 remains at 238 V. However, the motor must now operate as a generator and so the 60 A braking current flows out of the (+) terminal, as shown in Fig. 22.22.

The voltage drop across the armature resistance is $0.15\ \Omega \times 60\ A = 9$ V.

The dc voltage between terminals A, B is $(238 - 9) = 229$ V, which is the required *average* output voltage E_{LL} of the converter.

To calculate the dc input voltage E_H between terminals 1, 2 of the converter, we reason as follows:

Due to the large inertia, the speed will remain essentially constant at 900 r/min for, say, 10 cycles of the converter switching frequency.

The power output of the generator during this 10-cycle period is equal to the power absorbed by the 20 Ω braking resistor. Thus,

$$229\ V \times 60\ A = (E_H)^2/20\ \Omega$$

hence $\qquad E_H = E_{12} = 524$ V

This voltage is much higher than the previous operating voltage of 324 V. It is actually an advantage because the higher voltage automatically prevents the input rectifier from continuing to feed power to the drive system. On the other hand, the voltage should not be too high, otherwise it could exceed the withstand capability of the switching IGBT devices.

The *average* current in the resistor is 524 V/20 Ω = 26 A.

b. Knowing the input and output voltages of the converter, we can determine the value of the duty cycle:

$$E_{LL} = E_H(2D - 1) \qquad (21.24)$$

$$229 = 524(2D - 1)$$

Therefore

$$D = 0.72$$

The *on* and *off* times of Q1 (and Q4) are, therefore,

$$T_a = DT = 0.72 \times 500 = 360\ \mu s$$

$$T_b = 500 - 360 = 140\ \mu s$$

It follows that the corresponding *on* and *off* times of Q2 (and Q3) are 140 μs and 360 μs. Q1 and Q4 still operate simultaneously, as do Q2 and Q3.

When Q2 and Q3 are closed, the armature current follows the path shown in Fig. 22.23. This lasts for 140 μs and during this time I_1 (= 60 A) flows out of terminal 1. The current in the resistor is still 26 A. It follows that a current (60 + 26) = 86 A must come from the capacitor. The capacitor discharges, causing the voltage across it to drop by an amount E given by

$$\Delta E = Q/C = 86\ A \times 140\ \mu s/500\ \mu F = 24\ V$$

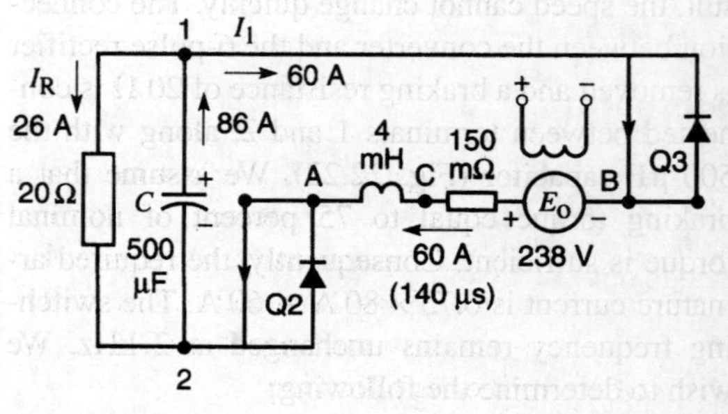

Figure 22.23
Current flows through IGBTs Q2 and Q3.

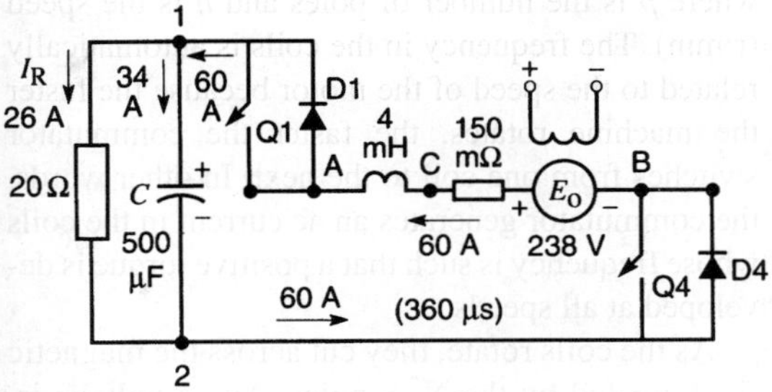

Figure 22.24
Current flows through diodes D1 and D4.

Next, when Q2, Q3 open and Q1, Q4 close, the current has to circulate via diodes D1 and D4 (Fig. 22.24). Applying KCL, a current of (60 − 26) = 34 A must flow into the capacitor during 360 µs. The resulting increase in voltage is

$$\Delta E = Q/C = 34 \text{ A} \times 360 \text{ µs}/500 \text{ µF} = 24 \text{ V}$$

Thus, the increase in voltage during 360 µs is exactly equal to the decrease during the remaining 140 µs of the switching cycle. The voltage across the resistor fluctuates between 524 + 12 = 536 V and 524 − 12 = 512 V.

This example shows that the converter can transfer power to the passive braking resistor. In so doing, the motor will slow down and the voltage between terminals A, B will decrease progressively. By continually adjusting the duty cycle during the deceleration period, it is possible to maintain the 60 A braking current until the speed is only a fraction of its rated value. This adjustment is of course done automatically by means of an electronic control circuit.

22.12 Introduction to brushless dc motors

Some electronic drives involve direct-current motors that do not look at all like dc machines. The reason is that the usual rotating commutator is replaced by a stationary electronic converter. We now discuss the theory behind these so-called "brushless" dc machines.

Consider a 2-pole dc motor having three independent armature coils A, B, and C spaced at 120° to

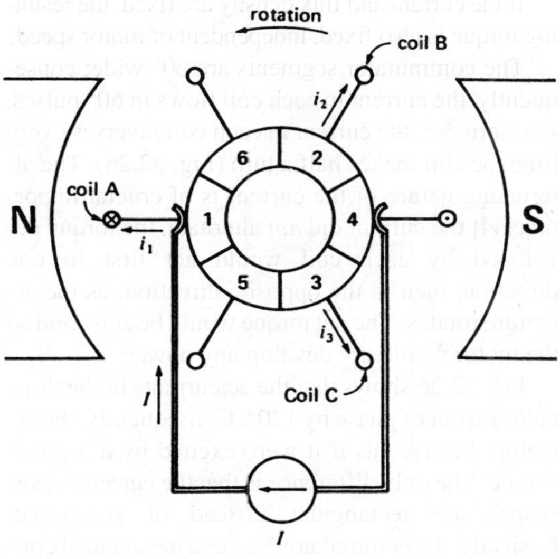

Figure 22.25
Special current-fed dc motor.

each other (Fig. 22.25). The two ends of each coil are connected to diametrically opposite segments of a 6-segment commutator. Two narrow brushes are connected to a *constant-current* source that successively feeds current into the coils as the armature rotates. A permanent magnet N, S creates the magnetic field.

With the armature in the position shown, current flows in coil A and the resulting torque causes the armature to turn counterclockwise. As soon as contact is broken with this coil, it is immediately established in the next coil. Consequently, conductors facing the N pole always carry currents that flow into the page, while those facing the S pole carry currents that flow out of the page (toward the reader). The motor torque is, therefore, continuous and may be expressed by

$$T = kIB \tag{22.7}$$

where

T = motor torque [N·m]

I = current in the conductors [A]

B = average flux density surrounding the current-carrying conductors [T]

k = a constant, dependent upon the number of turns per coil and the size of the armature

If the current and flux density are fixed, the resulting torque is also fixed, independent of motor speed.

The commutator segments are 60° wide; consequently, the current in each coil flows in 60° pulses. Furthermore, the current in each coil reverses every time the coil makes half a turn (Fig. 22.26). The alternating nature of the current is of crucial importance. If the current did *not* alternate, the torque developed by each coil would act first in one direction, then in the opposite direction, as the armature rotates. The net torque would be zero, and so the motor would not develop any power.

Fig. 22.26 shows that the ac currents in the three coils are out of phase by 120°. Consequently, the armature behaves as if it were excited by a 3-phase source. The only difference is that the current waveshapes are rectangular instead of sinusoidal. Basically, the commutator acts as a mechanical converter, changing the dc current from the dc source into ac current in the coils. The frequency of the current is given by

$$f = pn/120 \tag{22.8}$$

Figure 22.26
The dc current changes to ac current in the coils.

where p is the number of poles and n is the speed (r/min). The frequency in the coils is automatically related to the speed of the motor because the faster the machine rotates, the faster the commutator switches from one coil to the next. In other words, the commutator generates an ac current in the coils whose frequency is such that a positive torque is developed at all speeds.

As the coils rotate, they cut across the magnetic field created by the N, S poles. An ac voltage is, therefore, induced in each coil, and its frequency is also given by Eq. 22.8. Furthermore, the voltages are mutually displaced at 120° due to the way the coils are mounted on the armature. The induced ac voltages appear as a dc voltage between the brushes. The reason is that the brushes are always in contact with coils that are moving in the same direction through the magnetic field; consequently, the polarity is always the same (see Section 4.2).

If the brushes were connected to a dc *voltage source E,* the armature would accelerate until the induced voltage E_0 was about equal to E (Section 5.2). What determines the speed when the armature is fed from a *current source,* as it is in our case? The speed will increase until the load torque is equal to the torque developed by the motor. Thus, while the speed of a voltage-fed armature depends upon equilibrium between induced voltage and applied voltage, the speed of a *current-fed* armature depends upon equilibrium between motor torque and load torque. The torque of a mechanical load always rises with increasing speed. Consequently, for a given motor torque, a state of torque equilibrium is always reached, provided the speed is high enough. Care must be taken so that current-fed motors do not run away when the load torque is removed.

22.13 Commutator replaced by reversing switches

Recognizing that each coil in Fig. 22.25 carries an alternating current, we can eliminate the commutator by connecting each coil to a pair of slip-rings and bringing the leads out to a set of mechanical reversing switches (Fig. 22.27). Each switch has four

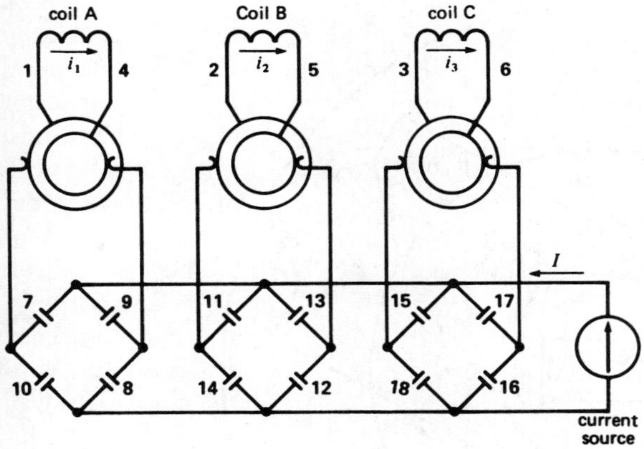

Figure 22.27
The commutator can be replaced by an array of mechanical switches and a set of slip-rings.

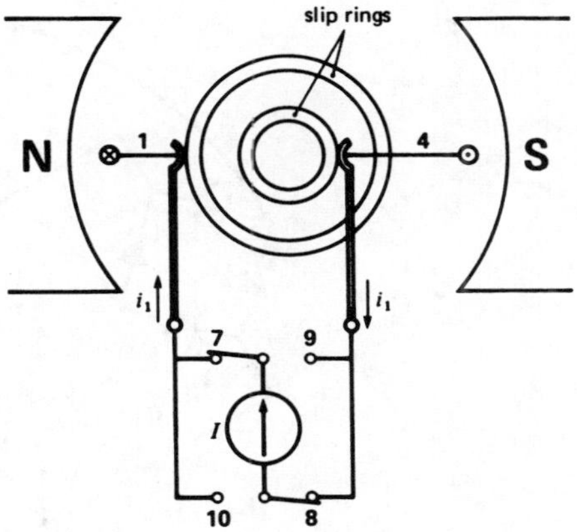

Figure 22.28
Circuit showing how current is controlled in coil A.

normally open contacts. Considering coil A, for example, switch contacts 7 and 8 are closed during the 60° interval when coil side 1 faces the N pole (Fig. 22.28). The contacts are then open for 120° until coil side 4 faces the N pole, whereupon contacts 9 and 10 close for 60°. Consequently, by synchronizing the switch with the *position* of coil A, we obtain the same result as if we used a commutator.

Coils B and C operate the same way, but they are energized at different times. Fig. 22.27 shows how the array of 12 contacts and 6 slip-rings are connected to the current source. The reversing switches really act as a 3-phase mechanical inverter, changing dc power into ac power. The slip-rings merely provide electrical contact between the revolving armature and the stationary switches and the dc power supply.

Clearly, the switching arrangement of Fig. 22.27 is more complex than the original commutator. However, we can simplify matters by making the armature stationary and letting the permanent magnets rotate. By thus literally turning the machine inside out, we can eliminate 6 slip-rings. Then, as a final step, we can replace each contact by a GTO thyristor (Fig. 22.29). The 12 thyristors are triggered by gate signals that depend upon the instantaneous *position* of the revolving rotor.

The dc motor in Fig. 22.29 looks so different from the one in Fig. 22.25 that we would never suspect they have the same properties. And yet they do. For example

1. If we increase the dc current I or the field strength of poles N, S, the torque increases, and consequently, the speed will increase.
2. If we shift the brushes against the direction of rotation in Fig. 22.25, current will start flowing in each coil a little earlier than before. Consequently, the ac current in each coil will *lead* the ac voltage induced across its terminals. We can produce exactly the same effect by firing the thyristors a little earlier in Fig. 22.29. Under these circumstances, the machine furnishes reactive power to the three thyristor bridges, at the same time as it absorbs active power from them.
3. If we shift the brushes by 180°, the current in each *coil* flows in the opposite direction to that shown in Fig. 22.25. However, the induced voltage in each coil remains unchanged because it depends only on the speed and direction of rotation. Consequently, the machine becomes a generator, feeding dc power back into the current source.

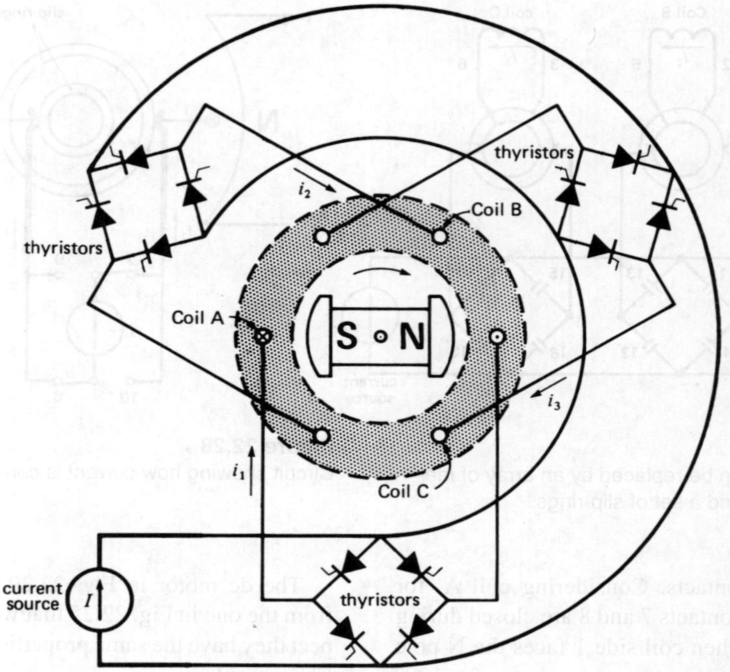

Figure 22.29
The armature is now the stator, and the switches have been replaced by thyristors.

> The same result occurs if we fire the thyristors 180° later in Fig. 22.29. The thyristors then behave as rectifiers feeding power back to the dc current source.

It is now clear that the machines in Figs. 22.25 and 22.29 behave the same way. The only difference between them is that one is equipped with a rotating mechanical commutator, while the other has a stationary electronic commutator composed of 12 thyristors. By firing the thyristors earlier or later, we produce the same effect as shifting the brushes.

22.14 Synchronous motor as a brushless dc machine

The revolving-field motor in Fig. 22.29 is built like a 3-phase synchronous motor. However, because of the way it receives its ac power, it behaves like a "brushless" dc machine. This has a profound effect upon its performance.

First, the "synchronous motor" can never pull out of step because the stator frequency is not fixed, but changes automatically with speed. The reason is that the gates of the SCRs are triggered by a signal that depends upon the instantaneous position of the rotor. For the same reason, the machine has no tendency to oscillate or hunt under sudden load changes.

Second, the phase angle between the ac current in a winding and the ac voltage across it can be modified by altering the timing of the gate pulses. This enables the synchronous motor to operate at leading, lagging, or unity power factor.

Third, because the phase angle between the respective voltages and currents can be fully controlled, the machine can even function as a generator, feeding power back to the dc current source. The thyristor bridges then operate as rectifiers.

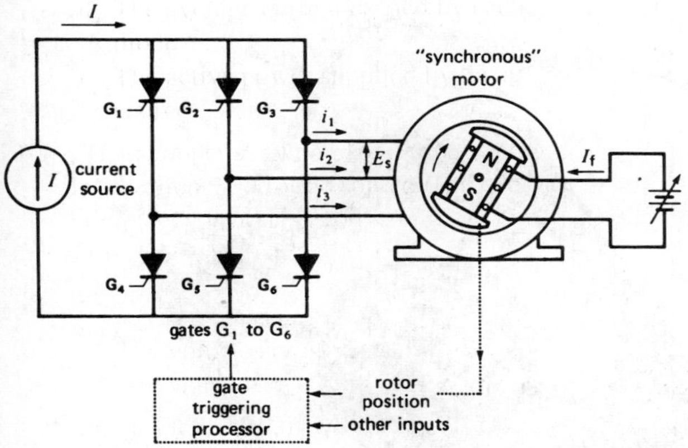

Figure 22.30
Brushless dc motor being driven by a converter.

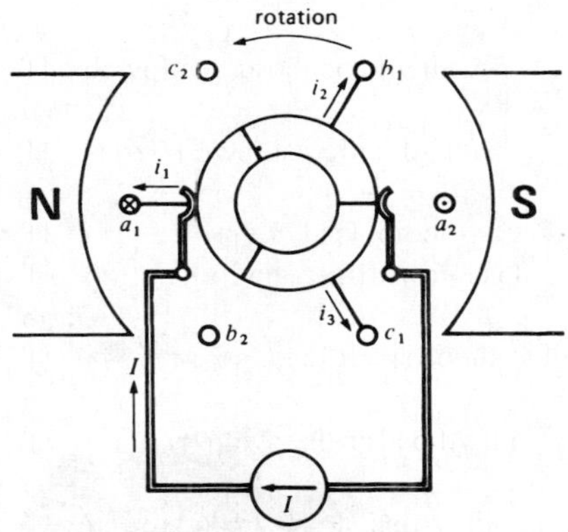

Figure 22.31
This elementary dc motor is equivalent to the entire circuit of Fig. 22.30.

Currents i_1, i_2, i_3 in Fig. 22.29 flow only during 60-degree intervals, as they did in the original dc machine. In practice, the conduction period can be doubled to 120°, by connecting the coils in wye and exciting them by a 3-phase, 6-pulse converter (Fig. 22.30). This reduces the number of thyristors by half. Furthermore, it improves the current-carrying capacity of the windings because the duration of current flow is doubled. Gate triggering is again dependent upon the position of the rotor. The phase angle between line voltage E_s and line current I is modified by firing the gates earlier or later. In the circuit of Fig. 22.30, the power factor of the motor has to be slightly leading to provide the reactive power absorbed by the converter.

As a matter of interest, the converter and motor of Fig. 22.30 could be replaced by the dc motor shown in Fig. 22.31. The armature coils are connected in wye and the 3 leads are soldered to a 3-segment commutator. The respective voltages and currents are identical in the two figures.

22.15 Standard synchronous motor and brushless dc machine

The machine shown in Fig. 22.30 can be made to function as a conventional synchronous motor by applying a *fixed* frequency to the SCR gates. Under these conditions, the input to the gate-triggering processor no longer depends on rotor position or rotor speed.

Obviously then, the behavior of the machine as a commutatorless dc motor or synchronous motor depends upon the way the gates are fired. If the triggering frequency is constant, the machine acts as a synchronous motor. On the other hand, if the triggering frequency depends on the speed of the rotor, it behaves like a commutatorless dc motor.*

22.16 Practical application of a brushless dc motor

One practical application of the brushless dc motor is illustrated in Fig. 22.32. This small blower, rated at 12 V dc has an output of only 1 W. For all its miniature construction, it represents hi-tech concepts that reflect the theory we have just studied.

The motor is a permanent magnet synchronous machine in which the armature is stationary and the field rotates. The armature has four salient poles and two sets of identical coils, A, A and B, B. Coils A, A

* Readers familiar with feedback theory will recognize that the basic distinction between the two machines is that one functions on open loop while the other operates on closed loop.

Figure 22.32
This miniature blower, rated at 1 W, 12 V dc, 2500 r/min, is driven by a brushless dc motor. The 7-blade impeller on the left contains a circular 4-pole permanent magnet that constitutes the revolving field. The stationary armature on the right consists of four coils that are commutated by an electronic switch. The switch is timed by a position-sensing detector; together they behave like a pair of brushes riding on a 4-segment commutator.

are connected so as to produce two N poles when they are excited, as shown in Fig. 22.33. As a result, two consequent south poles are created (S_c in the figure). The same remarks apply to coils B, B; when they are excited, they create two N poles where the two consequent S_c poles existed before. The stationary coil sets A, A and B, B are excited sequentially for equal lengths of time by two electronic switches. We are, therefore, dealing with a brushless dc motor that is actually a 2-phase synchronous motor.

The rotor has four permanent magnet poles and we assume it is rotating clockwise. A stationary pickup device H detects the successive presence of the N and S poles as the rotor sweeps by. If the pickup happens to be under the influence of a rotating N pole, as shown in Fig. 22.33, it produces a signal that causes one of the electronic switches to excite coil set A, A. This produces a cw magnetic torque between the rotor and stator poles, thereby sustaining the cw rotation. The flux pattern between the respective poles at this moment is shown in the figure.

On the other hand, when H lies momentarily under a S pole, it causes the other switch to close, which excites coil set B, B. At the same time, it causes coil set A, A to be de-energized. This also produces a cw torque. As a result, the successive switching action from one set of coils to the other keeps the rotor going. Thanks to the presence of the pickup device (which acts as a position detector), the switching frequency is always related to the speed of rotation.

Fig. 22.34 shows the switching converter that generates the 2-phase power. It consists of two transistors Q1 and Q2, which behave like switches. The

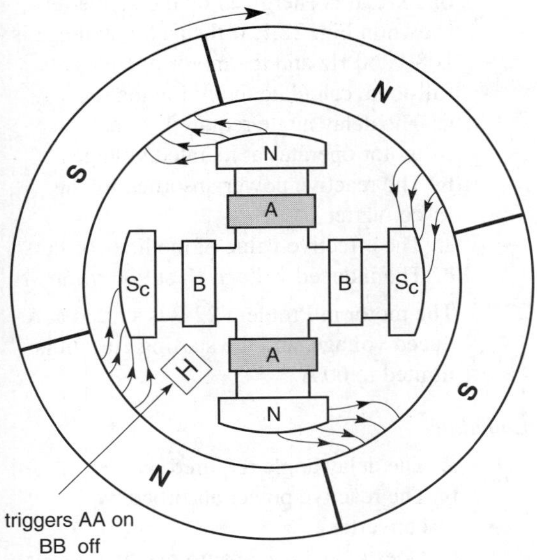

Figure 22.33
Construction of a 12 V, 1 W brushless dc motor for blower application. The coil structure is stationary. At this instant, the Hall detector H triggers coils A on and B off.

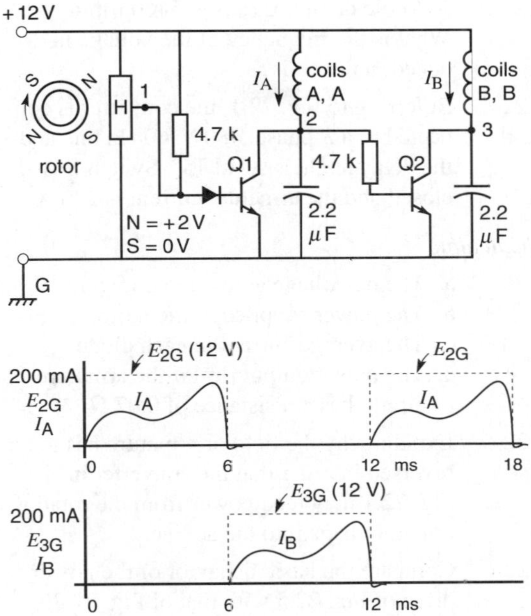

Figure 22.34
Switching circuit of brushless dc motor and waveshapes.

base of Q1 receives the signals from the pickup device H. The latter is actually a Hall effect detector, which produces a voltage of about +2V when under the influence of a N pole. The signal voltage is zero in the presence of a S pole. The 2.2 μF capacitors absorb the inductive energy released every time the coils are de-energized.

Fig. 22.34 also shows the waveshape of the currents in the coil sets. One cycle lasts for about 12 ms, which corresponds to half a turn. The frequency is, therefore, $1/0.012 = 83.3$ Hz and the speed is 2500 r/min.

This small blower serves to cool components in a computer. Its brushless motor offers several advantages. First, it requires absolutely no maintenance, even after thousands of hours of service. Second, it is pollution-free because no dust particles from worn-out brushes can contaminate surrounding components. Third, it is much quieter than a conventional dc motor because brushes are noisy, both mechanically and electrically, on account of brush friction and sparking. Finally, its high reliability ensures that vital computer components will not be damaged for lack of adequate cooling.

In the next chapter we will encounter brushless dc motors of several thousand horsepower. These machines are always connected to a large 3-phase ac source. For this reason, they are discussed in the chapter on ac motor drives.

Questions and Problems

Practical level

22-1 State in which quadrants a dc machine operates
  a. As a motor
  b. As a generator

22-2 A dc machine is turning clockwise in quadrant 3. Does it develop a clockwise or counter-clockwise torque?

22-3 A 2-pole dc motor runs at 5460 r/min. What is the frequency of the voltage induced in the coils?

22-4 Referring to Fig. 22.1, the converter is connected to a 3-phase, 480 V, 60 Hz line and the delay angle is set at 15°. Switch S is closed and the armature current is 270 A.

Calculate

a. The dc voltage across the armature
b. The power supplied to the motor
c. The average current in each diode
d. The power output [hp] if the armature circuit has a resistance of 0.07 Ω

22-5 Explain why the field or armature has to be reversed in order that the converter in Fig. 22.1 may feed power from the rotating armature back into the ac line.

22-6 Compare the basic behavior of the power drive of Fig. 22.5 with that of Fig. 22.8.

22-7 **a.** What is meant by the term commutatorless dc machine? Describe its construction and principle of operation.
b. What is meant by a half-bridge converter? What advantages does it have over a conventional 3-phase bridge converter?

Intermediate level

22-8 The motor shown in Fig. 22.1 has a shunt field rated at 180 V, 2 A.
a. Calculate the effective value of the 60 Hz ac voltage that should be applied to the single-phase bridge circuit.
b. What is the peak-to-peak voltage ripple across the field terminals?
c. Does the field current contain a substantial ripple? Explain.
d. Draw the waveshape of the current in the ac line.
e. What is the effective value of the ac line current?

22-9 A 10 hp, 240 V, 1800 r/min permanent magnet dc motor has an armature resistance of 0.4 Ω and a rated armature current of 35 A. It is energized by the converter shown in Fig. 22.1. If the ac line voltage is 208 V, 60 Hz and the motor operates at full-load, calculate the following:
a. The delay angle required so that the motor operates at its rated voltage
b. The reactive power absorbed by the converter
c. The effective value of the line currents
d. The induced voltage E_0 at 900 r/min

22-10 The motor in Problem 22-9 is started at reduced voltage, and the starting current is limited to 60 A.

Calculate

a. The delay angle required
b. The reactive power absorbed by the converter
c. Does inductor L absorb reactive power from the ac line?

22-11 Referring to Fig. 22.5, an ac ammeter inserted in series with line 1 gives a reading of 280 A. Furthermore, a 3-phase power factor meter indicates a lagging displacement power factor of 0.83.

Calculate

a. The value of the dc load current I_d
b. The approximate delay angle if converter 1 is operating alone as an inverter

22-12 The hoist motor shown in Fig. 22.9 is lifting a mass of 5000 lb at a constant speed of 400 ft/min.
a. Neglecting gear losses, calculate the value of E_0 if the armature current I_d is 150 A.
b. Knowing that $R_a = 0.1\ \Omega$, calculate the value of converter voltage E_d.

22-13 In Problem 22-12 (and referring to Fig. 22.9), if the same mass is lowered at a constant speed of 100 ft/min, calculate the following:
a. The armature current and its direction
b. The value of E_0 and its polarity

c. The value of E_d and its polarity
d. In which direction does the active power flow in the ac line?

22-14 In Problem 22-12, if the mass is simply held still in midair, calculate the following:
a. The value of E_0
b. The armature current I_d
c. The value and polarity of E_d

22-15 If the 3-phase line voltage is 240 V, 60 Hz, calculate the delay angle required
a. In Problem 22-13
b. In Problem 22-14

22-16 a. Referring to Fig. 22.18a, calculate the average current and also the peak current carried by the freewheeling diode.
b. What is the PIV across the diode?

22-17 An electronic chopper is placed between a 600 V dc trolley wire and the armature of a series motor. The switching frequency is 800 Hz, and each power pulse lasts for 400 μs. If the dc current in the trolley wire is 80 A, calculate the following:
a. The armature voltage
b. The armature current
c. Draw the waveshape of the current in the freewheeling diode, assuming the armature inductance is high.

Advanced level

22-18 Referring to Fig. 22.8, the cemf E_0 has the polarity shown when the armature turns clockwise. Furthermore, when the armature current actually flows in the direction shown and the machine is turning clockwise, it operates in quadrant 1. State whether converters 1 and 2 are acting as rectifiers or inverters when the machine operates
a. In quadrant 2
b. In quadrant 3
c. In quadrant 4
d. Make a sketch of the actual direction of current flow and the actual polarity of E_0 in each case.

22-19 A 200 hp, 250 V, 600 r/min dc motor is driven by a 4-quadrant converter similar to the one shown in Fig. 22.20. GTOs are used operating at a frequency of 125 Hz, and the voltage of the dc source is 280 V. The motor has the following characteristics:

armature resistance: 12 mΩ

armature inductance: 350 μH

rated armature current: 620 A

During start-up, the average armature current is maintained at 620 A. In order to limit the current fluctuations, the Q4 GTO is always maintained closed and the Q3 GTO is kept open. As a result, the converter acts as a 2-quadrant converter during the start-up phase.
a. Assuming the voltage drop across the switches is negligible, calculate the duty cycle needed to establish an average current of 620 A in the armature when it is stalled.
b. Calculate the peak-to-peak current ripple under these conditions.
c. If the voltage drop across the switches is 2 V, calculate the new duty cycle and the peak-to-peak current ripple.
d. During the start-up phase, would the current ripple be seriously affected if the converter were operated as a 4-quadrant unit?

22-20 The following specifications are given for the motor shown in Fig. 22.25:

armature diameter: 100 mm

armature axial length: 50 mm

turns per coil: 200

rotational speed: 840 r/min

flux density in air gap: 0.5 T

armature current: 5 A

Using this information, calculate the following:
a. The voltage induced in each coil
b. The dc voltage between the brushes

c. The frequency of the voltage in each coil
d. The frequency of the current in each coil
e. The power developed by the motor
f. The torque exerted by the motor

22-21 **a.** Referring to Fig. 22.17, what would be the effect if capacitor C_1 were removed?
b. In Fig. 22.18a, calculate the approximate value of capacitor C_1 [μF] so that the voltage across it does not drop by more than 50 V during the time of a current pulse.

22-22 A 3-phase, 6-pulse rectifier is equipped with a freewheeling diode. The 3-phase feeder has a line voltage of 240 V and the dc load is composed of an armature having a resistance of 0.4 Ω. The rated armature current is 40 A.

Calculate

a. The voltage needed to cause 60 A to flow through the armature when it is at standstill
b. The firing angle needed to attain this current
c. The reactive power absorbed by the converter

Industrial application

22-23 Referring to Fig. 22.21, suppose the 80 A armature current is actually flowing in the direction shown. If the current is decreasing, what is the polarity of terminal A with respect to terminal C?

22-24 Referring to Fig. 22.21a, I_a is +80 A, and increasing at the rate of 6000 A/s. Calculate the value of the current after an interval of 3 ms, and the voltage across the 4 mH inductance during the interval.

22-25 Referring to Fig. 22.20, it is known that at a given instant $I_d = +153$ A, $I_1 = +140$ A, $E_{12} = +300$ V, and $C = 7000$ μF. Calculate the value of I_2 and the rate at which the voltage across the capacitor is changing. Is the capacitor charging or discharging?

22-26 In Fig. 22.20, the following information is given:

$L_a = 20$ mH, $R_a = 1.2$ Ω, $E_0 = +65$ V, $I_A = +5$ A, $I_1 = -5$ A, $E_{AB} = +60$ V. Is I_A increasing or decreasing and at what rate is it changing?

CHAPTER 23

Electronic Control of Alternating-Current Motors

23.0 Introduction

We saw in Chapter 22 that the electronic control of dc motors enables us to obtain high efficiency at all torques and speeds. Full 4-quadrant control is possible to meet precise high-speed industrial standards. The same remarks apply to the electronic control of ac motors. Thus, we find that squirrel-cage and wound-rotor induction motors, as well as synchronous motors, lend themselves well to electronic control. Whereas dc machines are controlled by varying the voltage and current, ac machines are controlled by varying the voltage and frequency. Now, we may ask, if dc machines do such an outstanding job, why do we also use ac machines? There are several reasons:

1. AC machines have no commutators and brushes; consequently, they require less maintenance.
2. AC machines cost less (and weigh less) than dc machines.
3. AC machines are more rugged and work better in hostile environments.
4. AC machines can operate at much higher voltages: up to 25 kV. DC machines are limited to about 1000 V.
5. AC machines can be built in much larger sizes: up to 50 000 kW. DC machines are limited to about 2000 kW.
6. AC machines can run at speeds up to 100 000 r/min, whereas large dc machines are limited to about 2000 r/min.

In this chapter we cover 3-phase motor controls in keeping with the power emphasis of the book. However, the reader should first review the basic principles of electronic drives covered in Chapters 21 and 22. Furthermore, to understand the basic principles of ac motor control, the reader should also review Sections 20.18 and 20.20, which explain how variable frequency affects the behavior of a squirrel-cage induction motor.

23.1 Types of ac drives

Although there are many kinds of electronic ac drives, the majority can be grouped under the following broad classes:

1. Static frequency changers
2. Static voltage controllers
3. Rectifier-inverter systems with line commutation

4. Rectifier-inverter systems with self-commutation
5. Pulse-width modulation systems

Static frequency changers convert the incoming line frequency directly into the desired load frequency. Cycloconverters fall into this category, and they are used to drive both synchronous and squirrel-cage induction motors (Fig. 23.1).

Static voltage controllers enable speed and torque control by varying the ac voltage. They are used with squirrel-cage induction motors. Static voltage controllers are also used to soft-start induction motors (Fig. 23.2).

Rectifier-inverter systems with line commutation rectify the incoming line frequency to dc, and the dc is reconverted to ac by an inverter. The inverter, in turn, is line-commutated by the very motor it drives. Such systems are mainly used to control synchronous motors (Fig. 23.3). Similar systems are used to control the speed of wound-rotor induction motors (Fig. 23.4).

Rectifier-inverter systems with self-commutation rectify the incoming line frequency to dc, and the dc is reconverted to ac by an inverter. However, the inverter is self-commutated, generating its own frequency. Such rectifier-inverter systems are used to control squirrel-cage induction motors (Figs. 23.5 and 23.6).

Pulse-width modulation systems are a relatively new development as far as widespread industrial applications are concerned. They enable variable speed induction motor drives ranging from zero speed and up. Their appearance in the marketplace is directly due to the availability of high-speed switching devices such as IGBTs (Fig. 23.7).

The seven block diagrams shown in Figs. 23.1 through 23.7 are examples of these ac drives.

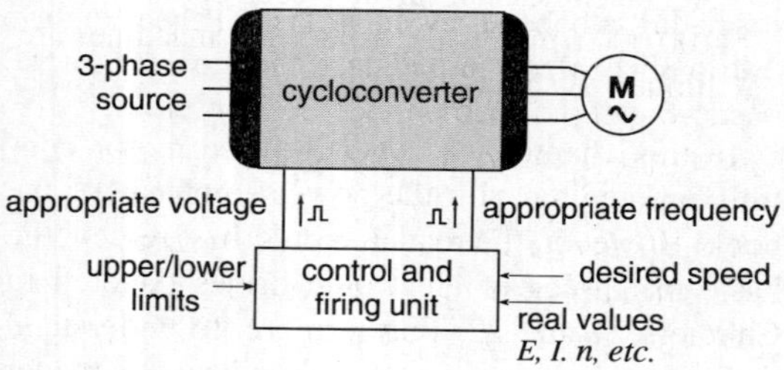

Figure 23.1
Variable-speed drive system using a cycloconverter (see Sections 23.3 and 23.5).

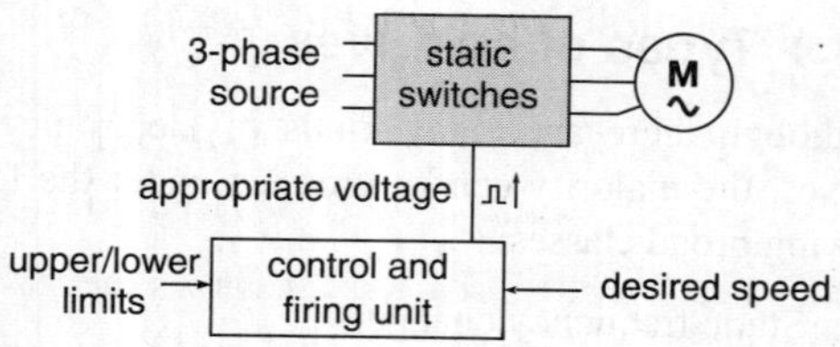

Figure 23.2
Variable-speed drive using a static switch (see Section 23.6).

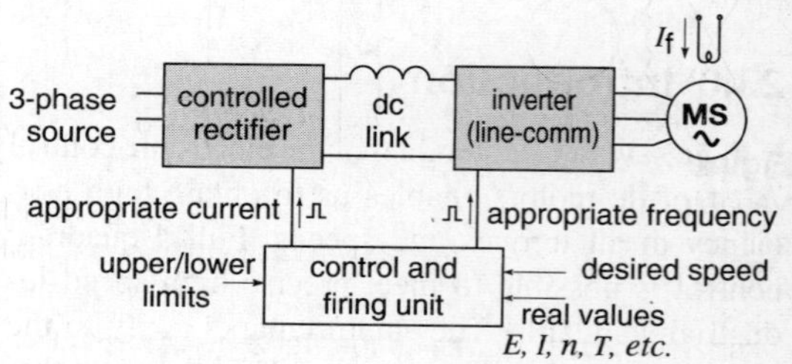

Figure 23.3
Variable-speed synchronous motor drive using a controlled rectifier and a line-commutated inverter fed from a dc link current source (see Section 23.2).

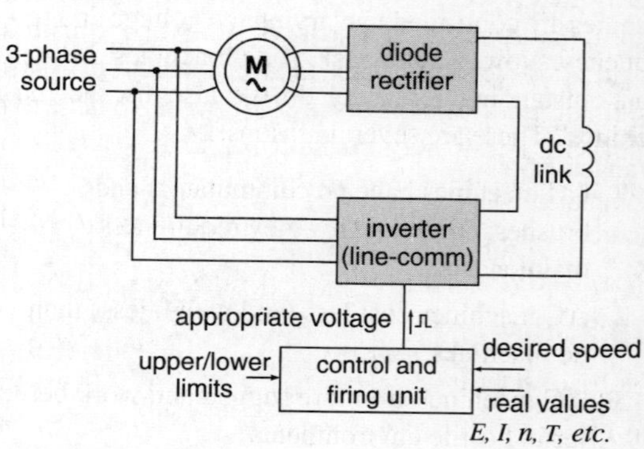

Figure 23.4
Variable-speed drive for a wound-rotor induction motor (see Section 23.12).

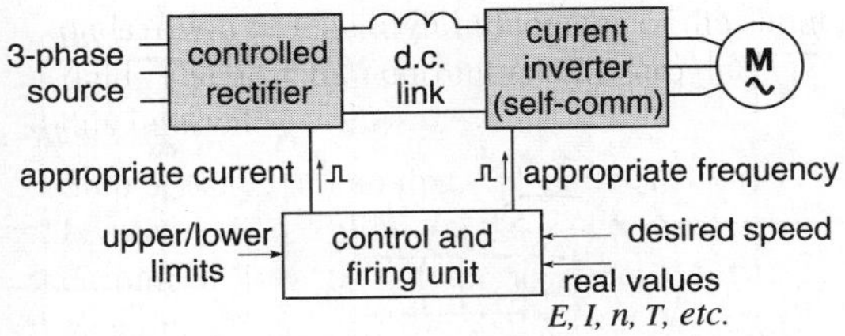

Figure 23.5
Variable-speed drive using a controlled rectifier and a self-commutated inverter fed from a dc link current source (see Section 23.9).

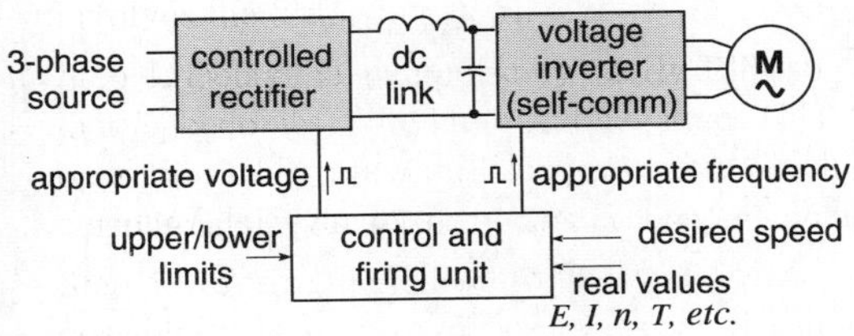

Figure 23.6
Variable-speed drive using a controlled rectifier and a self-commutated inverter fed from a dc link voltage source (see Section 23.10).

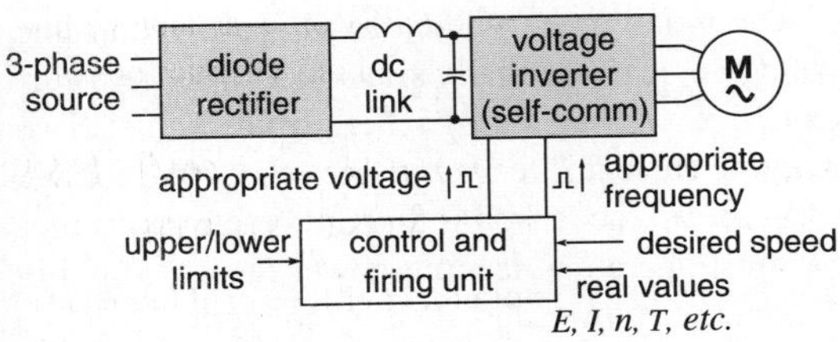

Figure 23.7
Variable-speed drive using a diode rectifier and a self-commutated PWM inverter fed from a dc link voltage source (see Section 23.13).

23.2 Synchronous motor drive using current-source dc link

In Chapter 22, Sections 22.14 and 22.15, we saw that the combination of a synchronous motor and its position-commutated inverter behaved like a brushless dc motor. This presents a bit of a dilemma, because large synchronous motors are generally considered to be alternating-current machines. The reader may therefore consider that in electronic drives the synchronous motor is a sort of hybrid animal that can be treated either as an ac machine or as a brushless dc machine, depending upon the point of view. In this chapter, we consider it to be an ac machine when fed from a 3-phase source.

Fig. 23.8 shows a typical synchronous motor drive. It consists of two converters connected between a 3-phase source and the synchronous motor. Converter 1 acts as a controlled rectifier, feeding dc power to converter 2. The latter behaves as a line-commutated inverter whose ac voltage and frequency are established by the motor.

A smoothing inductor L maintains a ripple-free current in the *dc link* between the two converters. Current I is controlled by converter 1, which acts as a current source. A smaller bridge rectifier (converter 3) supplies the field excitation for the rotor.

Converter 2 is naturally commutated by voltage E_S induced across the terminals of the motor. This voltage is created by the revolving magnetic flux in the air gap. The flux depends upon the stator currents and the exciting current I_f. The flux is usually kept fixed; consequently, the induced voltage E_S is proportional to the motor speed.

Gate triggering of converter 1 is done at line frequency (60 Hz) while that of converter 2 is done at motor frequency. The latter is directly proportional to the motor speed.

With regard to controls, information picked off at various points is assimilated in the gate-triggering processors, which then send out appropriate gate-firing pulses to converters 1 and 2. Thus, the processors receive information as to desired speed of rotation, actual speed, instantaneous rotor position, stator voltage, stator current, field current, etc. They interpret whether these inputs represent normal or abnormal conditions and emit appropriate gate pulses to correct the situation or to meet a specific command.

The gate pulses of converter 2 are controlled by the position of the rotor. This is accomplished by a set of transducers that sense the revolving magnetic field. They are mounted on the stator next to the air

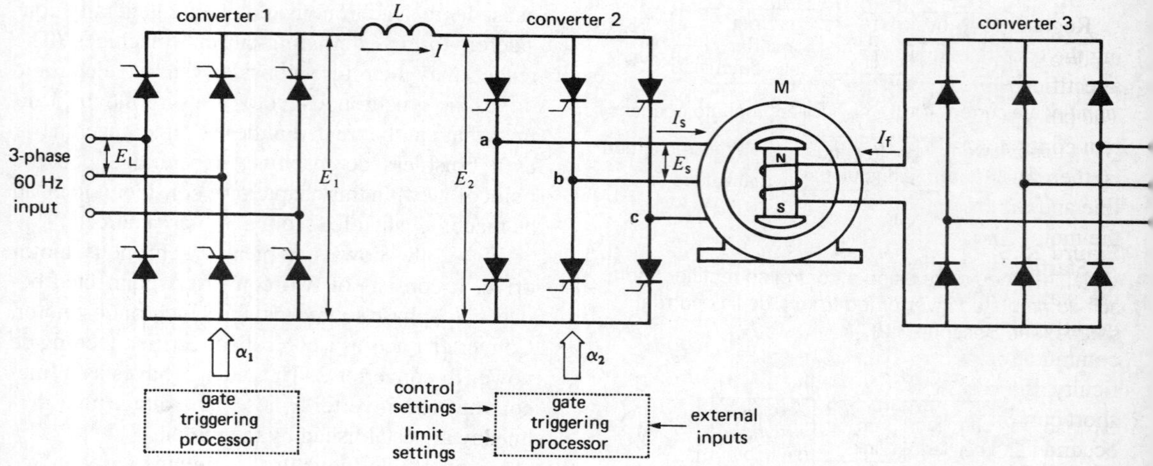

Figure 23.8
Synchronous motor driven by a converter with a dc link. The output frequency can be considerably greater than 60 Hz, thus permitting high speeds.

gap. Other methods employ position transducers mounted on the end of the shaft. Due to this method of gate control, the synchronous motor acts the same way as a brushless dc machine. The motor speed may be increased by raising either the dc link current I or the field current I_f.

Stator voltage E_s produces a dc emf E_2 given by

$$E_2 = 1.35\ E_s \cos \alpha_2 \qquad (21.13)$$

where

E_2 = dc voltage generated by converter 2 [V]

E_s = effective line-to-line stator voltage [V]

α_2 = firing angle of converter 2 [°]

Similarly, the voltage produced by converter 1 is given by

$$E_1 = 1.35\ E_L \cos \alpha_1$$

Link voltages E_1 and E_2 are almost equal, differing only by the negligible *IR* drop in the inductor. Firing angle α_1 is automatically controlled so that the magnitude of the link current is just sufficient to develop the required torque.

The stator line current I_s flows in 120° rectangular pulses, as shown in Fig. 23.9. These step-like currents produce a revolving MMF that moves in jerks around the armature. This produces torque pulsations, but they are almost completely damped out (except at low speeds), due to the inertia of the rotor. The shaft therefore turns smoothly when running at rated speed.

The motor line-to-neutral voltage E_{LN} and line voltage E_s are essentially sinusoidal. The field current, line current, and triggering are adjusted so that line current I_s leads the line-to-neutral voltage (Fig. 23.9). The reason is that the synchronous motor must operate at leading power factor to supply the reactive power absorbed by converter 2.

Converter 1 is designed so that under full-load conditions, firing angle α_1 is about 15°, to minimize the reactive power drawn from the 60 Hz ac line.

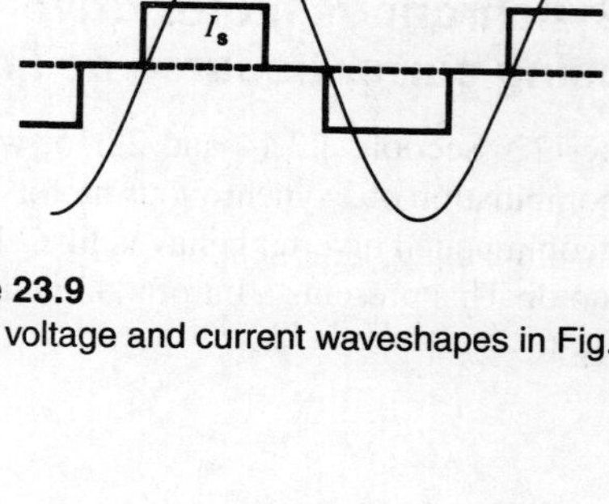

Figure 23.9
Typical voltage and current waveshapes in Fig. 23.8.

Regenerative braking is accomplished by shifting the gate-firing pulses so that converter 2 acts as a rectifier while converter 1 operates as an inverter. The polarity of E_2 and E_1 reverses, but the link current continues to flow in the same direction. Power is, therefore, pumped back into the 3-phase, 60 Hz line and the motor slows down. During this period the motor functions as an ac generator.

Starting the motor creates a problem, because the stator voltage E_2 is zero at standstill. Consequently, no voltage is available to produce the line commutation of converter 2. To get around this difficulty, the converters are fired in such a way that short current pulses flow successively in phases ab, bc, and ca. The successive pulses create N, S poles in the stator that are always just ahead of their opposite poles on the rotor. Like a dog chasing its tail, the rotor accelerates and, when it reaches about 10 percent of rated speed, converter 2 takes over and commutation takes place normally. This pulse mode of operation is also used to brake the motor as it approaches zero speed.

The speed control of synchronous motors using a current-source dc link is applied to motors ranging from 1 kW to several megawatts. Permanent magnet synchronous motors for the textile industry and brushless synchronous motors for nuclear reactor circulating pumps are two examples. Pumped-storage hydropower plants also use this method to bring the huge synchronous machines up to speed so they may be smoothly synchronized with the line.

Example 23-1

A 3-phase synchronous motor rated at 200 kW, 480 V, 60 Hz, 450 r/min, is connected to a drive similar to that shown in Fig. 23.8. The three-phase electric utility voltage is 600 V, 60 Hz.

The motor runs at a speed of 535 r/min. The effective terminal voltage is 511 V and the motor draws an effective line current I_s of 239 A at a power factor of 95%. The motor has an efficiency of 93%. Neglecting the losses in the converters, calculate

a. The frequency applied to the stator
b. The fundamental component of the stator current I_s
c. The current I flowing in the dc link
d. The firing angle α_2 of converter 2
e. The voltage E_2 of the dc link
f. The firing angle α_1 of converter 1
g. The reactive power supplied to converter 1
h. The mechanical power developed by the motor

Solution

a. The frequency applied to the motor is proportional to its speed. Because the rated speed is 450 r/min at a frequency of 60 Hz, the frequency at 535 r/min is

$$f = \frac{535 \text{ r/min}}{450 \text{ r/min}} \times 60 \text{ Hz} = 71.3 \text{ Hz}$$

b. Fundamental component of the stator current

$$I_F = 0.955\, I_s \tag{21.8}$$
$$= 0.955 \times 239 = 228 \text{ A}$$

c. Current in the dc link

$$I_d = \frac{I_F}{0.78} \tag{21.7}$$
$$= \frac{228}{0.78} = 293 \text{ A}$$

d. Firing angle α_2
Converter 2 acts as an inverter, consequently,

$$\alpha_2 = -\arccos FP = -\arccos 0.95$$
$$= 180° - 18.2° = 161.8°$$

e. Voltage E_2 of the dc link

$$E_2 = 1.35\, E_s \cos \alpha_2 \tag{21.4}$$
$$= 1.35 \times 511 \times \cos 161.8° = -655 \text{ V}$$

The dc voltage drop across inductor L is negligible, consequently, $E_1 = E_2 = 655$ V

f. Firing angle α_1
Converter 1 acts as a rectifier, hence

$$E_1 = 1.35\, E_L \cos \alpha_1 \tag{21.4}$$
$$655 = 1.35 \times 600 \times \cos \alpha_1$$
$$\alpha_1 = \arccos 0.808 = 36.0°$$

g. Active power supplied to converter 1

$$P = E_1 I = 655 \times 293 = 191\,915 \text{ W} = 192 \text{ kW}$$

Displacement power factor of converter 1

$$PF = \cos \alpha_1 = \cos 36.0° = 0.809 = 80.9\%$$

Apparent power absorbed by converter 1

$$S = 192 \text{ kW}/0.809 = 237 \text{ kVA}$$

Reactive power absorbed by converter 1

$$Q = \sqrt{S^2 - P^2}$$
$$= \sqrt{237^2 - 192^2} = 139 \text{ kvar}$$

h. Mechanical power developed by the motor

$$P_m = 192 \text{ kW} \times 0.93 = 179 \text{ kW} \approx 240 \text{ hp}$$

23.3 Synchronous motor and cycloconverter

We have seen that cycloconverters can directly convert ac power from a higher frequency to a lower frequency (Section 21.24). These converters are sometimes used to drive slow-speed synchronous motors rated up to several megawatts. If a 60 Hz source is used, the cycloconverter output frequency is typically variable from zero to 10 Hz. Such a low frequency permits excellent control of the waveshape of the output voltage by computer-controlled firing of the thyristor gates. The thyristors are line-commutated, with the result that the complexity of the electronics surrounding each SCR is considerably reduced.

Fig. 23.10 shows three cycloconverters connected to the wye-connected stator of a 3-phase synchronous motor. Each cycloconverter produces a single-phase output, based upon the principle explained in Section 21.24. Referring to phase A, the associated cycloconverter is composed of two 3-phase bridges, +A and −A, each fed by the same 3-phase, 60 Hz line.

Bridge +A generates the positive half-cycle of voltage for line a, while bridge −A generates the negative half. The two bridges are prevented from operating at the same time so as to prevent circulating currents between them. The resulting low-frequency wave is composed of segments of the 60 Hz voltage between lines 1, 2, 3. By appropriate gate firing, the low-frequency voltage can be made to approach a sine wave quite closely (Fig. 23.11). However, to reduce the reactive power absorbed from the 60 Hz line, the output voltage is usually designed to have a trapezoidal, flat-topped waveshape.

The 3-phase controlled rectifier supplying the field current I_f functions as a current source. The magnitudes of the three stator currents and of I_f are controlled so as to keep a constant flux in the air gap. Furthermore, the gate pulses are timed and the excitation is adjusted so that the motor operates at unity power factor at low frequency. However, even at unity power factor (I_a, I_b, I_c, respectively, in phase with E_{aN}, E_{bN}, E_{cN}), the cycloconverter absorbs reactive power from the 60 Hz line. The reason is that delayed triggering is needed on the 60 Hz line to generate the sinusoidal low-frequency voltage. The input power factor is typically 85 percent when the motor runs at rated power and speed.

Fig. 23.12 shows a large low-speed synchronous motor that is driven by a cycloconverter. The speed can be continuously varied from zero to 15 r/min. The low speed permits direct drive of the ball-mill without using a gear reducer. The motor is stopped by altering the gate firing so that the motor acts as a generator, feeding power back into the ac line.

Similar high-power, low-speed cycloconverter drives are being used with propulsion motors on board ships. For example, a popular 70 000 ton cruise liner (Fig. 23.59), is propelled by two 14 MW synchronous motors. The motors are directly coupled to propeller shafts that are driven at speeds of zero to 140 r/min.

23.4 Cycloconverter voltage and frequency control

Returning to Fig. 23.11 we can see that the low-frequency output voltage is composed of selected segments of the 3-phase, 60 Hz line voltage. The segments are determined by the gate firing of the SCRs. The triggering is identical to that of a conventional 6-pulse rectifier, except that the firing angle is continually varied during each low-frequency

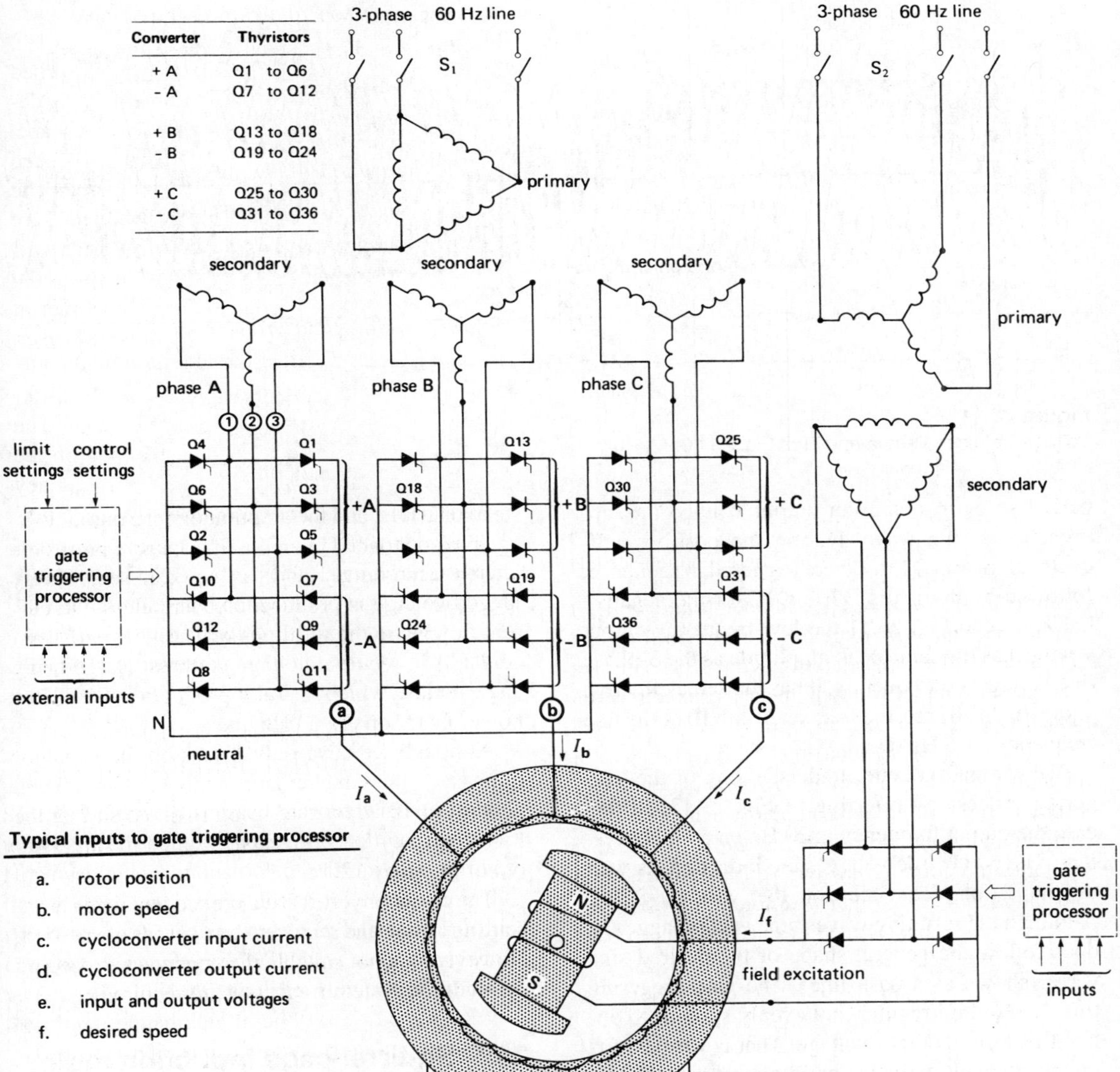

Figure 23.10
Cycloconverter driving a large synchronous motor. The output voltage associated with phase A is a slowly changing sine wave having a frequency of 6 Hz, which is 10 times less than the supply frequency. Thyristors Q1 to Q12 are triggered so as to track the desired sine wave as closely as possible. This produces the sawtooth output voltage shown in Fig. 23.11. The power factor at the input to the motor is assumed to be unity. The corresponding power factor at the input to the cycloconverter is less than unity, due to the delayed firing angles.

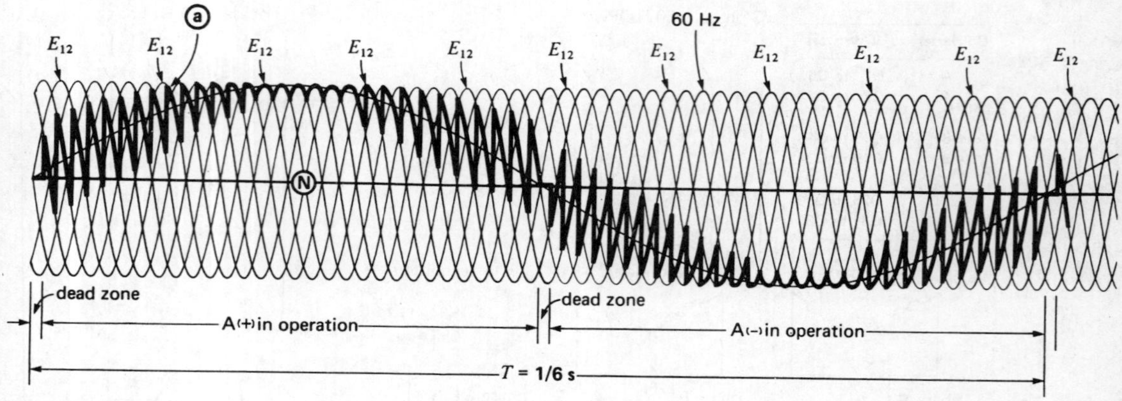

Figure 23.11
Voltage between lines a and N of Fig. 23.10.

period so as to obtain an output voltage that approaches a sine wave. During the positive half-cycle, thyristors Q1 to Q6 are triggered in sequence, followed by thyristors Q7 to Q12 for the negative half-cycle. In Fig. 23.11 the low-frequency output voltage has the same peak amplitude as the 3-phase line voltage; consequently, it has the same effective value. In this figure, the frequency is 1/10 of the line frequency, or 6 Hz on a 60 Hz system.

We can gain a better understanding of the triggering process by referring to Fig. 23.13. In this case the output frequency is 20 Hz on a 60 Hz system. The 60 Hz line voltages are indicated, as well as the firing sequence for the various SCRs. Although the resulting waveshape is very jagged, it does follow the general shape of the desired sine wave (shown as a dash line). The gate-triggering times are quite irregular (not evenly spaced) to obtain the desired output voltage. That is why the firing program has to be under computer control.

If this 20 Hz voltage is applied to the motor of Fig. 23.10, the resulting current will be a reasonably good sine wave. In effect, the inductance of the windings smooths out the ragged edges that would otherwise be produced by the sawtooth voltage wave.

To reduce the speed, both the frequency and voltage have to be reduced in the same proportion. Thus, in Fig. 23.14 the frequency is now 10 Hz instead of 20 Hz, and the amplitude of the output voltage is also reduced by one-half. The gate pulses are altered accordingly and, as we can see, a very jagged voltage is produced. Nevertheless, the current flowing in the windings will still be quite sinusoidal. A low-output voltage requires a large firing angle delay, which in turn produces a very low power factor on the 60 Hz line.

Although we have only discussed the behavior of phase A, the same remarks apply to phases B and C (Fig. 23.10). The gate firing is timed so that the low-frequency line currents I_a, I_b, I_c are mutually out of phase by 120°.

The cycloconverter drive is excellent when high-starting torque and relatively low speeds are needed. However, it is not suitable if frequencies exceeding one-half the system frequency are required.

23.5 Squirrel-cage induction motor with cycloconverter

Fig. 23.15 shows a 3-phase, squirrel-cage induction motor connected to the output of a 3-phase cycloconverter. The circuit arrangement is similar to that of Fig. 23.10, except that the windings are directly fed from a 3-phase line. Consequently, the windings cannot be connected in wye or delta but must be isolated from each other. Motor speed is

Figure 23.12a
Stator of a 3-phase synchronous motor rated 6400 kW (8576 hp), 15 r/min, 5.5 Hz, 80°C used to drive a ball-mill in a cement factory. The stator is connected to a 50 Hz cycloconverter, whose output frequency is variable from zero to 5.5 Hz. Internal diameter of stator: 8000 mm; active length of stacking: 950 mm; slots: 456.
(Courtesy of ABB)

Figure 23.12b
The 44 rotor poles are directly mounted on the ball-mill so as to eliminate the need of a gearbox. The two slip-rings on the right-hand side of the poles bring the dc current into the windings.

Figure 23.12c
End view of the ball-mill showing the enclosed stator frame in the background. The mill contains 470 tons of steel balls and 80 tons of crushable material. The motor is cooled by blowing 40 000 m^3 of fresh air over the windings, per hour. *(Courtesy of ABB)*

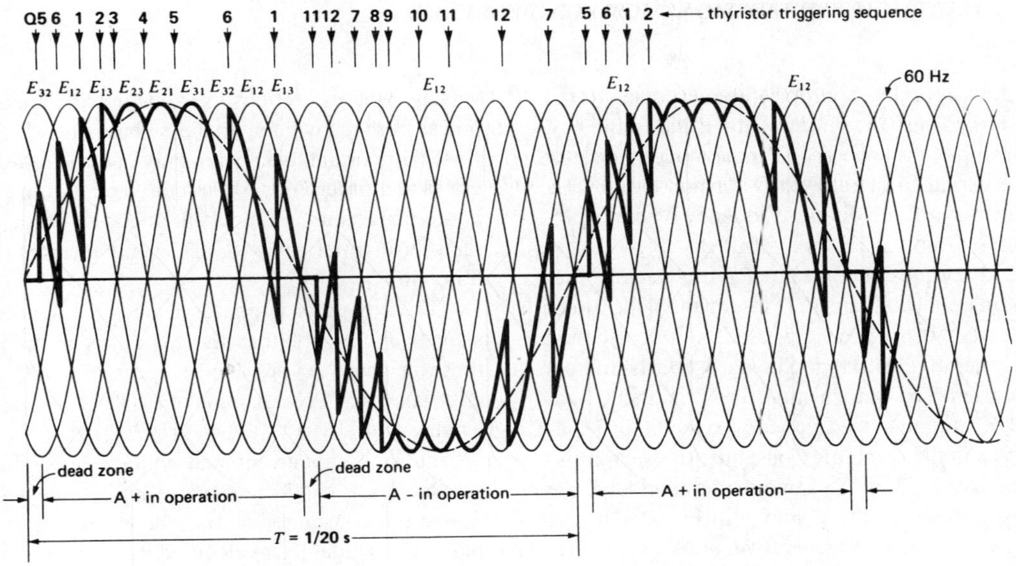

Figure 23.13
Waveshape of the output voltage E_{aN} in Fig. 23.10 at a frequency of 20 Hz. The effective output voltage has the same value as the effective input voltage between the 3-phase lines.

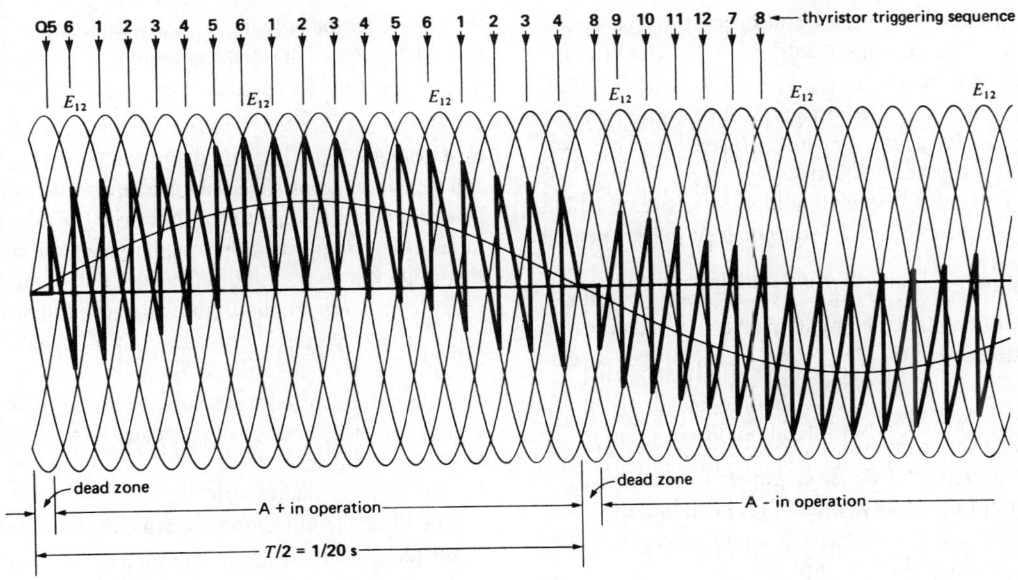

Figure 23.14
Waveshape of E_{aN} in Fig. 23.10 at a frequency of 10 Hz. The thyristors are triggered later in the cycle so that the effective value of the output voltage is only half that between the 3-phase lines. As a result, the flux in the air gap is the same in this figure as it is in Fig. 23.13.

varied by applying appropriate gate pulses to the thyristors to vary the output voltage and frequency. For example, the speed of a 2-pole induction motor can be varied from zero to 1500 r/min on a 60 Hz line by varying the output frequency of the cycloconverter from 0.1 Hz to 25 Hz.

Good torque-speed characteristics in all four quadrants can be obtained. Consequently, the motor can be started, stopped, reversed, and decelerated by regenerative braking. Standard 60 Hz motors can be used. The stator voltage is automatically adjusted in relation to the frequency to maintain a constant flux in the machine. Consequently, the torque-speed curves follow the same pattern and have the same properties as those shown in Fig. 23.16. For example, to obtain regenerative braking, the frequency produced by the cycloconverter must be slightly less than the frequency corresponding to the speed of the motor. Thus, if a 4-pole induction motor turns at 495 r/min, the cycloconverter frequency must be slightly less than $(495 \times 4)/120 = 16.5$ Hz in order to feed power back into the line.

To understand the operation of the cycloconverter, consider phase A in Fig. 23.15. The voltage across the winding is E_a and the ac current through it is I_a. The current is, therefore, alternatively positive and negative. Because of the inductive nature of a squirrel-cage motor, I_a lags behind E_a by an angle of about 30° (Fig. 23.17). Suppose the cycloconverter generates a frequency of 15 Hz.

Referring now to Fig. 23.15, a positive current I_a can only be furnished by converter 1, because only thyristors Q1, Q3, Q5 "point" in the proper direction. The current obviously returns by way of thyristors Q2, Q4, Q6. This converter can act either as a rectifier or inverter. When E_a is positive, it acts as a rectifier and delivers power to the phase A winding. Conversely, when E_a is negative, the converter acts as an inverter, delivering power from the phase A winding to the 3-phase line.

Similarly, a negative current I_a can only be furnished by converter 2. This converter acts as a rectifier when E_a is negative, and during this period the converter supplies power to the winding. Conversely, when E_a is positive, converter 2 transfers power from the winding to the 3-phase line.

It is important to note that only one converter operates at a time. Thus, when converter 1 is in operation, converter 2 is blocked, and vice versa. The rectifier/inverter behavior of the converters is illustrated in Fig. 23.17.

The converters in phases B and C function the same way, except that the thyristors (similar to those in phase A) are fired respectively 120° and 240° later. At 15 Hz an angle of 120° corresponds to a delay of $(1/15) \times (120/360) = 22.2$ ms.

The smooth current and voltage waveshapes shown in Fig. 23.17 are actually jagged sine waves, due to the constant switching between output and input. Consequently, cycloconverter-fed motors run about 10°C hotter than normal and adequate cooling must be provided. A separate blower may be needed at low speeds.

The cycloconverter can furnish the reactive power absorbed by the induction motor. However, a lot of reactive power is drawn from the 60 Hz line; the power factor is therefore poor. Indeed, with sinusoidal outputs the displacement power factor is always less than 84 percent, even for resistive loads.

Example 23-2

A 3-phase, squirrel-cage induction motor has a full-load rating of 25 hp, 480 V, 1760 r/min, 60 Hz. The three independent windings each carry a rated current of 20 A.

This motor is connected as shown in Fig. 23.15. The cycloconverter is connected to a 3-phase, 60 Hz line and generates a frequency of 8 Hz. Calculate the approximate value of the following:

a. The effective voltage across each winding
b. The no-load speed
c. The speed at rated torque
d. The effective current in the windings at rated torque
e. The effective voltage of the 60 Hz line

Solution

a. The flux in the motor should remain the same at all frequencies. Consequently, for a frequency

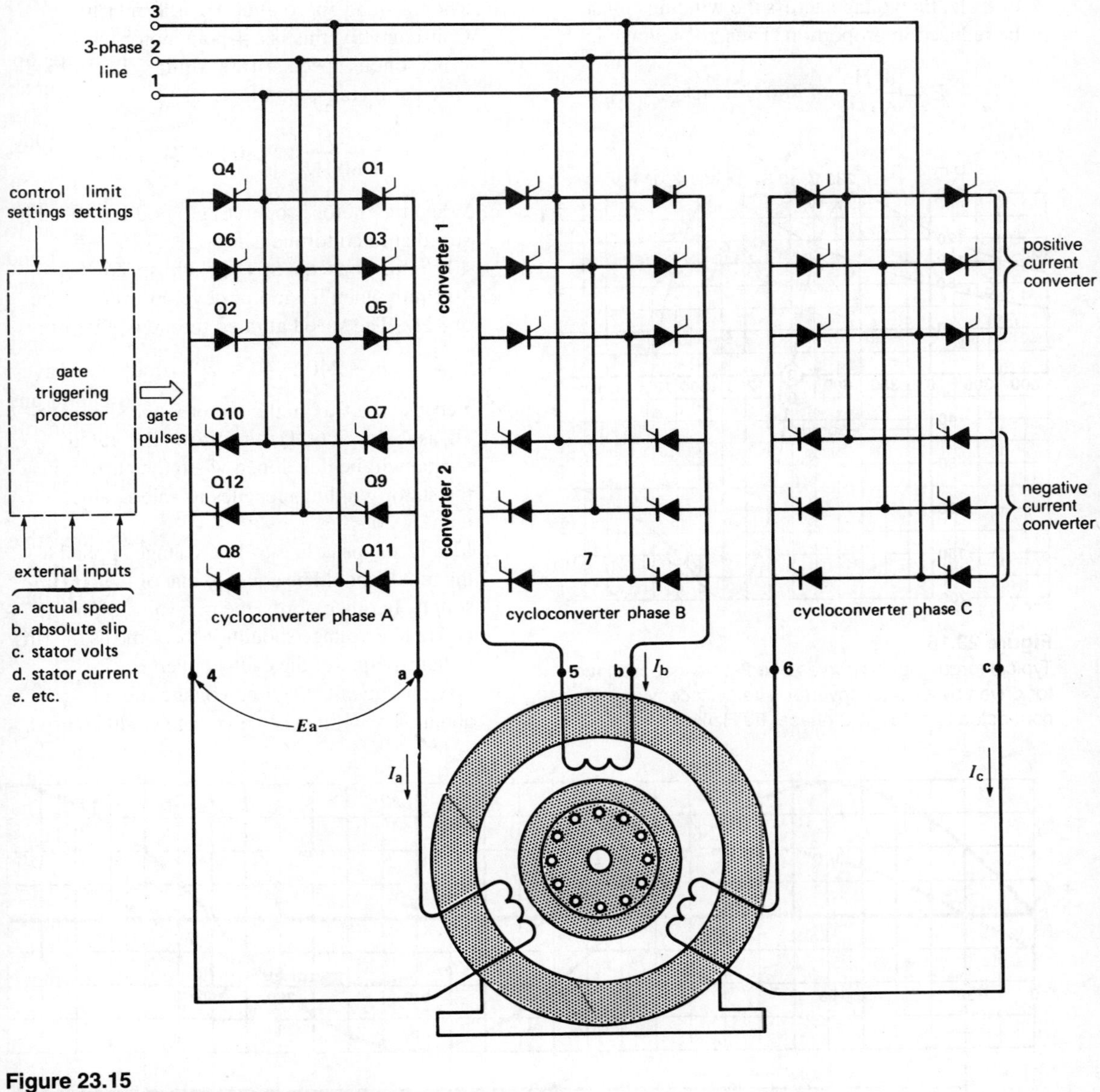

Figure 23.15
Squirrel-cage induction motor fed from a 3-phase cycloconverter.

of 8 Hz, the voltage across the windings must be reduced in proportion. Thus, the voltage is

$$E = \frac{8 \text{ Hz}}{60 \text{ Hz}} \times 480 \text{ V} = 64 \text{ V}$$

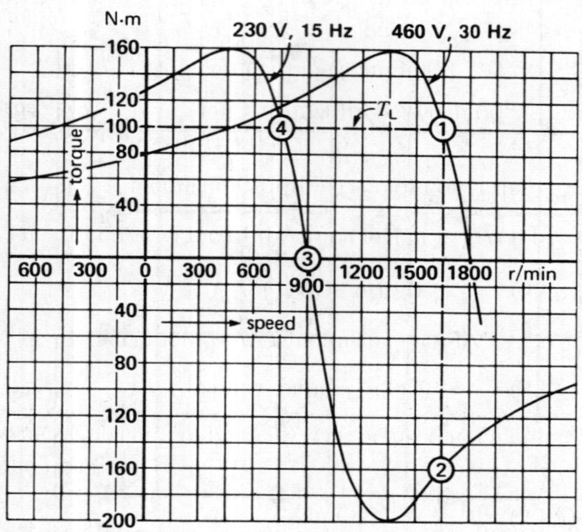

Figure 23.16
Typical torque-speed curves of a 2-pole induction motor driven by a cycloconverter. The cycloconverter is connected to a 460 V, 3-phase, 60 Hz line.

b. The full-load speed at 60 Hz is 1760 r/min. Consequently, this is a 4-pole motor whose synchronous speed is 1800 r/min. The no-load speed at 8 Hz is, therefore,

$$n = \frac{8 \text{ H}}{60 \text{ Hz}} \times 1800 = 240 \text{ rmin}$$

c. When the motor is operating on 60 Hz, the slip speed at rated torque is (1800 − 1760) = 40 r/min. Consequently, the slip speed is again 40 r/min when the motor develops rated torque at 8 Hz. The speed at rated torque is, therefore,

$$n = 240 - 40 = 200 \text{ r/min}$$

d. Because the flux in the motor is the same at 8 Hz as it was at 60 Hz, it follows that rated torque will be developed when the current in the stator windings reaches its rated value, namely 20 A.

e. Ideally, the peak line-to-line voltage applied to the motor should be equal to that of the 60 Hz supply. In other words, the rms value of the 60 Hz line voltage should be the same as the rms voltage output of the cycloconverter.

Consequently, the line voltage should be about 64 V. A higher line voltage could be used,

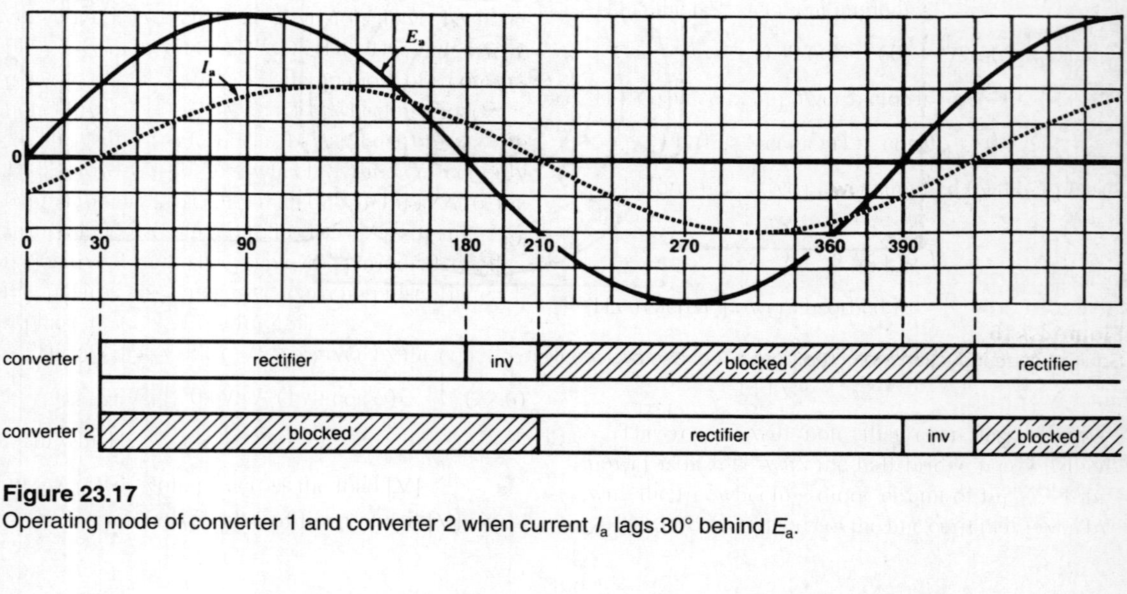

Figure 23.17
Operating mode of converter 1 and converter 2 when current I_a lags 30° behind E_a.

but this would require a greater lag in the firing angle to obtain the desired output voltage. The converter would draw more reactive power from the line and the power factor would be poorer.

23.6 Squirrel-cage motor and static voltage controller

The speed of a 3-phase, squirrel-cage induction motor can be varied by simply varying the stator voltage. This method of speed control is particularly useful for a motor driving a blower or centrifugal pump. To understand why, suppose the stator is connected to a variable-voltage 3-phase autotransformer (Fig. 23.18).

At rated voltage, the torque-speed characteristic of the motor is given by curve 1 of Fig. 23.19. If we apply half the rated voltage, we obtain curve 2. Because torque is proportional to the square of the applied voltage, the torques in curve 2 are only 1/4 of the corresponding torques in curve 1. For example, the breakdown torque drops from 184% to 46%. Similarly, the torque at 60-percent speed drops from 175% to 43.75%.

The load torque of a blower varies nearly as much as the square of the speed. This typical characteristic, shown by curve 3, is superimposed on the motor torque-speed curves. Thus, at rated voltage, the intersection of curves 1 and 3 shows that the blower runs at 90 percent of synchronous speed. On the other hand, at half rated voltage, the blower rotates at only 60 percent of synchronous speed. By varying the voltage this way, we can control the speed.

The variable-voltage autotransformer can be replaced by three sets of thyristors connected back-to-back, as shown in Fig. 23.20. The sets are called valves. To produce rated voltage across the motor, the respective thyristors are fired with a delay θ equal to the phase angle lag that *would* exist if the motor were directly connected to the line. Fig. 23.21 shows the resulting current and line-to-neutral voltage for phase A. The valves in phases B and C are triggered the same way, except for an additional delay of 120° and 240°, respectively.

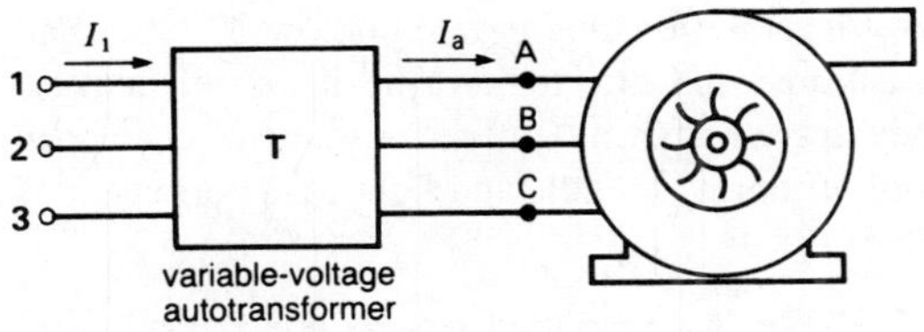

Figure 23.18
Variable-speed blower motor.

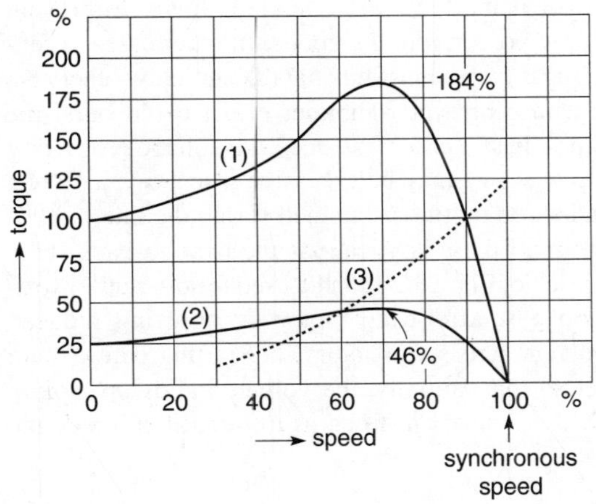

Figure 23.19
Torque-speed curve of blower motor at rated voltage (1) and 50 percent rated voltage (2). Curve 3 is the torque-speed characteristic of the fan.

To reduce the voltage across the motor, the firing angle θ is delayed still more. For example, to obtain 50 percent rated voltage, all the pulses are delayed by about 100°. The resulting distorted voltage and current waveshape for phase A are pictured very approximately in Fig. 23.22. The distortion increases the losses in the motor compared to the autotransformer method. Furthermore, the power factor is considerably lower because of the large phase angle lag θ. Nevertheless, to a first approximation, the torque-speed characteristics shown in Fig. 23.19 still apply.

Due to the considerable I^2R losses and lower power factor, this type of electronic speed control is only feasible for motors rated below 20 hp. Small hoists are also suited to this type of control, because they operate intermittently. Consequently, they can cool off during the idle and light-load periods.

23.7 Soft-starting cage motors

In many applications an induction motor must not accelerate too quickly when switched across the power line. For example, some loads, such as conveyor belts, have to be started slowly to prevent tipping or spilling the goods. In other cases, a centrifugal pump must not start too quickly, otherwise a damaging water-hammer effect could burst the pipes. In still other instances, the voltage drop along a power line may be excessive when, say, a 500 hp induction motor is slammed across the line.

In all these applications the back-to-back static switch of Fig. 23.20 can be used to soft-start or soft-stop a squirrel-cage motor by applying reduced voltage across the stator. The starting controls are set so that, initially, the voltage builds up rapidly until the motor just begins to turn, after which the voltage increases linearly with time until full voltage is reached. Some of these ramp-up schedules incorporate a short pulse of full voltage to overcome the static friction of machinery that has not operated for some time or that is covered with frost. In other schedules the starting current can be limited automatically to, say, four times the rated current. Some of the starting and stopping features offered are illustrated in Fig. 23.23a.

Once the motor reaches rated speed, a bypass contactor is sometimes used to short-circuit the thyristors to eliminate the heat loss. Due to the voltage drop between the anode and cathode, the total 3-phase loss amounts to about 3.5 W per ampere. Thus, the thyristors of a 600 hp motor drawing a line current of, say 500 A, will dissipate about 3.5 × 500 = 1750 W. In

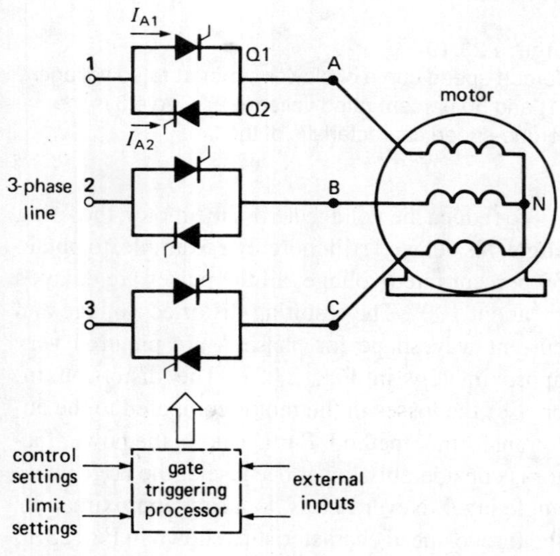

Figure 23.20
Variable-voltage speed control of a squirrel-cage induction motor using back-to-back thyristors.

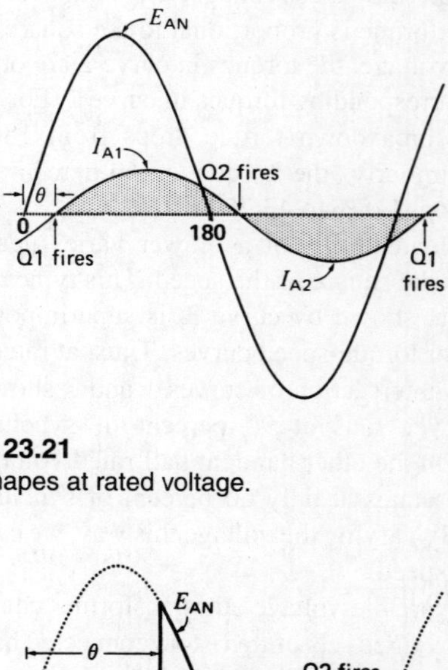

Figure 23.21
Waveshapes at rated voltage.

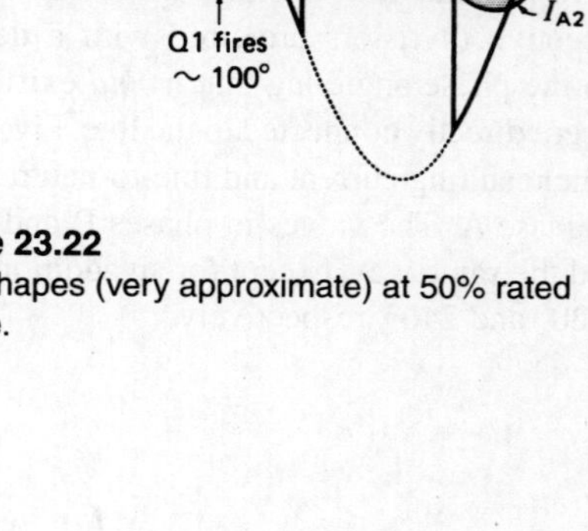

Figure 23.22
Waveshapes (very approximate) at 50% rated voltage.

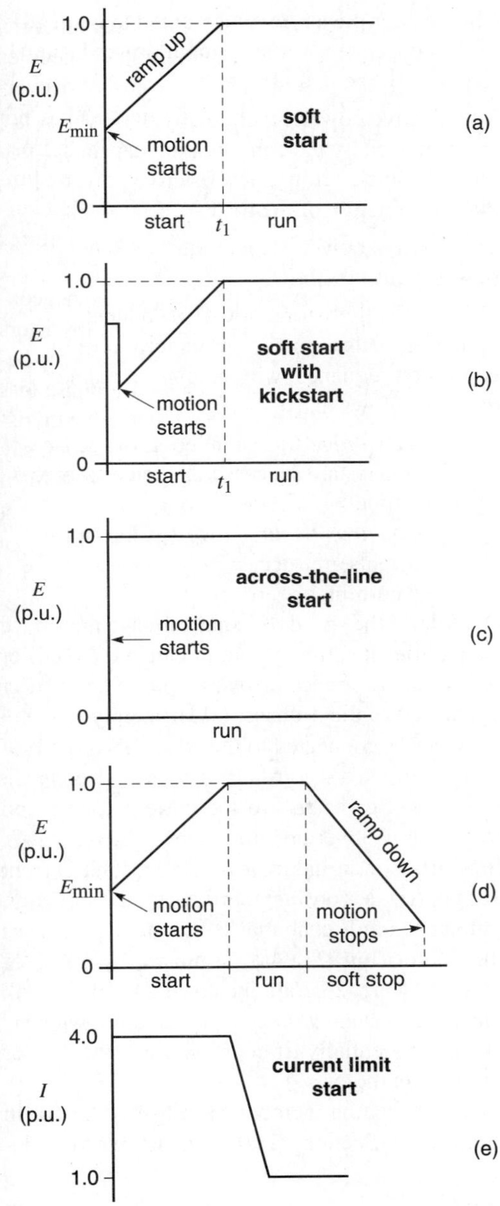

Figure 23.23a
Five typical options to control the soft starting and soft stopping of a cage induction motor (per-unit values).

the absence of a bypass contactor, forced cooling would have to be used to get rid of the heat.

When power is shut off, the motor may coast to a stop too quickly. In such cases the slow ramp-down feature of the electronic starter is an advantage. During this phase the voltage across the motor terminals is reduced gradually until the motor comes to rest. The starter can be programmed in the field to generate the ramp-up and ramp-down features that are best suited to the load (Fig. 23.23b).

Another feature of soft starters is their reliability and absolutely silent operation. No mechanical contacts clap when they open and close, no noisy holding coil to worry about, and—most importantly—no worn contacts to replace.

Soft starting of induction motors is available from 1 hp up to several thousand horsepower. It offers an excellent alternative choice to series resistance and autotransformer starters as well as wye-delta and part-winding starters. Retrofitting older starters is an important application of soft starters.

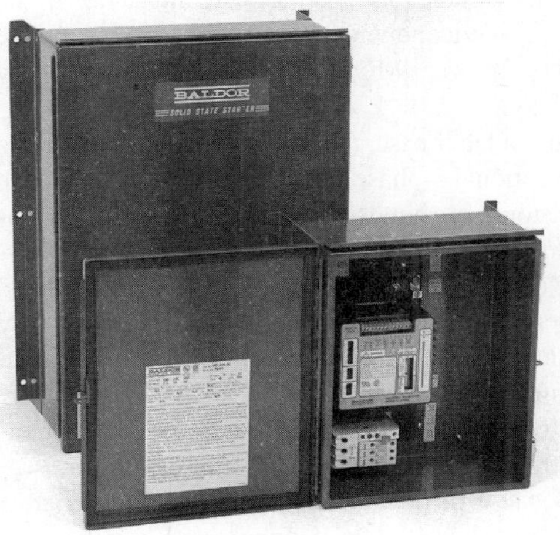

Figure 23.23b
Solid-state soft starter rated 5 hp, 460 V, 60 Hz. Start-up time adjustable 5–50 s; initial torque adjustment 0–75%; current limit schedule 75%–400%; kick-start time adjustable 0–1.5 s. In background is 40 hp, 460 V soft starter.
(Courtesy of Baldor Electric Company)

SELF-COMMUTATED INVERTERS

23.8 Self-commutated inverters for cage motors

In Section 23.2 we saw that a synchronous motor can be driven by a line-commutated inverter. This is possible because the synchronous motor can provide the reactive power needed by the inverter. Unfortunately, if the synchronous motor is replaced by an induction motor, the frequency conversion system breaks down, because an induction motor cannot deliver reactive power. Worse still, it actually absorbs reactive power.

Nevertheless, we can drive an induction motor using a *self-commutated inverter* (also called *force-commutated inverter*). It operates quite differently from a line-commutated inverter. First, it can generate its own frequency, determined by the frequency of the pulses applied to the gates. Second, it can either absorb or deliver reactive power. The reactive power generated or absorbed depends upon the nature of the load and the switching action of the power semiconductors. The switches may be IGBTs, power MOSFETs, GTOs, or ordinary thyristors.

In the latter case, the thyristors are arranged in a conventional 3-phase bridge circuit. However, each thyristor is surrounded by an array of capacitors, inductors, diodes, and auxiliary thyristors. The purpose of these auxiliary components is to force some power thyristors to conduct when normally they would not, and to force other thyristors to stop conducting before their "natural" time. It is precisely this forced switching action that enables these converters to generate and absorb reactive power.

Because of the variety of the switching circuits used, we show the self-commutated inverter as a simple 5-terminal device having two dc input terminals and three ac output terminals to provide 3-phase power to the motor. There are two basic types of inverters: current-source inverters (Fig. 23.24a) and voltage-source inverters (Fig. 23.26a). This simple representation helps us understand the basic features of all self-commutated inverters:

- The inverter power loss is assumed to be negligible; consequently, the dc input power is equal to the active ac output power.
- The reactive power generated by the inverter is not produced by the commutating capacitors included in the circuitry. The reactive power is due to the nature of the load.
- The reactive power output requires no net dc power input.
- The IGBTs, thyristors, or GTOs connect the dc input terminals to the ac output terminals in a controlled sequence, with negligible voltage drop. It follows that
  a. In a *voltage source* inverter, the ac line voltages are successively equal to ± the dc input voltage, or zero
  b. In a *current source* inverter, the ac line currents are successively equal to ± the dc current, or zero

To control the speed of a squirrel-cage motor, we use a rectifier-inverter system in which the rectifier and inverter are connected by a *dc link*. The rectifier is connected to the 3-phase, 60 Hz supply line and the inverter is connected to the stator. Two types of dc links are used—constant current and constant voltage. This gives rise to the current-source and voltage-source inverters* mentioned above.

By virtue of an inductor *L*, the constant current link supplies a constant current to the inverter, which is then fed sequentially into the three phases of the motor (Fig. 23.24a). Similarly, by virtue of capacitor *C* (Fig. 23.26a), the constant-voltage link furnishes a constant voltage to the inverter, which is switched sequentially from one phase to the next of the induction motor.

Many switching methods have been devised. In the following Sections 23.9 to 23.12, we first de-

* In 2-quadrant and 4-quadrant motor drives, the term *inverter* is somewhat misleading because power can flow not only from the dc side to the ac side (inverter mode), but also from the ac side to the dc side (rectifier mode). For this reason we prefer the term *converter* rather than inverter whenever ac/dc power can flow in both directions.

scribe the methods that generate a rectangular wave current or a rectangular wave voltage. We then go on to describe pulse-width modulation methods.

23.9 Current-source self-commutated frequency converter (rectangular wave)

The current-source frequency converter shown in Fig. 23.24a is used to control the speed of *individual* cage motors. The switching action of the inverter is such that the current in each phase is a rectangular pulse that flows for 120°. Nevertheless, the resulting voltage between lines A, B, C is nearly sinusoidal. The reason is that the 3-phase rectangular current pulses together produce a revolving magnetic field that is almost sinusoidal in shape. Fig. 23.24b shows the line current I_a in one phase, and the associated line-to-neutral voltage E_{AN}. Phase angle θ corresponds to the operating power factor of the motor. It depends upon the properties of the motor itself and not upon the switching action of the inverter. In effect, although instant t_1 coincides with the firing of the thyristor connected to phase A, the *timing* of the pulse is not determined by the zero crossing point of voltage E_{AN}. The voltage finds its own place, so to speak, depending upon the particular speed, torque, and direction of rotation the motor happens to have.

We can obtain regenerative braking (generator action) by changing the firing angle and reducing the gate pulse frequency of converter 2, as was explained in Section 20.20. This reverses the polarity of E_2. However, the dc current continues to flow in the same direction and so converter 2 feeds power into the dc link. By simultaneously retarding the triggering of the thyristors in converter 1, we also reverse the polarity of E_1. Consequently, converter 1 now acts as an inverter, feeding power back into the 3-phase line. The new phase relationship between stator voltage and stator current is shown in Fig. 23.24c. Note that converter 2 continues to supply reactive power to the motor during this regenerative braking period.

The direction of rotation is easily changed by altering the phase sequence of the pulses that trigger the gates of converter 2. Consequently, this static frequency converter can operate in all four quadrants with high efficiency. By changing the frequency, the torque-speed curve can be moved back and forth, as shown in Fig. 23.16. High-inertia loads can be quickly brought up to speed by designing the

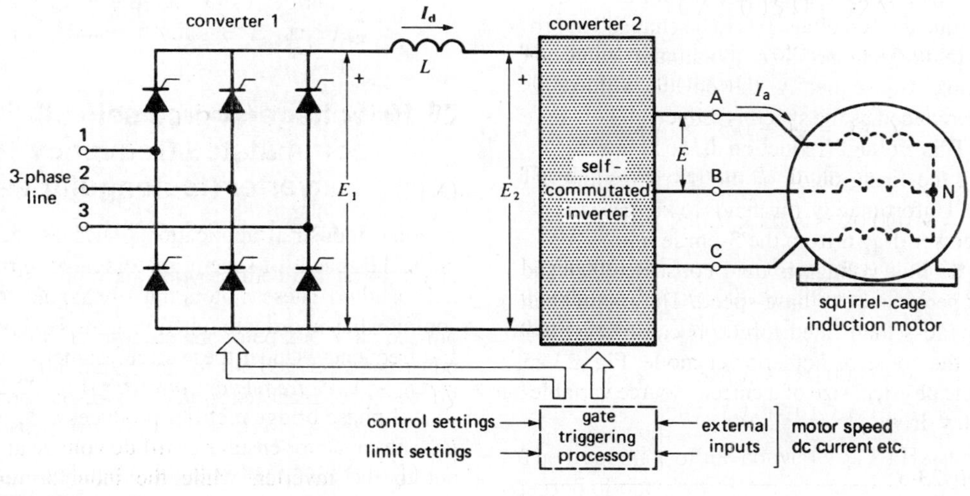

Figure 23.24a
Current-fed frequency converter.

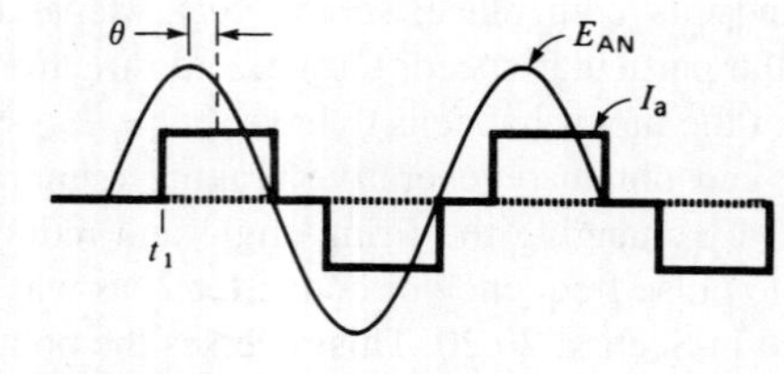

Figure 23.24b
Motor voltage and current.

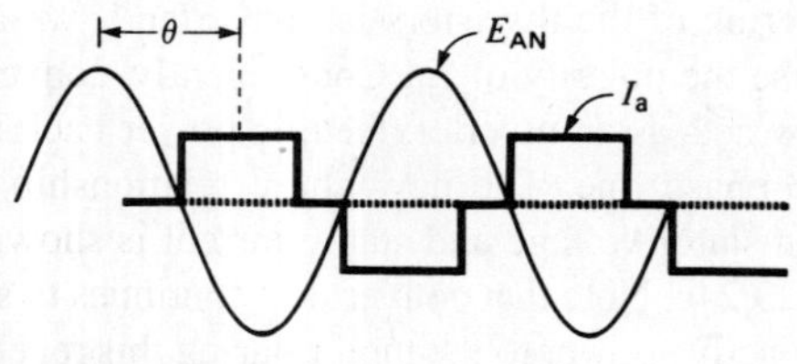

Figure 23.24c
Asynchronous generator voltage and current.

control system so that full-load torque is developed as the motor accelerates.

In practice, the output frequency of such a rectangular wave inverter using thyristors may be varied over a range of 10:1, with top frequencies of about 400 Hz. However, in commercial applications, frequencies are usually less than 200 Hz. At rated torque the ac voltage has to be changed in proportion to the frequency so as to maintain a constant stator flux. Consequently, the dc link voltage E_1 must be reduced as the speed is reduced below base speed. This voltage reduction is achieved by increasing the firing angle of the thyristors in converter 1. Unfortunately, this tends to increase the reactive power drawn from the 3-phase line.

The dc link voltage is held constant when the motor operates above base speed. The motor then develops less than rated torque because it is running in the constant horsepower mode. Fig. 23.25 shows the physical size of a current-source variable-frequency drive.

Example 23-3

A 40 hp, 1165 r/min, 460 V, 52 A, 60 Hz, 3-phase motor is driven by a current-source frequency converter. The efficiency of the motor is 88% and that of the inverter is 99.4%. Referring to Fig. 23.24, calculate the approximate value of the following:

a. The dc power input to converter 2
b. The current in the dc link
c. The dc voltage E_1 produced by converter 1

Solution

a. The active power absorbed by the motor is

$$P = \frac{40 \times 746}{0.88} = 33.9 \text{ kW}$$

The active power absorbed by converter 2 (the inverter) is

$$P_2 = \frac{33.9}{0.994} = 34.1 \text{ kW}$$

b. The effective value of the full-load current is 52 A, stamped on the nameplate. This is the fundamental component of current I_a (Fig. 23.24b). Consequently, the dc current has an approximate value of

$$I_\delta = \frac{52}{0.78} = 66.7 \text{ A} \qquad (21.7)$$

c. The dc value of E_1 (and of E_2) is

$$E_1 = \frac{P_2}{I_d} = \frac{34.1 \times 10^3}{66.7} = 511 \text{ V}$$

23.10 Voltage-source self-commutated frequency converter (rectangular wave)

In some industrial applications, such as in textile mills, the speeds of several motors have to rise and fall together. These motors must be connected to a common bus in order to function at the same voltage and frequency. Under these circumstances we use a *voltage-source frequency converter* (Fig. 23.26a).

A 3-phase bridge rectifier produces a dc voltage E_1. The capacitor ensures a stiff dc voltage at the input to the inverter, while the inductor tends to smooth out the current I_d supplied by the rectifier. The inverter successively switches voltage E_2 across

Figure 23.25
Current-source variable-frequency electronic drive for a conventional 500 hp, 460 V, 1780 r/min, 3-phase, 60 Hz induction motor. The output frequency can be varied from zero to 72 Hz and the efficiency at rated load and speed is 95%. The design is a current-source, 6-step output that can operate in all 4 quadrants.
(Courtesy of Robicon Corporation)

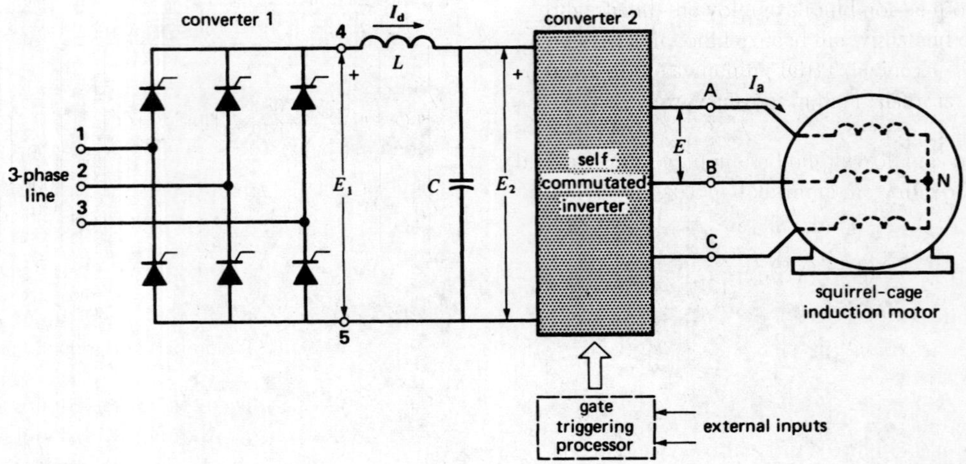

Figure 23.26a
Voltage-fed frequency converter.

the lines of the 3-phase motor. The switching produces positive and negative rectangular voltage pulses of 120° duration (Fig. 23.26b). The frequency ranges typically from about 10 Hz to 200 Hz.

The fundamental component of the line-to-line voltage is directly related to the dc voltage by the expression

$$E_{\text{line}} = 0.78\,E_{\text{d}} \tag{23.1}$$

where

E_{line} = effective fundamental component of line-to-line voltage [V]

E_{d} = dc voltage at input to converter [V]

0.78 = constant [exact value = $\sqrt{6}/\pi$]

Up to base speed, the amplitude of the inverter output voltage E_{line} is varied in proportion to the frequency so as to maintain a constant flux in the motor (or motors). Because the flat-topped ac voltage is equal to the dc voltage E_{d} (= E_2), it follows that rectifier voltage E_1 must be varied as the frequency varies. The speed of the motor can therefore be controlled from a few revolutions per minute to maximum while developing full torque.

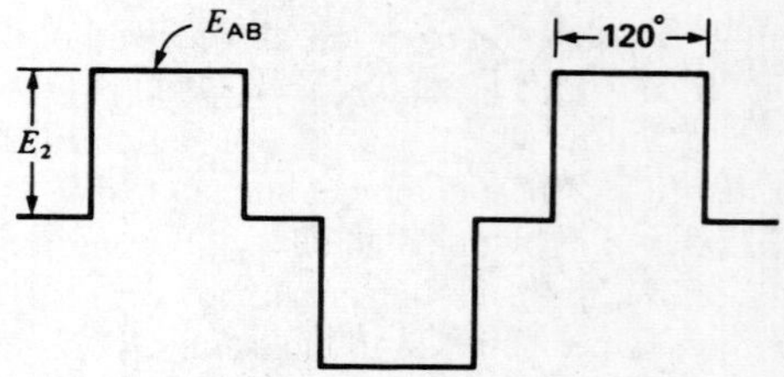

Figure 23.26b
Motor line-to-line voltages.

Above base speed all the voltages are held constant while the frequency continues to increase. In this constant horsepower mode, the torque decreases as the speed rises.

Regenerative braking is possible, but the link current I_{d} reverses when the motor acts as a generator. Voltage E_2 does not change polarity as it does in a current-source inverter. Because converter 1 cannot accept reverse current flow, a third converter (not shown) has to be installed in reverse parallel with converter 1 to permit regenerative braking. The third converter functions as an inverter and, while it operates, converter 1 is blocked. As a result, voltage-source drives that actually return power to

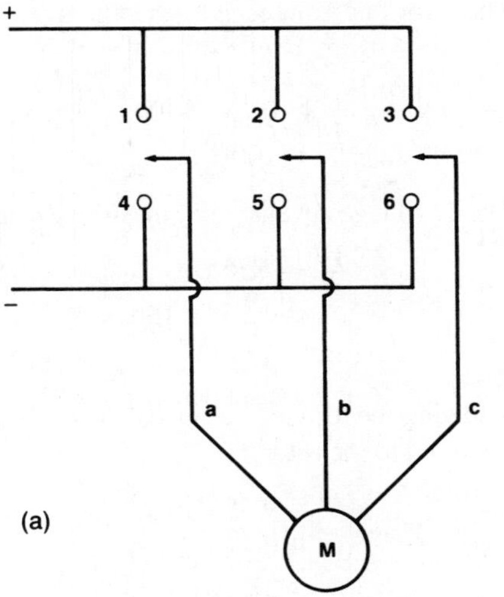

(a)

Time intervals

contacts	T1	T2	T3	T4	T5	T6	T7	T8	T9	T10	T11
1		x	x	x				x	x	x	
2				x	x	x				x	x
3	x	x				x	x	x			
4	x				x	x	x				x
5	x	x	x				x	x	x		
6			x	x	x				x	x	x

(b)

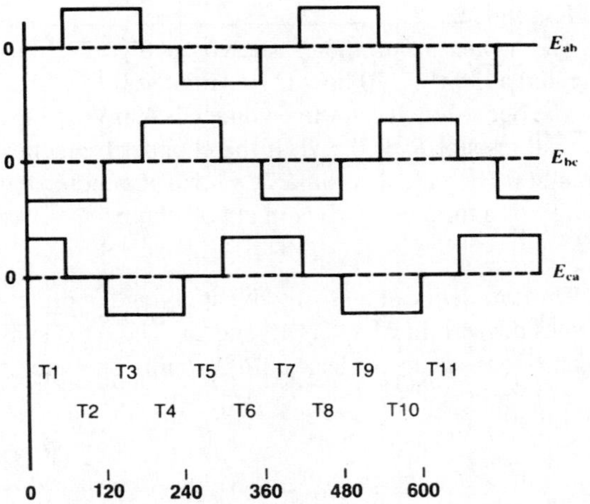

(c)

Figure 23.27
a. Three mechanical switches could produce the same voltage pulses as a voltage-fed inverter.
b. Table showing the switching sequence of the switches.
c. Voltages produced across the motor terminals.

the ac line tend to be more expensive than current-source drives. In many cases a resistor is used to absorb the power delivered during the braking process. Unless the power is large, such dynamic braking is much cheaper than feeding power back into the line. In other installations a dc current is injected into the stator windings (see Section 14.9).

The switching action of converter 2 can be represented by three mechanical switches, as shown in Fig. 23.27a. The opening and closing sequence is given in the chart (b), together with the resulting rectangular line voltages. An X indicates that a switch contact is closed. This mechanical model illustrates that thyristors and other electronic devices in converter 2 really act as high-speed switches. The switching action is called 6-step because the switching sequence repeats after every 6th step, as can be seen from the chart.

23.11 Chopper speed control of a wound-rotor induction motor

We have already seen that the speed of a wound-rotor induction motor can be controlled by placing three variable resistors in the rotor circuit (Section 13.16). Another way to control the speed is to connect a 3-phase bridge rectifier across the rotor terminals and feed the rectified power into a *single* variable resistor. The resulting torque-speed characteristic is identical to that obtained with a 3-phase rheostat. Unfortunately, the single rheostat still has to be varied mechanically in order to change the speed.

We can make an all-electronic control (Fig. 23.28) by adding a chopper and a fixed resistor R_0 to the secondary circuit. In this circuit, capacitor C supplies the high current pulses drawn by the chopper. The purpose of inductor L and freewheeling diode D has already been explained in Section 21.37. By varying the chopper on-time T_a, the apparent resistance across the bridge rectifier can be made either high or low. The relationship is given by

$$R_d = R_0/D_2 \qquad (21.22)$$

where R_d is the apparent resistance between terminals A1, A2, and D is the chopper duty cycle.

Example 23-4

The wound-rotor motor shown in Fig. 23.28 is rated at 30 kW (40 hp), 1170 r/min, 460 V, 60 Hz. The open-circuit rotor line voltage is 400 V, and the load resistor R_0 is 0.5 Ω. If the chopper frequency is 200 Hz, calculate time T_a so that the motor develops a torque of 200 N·m at 900 r/min.

Solution

This problem can be solved by applying the principles covered in Chapters 13 and 21. The rated synchronous speed is clearly 1200 r/min. The slip at 900 r/min is

$$\begin{aligned} s &= (n_s - n)/n_s \qquad (13.2)\\ &= (1200 - 900)/1200\\ &= 0.25 \end{aligned}$$

The rotor line voltage at 900 r/min is

$$\begin{aligned} E &= sE_{oc} \qquad (13.4)\\ &= 0.25 \times 400\\ &= 100 \text{ V} \end{aligned}$$

The dc voltage developed by the bridge rectifier is

$$\begin{aligned} E_d &= 1.35\ E \qquad (21.4)\\ &= 1.35 \times 100\\ &= 135 \text{ V} \end{aligned}$$

Knowing the torque, we can calculate the power P_r delivered to the rotor:

$$\begin{aligned} T &= 9.55\ P_r/n_s \qquad (13.19)\\ 200 &= 9.55\ P_r/1200\\ P_r &= 25\ 130 \text{ W} \end{aligned}$$

Part of P_r is dissipated as heat in the rotor circuit:

$$\begin{aligned} P_{jr} &= sP_r \qquad (13.7)\\ &= 0.25 \times 25\ 130\\ &= 6282 \text{ W} \end{aligned}$$

The power of 6282 W is actually dissipated in resistor R_0, but it is obviously equal to the rectifier output E_dI_d. Thus,

$$\begin{aligned} E_dI_d &= P_{jr}\\ 135\ I_d &= 6282\\ I_d &= 46.5 \text{ A} \end{aligned}$$

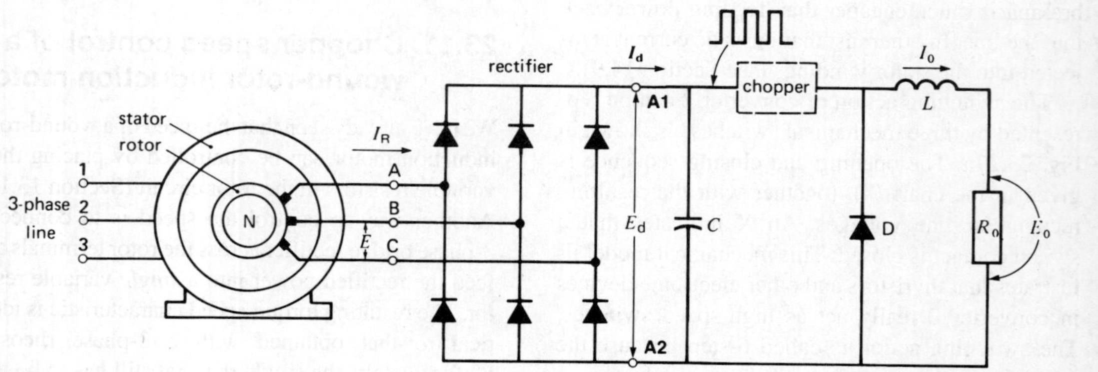

Figure 23.28
Speed control of a wound-rotor induction motor using a load resistor and chopper.

The apparent resistance at the input to the chopper circuit is, therefore,

$$R_d = E_d/I_d = 135/46.5 = 2.9\ \Omega$$

Given that $R_0 = 0.5\ \Omega$, and applying Eq. 21.22, we have

$$0.5 = 2.9 \times D^2$$
$$D = 0.415$$
$$T_a = \frac{D}{f} = \frac{0.415}{200} = 2.08 \text{ ms}$$

The chopper on-time is therefore 2.08 ms.

Example 23-5
In Example 23-3, calculate the magnitude of the current pulses drawn from the capacitor.

Solution
The current I_0 flowing in R_0 is a steady current given by

$$I_0^2 R_0 = P_{jr}$$
$$I_0^2 \times 0.5 = 6282$$
$$I_0 = 112 \text{ A}$$

The capacitor therefore delivers current pulses having an amplitude of 112 A. The pulse width is 2.08 ms and the repetition rate is 200 pulses per second. On the other hand, the rectifier continuously charges the capacitor with a current I_d of 46.5 A.

23.12 Recovering power in a wound-rotor induction motor

Instead of dissipating the rotor power in a resistor, we could use it to charge a large dc battery (Fig. 23.29). Assuming the battery voltage E_2 can be varied from zero to some arbitrary maximum value, let us analyze the behavior of the circuit.

The ac voltage E across the rotor terminals is given by

$$E = sE_{oc} \tag{13.4}$$

where s is the slip and E_{oc} is the open-circuit rotor voltage at standstill (Section 13.10).

On the other hand, rectified output voltage E_d is given by

$$E_d = 1.35\ E \tag{21.4}$$

Because the IR drop in the smoothing inductor is negligible, $E_d = E_2$. Combining Eqs. 13.4 and 21.4, we obtain

$$s = \frac{E_2}{1.35\ E_{oc}}$$

Recognizing that E_{oc} is a fixed quantity, the equation shows that the slip depends exclusively upon the battery voltage E_2. Consequently, we could vary the speed from essentially synchronous speed ($s = 0$) to zero ($s = 1$) by varying the battery voltage from zero to 1.35 E_{oc}.

In practice, instead of charging a battery to absorb the rotor power, we use a 3-phase inverter that

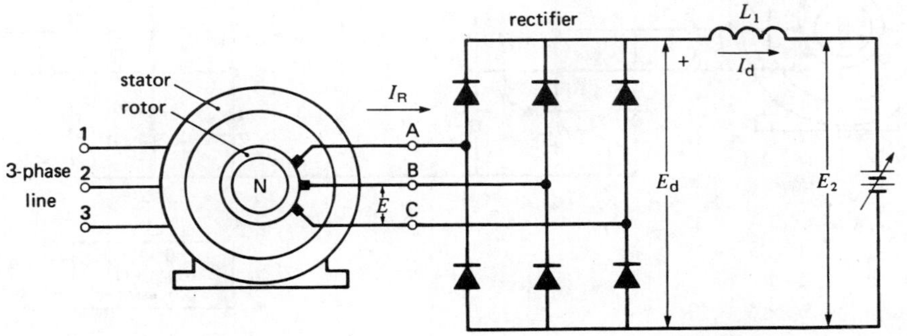

Figure 23.29
Speed control using a variable-voltage battery.

returns the power to the ac source. The line-commutated inverter is connected to the same feeder that supplies power to the stator (Fig. 23.30). A transformer T is usually added, so that the effective value of E_T lies between 80 and 90 percent of E_2. This ensures that the firing angle is reasonably close to the permissible limit of 165° while reducing the reactive power absorbed by the inverter. As usual, the voltages are related by the equation

$$E_2 = 1.35\, E_T \cos \alpha \qquad (21.13)$$

where

E_2 = dc voltage developed by the inverter [V]

E_T = secondary line voltage of transformer T [V]

α = firing angle [°]

This method of speed control is very efficient because the rotor power is not dissipated in a group of resistors, but is returned to the line. Another advantage is that for any given setting of E_T, the speed is practically constant from no-load to full-load.

Fig. 23.31a shows the torque-speed curves for two settings of E_T. When $E_T = 0$, both E_2 and E_d are zero. Consequently, the slip-rings are short-circuited, thus yielding curve 1. When E_T is adjusted to equal 0.4 E_{oc}, the torque-speed characteristic (curve 2) has the same shape but is shifted to the left. Note that the speed decreases only slightly with increasing torque.

The rotor current I_R is rectangular and flows during 120° intervals (Fig. 23.31b). It is symmetrical with respect to the respective line-to-neutral rotor voltage E_{AN}. Consequently, the displacement power factor of the load across the rotor is always unity.

This method of speed control is economical because the rectifier and inverter only have to carry the *slip* power of the rotor, which is considerably less than the input power to the stator. For example, if the lowest desired motor speed is 80% of synchronous speed, the power handled by the converters (at rated torque) is only 20% of the input power to the stator. It follows that the converters are much smaller than if they were placed in the stator circuit where the full stator power would have to be controlled.

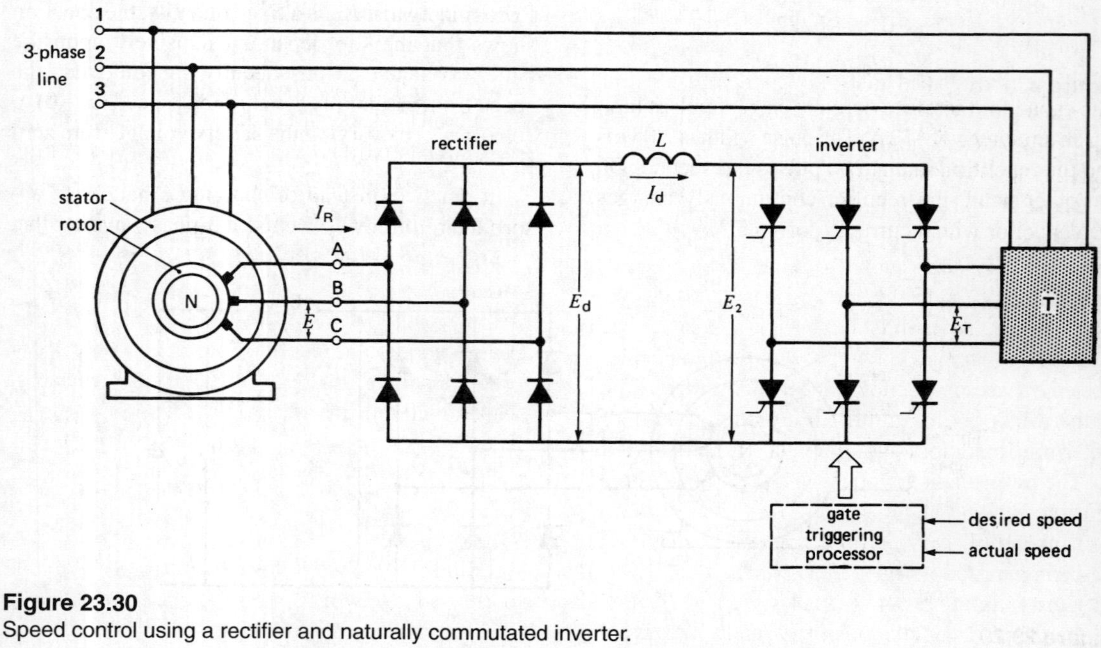

Figure 23.30
Speed control using a rectifier and naturally commutated inverter.

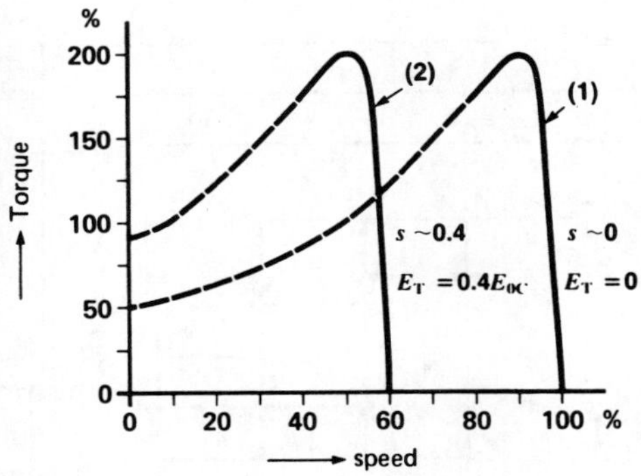

Figure 23.31a
Torque-speed characteristics of a wound-rotor motor for two settings of voltage E_T.

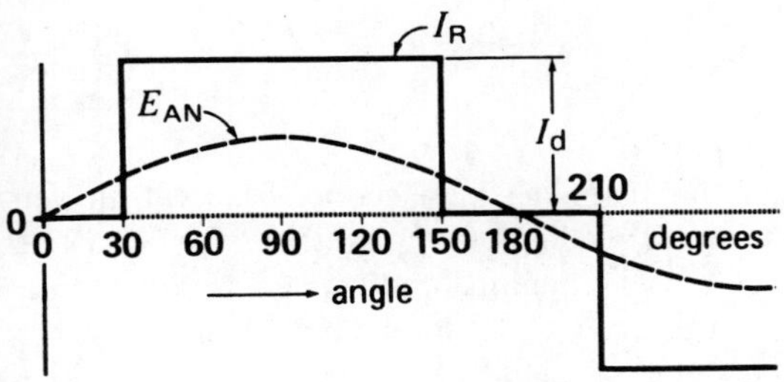

Figure 23.31b
Rotor voltage and current in Fig. 23.30.

Example 23-6

A 3-phase, 3000 hp, 4000 V, 60 Hz, 8-pole, wound-rotor induction motor drives a variable-speed centrifugal pump. When the motor is connected to a 4160 V line, the open-circuit rotor line voltage is 1800 V. A 3-phase, 4160 V/480 V transformer is connected between the inverter and the line (Fig. 23.32). If the motor has to develop 800 kW at a speed of 700 r/min, calculate the following:

a. The power output of the rotor
b. Rotor voltage and link voltage
c. Link current I_d and rotor current
d. Firing angle of the inverter
e. Current in the primary and secondary lines of transformer T

Solution

a. Synchronous speed is

$$n_s = 120\,f/p \quad (13.1)$$
$$= 120 \times 60/8$$
$$= 900\ \text{r/min}$$

Slip is

$$s = (n_s - n)/n_s \quad (13.2)$$
$$= (900 - 700)/900$$
$$= 0.222$$

Mechanical power is

$$P_m = 800\ \text{kW}\ (= 1072\ \text{hp})$$

but

$$P_m = P_r(1 - s) \quad (13.8)$$
$$800 = P_r(1 - 0.222)$$

Power supplied to rotor is

$$P_r = 1028\ \text{kW}$$

Electric power output of rotor

$$P_{jr} = sP_r \quad (13.7)$$
$$= 0.222 \times 1028$$
$$= 228\ \text{kW}$$

Consequently, 228 kW is fed back to the ac line.

b. Rotor line-to-line voltage

$$E = sE_{oc} \quad (13.4)$$
$$E = 0.222 \times 1800$$
$$= 400\ \text{V}$$

DC link voltage

$$E_d = 1.35\,E$$
$$= 1.35 \times 400 = 540\ \text{V}$$

c. DC link current

$$I_d = P_{jr}/E_d = 228\,000/540$$
$$= 422\ \text{A}$$

The effective value of the rotor current is

$$I_R = 0.816\,I_d \quad (21.6)$$
$$= 0.816 \times 422$$
$$= 344\ \text{A}$$

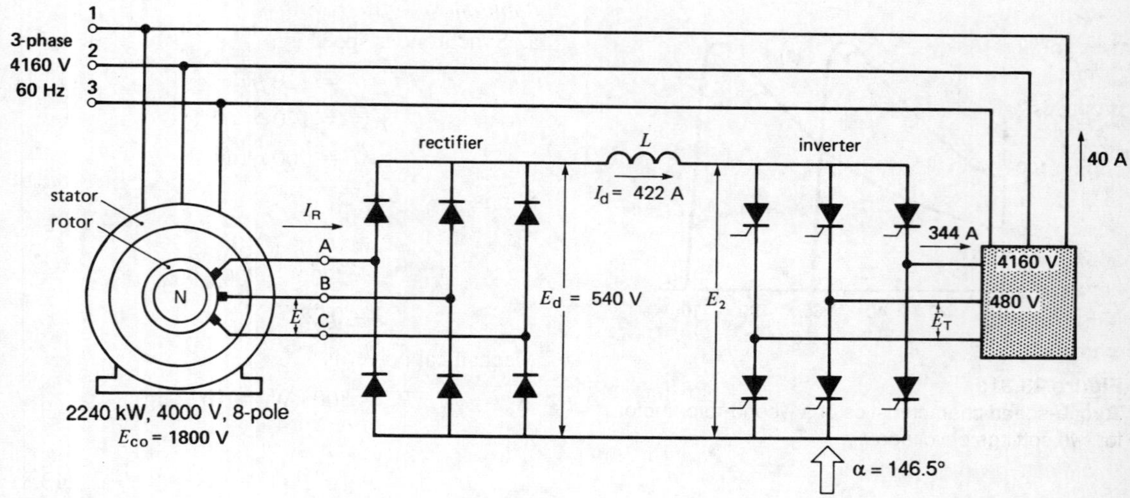

Figure 23.32
See Example 23-5.

d.

$$E_2 = 1.35\,E_T \cos\alpha$$
$$540 = 1.35 \times 480 \cos\alpha$$
$$\alpha = 33.5°$$

The firing angle is actually (180 − 33.5) = 146.5° because the converter acts as an inverter.

e. The current in each phase of the 480 V line flows during 120° intervals and has a peak value of 422 A. The effective value is given by Eq. 21.6:

$$I = 344\text{ A}$$

Effective line current on the 4160 V side is

$$I = (480/4160) \times 344 = 40\text{ A}$$

PULSE-WIDTH MODULATION DRIVES

23.13 Review of pulse-width modulation

The self-commutated frequency converters discussed so far generate rectangular waveshapes that contain substantial 5th and 7th harmonic voltages and currents. When these harmonic currents flow in the motor windings, they produce torque pulsations that are superimposed on the main driving torque. The frequency of the torque pulsation is six times that of the fundamental frequency.

For example, suppose the drive involves a 4-pole induction motor. When the frequency of the rectangular wave is 60 Hz, the synchronous speed is 1800 r/min and the corresponding torque pulsation is 60 × 6 = 360 Hz. On the other hand, when a frequency of 1.5 Hz is applied to the stator, the synchronous speed is 45 r/min and the associated torque vibration is 1.5 × 6 = 9 Hz.

Torque pulsations, such as 360 Hz, are damped out at moderate and high speeds, due to mechanical inertia. However, at low speeds (such as 45 r/min), a 9 Hz vibration is very noticeable. Such torque fluctuations are unacceptable in some industrial applications, where fine speed control down to zero speed is required. Under these circumstances, instead of using rectangular waveshapes, the motor is driven by *pulse-width modulation* techniques. Converters that generate PWM outputs were covered in Chapter 21, Sections 21.45 to 21.48.

To briefly review the basic principles, consider the voltage-source frequency converter system shown in Fig. 23.33. A 3-phase bridge rectifier 1 produces a fixed dc voltage E_1, which appears essentially undiminished as E_2 at the input to the self-commutated converter 2. The converter is triggered in a special way so that the output voltage is composed of a series of short positive pulses of constant amplitude followed by an equal number of short negative pulses (Fig. 23.34a). The pulse widths and pulse spacings are arranged so that their weighted average approaches a sine wave, as shown in the figure. This wanted sine wave is called the *fundamental* and its frequency ranges typically from 0.1 Hz to 400 Hz. The frequency of the pulses, called *carrier frequency,* can range from 200 Hz to 20 kHz, depending on the application and the type of switch employed (GTO, IGBT, etc.).

The pulses in the figure all have the same width, but in practice, the ones near the middle of the sine wave are made broader than those near the edges. By increasing the number of pulses per half-cycle, we can make the fundamental output frequency as low as we please. Thus, to reduce the output frequency of Fig. 23.34a by a factor of 10, we increase the number of pulses per half-cycle from 5 to 50. At the same time, the pulse spacings are rearranged so that their weighted average again approaches a sine wave.

In some cases the output voltage has to be reduced while maintaining the same fundamental frequency. This is done by reducing all the pulse widths in proportion to the desired reduction in output voltage. Thus, in Fig. 23.34b, the pulses are half as wide as those in Fig. 23.34a, yielding an output voltage half as great, but having the same frequency.

We can therefore vary both the output frequency and output voltage using a fixed dc input voltage. As a result, a simple diode bridge rectifier can be used to supply the fixed dc link voltage. The displacement power factor of the 3-phase supply line is therefore close to unity.

The presence of the carrier frequency eliminates the low-frequency harmonics of the embedded fundamental frequency. The only harmonics present are the carrier frequency itself and close multiples thereof. Thus, a PWM drive that generates a fundamental frequency of 2 Hz, using a carrier frequency of 2500 Hz, would have harmonics clustered around 2500 Hz and multiples of 2500 Hz. The harmonics of 2 Hz do not show up. Consequently,

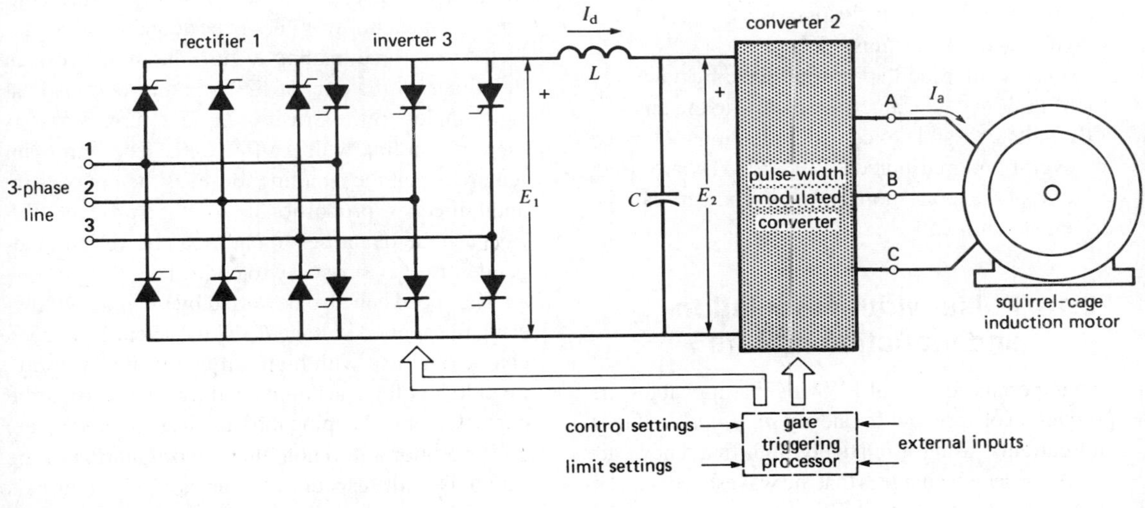

Figure 23.33
Speed control by pulse width modulation.

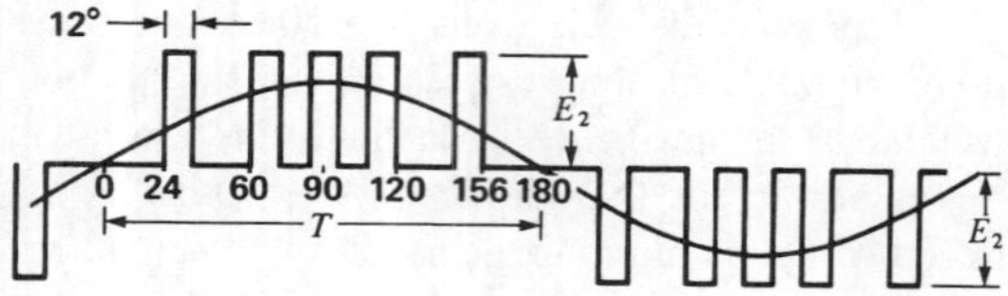

Figure 23.34a
Voltage waveform across one phase.

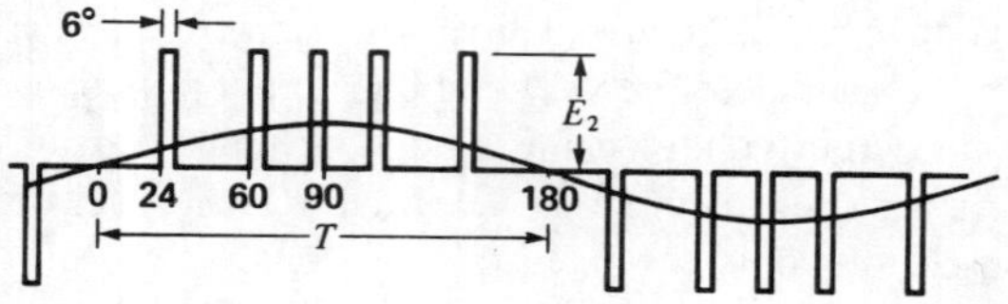

Figure 23.34b
Waveform yielding the same frequency but half the voltage.

torque vibrations at low speeds (and even zero speed) are imperceptible.

However, the distortion of current due to the carrier frequency increases the copper losses in the motor windings. In addition, the carrier frequency voltage that appears across the windings increases the iron losses. As a result, standard induction motors run about 10°C to 20°C hotter when supplied by a 60 Hz PWM voltage source as compared to a conventional 60 Hz sinusoidal source.

Pulse-width modulation is affected by computer control of the gate triggering. By firing the gates of IGBTs, it is possible to control induction motors up to several hundred horsepower. If GTOs are used, motors of several thousand horsepower can be driven electronically.

23.14 Pulse-width modulation and induction motors

The important feature of PWM is that it enables the production of very low-frequency *sinusoidal* voltages and currents, using a relatively high-frequency carrier. A further advantage is that the waveshapes can be altered in a fraction of a millisecond. Consequently, even low-frequency sinusoidal voltages can be transformed almost instantaneously into higher frequencies of any arbitrary shape. As a result, induction motor servo drives can now respond to commands as quickly as the best dc drives. Fig. 23.35 illustrates a typical application of PWM drives.

In order to understand the application of PWM to induction motor drives, it is necessary to look at this motor in a somewhat different light. The reason is that induction motors have traditionally operated at fixed frequencies and whenever a variable-speed drive was needed, the immediate solution was to use a dc drive. Consequently, not much attention was directed to variable-speed induction motor behavior. In the sections that follow, we examine this aspect of induction motors.

TORQUE AND SPEED CONTROL OF INDUCTION MOTORS

23.15 DC motor and flux orientation

We begin our discussion of speed and torque control by referring to a dc motor (Fig. 23.36a). The field produces a flux Φ that is stationary in space and which can be varied by means of the field current. When the brushes are in the neutral position, the armature current I flows in the armature conductors in such a way that every conductor is subjected to a force tending to turn the motor ccw. In this diagram the axis of the armature current is at right angles to the brush axis. The current axis is therefore in line with the field axis. The important feature is that the resulting torque is then maximum and directly proportional to the product ΦI. Because the quantities Φ and I can be varied independently, it is very easy to control the torque.

The speed can also be varied by raising and lowering the applied voltage E_s. Thus, a very low speed can be obtained with high torque by simply applying a low voltage accompanied by a large armature current I, while keeping the flux Φ at its rated value.

It is important to note that the orientation of the flux axis with respect to the armature current axis has a direct impact on the torque. For example, if the brushes are shifted as shown in Fig. 23.36b, the

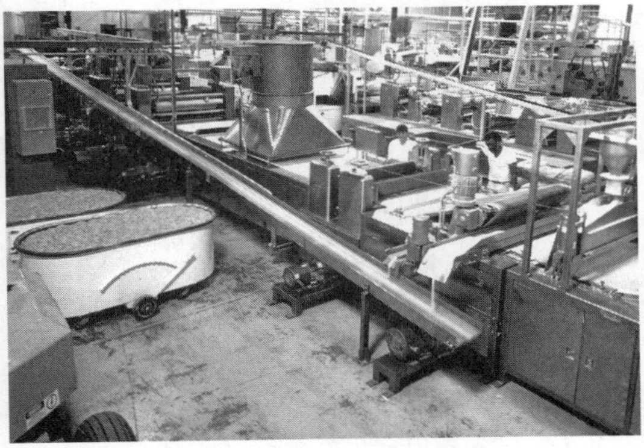

Figure 23.35
Food processing is one of countless industrial applications where PWM drives are used. A good example is the production line at the Wortz® Company in Poteau, Oklahoma, pictured here. This 700-foot long baking and packaging line, which produces 1000 boxes of saltine crackers every 10 minutes, is equipped with 44 PWM drives plus 35 other individual motors. The drives allow precise control over the entire production process. Downtime and maintenance of the drive system are much less compared to older baking lines that use mechanical drives.
(Courtesy of Baldor Electric Company)

angle between the flux axis and current axis is altered and this will produce a smaller torque. Indeed, it can be seen that if the brushes were shifted off neutral by 90°, the angle between the flux and current axes would also shift by 90° and the resulting torque would be zero. The reason is that the forces on the armature conductors now cancel each other. Thus, *flux orientation* relative to the armature current axis is just as important as are the Φ and I values themselves.

23.16 Slip speed, flux orientation, and torque

The fundamental behavior of an induction motor having p poles can be understood by reference to Fig. 23.37. It shows two successive N, S poles, created by the stator (not shown), sweeping to the right at synchronous speed n_s. The flux per pole is distributed sinusoidally, with a peak flux density $B_{peak} = 0.8$ T. The flux in question is the mutual flux that crosses the air gap (see Section 13.11).

The rotor and its rotor bars are also moving to the right, but at a speed n, where n is less than n_s. It follows that the flux is cutting across the rotor bars at a *slip speed* given by

$$S = (n_s - n)$$

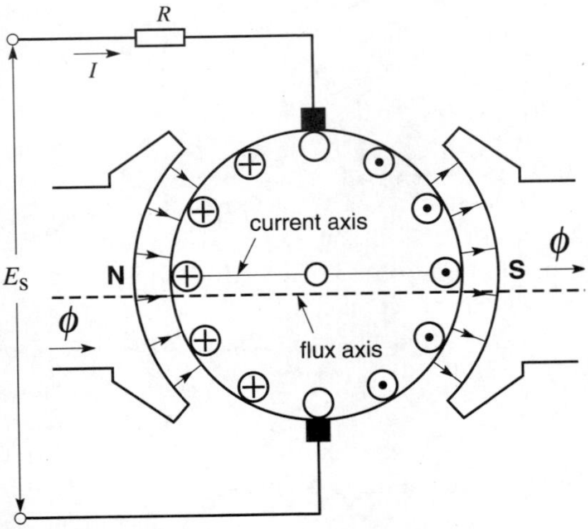

Figure 23.36a
Speed and torque control of a dc motor.

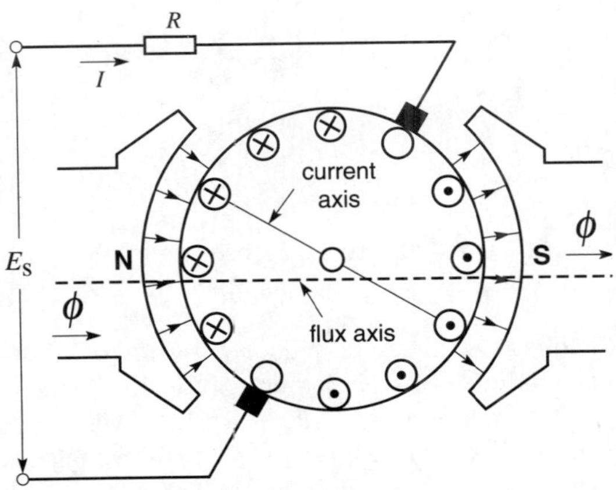

Figure 23.36b
DC motor with brushes off neutral.

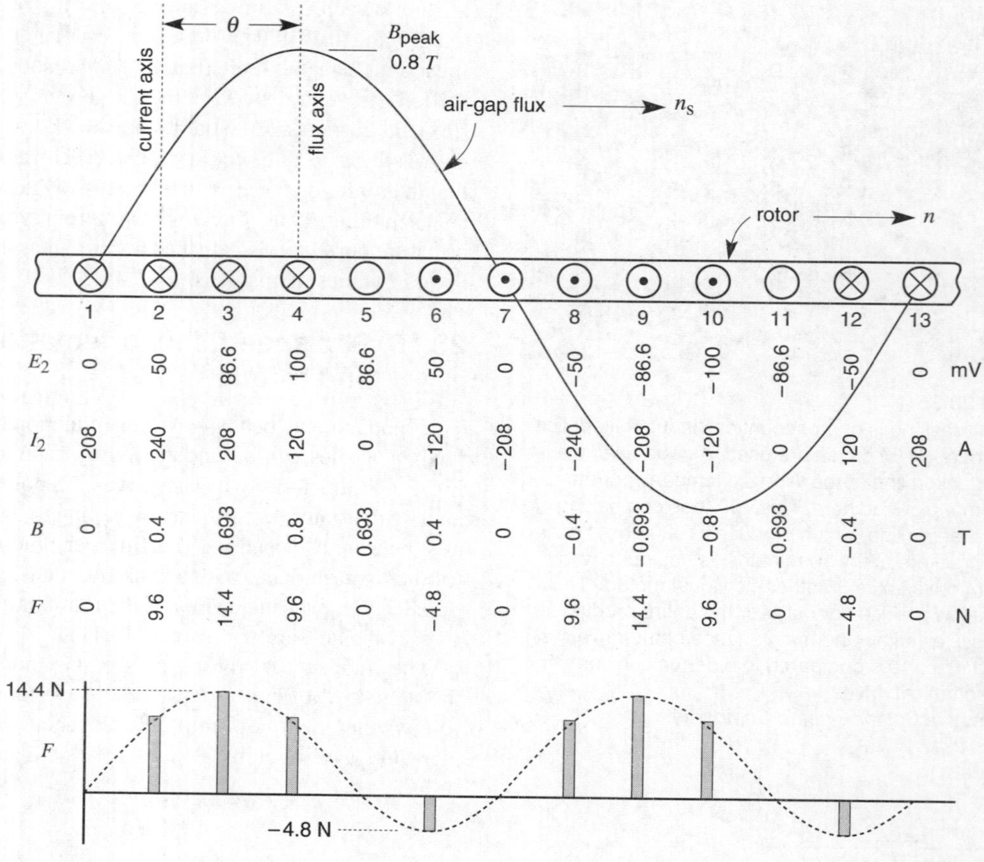

Figure 23.37
Air-gap flux and resultant voltages, currents, and forces produced in rotor.

where

S = slip speed [r/min]
n_s = synchronous speed [r/min]
n = rotor speed [r/min]

A voltage is, therefore, induced in each rotor bar, the amplitude of which is proportional to the slip speed S multiplied by the flux density in which the bar happens to be immersed. Thus, the voltage is momentarily maximum in bars 4 and 10, and zero in bars 1, 7, and 13.

There are six rotor bars per pole and so the electrical angle separating them is 180°/6 = 30°.

As the flux cuts across the bars, the voltage induced in each will vary sinusoidally in time. We learned in Chapter 13 that the following equations apply to an induction motor:

The rotor frequency f_2 is related to the stator frequency f by the expression

$$f_2 = sf \qquad (13.3)$$

Furthermore, the slip s is given by

$$s = (n_s - n)/n_s \qquad (13.2)$$

and, finally, n_s is related to the stator frequency f and the number of poles p by the equation

$$n_s = 120 f/p \quad (13.1)$$

From these equations we deduce the following expression:

$$f_2 = Sp/120 \quad (23.3)$$

where

f_2 = rotor frequency [Hz]
S = slip speed [r/min]
p = number of poles

The rotor frequency is therefore directly proportional to the slip speed. Frequency plays an important role in the flux orientation of the induction motor. At full-load and rated torque, the rotor frequency of conventional motors is 2 Hz or less.

Rotor Current. The voltage induced in a particular rotor bar will cause a current to flow in the bar equal to the voltage divided by the bar impedance. The latter, in turn, depends upon the resistance of the bar and its reactance. Because of the reactance, the current in a particular bar will lag behind the voltage, which means that it reaches its maximum value a brief instant after the voltage has reached its maximum. For example, referring to Fig. 23.37, the current is assumed to lag 60° behind the voltage; consequently, the current reaches its maximum in bar 2 because this bar is 60° behind bar 4, which is the position bar 2 occupied at the instant *its* voltage was momentarily maximum.

The axis of the currents in the rotor is therefore displaced from the axis of the air gap flux by an angle of 60°. This is equivalent to shifting the brushes of a 2-pole dc motor by 60° from the neutral. The flux orientation in this figure is therefore poor.

However, given that the rotor frequency at full-load is typically less than 2 Hz, it follows that the reactance of a rotor bar is very low compared to its resistance. At full-load the phase angle between the current and the voltage is typically less than 5°. The current distribution in the rotor bars is, therefore, essentially the same as the voltage distribution. This means that the rotor bar in which the induced voltage is maximum will also carry the maximum current. As a result, the axis of the current in the rotor is almost directly in line with the axis of the flux from the stator for all loads between zero and full-load. Clearly, under these conditions the induction motor compares very favorably with a dc motor as far as flux orientation is concerned.

However, when the rotor frequency is high (say, 30 Hz or more), the reactance of the rotor bar is considerably greater than its resistance. Consequently, the current will lag significantly behind the voltage. Thus, in Fig. 23.37, where the rotor frequency is 40 Hz, the current lags 60° behind the voltage.

We conclude that to ensure good flux orientation at all speeds, the frequency in the rotor must be kept low: typically, 2 Hz or less.

Torque. The force exerted on each rotor bar is proportional to the product of the current flowing through it and the flux density in which it happens to be. For example, in Fig. 23.37, the force on bar 3 is proportional to the current (208 A) times the flux density (0.693 T). Using $F = BLI$ (Eq. 2.26), this yields a force of 14.4 N for a rotor bar having a length of 10 cm. The sum of all the forces acting on the rotor bars, multiplied by the radius arm, is equal to the torque developed by the motor. Fig. 23.37 illustrates the voltage, current, flux density, and force for the individual rotor bars.

23.17 Features of variable-speed control–constant torque mode

Before going into a detailed analysis of speed and torque control, which involves using the equivalent circuit diagram of the induction motor, it is useful to look at the main features. Fig. 23.38 shows six operating modes of a 1 kW, 4-pole, 1740 r/min induction motor. It has a nominal rating of 416 V, 3-phase, 60 Hz but is designed to run over a broad range of speeds, including zero speed, by varying the stator frequency.

In these six modes we assume that the torque is held constant at its rated value. Furthermore, the flux in the air gap is held constant with a peak flux density B_{peak} = 0.8 T. The first example (Fig. 23.38a) exhibits *rated* operating conditions, together with information on rotor voltages and currents. These

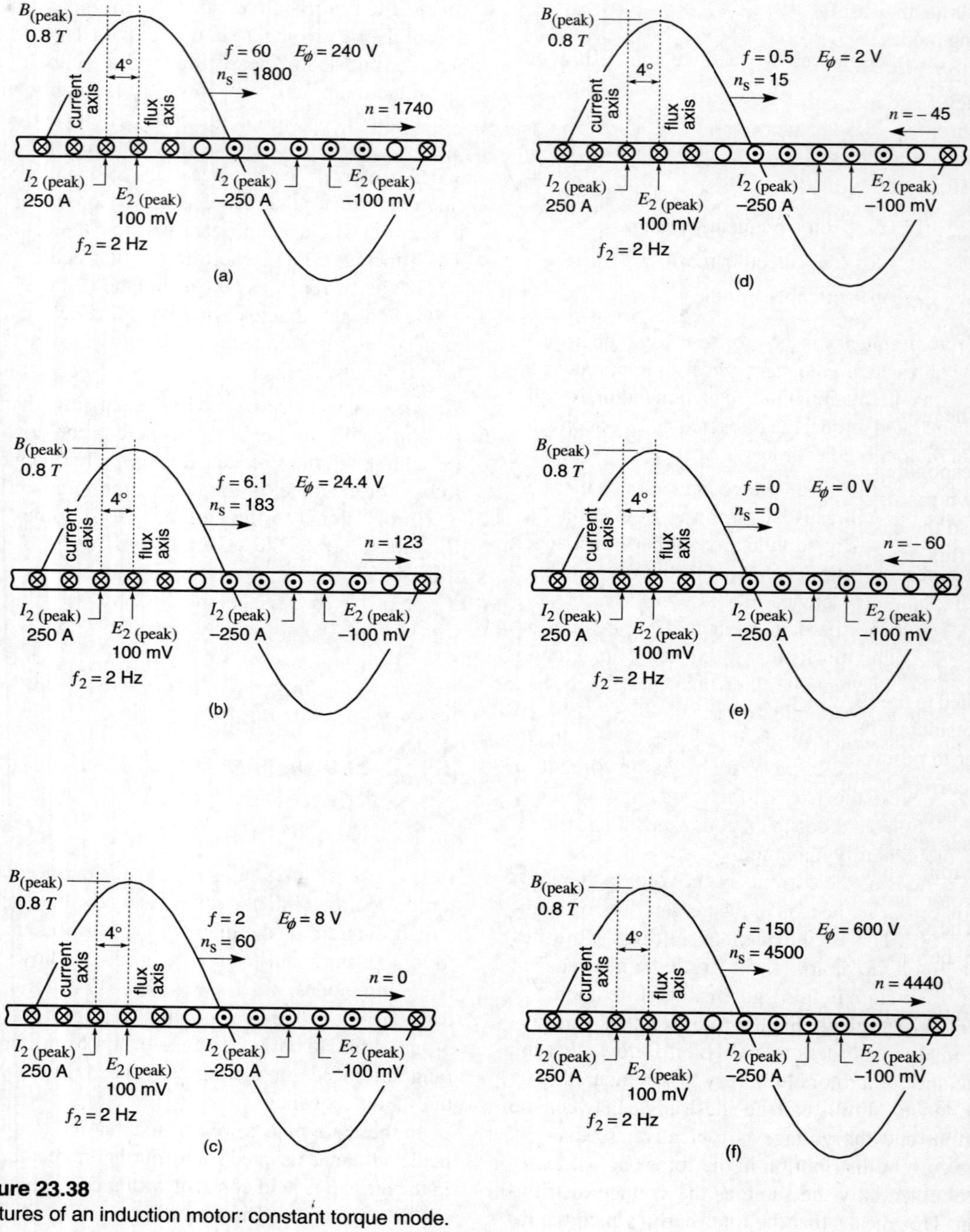

Figure 23.38
Features of an induction motor: constant torque mode.

details are then used to analyze in the subsequent operating modes (Fig. 23.38b to 23.38f).

Fig. 23.38a: Rated Operating Mode. The frequency f applied to the stator is 60 Hz, and so the synchronous speed is 1800 r/min. The motor develops rated torque at 1740 r/min, which corresponds to a slip speed of (1800 − 1740) = 60 r/min. The corresponding rotor frequency is therefore given by Eq. 23.3:

$$f_2 = Sp/120 \tag{23.3}$$

and so

$$f_2 = (60 \times 4)/120 = 2 \text{ Hz}$$

The peak voltage induced in each rotor bar under these conditions is known to be 100 mV and the corresponding peak current is 250 A. It is also known that the current lags 4° behind the voltage and so the current axis lies 4° behind the flux axis. The flux orientation is excellent.

As the mutual flux sweeps across the stationary stator windings, it induces in each phase a voltage E_ϕ of 240 V, at a frequency of 60 Hz.

Fig. 23.38b: Operation at 6.1 Hz. The frequency applied to the stator has been reduced to 6.1 Hz, with the result that the synchronous speed is 183 r/min. In order to produce the same torque as in Fig. 23.38a, the current in the rotor bars must be exactly as it was before in magnitude, frequency, and phase. This is realized when the slip speed ($n_s - n$) is again 60 r/min. Thus, full-load torque is produced when the rotor turns at (183 − 60) = 123 r/min.

The voltage E_ϕ induced in the stator is now less than before, because the flux is only turning at 183 r/min. The value of E_ϕ is readily calculated by the ratio method:

$$E_\phi = 240 \times 183/1800 = 24.4 \text{ V; frequency 6.1 Hz}$$

Fig. 23.38c: Motor Stalled. The stator frequency is now reduced to 2 Hz and so the synchronous speed is 60 r/min. To produce rated torque, the slip speed must again be 60 r/min. This means that n = (60 − 60) = 0 and so the motor is not turning at all.

The voltage induced in the stator by the mutual flux is

$$E_\phi = 240 \times 60/1800 = 8 \text{ V; frequency 2 Hz}$$

Fig. 23.38d: Motor Operating as a Brake. The stator frequency is dropped still further to 0.5 Hz, with the result that the synchronous speed becomes 15 r/min. However, the motor can still develop rated torque provided the slip speed is maintained at 60 r/min. This is achieved if the rotor turns in the *opposite* direction to the flux at a speed of (15 − 60) = −45 r/min. However, in this mode when the flux and rotor turn in opposite directions, the motor acts as a brake. The voltage induced in the stator is 2 V.

Fig. 23.38e: Stator Excited by DC. The stator frequency is now zero, which means that a dc current is flowing in the stator windings. Nevertheless, the rated torque can again be obtained provided the relative speed is 60 r/min. This happens when the rotor turns at 60 r/min in either direction. Again, the motor acts as a brake. The flux is not rotating and so $E_\phi = 0$.

Fig. 23.38f: Operation Above Base Speed. As another example of motor performance in the constant torque mode, the stator frequency is raised to 150 Hz, giving a synchronous speed of 4500 r/min. Rated torque is again obtained when the slip speed is 60 r/min. The rotor is, therefore, turning at 4440 r/min. Note that E_ϕ induced in the stator is now quite high, reaching $E_\phi = 240 \times 4500/1800 = 600$ V.

It is revealing that in all six modes examined above the rotor conditions are identical. The peak voltage induced in the rotor bars remains at 100 mV, the peak current remains at 250 A, and the frequency is unchanged at 2 Hz. In effect, as the stator frequency is varied, the entire behavior of the motor is seen to depend upon the slip speed S. It is important to recall that the flux per pole was kept fixed. To meet this requirement, the magnetizing current that produces the mutual flux must somehow be held constant.

23.18 Features of variable-speed control–constant horsepower mode

Returning to the motor described by Fig. 23.38a, suppose the electronic power supply can only deliver the rated maximum of 240 V, but that the frequency can be raised to 400 Hz, if need be. We wish to raise the motor speed to about 4500 r/min, which means raising the stator frequency to 150 Hz. If the peak flux density were held at its normal level, the stator voltage would have to be 600 V, as previously seen in Fig. 23.38f. But because the stator voltage is limited to 240 V, the peak flux density will automatically fall in proportion to the increase in frequency. Thus,

$$B_{peak} = (60/150) \times 0.8\ \text{T} = 0.32\ \text{T}$$

This flux density is 2.5 times less than the rated peak value. The situation is depicted in Fig. 23.39. To see what happens to the torque and speed, we reason as follows:

1. In order to develop the maximum possible torque, the current in the rotor bars should be as large as possible, without, however, exceeding the thermal limits. This means that the peak current should again be 250 A.
2. To produce 250 A, the peak voltage E_2 induced in the rotor bars must again be 100 mV.
3. If B_{peak} were equal to 0.8 T, a slip speed of 60 r/min would suffice to generate 100 mV. But B_{peak} is now only 0.32 T, which is 2.5 times less. Therefore, the only way to make E_2 equal to 100 mV is for the slip speed to increase by a factor of 2.5. The required slip speed must therefore be $2.5 \times 60 = 150$ r/min. The resulting motor speed is $4500 - 150 = 4350$ r/min.
4. The flux per pole is only 1/2.5 of its rated value, and so the torque is also 1/2.5 of its rated value. However, the motor speed is nearly 2.5 times its rated base speed and so the horsepower remains at its rated value. The motor is operating in the constant horsepower mode.

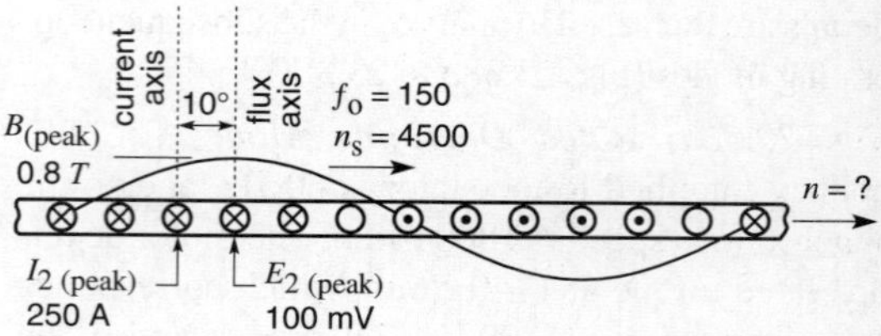

Figure 23.39
Features of an induction motor: constant horsepower mode.

5. The frequency in the rotor is no longer 2 Hz because the slip speed is 2.5 times greater than in Fig. 23.38a. The rotor frequency is 2.5×2 Hz $= 5$ Hz. This higher frequency will cause the current to lag a few extra degrees behind E_2. The angle between the flux axis and current axis is larger than in Fig. 23.38, but the reduction in torque due to this change in flux orientation is minimal.

However, if the speed had to be raised by a factor of 20 (i.e., to $20 \times 1800 = 36\,000$ r/min), while limiting E_ϕ to 240 V, the flux density would have to be reduced by a factor of 20. To generate the 100 mV in the rotor bars, the slip speed would have to be $20 \times 60 = 1200$ r/min. This corresponds to a rotor frequency of 20×2 Hz $= 40$ Hz. The flux orientation would be poor, and the resulting drop in torque would be so serious that the constant horsepower mode could probably not be sustained.

23.19 Feature of variable-speed control–generator mode

In variable-speed induction motor drives, the generator mode of operation comes into play very frequently. We recall that an induction motor becomes a generator whenever the stator flux turns in the same direction as the rotor, but at a slower speed.

We will study two cases, one where the motor is running at close to rated speed and another where the speed is much lower. These conditions are repre-

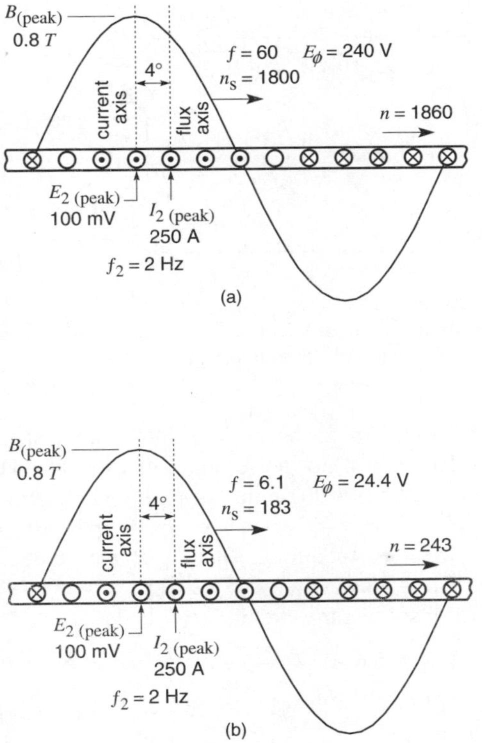

Figure 23.40
Features of an induction motor: generator mode.

sented in Figs. 23.40a and 23.40b. The generator torque in both cases is equal to the rated torque, and the same data is used as in Figs. 23.38 and 23.39.

Fig. 23.40a: Generator Mode, Rated Speed. The stator frequency is 60 Hz and so the synchronous speed is 1800 r/min. The rotor turns at 1860 r/min; consequently, the slip speed is 60 r/min. As in the previous examples, it follows that the rotor frequency is 2 Hz and the current again lags behind E_2 by 4°. However, there is an important difference because the direction of current flow is the reverse of what it was in Fig. 23.38a. Furthermore, the current axis is now slightly *ahead* of the flux axis, leading it by 4°. The important point to remember is the reversal of the rotor current. It is the reversal that produces the generator action of the motor.

Fig. 23.40b: Generator Mode, Low Speed. The stator frequency in this case is 6.1 Hz, producing a synchronous speed of 183 r/min. The rotor turns at 243 r/min, and the slip speed is again 60 r/min. The rotor voltages and currents are, therefore, the same as in Fig. 23.40a. Power is again being fed from the rotor to the stator.

23.20 Induction motor and its equivalent circuit

Torque and speed control of a squirrel-cage induction motor is more difficult to achieve than in a dc motor because the rotor is not accessible, and so the rotor current cannot be controlled directly. The rotor current is induced by the current flowing in the stator. Furthermore, the stator current also produces the very flux that is needed to produce the torque. This complex situation can best be resolved by referring to the equivalent circuit of a 3-phase induction motor.

The complete circuit for one phase (drawn from Chapter 15), is shown in Fig. 23.41. It is very similar to the circuit diagram of a transformer. The parameters of the motor are listed as follows:

r_1 = stator resistance
x_1 = stator leakage reactance
x_2 = rotor leakage reactance referred to the stator
r_2 = rotor resistance referred to the stator
x_m = stator magnetizing reactance
s = slip (not slip speed)

In this figure, in the interest of simplicity, we have not included the branch representing the iron losses.

The applied voltage E between line 1 and neutral N produces a stator current I_1, which consists of two parts, I_m and I_2. Current I_m is the magnetizing current that produces the flux Φ in the air gap. Current I_2 is a reflection of the current that actually flows in the rotor; it is the torque-producing component of stator current. Flux Φ is the mutual flux that links

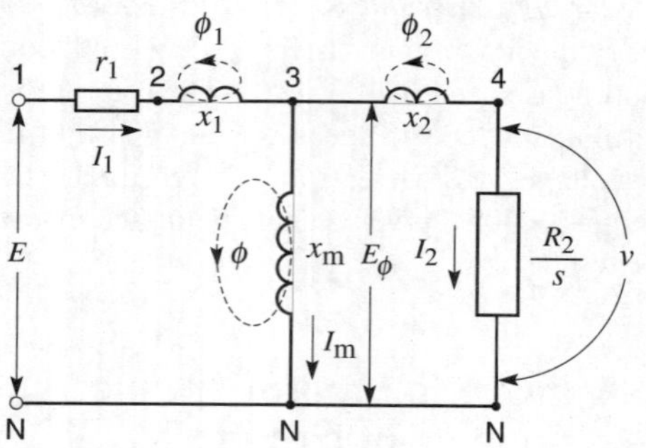

Figure 23.41
Equivalent circuit for one phase of a 3-phase induction motor (see Chapter 15).

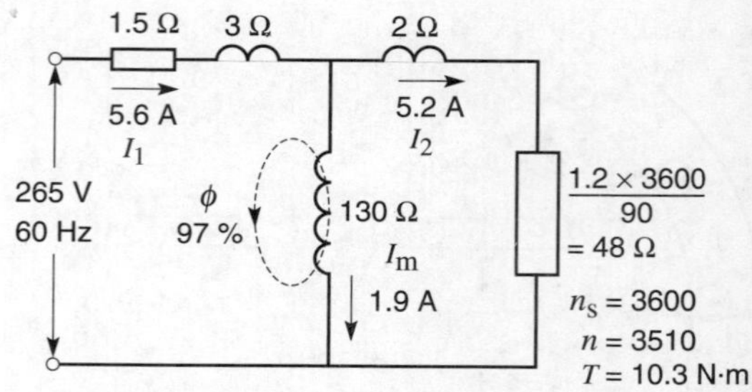

Figure 23.42a
Equivalent circuit of a 5 hp, 2-pole, 460 V, 3-phase, 60 Hz induction motor at full-load.

the stator and rotor. It is precisely the flux illustrated in Figs. 23.38, whose peak flux density is $B_{(peak)}$ and which induces voltage E_ϕ.

The fluxes Φ_1 and Φ_2, associated with x_1 and x_2, are the leakage fluxes for the stator and rotor respectively. The sum of Φ and Φ_1 is the total flux linking the stator. It induces voltage E_{2N} in the stator. Similarly, the sum of Φ and Φ_2 is equal to the total flux linking the rotor. It induces E_{4N} in the rotor.

The resistance R_2/s is a simulated way of representing the active power P_r that is transmitted across the air gap, from stator to rotor, by induction. This "power resistance" can be expressed in terms of the slip speed S:

$$\text{power resistance} = \frac{R_2}{s} = \frac{R_2 n_s}{S} \qquad (23.4)$$

23.21 Equivalent circuit of a practical motor

What information can such a circuit diagram yield in the case of a practical motor? Consider Fig. 23.42a, which shows the equivalent circuit of a commercial 5 hp, 460 V, 3-phase, 60 Hz, 3510 r/min cage motor. The parameters at 60 Hz are listed as follows:

$r_1 = 1.5\ \Omega$	$x_1 = 3\ \Omega$
$r_2 = 1.2\ \Omega$	$x_2 = 2\ \Omega$
$x_m = 130\ \Omega$	$n_s = 3600$ r/min

When the motor operates at full-load, the speed is 3510 r/min, which corresponds to a slip speed of (3600 − 3510) = 90 r/min. The line-to-neutral voltage E is $460/\sqrt{3} = 265$ V. The power resistance in the circuit is, therefore, equal to $R_2 n_s/S = 1.2 \times 3600/90 = 48\ \Omega$.

After solving the circuit, it is found that

$$I_1 = 5.6\text{ A} \quad I_2 = 5.2\text{ A} \quad I_m = 1.9\text{ A}$$

The full-load torque developed by all 3 phases is given by

$$T = \frac{9.55\, P_r}{n_s} \times 3 \qquad (13.9)$$

$$= \frac{9.55 \times 5.2^2 \times 48}{3600} \times 3 = 10.3\text{ N·m}$$

The magnetizing current I_m produces the flux Φ in the air gap. Its value at full-load is 97% of its no-load value, which is the reason for designating Φ as 97%.

When these currents are observed in the actual machine, we obtain the picture shown in Fig. 23.42b. The flux is rotating ccw at 3600 r/min, dragging the rotor along with it. We discover that the axis of the rotor current lags only 2.4° behind the axis of the flux. Consequently, the flux orientation is excellent. The reader will note that the 2.4° is equal to the phase angle determined by the power resistance (48 Ω) and the leakage reactance x_2 (2 Ω) of the rotor.

Consider now the situation when the rotor is locked, with full voltage applied to the stator

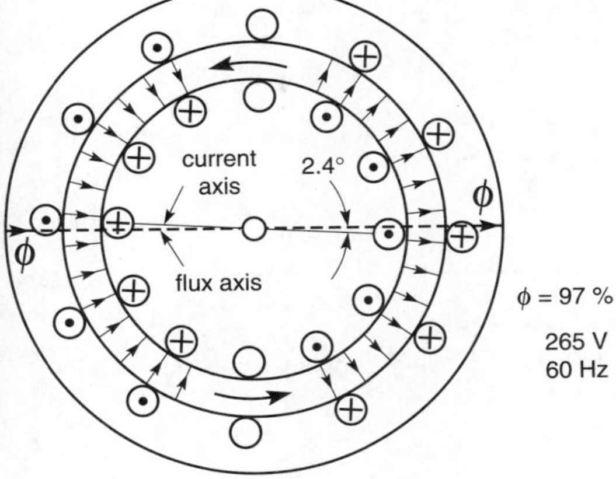

Figure 23.42b
At full-load, flux in the air gap is oriented at 2.4° with respect to rotor current. Flux rotating ccw.

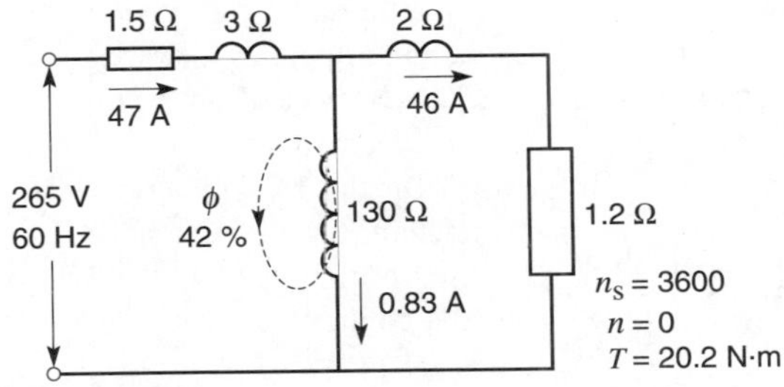

Figure 23.43a
Equivalent circuit of 5 hp induction motor with locked rotor at rated voltage and frequency.

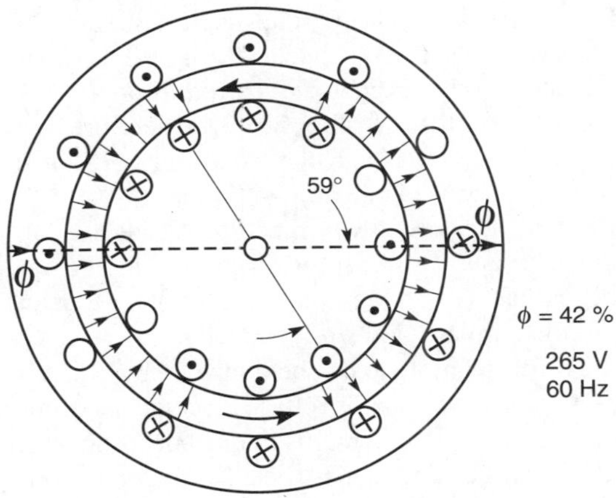

Figure 23.43b
At locked rotor, flux in the air gap is oriented at 59° with respect to rotor current. Flux rotating ccw.

(Fig. 23.43a). The power resistance is now simply equal to R_2, or 1.2 Ω. After solving the circuit, it is found that the currents are much larger, and the orientation of Φ and I_2 have changed. Indeed, the rotor current axis lags 59° behind the flux axis; consequently, there is a large reduction in the torque that would otherwise be available. Furthermore, the air gap flux has dropped to 42% of its rated value, as witnessed by the drop in the magnetizing current, which is now only 0.83 A. Clearly, this is an unsatisfactory condition as far as torque production is concerned. It is directly attributable to the high slip speed (S = 3600 r/min) and the consequent high rotor frequency (60 Hz).

Using this background information, we will now analyze the behavior of the motor when it is driven by a variable frequency source.

23.22 Volts per hertz of a practical motor

We saw in Sections 20.18 and 20.19 that in variable-speed drives, the torque-speed curve and current-speed curve retain the same shape provided that the voltage is varied in proportion to the frequency. This has given rise to the so-called constant volts per hertz rule. When the volts/hertz ratio is held constant, the flux in the motor remains essentially the same over a broad speed range. However, a problem arises at low speeds. For example, let us see how this rule works out when our 5 hp, 3510 r/min, 460 V, 60 Hz commercial motor is driven by a 6 Hz source, which is one-tenth of the base frequency.

If we apply the volts per hertz rule, the line voltage is one-tenth of 460 V, or 46 V. The line-to-neutral voltage is, therefore, 26.5 V. The reactances are all diminished by a factor of 10, as can be seen in Fig. 23.44a. Assuming the same slip speed of 90 r/min in order to get rated torque, it follows that the power resistance is equal to 4.8 Ω. Thus, all the impedances in Fig. 23.44a are ten times less than those in Fig. 23.42a—except for the 1.5 Ω stator resistance which remains unchanged.

After solving the circuit of Fig. 23.44a, we discover that the torque due to the three phases is

$$T = \frac{9.55\ P_r}{n_s} \times 3 \qquad (13.9)$$

$$= \frac{9.55 \times 4^2 \times 4.8}{360} \times 3 = 6.1\ \text{N·m}$$

This torque is much less than the rated value of 10.3 N·m. What has happened? The calculations indicate that the magnetizing current is only 1.5 A compared to 1.9 A in Fig. 23.42a. Therefore, the flux in the air gap is much less than before. That is the reason for the large drop in torque.

Thus, the constant volts/hertz rule leads to a big drop in torque at lower speeds. The culprit is the stator resistance. If it were not present, the constant volts/hertz rule would work perfectly.

The drop in torque can be remedied by systematically raising the stator voltage, to compensate for the *IR* drop in the stator. This torque boost compensation can be introduced when the motor is controlled electronically by a PWM drive.

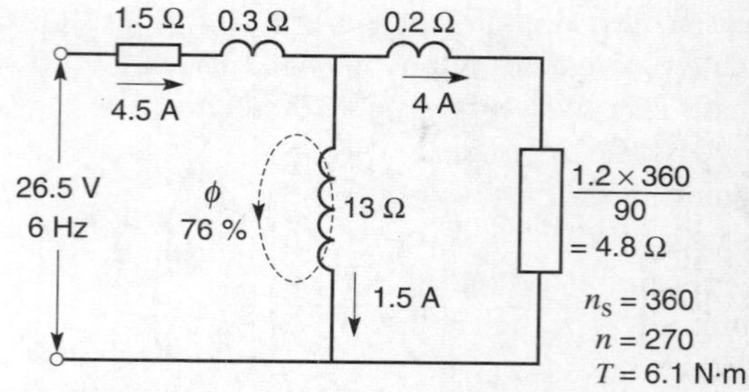

Figure 23.44a
5 hp induction motor operating at one-tenth of rated voltage and frequency.

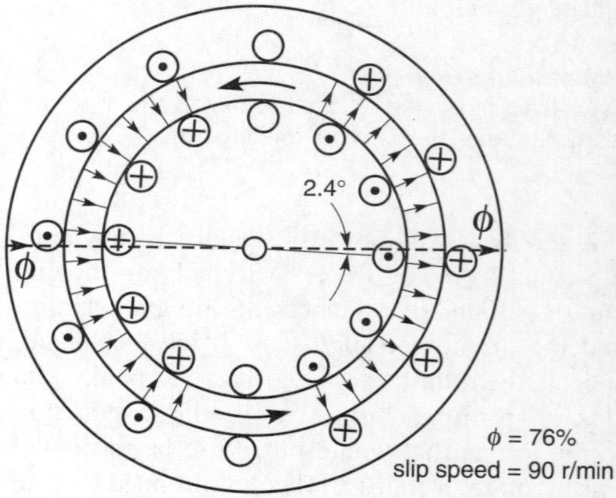

Figure 23.44b
Motor rotating at 270 r/min.

23.23 Speed and torque control of induction motors

The problem in controlling torque and speed is that the magnetizing current I_m and the torque-producing current I_2 are merged into a single current, namely the current I_1 flowing in the stator. In order to control the torque, this current must be split into its I_m and I_2 components. Furthermore, it is advantageous that I_m be held close to its rated value, to ensure the flux is as great as possible without excessive saturation of the iron.

To keep track of all these variables, the circuit parameters of the motor must be known. Toward this end, some PWM control systems incorporate a feature that actually measures the rotor and stator parameters. This measurement is done once, at the time when the drive is installed.

When the motor is in operation, the stator voltage, stator current, frequency, and speed are sensed by transducers and compared with the wanted values. The computer in the control system then determines the I_m and I_2 components and automatically sets the required voltage, frequency, and current that are required.

Sensing the speed creates a problem, because shaft encoders have to be added. This is not an easy matter for motors that are already installed and whose shaft extensions are not accessible. For this reason other algorithms exist whereby the computer can *estimate* the speed, without feedback from the shaft. This gives good results, if the speed is not too low. But if the speed is only a few revolutions per minute, or if a servo position control is required, it is mandatory to use an encoder.

Having a computer in charge of speed and torque, it is possible to include many extra features such as rate of acceleration, deceleration, overcurrent protection, and so forth, as part of the control system. Furthermore, special features can be programmed into the computer by the ultimate user.

The computer makes the high-speed calculations and sends signals to the converter driving the motor, to achieve the desired result. Thus, PWM control of induction motors is made possible thanks to many sophisticated devices, in addition to the switching converter.

23.24 Carrier frequencies

PWM drives for induction motors use various carrier frequencies, ranging from 1 kHz to about 16 kHz. These frequencies can often be changed in the field to satisfy particular needs. One of the concerns is noise which, in quiet environments, is particularly noticeable in the 1 kHz to 2 kHz range. For this reason, carrier frequencies have been raised to 10 kHz and more because they are beyond the range of human audibility. Unfortunately, the higher frequencies always require a decrease in the power-handling capability of the semiconductors.

The sharp rise-time of the carrier voltage has also created problems in some motors, as regards the insulation. The fast rise time produces two effects. First, owing to the mismatch between the high-frequency impedance of the motor windings and that of the connecting cable, the voltage across the motor terminals tends to double for a fraction of a microsecond during every impulse of the PWM voltage. Second, during these sharp peaks, the distributed inductance and capacitance of the motor windings causes the doubled voltage to appear across the first few turns of the motor windings. As a result, the dielectric stress on these turns is much greater than normal, causing an eventual breakdown of the insulation. In some cases, line filters have been added to attenuate the effect, particularly when the motor is located more than 50 m from the converter.

23.25 Dynamic control of induction motors

If a PWM drive is used to vary the speed of a compressor or fan, the change in speed is usually made rather slowly and once set, the motor runs essentially at constant speed. Under these conditions, the motor behaves like an ordinary induction motor, except that the frequency is, say, 47 Hz instead of 60 Hz. The fundamental voltages and currents are sinusoidal and the equivalent circuit diagram is sufficient to describe the motor behavior, even while the speed is changing.

However, in some machine-tool applications, the motor must rapidly accelerate, reverse, stop, and start while responding to torques that may suddenly change without warning, all in a matter of milliseconds. Under such conditions, the behavior of the motor can only be described by special equations that are far more complex than those covered here by the equivalent circuit. During such transient conditions, the voltages and currents are no longer sinusoidal, and the computer-generated waveshapes change from instant to instant. During these transition periods, the flux must be maintained both in value and orientation so as to instantaneously develop the required torque.

It is the fast switching of IGBTs operating at carrier frequencies of several kilohertz, in conjunction with high-speed computers, that makes this type of dynamic control possible. It is often called *flux vector control,* but other names are also used. Obviously, vector control is not needed to drive a fan or compressor, where fast changes of speed are not required. Nor is vector control necessary to drive high-inertia loads that inherently take considerable time to change speed. Indeed, inertia plays an important role in the setting of all PWM drives.

There are many ways of designing high-response induction motor drives, but so far no single best method has evolved. However, a few basic principles are common to all vector drives, and we will describe them briefly in the next section.

23.26 Principle of flux vector control

When an induction motor runs at steady-state, we can use any one of the three phases as a model for all. In this way we arrive at a simple circuit diagram and a few simple equations that adequately describe the behavior of the motor. The respective phase voltages and currents have sinusoidal waveshapes, whose frequency is constant, all neatly separated by phase angles of 120°.

This reassuring situation is completely upset when the motor is subjected to rapidly changing torques, or if it suddenly has to change speed. The behavior is particularly complex when the inertia of the drive is so small that its mechanical time constant is of the same order of magnitude as the electrical time constant of the drive. When such high response drives are subjected to disturbances, or when they must follow rapidly changing commands, the voltages and currents are no longer sinusoidal, and the term *phase angle* loses its meaning.

Under these special conditions, the currents and voltages in all three phases must be considered on an instantaneous basis, both for the stator and the rotor. In the explanation that follows, we assume a wound-rotor motor so that it is easier to visualize the currents and rotor position. Nevertheless, a motor having a cage rotor performs the same way.

Fig. 23.45 is a schematic diagram of a 2-pole, 3-phase motor. Suppose the instantaneous currents flowing in the stator and rotor windings are as shown. The stator currents of 32A, 18A, and 14A are generated by an appropriate current source, which establishes both their instantaneous magnitudes and instantaneous rates of change. The instantaneous magnitudes induce *speed* voltages in the rotor windings that are proportional to the speed of rotation. On the other hand, the instantaneous rates of change of the stator currents induce voltages in the rotor windings by *induction.* The sum of the *speed* voltages and

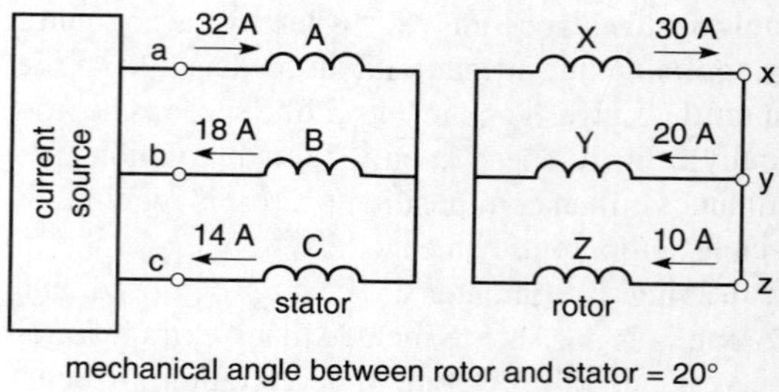

Figure 23.45
Instantaneous currents in rotor and stator windings of a 2-pole, 3-phase induction motor.

induction voltages give rise to the rotor currents. Unfortunately, the rotor currents cannot change instantaneously in response to changes in these two types of voltages. The delay is due to the inductance of the rotor windings. Consequently, the L_2/R_2 time constant of the rotor (per phase) plays an important role in the response of high-performance drives.

The current source is designed to produce fast changes in selected rotor currents by modifying both the magnitude and rate of change of specific stator currents. Therefore, one of the duties of a vector drive is to target those stator currents that will produce the desired changes in specific rotor currents while developing the required torque and maintaining the rated flux and its proper orientation in the air gap. Evidently, this is no small feat.

In explaining the principle of a vector drive, it is much easier to use a numerical example. Thus, the magnitudes and directions of the instantaneous currents are shown schematically in Fig. 23.45. The physical location of the stator windings A, B, C and instantaneous position of the rotor windings X, Y, Z are shown in Fig. 23.46. The distributed stator and rotor windings are shown as single coils. The instantaneous current flows in the respective coils are also shown. The individual coils are assumed to have 10 turns. The rotor is rotating clockwise. At this instant, its position is such that windings X, Y, Z are displaced by 20° clockwise from the corresponding stator windings A, B, C.

The currents in the three stator coils produce magnetomotive forces that are oriented at right angles to the plane of the individual coils. Thus, by applying the right-hand rule, phase A produces an mmf of 32 A × 10 turns = 320 A, directed vertically upward (Fig. 23.47). Similarly, phase B produces an mmf of 18 A × 10 turns = 180 A, directed to the left at an angle of 60° from the vertical. In turn, phase C produces an mmf of 14 A × 10 turns = 140 A, slanted to the right at 60° from the vertical.

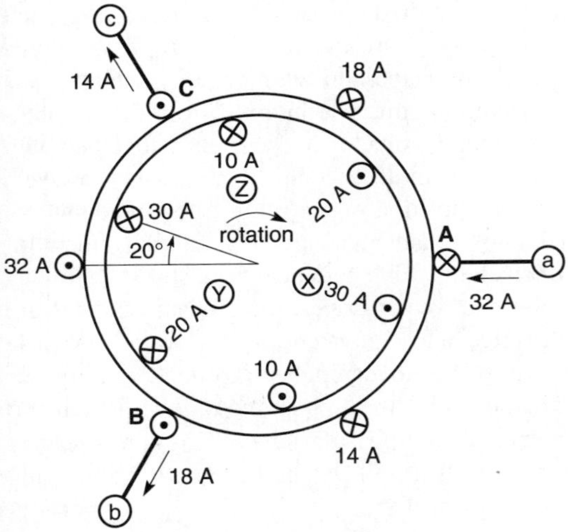

Figure 23.46
Instantaneous position of the rotor and stator windings.

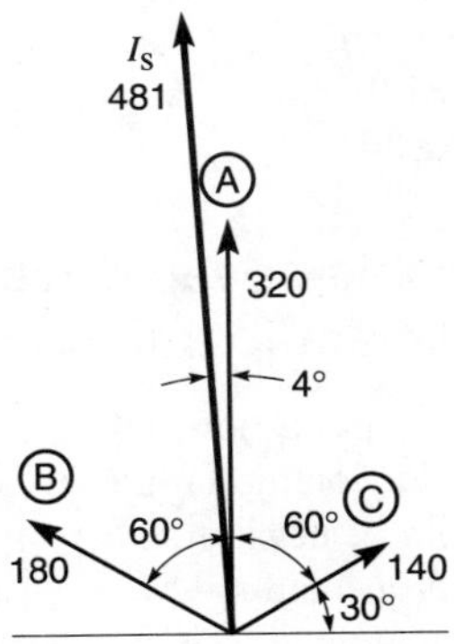

Figure 23.47
Instantaneous magnitude and orientation in space of the stator mmfs.

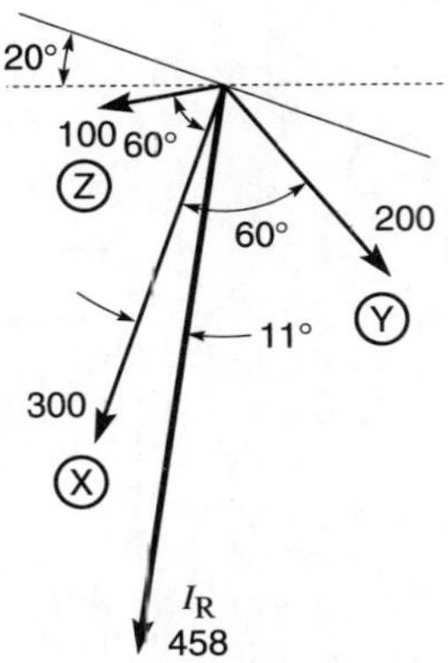

Figure 23.48
Instantaneous magnitude and orientation in space of the rotor mmfs.

The vector sum of these mmfs gives a resultant stator mmf I_s of 481 A, slanted at 4° to the vertical. This single mmf represents the combined effect of all three phases. It is as if the entire stator were replaced at this particular moment by a single 10-turn coil carrying a current of 48.1 A. The plane of this fictitious coil is tilted at 4° to the horizontal.

Now let us consider the rotor. The individual coils produce oriented mmfs the same way as in the case of the stator. Thus, the respective currents produce mmfs of 300 A, 200 A, and 100 A, which are oriented at 60° to each other. However, on account of the position of the rotor relative to the stator, the entire group of mmfs is shifted by 20° (Fig. 23.48). The resultant of these mmfs is a rotor mmf I_R of 458 A directed downward at an angle of 9° clockwise to the vertical. Therefore, at this instant, the three rotor windings can be replaced by a single coil of 10 turns, carrying a current of 45.8 A. The plane of this fictitious coil is tilted at 9° to the horizontal.

Let us now combine the vectors in Figs. 23.47 and 23.48 into a single mmf vector diagram (Fig. 23.49). It again shows how the stator and rotor vectors combine to produce the resultant mmf vectors I_S and I_R. Their respective values are 486A and 456A (not shown). However, it also reveals that the vector sum of I_S and I_R produces a vector I_M. It is this important

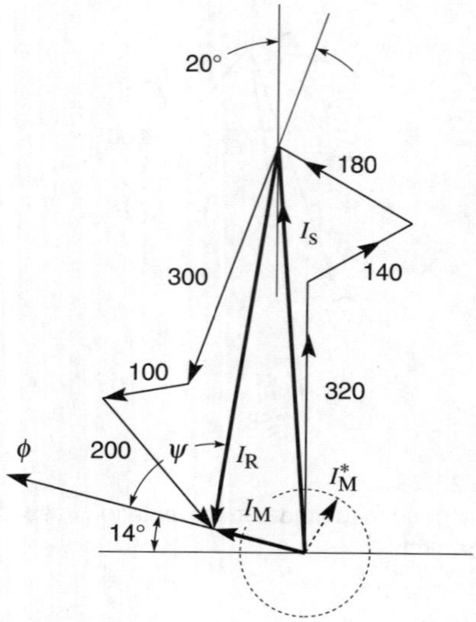

Figure 23.49
The sum of the stator and rotor mmf's produces a resultant mmf I_M, which creates the flux in the air gap.

net mmf that produces the mutual flux Φ in the air gap. This is the same flux that appears in Fig. 23.41 and elsewhere in this chapter. The mmf I_M has a magnitude of 110 A, inclined at 14° to the horizontal.

The torque is created by the interaction of the rotor mmf I_R and the mutual flux Φ. The relationship is given by

$$T = I_R \Phi \sin \psi \qquad (23.5)$$

In order to maximize the torque, angle ψ should be close to 90°, and that is one of the objectives of the PWM vector control unit. Another objective is to adjust the magnitude of I_M to produce rated flux Φ in the air gap. Thus, the actual magnitude of I_M should be adjusted to equal the desired I^*_M. In Fig. 23.49 the value of I_M is a little too large because ideally the tip of I_M should lie on the dotted circle having a radius I^*_M.

We recall that one of the objectives of vector control is to decompose the stator mmf I_S into two parts: the component that produces the flux Φ and the component that produces the torque. These components are made evident in Fig. 23.49; they correspond respectively to vectors I_M and I_R.

In observing Fig. 23.49, it is obvious that the six vectors generated by the six windings will change instant by instant, both in magnitude and direction. The challenge of vector control in the face of changing torques and speeds, is (1) to keep vector I_M on the dotted circle, (2) to keep angle ψ close to 90°, and (3) to keep I_S from exceeding its maximum permissible limits.

The reader will note that the accent is on the control of *current* in the three stator windings. To produce the required currents, the voltages generated by the PWM converter must, in turn, have appropriate waveshapes. In addition, the instantaneous rotor currents must be inferred from the instantaneous stator voltages and currents, together with feedback from an encoder (if necessary) to determine the position of the rotor. These readings are fed into a mathematical model of the motor, in which all the drive parameters are stored.

In most vector drives, the 3-phase readings are converted into equivalent 2-phase values because they are easier to manipulate. In effect, for purposes of computation, the 3-phase motor is converted into an equivalent 2-phase machine. This approach permits expressing all values in terms of direct and quadrature axes.

It is a tribute to the designers of vector drives that such sophisticated control systems have been invented. But a glance at the ever-changing vectors in Fig. 23.49, and their underlying concept, reveals that fast PWM switching and nanosecond computer response in real time, is what makes such remarkable drives possible.

23.27 Variable-speed drive and electric traction

There are many applications where the torque and speed of an induction motor have to be controlled. We will examine electric traction because in this category the torque and speed cover a particularly broad range, including generator action.

Electric traction is also interesting because many power lines for electric trains furnish 60 Hz, single-phase power, at voltages from 5 kV to 25 kV. The power factor of the transportation vehicle should be

Figure 23.50
This blower-cooled, flux vector-controlled motor is equipped with an optical encoder (not visible) that permits accurate sensing of the shaft position at any instant of time. Standard encoders produce 1024 pulses per revolution. Nominal rating of motor: 10 hp, 230 V, 3-phase, 60 Hz, base speed 1800 r/min. The speed is variable from zero to 4500 r/min. PWM carrier frequency is nominally 2.5 kHz or 8 kHz.
(Courtesy of Baldor Electric Company)

Figure 23.51
Internal view of a PWM flux vector control unit showing the complex circuitry. It comprises IGBTs, amplifiers, filters, and a host of other components under the control of a microprocessor. The feedback from the encoder, together with information provided by the keypad instructions, permits an extremely wide range of position and speed control. Thus, torque can be programmed according to position and speed, ranging from zero to several thousand revolutions per minute. Typical features are 0.01 percent speed regulation, 1 ms torque reversal, and smooth vibration-free motoring down to zero speed.
(Courtesy of Baldor Electric Company)

as close as possible to unity so as to minimize the line voltage drop. In addition, the current it draws from the line should be sinusoidal and free from harmonics, so as to prevent interference with adjacent telephone lines. As we will see, the PWM switching converter offers an elegant way of meeting these requirements without having to resort to huge filters and power factor correcting capacitors.

Traction motors are relatively large and hence GTOs are often used. The switching frequency of

GTOs is variable but is typically limited to a maximum of about 250 Hz. This relatively low carrier frequency demands particular attention when PWM methods are applied.

In the range from 60 Hz and up, the switching converters are arranged to deliver rectangular waveshapes, as already discussed in Section 23.10. There is an important advantage in doing so, because for a given dc link voltage, the fundamental rms voltage is higher when using a rectangular wave rather than a PWM wave. Although the voltage harmonics are important at these frequencies, the corresponding current harmonics are damped out by the reactance of the motor windings. The 5th and 7th harmonics are dominant: on a 60 Hz fundamental, they correspond to frequencies of 300 Hz and 420 Hz.

However, if a rectangular wave is used at *low* frequencies the corresponding current harmonics become too great, and PWM methods must be used. Pulse-width modulation can be synchronized or unsynchronized. Synchronization means that the carrier frequency is arranged to be an exact integral multiple of the wanted fundamental frequency. The multiple is preferably an odd number such as 3, 5, 7, and so forth.

Figure 23.52
This 3 hp, 460 V PWM drive and keypad integrates the control unit and motor into a single package. At constant torque the speed can be varied from 180 r/min to 1800 r/min. Above 1800 r/min—up to a maximum of 3600 r/min—the motor operates in the constant horsepower mode. For optimal performance the carrier frequency can be set to any value between 1125 Hz and 18 kHz, albeit with progressive power derating.
(Courtesy of Baldor Electric Company)

It has been found that synchronization is advantageous whenever the carrier frequency is less than ten times the wanted frequency. Thus, if the carrier frequency is variable but limited to a maximum, say, of 250 Hz, it should be synchronized whenever the wanted frequency exceeds 25 Hz. For example, if the wanted frequency happens to be 43.67 Hz, the carrier should be set at the highest odd multiple of this frequency that does not exceed the 250 Hz limit of the GTO. Thus, the carrier should be set at 5 × 43.67 = 218.35 Hz exactly.

If the wanted frequency is less than 25 Hz, the unsynchronized PWM method can be employed, wherein the carrier is simply held fixed at the GTO limit, namely 250 Hz. In this mode, the harmonics are clustered around multiples of 250 Hz.

These points are brought out more clearly in the following example.

23.28 Principal components

Fig. 23.53 shows the basic elements of a drive for a transportation vehicle. The catenary line supplies single-phase power at 15 kV, 60 Hz to a transformer that steps the voltage down to 530 V. The voltage is fed into a PWM converter (3) that delivers 700 V to the dc link. The link voltage is held stiff by capacitor (6), and switching converter (7) furnishes the 3-phase power to traction motor (8).

A braking resistor and chopper (4) absorb power in the event that the catenary line cannot absorb it all during a fast stop. A 120 Hz series-tuned filter (5) absorbs the double frequency current generated by converter (3) and thereby helps reduce the ripple in the dc link voltage.

When the system is first connected to the power line, switch (11) and resistor (12) limit the inrush current due to the presence of capacitor (6). Switch (13) is immediately closed thereafter.

Inductive reactance (2) acts as a filter for the carrier frequency generated by the converter (3). At the same time, it establishes the nature of the active and reactive power flow between converter (3) and transformer (1). In practice, the leakage reactance of the transformer fills the role of inductive reactance.

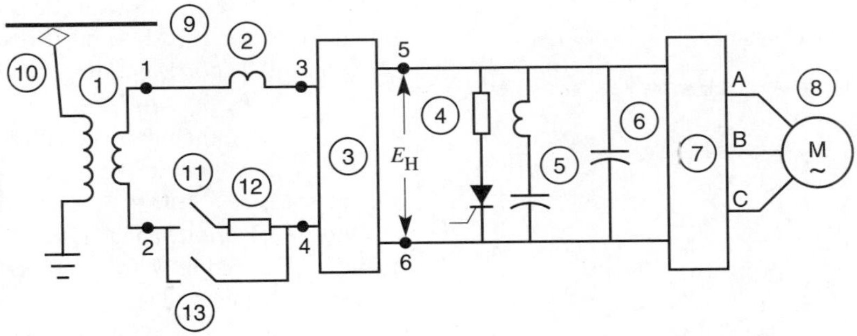

(1) single phase transformer
(2) inductor
(3) PWM converter
(4) braking resistor and chopper
(5) filter
(6) capacitor
(7) PWM converter
(8) traction motor
(9) trolley line
(10) pantograph
(11) switch
(12) resistor
(13) switch

Figure 23.53
Schematic diagram of a traction drive.

It must be understood that the circuit of Fig. 23.53 has been highly simplified to illustrate only those points we want to emphasize.

The 3-phase, 4-pole traction motor is described as follows:

type: squirrel-cage induction

power: 160 kW

rated voltage: 545 V

speed range: 0 to 3000 r/min

base speed: 1800 r/min

temperature class: H

forced ventilation: 12 m^3/min

mass: 520 kg

23.29 Operating mode of the 3-phase converter

The operating mode of converter (7) can be followed by referring to Fig. 23.54. The GTOs have a frequency limit of, say, 300 Hz. We assume that in the PWM mode the carrier frequency will be held between a minimum of 200 Hz and a maximum of 300 Hz. The minimum is a question of choice regarding the level of current harmonics that are permissible. The maximum depends upon the allowable switching losses in the GTOs, plus safety margins.

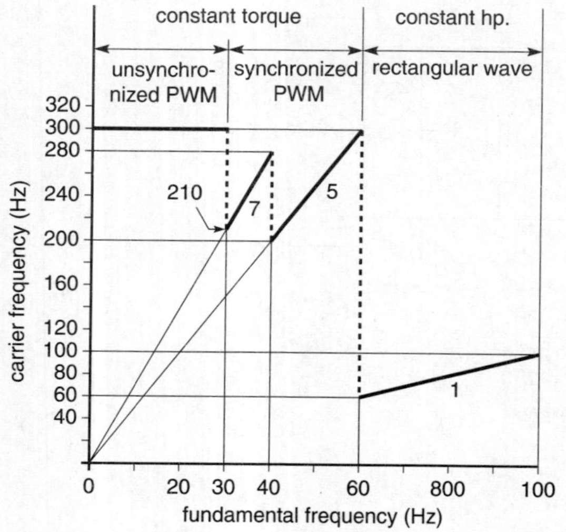

Figure 23.54
Generating variable fundamental frequencies with moderate carrier frequencies.

When the motor runs between 1800 r/min (base speed) and 3000 r/min, the corresponding frequencies lie between 60 Hz and 100 Hz. A rectangular 6-step waveshape is used in this range; thus, the full 700 V dc link voltage is available. The motor operates in the constant horsepower mode, and the fundamental rms voltage across the motor terminals is given by

$$E_{\text{line}} = 0.78\, E_{\text{d}} = 0.78 \times 700 = 546 \text{ V} \qquad (23.1)$$

At frequencies immediately below 60 Hz, where the harmonics begin to be more important, the synchronized PWM mode is initiated. Bearing in mind that the GTO frequency must not exceed 300 Hz, it follows that a frequency ratio of 5 must be used to generate frequencies of 60 Hz and below. As the wanted frequency is lowered, the carrier frequency must be decreased in proportion, both frequencies following the sloped line 5. When the lower 200 Hz limit is reached, it is evident that the corresponding fundamental frequency is $200 \div 5 = 40$ Hz.

The schedule then jumps to a frequency ratio of 7. On this new operating line, the GTO carrier frequency starts at $7 \times 40 = 280$ Hz, which is just below the 300 Hz limit. Then, as the fundamental frequency falls gradually from 40 Hz to 30 Hz, the carrier frequency keeps track so that it is always exactly 7 times the fundamental frequency. When 30 Hz is reached, the motor is running at about 900 r/min, and the carrier frequency is 210 Hz—just above the 200 Hz minimum.

At this point, a transition is made to the unsynchronized PWM mode, using the maximum GTO frequency (300 Hz), which is 10 times the wanted frequency (30 Hz). Thus, for fundamental frequencies below 30 Hz, the GTO frequency is held constant at 300 Hz, as shown by the bold horizontal line (Fig. 23.54).

Fig. 23.55 illustrates the typical waveshapes of the line-to-line motor voltage E_{AB} for the four operating modes of the converter displayed in Fig. 23.54.

We recall that E_{AB} is the difference between the voltages E_{AN} and E_{BN} that are produced by the two arms of the 3-phase converter (see Fig. 21.86, Chapter 21).

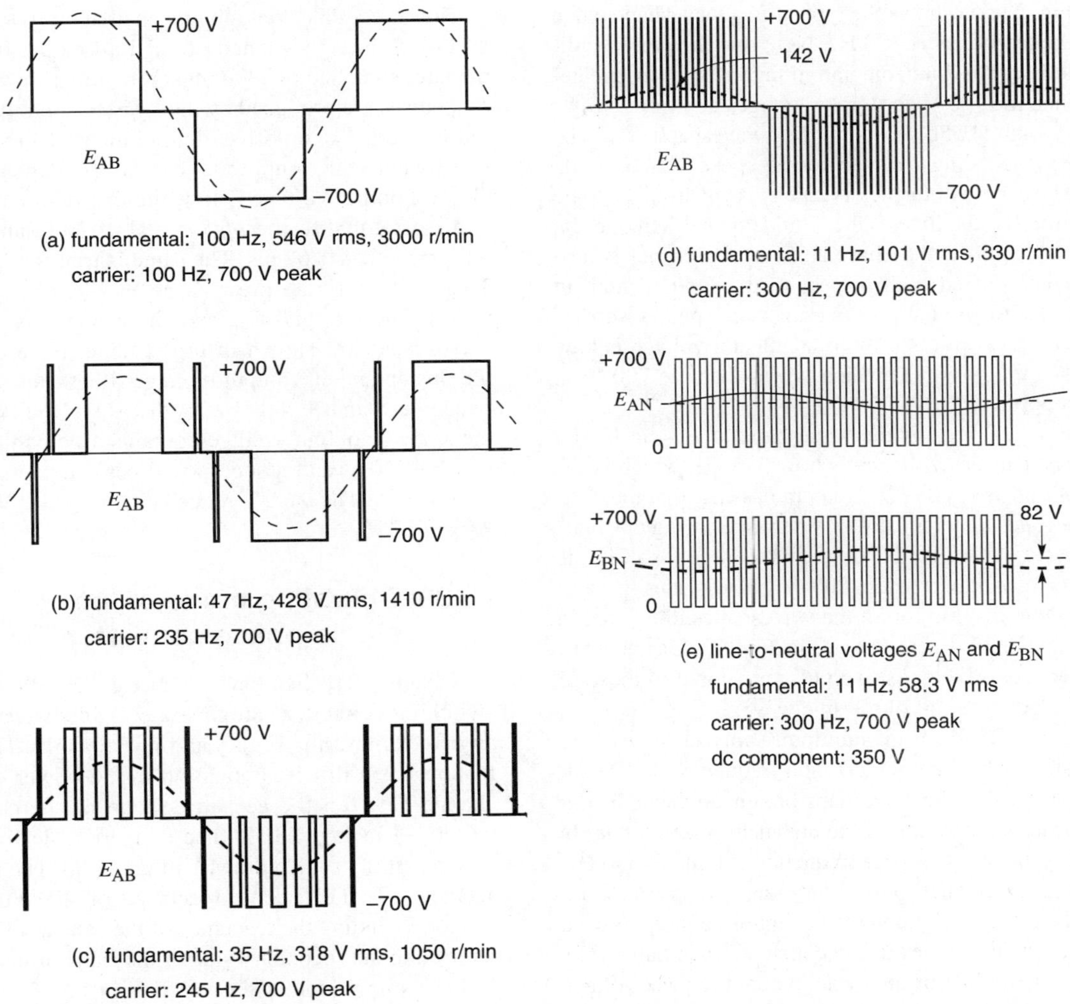

(a) fundamental: 100 Hz, 546 V rms, 3000 r/min
carrier: 100 Hz, 700 V peak

(b) fundamental: 47 Hz, 428 V rms, 1410 r/min
carrier: 235 Hz, 700 V peak

(c) fundamental: 35 Hz, 318 V rms, 1050 r/min
carrier: 245 Hz, 700 V peak

(d) fundamental: 11 Hz, 101 V rms, 330 r/min
carrier: 300 Hz, 700 V peak

(e) line-to-neutral voltages E_{AN} and E_{BN}
fundamental: 11 Hz, 58.3 V rms
carrier: 300 Hz, 700 V peak
dc component: 350 V

Figure 23.55
Waveshapes of line-to-line voltage for operating modes shown in Fig. 23.54.
a. Constant horsepower mode: 100 Hz, 3000 r/min.
b. Synchronized PWM at 47 Hz; $m_t = 5$.
c. Synchronized PWM at 35 Hz; $m_t = 7$.
d. Unsynchronized PWM at 11 Hz; $m_t = 27.27$.
e. Line-to-neutral voltages of individual switching arms E_{AN} and E_{BN}.

For speeds above base speed (1800 r/min), implying frequencies above 60 Hz, the converter operates in the rectangular wave mode. The step voltage is applied during 120° intervals and the effective line-to-line voltage is held constant at 546 V. Fig. 23.55a shows the typical E_{AB} waveshape when the frequency is 100 Hz. Note that the peak amplitude of the fundamental voltage is slightly greater than the 700 V dc supply voltage.

Fig. 23.55b shows the E_{AB} waveshape at 47 Hz, corresponding to a synchronous speed of 1410 r/min. The carrier frequency is 235 Hz, synchronized to be *exactly* 5 times the fundamental frequency. Furthermore, the phase angle of the carrier is also synchronized with respect to the fundamental, in order to produce the symmetrical pulses shown. The peak value of the fundamental voltage is now $428\sqrt{2} = 605$ V, which is less than the 700 V dc supply voltage.

Fig. 23.55c is the waveshape of E_{AB} at 35 Hz. The carrier frequency is now 245 Hz, which is *exactly* 7 times 35 Hz. Note, in passing, that the volt-seconds under the dotted sine wave during one half-cycle are equal to the volt-seconds of the corresponding seven 700 V pulses. This general rule holds true for all the waveshapes illustrated in Fig. 23.55. For example, in Fig. 23.55a the volt-seconds of the positive pulse are equal to those of the positive half of the sine wave.

Fig. 23.55d is the multipulse waveshape E_{AB} obtained when the fundamental frequency is 11 Hz. It is typical of the waveshape obtained when the converter is operating in the unsynchronized mode. In this mode, the carrier frequency is fixed at 300 Hz. The individual pulse durations are very short. Nevertheless, although the figure cannot show it, their width varies in the course of each half-cycle. In the middle of the cycle, where the peak voltage is 142 V, the pulse width is only 0.68 ms. The calculation is made as follows:

The duration of each pulse is equal to the period of the carrier frequency, which is $T = 1/300$ Hz $=$ 0.00333 s $=$ 3.33 ms. When the voltage of the fundamental is momentarily 142 V, the volt-seconds during 3.33 ms amount to $142 \times 3.33 = 473$ mVs. However, these volt-seconds are provided by the 700 V dc supply. Consequently, the duration of the *on* pulse must be 473 V·s $\div$ 700 V $=$ 0.68 ms. Clearly, the pulse widths are even shorter when the momentary fundamental voltage is less than 142 V.

However, this does not mean that individual GTOs are being switched on, and a fleeting 0.68 ms later switched off. We must remember that the E_{AB} pulses are produced by the *difference* between the E_{AN} and E_{BN} on/off switching intervals. In effect, when the amplitude of the fundamental (11 Hz) output voltage is low, the E_{AN} *on* interval is almost equal to the *off* interval, namely about 3.33 ms $\div$ 2 $=$ 1.67 ms. The same is true for E_{BN}. This switching rate presents no problem for the GTOs. The E_{AN} and E_{BN} switching intervals and waveshapes are shown in Fig. 23.55e. Note that the instantaneous output voltage fluctuates between zero and +700 V in both cases. However, the *average* output voltage contains a dc component of 350 V and a superposed peak ac component of 82 V. The latter is related to E_{AB} by 142 V $\div$ $\sqrt{3} = 82$ V.

23.30 Operating mode of the single-phase converter

In Chapter 21, Section 21.46 we saw that a switching converter can generate a sine wave of any frequency, amplitude, and phase angle. This feature has a direct application in the power exchange between the ac and dc side of the converter (3) in Fig. 23.53. The converter, dc link, and transformer are redrawn in Fig. 23.56. The reactance x is the leakage reactance of the transformer, including the reactance of the catenary line referred to the secondary side of the transformer.

Let us now look at the voltages in Fig. 23.56. Voltage E_{12} on the secondary side of the transformer is fixed because its frequency and amplitude are directly related to the catenary power line network. On the other hand, the magnitude and phase of E_{34} is determined by the switching action of the converter (3). By controlling the magnitude and phase angle of E_{34}, it is possible to control the active and reactive power flow between the secondary side of the transformer and the converter.

Consider, for example, Fig. 23.57a wherein the phase angle of E_{34} is adjusted so it lags behind E_{12} by an angle θ_1. Furthermore, suppose $E_{34(rms)}$, (the rms value of E_{34}) is adjusted so it is equal to $E_{12(rms)}/\cos\theta_1$. Under these conditions the resulting I is *forced* to be in phase with E_{12}. As a result, only active power is delivered from the transformer to the converter; consequently, the catenary supplies power at unity power factor. The active power P that is transferred is given by

$$P = \frac{E_{12}E_{34}}{x}\sin\theta_1 \qquad (16.8)$$

Next, suppose the vehicle is coasting downhill. Instead of applying the brakes, the drag is obtained by having the motor run as an asynchronous generator. The power furnished to the dc link by converter 7 (Fig. 23.53) has now to be fed into the transformer by converter 3. This power reversal is obtained by shifting the phase of voltage E_{34} so that it *leads* E_{12} by an angle θ_2. At the same time, the converter adjusts the magnitude of E_{34} so that the resulting current is 180° out of phase with E_{12} (Fig. 23.57b). As a result, the power factor is again unity as far as the catenary power line is concerned.

The 60 Hz voltage E_{34} generated by the converter is pulse-width modulated at a carrier frequency of, say, 4 kHz. The voltage between terminals 3 and 4 is composed of 700 V impulses that are modulated at 60 Hz. It can be shown that the principal harmonic frequencies generated at these terminals are given by the equation:

$$f_H = 2f_c \pm f$$

wherein f_H is the harmonic frequency, f_c is the carrier frequency and f is the wanted frequency. In our case, $f_H = 2 \times 4000 \pm 60 = 8060$ Hz and 7040 Hz. These frequencies are so high that the corresponding ac currents are almost completely filtered out by the reactance x. As a result, the current I (Fig. 23.56) is nearly a pure sine wave.

The 60 Hz sinusoidal current I appears as a rectified current I_d on the dc side of the converter. Thus, I_d consists of chopped rectified sine waves that contain a strong 120 Hz component. This component is short-circuited by the LC series filter (5) that is tuned to 120 Hz. As a result, the dc link voltage E_{56} contains only a small 120 Hz ripple.

The converter feeding the ac motor does not experience the same problem because in balanced 3-phase systems the instantaneous power is constant, so there is no ripple on this account. The only ripple is that caused by the switching action of the converter at carrier frequency.

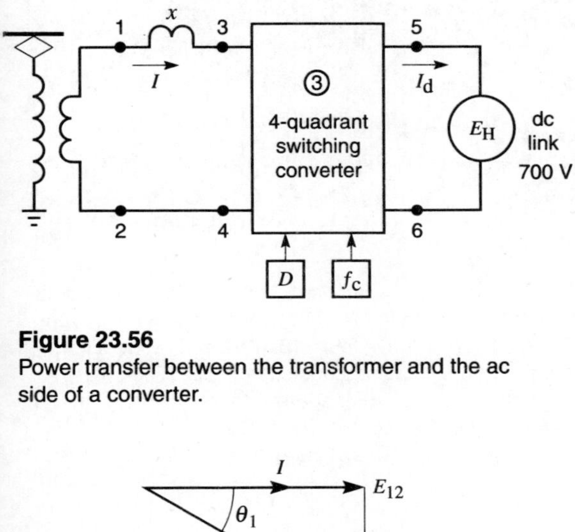

Figure 23.56
Power transfer between the transformer and the ac side of a converter.

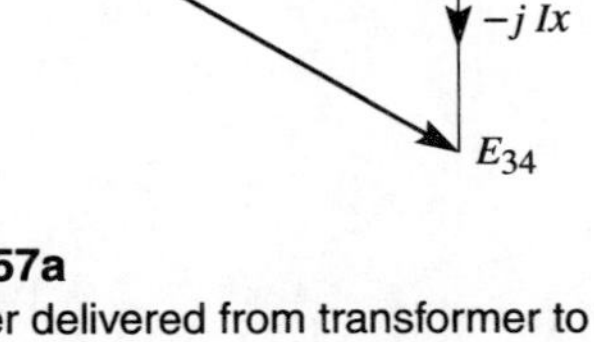

Figure 23.57a
Active power delivered from transformer to converter.

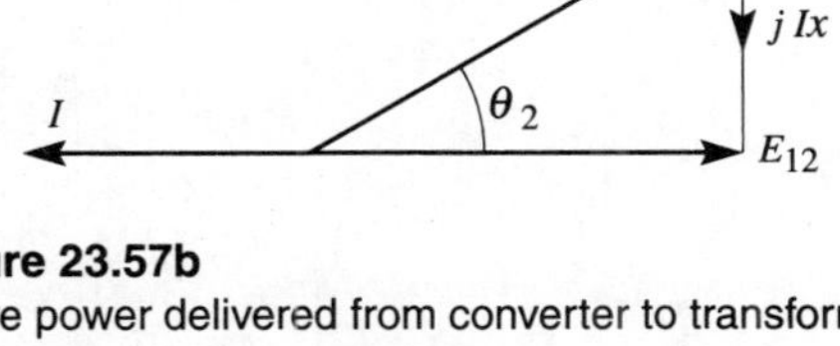

Figure 23.57b
Active power delivered from converter to transformer.

Figure 23.58
This tilt-body electric train draws its power from an 11 kV, 25 Hz, single-phase catenary. The ac voltage is rectified to produce a fixed dc voltage of 2400 V for the dc link. The GTO thyristors in the PWM converters generate a variable frequency (0–120 Hz) and variable 3-phase voltage (0–1870 V). They drive four 815 kW, 3-phase induction motors. The fully loaded trainset is 140 m long and has a mass of 343 t. It has reached speeds of 277 km/h (172 mi/h). The tilt-body feature enables the train to move through curves at higher speeds, thereby saving time while ensuring passenger comfort. Vehicle dynamic tests, carried out in the U.S. Northeast Corridor on this ABB X2000 tilt-body trainset were sponsored by Amtrak, by SJ (Swedish State Railways), and by ABB, and supported by the Federal Railroad Administration.
(Courtesy of ABB Traction Inc.)

Figure 23.59

This 70 367-ton Superliner *MS Fascination* contains a power plant composed of six diesel-electric synchronous generators, four of which are rated at 10 260 kVA and two at 6820 kVA. The 6600 V, 3-phase, 60 Hz, 75% power factor generators are respectively driven by four 12-cylinder and two 8-cylinder, 512 r/min diesel engines. The number of diesel engines in service at a given time depends upon the electrical load. Generators that are brought on line are synchronized automatically.

The propulsion system comprises two 14 MW, 1000 V, 3-phase, 14-pole synchronous motors that are directly coupled to two propeller shafts driven at speeds ranging from 50 r/min to 140 r/min. The motors each have two 3-phase windings which can be operated independently or in tandem. Each winding has a rating of 7 MVA.

The rotating field is supplied by the excitation unit which provides the excitation current for the Propulsion Motor. The excitation unit is supplied from the 450 V network through a 450 V/400 V, 400 kVA excitation transformer.

A control unit controls both the excitation current of the Propulsion Motor and the output currents of the cycloconverters, i.e., the stator currents of the Propulsion Motor. In addition, the control unit takes care of the speed control of the motor, overload protection of the supply network, and the synchronization to the propellers.

The 6.6 kV main bus voltage is stepped down to 1500 V by means of transformers. The secondary sides are connected to the input of four cycloconverters, two of which are used for each propulsion motor. The cycloconverters each employ 36 thyristors.

This ultramodern Superliner has a length of 260.6 m, a beam of 31.5 m, and operates at a service speed of 19.5 knots. The passenger capacity is 2040, complemented by a captain and crew of 920.

(Courtesy of Carnival Cruise Lines)

Figure 23.60
The training of technical personnel is an important step toward the creation of new jobs. The inroad of computers and electronics into every sector of commerce and industry has now expanded into the electric power sector as well. Thus, electric power technology is rapidly changing to embrace these new devices and concepts.
Top left: This modular educational console employs 200 W machines (dc, synchronous, induction) for direct hands-on training of electronic drives. Physical connections between machines and electronic converters are made, using protected leads. Measurements are taken using standard instruments. The student observes the physical reality of torque, inertia, overloads, sudden changes in speed, and so forth.

Top right: In a more advanced program, data acquisition is used to display waveshapes, voltages, currents, active and reactive power, as well as harmonics. A computer makes the necessary calculations in real-time, thus permitting torque-speed characteristics and other drive features to be observed. Printouts of observations save valuable time for students and instructors alike. By becoming accessible and visible, harmonics lose their mystery and become a source of interest and even fascination.

Lower right: Simulation is becoming a popular way of performing experiments without using any hardware at all. The special program pictured here permits simulated modules to be taken from "inventory," pulled into the "console," connected with flexible "wires," and mechanically coupled to "loads." The "modules" are exact replicas of those shown in the picture at left. The interesting feature of this simulation program is that the static and dynamic properties of the individual machines (and loads) are stored in the computer. As a result, the steady-state and transient state behavior of a drive can be observed as if the real machines and converters were present.
(Courtesy of Lab-Volt Ltd.)

23.31 Direct Torque Control

Among the several methods used to control induction motors, the so-called Direct Torque Control technique, or DTC, occupies an important place. This technique involves the respective control of torque and stator flux within two distinct bands. This means that the torque and flux are constrained to lie respectively within a set of upper and lower limits.

Before explaining the DTC technique, let us see how the flux and torque can be measured. Consider the circuit of Fig. 23.61a which shows one phase of a 3-phase induction motor connected to a sinusoidal voltage source. We recognize the stator resistance r_1, the stator leakage flux ϕ_1, the mutual flux ϕ, the rotor leakage flux ϕ_2, and resistance r_2/s which absorbs the active power P_r transmitted to the rotor. The total flux ϕ_S linked by the stator is equal to the vector sum of ϕ_1 and ϕ. Thus, $\phi_s = \phi_1 + \phi$.

The total torque T_M developed by the three phases is given by the expression:

$$T_M = \frac{9.55\, P_r}{n_s} \times 3 \qquad (13.9)$$

The power P_r absorbed between points 4 and N is given by $P_r = E_{4N} I_2$. This active power corresponds to the power that flows into the stator between points 2 and N because the reactive elements x_1, x_m, and x_2 do not absorb any active power. We can therefore write

$$P_r = E_{2N} I_1 \cos \theta_s \qquad (23.6)$$

where

P_r = active power supplied to the rotor, per phase [W]

E_{2N} = voltage induced by flux ϕ_s linked by the stator [V]

I_1 = stator current [A]

θ_s = phase angle between E_{2N} and I_1

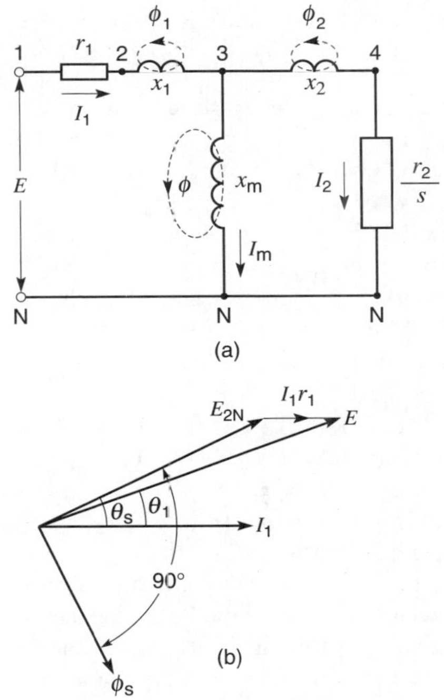

Figure 23.61

a. Equivalent circuit diagram of one phase of a 3-phase induction motor.

b. Phasor diagram of the voltages and current in the stator.

Voltage E_{2N} is not accessible, but its value is easy to calculate by measuring the voltage E_{1N} at the terminals of the stator and taking the I_1r_1 voltage drop into account.

Note that flux ϕ_S is proportional to voltage E_{2N} and lags 90° behind it. The phasor diagram (Fig. 23.61b) shows the current and voltages of the stator as well as the voltage drop in resistance r_1.

Equations 13.9 and 23.6 enable us to calculate the torque when we know the voltage E_{2N}, the current I_1, and the phase angle θ_S between them. Knowing E_{2N}, we can also determine the relative magnitude of the flux ϕ_S (per unit values).

In the explanations that follow, we will neglect the stator resistance r_1.

23.32 Controlling the flux and torque by hysteresis

Fig. 23.62 shows a 3-phase induction motor powered by a mechanical converter equipped with three double-pole switches that offer six switching positions. The converter is connected to a dc voltage source E_d. The switches open and close according to a special program. Contrary to the PWM technique, the switching frequency is not constant, but depends upon the instantaneous values of the torque T_M developed by the motor and the flux ϕ_S of the stator.

The desired flux ϕ_S can have any value between an upper limit ϕ_A and a lower limit ϕ_B. The narrower the band, the closer the flux will be controlled. This is sometimes called bang-bang control or hysteresis control. When the flux drops below ϕ_B, a logic signal transmitted to the converter indicates which switches should change state in order to increase the flux. Similarly, when the flux becomes greater than ϕ_A a logic signal indicates which switches should change state in order to reduce the flux. Finally, when ϕ_S lies within the tolerance band, the momentary state of the switches remains unchanged—provided that the torque also has the desired value. In response to these requirements, the flux continually fluctuates between the limits ϕ_A and ϕ_B.

The same remarks apply to torque T_M which must be kept between the levels T_A and T_B (Fig. 23.62). For example, if the motor torque falls below T_B, the converter receives a logic signal to change the state of the switches, so as to increase T_M. Conversely, when T_M is greater than T_A, a logic signal causes the switches to change state so as to reduce T_M. Just as in the case of the flux ϕ_S, this adjustment procedure causes the torque to oscillate rapidly and continually between the limits T_A and T_B.

The nominal value of ϕ_S corresponds to the average value of ϕ_A and ϕ_B. However, when the motor is lightly loaded we do not need to operate at rated flux. Consequently, we reduce the flux ϕ_S to reduce the iron losses. To do so, we lower the levels of both ϕ_A and ϕ_B, without changing the width of the tolerance band.

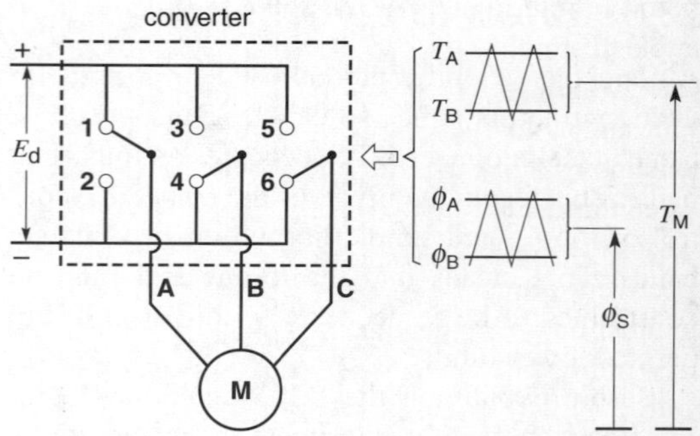

Figure 23.62
Three-phase mechanical converter wherein the instantaneous position of the switches is determined by the flux ϕ_S of the stator and the torque T_M developed by the motor. The flux is allowed to have any value between ϕ_A and ϕ_B. The torque is allowed to have any value between T_A and T_B.

23.33 Controlling the speed

Speed control is done via the torque T_M. Thus, when the speed is lower than the desired value, the control circuit raises the levels of both T_A and T_B. Consequently, the torque developed by the motor is suddenly below T_B and the system reacts to increase the torque. Therefore, the motor accelerates. When the speed has attained the desired value, the torque T_M fluctuates between the new settings of T_A and T_B. During this interval, the same switches continue to keep the flux within the levels ϕ_A and ϕ_B.

23.34 Producing a magnetic field in a 2-phase motor

When a dc source E_d is applied to the converter (Fig. 23.62), we may wonder how it can be used to produce a revolving field in a motor. To simplify the explanation we will use a 2-phase instead of a 3-phase motor. Furthermore, we will adopt a numerical example to simplify the explanation. We represent the stator windings by two phases X and Y that are at right angles to each other (Fig. 23.63). Each pole contains 10 turns, thus making a total of 20 turns between terminals x_1 and x_2. A similar set of windings exists between terminals y_1 and y_2. The windings respectively produce fluxes ϕ_X and ϕ_Y. Suppose the nominal flux per pole is 25 mWb (milliwebers).

Windings X and Y are connected to a 200 V dc source by way of a converter that comprises four switches (Fig. 23.64). As far as phase X is concerned, there are four ways of making the connections to the + and − terminals of the source. Consequently, there are four combinations of polarities for terminals x_1 and x_2: (+−), (−+), (++), and (−−). When the polarities are the same, the terminals are obviously short-circuited. As a result, there are only three distinct ways to make the connections. Note that the circuit of coil X is arranged so that it is *never* open-circuited. As a result, if the coil happens to carry a current I_X, the latter is never interrupted during a switching commutation.

The same remarks apply to winding Y. Therefore, there are $3 \times 3 = 9$ distinct ways whereby the X and Y windings can be connected to the (+) and (−) terminals of source E_d. These switching combinations enable us to vary the magnitude and direction of fluxes ϕ_X and ϕ_Y.

For example, suppose that the flux ϕ_X in Fig. 23.63 is directed to the right and that it is *increasing*. According to Lenz's Law, terminal x_1 will be positive with respect to terminal x_2. Consequently, by virtue of the indicated polarity marks in Fig. 23.63, E_X is positive (+).

Therefore, when the external source is connected to winding X so that E_X is positive, the flux will tend to increase towards the right. In effect, as soon as a voltage is connected to terminals x_1 and x_2 the flux ϕ_X will begin to change. The rate of change is given by Faraday's Law:

$$\frac{\Delta\phi_X}{\Delta t} = \frac{E_X}{N} \tag{2.24}$$

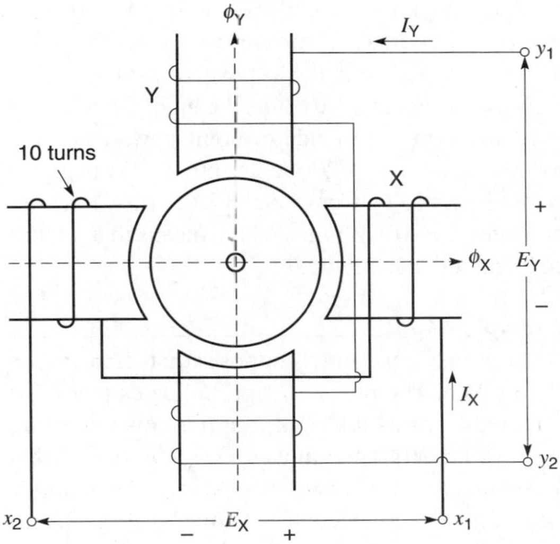

Figure 23.63
Schematic diagram of a 2-phase induction motor. The value and direction of fluxes ϕ_X and ϕ_Y depends upon the volt-seconds applied to the respective windings.

In our case, $E_X = E_d = 200$ V and $N = 20$ turns. As a result, $\Delta\phi_X/\Delta t = 200$ V/20 turns $= 10$ Wb/s, which is the same as 10 mWb/ms. (We prefer to deal with milliseconds because the switching intervals are very brief.) When E_X is zero (terminals in short-circuit), the flux ϕ_X does not change; it remains at the value it had when the short-circuit took place.

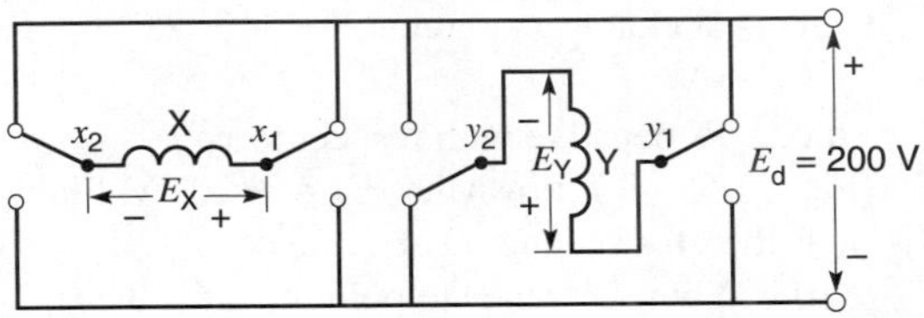

Figure 23.64
The four switches offer nine ways of connecting the windings X and Y to the 200 V dc source. At any given instant at least one of the two windings is in short-circuit.

The same remarks apply to winding Y. When the external dc source is connected to winding Y so that $E_Y = +200$ V, terminal y_1 is positive with respect to y_2. That means that flux ϕ_Y is changing at a rate of $+10$ mWb/ms and tends to point upwards. However, when $E_Y = -200$ V, terminal y_1 is negative with respect to y_2. Consequently, the flux ϕ_Y varies at a rate of -10 mWb/ms, which means that it tends to be directed downwards.

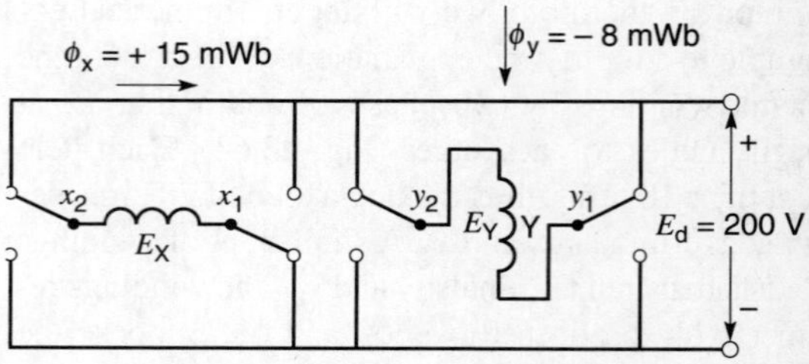

Figure 23.65
See Example 23-7.

Example 23-7

At a given moment, suppose that flux ϕ_X is $+15$ mWb. The plus (+) sign indicates that ϕ_X is directed towards the right. Suppose also that flux $\phi_Y = -8$ mWb. The minus (−) sign indicates that ϕ_Y is directed downwards. Suddenly, the X and Y windings are connected as shown in Fig. 23.65. Determine

a. The initial value of the resultant flux ϕ_S and its orientation in space
b. The value of flux ϕ_S and its orientation 2.2 ms later

Solution

a. Because coils X and Y are displaced 90° in space, the initial orientation of the fluxes is as shown in Fig. 23.66a. It follows that ϕ_S is given by

$$\phi_S = \sqrt{\phi_X^2 + \phi_Y^2}$$

$$= \sqrt{15^2 + (-8)^2} = 17 \text{ mWb}$$

It is directed at an angle:

$$\alpha_S = \arctan \frac{\phi_Y}{\phi_X} = \arctan \frac{-8}{15} = -28°$$

b. Since x_1 is negative with respect to x_2 (Fig. 23.65), it follows that $E_X = -200$ V. Flux ϕ_X is therefore changing at a rate of -10 mWb/ms. It tends to point towards the left. However, because $E_Y = 0$, flux ϕ_Y does not change, and so it remains at -8 mWb.

Change of flux ϕ_X during 2.2 ms

$$2.2 \text{ ms} \times -10 \text{ mWb/s} = -22 \text{ mWb}$$

New flux ϕ_X (Fig. 23.66b)

$$+15 \text{ mWb} - 22 \text{ mWb} = -7 \text{ mWb}$$

During this interval of 2.2 ms, flux ϕ_X has gradually dropped to zero and then reversed to reach -7 mWb. The minus sign shows that ϕ_X is directed to the left.

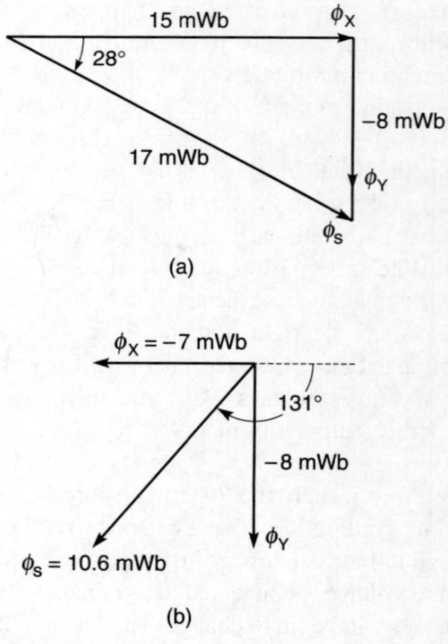

Figure 23.66
a. Initial position of flux ϕ_S.
b. Final position of flux ϕ_S (see Example 23-7).

Resulting flux ϕ_S

$$\phi_S = \sqrt{\phi_X^2 + \phi_Y^2}$$
$$= \sqrt{(-7)^2 + (-8)^2} = 10.6 \text{ mWb}$$

Its orientation in space is

$$\alpha_S = \arctan \frac{\phi_Y}{\phi_X} = \arctan \frac{-8}{-7} = -131°$$

We can see that during the interval of 2.2 ms, the spatial flux has moved from −28° to −131°. It has therefore turned clockwise through an angle of 103°. This proves that we can create a revolving field by opening and closing the switches in an appropriate way.

Strange as it may seem, the flux changes are not created by the current that happens to flow in a particular winding. Because the resistances are assumed to be negligible, the change of fluxes ϕ_X and ϕ_Y depends *exclusively* upon the volt-seconds that are applied to the terminals of the respective windings.

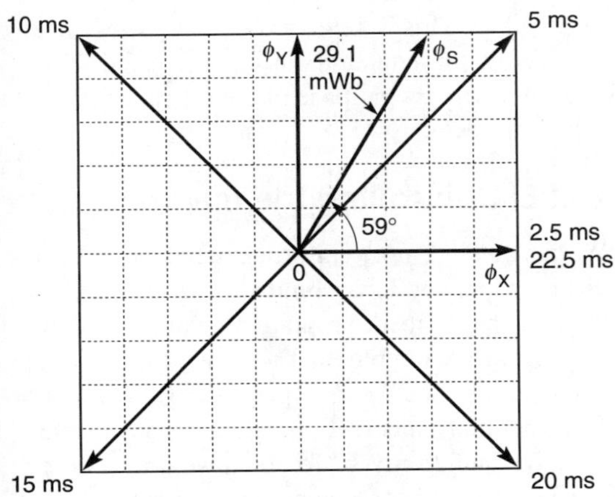

Figure 23.67
This diagram shows the value and position of the flux ϕ_S at different instants. It also enables us to visualize the components ϕ_X and $_Y$.

23.35 Producing a rotating field

We will now demonstrate how a rotating field is created in the 2-phase motor of Fig. 23.63. To do so, we will perform six switching operations, as indicated by steps 1 to 6 below. Fig. 23.67 enables us to observe the successive values of ϕ_X and ϕ_Y. Their nominal values are 25 mWb.

Step 1. ($0 > t > 2.5$ ms): $E_X = +200$ V; $E_Y = 0$
Suppose that the initial flux in the motor is zero, so that $\phi_X = \phi_Y = 0$. We then close the switches so that $E_X = +200$ V and $E_Y = 0$. Flux ϕ_X will begin to increase to the right at a rate of 10 mWb/ms. It will reach its nominal value of 25 mWb after an interval of 2.5 ms. We do not want to increase the flux beyond this value, and so we short-circuit terminals x_1 and x_2 at the end of this step.

Step 2. ($2.5 > t > 5$ ms): $E_X = 0$; $E_Y = +200$ V
While terminals x_1 and x_2 are still short-circuited, we close the switches so that $E_Y = +200$ V. Flux ϕ_Y is initially zero, but it immediately begins to increase, directed upwards. The applied voltage is kept unchanged until ϕ_Y reaches *its* nominal value of 25 mWb. The time required to reach this value is

$$\Delta t = 25 \text{ mWb}/(10 \text{ mWb/ms}) = 2.5 \text{ ms}$$

Since flux ϕ_Y must not exceed 25 mWb, terminals y_1 and y_2 are short-circuited so that $E_Y = 0$ at the end of this step.

Step 3. ($5 > t > 10$ ms): $E_X = -200$ V; $E_Y = 0$
During this step, we apply a negative voltage E_X across winding X. Consequently, flux ϕ_X will tend to be directed to the left, increasing at a rate of 10 mWb/ms. Since the initial value of ϕ_X is +25 mWb, it will become zero after an interval of 2.5 ms.

If we keep the switches in the same state, flux ϕ_X will continue to build up towards the left. It will reach its nominal value of −25 mWb after a further interval of 2.5 ms. At this very moment, we short-circuit terminals x_1 and x_2 so that the flux stops changing.

Step 4. ($10 > t > 15$ ms): $E_X = 0$; $E_Y = -200$ V
We now apply voltage $E_Y = -200$ V across coil Y. Consequently, flux ϕ_Y tends to be oriented downwards, increasing negatively at a rate of 10 mWb/ms.

After 5 ms, flux $\phi_Y = -25$ mWb and we short-circuit terminals y_1 and y_2.

Step 5. ($15 > t > 20$ ms): $E_X = +200$ V; $E_Y = 0$
Flux ϕ_X increases, while being directed to the right. When it reaches +25 mWb, terminals x_1 and x_2 are short-circuited so that the flux ceases to increase any more.

Step 6. ($20 > t > 22.5$ ms): $E_X = 0$; $E_Y = +200$ V
Flux ϕ_Y is directed upwards, increasing positively at a rate of 10 mWb/ms. Since its initial value is −25 mWb, it will reach 0 mWb after an interval of 2.5 ms.

We see that the flux ϕ_S has made one complete turn.

The instantaneous values of E_X, E_Y, ϕ_X and ϕ_Y are shown in Fig. 23.68. The figure shows that the waveshapes of the fluxes are trapezoidal whereas the voltages are rectangular.

The graph of Fig. 23.67 is particularly useful because it enables us to observe the spatial orientation of the resulting flux ϕ_S.
For example, at instant $t = 6$ ms where $\phi_X = +15$ mWb and $\phi_Y = +25$ mWb, the resulting flux ϕ_S is

$$\phi_S = \sqrt{\phi_X^2 + \phi_Y^2}$$
$$= \sqrt{15^2 + 25^2} = 29.1 \text{ mWb}$$

The flux is oriented at an angle given by arctan 25/15, which is 59° counterclockwise from its initial horizontal position. A complete turn is made in 20 ms which corresponds to a speed of 50 turns per second or 3000 r/min.

There remains one troubling situation: The nominal flux is 25 mWb but we note that at the four corners of the square in Fig. 23.67, the resulting flux ϕ_S reaches a value of $25\sqrt{2} = 35$ mWb. This is 40% greater than the nominal flux and this situation must be corrected. That is precisely the purpose of the tolerance band.

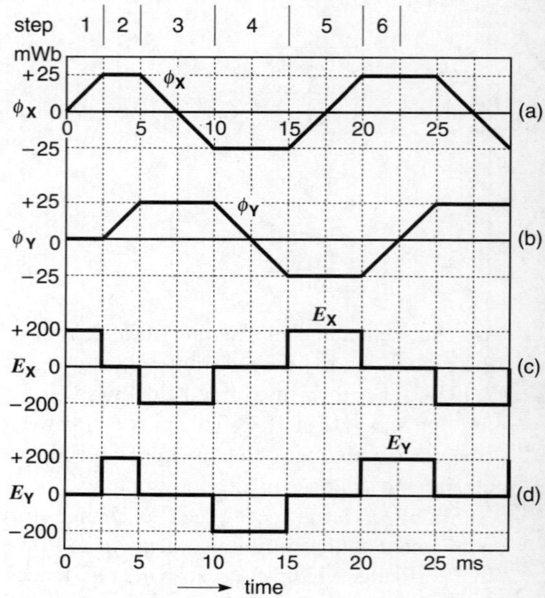

Figure 23.68
Changes in ϕ_X and ϕ_Y produced by successively applying ±200 V to the X and Y windings.

23.36 Controlling the magnetic flux

We can obtain a more uniform magnetic flux by imposing upper and lower limits to its value. This requires a change in the programming of the switches. Suppose, for example, that we wish to restrict the values of flux between upper and lower limits of 1 pu (per unit) and 1.12 pu, which means between 25 mWb and 28 mWb. To do so we draw two circles having radii corresponding to 25 mWb and 28 mWb, respectively (Fig. 23.69). Suppose the initial flux is $\phi_S = 25$ mWb and that it is directed to the right. Starting from point 1, we keep ϕ_X constant and apply $E_Y = +200$ V to coil Y. As we have already stated, this causes flux ϕ_Y to increase upwards

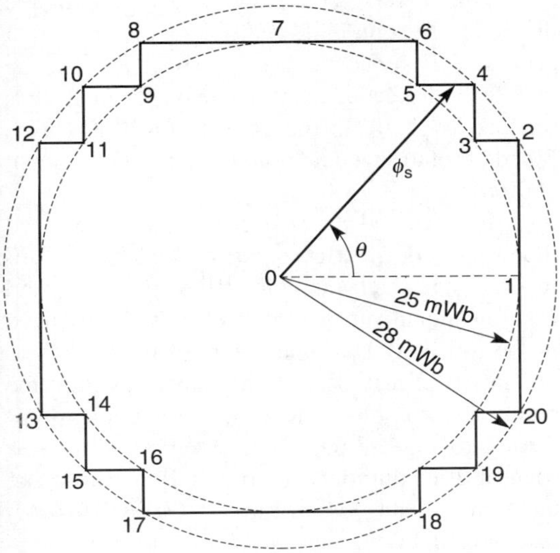

Figure 23.69
The bang-bang method of control forces the flux ϕ_S to stay within the limits of 25 mWb and 28 mWb. The short vertical and horizontal zig-zag lines show the path followed by the flux during one revolution. The value and position of the flux are indicated at each instant by the position and amplitude of the vector ϕ_S.

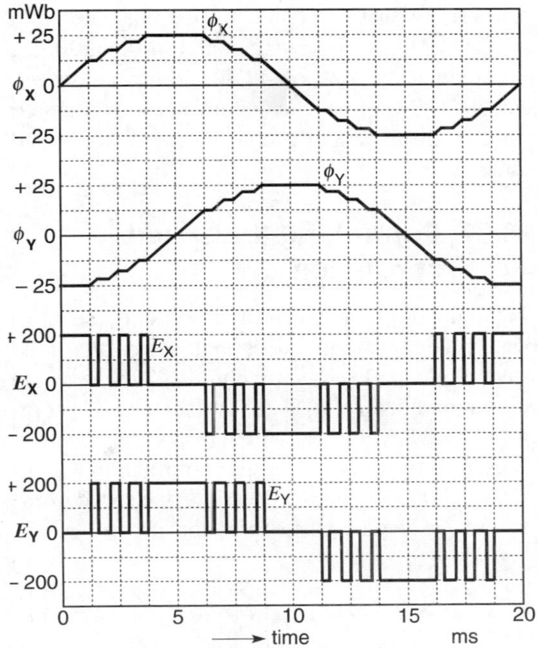

Figure 23.70
Waveshape of fluxes ϕ_X and ϕ_Y linked by the X and Y windings. The voltages E_X and E_Y (and not the currents) are at the origin of these fluxes.

at the rate of 10 mWb per millisecond. As soon as the resultant flux is equal to 28 mWb (point 2 on the external circle), we reduce E_Y to zero by short-circuiting y_1 and y_2.

Next, we apply $E_X = -200$ V, which diminishes ϕ_X without affecting ϕ_Y. Having arrived at point 3 on the internal circle where $\phi_S = 25$ mWb, we reduce E_X to zero. Then, we briefly apply $E_Y = +200$ V, which raises the flux to point 4, after which we set $E_Y = 0$. Again applying $E_X = -200$ V, the flux is displaced to the left. Arriving at point 5 where $\phi_S =$ 25 mWb, we set $E_X = 0$.

Proceeding this way between the limits imposed by the two circles, we obtain the revolving flux ϕ_S which passes through points 1, 2, 3, . . . 6, 7, 8, and so on. Point 7 barely touches the interior circle; consequently, it is not necessary to change the state of the switches at this moment. The result is 20 commutations per revolution (Fig. 23.69) compared to 4 in Figure 23.67. In this manner, the amplitude of the flux is kept at 26.5 mWb ± 6%.

Knowing that the radii of the inner and outer circles correspond to 25 mWb and 28 mWb, respectively, it is easy to calculate the value and orientation of flux ϕ_S anywhere along its path.

Fig. 23.70 shows the waveshapes of fluxes ϕ_X and ϕ_Y as well as those of E_X and E_Y. The chopped voltage waveshapes look like PWM, but the switching periods are not constant as they would be if the PWM technique were used. The reader should compare these waveshapes with those of Fig. 23.68.

We can reduce the difference between the upper and lower values of flux ϕ_S by reducing the tolerance band. For example, by choosing ϕ_S between 1 p.u. and 1.06 p.u. we can attain a precision of

±3%. However, this requires 44 commmutations per revolution. Since one revolution is made in 20 ms, this amounts to 44/20 ms = 2200 commutations per second. Thus, a higher switching speed is required if we wish to obtain a more precisely controlled value of ϕ_S.

23.37 Controlling the speed of rotation

It is important to note that the increase in the number of commutations does not affect the time needed to complete one revolution. As long as the minimum flux level ϕ_S is 25 mWb, the time to complete one revolution will always be 20 ms. Consequently, the average speed of rotation will always be 3000 r/min. To generalize, the speed of rotation n_R is given by the expression:

$$n_R = \frac{kE_d}{\phi_S} \tag{23.7}$$

where

n_R = speed of rotation of the flux ϕ_S [r/min]
E_d = dc voltage of the source [V]
ϕ_S = rated flux per pole [Wb]
k = constant that depends upon the construction of the motor: number of turns per pole, etc.

According to this equation, the speed of a given motor can be changed in two ways: change the dc voltage E_d, or change the value of the flux ϕ_S.

To increase the speed, we can raise the dc voltage E_d above 200 V. Because the flux is constrained to remain within the two circles of Fig. 23.69, each step will take less time. In effect, the height and depth of each step corresponds to a precise number of volt-seconds. Thus, if we increase the voltage from 200 V to, say, 300 V, the speed will increase from 3000 r/min to 4500 r/min. In practice, however, the supply voltage E_d is fixed.

Another way of increasing the speed is to reduce the flux ϕ_S. This is equivalent to reducing the diameters of the limiting circles, while keeping the voltage E_d at 200 V. For example, by reducing the diameters by one-half, the height and depth of each step is reduced by half. Consequently, the volt-seconds needed to complete one revolution is reduced by half. In the case of Fig. 23.69, the speed of rotation would double from 3000 r/min to 6000 r/min.

A third method can be used to control the speed of the rotating flux. It consists of introducing "zeros" during which moments the voltages E_X and E_Y are simulaneously kept at zero (both windings in short-circuit). During these intervals, the flux ϕ_S remains frozen in space. This increases the time required to complete one turn. For example, in referring to Fig. 23.69, if we introduce 40 zeros, each of 2 ms duration, the time required to make one turn is 20 ms + 40 × 2 ms = 100 ms. This corresponds to an *average speed* of 10 turns per second or 600 r/min.

Note that when E_X and E_Y are simultanteously zero, the flux ϕ_S is momentarily stationary in space. However, as soon as the short-circuit is removed, the flux again rotates at a speed of 3000 r/min. Thus, the flux can be made to constantly advance and stop, its speed fluctuating between 3000 r/min and zero.

As we will explain in the next section, the windings are short-circuited when the motor torque T_M is greater than torque T_A. This means that the "zeros" are generated by the control process itself.

23.38 Programming logic of the switching procedure

Knowing that we want to keep the flux and torque within their respective upper and lower limits (25 mWb and 28 mWb for flux, and T_A and T_B for torque), how can we program the switching process to attain these objectives?

Suppose the flux ϕ_S has the momentary value and position indicated by flux vector ϕ_{S1} and that it is rotating counterclockwise at 3000 r/min (Fig. 23.71). Furthermore, suppose the rotor is turning in the same counterclockwise direction, but at a constant speed of 600 r/min.

Since ϕ_{S1} is less than 25 mWb, windings X and Y must be activated so as to bring the flux within the desired zone. Five options are then possible:

1. Apply a voltage of +200 V to winding X. This will move the flux to the right.
2. Apply a voltage of −200 V to winding X. This will move the flux to the left.
3. Apply a voltage of +200 V to winding Y. This will move the flux upwards.
4. Apply a voltage of −200 V to winding Y. This will move the flux downwards.
5. Apply zero voltage to both windings by short-circuiting them.

Of these possible choices for ϕ_{S1} (Fig. 23.71), it is clear that options 2 and 4 must be rejected because the flux ϕ_{S1} will move even further away from the desired value. Option 5 must also be rejected because the flux will then only stay in place. Thus, only options 1 and 3 remain. To determine which one of the two is preferred, we must now look at the position of the motor torque T_M.

Referring now to Fig. 23.72, if we choose option 1, the flux ϕ_{S1}, while increasing to ϕ_{S1a}, it will move clockwise, which is opposite to the direction of rotation of the rotor. This will produce a braking effect on the rotor*. Consequently, this choice is appropriate if torque T_M is, at this moment, greater than the maximum allowable value T_A.

However, if we choose option 3, the flux ϕ_{S1}, while rising towards ϕ_{S1b}, it will move in the same direction as the rotor. Since the flux is moving much faster than the rotor, the effect will be to accelerate the rotor. This is the option that should be taken *provided* that the torque T_M is, at this moment, less than T_B. Finally, if torque T_M is already within the tolerance band (between T_A and T_B), we will select option 3 because it produces a torque in the same direction as the rotation of the rotor.

Let us now consider the case of the flux vector ϕ_{S2} (Fig. 23.71). Since it is greater than 25 mWb, the X and Y windings must be excited so that it falls inside the tolerance zone. We have the same options as in the previous example.

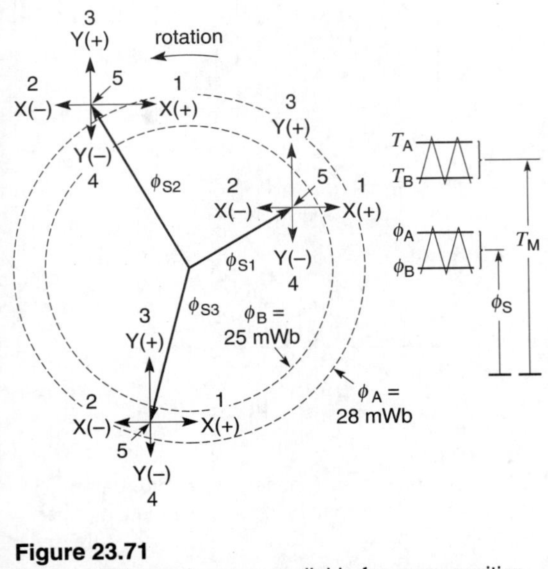

Figure 23.71
Five switching options are available for every position of the flux ϕ_S.

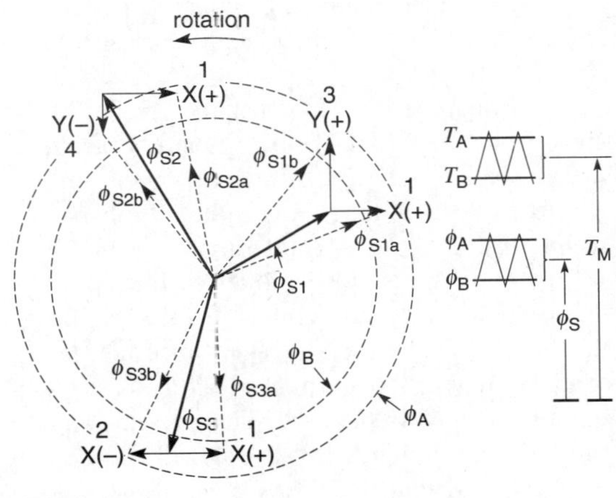

Figure 23.72
The selection of the switches depends upon the momentary state of the flux ϕ_S and the torque T_M.

* The phenomenon of torque creation is explained in Sections 13.2, 13.3, and 13.7 of Chapter 13.

Of these choices, options 2 and 3 can be rejected because the flux would be still further removed from the desired value. Option 5 is also rejected because it would freeze the flux in its current position. We are therefore left with options 1 and 4.

Referring to Fig. 23.72, if we select option 1, the flux ϕ_{S2}, while dropping towards ϕ_{S2a}, it moves clockwise, which is opposite to the rotation of the rotor. Thus, a braking torque will be developed. Consequently, this option is valid *provided* that the motor torque T_M is, at this moment, greater than the upper limit T_A.

However, if we choose option 4, the flux ϕ_{S2}, while dropping towards ϕ_{S2b}, it will move simultaneously in the direction of rotation of the rotor. This will produce an accelerating torque on the rotor. Hence, this option is the one to take *provided* that torque T_M is, at this moment, less than T_B.

We are left with a final possibility: that the flux vector ϕ_{S3} is already within the tolerance band (Fig 23.71). We again have five optional ways of exciting the windings.

If the torque T_M is less than T_B, the torque must be raised by using option 1. The flux ϕ_{S3} will move towards ϕ_{S3a}, while dropping slightly in amplitude (Fig. 23.72).

However, if at this moment the torque T_M is greater than T_B, we will choose option 2 because ϕ_{S3} will move towards ϕ_{S3b}. A strong braking torque will result because the flux cuts the rotor bars at a speed of $3000 + 600 = 3600$ r/min.

Having said this, we could also select option 5 (both windings in short-circuit). In this case, the flux will be stationary in space. Since the motor continues to turn at 600 r/min, a braking torque will again be applied to the rotor. This presents an advantage over option 2 because it will reduce the number of commutations per second.

To summarize, the switching program depends entirely upon the instantaneous values of the flux ϕ_S and the motor torque T_M as compared to their respectively designated upper and lower limits.

23.39 Instantaneous slip and production of torque

To better understand the nature of the torque T_M, suppose that our 2-phase motor is connected to a 200 V source and the flux ϕ_S is kept within the limits ϕ_A and ϕ_B. The flux therefore turns counterclockwise at 3000 r/min except when the windings are short-circuited, in which case it is momentarily frozen in space. Let us further assume the motor is running counterclockwise at 600 r/min.

The flux cuts the rotor bars at a relative speed of $3000 - 600 = 2400$ r/min. This slip speed is very high and so the voltage E_R induced in the rotor bars is quite high (Fig. 23.73a). It will induce a rotor current I_R that rises very quickly. The rate of rise is determined by the voltage E_R and the leakage inductance of the rotor and stator windings. The rotor current lies in the magnetic field produced by the stator; as a result, the rotor torque T_M also increases rapidly (Fig. 23.73b). Thus, after an interval t_1, the

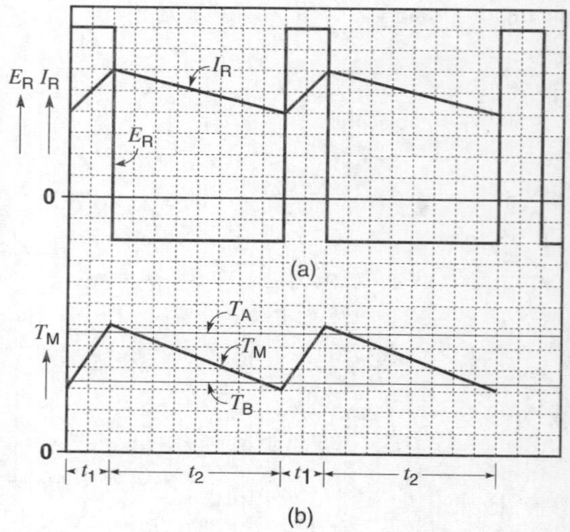

Figure 23.73
a. Voltage and current induced in the rotor bars.
b. Torque T_M developed by the motor, and the upper and lower limits T_A and T_B.

torque T_M reaches the level T_A, upon which the switches short-circuit the X and Y windings.

This freezes the flux in space and so it stops turning. However, the rotor continues to turn at 600 r/min, on account of its inertia. The slip speed is now −600 r/min; it induces in the rotor bars a negative voltage E_R that is 4 times smaller than during interval t_1.

Consequently, the rotor current decreases at a rate that is one quarter of what it was before. The torque decreases at the same rate, as shown in Fig. 23.73b. During interval t_2 and as soon as the torque has attained the lower limit T_B, the switches change state and the flux resumes its speed of 3000 r/min. The slip speed is again 2400 r/min, the accelerating torque increases rapidly, and the operating cycle repeats itself. The sum of the intervals t_1 and t_2 is a few milliseconds.

Thus, the flux continually advances and stops so that its average speed is far below the instantaneous speed of 3000 r/min. In fact, the average speed is slightly greater than the 600 r/min of the rotor.

23.40 Control of 3-phase motors

We have now covered the switching procedure for a 2-pole, 2-phase motor. How does it compare with that of a 3-phase motor? The windings in a 2-pole, 3-phase motor are connected in star, displaced 120° in space. Consequently, if we use a 6-pulse converter such as shown in Fig. 23.62, there will exist seven switching combinations to power the three windings. These combinations connect the (+) and (−) terminals of the dc source to windings A, B, and C (Fig. 23.74a). The seventh combination short-circuits all three windings. Thus, for the A (+) combination, winding A is connected to the (+) terminal and windings B and C are connected to the negative (−) terminal. It follows that the flux ϕ_s is directed to the right. However, for the A (−) combination, winding A is connected to the (−) terminal and windings B and C are connected to the (+) terminal. Flux ϕ_s is then directed to the left.

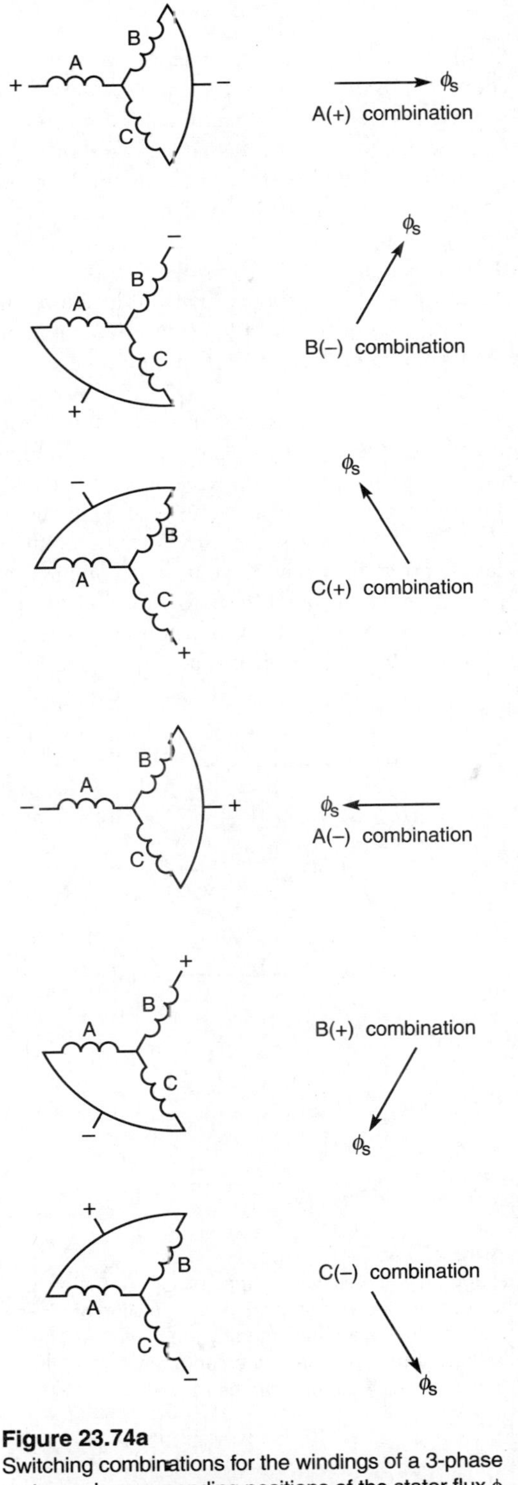

Figure 23.74a
Switching combinations for the windings of a 3-phase motor and corresponding positions of the stator flux ϕ_S.

Similarly, for the B(−) combination, winding B is connected to the (−) terminal and windings A and C are connected to the (+) terminal. Flux ϕ_s is then directed counterclockwise at an angle of 60°.

Suppose that the stator flux in this 3-phase motor should not go beyond the dotted circle (Fig. 23.74b). For each combination A (+), A (−), B (+), B (−), C (+), C (−), the flux will be directed in one of the six positions indicated by the "vectors" in the center of the figure. To complete one turn, a minimum of six commutations are required.

For example, suppose that the initial flux is represented by the vector 0-1. By using the combination C (+), the flux will move along the path 1-2. Having arrived at point 2, we use the combination A (−), which moves the flux toward point 3. Having arrived at point 3, we use the combination B (+) to move to point 4, and so forth. Thus, the flux in space of a 3-phase motor follows a hexagonal path instead of the square path of a 2-phase motor. The ratio of the maximum flux ϕ_S to the minimum is imposed by the geometry of the hexagon, namely $2/\sqrt{3} = 1.155$. If six switchings are allowed per revolution, the width of the tolerance band is 0.155 p.u.

Just as in the case of a 2-phase motor, by setting upper and lower limits to the tolerance band, the number of commutations per revolution will rise. For example, by reducing the band to 0.1 pu, the excursion is reduced to ±5% of the average flux. However the number of commutations per turn rises to 18 (Fig. 23.75). If the time required to make one complete turn is, say, 15 ms, that is equivalent to a switching frequency of 18/0.015 = 1200 Hz. Since the switching intervals are not fixed, the associated acoustic noise is less perceptible.

The path of Fig. 23.75 can be seeded with momentary stops that correspond to "zero" intervals where the three windings are in short-circuit. Each dot represents a stop lasting a fraction of a millisecond to several milliseconds. Thus, the numerous

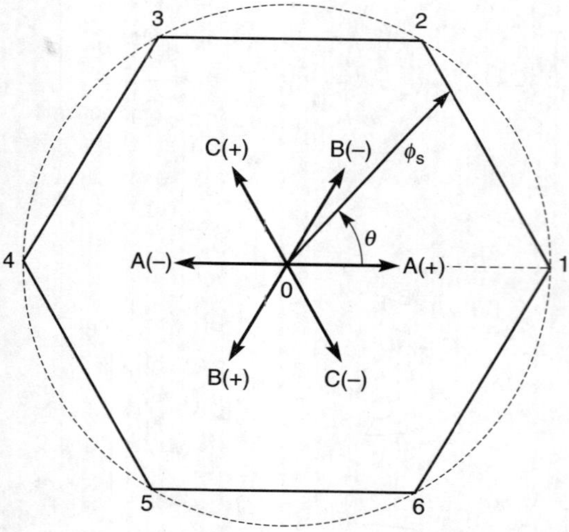

Figure 23.74b
Hexagonal path followed by the flux ϕ_S in a 6-step, 3-phase converter. The amplitude and position of the instantaneous flux are indicated by the vector ϕ_S. The six arrows emanating from the center show the six directions in which the flux can be moved.

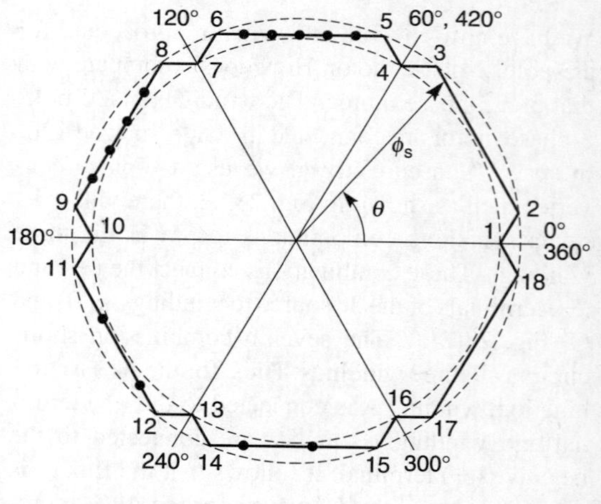

Figure 23.75
Path followed by the flux ϕ_S in a 3-phase converter when the amplitude is forced to lie between upper and lower limits of 1.0 pu and 1.1 pu. The bold dots represent "zero" periods when the windings are in short-circuit and the flux ϕ_S is frozen in space.

dots between 60° and 180° indicate that the average speed of the flux is rather low during this period. In counterpoint, between 180° and 300°, the flux turns quicker, and its average speed is maximum between 300° and 420° where the "zeros" are absent.

As in the case of a 2-phase motor, the number of stops depends upon the signals that control the torque. Each stop corresponds to an instant where the torque T_M exceeds the level T_A. It is obvious that the number of zeros will increase everywhere when the motor runs at low speed.

In order to understand the commutation process of a 3-phase motor, consider the case where the rotor and the flux rotate counterclockwise (Fig. 23.76). As before, the windings are connected to a converter that offers seven distinct switching positions (Fig. 23.62). Six combinations correspond to windings that are excited and one combination has all three windings in short-circuit.

Suppose that the flux ϕ_{S1} is momentarily less than the minimum flux ϕ_B. To correct this situation, we can connect the windings to the dc source in seven different ways. Thus, option A (+) produces

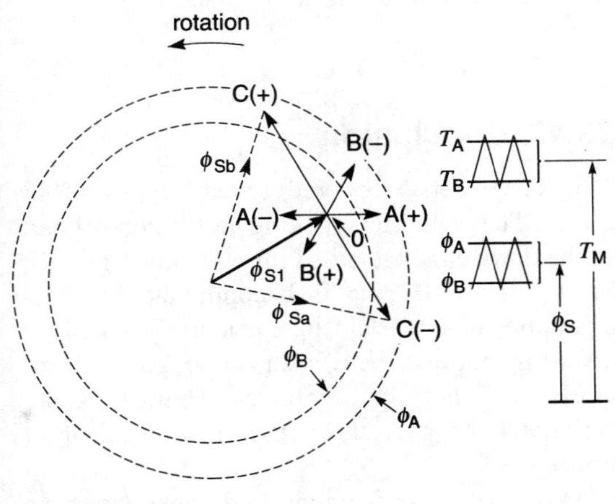

Figure 23.76
When ϕ_{S1} is less than ϕ_B, the flux can be increased by selecting one of the following options: A (+), B (−), C (+), or C (−).

a flux that is directed to the right, while option C (+) produces a flux that is oriented at 120° to the horizontal. Option "zero" produces a flux that is fixed in space because the windings are in short-circuit.

Recalling the remarks made in the case of the 2-phase motor, options A (−), B (+), and zero are rejected, but options A (+), B (−), C (+), and C (−) are plausible. The choice depends upon the instantaneous value of the torque T_M. If $T_M < T_B$ we select option C (+) because it produces an important movement of the flux in the direction of rotation of the motor, hence a strong accelerating torque. However, if $T_M > T_A$, we choose option A (+). Finally, if T_M lies between T_A and T_B, we choose B (−) rather than option A (+) because, while increasing the flux, it also produces a slight torque in the direction of rotation of the motor.

23.41 Schematic diagram of a DTC

As in all sophisticated control systems, the variable-speed controller (Fig. 23.77) rests upon a virtual model of the motor. The properties of the virtual motor are defined when the variable-speed system is being installed. A series of preliminary tests are carried out by the controller and in a few minutes the parameters of the real motor are determined, along with the moment of inertia of the system. The virtual motor is therefore the computer image of the actual motor.

By capturing the stator currents and voltages, and the dc voltage E_d, as well as the state of the switches (Fig. 23.62), the controller will automatically calculate the torque, speed, and flux ϕ_S in the real motor.

Figure 23.77 is a simplified sketch of the Direct Torque Control or DTC system. The diode rectifier is powered by the 3-phase source and the dc output voltage E_d is connected to the converter. We can understand the general operation of the system by following the input and output signals of the various blocks. In particular, the best switch state box sends logic signals to the converter, indicating at every instant which of the switches should be open or closed.

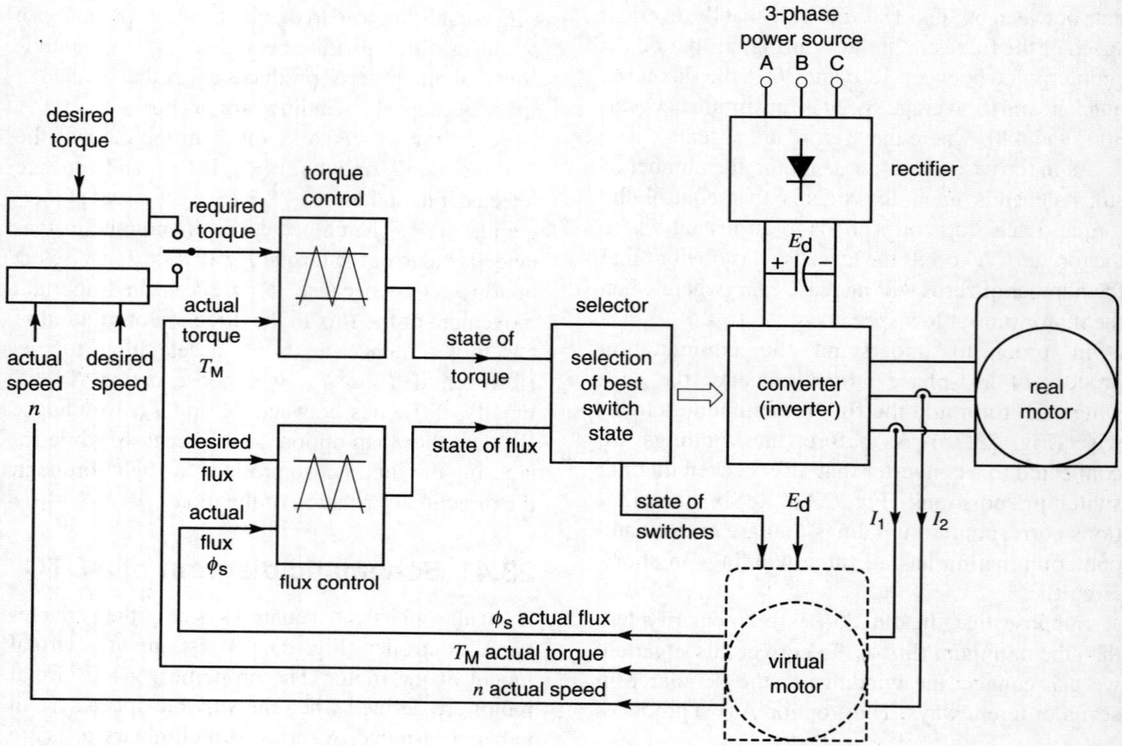

Figure 23.77
Schematic diagram of a Direct Torque Control (DTC) system. This highly simplified diagram illustrates the basic principle of the system.

Note that either the torque *or* the speed of the motor can be controlled at any one time. We cannot control both simultaneously. The reason is that the torque-speed relationship depends upon the characteristics of the load.

Direct torque control is used in many applications. It enables the control of speed and torque over a very broad range. The torque response is particularly fast. Consequently, it is possible to maintain constant speed, even when the mechanical load imposes sudden and unexpected mechanical shocks.

Figures 23.78a and 23.78b show the components of a DTC controller. Figure 23.79 shows a typical industrial application of a Direct Torque Control system.

23.42 Conclusion

This chapter has covered several types of ac drives. The converters making up the control part of the drive can be classed into two main groups: line-commutated and self-commutated. Line-commutated converters are particularly suited for thyristors because the current is extinguished naturally as the line voltages change. Line-commutated converters are used in large ac motor drives.

Drives using self-commutated converters have come to the fore mainly because of two factors: the availability of high-power switches such as GTOs and IGBTs, and the ability of high-speed computers

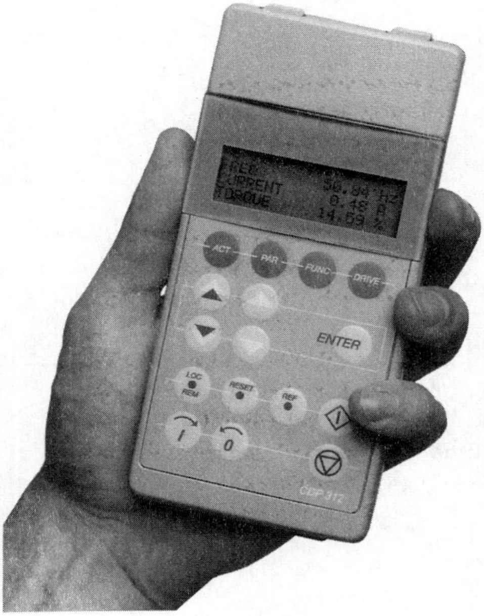

Figure 23.78a
This portable micro-console is a component of the DTC system. It provides information as to the real values of speed, torque, current, and so on, in 10 languages. It also registers the last five problems that occurred, and at what time.
(Courtesy of ABB)

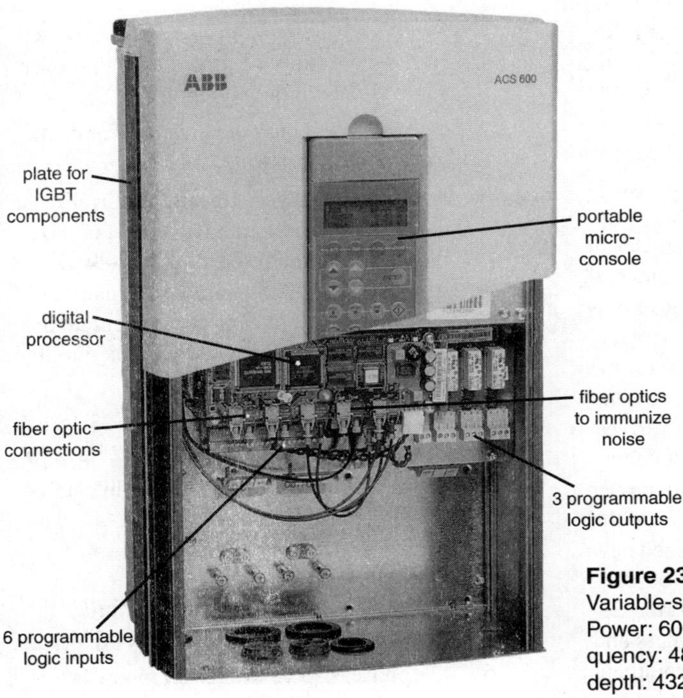

Figure 23.78b
Variable-speed controller using the DTC technology. Power: 60 hp; voltage 600 V, 3-phase; input frequency: 48 to 63 Hz; height: 715 mm; width: 306 mm; depth: 432 mm; weight: 50 kg.
(Courtesy of ABB)

Figure 23.79
The torque in this paper-winding machine is controlled with high precision using a conventional induction motor and without requiring an encoder. An interesting application of DTC.
(Courtesy of ABB)

and microprocessors to process signals in real-time. In addition, the ability of PWM switching converters to generate complex waveshapes of any frequency and phase has opened the way to induction motor drives that perform as well as dc drives do.

Another factor of great importance is that switching converters, connected to electric utility feeders, can convert ac power to dc power and vice versa while operating *sinusoidally* at unity power factor. This is made possible by operating the converter in the PWM mode and phase shifting the fundamental voltage while filtering out the high-frequency components with relatively inexpensive filters. The fact that power can be drawn from, or fed back to, the line at high-power factor and low-harmonic content, augurs well for all induction motor electronic drives.

Indeed, the inherent property of PWM switching converters to generate or absorb reactive power while permitting real power to flow freely from the ac side to the dc side and vice versa has opened new frontiers in all areas where power has to be controlled. Thus, the PWM switching converter deserves a special place, along with transformers and rotating machines, in the hierarchy of prominent power apparatus.

Questions and Problems

Practical level

23-1 Name three types of drives used to power squirrel-cage induction motors.

23-2 Why are two converters needed for each phase winding in Fig. 23.15?

23-3 A standard 3-phase, 16-pole, squirrel-cage induction motor is rated at 460 V, 60 Hz. We want the motor to run at a no-load speed of about 225 r/min while maintaining the same flux in the air gap. Calculate the voltage and frequency to be applied to the stator.

23-4 The blower motor shown in Fig. 23.18 has 4 poles and a full-load rating of 2 hp, 240 V, 3-phase, 60 Hz. It has the torque-speed characteristic shown in Fig. 23.19.

Calculate

a. The full-load rated speed [r/min]
b. The full-load rated torque [N·m]

23-5 A 3-phase, 6-pole induction motor is driven by a cycloconverter that is fed from a 60 Hz line. What is the approximate maximum speed that can be attained with this arrangement?

23-6 What is the basic difference between a line-commutated and a self-commutated inverter?

23-7 A line-commutated inverter can be used to drive a 3-phase synchronous motor but not a 3-phase induction motor. Explain why.

23-8 In comparing the physical arrangement of the bridge rectifiers in one phase of the cycloconverter of Fig. 23.15, is there any difference with the bridge rectifier arrangement of Fig. 23.33?

23-9 A large squirrel-cage induction motor has to run at a very low, steady speed. If electronic control is required, what type of control would be most appropriate?

Intermediate level

23-10 The induction motor in Fig. 23.15 has six poles and runs at a no-load speed of 160 r/min. The effective voltage across the windings is 42 V.

Calculate

a. The frequency generated by the cycloconverter [Hz]
b. The smallest possible effective line voltage of the 60 Hz source [V]

23-11 When the induction motor in Problem 23-10 operates at full-load (with the frequency unchanged) its power factor is 80 percent.

Calculate

a. The time during which converter 1 acts as a rectifier [ms]
b. The time during which it acts as an inverter [ms]

23-12 The motor and blower shown in Fig. 23.18 have the properties shown in Fig. 23.19. The synchronous speed is 1200 r/min, the rated torque is 8 N·m, and the rated voltage is 240 V.

Calculate

a. The torque, speed, and horsepower when the voltage is 240 V
b. The torque, speed, and horsepower when the voltage is 120 V

23-13 Referring to Fig. 23.24a, the dc link voltage and current are respectively 250 V and 60 A. The 3-phase line voltage is 240 V, 60 Hz. The motor has an efficiency of 82 percent.

Calculate

a. The approximate mechanical power developed by the motor [hp]
b. The firing angle of converter 1
c. The reactive power absorbed by converter 1

23-14 Why is it easier to achieve regenerative braking with a current-fed drive than with a voltage-fed drive?

23-15 Referring to Fig. 23.32, calculate the following:

a. The average current in each diode
b. The peak current in each diode
c. The peak inverse voltage across each diode
d. The frequency of rotor current I_R

23-16 In Fig. 23.33 the value of E_2 remains fixed, but in Fig. 23.26 it varies linearly with the frequency generated by converter 2. Can you explain why?

23-17 The blower motor in Fig. 23.18 has a nominal rating of 1/4 hp, 1620 r/min, 3-phase, 460 V. The respective torque-speed characteristics of the motor and blower are given in Fig. 23.19. Calculate the rotor I^2R losses (with the motor coupled to the blower).

a. When the motor runs at rated voltage
b. When the stator voltage is reduced to 230 V
c. Is the rotor hotter in (a) or (b)?

23-18 In Problem 23-17 calculate the stator voltage required so that the blower runs at a speed of 810 r/min.

23-19 A 30 hp, 208 V, 3-phase, 3500 r/min, 60 Hz, wound-rotor induction motor produces an open-circuit rotor line voltage of 250 V. We wish to limit the locked-rotor torque to a maximum value of 40 N·m so as to ensure a small starting current. A 3-phase bridge rectifier composed of six diodes is connected to the three slip-rings. A single manual rheostat is connected across the dc output of the rectifier.

Calculate

a. The synchronous speed of the motor
b. The power that is dissipated in the rotor circuit under locked-rotor conditions
c. The approximate dc output voltage
d. The approximate resistance of the rheostat and its power-handling capacity

23-20 In Problem 23-19 a dc chopper is connected between the dc output of the rectifier and a 0.2 Ω resistor. If the chopper operates at a fixed frequency of 500 Hz, calculate the duration of the on-time T_a under locked-rotor conditions.

Advanced level

23-21 **a.** The squirrel-cage induction motor shown in Fig. 23.15 has a nominal rating of 50 hp, 460 V per phase, 60 Hz, 1100 r/min. The 3-phase line voltage is 208 V, 60 Hz. If we want the motor to run at a speed of about 200 r/min, while developing full-load torque, calculate the approximate voltage and frequency to be applied to the stator windings.
b. If current I_a has an effective value of 60 A, calculate the approximate value of the peak current carried by each thyristor.

23-22 The self-commutated inverter in Fig. 23.24a furnishes a motor current having an effective value of 26 A. What is the value of the dc link current?

23-23 A standard 50 hp, 1750 r/min, 3-phase, 200 V, 60 Hz, squirrel-cage induction motor is driven by a current-fed self-commutated inverter shown in Fig. 23.24a. Calculate the voltage and frequency to be applied to the stator so that the motor develops its rated torque at 400 r/min. Assume that the flux in the machine is constant.

Industrial application

23-24 A 50 hp dc motor is required to drive a centrifuge at a speed ranging between 18 000 and 30 000 r/min. Owing to commutation problems associated with a standard commutator at these speeds, it is decided to use a commutatorless dc motor driven by two converters with a dc link (Fig. 23.8). A 2-pole motor is selected having a nominal rating of 50 hp, 30 000 r/min, 460 V, 60 A, 90 percent power factor leading. When the motor delivers its rated output, the delay angle for converter 2 is 155°. If the available 60 Hz line voltage is 575 V, calculate the following:

a. The triggering frequency applied to the gates of converter 2
b. The dc link voltage
c. The delay angle of converter 1
d. The dc link current if the motor draws an input power of 41.5 kW
e. The fundamental ripple frequency in E_1
f. The fundamental ripple frequency in E_2
g. The power factor of the 60 Hz line
h. The effective value of I_s
i. Show the flow of active and reactive power in the converters.

23-25 The solid-state starter illustrated in Fig. 23.23b is used with a 5 hp, 460 V, 3-phase, 1760 r/min motor that drives a belt conveyor. The motor has a starting torque of 2 pu. The kick-start voltage is set at 0.8 pu and the initial voltage is set at 0.4 pu.

a. Calculate the value of the kick-start torque and the initial torque.

b. Knowing that the full-load current is 6.2 A, calculate the approximate thermal power dissipated in the starter.

23-26 **a.** Referring to Fig. 23.37 calculate the net tangential force exerted on the rotor bars, per pole.

b. If the rotor bar currents were in phase with the rotor bar voltages, what would be the net tangential force exerted on the rotor bars, per pole? The peak current is assumed to remain at 240 A and the length of the rotor bars is 10 cm.

23-27 The motor shown in Fig. 23.37 has 8 poles and it is connected to a 60 Hz source. The rotor has a diameter of 140 mm and the rotor frequency is 40 Hz. Calculate

a. The speed of the rotor [r/min]

b. The torque developed by the rotor [N·m]

23-28 In the equivalent circuit of Fig. 23.44a, calculate the line-to-line stator voltage that is needed in order that the motor will develop its rated torque of 10.1 N·m.

23-29 The full-load efficiency of the 14 MW propulsion motor described in Fig. 23.59 is 97.3% when it operates at unity power factor.

a. Taking into account the losses of the dc field, which amount to 84 kW, calculate the nominal stator current at full-load.

b. Calculate the nominal stator current per winding.

c. Calculate the peak current carried by the thyristors.

23-30 In reference to Fig. 23.59, calculate the following:

a. The frequency range of the cycloconverters

b. The rated active and reactive power supplied by each of the 10 260 MVA diesel-electric generators

c. The 75% power factor that the diesel-electric generators can supply is much lower than the 90% lagging power factor rating of most alternators. Can you give a plausible reason for this low power factor rating?

d. The time required to cover a distance of 500 miles when this Superliner runs at its rated service speed

23-31 In Fig. 23.56 it is given that $E_{12} = 420\angle 37°$; $I = 330\angle 42°$ $x = 0.2\ \Omega$. Determine the following:

a. The magnitude and phase of E_{34}

b. The active and reactive power delivered to, or received by, the converter

23-32 Referring to the electric vehicle drive of Fig. 23.56, the 4-quadrant single-phase converter produces a dc voltage of 805 V between terminals 5 and 6. The magnitude and phase angle of the ac voltage between terminals 3 and 4 can be adjusted by continually varying the duty cycle. The carrier frequency of f_c is 800 Hz and the fundamental frequency is equal to that of the 60 Hz power line. The reactance x has a 60 Hz impedance of 0.8 Ω, and the voltage on the secondary side of the transformer is $E_{12} = 400\angle 62°$. The magnitude and phase of E_{34} are adjusted so that the converter supplies 161 kW to the dc link, while ensuring that the current I is in phase with E_{12}. Neglecting the losses in the converter, calculate the following:

a. The magnitude of I_d

b. The magnitude and phase of I

c. The magnitude and phase of E_{34}

d. The amplitude modulation ratio

23-33 A single-phase, 60 Hz converter such as shown in Fig. 23.56, operates at a synchronous carrier frequency of 300 Hz. The dc link voltage is 680 V and the effective value of the 60 Hz fundamental voltage E_{34} is 430 V. Calculate the duty cycle D and the on/off time when the ac voltage is momentarily:

a. +500 V
b. −30 V.

23-34 The equivalent circuit of a 2-pole, 5 hp, 480 V, 3-phase, 60 Hz motor is shown in Fig. 23.42a. Determine the equivalent circuit per phase when the motor runs at 600 r/min while operating at a frequency of 12 Hz and a line-to-line voltage of 92 V. Calculate the following:

a. The value of the power resistance
b. The stator current
c. The magnetizing component of the stator current
d. The torque-producing component of the stator current
e. The total torque

23-35 Referring to Fig. 23.44a, but assuming a greater load, calculate the line current, magnetizing current, and torque if the motor turns at 90 r/min instead of 270 r/min.

PART FOUR

Electric Utility Power Systems

Chapter 24

Generation of Electrical Energy

24.0 Introduction

Now that we are familiar with the principal machines, transformers, and other power devices, we are in a position to see how they are used in a large electrical system. Such a system comprises all the apparatus used in the generation, transmission, and distribution of electric energy, starting from the generating station and ending up in the most remote summer home in the country. This chapter and the next three chapters are, therefore, devoted to the following major topics:

- the generation of electrical energy
- the transmission of electrical energy
- the distribution of electrical energy
- the cost of electricity

24.1 Demand of an electrical system

The total power drawn by the customers of a large utility system fluctuates between wide limits, depending on the seasons and time of day. Fig. 24.1 shows how the system demand (power) varies during a typical day in the summer and a typical day in the winter. The pattern of the daily demand is remarkably similar for the two seasons. During the winter the peak demand of 15 GW (= 15 000 MW)

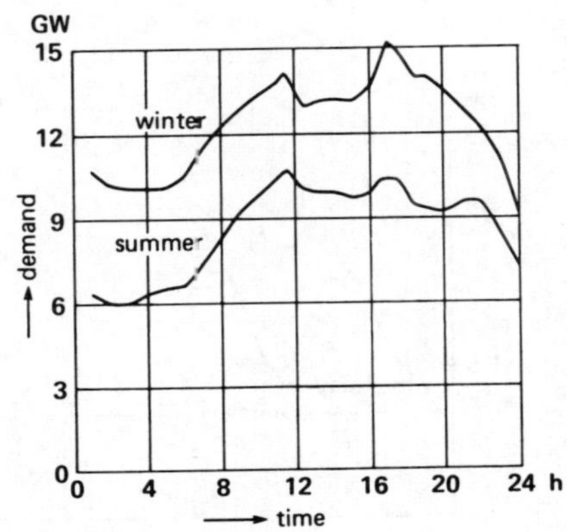

Figure 24.1
Demand curve of a larger system during a summer day and a winter day.

is higher than the summer peak of 10 GW. Nevertheless, both peaks occur about 17:00 (5 P.M.) because increased domestic activity at this time coincides with industrial and commercial centers that are still operating at full capacity.

The load curve of Fig. 24.2 shows the *seasonal* variations for the same system. Note that the peak demand during the winter (15 GW) is more than twice the minimum demand during the summer (6 GW).

In examining the curve, we note that the demand throughout the year never falls below 6 GW. This is the *base load* of the system. We also see that the annual *peak load* is 15 GW. The base load has to be fed 100 percent of the time, but the peak load may occur for only 0.1 percent of the time. Between these two extremes, we have *intermediate loads* that have to be fed for less than 100 percent of the time.

If we plot the duration of each demand on an annual base, we obtain the *load duration curve* of Fig. 24.3. For example, the curve shows that a demand of 9 GW lasts 70 percent of the time, while a demand of 12 GW lasts for only 15 percent of the time. The graph is divided into base, intermediate, and peak-load sections. The peak-load portion usually includes demands that last for less than 15 percent of the time. On this basis the system has to deliver 6 GW of base power, another 6 GW of intermediate power, and 3 GW of peak power.

These power blocks give rise to three types of generating stations:

a. **Base-power stations** that deliver full power at all times: Nuclear stations and coal-fired stations are particularly well adapted to furnish base demand.
b. **Intermediate-power stations** that can respond relatively quickly to changes in demand, usually by adding or removing one or more generating units: Hydropower stations are well adapted for this purpose.
c. **Peak-generating stations** that deliver power for brief intervals during the day: Such stations must be put into service very quickly. Consequently, they are equipped with prime movers such as diesel engines, gas turbines, compressed-air motors, or pumped-storage turbines that can be started up in a few minutes. In this regard, it is worth mentioning that thermal generating stations using gas or coal take from 4 to 8 hours to start up, while nuclear stations may take several days. Obviously, such generating stations cannot be used to supply short-term peak power.

Returning to Fig. 24.3, it so happens that the areas of the dotted and cross-hatched parts are proportional to the relative amount of energy (kW·h) associated with the base, intermediate, and peak

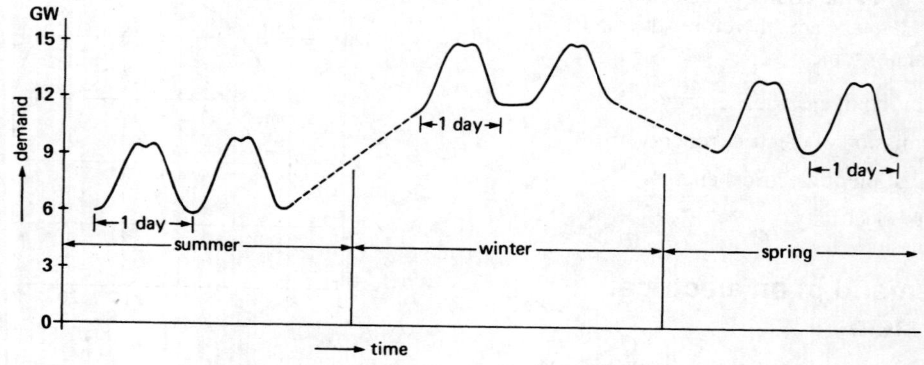

Figure 24.2
Demand curve of a large electric utility system during one year.

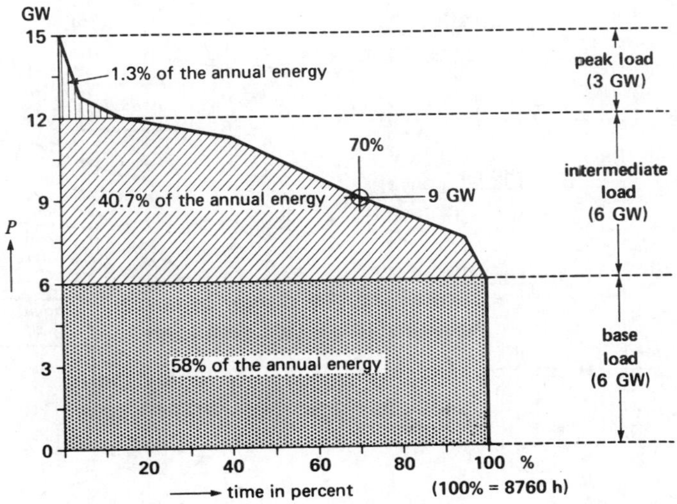

Figure 24.3
Load duration curve of a large electric utility system.

loads. Thus, the base-power stations supply 58 percent of the total annual energy requirements, while the peak-load stations contribute only 1.3 percent. The peak-load stations are in service for an average of only 1 hour per day. Consequently, peak power is very expensive because the stations that produce it are idle most of the time.

24.2 Location of the generating station

In planning an electric utility system, the physical location of the generating station, transmission lines, and substations must be carefully planned to arrive at an acceptable, economic solution. We can sometimes locate a generating station next to the primary source of energy (such as a coal mine) and use transmission lines to carry the electrical energy to where it is needed. When this is neither practical or economical, we have to transport the primary energy (coal, gas, oil) by ship, train, or pipeline to the generating station (Fig. 24.4). The generating station may, therefore, be near to, or far away from, the ultimate user of the electrical energy. Fig. 24.4 also shows some of the obstacles that prevent transmission lines from following the shortest route. Due to these obstacles, both physical and legal, transmission lines often follow a zigzag path between the generating station and the ultimate user.

24.3 Types of generating stations

There are three main types of generating stations:

1. Thermal generating stations
2. Hydropower generating stations
3. Nuclear generating stations

Thermal generating stations produce most of the electrical energy in the United States. Nevertheless, important hydropower stations and nuclear generating stations produce about 20 percent of the total requirements.

Some of the largest hydropower stations are located in Quebec and British Columbia, in Canada.

Although we can harness the wind, tides, and solar energy, these energy sources represent a tiny part of the total energy we need.

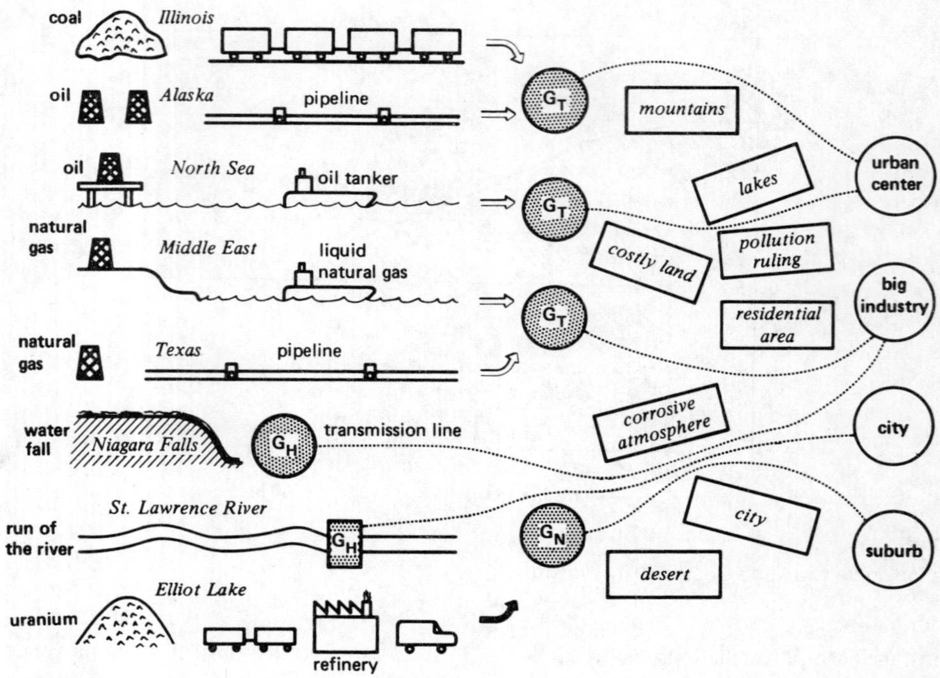

Figure 24.4
Extracting, hauling, and transforming the primary sources of energy is done in different ways. The dotted transmission lines connecting the generating stations G with the consumers must go around various obstacles. G_T: thermal station; G_H: hydro station; G_N: nuclear station.

24.4 Controlling the power balance between generator and load

The electrical energy consumed by the thousands of customers must immediately be supplied by the ac generators because electrical energy cannot be stored. How do we maintain this almost instantaneous balance between customer requirements and generated power? To answer the question, let us consider a single hydropower station supplying a regional load R_1 (Fig. 24.5). Water behind the dam flows through the turbine, causing the turbine and generator to rotate.

The mechanical power P_T developed by the turbine depends exclusively on the opening of the wicket gates that control the water flow. The greater the opening, the more water is admitted to the turbine and the increased power is immediately transmitted to the generator.

On the other hand, the electric power P_L drawn from the generator depends exclusively on the load. When the mechanical power P_T supplied to the rotor is equal to the electrical power P_L consumed by the load, the generator is in dynamic equilibrium and its speed remains constant. The electrical system is said to be *stable.*

However, we have just seen that the system demand fluctuates continually, so P_L is sometimes greater and sometimes less than P_T. If P_L is greater than P_T, the generating unit (turbine and generator) begins to slow down. Conversely, if P_L is less than P_T, the generating unit speeds up.

The speed variation of the generator is, therefore, an excellent indicator of the state of equilibrium be-

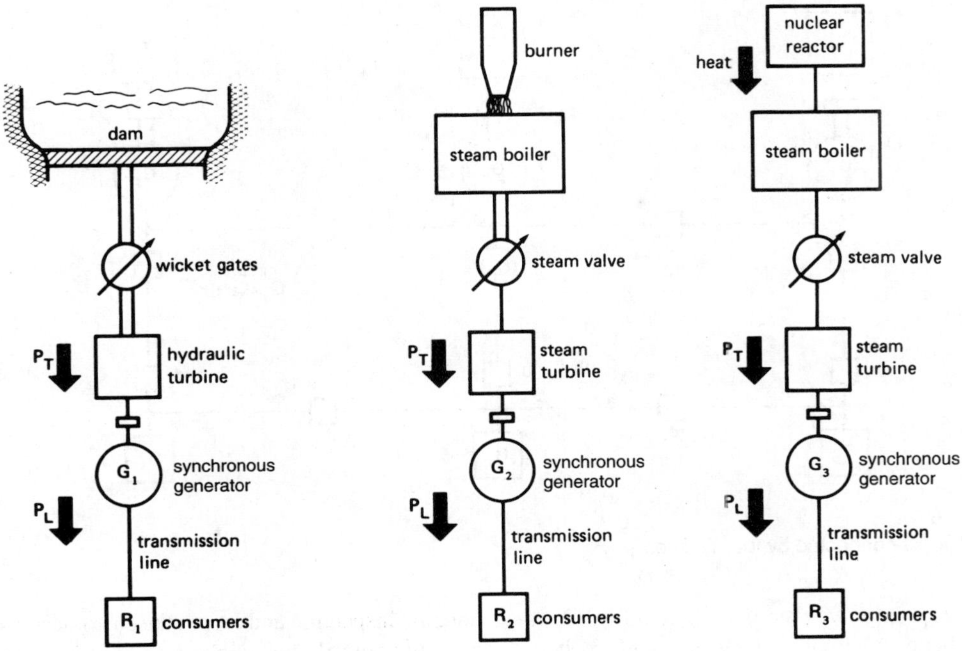

Figure 24.5
Power supplied to three independent regions.

tween P_L and P_T and, hence, of the stability of the system. If the speed falls the wicket gates must open, and if it rises they must close so as to maintain a continuous state of equilibrium between P_T and P_L. Although we could adjust the gates manually by observing the speed, an automatic speed regulator is always used.

Speed regulators, or governors, are extremely sensitive devices. They can detect speed changes as small as 0.02 percent. Thus, if the speed of a generator increases from 1800 r/min to 1800.36 r/min, the governor begins to act on the wicket gate mechanism. If the load should suddenly increase, the speed will drop momentarily, but the governor will quickly bring it back to rated speed. The same corrective action takes place when the load is suddenly removed.

Clearly, any speed change produces a corresponding change in the system frequency. The frequency is therefore an excellent indicator of the stability of a system. *The system is stable so long as the frequency is constant.*

The governors of thermal and nuclear stations operate the same way, except that they regulate the steam valves, allowing more or less steam to flow through the turbines (Fig. 24.5). The resulting change in steam flow has to be accompanied by a change in the rate of combustion. Thus, in the case of a coal-burning boiler, we have to reduce combustion as soon as the valves are closed off, otherwise the boiler pressure will quickly exceed the safety limits.

24.5 Advantage of interconnected systems

Consider the three generating stations of Fig. 24.5, connected to their respective regional loads R_1, R_2, and R_3. Because the three systems are not connected, each can operate at its own frequency, and a disturbance on one does not affect the others. However, it is preferable to interconnect the systems

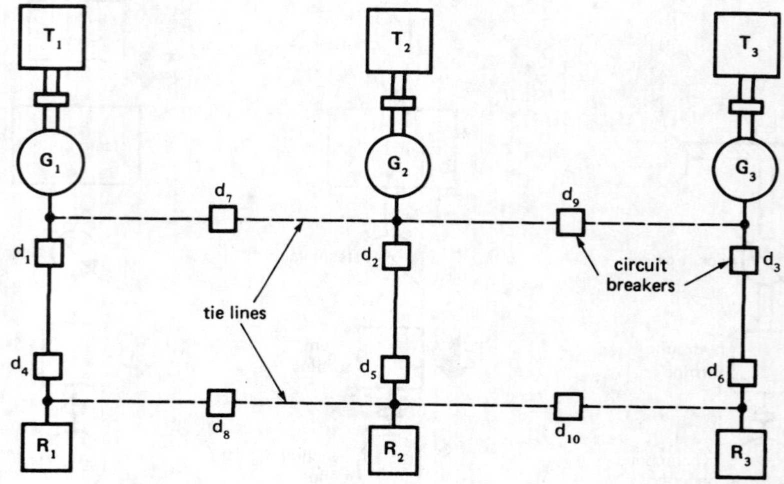

Figure 24.6
Three networks connected by four tie lines.

because (1) it improves the overall stability, (2) it provides better continuity of service, and (3) it is more economical. Fig. 24.6 shows four interconnecting transmission lines, tying together both the generating stations and the regions being serviced. High-speed circuit breakers d_1 to d_{10} are installed to automatically interrupt power in case of a fault and to reroute the flow of electric power.* We now discuss the advantages of such a network.

1. Stability. Systems that are interconnected have greater reserve power than a system working alone. In effect, a large system is better able to withstand a large disturbance and, consequently, it is inherently more stable. For example, if the load suddenly increases in region R_1, energy immediately flows from stations G_2 and G_3 and over the interconnecting tie-lines. The heavy load is, therefore, shared by all three stations instead of being carried by one alone.

2. Continuity of Service. If a generating station should break down, or if it has to be shut down for annual inspection and repair, the customers it serves can temporarily be supplied by the two remaining stations. Energy flowing over the tie-lines is automatically metered and credited to the station that supplies it, less any wheeling charges. A *wheeling charge* is the amount paid to another electric utility when its transmission lines are used to deliver power to a third party.

3. Economy. When several regions are interconnected, the load can be shared among the various generating stations so that the overall operating cost is minimized. For example, instead of operating all three stations at reduced capacity during the night when demand is low, we can shut down one station completely and let the others carry the load. In this way we greatly reduce the operating cost of one station while improving the efficiency of the other stations, because they now run closer to their rated capacity.

Electric utility companies are, therefore, interested in grouping their resources by a grid of interconnecting transmission lines. A central dispatching office (control center) distributes the load among the various companies and generating stations so as to minimize the costs (Fig. 24.7). Due to the complex-

* The IEEE Std 100-1992 states that a fault is a physical condition that causes a device, a component, or an element to fail to perform in a required manner, for example, a short-circuit, a broken wire, or an intermittent connection.

Figure 24.7
Technicians in the control rooms of two generating stations communicate with each other, or with a central dispatching office, while supervising the operation of their respective generating units.

ity of some systems, control decisions are invariably made with the aid of a computer. The dispatching office also has to predict daily and seasonal load changes and to direct the start-up and shut-down of generating units so as to maintain good stability of the immense and complicated network.

For example, the New England Power Exchange (NEPEX) coordinates the resources of 13 electrical utility companies serving Connecticut, Rhode Island, Maine, and New Hampshire. It also supervises power flow between this huge network and the state of New York and Canada.

Although such interconnected systems must necessarily operate at the same frequency, the load can still be allocated among the individual generating units, according to a specific program. Thus, if a generating unit has to deliver more power, its governor setting is changed slightly so that more power is delivered to the generator. The increased electrical output from this unit produces a corresponding decrease in the total power supplied by all the other generating units of the interconnected system.

24.6 Conditions during an outage

A major disturbance on a system (called *contingency*) creates a state of emergency and immediate steps must be taken to prevent it from spreading to other regions. The sudden loss of an important load or a permanent short-circuit on a transmission line constitutes a major contingency.

If a big load is suddenly lost, all the turbines begin to speed up and the frequency increases everywhere on the system. On the other hand, if a generator is disconnected, the speed of the remaining generators decreases because they suddenly have to carry the entire load. The frequency starts to decrease—sometimes at the rate of 5 Hz per second. Under these conditions, no time must be lost and, if conventional methods are unable to bring the frequency back to normal, one or more loads must be dropped. Such *load shedding* is done by frequency-sensitive relays that open selected circuit breakers as the frequency falls. For example, on a 60 Hz system the relays may be set to shed 15 percent of the system load when the frequency reaches 59.3 Hz, another 15 percent when it reaches 58.9 Hz, and a final 30 percent when the frequency is 58 Hz. Load shedding must be done in less than one second to save the loads judged to be of prime importance. As far as the disconnected customers are concerned, such an outage creates serious problems. Elevators stop between floors, arc furnaces start to cool down, paper tears as it moves through a paper mill, traffic lights stop functioning, and so forth. Clearly, it is in everyone's interest to provide uninterrupted service.

Experience over many years has shown that most system short-circuits are very brief. They may be caused by lightning, by polluted insulators, by falling trees, or by overvoltages created when circuit breakers open and close. Such disturbances usually produce a short-circuit between two phases or between one phase and ground. Three-phase short-circuits are very rare.

Because line short-circuits are, in general, very brief, a major outage can usually be prevented by simply opening a short-circuited line and reclosing it very quickly. Naturally, such fast switching of circuit breakers is done automatically because it all happens in a matter of a few cycles.

24.7 Frequency and electric clocks

The frequency of a system fluctuates as the load varies, but the turbine governors always bring it back to 60 Hz. Owing to these fluctuations, the system gains or loses a few cycles throughout the day. When the accumulated loss or gain is about 180 cycles, the error is corrected by making all the generators turn either faster or slower for a brief period. The frequency correction is affected according to instructions from the dispatching center. In this way a 60 Hz network generates exactly 5 184 000 cycles in a 24-hour period. Electric clocks connected to the network indicate the correct time to within 3 seconds, because the position of the second hand is directly related to the number of elapsed cycles.

HYDROPOWER GENERATING STATIONS

Hydropower generating stations convert the energy of moving water into electrical energy by means of a hydraulic turbine coupled to a synchronous generator.

24.8 Available hydro power

The power that can be extracted from a waterfall depends upon its height and rate of flow. The size and physical location of a hydropower station depends, therefore, on these two factors. The available hydro power can be calculated by the equation

$$P = 9.8\,qh \tag{24.1}$$

where

P = available water power [kW]
q = water rate of flow [m^3/s]
h = head of water [m]
9.8 = coefficient to take care of units

Owing to friction losses in the water conduits, turbine casing, and the turbine itself, the mechanical power output of the turbine is somewhat less than that calculated by Eq. 24.1. However, the efficiency of large hydraulic turbines is between 90 and 94 percent. The generator efficiency is even higher, ranging from 97 to 99 percent, depending on the size of the generator.

Example 24-1

A large hydropower station has a head of 324 m and an average flow of 1370 m^3/s. The reservoir of water behind the dams and dikes is composed of a series of lakes covering an area of 6400 km^2.

Calculate

a. The available hydraulic power
b. The number of days this power could be sustained if the level of the impounded water were allowed to drop by 1 m (assume no precipitation or evaporation and neglect water brought in by surrounding rivers and streams)

Solution

a. The available hydropower is

$$\begin{aligned} P &= 9.8\,qh \\ &= 9.8 \times 1370 \times 324 \\ &= 4\,350\,000 \text{ kW} = 4350 \text{ MW} \end{aligned}$$

b. A drop of 1 m in the water level corresponds to 6400×10^6 m^3 of water. Because the flow is 1370 m^3/s, the time for all this water to flow through the turbines is

$$\begin{aligned} t &= 6400 \times 10^6/1370 \\ &= 4.67 \times 10^6 \text{ s} \\ &= 1298 \text{ h} = 54 \text{ days} \end{aligned}$$

As a matter of interest, a flow of 1370 m^3/s is about 10 times the amount of water used by the city of New York and its suburbs.

24.9 Types of hydropower stations

Hydropower stations are divided into three groups depending on the head of water:

1. High-head development
2. Medium-head development
3. Low-head development

High-head developments have heads in excess of 300 m, and high-speed Pelton turbines are used. Such generating stations are found in the Alps and other mountainous regions. The amount of impounded water is usually small.

Medium-head developments have heads between 30 m and 300 m, and medium-speed Francis turbines are used. The generating station is fed by a huge reservoir of water retained by dikes and a dam. The dam is usually built across a river bed in a relatively mountainous region. A great deal of water is impounded behind the dam (Fig. 24.8).

Low-head developments have heads under 30 m, and low-speed Kaplan or Francis turbines are used. These generating stations often extract the energy from flowing rivers. The turbines are designed to handle large volumes of water at low pressure. No reservoir is provided (Fig. 24.9).

Figure 24.8
Grand Coulee Dam on the Columbia River in the state of Washington is 108 m high and 1270 m wide. It is one of the large hydropower plants in the world, having 18 generating units of 125 MW each and 12 generating units of 600 MW each, for a total of 9450 MW of installed capacity. The spillway can be seen in the middle of the dam. *(Courtesy of General Electric)*

Figure 24.9
The Beauharnois generating station on the St. Lawrence River contains 26 3-phase alternators rated 50 MVA, 13.2 kV, 75 r/min, 60 Hz at a power factor of 0.8 lagging. An additional 10 units rated 65 MVA, 95.7 r/min make up the complete installation. The output ranges between 1000 MW and 1575 MW depending upon the seasonal water flow.
(Courtesy of Hydro-Québec)

24.10 Makeup of a hydropower plant

A hydropower installation consists of dams, waterways, and conduits that form a reservoir and channel the water toward the turbines. These, and other items described, enable us to understand some of the basic features and components of a hydropower plant (see Fig. 24.10).

1. ***Dams.*** Dams made of earth or concrete are built across river beds to create storage reservoirs. Reservoirs can compensate for the reduced precipitation during dry seasons and for the abnormal flows that accompany heavy rains and melting snow. Dams permit us to regulate the water flow throughout the year, so that the powerhouse may run at close to full capacity.

Spillways adjacent to the dam are provided to discharge water whenever the reservoir level is too high. We have seen that the demand for electricity varies considerably throughout the day, and from season to season. Consequently, the available water cannot always be used to supply energy to the system. If the water reservoir is small or almost nonexistent (such as in run-of-river stations), we unfortunately have to let the water through the spillway without using it.

Dams often serve a dual purpose, providing irrigation and navigation facilities, in addition to their power-generating role. The integrated system of the Tennessee Valley Authority is a good example.

2. ***Conduits, Penstocks, and Scroll-Case.*** In large installations, conduits lead the water from the dam site to the generating plant. They may be open canals

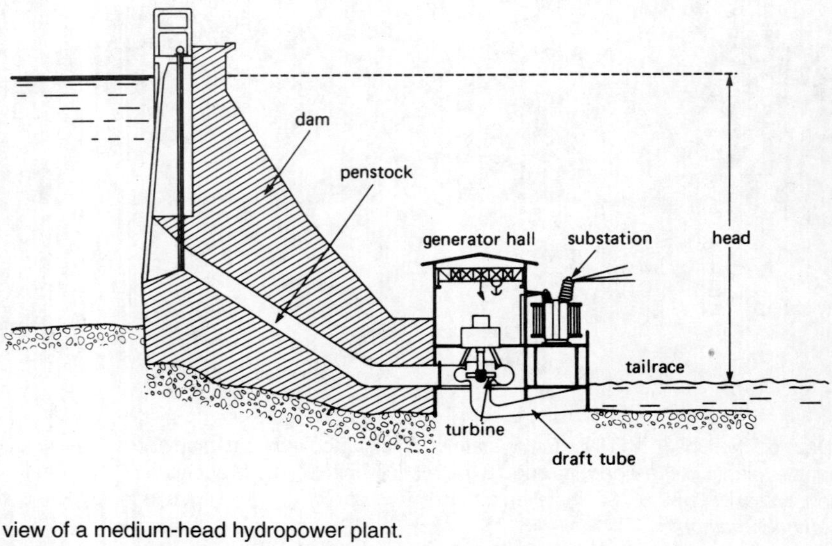

Figure 24.10
Cross-section view of a medium-head hydropower plant.

or tunnels carved through rock. The conduits feed one or more penstocks (huge steel pipes), which bring the water to the individual turbines. Enormous valves, sometimes several meters in diameter, enable the water supply to be shut off in the conduits.

The penstocks channel the water into a scroll-case that surrounds the runner (turbine) so that water is evenly distributed around its circumference. Guide vanes and wicket gates control the water so that it flows smoothly into the runner blades (see Figs. 24.11, 24.12, and 24.13). The wicket gates open and close in response to a powerful hydraulic mechanism that is controlled by the respective turbine governors.

*3. **Draft Tube and Tailrace.*** Water that has passed through the runner moves next through a carefully designed vertical channel, called draft tube. The draft tube improves the hydraulic efficiency of the turbine. It leads out to the tailrace, which channels the water into the downstream river bed.

*4. **Powerhouse.*** The powerhouse contains the synchronous generators, transformers, circuit breakers, etc., and associated control apparatus. Instruments, relays, and meters are contained in a central room where the entire station can be monitored and controlled. Finally, many other devices (too numerous to mention here) make up the complete hydropower station.

Figure 24.11
Spiral case feeds water around the circumference of a 483 MW turbine.
(Courtesy of Marine Industrie)

Figure 24.12
Inside the spiral case, a set of adjustable wicket gates control the amount of water flowing into the turbine.
(Courtesy of Marine Industrie)

Figure 24.13
Runner of a Francis-type turbine being lowered into position at the Grand Coulee Dam. The turbine is rated at 620 MW, 72 r/min and operates on a nominal head of 87 m. Other details: runner diameter: 10 m; runner mass: 500 t; maximum head: 108 m; minimum head: 67 m; turbine efficiency: 93 percent; number of wicket gates: 32; mass per wicket gate: 6.3 t; turbine shaft length: 6.7 m; mass of shaft: 175 t.
(Courtesy of Les Ateliers d'Ingénierie. Dominion)

24.11 Pumped-storage installations

We have already seen that peak-power stations are needed to meet the variable system demand. To understand the different types of peaking systems used, consider a network (electric system) in which the daily demand varies between 100 MW and 160 MW, as shown in Fig. 24.14. One obvious solution to this variable demand is to install a 100 MW base-power station and a peak-power unit of 60 MW, driven intermittently by a gas turbine.

However, another solution is to install a larger base-power unit of 130 MW and a smaller peaking station of 30 MW. The peaking station must be able to both deliver and absorb 30 MW of electric power. During lightly loaded periods (indicated by a minus sign in Fig. 24.15), the peaking station receives and stores energy provided by the base-power generating plant. Then, during periods of heavy demand (shown by a plus), the peaking station returns the energy it had previously stored.

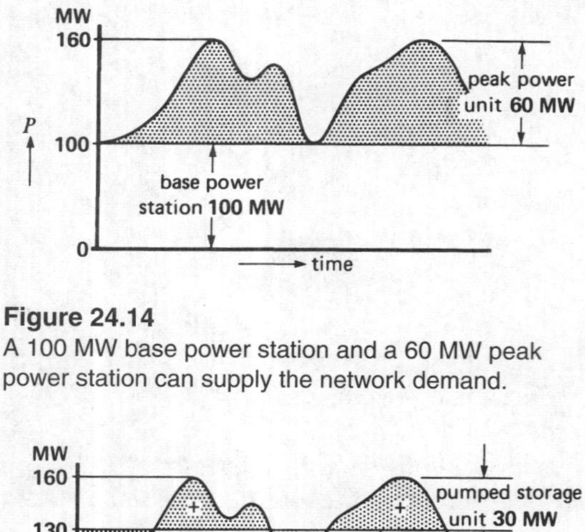

Figure 24.14
A 100 MW base power station and a 60 MW peak power station can supply the network demand.

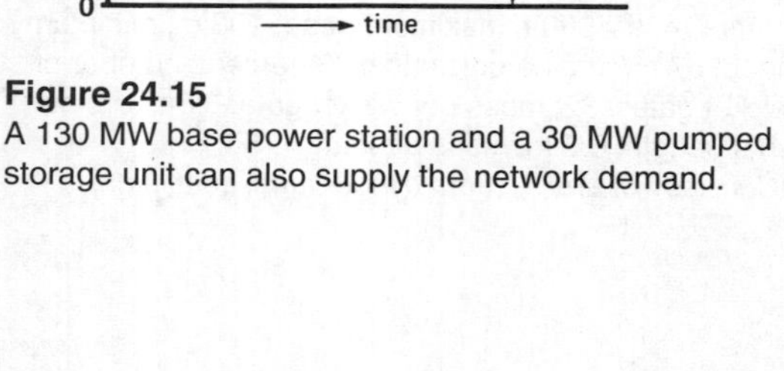

Figure 24.15
A 130 MW base power station and a 30 MW pumped storage unit can also supply the network demand.

This second solution has two advantages:

1. The base-power station is larger and, consequently, more efficient.
2. The peak-power station is much smaller and, therefore, less costly.

Large blocks of energy can only be stored mechanically, and that is why we often resort to a hydraulic pumped-storage station. Such a peak-power generating station consists of an upper and a lower reservoir of water connected by a penstock and an associated generating/pumping unit. During system peaks the station acts like an ordinary hydropower generating station, delivering electrical energy as water flows from the upper to the lower reservoir. However, during light load periods the process is reversed. The generator then operates as a synchronous motor, driving the turbine as an enormous pump. Water now flows from the lower to the upper reservoir, thereby storing energy in preparation for the next system peak (Fig. 24.16).

The generating/pumping cycle is repeated once or twice per day, depending on the nature of the system load. Peak-power generators have ratings between 50 MW and 500 MW. They are reversible because the direction of rotation has to be changed when the turbine operates as a pump. Starting such big synchronous motors puts a heavy load on the transmission line, and special methods must be used to bring them up to speed. Pony motors are often used, but static electronic frequency converters are also gaining ground. (A *pony motor* is a machine that brings a much larger machine up to speed.)

Pumped-storage installations operating in conjunction with nuclear plants make a very attractive combination because nuclear plants give best efficiency when operating at constant load.

THERMAL GENERATING STATIONS

The hydraulic resources of most modern countries are already fully developed. Consequently, we have to rely on thermal and nuclear stations to supply the growing need for electrical energy.

Figure 24.16
This pumped storage station in Tennessee pumps water from Lake Nickajack to the top of Raccoon Mountain, where it is stored in a 2 km^2 (≈500 acres) reservoir, giving a 316 m head. The four alternator/pump units can each deliver 425 MVA during the system peaks. The units can be changed over from generators to pumps in a few minutes.
(Courtesy of Tennessee Valley Authority)

Thermal generating stations produce electricity from the heat released by the combustion of coal, oil, or natural gas. Most stations have ratings between 200 MW and 1500 MW so as to attain the high efficiency and economy of a large installation. Such a station has to be seen to appreciate its enormous complexity and size.

Thermal stations are usually located near a river or lake because large quantities of cooling water are needed to condense the steam as it exhausts from the turbines.

The efficiency of thermal generating stations is always low because of the inherent low efficiency of the turbines. The maximum efficiency of any machine that converts heat energy into mechanical energy is given by the equation

$$\eta = (1 - T_2/T_1)\ 100 \qquad (24.2)$$

where

η = efficiency of the machine [%]
T_1 = temperature of the gas entering the turbine [K]
T_2 = temperature of the gas leaving the turbine [K]

In most thermal generating stations the gas is steam. In order to obtain a high efficiency, the quotient T_2/T_1 should be as small as possible. However, temperature T_2 cannot be lower than the ambient temperature, which is usually about 20°C. As a result, T_2 cannot be less than

$$T_2 = 20° + 273° = 293 \text{ K}$$

This means that to obtain high efficiency, T_1 should be as high as possible. The problem is that we cannot use temperatures above those that steel and other metals can safely withstand, bearing in mind the corresponding high steam pressures. It turns out that the highest feasible temperature T_1 is about 550°C. As a result,

$$T_3 = 550° + 273° = 823 \text{ K}$$

It follows that the maximum possible efficiency of a turbine driven by steam that enters at 823 K and exists at 293 K is

$$\eta = (1 - 293/823)\ 100 = 64.4\%$$

Due to other losses, some of the most efficient steam turbines have efficiencies of 45%. This means that 65% of the thermal energy is lost during the thermal-to-mechanical conversion process. The enormous loss of heat and how to dispose of it represents one of the major aspects of a thermal generating station.

24.12 Makeup of a thermal generating station

The basic structure and principal components of a thermal generating station are shown in Fig. 24.17. They are itemized and described below.

- A huge boiler (1) acts as a furnace, transferring heat from the burning fuel to row upon row of water tubes S_1, which entirely surround the flames. Water is kept circulating through the tubes by a pump P_1.
- A drum (2) containing water and steam under high pressure produces the steam required by the turbines. It also receives the water delivered by boiler-feed pump P_3. Steam races toward the high-pressure turbine HP after having passed through superheater S_2. The superheater, composed of a series of tubes surrounding the flames, raises the steam temperature by about 200°C. This increase in temperature ensures that the steam is absolutely dry and raises the overall efficiency of the station.
- A high-pressure (HP) turbine (3) converts thermal energy into mechanical energy by letting the steam expand as it moves through the turbine blades. The temperature and pressure at the output of the turbine are, therefore, less than at the input. In order to raise the thermal efficiency and to prevent premature condensation, the steam passes through a reheater S_3, composed of a third set of heated tubes.
- The medium-pressure (MP) turbine (4) is similar to the high-pressure turbine, except that it is bigger so that the steam may expand still more.

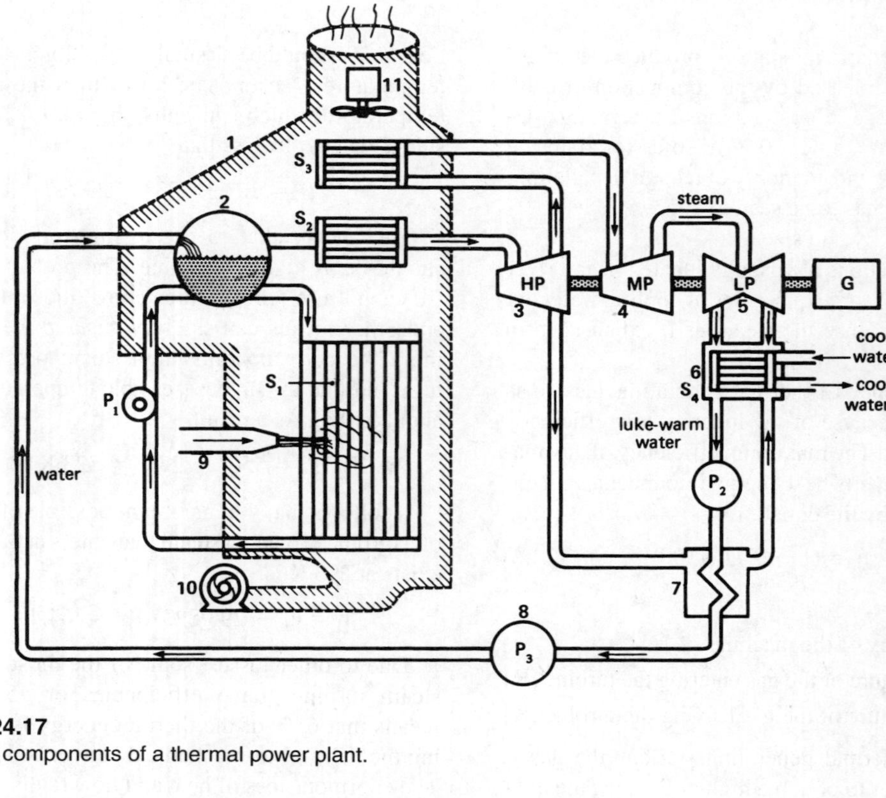

Figure 24.17
Principal components of a thermal power plant.

- The low-pressure (LP) turbine (5) is composed of two identical left-hand and right-hand sections. The turbine sections remove the remaining available energy from the steam (Fig. 24.18). The steam flowing out of LP expands into an almost perfect vacuum created by the condenser (6).
- Condenser (6) causes the steam to condense by letting it flow over cooling pipes S_4. Cold water from an outside source, such as a river or lake, flows through the pipes, thus carrying away the heat. It is the condensing steam that creates the vacuum.

A condensate pump P_2 removes the lukewarm condensed steam and drives it through a reheater (7) toward a feedwater pump (8).

- The reheater (7) is a heat exchanger. It receives hot steam, bled off from high-pressure turbine HP, to raise the temperature of the feedwater. Thermodynamic studies show that the overall thermal efficiency is improved when some steam is bled off this way, rather than letting it follow its normal course through all three turbines.
- The burners (9) supply and control the amount of gas, oil, or coal injected into the boiler. Coal is pulverized before it is injected. Similarly, heavy bunker oil is preheated and injected as an atomized jet to improve surface contact (and combustion) with the surrounding air.
- A forced-draft fan (10) furnishes the enormous quantities of air needed for combustion (Fig. 24.19).
- An induced-draft fan (11) carries the gases and other products of combustion toward cleansing apparatus and from there to the stack and the outside air.
- Generator G, directly coupled to all three turbines, converts the mechanical energy into electrical energy.

In practice, a steam station has hundreds of other components and accessories to ensure high efficiency, safety, and economy. For example, control

Figure 24.18
Low-pressure section of a 375 MW, 3600 r/min steam-turbine generator set, showing the radial blades.
(Courtesy of General Electric)

Figure 24.19
This forced-draft fan provides 455 m^3/s of air at a pressure difference of 5.8 kPa for a thermal power station. It is driven by a 3-phase induction motor rated 12 000 hp (8955 kW), 60 Hz, 890 r/min.
(Courtesy of Novenco Inc.)

valves regulate the amount of steam flowing to the turbines; complex water purifiers maintain the required cleanliness and chemical composition of the feedwater; and oil pumps keep the bearings properly lubricated. However, the basic components we have just described enable us to understand the operation and some of the basic problems of a thermal station.

24.13 Turbines

The low-, medium-, and high-pressure turbines possess a series of blades mounted on the drive shaft (Fig. 24.18). The steam is deflected by the blades, producing a powerful torque. The blades are made of special steel to withstand the high temperature and intense centrifugal forces.

The HP, MP, and LP turbines are coupled together to drive a common generator. However, in some large installations the HP turbine drives one generator while the MP and LP turbines drive another one having the same rating.

24.14 Condenser

We have seen that about one-half the energy produced in the boiler has to be removed from the steam when it exhausts into the condenser. Consequently, enormous quantities of cooling water are needed to carry away the heat. The temperature of the cooling water increases typically by 5°C to 10°C as it flows through the condenser tubes. The condensed steam (condensate) usually has a temperature between 27°C and 33°C and the corresponding absolute pressure is a near-vacuum of about 5 kPa. The cooling water temperature is only a few degrees below the condensate temperature (see Fig. 24.20).

24.15 Cooling towers

If the thermal station is located in a dry region, or far away from a river or lake, we still have to cool the condenser, one way or another. We often use *evaporation* to produce the cooling effect. To understand the principle, consider a lake that exposes a large surface to the surrounding air. A lake evaporates continually, even at low temperatures, and it is known that for every kilogram of water that evaporates, the lake loses 2.4 MJ of heat. Consequently, evaporation causes the lake to cool down.

Figure 24.20
Condenser rated at 220 MW. Note the large pipes feeding cooling water into and out of the condenser. The condenser is as important as the boiler in thermal and nuclear power stations.
(Courtesy of Foster-Wheeler Energy Corporation)

Consider now a tub containing 100 kg of water at a certain temperature. If we can somehow cause 1 kg of water to evaporate, the temperature of the remaining 99 kg will inevitably drop by 5.8°C. We conclude that whenever 1 percent of a body of water evaporates, the temperature of the remaining water drops by 5.8°C. Evaporation is, therefore, a very effective cooling process.

But how can we produce evaporation? Surprisingly, all that is needed is to expose a large surface of water to the surrounding air. The simplest way to do this is to break up the water into small droplets, and blow air through this artificial rain.

In the case of a thermal station, the warm cooling water flowing out of the condenser is piped to the top of a cooling tower (Fig. 24.21) where it is broken up into small droplets. As the droplets fall toward the open reservoir below, evaporation takes place and the droplets are chilled. The cool water is pumped from the reservoir and recirculated through the condenser, where it again removes heat from the condensing steam. The cycle then repeats. Approximately 2 percent of the cooling water that flows through the condenser is lost by evaporation. This loss can be made up by a stream, or small lake.

24.16 Boiler-feed pump

The boiler-feed pump drives the feedwater into the high-pressure drum. The high back pressure together with the large volume of water flowing through the pump requires a very powerful motor to drive it. In modern steam stations the pumping power represents about 1 percent of the generator output. Although this appears to be a significant loss, we must remember that the energy expended in the pump is later recovered when the high-pressure steam flows through the turbines. Consequently, the energy supplied to the feed pump motor is not really lost, except for the small portion consumed by the losses in the motor and pump.

Figure 24.21
Cooling tower installed in a nuclear power station in Oregon. The generator output is a 1280 MVA at a power factor of 0.88. Tower characteristics: height: 152 m; diameter at the base: 117 m; diameter at the top: 76 m; cooling water: 27 m^3/s; water loss by evaporation: 0.7 m^3/s. The temperature of the cooling water drops from 44.5° to 24° as it passes through the tower. *(Courtesy of Portland General Electric Company)*

24.17 Energy flow diagram for a steam plant

Modern thermal generating stations are very similar throughout the world because all designers strive for high efficiency at lowest cost. This means that materials are strained to the limits of safety as far as temperature, pressure, and centrifugal forces are concerned. Because the same materials are available to all, the resulting steam plants are necessarily similar. Fig. 24.22 shows a typical 540 MW turbine-generator set, and Fig. 24.23 is a view of the control room.

Most modern boilers furnish steam at a temperature of 550°C and a pressure of 16.5 MPa. The overall efficiency (electrical output/thermal input) is then about 40 percent. The relative amounts of energy, steam flow, losses, and so forth, do not change very much, provided the temperature and pressure have the approximate values indicated above. This enables us to draw a diagram showing the energy flow, steam flow, water flow, and so on, in a reduced-scale model of a typical thermal generating

Figure 24.22
This 540 MW steam-turbine generator set runs at 3600 r/min, generating a frequency of 60 Hz. The low-pressure turbine and alternator are in the background. *(Courtesy of General Electric)*

Figure 24.23
Control room of the 540 MW generator set.
(Courtesy of General Electric)

station. Fig. 24.24 shows such a model producing 12 MW of electrical power.

Using this model, we can estimate the characteristics of any thermal power station. For example, a 480 MW station (40 times more powerful than the model) has the following approximate characteristics:

Electric power output	40 × 12 MW	480 MW
Coal consumption	40 × 1 kg/s	40 kg/s
Air intake	40 × 10 kg/s	400 kg/s
Boiler thermal power	40 × 30 MW	1 200 MW
Steam output	40 × 8 kg/s	320 kg/s
Cooling water	40 × 360 kg/s	14 400 kg/s
Heat carried away by the cooling water	40 × 15 MW	600 MW

If a large river or lake is not available and a cooling tower is required, it would have to evaporate

$$q = 2\% \times 14\,400 = 288 \text{ kg/s}$$

of cooling water. This loss by evaporation has to be made up by a local source of water.

24.18 Thermal stations and the environment

The products of combustion of thermal generating stations are an increasing subject of concern, due to their impact on the environment.

Carbon dioxide (CO_2), sulfur dioxide (SO_2), and water are the main products of combustion when oil, coal, or gas are burned. Carbon dioxide and water produce no immediate environmental effects, but sulfur dioxide creates substances that give rise to acid rain. Dust and fly ash are other pollutants that may reach the atmosphere. Natural gas pro-

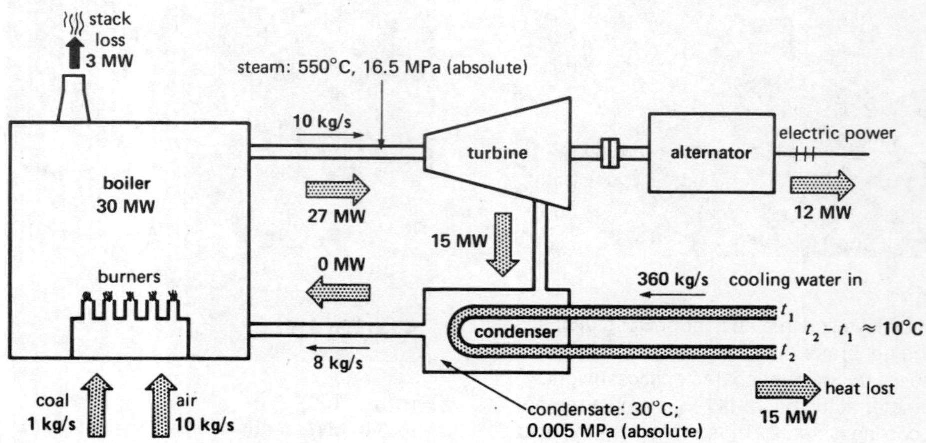

Figure 24.24
Scale model of a typical thermal generating station.

duces only water and CO_2. This explains why gas is used (rather than coal or oil), when atmospheric pollution must be reduced to a minimum.

A good example of pollution control is the large Eraring generating station located in Newcastle, Australia, about 100 km north of Sydney (Fig. 24.25). It is equipped with a special fabric filter flue gas cleaning system (Fig. 24.26). The fabric filters act like huge vacuum cleaners to remove particles from the boiler-gas flue stream. The fabric filter for each boiler is composed of 48 000 filter bags, each 5 m long and 16 cm in diameter (Fig. 24.27). When a boiler operates at full capacity, they capture dust particles at the rate of 28 kg/s. A substantial proportion of this material is later mixed with concrete for road-building projects. The following technical specifications enable us to appreciate the size of this station.

Electrical data

number of generators: 4
power per generator: 660 MW
speed: 3000 r/min
voltage: 23 000 V
frequency: 50 Hz, phases: 3

Thermal and mechanical data

number of steam turbines: 4
number of condensers: 4
number of boilers: 4
steam flow per turbine: 560 kg/s
steam temperature: 540°C
steam pressure: 16.55 MPa
cooling water per condenser: 21 000 kg/s
coal consumption per boiler: 51.5 kg/s
dust captured by cleaning system: 28 kg/s

Figure 24.25
View of the Eraring Power Station in Newcastle, Australia. The large building on the left is the turbine-generator hall: 27 m wide × 38 m high × 418 m long. To the right can be seen the four structures that house the steam boilers. A portion of the flue gas cleaning system can be seen between the emission stack in the foreground and the boiler structures. *(Courtesy of the Electricity Commission of New South Wales)*

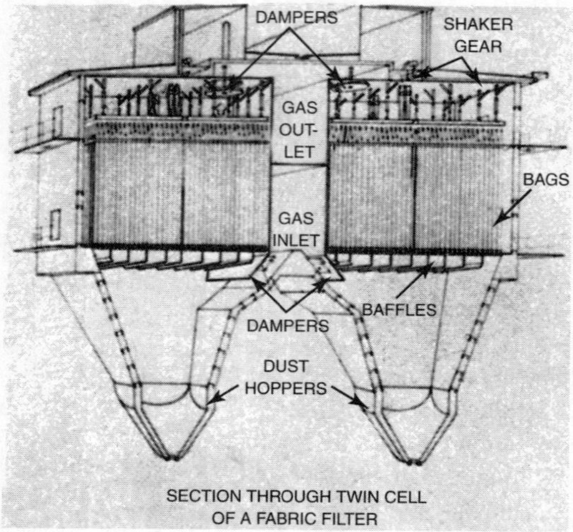

Figure 24.26
General construction of the flue gas cleaning system showing the filter bags that capture the dust, which then falls into the hoppers below.
(Courtesy of Electricity Commission of New South Wales)

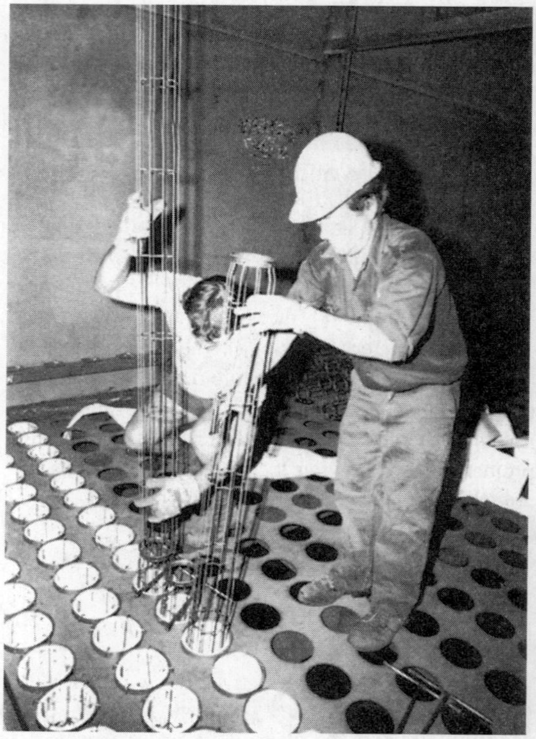

Figure 24.27
Installation of the fabric filter bags. Each bag is 15 m long and 16 cm in diameter.
(Courtesy of Electricity Commission of New South Wales)

length of one turbine-generator unit: 50 m
weight of one turbine-generator unit: 1342 tons
number of emission stacks: 2
height of emission stack: 200 m
outside diameter at bottom: 20 m
outside diameter at top: 11.6 m

Another interesting feature is that coal for the station is brought in by conveyor belts from two mines that are only 1.5 km and 4.5 km away. Thus, the station is ideally located near its source of fuel and near its source of cooling water, on the shore of Lake Macquarie.

NUCLEAR GENERATING STATIONS

Nuclear stations produce electricity from the heat released by a *nuclear reaction*. When the nucleus of an atom splits in two (a process called atomic fission), a considerable amount of energy is released. Note that a chemical reaction, such as the combustion of coal, produces only a rearrangement of the atoms, without in any way affecting their nuclei.

A nuclear station is identical to a thermal station, except that the boiler is replaced by a nuclear reactor. The reactor contains the fissile material that generates the heat. A nuclear station, therefore, contains a synchronous generator, steam turbine, condenser, and so on, similar to those found in a conventional thermal station. The overall efficiency is also similar (between 30 and 40 percent), and a cooling system must be provided for. Consequently, nuclear stations are also located close to rivers and lakes. In dry areas, cooling towers are installed. Owing to these similarities, we will only examine the operating principle of the reactor itself.

24.19 Composition of an atomic nucleus; isotopes

The nucleus of an atom contains two types of particles—protons and neutrons. The proton carries a positive charge, equal to the negative charge on an electron. The neutron, as its name implies, has no electric charge. Neutrons are, therefore, neither attracted to nor repelled by protons and electrons.

Protons and neutrons have about the same mass, and both weigh 1840 times as much as electrons do. The mass of an atom is concentrated in its nucleus.

The number of protons and neutrons in the nucleus depends upon the element. Furthermore, because an atom is electrically neutral, the number of electrons is equal to the number of protons. Table 24A gives the atomic structure of a few important elements used in nuclear reactors. For example, there are two types of hydrogen atoms that can be distinguished from each other only by the makeup of the nucleus. First, there is ordinary hydrogen (H), whose nucleus contains 1 proton and no neutrons. Next, there is a rare form, deuterium (D), whose nuclei contain 1 neutron, in addition to the usual proton. This rare form is called an *isotope* of hydrogen.

When two atoms of ordinary hydrogen unite with one atom of oxygen, we obtain ordinary water (H_2O) called *light* water. On the other hand, if 2 atoms of deuterium unite with 1 atom of oxygen, we obtain a molecule of *heavy* water (D_2O). The oceans contain about 1 kg of heavy water for every 7000 kg of sea water.

In the same way, two isotopes of uranium are found in nature: uranium 238 (^{238}U) and uranium 235 (^{235}U). Each contains 92 protons, but ^{238}U has 146 neutrons and ^{235}U has 143. Uranium 238 is very common, but the isotope ^{235}U is rare.

Uranium 235 and heavy water deserve our attention because both are essential to the operation of the nuclear reactors we are about to discuss.

24.20 The source of uranium

Where does uranium come from? It is obtained from the ore found in uranium mines. This ore contains the compound U_3O_8 (3 atoms of uranium and 8 atoms of oxygen). It so happens that U_3O_8 is actually composed of $^{238}UO_8$ and $^{235}UO_8$ in the relatively precise ratio of 1398:10.

In other words, the ore contains 1398 parts of the less interesting ^{238}U for every 10 parts of the isotope ^{235}U. It is very difficult to separate $^{238}UO_8$ from $^{235}UO_8$ because they possess identical chemical properties.

In order to use these substances in nuclear reactors, they are processed into uranium dioxide (UO_2). The natural UO_2 again contains $^{238}UO_2$ and $^{235}UO_2$ in the ratio of 1398:10.

Some nuclear reactors require UO_2 that has more of the isotope ^{235}U than natural UO_2 does. This is produced by an enrichment process whereby the ratio of $^{235}UO_2$ to $^{238}UO_2$ is raised to 50:1398 rather than the natural ratio of 10:1398. In this enrichment process a lot of $^{238}UO_2$ is obtained as a by-product that must be stored. As we shall see, this by-product also has useful applications.

TABLE 24A ATOMIC STRUCTURE OF SOME ELEMENTS

Element	Symbol	Protons	Electrons	Neutrons	Mass number (neutrons + protons)
hydrogen	H	1	1	0	1
deuterium	D	1	1	1	2
tritium	^3H	1	1	2	3
helium	He	2	2	2	4
carbon	C	6	6	6	12
iron	Fe	26	26	30	56
uranium 235	^{235}U	92	92	143	235
uranium 238	^{238}U	92	92	146	238

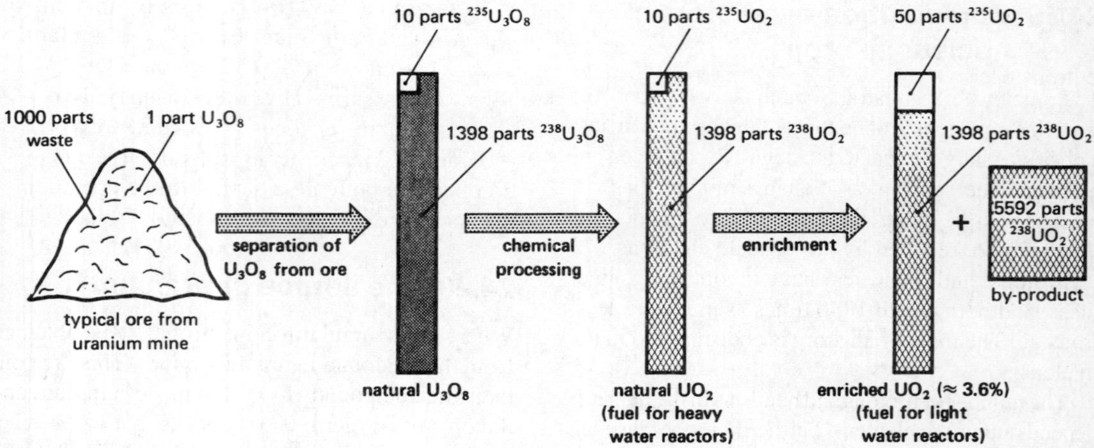

Figure 24.28
Various steps in the manufacture of nuclear fuel for heavy-water and light-water reactors. This extremely simplified diagram shows that in the process of enriching uranium dioxide, it is inevitable that large amounts of $^{238}UO_2$ remain as a by-product.

The process of converting uranium ore into these uranium derivatives is shown in highly simplified form in Fig. 24.28.

24.21 Energy released by atomic fission

When the nucleus of an atom fissions, it splits in two. The total mass of the two atoms formed in this way is usually less than that of the original atom. If there is a loss in mass, energy is released according to Einstein's equation:

$$E = mc^2 \tag{24.3}$$

where

E = energy released [J]

m = loss of mass [kg]

c = speed of light [3×10^8 m/s]

An enormous amount of energy is released because, according to this formula, a loss in mass of only one gram produces 9×10^{13} J, which is equivalent to the heat given off by burning 3 thousand *tons* of coal. Uranium is one of those elements that loses mass when it fissions. However, uranium 235 is fissionable, whereas uranium 238 is not, and so large separating plants have been built to isolate molecules containing ^{235}U from those containing ^{238}U.

24.22 Chain reaction

How can we provoke the fission of a uranium atom? One way is to bombard its nucleus with neutrons. A neutron makes an excellent projectile because it is not repelled as it approaches the nucleus and, if its speed is not too great, it has a good chance of scoring a hit. If the impact is strong enough, the nucleus will split in two, releasing energy. The fission of one atom of ^{235}U releases 218 MeV of energy, mainly in the form of heat. Fission is a very violent reaction on an atomic scale, and it produces a second important effect: It ejects 2 or 3 neutrons that move at high speed away from the broken nucleus. These neutrons collide with other uranium atoms, breaking them up, and a chain reaction quickly takes place, releasing a tremendous amount of heat.

This is the principle that causes atomic bombs to explode. Although a uranium mine also releases neutrons, the concentration of ^{235}U atoms is too low to produce a chain reaction.

In the case of a nuclear reactor, we have to slow down the neutrons to increase their chance of striking other uranium nuclei. Toward this end, small fissionable masses of uranium fuel (UO_2) are immersed in a *moderator*. The moderator may be ordinary water, heavy water, graphite, or any other material that can slow down neutrons without absorbing them. By using an appropriate geometrical distribution of the uranium fuel within the moderator, the speed of the neutrons can be reduced so they have the required velocity to initiate other fusions. Only then will a chain reaction take place, causing the reactor to *go critical*.

As soon as the chain reaction starts, the temperature rises rapidly. To keep it at an acceptable level, a liquid or gas has to flow rapidly through the reactor to carry away the heat. This *coolant* may be heavy water, ordinary water, liquid sodium, or a gas like helium or carbon dioxide. The hot coolant moves in a closed circuit which includes a heat exchanger. The latter transfers the heat to a steam generator that drives the turbines (Fig. 24.29). Thus, contrary to what its name would lead us to believe, the coolant is not cool but searingly hot.

24.23 Types of nuclear reactors

There are several types of reactors, but the following are the most important:

1. ***Pressure-Water Reactor (PWR).*** Water is used as a coolant and it is kept under such high pressure that it cannot boil off into steam. Ordinary water, as in light-water reactors may be used, or heavy water, as in CANDU* reactors.

2. ***Boiling-Water Reactors (BWR).*** The coolant in this reactor is ordinary water boiling under high pressure and releasing steam. This eliminates the need for a heat exchanger, because the steam circulates directly through the turbines. However, as in all light-water reactors, enriched uranium dioxide must be used containing about 3 percent ^{235}U.

3. ***High-Temperature Gas Reactor (HTGR).*** This reactor uses an inert gas coolant such as helium or carbon dioxide. Due to the high operating tempera-

* CANDU: Canada Deuterium Uranium, developed by the Atomic Energy Commission of Canada.

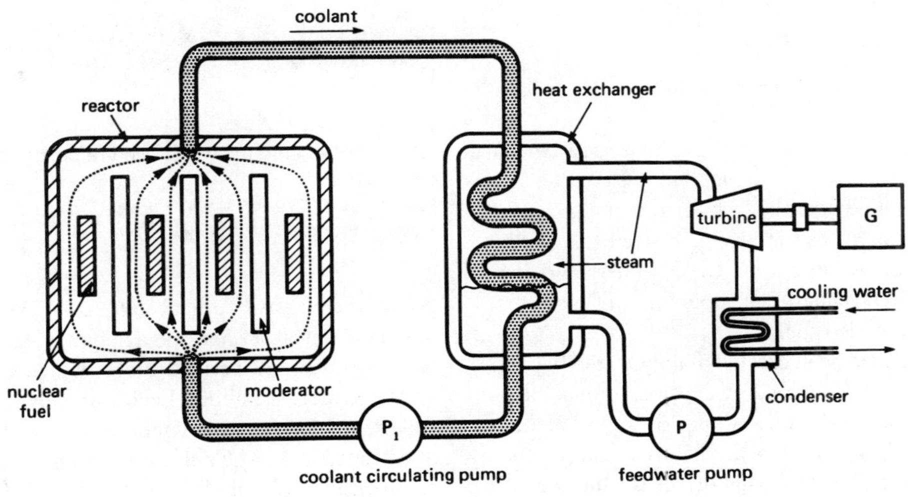

Figure 24.29
Schematic diagram of a nuclear power station.

Figure 24.30
Aerial view of a light-water nuclear generating station. The large rectangular building in the foreground houses a 667 MVA, 90 percent power factor, 19 kV, 60 Hz, 1800 r/min turbo-generator set; the circular building surrounds the reactor.
(Courtesy of Connecticut Yankee Atomic Power Company; photo by Georges Betancourt)

ture (typically 750°C), graphite is used as a moderator. The steam created by the heat exchanger is as hot as that produced in a conventional coal-fired steam boiler. Consequently, the overall efficiency of HTGR stations is about 40 percent.

4. Fast Breeder Reactor (FBR). This reactor has the remarkable ability to both generate heat and create additional nuclear fuel while it is in operation.

24.24 Example of a light-water reactor

Reactors that use ordinary water as a moderator are similar to those using heavy water, but the uranium-dioxide fuel has to be enriched. Enrichment means that the fuel bundles contain between 2 and 4 percent of ^{235}U, the remainder being ^{238}U. This enables us to reduce the size of the reactor for a given power output. On the other hand, the reactor has to be shut down about once a year to replace the expended fuel.

The generated heat, created mainly by the fission of uranium 235, is carried away by a coolant such as ordinary water, liquid sodium, or a gas such as CO_2. As it flows through the heat exchanger, the coolant creates the steam that drives the turbine.

A typical nuclear power station (Figs. 24.30 and 24.31) possesses a light-water reactor that is composed of a massive vertical steel tank having an external diameter of 4.5 m and a height of 12.5 m. The tank contains 157 vertical tubes, which can lodge 157 large fuel assemblies. Each assembly is 3 m long and groups 204 fuel rods containing a total of 477 kg of enriched UO_2. The nuclear reaction is kept under control by 45 special-alloy control rods. When these rods are gradually lowered into the moderator, they absorb more and more neutrons. Consequently, they

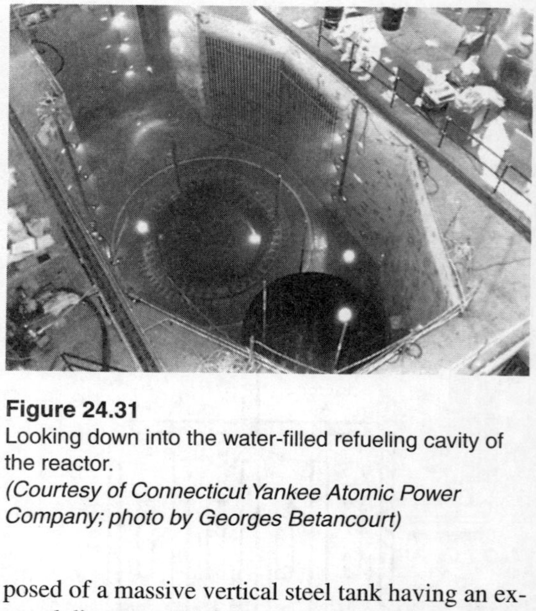

Figure 24.31
Looking down into the water-filled refueling cavity of the reactor.
(Courtesy of Connecticut Yankee Atomic Power Company; photo by Georges Betancourt)

control the rate of the nuclear reaction and, hence, the amount of heat released by the reactor.

The nuclear station drives a 3-phase, 667 MVA, 90 percent power factor, 19 kV, 60 Hz, 1800 r/min synchronous generator.

24.25 Example of a heavy-water reactor

The CANDU reactor uses heavy water, both as moderator and coolant. It differs from all other reactors in that it uses *natural* uranium dioxide as a fuel. One of the biggest installations of its kind is located at Pickering, a few kilometers east of Toronto, Canada. The nuclear station has 4 reactors. Each reactor is coupled to 12 heat exchangers that provide the interface between the heavy-water coolant and the ordinary steam that drives the turbines (Fig. 24.32).

Each reactor is enclosed in a large horizontal vessel (calandria) having a diameter of 8 m and a length of 8.25 m. The calandria possesses 390 horizontal tubes, each housing 12 fuel bundles containing 22.2 kg of UO_2. Each bundle releases about 372.5 kW while it is in operation. Because there is a total of 4680 bundles, the reactor develops 1740 MW of thermal power.

Twelve pumps, each driven by an 1100 kW motor, push the heavy-water coolant through the reactor and the heat exchangers in a closed loop. The heat exchangers produce the steam to drive the four turbines. The steam exhausts into a condenser that is cooled by water drawn from Lake Ontario.

Each turbine drives a 3-phase, 635 MVA, 85 percent power factor, 24 kV, 1800 r/min, 60 Hz alternator.

The fuel bundles are inserted at one end of the calandria and, after a 19-month stay in the tubes, they are withdrawn from the other end. The bundles are inserted and removed on a continuous basis—an average of nine bundles per day.

Table 24B compares the typical characteristics of light-water and heavy-water reactors.

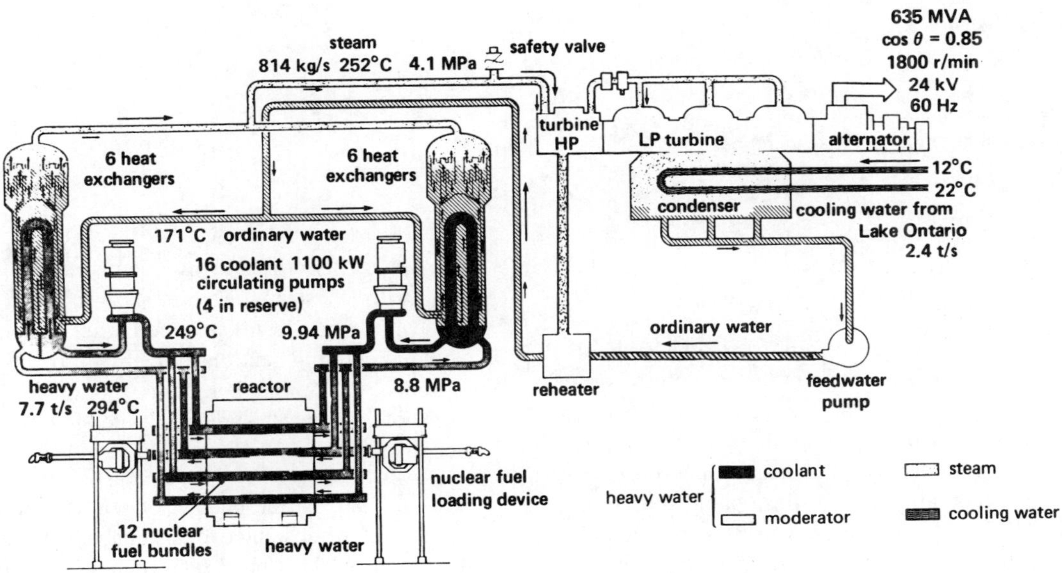

Figure 24.32
Simplified schematic diagram of a CANDU nuclear generating unit composed of one heavy-water reactor driving one alternator.
(Courtesy of Atomic Energy of Canada)

TABLE 24B TYPICAL LIGHT-WATER AND HEAVY-WATER REACTORS

	Light-water reactor	Heavy-water reactor
Reactor Vessel		
external diameter	4.5 m	8 m
length	12.5 m	8.25 m
vessel thickness	274 mm	25.4 mm
weight empty	416 t	604 t
position	vertical	horizontal
number of fuel canals	157	390
type of fuel	enriched UO_2 (3.3%)	natural UO_2
total mass of fuel	75 t	104 t
Moderator		
type	light-water	heavy-water
volume	13.3 m^3	242 m^3
Reactor Cooling		
heat produced in reactor	1825 MW	1661 MW
coolant	light-water	heavy-water
volume	249 m^3	130 m^3
flow rate	128 t/s	7.73 t/s
coolant temperature entering the reactor	285°C	249°C
coolant temperature leaving the reactor	306°C	294°C
coolant pumps	4	12
total pump power	12 MW	14 MW
Electrical Output		
3-phase, 1800 r/min, 60 Hz synchronous generator	600 MW	540 MW

24.26 Principle of the fast breeder reactor

A fast breeder reactor differs from other reactors because it can extract more of the available energy in the nuclear fuel. It possesses a central core containing fissionable plutonium 239 (^{239}Pu). The core is surrounded by a blanket composed of substances containing nonfissionable uranium 238 (^{238}U). No moderator is used; consequently, the high-speed (fast) neutrons generated by the fissioning ^{239}Pu bombard the nonfissionable atoms of ^{238}U. This nuclear reaction produces two important results:

a. The heat released by the fissioning core can be used to drive a steam turbine.
b. Some atoms of ^{238}U in the surrounding blanket capture the flying neutrons, thereby becoming fissionable ^{239}Pu. In other words, the passive atoms of uranium 238 are transmuted into fissionable atoms of plutonium 239.

As time goes by, the blanket of nonfissionable ^{238}U is gradually transmuted to fissionable ^{239}Pu and waste products. The blanket is periodically removed and the materials are processed to recover the substances containing ^{239}Pu. The nuclear fuel recovered is placed in the central core to generate heat and to produce still more fuel in a newly relined blanket of substances containing uranium 238.

This process can be repeated until nearly 80 percent of the available energy in the uranium is extracted. This is much more efficient than the 2 percent now being extracted by conventional reactors.

The breeder reactor is particularly well adapted to complement existing light-water reactors. The reason is that a great deal of ^{238}U is available as a byproduct in the manufacture of enriched ^{235}U (see Fig. 24.28). This otherwise useless material (now being stored) could be used to surround the core of a fast breeder reactor. By capturing fast neutrons, it could be rejuvenated, as explained above, until most of the potential energy in the uranium is used up.

24.27 Nuclear fusion

We have seen that splitting the nucleus of a heavy element such as uranium results in a decrease in mass and a release of energy. We can also produce energy by *combining* the nuclei of two light elements in a process called *nuclear fusion*. For example, energy is released by the fusion of an atom of deuterium with an atom of tritium. However, owing to the strong repulsion between the two nuclei (both are positive), they only unite (fuse) when they approach each other at high speed. The required velocity is close to the speed of light and corresponds to a thermodynamic temperature of several million degrees. If both the atomic concentration and speed are high enough, a self-sustaining chain reaction will result.

We can, therefore, produce heat by the fusion of two elements, and the hydrogen bomb is a good example of this principle. Unfortunately, we run into almost insurmountable problems when we try to *control* the fusion reaction, as we must do in a nuclear reactor. Basically, scientists have not yet succeeded in confining and controlling high-speed particles without at the same time slowing them down.

A major worldwide research effort is being devoted to solve this problem. If scientists succeed in domesticating nuclear fusion, it could mean the end of the energy shortage because hydrogen is the most common element on earth.

WIND-GENERATING STATIONS

Energy drawn from the wind offers an interesting supplement to coal and gas-fired power stations that generate electricity. In this section, we examine the properties of the wind and how it is currently used to generate electric power.

24.28 Properties of the wind

The wind possesses energy by virtue of its mass and speed. For example, consider a cubic meter of air moving at a speed of 10 m/s. Knowing that a cubic meter has a mass of about 1.2 kg, it possesses a kinetic energy given by

$$E_k = 1/2\, mv^2 \qquad (3.7)$$
$$= 1/2 \times 1.2 \times 10^2 = 60 \text{ J}$$

If the air is slowed down by a mechanical device of some kind (such as a wind turbine) the wind will give up some of its kinetic energy. Consequently, the wind turbine will produce a mechanical power output that can be used to drive an electric generator.

Using Eq. 3.7, we can deduce that the inherent power of the wind is given by the approximate formula:

$$P_a = 0.6\, v^3 \qquad (24.4)$$

where

P_a = power per square meter facing the wind [W/m^2]

v = speed of the wind [m/s]

Equation 24.4 assumes that the wind, if harnessed, would continuously be brought to a standstill from its original speed *v*. In practice, it is impossible for a wind turbine to bring the wind to a complete stop. Consequently, the maximum power that can be extracted from the wind is about 30% to 40% of that given by Eq. 24.4.

As regards intensity, the wind is roughly classified as follows:

light breeze	3 m/s	11 km/h
moderate breeze	7 m/s	25 km/h
strong breeze	12 m/s	43 km/h
gale	18 m/s	65 km/h
hurricane	>32 m/s	>115 km/h

For wind-power applications, the utilizable wind speed lies between 5 m/s and 15 m/s.

In order to harness the wind, we must consider the following factors:

1. The speed of the wind can fluctuate by ±25% within a period of a few minutes.
2. The direction of the wind changes; therefore, the orientation of the wind turbine must be changed while the wind is blowing so as to extract the greatest amount of the available wind power.
3. The constancy and speed of the wind depend upon its location. Thus, before a satisfactory place can be selected, a yearly record of the direction, speed, and duration of the wind must be known.
4. Whenever the power of the wind exceeds that of the generator, means must be taken to limit the electric power.
5. When gale and hurricane winds come into play, the turbine blades must be pitched accordingly, or brought to a complete halt so as not to damage the turbine and its tower.
6. On account of their great height, the turbine blades are a natural target for lightning.
7. Snow and sleet during the winter demand particular attention.
8. The power generated by a wind farm usually has to be fed into an existing power grid.
9. Wind energy costs nothing and is absolutely pollution-free.

In discussing wind turbines, we will limit our remarks to the 3-blade types that generate electric power in the 100 kW to 3000 kW range (Fig. 24.38). Some wind turbines are designed to generate as much as 5 MW. In commercial applications, the wind turbines are grouped together in so-called wind farms.

In order to extract the maximum energy from the wind, the turbine speed of rotation must be a specific fraction of the wind speed. As a rule of thumb, and depending upon the rated power of the turbine, the tip speed of the blades should lie between 4 and 8 times the wind speed. Since the wind speed can cover a broad range, the speed of rotation of the turbine should ideally be variable. However, many wind turbines are designed to operate at essentially constant speed.

Example 24-2

A 400 kW, 3-blade wind turbine is designed to deliver full power at a wind speed of 15 m/s. The blades have a length of 14 m and the rated speed of the turbine is 48 r/min.

Calculate

a. The area swept out by the turbine blades
b. The wind power available to drive the turbine
c. The ratio of the 400 kW output to the available wind power, in percent
d. The tip speed of the turbine blades
e. The ratio of the tip speed to wind speed

Solution

a. Area swept out by the turbine blades

$$A = \pi r^2 = \pi \times 14^2 = 616 \text{ m}^2$$

b. Available wind power per square meter

$$P_a = 0.6\, v^3 \tag{24.4}$$

$$= 0.6 \times 15^3 = 2025 \text{ W/m}^2$$

Wind power available to drive the turbine

$$P = P_a A = 2025 \times 616 = 1\,247\,400 \text{ W}$$
$$= 1247 \text{ kW}$$

c. $$\frac{\text{generator output power}}{\text{available wind power}} = \frac{400 \text{ kW}}{1247 \text{ kW}}$$

$$= 0.3208 = 32\%$$

d. Circumference of turbine at the blade tips

$$C = 2\pi r = 2 \times \pi \times 14 \text{ m} = 88 \text{ m}$$

$$\text{Tip speed} = C \times \text{r/min} = 88 \times 48 = 4224 \text{ m/min}$$
$$= 70.4 \text{ m/s or } 253 \text{ km/h}$$

e. Tip speed/wind speed = 70.4/15 = 4.7

24.29 Harnessing wind power

Five main methods are used to generate electricity from the wind:

1. Turbine driving a dc generator (Fig. 24.33)
2. Turbine driving an asychronous generator at constant speed (Fig. 24.34)
3. Turbine driving an asynchronous generator at variable speed (Fig. 24.35)
4. Turbine driving a doubly-fed induction generator at variable speed (Fig. 24.36)
5. Turbine driving a permanent magnet generator at variable speed (Fig. 24.37)

We now explain the basic principles of these wind-driven generators.

24.30 Wind turbine driving a dc generator

Figure 24.33 shows the blades (1) of a simple windmill supported on a tall mast (2) driving a dc generator (4). The gear box (3) multiplies the speed of the windmill 20 or 30 times, which permits the use of a relatively small generator.

The energy delivered by the generator is stored in a battery (5) which acts as a continuous and reliable source of power for the dc load (6). The load may consist of a few 12-volt lamps and a dc/ac converter to power a TV set. Such wind-driven dc generators are only used in remote locations, far from other sources of electric power. Their power is usually limited to a few hundred watts.

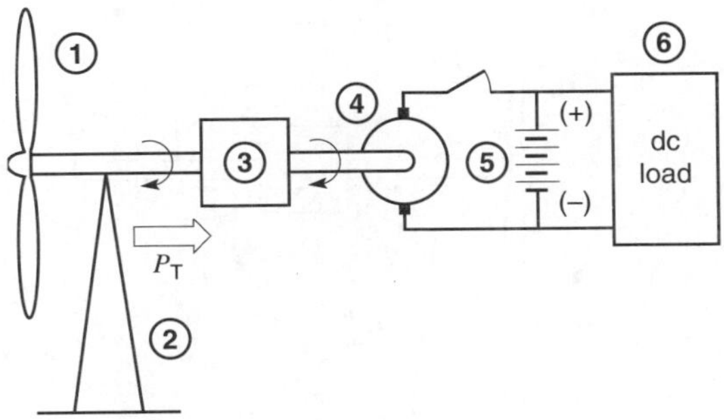

Figure 24.33
Windmill driving a small dc generator.

24.31 Turbine driving an asychronous generator at constant speed

Figure 24.34 shows a large commercial wind turbine (1) that drives a squirrel-cage induction generator (4) by means of a gear box (3). The stator of the generator is connected to the power grid (7) of the electric utility company by means of a step-up transformer (6). As a result, the magnetic flux in the stator rotates at synchronous speed corresponding to the grid frequency, and the rotor turns only slightly faster.

The turbine therefore runs at essentially constant speed. This means that it cannot extract the maximum amount of energy in the wind at all times.

The reactive power absorbed by the generator is provided by the capacitors (5). The power delivered to the grid is therefore close to unity power factor. The active power P_T developed by the turbine is transmitted to the electric utility grid, minus the losses in the gear box, the generator, and the transformer. The power of the asynchronous generators is typically between 100 kW and 800 kW.

Some asynchronous generators are equipped with two stator windings having 4 poles and 6 poles, respectively. When the wind speed is high, the lower number of poles is used because it corresponds to a higher generator speed. Conversely, the winding

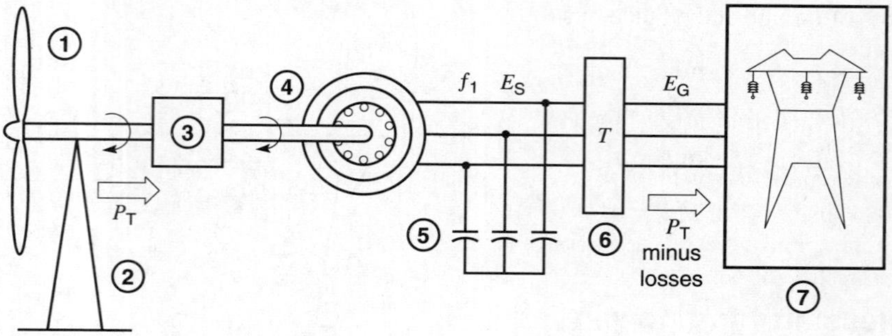

Figure 24.34
Wind turbine driving an asynchronous generator by means of a gear box. The speed of the generator is practically constant and so it cannot, at all times, extract the maximum energy from the wind.

with the higher number of poles is used when the wind speed is low. The transfer from one winding to the other is programmed to extract the maximum energy from the wind as its velocity changes.

The principle of the induction generator is described in Sections 14.15 and 15.8.

24.32 Turbine driving an asynchronous generator at variable speed

Figure 24.35 is similar to Fig. 24.34 except that the stator of the squirrel-cage induction generator is connected to a converter (5) that generates a variable frequency. As a result, the synchronous speed of the generator can be varied at will. It is varied according to the speed of the wind (captured by an anemometer) and in such a way as to extract the maximum amount of available energy. In effect, by imposing an optimal speed on the induction generator, we automatically impose the optimal speed on the wind turbine.

Converter (5) absorbs the active power P_T delivered by the turbine and, at the same time, it furnishes the reactive power drawn by the generator. The constant-voltage dc link between converter (5)

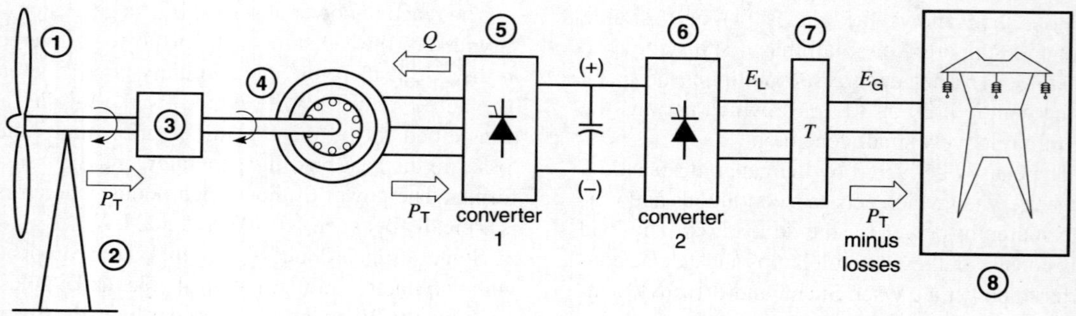

Figure 24.35
Wind turbine driving an asynchronous generator that is connected to a variable frequency converter. This enables the maximum amount of energy to be extracted from the wind at all times.

and converter (6) carries the active power to converter (6) where it is converted to 3-phase, 60 Hz (or 50 Hz) power, and thence to the electric utility grid. Note that each converter must carry the full power delivered by the generator. Some converters generate sinusoidal pulse-width modulated (PWM) voltages which prevent undesirable harmonics from reaching the generator and the power grid.

24.33 Turbine driving a doubly-fed induction generator

Figure 24.36 displays a wind turbine driving a wound-rotor induction generator (4), by way of a gear box (3). The electric utility grid voltage E_G is stepped down to a lower voltage E_S by means of a transformer (7).

Converter (6) transforms the line voltage E_S to a constant dc voltage E_d. Power can flow from the ac side to the dc side of this converter and vice versa.

Converter (5) transforms the dc voltage E_d into a voltage E_R whose magnitude, frequency, phase shift, and phase sequence can be varied at will. Once again, power can flow from the dc side to the ac side (and vice versa) of the converter.

The stator of the wound-rotor induction generator is connected directly to the power line whose frequency f is 50 Hz or 60 Hz. Consequently, the stator voltage E_S and its frequency are the same as those of the line voltage. The rotor is connected to converter (5) whose 3-phase output voltage E_R and frequency f_2 can be varied, as mentioned before. In some cases, converters (5) and (6) generate sinusoidal PWM voltages.

The wound-rotor machine is therefore fed from two sources E_S and E_R. The principle of this doubly-fed induction generator is described in Sections 13.23 to 13.26. The reader should read them to fully understand how the generator operates. Briefly, the frequency and phase sequence of voltage E_R (together with the stator frequency f) determine the speed of rotation of the machine. Since the stator frequency is fixed, the speed of rotation is essentially imposed by the rotor frequency f_2. As a result, the wind turbine can be forced to rotate at that optimal speed which extracts the maximum amount of power from the wind. To achieve this result, the wind speed is monitored by an anemometer and the information is fed into the control circuit of converter (5).

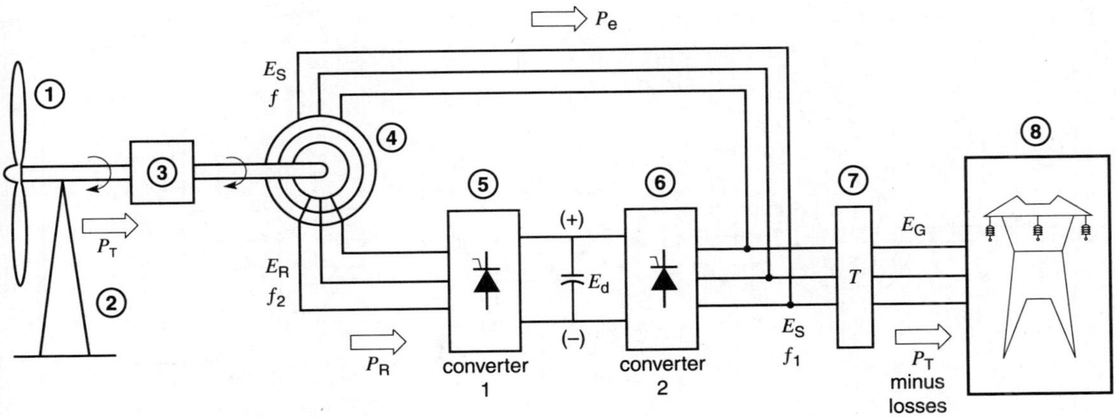

Figure 24.36
Wind turbine connected to a doubly-fed induction generator. Converters 1 and 2 only have to carry a small portion of the power P_T generated by the wind turbine.

During a moderate breeze, the rotor must turn slowly and so the generator is made to run at subsynchronous speed. However, when the wind is strong, the rotor turns more rapidly at supersynchronous speed. The magnitudes of the supersynchronous and subsynchronous speeds are given by Eqs. 13.13a and 13.13b (see Section 13.23).

Supersynchronous speed

$$n = \frac{120}{p}(f + f_2) \qquad (13.13a)$$

Subsynchronous speed

$$n = \frac{120}{p}(f - f_2) \qquad (13.13b)$$

where

n = generator rotor speed [r/min]
120 = numerical value to take care of units
p = number of poles
f = line frequency applied to the stator [Hz]
f_2 = frequency applied to the rotor [Hz]

The mechanical power produced by the wind turbine is converted into electric power by the generator. When the generator runs at supersynchronous speed, both the rotor and stator deliver power to the grid, as shown in Fig. 13.38 (Section 13.26).

When the generator runs at subsynchronous speed, the stator continues to deliver power to the grid. However, under these conditions, the rotor *absorbs* power from the grid, as shown in Fig. 13.37 (Section 13.26).

The setup of Fig. 24.36 has certain advantages over that of Fig. 24.35. The reason is that only a small portion of the total power P_T has to be handled by the electronic converters. However, the wound-rotor generator is more complex than a squirrel-cage generator and the brushes on the slip-rings require occasional inspection and replacement.

24.34 Turbine directly driving a permanent magnet alternator

Figure 24.37 shows a wind turbine directly connected to a permanent magnet alternator. Converters (4) and (5) and transformer (6) fill the same role as converters (5) and (6) and transformer (7) in Fig. 24.35.

The frequency f_1 generated by converter (4) imposes the optimal speed of rotation on the generator. Note that the converters have to carry the entire

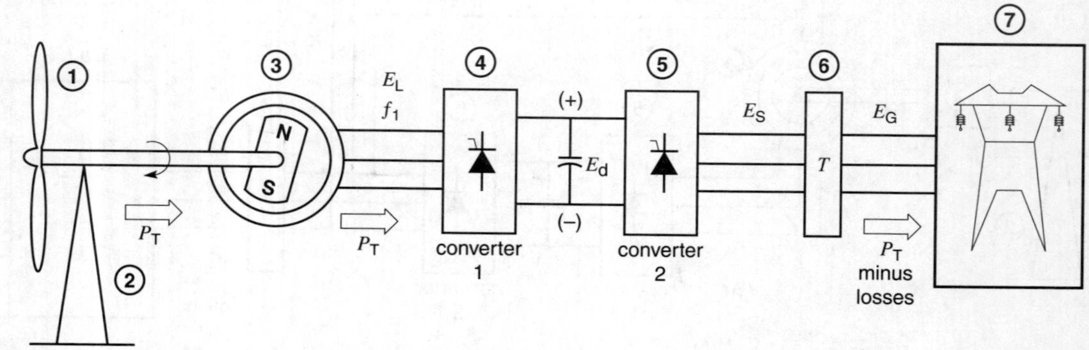

Figure 24.37
Turbine directly driving a high-power permanent magnet alternator. The absence of a gear box eliminates a component that requires occasional maintenance.

power developed by the turbine; consequently, they are inherently larger than those in the doubly-fed generator.

The direct drive has the advantage of eliminating the speed-multiplying gear box. However, since the turbine speed is of the order of 30 r/min or less, the alternator has to be much larger than if it were designed to run, say, at 1200 r/min. However, the permanent magnet alternator does not require any brushes and the rotor losses are nil. For these reasons, the arrangement of Fig. 24.37 is sometimes preferred in turbines that generate power in the 2 MW to 5 MW range.

24.35 Examples of wind-generating stations

It is instructive to present some examples of wind-generating stations, as follows.

*1. **Le Nordais Wind Farm.*** Figure 24.38a shows 11 of a total of 57 wind turbines installed in the Le Nordais wind farm in the Gaspé region near Matane, Québec. Each turbine has a nominal rating of 750 kW. The generator is a two-winding induction machine that can develop 200 kW at 1200 r/min and 750 kW at 1800 r/min. The speeds respectively correspond to a 4-pole and 6-pole stator connection. The generator develops 690 V, 3-phase, 60 Hz power which is stepped up to 230 kV by means of a transformer for direct connection to the local Hydro-Québec grid.

Figure 24.38b shows one of the wind turbines with its 3-blade propeller. It is manufactured by NEG Micon of Denmark. The base of the 55 m tubular steel tower has a diameter of 4.5 m; its sealed door gives access to the interior and to the nacelle above (Fig. 24.38c). Table 24C gives additional technical information on this wind turbine.

*2. **Stateline Wind Energy Center.*** The Stateline wind-generating station is located between the states of Oregon and Washington in the western United States. It consists of 399 wind turbines each having a capacity of 660 kW (Fig. 24.39). The tubular steel towers are 50 m high and the blades

Figure 24.38a
Portion of Le Nordais wind farm in Matane, Québec. It operates in both summer and bitterly cold winters.

Figure 24.38b
The nacelle (also called pod) is set on top of a 55 m steel tower. The pod is 8.5 m long and it automatically yaws to face the wind at all times. It is equipped with a lightning arrestor and is heated during the winter.

TABLE 24C SPECIFICATIONS OF LE NORDAIS WIND TURBINES

Average wind speed in the region	28 km/h
Wind speed to produce 200 kW	15 km/h
Wind speed to produce 750 kW	51 km/h
Maximum wind speed (turbine stops)	85 km/h
Height of tower	55 m
Length of blades	14 m
Length of nacelle	8.5 m
Weight of one blade	3 t
Weight of nacelle	19.5 t
Weight of electric generator	5 t
Weight of entire installation	75 t
Gear box ratio	80:1
Lower speed of blades	15 r/min
Higher speed of blades	22.5 r/min

Note: t stands for metric ton.

Figure 24.38c
The base of the steel tower has a diameter of 4.5 m. The door gives access to the inside and upwards to the nacelle. The transformer connecting the turbine to the 230 kV grid can be seen in the background. The connection to the grid is made by means of an underground cable.

sweep out a circular area having a diameter of 47 m. The nominal speed of rotation is 28.5 r/min. The pitch of the blades is automatically regulated according to the speed of the wind. The cut-in wind speed is 4 m/s, the nominal wind speed is 15 m/s, and during gale winds the stop speed is 25 m/s.

The induction generator has a wound rotor whose terminals are connected to a set of resistors whose resistance can be rapidly changed by means of an electronic converter. The converter and the resistors are mounted on the rotor itself; consequently, no brushes or slip-rings are required. The resistance is controlled by means of an optical signal that is transmitted to the revolving converter.

The advantage of this Vestas Optislip® technology is that during a violent gust of wind, the speed of the blades and the rotor can be allowed to quickly increase by immediately raising the resistance in series with the rotor. This diminishes the mechanical shock and allows time for the pitch of the blades to readjust to the higher wind speed. As soon as the pitch is properly adjusted, the resistance in series with the rotor is again effectively reduced to zero.

Figure 24.39
This impressive Stateline Wind Energy Center, composed of 399 wind turbines, is located between Oregon and Washington. The 660 kW, 3-phase induction generators operate at 690 V, 60 Hz and run normally at a geared-up speed between 1800 and 1818 r/min. During gusty wind conditions, the speed is allowed to rise temporarily to as much as 1980 r/min. The turbine is brought to a stop whenever the gale winds exceed 25 m/s.
(Courtesy of Vestas Wind Systems A/S)

Consequently, the losses due to the varying external rotor resistance remain minimal.

3. Nakskov Wind Turbines. Three large wind turbines, Vestas model V90-3.0 MW, each having a capacity of 3 MW, are installed in the city of Nakskov, in Denmark. These turbines are equipped with 3 MW, 1500 r/min, 50 Hz doubly-fed wound-rotor induction generators (Figure 24.40). The tower is 75 m high and the blades have a length of 44 m. The blades rotate at speeds ranging from 9 to 19 r/min; rated power is obtained at the nominal speed of 16.1 r/min. The cut-in wind speed is 4 m/s, the nominal wind speed is 15 m/s, and the gale wind stop speed is 25 m/s. Figure 24.41 shows the output power of the wind turbine as a function of wind speed. Note that when the wind speed increases from 5 m/s to 12.5 m/s (a factor of 2.5) the power increases from 250 kW to 2500 kW (a factor of 10). Thus, the power increases very quickly as the wind speed rises. For reasons of safety and the protection of equipment, the power output flattens off at 3 MW when the wind speed approaches gale proportions.

4. Offshore Wind Farms. Offshore wind farms are also being installed when wind conditions are favorable. One example is the Middelgrunden Offshore Wind Farm installed in Copenhagen Harbour, in Denmark. It consists of twenty 2 MW turbines manufactured by Bonus Energy. A picture of this important installation appears in Chapter 13, Figure 13.40.

Questions and Problems

Practical level

24-1 Explain the difference between a base-load and a peak-load generating plant.

24-2 Why are nuclear power stations not suited to supply peak loads?

24-3 Referring to the coal mine in Fig. 24.4, we have the choice of hauling the coal to a generating plant or installing the generating plant next to the mine mouth. What factors come into play in determining the best solution?

24-4 What is the best indicator of stability (or instability) of an electric utility system?

24-5 What is meant by the term *network?*

24-6 Give two reasons why electric utility systems are interconnected.

24-7 The river flow in Fig. 24.9 is 5000 m^3/s at a height of 24 m. Calculate the available hydraulic power.

24-8 Explain the operating principle of a thermal plant, a hydropower plant, and a nuclear plant.

24-9 Name two basic differences between a light-water reactor and a heavy-water reactor.

24-10 Explain what is meant by *moderator, fission, fusion, neutron,* and *heavy water.*

Intermediate level

24-11 The Zaïre River, in Africa, discharges at a constant rate 1300 km^3 of water per year. It has been proposed to build a series of dams in the region of Inga, where the river drops by 100 m.

Calculate

a. The water flow [m^3/s]
b. The power that could be harnessed [MW]
c. The discharge in cubic miles per year

24-12 For how long does a 1500 MW generator have to run to produce the same quantity of energy as that released by a 20 kiloton atomic bomb? (See conversion charts in Appendix.)

24-13 The demand of a municipality regularly varies between 60 MW and 110 MW in the course of one day, the average power being 80 MW. To produce the required energy, we have the following options:

a. Install a base-power generating unit and a diesel-engine peaking plant.
b. Install a base-power generating unit and a pumped-storage unit.

Figure 24.40
This 3 MW wind turbine contains a 4-pole, doubly-fed wound-rotor induction generator equipped with slip-rings and brushes. The synchronous speed is 1500 r/min. The converter that is connected to the rotor permits operation at subsynchronous and supersynchronous speeds. The nacelle weighs 66 t and the 3-blade rotor weighs 38 t.
(Courtesy of Vestas Wind Systems A/S)

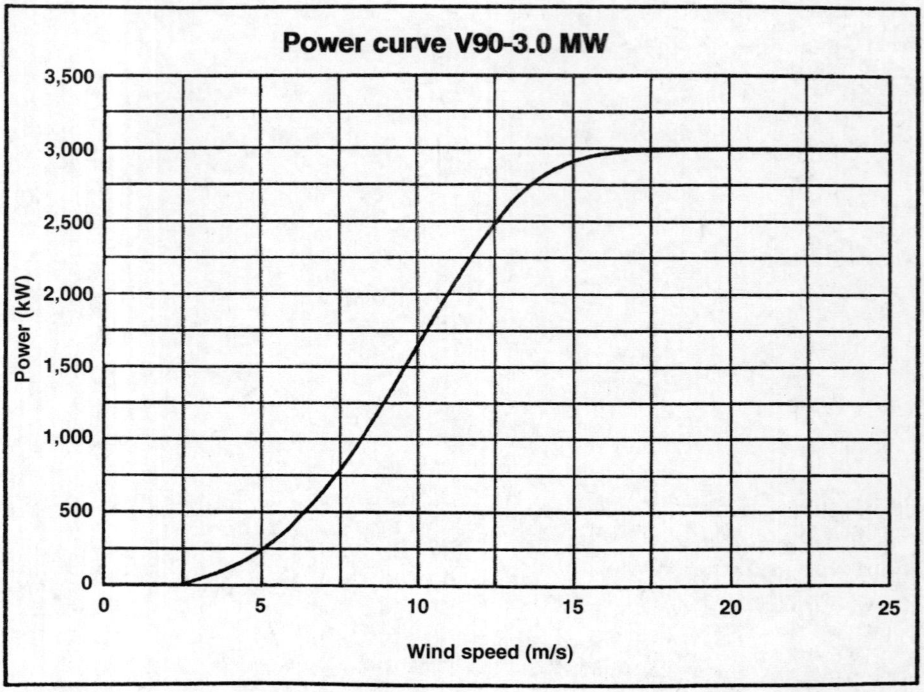

Figure 24.41
Power output versus wind speed for the 3 MW turbine illustrated in Figure 24.40. The output automatically flattens off at wind speeds above 15 m/s in order to prevent overloading the generator.
(Courtesy of Vesta Wind Systems A/S)

What are the respective capacities of the base power and peaking power plants in each case?

24-14 On a particular day, the head of Grand Coulee dam is 280 ft and the generators deliver 6000 MVA at a power factor of 0.9 lagging. Assuming the average turbine efficiency is 0.92 and the average generator efficiency is 0.98, calculate the following:

a. The active power output [MW]

b. The reactive power supplied to the system [Mvar]

c. The amount of water flowing through the turbines [yd^3/s]

24-15 Explain the principle of operation of a cooling tower.

24-16 A modern coal-burning thermal station produces an electrical output of 720 MW. Calculate the approximate value of the following:

a. The amount of coal consumed [tons (not tonnes) per day]

b. The amount of smoke, gas, and fly ash released [tons per day]

c. The cooling water flowing through the condenser, assuming a temperature rise of 10°C [m^3/s]

24-17 In Problem 24-16, if a cooling tower is required, how much water must be drawn from a local stream [m^3/s]? Can this water be recycled?

24-18 A fuel bundle of natural uranium dioxide has a mass of 22.2 kg when first inserted into a heavy-water reactor. If it releases an average of 372.5 kW of thermal energy during its 19-month stay in the reactor, calculate the following:

a. The total amount of heat released [J] and [Btu]

b. The reduction in weight of the bundle, due to the energy released [g]

Advanced level

24-19 **a.** Calculate the annual energy consumption [TW·h] of the electric utility system having the load duration curve given in Fig. 24.3.

b. If this energy were consumed at an absolutely uniform rate, what would the peak load be [GW]?

24-20 Referring to Fig. 24.32, the temperature of the heavy-water coolant drops from 294°C to 249°C in passing through the heat exchangers. Knowing that the reactor is cooled at the rate of 7.7 t/s of heavy water, calculate the heat [MW] transmitted to the heat exchangers (specific heat of heavy water is 4560 J/kg).

Industrial Application

24-21 On November 12, 1992, at 10:09 AM a large generator on the East Coast tripped out, causing the interconnected power pool of 18 823 MW to suddenly lose 1050 MW of generating power. In a matter of seconds, the system frequency fell from 60 Hz to 59.97 Hz. The power output of the other generators on the system was selectively increased and the rated 60 Hz frequency was restored after an interval of about 7.5 minutes. The frequency was then raised above 60 Hz for a time to recover the cycles lost, thereby correcting the electric clocks. The behavior of the frequency before and after the incident is shown in Fig. 24.42.

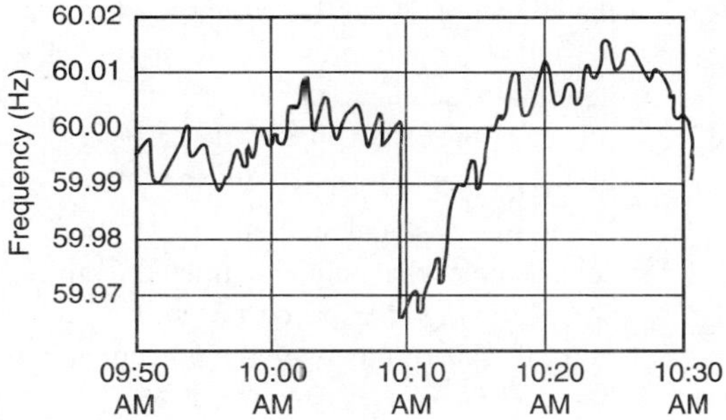

Figure 24.42
See Problem 24-21.

Calculate

a. The average frequency during the 7.5-minute restoration period

b. The number of cycles generated during the 7.5-minute period

c. The number of cycles that would have been generated during the 6-minute interval if the accident had not occurred and the frequency had stayed at 60 Hz

d. Electric clocks are designed so that the minute hand makes one complete turn in exactly one minute when the frequency is exactly 60 Hz. How many turns did the minute hand make during the 7.5-minute interval? What is the error in the minute-hand reading, expressed in milliseconds?

24-22 In Problem 24-21 we assume that half the 18 823 MW load consists of induction motors. Some motors drive fans and similar loads wherein the power varies as the cube of the speed. Calculate the drop in power of a 10 000 hp blower motor when the frequency falls from 60 Hz to 59.97 Hz.

24-23 A summer camp is located near a 55 ft waterfall. Tests show that the stream delivers a minimum of 270 cubic feet per minute in the course of a year. It is proposed to install a 3-phase induction motor and drive it as a generator. Calculate the approximate horsepower of the motor that could harness 80 percent of the capacity of the falls.

24-24 Using Eq. 24.4, calculate the power per square meter that can be extracted from a wind blowing at a speed of 35 miles per hour, if 24% of the available power can be harnessed.

24-25 The propeller of a small wind turbine has a diameter of 1.5 m. Estimate the power that the turbine can develop when the wind blows at a speed of 45 km/h and supposing that 25% of the available wind energy can be extracted.

24-26 The wind turbine in Fig. 24.40 develops its rated output of 3 MW when the blades rotate at 16.1 r/min. Calculate

a. The torque [kN·m] exerted on the hub and shaft

b. The horsepower rating of the wind turbine

24-27 Referring to Fig. 24.34, the induction generator produces a 3-phase output of 750 kW at 690 V with a power factor of 86% lagging. Calculate

a. The apparent power at the terminals of the generator [kVA]

b. The current per phase delivered by the generator [A]

c. The kvar rating of the capacitor bank if the power factor at the terminals of the grid is to be 100% [kvar]

24-28 Referring to Fig. 24.34, the wind turbine produces a power P_T of 420 kW. The gear box has losses of 1.2%, the generator losses amount to 5.4%, and the transformer losses are 1.4%. Calculate

a. The net power that is injected into the utility power grid [kW]

b. The overall efficiency of the system [%]

24-29 Referring to Fig. 24.35, converter (5) generates a frequency of 57.6 Hz and the induction generator has 4 poles. Knowing that the gear box has a ratio of 45, calculate the exact speed of rotation of the blades [r/min].

24-30 Knowing that the average height of one story of a commercial building is 10 feet, calculate the number of stories corresponding to the height of the tower in Fig. 24.40.

24-31 Referring to Fig. 24.38b and Table 24C, the speed of the blades is found to be exactly 23.75 r/min. Knowing that the induction generator delivers a power output of 672 kW, estimate the power dissipated in the rotor in the form of heat [kW].

24-32 Using Fig. 24.41, calculate the power delivered by the 3 MW wind turbine when the wind blows at 28 mi/h [kW].

24-33 Referring to Fig. 24.41, the turbine develops 3 MW when the wind speed is 17.5 m/s. The corresponding speed of rotation of the blades is 19.1 r/min. Calculate

a. The linear speed of the tips of the blades [km/h]

b. The ratio of the tip speed to the wind speed

24-34 Calculate the combined maximum power of the wind turbines that appear in Fig. 24.38a. If the average household consumes 5 kW of power, how many households can these turbines furnish?

24-35 Referring to Chapter 13, Fig. 13.40, calculate the total energy in MW·h that the 20 turbines could deliver theoretically if they operated at full capacity all year round. What is the ratio of the guaranteed minimum energy of 89 000 MW·h to this theoretical maximum [%]?

24-36 Referring to Figs. 24.40 and 24.41 and the text concerning the Nakskov wind turbine, calculate the ratio of the power developed by the turbine to the total available power in the wind when the wind speed is 12.5 m/s [%].

24-37 A 3 MW wind turbine, similar to the one illustrated in Fig. 24.40, possesses the basic circuit diagram shown in Fig. 24.36. The turbine speed ranges from 13 r/min to 20 r/min and the gear box has a ratio of 1:90. The output of the doubly-fed generator is connected to a 50 Hz grid and the stator has 4 poles. The turbine produces its rated output of 3 MW when the blades rotate at 20 r/min. Neglecting all power losses in the various components, calculate

a. The synchronous speed of the generator
b. The speed of rotation of the rotor
c. The value of the slip speed
d. The value of the slip
e. The power output of the stator [MW]
f. The power output of the rotor to converter (5) [MW]
g. The power carried respectively by converters (5) and (6) [MW]
h. The ratio of the power carried by converter (5) to the total power (3 MW) produced by the turbine [%]
i. The frequency generated by converter (5) [Hz]
j. If the converter (5) generates a frequency of 7.6 Hz and the generator is running at subsynchronous speed; calculate the speed of rotation of the blades [r/min]

CHAPTER 25

Transmission of Electrical Energy

25.0 Introduction

The transmission of electrical energy does not usually raise as much interest as does its generation and utilization; consequently, we sometimes tend to neglect this important subject. This is unfortunate because the human and material resources involved in transmission are much greater than those employed in generation.

Electrical energy is carried by conductors such as overhead transmission lines and underground cable. Although these conductors appear very ordinary, they possess important electrical properties that greatly affect the transmission of electrical energy. In this chapter, we study these properties for several types of transmission lines: high-voltage, low-voltage, high-power, low-power, aerial lines, and underground lines. We then show some of the ways whereby the voltage and power flow are controlled in an electric utility system.

25.1 Principal components of a power distribution system

In order to provide electrical energy to consumers in usable form, a transmission and distribution system must satisfy some basic requirements. Thus, the system must

1. Provide, at all times, the power that consumers need
2. Maintain a stable, nominal voltage that does not vary by more than ±10%
3. Maintain a stable frequency that does not vary by more than ±0.1 Hz
4. Supply energy at an acceptable price
5. Meet standards of safety
6. Respect environmental standards

Fig. 25.1 shows an elementary diagram of a transmission and distribution system. It consists of two generating stations G_1 and G_2, a few substations, an interconnecting substation and several commercial, residential, and industrial loads. The energy is carried over lines designated *extra-high* voltage (EHV), *high* voltage (HV), *medium* voltage (MV), and *low* voltage (LV). This voltage classification is made according to a scale of standardized voltages whose nominal values are given in Table 25A.

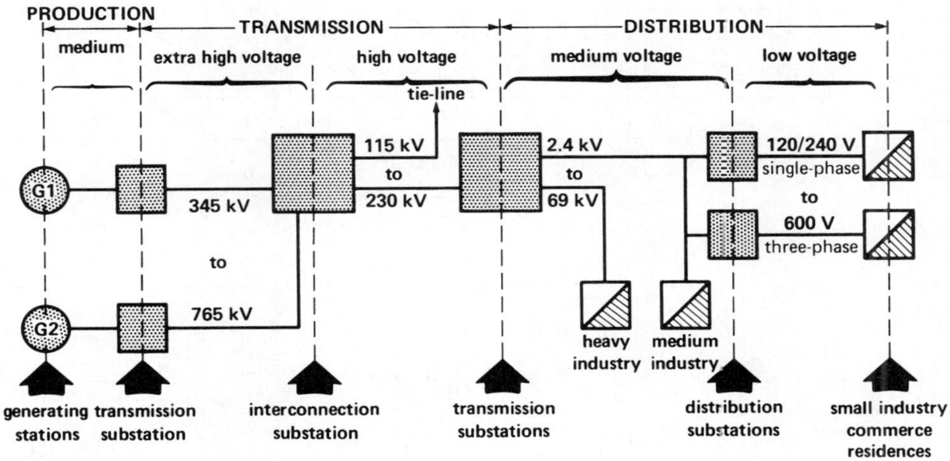

Figure 25.1
Single-line diagram of a generation, transmission, and distribution system.

Transmission substations (Fig. 25.1) change the line voltage by means of step-up and step-down transformers and regulate it by means of static var compensators, synchronous condensers, or transformers with variable taps.

Distribution substations change the medium voltage to low voltage by means of step-down transformers, which may have automatic tap-changing capabilities to regulate the low voltage. The low voltage ranges from 120/240V single phase to 600 V, 3 phase. It serves to power private residences, commercial and institutional establishments, and small industry.

Interconnecting substations tie different power systems together, to enable power exchanges between them, and to increase the stability of the overall network.*

These substations also contain circuit breakers, fuses, and lightning arresters, to protect expensive apparatus, and to provide for quick isolation of faulted lines from the system. In addition, control apparatus, power measuring devices, disconnect switches, capacitors, inductors, and other devices may be part of a substation.

Electrical power utilities divide their power distribution systems into two major categories:

1. **Transmission systems** in which the line voltage is roughly between 115 kV and 800 kV
2. **Distribution systems** in which the voltage generally lies between 120 V and 69 kV. Distribution systems, in turn, are divided into *medium-voltage* distribution systems (2.4 kV to 69 kV) and *low-voltage* distribution systems (120 V to 600 V).

25.2 Types of power lines

The design of a power line depends upon the following criteria:

1. The amount of active power it has to transmit
2. The distance over which the power must be carried
3. The cost of the power line
4. Esthetic considerations, urban congestion, ease of installation, and expected load growth

* A network is "an aggregation of interconnected conductors consisting of feeders, mains and services" (ref. *IEEE Standard Dictionary of Electrical and Electronics Terms*).

TABLE 25A VOLTAGE CLASSES AS APPLIED TO INDUSTRIAL AND COMMERCIAL POWER

	Nominal system voltage		
Voltage class	Two-wire	Three-wire	Four-wire
low voltage	120	120/240 □	—
	single phase	single phase	120/208 □
		480 V □	277/480 □
LV		600 V	347/600
medium voltage		2 400	
		4 160 □	
		4 800	
MV		6 900	
		13 800 □	7 200/12 470 □
		23 000	7 620/13 200 □
		34 500	7 970/13 800
		46 000	14 400/24 940 □
		69 000 □	19 920/34 500 □
high voltage		115 000 □	
		138 000 □	
		161 000	
HV		230 000 □	
extra-high voltage		345 000 □	
		500 000 □	
EHV		735 000–765 000 □	

All voltages are 3-phase unless indicated otherwise.
Voltages designated by the symbol □ are preferred voltages.
Note: Voltage class designations were approved for use by IEEE Standards Board (September 4, 1975).

We distinguish four types of power lines, according to their voltage class:

1. ***Low-voltage (LV) lines*** provide power to buildings, factories, and houses to drive motors, electric stoves, lamps, heaters, and air conditioners. The lines are insulated conductors, usually made of aluminum, often extending from a local pole-mounted distribution transformer to the service entrance of the consumer. The lines may be overhead or underground, and the transformer behaves like a miniature substation.

In some metropolitan areas, the distribution system feeding the factories, homes, and commercial buildings consists of a grid of underground cables operating at 600 V or less. Such a network provides dependable service, because even the outage of one or several cables will not interrupt customer service.

2. ***Medium-voltage (MV) lines*** tie the load centers to one of the many substations of the utility company. The voltage is usually between 2.4 kV and 69 kV. Such medium-voltage radial distribution systems are preferred in the larger cities. In radial systems the transmission lines spread out like fingers from one or more substations to feed power to various load centers, such as high-rise buildings, shopping centers, and campuses.

3. ***High-voltage (HV) lines*** connect the main substations to the generating stations. The lines are composed of aerial conductors or underground cables operating at voltages below 230 kV. In this category we also find lines that transmit energy between two power systems, to increase the stability of the network.

4. ***Extra-high-voltage (EHV) lines*** are used when generating stations are very far from the load centers. We put these lines in a separate class because of their special electrical properties. Such lines operate at voltages up to 800 kV and may be as long as 1000 km.

25.3 Standard voltages

To reduce the cost of distribution apparatus and to facilitate its protection, standards-setting organizations have established a number of standard voltages for transmission lines. These standards, given in Table 25A, reflect the various voltages presently used in North America. Voltages that bear the symbol □ are *preferred* voltages. Unless otherwise indicated, all voltages are 3-phase.

25.4 Components of a HV transmission line

A transmission line is composed of conductors, insulators, and supporting structures.

1. ***Conductors.*** Conductors for high-voltage lines are always bare. Stranded copper conductors, or steel-reinforced aluminum cable (ACSR) are used. ACSR conductors are usually preferred because they result in a lighter and more economical line. Conductors have to be spliced when a line is very long. Special care must be taken so that the joints have low resistance and great mechanical strength.

2. ***Insulators.*** Insulators serve to support and anchor the conductors and to insulate them from ground. Insulators are usually made of porcelain, but glass and other synthetic insulating materials are also used.

From an electric standpoint, insulators must offer a high resistance to surface leakage currents and must be sufficiently thick to prevent breakdown under the high-voltage stresses they have to withstand. To increase the leakage path (and hence the leakage resistance), the insulators are molded with wave-like folds. From a mechanical standpoint, they must be strong enough to withstand the dynamic pull and weight of the conductors.

There are two main types of insulators: *pin-type insulators* and *suspension-type insulators* (Figs. 25.2 and 25.3). The pin-type insulator has several porcelain skirts (folds) and the conductor is fixed at the top.

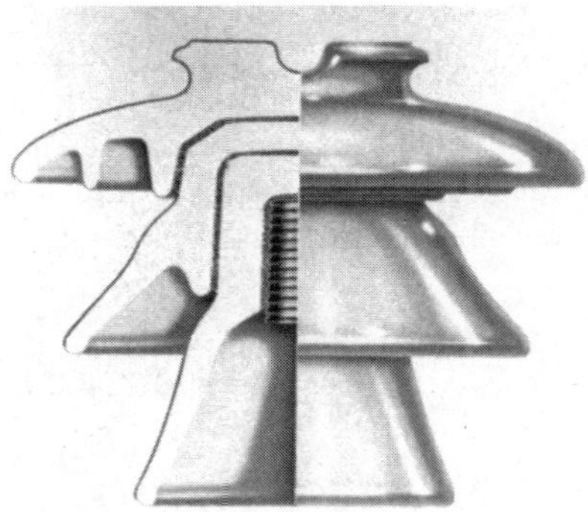

Figure 25.2
Sectional view of a 69 kV pin-type insulator. BIL: 270 kV; 60 Hz flash-over voltage under wet conditions: 125 kV.
(Courtesy of Canadian Ohio Brass Co. Ltd.)

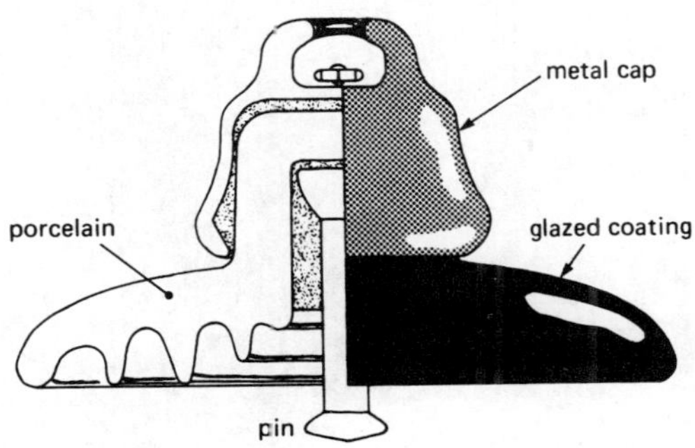

Figure 25.3
Sectional view of a suspension insulator. Diameter: 254 mm; BIL: 125 kV, 60 Hz flash-over voltage, under wet conditions: 50 kV.
(Courtesy of Canadian Ohio Brass Co. Ltd.)

A steep pin screws into the insulator so it can be bolted to a support.

For voltages above 70 kV, suspension-type insulators are used, strung together by their cap and pin metallic parts. The number of insulators depends upon the voltage: for 110 kV, we generally use from 4 to 7; for 230 kV, from 13 to 16. Fig. 25.4 shows an insulator arrangement for a 735 kV line. It is composed of 4 strings in parallel of 35 insulators each, to provide both mechanical and electrical strength.

*3. **Supporting structures.*** The supporting structure must keep the conductors at a safe height from the ground and at an adequate distance from each other. For voltages below 70 kV, we can use single wooden poles equipped with cross-arms, but for higher voltages, two poles are used to create an H-frame. The wood is treated with creosote or special metallic salts to prevent it from rotting. For very high-voltage lines, steel towers are used, made of galvanized angle-iron pieces that are bolted together.

The spacing between conductors must be sufficient to prevent arc-over under gusty wind conditions. The spacing has to be increased as the distance between towers and as the line voltages become higher.

25.5 Construction of a line

Once we know the conductor size, the height of the poles, and the distance between the poles (span), we can direct our attention to stringing the conductors. A wire supported between two points (Fig. 25.5) does not remain horizontal, but loops down at the middle. The vertical distance between the straight line joining the points of support and the lowest point of the conductor is called *sag*. The tighter the wire, the smaller the sag will be.

Figure 25.4
Lineman working bare-handed on a 735 kV line. He is wearing a special conductive suit so that his body is not subjected to high differences of potential. In the position shown, his potential with respect to ground is about 200 kV.
(Courtesy of Hydro-Québec)

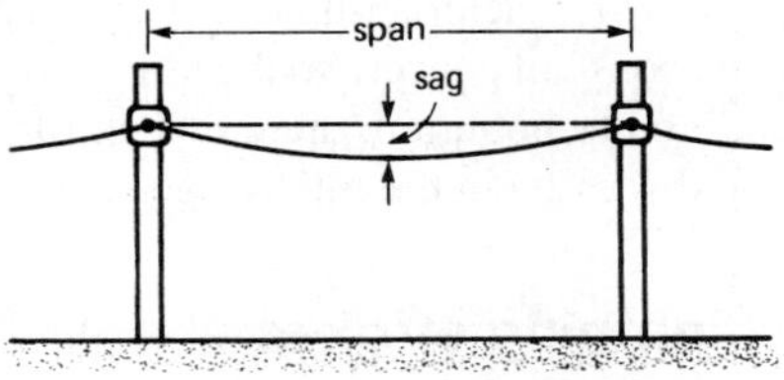

Figure 25.5
Span and sag of a line.

Before undertaking the actual construction of a line, it is important to calculate the permissible sag and the corresponding mechanical pull. Among other things, the summer to winter temperature range must be taken into account because the length of the conductor varies with temperature. Thus, if the line is strung in the winter, the sag must not be too great, otherwise the wire will stretch even more during the summer heat, with the result that the clearance to ground may no longer be safe. On the other hand, if the line is installed in the summer, the sag must not be too small otherwise the wire, contracting in winter, may become so dangerously tight as to snap. Wind and sleet add even more to the tractive force, which may also cause the wire to break (Fig. 25.6).

25.6 Galloping lines

If a coating of sleet is deposited on a line during windy conditions, the line may begin to oscillate. Under certain conditions, the oscillations may become so large that the line is seen to actually *gallop.* Galloping lines can produce short-circuits between phases or snap the conductors. To eliminate the problem, the line is sometimes equipped with special mechanical weights, to dampen the oscillations or to prevent them from building up.

25.7 Corona effect—radio interference

The very high voltages in use today produce a continual electrical discharge around the conductors, due to local ionization of the air. This discharge, or corona effect, produces losses over the entire length

Figure 25.6
During winter, steel towers must carry the combined weight of conductors and accumulated ice.
(Courtesy of Hydro-Québec)

of the transmission line. In addition, corona emits high-frequency noise that interferes with nearby radio receivers and TV sets. To diminish corona, we must reduce the electric field (V/m) around the conductors, either by increasing their diameter or by arranging them in sets of two, three, or more bundled conductors per phase (see Figs. 25.7a and 25.7b). This *bundling* arrangement also reduces the inductive reactance of the line, enabling it to carry more power. This constitutes an important additional benefit.

25.8 Pollution

Dust, acids, salts, and other pollutants in the atmosphere settle on insulators and reduce their insulating properties. Insulator pollution may produce short-circuits during storms or momentary overvoltages. The possibility of service interruption and

Figure 25.7a
Four bundled conductors make up this phase of a 3-phase, 735 kV line.
(Courtesy of Hydro-Québec)

Figure 25.7b
Details of the bundled conductors.

the necessity to clean insulators periodically is therefore a constant concern to the utility company.

In addition to pollution, there is the problem of lightning, discussed in the following sections.

25.9 Lightning strokes

During stormy weather, by a process not yet fully understood, a charge separation takes place inside clouds, so that positive charges move to the upper part of the cloud while negative charges stay below (Fig. 25.8). This transfer of electric charge sets up an electric field within the cloud. Furthermore, the negative charge at the base of the cloud repels the free electrons on the ground below. Consequently, region T becomes positively charged, by induction. It follows that an electric field and difference of potential will be established between the base of the cloud and the earth. Furthermore, another electric field exists between the electrons repelled from region T and the positive charge at the top of the cloud.

As more and more positive charges move upward within the cloud, the electric field below the cloud becomes more and more intense. Ultimately, it reaches the critical ionization level where air begins to break down. Ionization takes place first at the tips of church spires and the top of high trees, and may sometimes give rise to a bluish light. Mariners of old observed this light around the masts of their ships and called it St. Elmo's fire.

When the electric field becomes sufficiently intense, lightning will suddenly strike from cloud to earth. A single stroke may involve a charge transfer of from 0.2 to 20 coulombs, under a difference of potential of several hundred million volts. The current per stroke rises to a peak in one or two microseconds and falls to half its peak value in about 50 μs. What is visually observed as a single stroke is often composed of several strokes following each other in rapid succession. The total discharge time may last as long as 200 ms.

Discharges also occur between positive and negative charges within the cloud, rather than between the base of the cloud and ground.

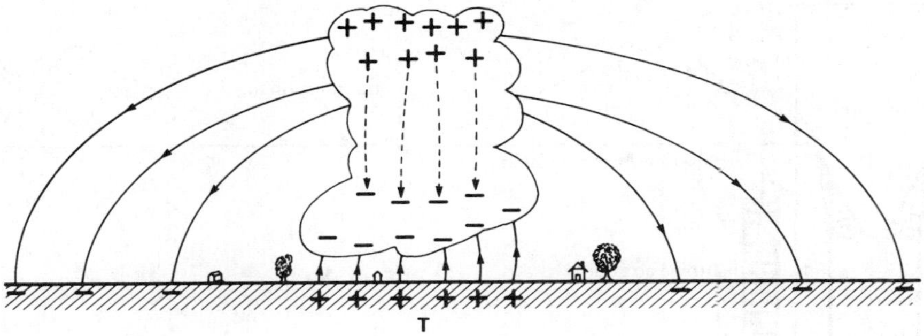

Figure 25.8
Electric fields created by a thundercloud.

The thunder we hear is produced by a supersonic pressure wave. It is created by the sudden expansion of air surrounding the intensely hot lightning stroke.

25.10 Lightning arresters on buildings

The simplest lightning arresters are metallic rods that rise above the highest point of a building, channeling the lightning toward a ground electrode by means of a conducting wire. This prevents the high current from passing through the building itself, which might cause a fire or endanger its occupants. A lightning arrester and anything connected to it can be dangerous to the touch; during a discharge, a very high voltage can exist between the protective system and ground. The reason is that the resistance between the ground rod and the ground itself is seldom less than 0.5 ohms. Thus, a discharge current of 10 kA can produce a momentary touch voltage of 5000 V.

Much more sophisticated lightning arresters are used on electrical utility systems. They divert lightning and high-voltage switching surges to ground before they damage costly and critical electrical equipment.

25.11 Lightning and transmission lines

When lightning makes a direct hit on a transmission line, it deposits a large electric charge, producing an enormous overvoltage between the line and ground. The dielectric strength of air is immediately exceeded and a flashover occurs. The line discharges itself and the overvoltage disappears in typically less than 50 μs.

Unfortunately, the arc between the line and ground (initiated by the lightning stroke), produces a highly ionized path which behaves like a conducting short-circuit. Consequently, the normal ac line voltage immediately delivers a large ac current that follows the ionized path. This *follow-through* current may sustain the arc until the circuit breakers open at the end of the line. The fastest circuit breakers will trip in about 1/15th of a second, which is almost 1000 times longer than the duration of the lightning stroke itself.

Direct hits on a transmission line are rare; more often, lightning will strike the overhead ground wire that shields the line. In the latter case, a local charge still accumulates on the line, producing a very high local overvoltage. This concentrated charge immediately divides into two waves that swiftly move in opposite directions at close to the speed of light (300 m/μs). The height of the impulse wave represents the magnitude of the surge voltage that exists from point to point between the line and ground (Fig. 25.9). The peak voltage (corresponding to the crest of the wave) may attain one or two million volts. Wave front **ab** is concentrated over a distance of about 300 m, while tail **bc** may stretch out over several kilometers.

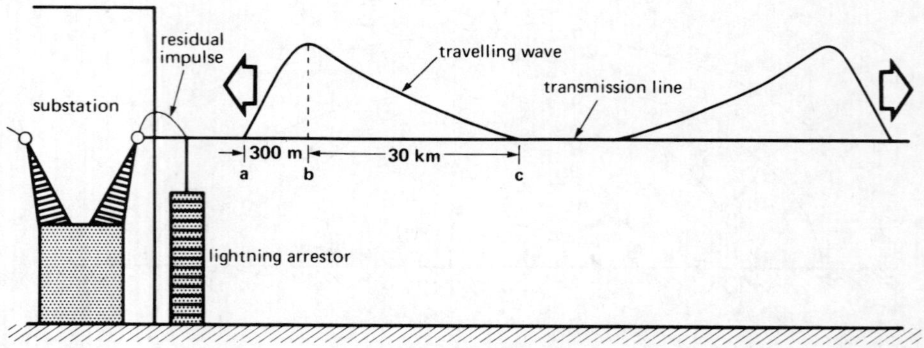

Figure 25.9
Flow of electric charge along a transmission line.

The wave also represents the point-to-point value of the current flowing in the line. For most aerial lines the ratio between surge voltage and surge current corresponds to a resistance of about 400 Ω. A surge voltage of 800 000 V at a given point is therefore accompanied by a local surge current of 800 000/400 = 2000 A.

As the wave travels along the line, the I^2R and corona losses gradually cause it to flatten out, and the peak of the surge voltage decreases.

Should the wave encounter a line insulator, the latter will be briefly subjected to a violent over-voltage. The over-voltage period is equal to the time it takes for the wave to sweep past the insulator. The voltage rises from its nominal value to several hundred kilovolts in about 1 μs, corresponding to the length of wavefront **ab.** If the insulator cannot withstand this overvoltage, it will flash over, and the resulting follow-through current will cause the circuit breakers to trip. On the other hand, if the insulator does not fail, the wave will continue to travel along the line until it eventually encounters a substation. It is here that the impulse wave can produce real havoc. The windings of transformers, synchronous condensers, reactors, etc., are seriously damaged when they flash over to ground. Expensive repairs and even more costly shut-downs are incurred while the apparatus is out of service. The overvoltage may also damage circuit breakers, switches, insulators, and relays, that make up a substation. To reduce the impulse voltage on station apparatus, lightning arresters must be installed on all incoming lines.

Lightning arresters are designed to clip off all voltage peaks that exceed a specified level, say, 400 kV. In turn, the apparatus within the substation is designed to withstand an impulse voltage, say 550 kV, that is considerably higher than the arrester *clipping voltage.* Consequently, if a 1000 kV surge voltage enters a substation, the 400 kV station arrester diverts a substantial part of the surge energy to ground. The residual impulse wave that travels beyond the arrester then has a peak of only 400 kV. This impulse will not damage station apparatus built to withstand an impulse of 550 kV.

25.12 Basic impulse insulation level (BIL)

How do insulating materials react to impulse voltages? Tests have shown that the withstand capability increases substantially when voltages are applied for very brief periods. To illustrate, suppose we wish to carry out an insulation test on a transformer, by applying a 60 Hz sinusoidal voltage between the windings and ground. As we slowly raise the voltage, a point will be reached where breakdown occurs. Let us assume that the breakdown voltage is 46 kV (RMS) or 65 kV crest.

On the other hand, if we apply a dc impulse voltage of extremely short duration between the wind-

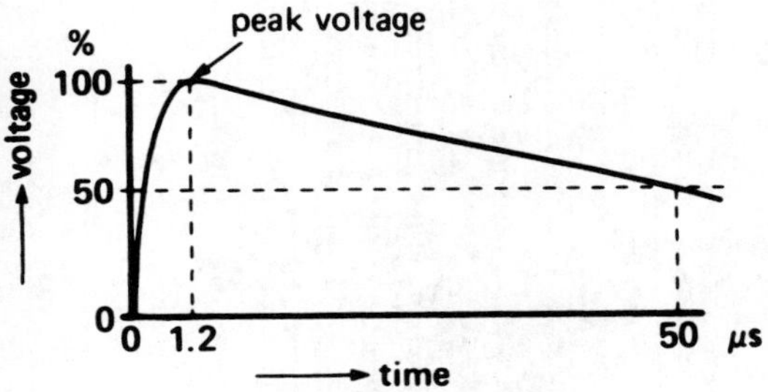

Figure 25.10
Standard shape of impulse voltage used to determine the BIL rating of electrical apparatus.

ings and ground, we discover that it takes about twice the peak voltage (or 130 kV) before the insulation breaks down. The same phenomenon is observed in the case of suspension insulators, bushings, spark gaps, and so on, except that the ratio between impulse voltage and crest ac voltage is closer to 1.5.

In the interest of standardization, and to enable a comparison between the impulse withstand capability of similar devices, standards organizations have defined the shape and crest values of several impulse waves. Fig. 25.10 shows one of these standard impulse waves. It attains its peak after 1.2 μs and falls to one-half the peak in 50 μs. The peak voltage has a defined set of values that range from 30 kV to 1550 kV (see Table 25B).

TABLE 25B TYPICAL PEAK VOLTAGES FOR 1.2 × 50 μs BIL TESTS

Values are in kilovolts

1550	825	250
1425	750	200
1300	650	150
1175	550	110
1050	450	90
900	350	30

The peak voltage is used to specify the basic impulse insulation level (BIL) of equipment. Thus, a piece of equipment (transformer, insulator, capacitor, resistor, bushing, etc.) that can withstand a 1.2 × 50 microsecond wave of 900 kV, is said to possess a *basic impulse insulation level* (or BIL) of 900 kV. Fig. 25.11 shows an insulator string being subjected to a BIL impulse test.

The BIL of a device is usually several times higher than its nominal ac operating voltage. For example, the standards require that a 69 kV distribution transformer must have a BIL of 350 kV. However, there is no special relationship between BIL and nominal voltage. As the BIL rises, we must increase the amount of insulation which, in turn, increases the size and cost of equipment.

In conclusion, the peak voltage at which an arrester begins to conduct must always be lower than the BIL of the apparatus it is intended to protect.

25.13 Ground wires

In Fig. 25.6 we can discern two bare conductors supported at the very top of the transmission-line towers. These conductors, called *ground wires,* are intended to shield the line and intercept lightning strokes so they do not hit the current-carrying conductors below. Grounding wires normally do not carry current; consequently, they are often made of steel. They are connected to ground at each tower.

25.14 Tower grounding

Transmission-line towers are always solidly connected to ground. Great care is taken to ensure that the ground resistance is low. In effect, when lightning hits a line, it creates a sudden voltage rise across the insulators as the lightning current discharges to ground. Such a voltage rise may produce a flash-over across the insulators and a consequent line outage, as shown by the following example.

Example 25-1

A 3-phase, 69 kV transmission line having a BIL of 300 kV is supported on steel towers and protected by a circuit breaker (Fig. 25.12). The ground resistance at each tower is 20 Ω whereas the neutral of the transmission line is *solidly* grounded at the transformer just ahead of the circuit breaker.

Figure 25.11
A 4 000 000 V impulse causes a flashover across an insulator string rated at 500 kV, 60 Hz. Such impulse tests increase the reliability of equipment in the field. The powerful impulse generator in the center of the photo is 24 m high and can deliver 400 kJ of energy at a potential of 6.5 MV.
(Courtesy of IREQ)

During an electric storm, one of the towers is hit by a lightning stroke of 20 kA.

a. Calculate the voltage across each insulator string under normal conditions
b. Describe the sequence of events during and after the lightning stroke

Solution

a. Under normal conditions, the line-to-neutral voltage is $69 \text{ kV}/\sqrt{3} = 40 \text{ kV}$ and the current flowing in the tower ground resistance is zero. The steel tower is therefore at the same potential as the ground. It follows that the peak voltage across each insulator string (line to tower) is $40\sqrt{2} = 57 \text{ kV}$.
b. When lightning strikes the tower, the voltage across the ground resistance suddenly leaps to $20 \text{ kA} \times 20 \ \Omega = 400 \text{ kV}$. The voltage between the tower and *solid* ground is therefore 400 kV, and so the potential difference across all three insulator strings jumps to the same value. Because this impulse exceeds the insulator BIL of 300 kV, a flashover immediately occurs across the insulators, short-circuiting all three lines to the steel cross-arm. The resulting 3-phase short-circuit initiated by the lightning stroke will continue to be fed and sustained by a heavy follow-through current from the 3-phase source. This short-circuit current I_{sc} will trip the circuit breaker, producing a line outage.

In view of the many customers affected by such a load interruption, we try to limit the number of outages by ensuring a low resistance between the towers and ground. In this example, if the tower resistance had been 10 Ω instead of 20 Ω, the impulse voltage across the insulators would have risen to 200 kV and no flashover would have occurred.

Note that lightning currents of 20 kA are quite frequent, and they last only a few microseconds.

Another way of avoiding a line outage is to use a circuit breaker that recloses automatically, a few cycles after it trips. By that time the disturbance due to lightning will have disappeared and normal operation of the system can resume.

25.15 Fundamental objectives of a transmission line

The *fundamental* purpose of a transmission or distribution line is to carry *active* power (kilowatts)

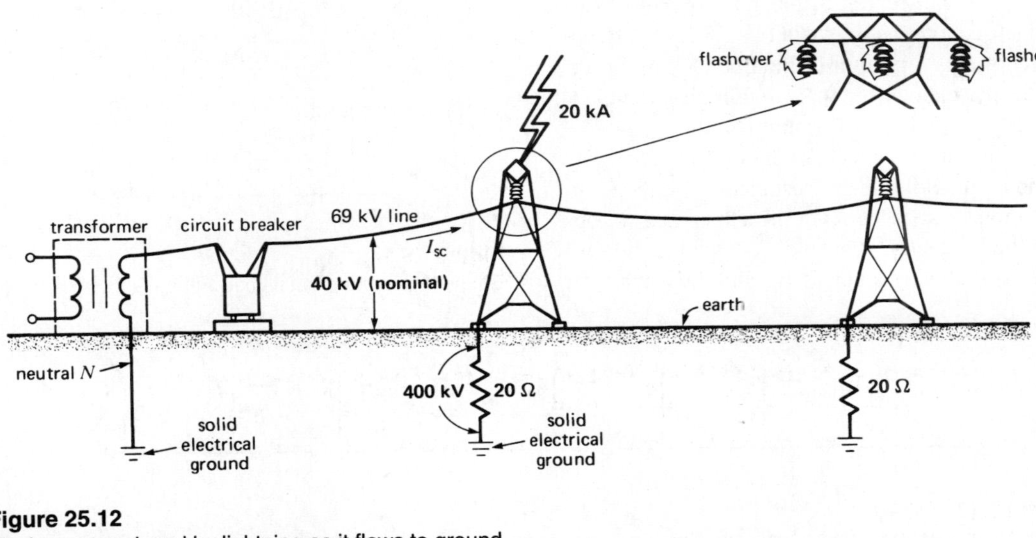

Figure 25.12
Flash-over produced by lightning as it flows to ground.

from one point to another. If it also has to carry reactive power, the latter should be kept as small as possible. In addition, a transmission line should possess the following basic characteristics:

1. The voltage should remain as constant as possible over the entire length of the line, from source to load, and for all loads between zero and rated load
2. The line losses must be small so as to attain a high transmission efficiency
3. The I^2R losses must not overheat the conductors

If the line alone cannot satisfy the above requirements, supplementary equipment, such as capacitors and inductors, must be added until the requirements are met.

25.16 Equivalent circuit of a line

In spite of their great differences in power rating, voltage levels, lengths, and mechanical construction, transmission lines possess similar electrical properties. In effect, an ac line possesses a resistance *R*, an inductive reactance X_L, and a capacitive reactance X_C. These impedances are uniformly distributed over the entire length of the line; consequently, we can represent the line by a series of identical sections, as shown in Fig. 25.13. Each section represents a portion of the line (1 km, for example), and elements *r*, x_L, x_C represent the impedances corresponding to this unit length.

We can simplify the circuit of Fig. 25.13 by lumping the individual resistances *r* together to yield a total resistance *R*. In the same way, we obtain a total inductive reactance X_L equal to the sum of the individual reactances x_L. Similarly, the total capacitive reactance X_C is equal to the sum of the x_C reactances, except they are connected in parallel. It is convenient to assume that the total capacitive reactance X_C of the line is composed of two parts, each having a value 2 X_C located at each end of the line. The resulting equivalent circuit of Fig. 25.14 is a good approximation of any 50 Hz or 60 Hz power line, provided its length is less than 250 km. Note that *R* and X_L increase as the length of the line increases, whereas X_C decreases with increasing length.

The equivalent circuit of Fig. 25.14 can also be used to represent one phase of a 3-phase line. Current *I* corresponds to the actual current flowing in one conductor and *E* is the voltage between the same conductor and neutral.

25.17 Typical impedance values

Table 25C gives typical values of the inductive and capacitive reactances per kilometer for practical transmission lines operating at 60 Hz. Surprisingly, the respective impedances per unit length are reasonably constant for all aerial lines. Thus, x_L is about 0.5 Ω/km and x_C is about 300 000 Ω·km

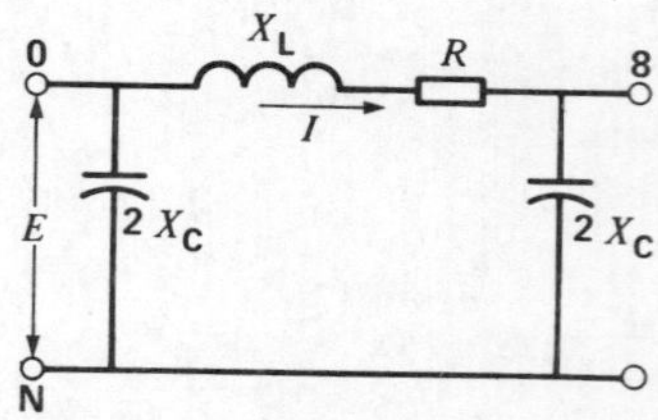

Figure 25.14
Equivalent lumped circuit of a transmission line.

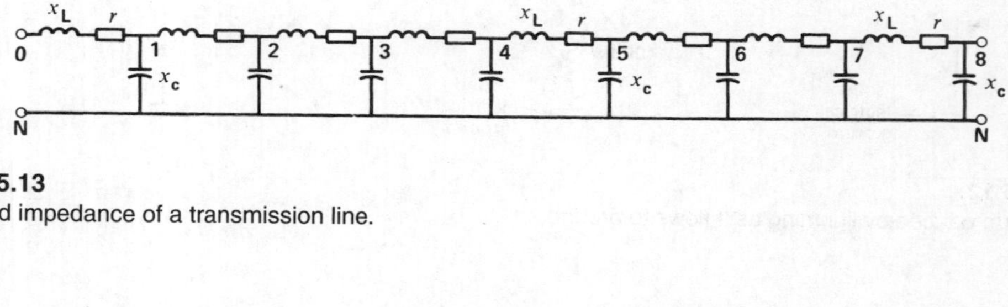

Figure 25.13
Distributed impedance of a transmission line.

whether the transmission line voltage is high or low, or whether the power is great or small.

TABLE 25C TYPICAL IMPEDANCE VALUES PER KILOMETER FOR 3-PHASE, 60 HZ LINES

Type of line	x_L [Ω]	x_C [Ω]
Aerial line	0.5	300 000
Underground cable	0.1	3 000

The same can be said of underground cables, except that the inductive and capacitive reactances of 3-phase cables are much smaller. Thus, x_C is about one hundred times smaller than that of aerial lines, whereas x_L is about five times smaller. This fact has a direct bearing on the maximum distance that ac power can be transmitted by cable.

The resistance r per unit length depends upon the size of the conductor. However, the size varies over such a wide range that it is impossible to assign a *typical* value to r. Table 25D gives the resistance and ampacity for several aerial conductors.

Example 25-2

A 3-phase, 230 kV transmission line having a length of 50 km is composed of three ACSR conductors having a cross-section of 1000 kcmil. The voltage of the source is 230 kV (line-to-line) and that at the load is 220 kV.

a. Determine the equivalent circuit, per phase.
b. Draw the complete equivalent circuit of the 3-phase line.

Solution

a. Referring to Tables 25C and 25D, the approximate line impedances per unit length are

$$r = 0.065\ \Omega/\text{km}$$
$$X_L = 0.5\ \Omega/\text{km}$$
$$X_C = 300\ \text{k}\Omega\cdot\text{km}$$

The line impedances, *per phase,* are

$$R = 0.065 \times 50 = 3.25\ \Omega$$
$$X_L = 0.5 \times 50 = 25\ \Omega$$
$$X_C = 300\ 000/50 = 6000\ \Omega$$

The capacitive reactance at each end of the line is

$$2\ X_C = 2 \times 6000 = 12\ \text{k}\Omega$$

The voltage per phase is $230/\sqrt{3} = 133$ kV at the source and $220/\sqrt{3} = 127$ kV at the load. The equivalent circuit per phase is shown in Fig. 25.15.

b. The complete equivalent circuit of the 3-phase line is shown in Fig. 25.16. Note that the line capacitance acts as if it were composed of six capacitors connected between the lines and ground. This circuit arrangement holds true even when the neutrals of the source and load

TABLE 25D RESISTANCE AND AMPACITY OF SOME BARE AERIAL CONDUCTORS

Conductor size		Resistance per conductor at 75°C		Ampacity in free air*	
AWG	Cross-section [mm²]	Copper [Ω/km]	ACSR [Ω/km]	Copper [A]	ACSR [A]
10	5.3	3.9	6.7	70	–
7	10.6	2.0	3.3	110	–
4	21.1	0.91	1.7	180	140
1	42.4	0.50	0.90	270	200
3/0	85	0.25	0.47	420	300
300 kcmil	152	0.14	0.22	600	500
600 kcmil	304	0.072	0.11	950	750
1000 kcmil	507	0.045	0.065	1300	1050

*The ampacity indicated is the maximum that may be used without weakening the conductor by overheating. In practice, the actual line current may be only 25 percent of the indicated value.

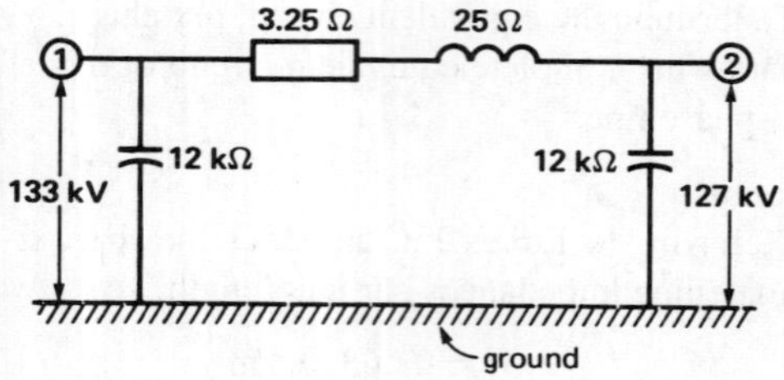

Figure 25.15
Equivalent circuit of one phase (Example 25-2).

are not grounded. The result is that the voltage across each capacitor is given by $E_c = E/\sqrt{3}$, where E is the respective line voltage at the source or load. Thus, knowing that the line voltage is 230 kV at the source and 220 kV at the load, the voltages across the respective capacitors are

$$E_{CS} = 230\sqrt{3} = 133 \text{ kV}$$

$$E_{CL} = 220\sqrt{3} = 127 \text{ kV}$$

25.18 Simplifying the equivalent circuit

We can often simplify the equivalent circuit of a transmission line by eliminating one, two, or all the elements shown in Fig. 25.14. The validity of this simplification depends upon the relative magnitude of the active and reactive powers P_J, Q_L, Q_C associated with the line, compared to the active power P that it delivers to the load. Referring to Fig. 25.17, these powers are

P = active power absorbed by the load
$P_J = I^2R$, active power dissipated in the line
$Q_L = I^2X_L$, reactive power absorbed by the line
$Q_C = E^2/X_C$, reactive power generated by the line (We assume the source and load voltages have the same magnitude.)

With the exception of P, these powers are all proportional to the length of the line. If one of them—P_J, Q_L, or Q_C—is negligible compared with the active power P, we can neglect the corresponding circuit element that produces it.

For example, low-voltage lines are always short and because the voltage is low, E^2/X_C is always negligible. Low-voltage lines can therefore be represented by the circuit of Fig. 25.18. If the conductor happens to be small, such as in house-wiring circuits, the resistance predominates and the inductive portion of Fig. 25.18 can also be neglected.

On the other hand, extra-high-voltage lines are always long, and so the reactive powers associated with the line capacitance and line inductance become important. Furthermore, because the efficiency is high, it follows that the I^2R losses are small. The equivalent circuit can therefore be represented by the circuit of Fig. 25.19.

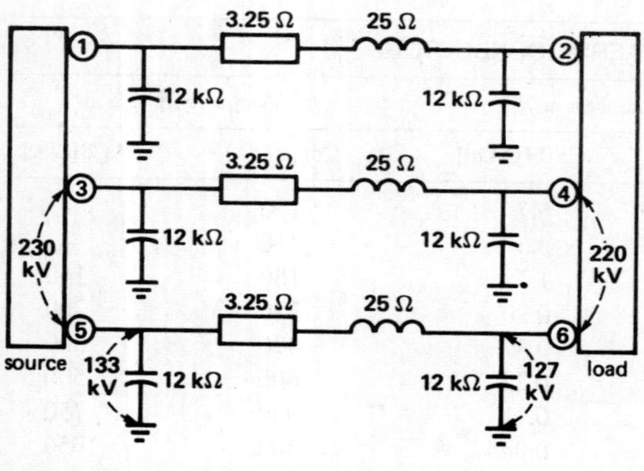

Figure 25.16
Equivalent circuit of a 3-phase line.

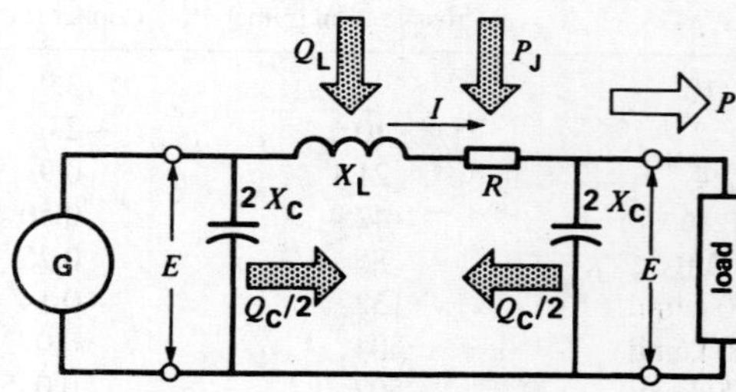

Figure 25.17
Active and reactive powers of a transmission line.

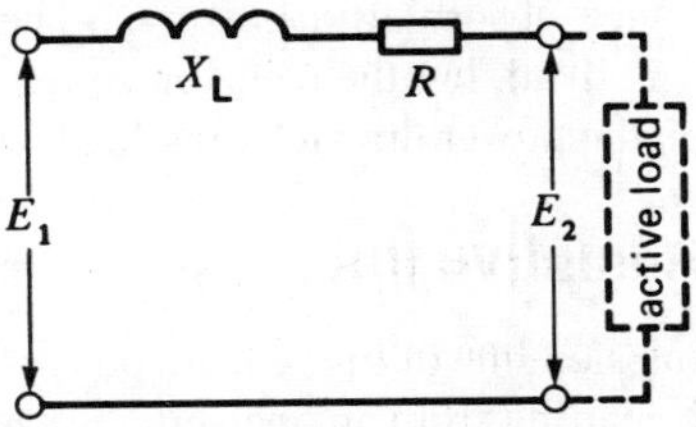

Figure 25.18
Equivalent circuit of a short LV line.

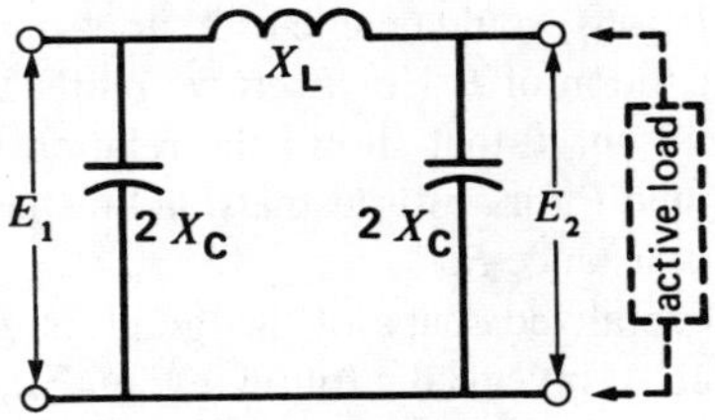

Figure 25.19
Equivalent circuit of a long HV line.

In general, medium-voltage and high-voltage lines can be represented by a simple inductive reactance. We will make use of this fact in developing the properties of transmission lines.

Example 25-3

The transmission line shown in Fig. 25.16 delivers 300 MW to the 3-phase load. If the line voltage at both the sending end (source) and receiving end (load) is 230 kV, determine the following:

a. The active and reactive powers associated with the line
b. The approximate equivalent circuit, per phase

Solution

Referring to Fig. 25.20a, we have

a. The line-to-neutral voltage at the load is

$$E = 230/\sqrt{3} = 133 \text{ k}\Omega$$

The active power transmitted to the load per phase is

$$P = 300 \text{ MW}/3 = 100 \text{ MW}$$

The load current is

$$I = 100 \text{ MW}/133 \text{ kV} = 750 \text{ A}$$

If we temporarily neglect the presence of the 12 kΩ capacitor in parallel with the load, the line current is equal to the load current (Fig. 25.20b). I^2R losses in the line are

$$P_J = I^2R = 3.25 \times 750^2$$
$$= 1.83 \text{ MW } (1.8 \text{ percent of } P)$$

Reactive power absorbed by the line is

$$Q_L = I^2X_L = 25 \times 750^2$$
$$= 14.1 \text{ Mvar } (14 \text{ percent of } P)$$

Reactive power generated by the line at each end is

$$Q = E^2/X_C = 133\,000^2/12\,000$$
$$= 1.47 \text{ Mvar}$$

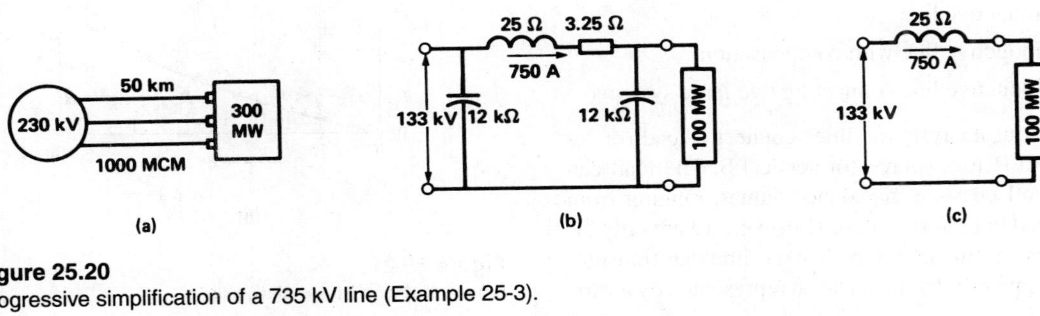

Figure 25.20
Progressive simplification of a 735 kV line (Example 25-3).

Total reactive power generated by the line is

$$Q_C = 2 \times 1.47$$
$$= 3 \text{ Mvar (3 percent of } P)$$

b. Comparing the relative values of P_J, Q_L, Q_C, and P, it is clear that we can neglect the resistance and the capacitance of the line. The resulting equivalent circuit is a simple inductive reactance of 25 Ω (Fig. 25.20c).

25.19 Voltage regulation and power-transmission capability of transmission lines

Voltage regulation and power-handling capacity are two important features of a transmission line. Thus, the voltage of a transmission line should remain as constant as possible even under variable load conditions. Ordinarily, the voltage regulation from zero to full-load should not exceed ±5% of the nominal voltage (though we can sometimes accept a regulation as high as ±10%).

As regards power-handling capacity, it may come as a surprise that a transmission line can deliver only so much power and no more. The power that can be transported from source to load depends upon the impedance of the line. We are mainly interested in transmitting active power because only it can do useful work. In order to determine the voltage regulation and to establish their power transmission capability, we now examine four types of lines:

1. Resistive line
2. Inductive line
3. Inductive line with compensation
4. Inductive line connecting two large systems

In our analysis the lines connect a load (or receiver) R to a source (or sender) S. The load can have all possible impedance values, ranging from no-load to a short-circuit. However, we are only interested in the *active* power the line can transmit. Consequently, the load can be represented by a variable resistance absorbing a power P. The sender voltage E_S is fixed, but the receiver voltage E_R depends upon the power drawn by the load.

25.20 Resistive line

The transmission line of Fig. 25.21a possesses a resistance R. Starting from an open circuit, we gradually reduce the load resistance until it becomes zero. During this process we observe the receiver voltage E_R across the load, as well as the active power P it absorbs. If numerical values were given, a few simple calculations would enable us to draw a graph of E_R as a function of P. However, we prefer to use a generalized curve that shows the relationship between E_R and P for *any* transmission line having an arbitrary resistance R.

The generalized shape of this graph is given in Fig. 25.21b. It reveals the following information:

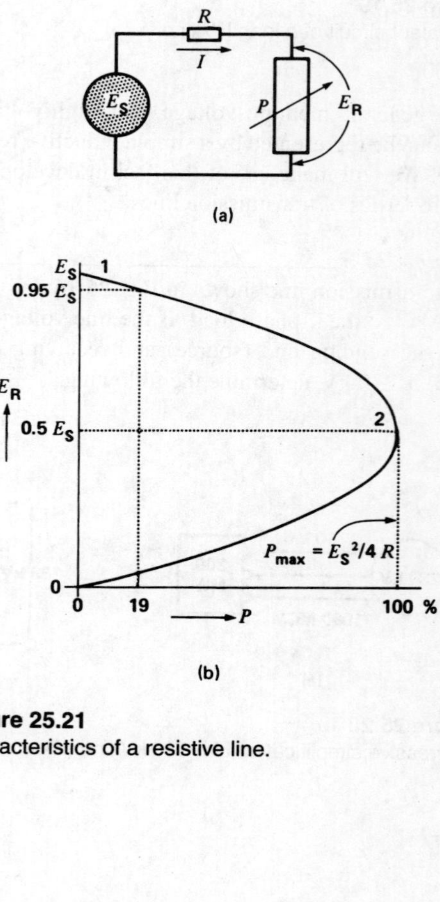

Figure 25.21
Characteristics of a resistive line.

a. There is an upper limit to the power the line can transmit to the load. In effect,

$$P_{max} = E_S^2/4\,R \qquad (25.1)$$

and this maximum is reached when the receiver voltage is

$$E_R = 0.5\,E_S$$

b. The power delivered to the load is maximum when the impedance of the load is equal to the resistance of the line.
c. If we permit a maximum regulation of 5 percent ($E_R = 0.95\,E_S$), the graph shows that the line can carry a load that is only 19 percent of P_{max}. The line could transmit more power, but the customer voltage E_R would then be too low.

Note that the sender must furnish the power P absorbed by the load, plus the I^2R losses in the line.

Example 25-4

A single-phase transmission line having a resistance of 10 Ω is connected to a fixed sender voltage of 1000 V.

Calculate

a. The maximum power the line can transmit to the load
b. The receiver power for a receiver voltage of 950 V

Solution

a. The maximum power that can be transmitted is

$$P_{max} = E_S^2/4\,R = 1000^2/(4 \times 10) = 25\text{ kW}$$

b. When E_R = 950 V, the voltage drop in the line is

$$E_S - E_R = 1000 - 950 = 50\text{ V}$$

The line current is, therefore,

$$I = (E_S - E_R)/R = 50/10 = 5\text{ A}$$

The receiver power is

$$P = E_S I = 950 \times 5 = 4750\text{ W} = 4.75\text{ kW}$$

Note that 4.75 kW/25 kW = 0.19, or 19%, which is the percentage predicted by the curve of Fig. 25.21b.

25.21 Inductive line

Let us now consider a line having negligible resistance but possessing an inductive reactance X (Fig. 25.22a). The receiver again operates at unity power factor, and so it can be represented by a variable resistance absorbing a power P. As in the case of a resistive line, voltage E_R diminishes as the load increases, but the regulation curve has a different shape (Fig. 25.22b). In effect, the generalized graph of E_R as a function of P reveals the following information:

a. The line can transmit a maximum power to the load given by

$$P_{max} = E_S^2/2\,X \qquad (25.5)$$

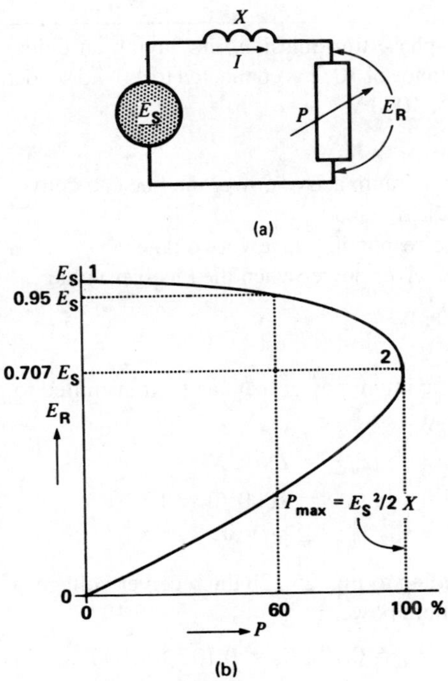

Figure 25.22
Characteristics of an inductive line.

The corresponding receiver voltage is

$$E_R = 0.707\ E_S$$

Thus, for a given line impedance and sender voltage, the reactive line can deliver twice as much power as a resistive line can (compare $P = E_S^2/2\ X$ and $P = E_S^2/4\ R$).

b. The power delivered to the load is maximum when the resistance of the load is equal to the reactance of the line.

c. If we again allow a maximum regulation of 5 percent, the graph shows that the line can carry a load that is 60 percent of P_{max}. Thus, for a given line impedance and a regulation of 5 percent, the inductive line can transmit *six* times as much active power as a resistive line can.

The sender has to supply the active power P consumed by the load plus the reactive power I^2X absorbed by the line.

Example 25-5

A single-phase transmission line having an inductive reactance of 10 Ω is connected to a fixed sender voltage of 1000 V.

Calculate

a. The maximum active power the line can deliver to a resistive load
b. The corresponding receiver voltage
c. The receiver power when the receiver voltage is 950 V

Solution

a. The maximum power that can be transmitted to the load is

$$P_{max} = E_S^2/2\ X = 1000^2/2 \times 10 = 50\ \text{kW}$$

b. According to Fig. 25.22b the receiver voltage at maximum power is

$$E_R = 0.707\ E_S = 0.707 \times 1000 = 707\ \text{V}$$

c. In order to calculate the receiver power when $E_R = 950$ V, we first calculate the value of the current I. Taking $E_R = 950$ V as the reference phasor, we draw the phasor diagram for the circuit of Fig. 25.23.

Current I is in phase with E_R because the load is resistive. Furthermore, we can write

$$E_S = E_R + jIX = 950 + 10\,jI$$

This equation corresponds to the phasor diagram of Fig. 25.24. From this diagram we can write, by inspection

$$E_S^2 = E_R^2 + (10\,I)^2$$
$$1000^2 = 950^2 + 100\,I^2$$

from which

$$I = \sqrt{975} = 31.22\ \text{A}$$

The power to the receiver is, therefore,

$$P = E_S I = 950 \times 31.22 = 29.66\ \text{kW}$$

Note that 29.66 kW is equal to 60 percent of P_{max} (50 kW), as predicted by the curve of Fig. 25.22.

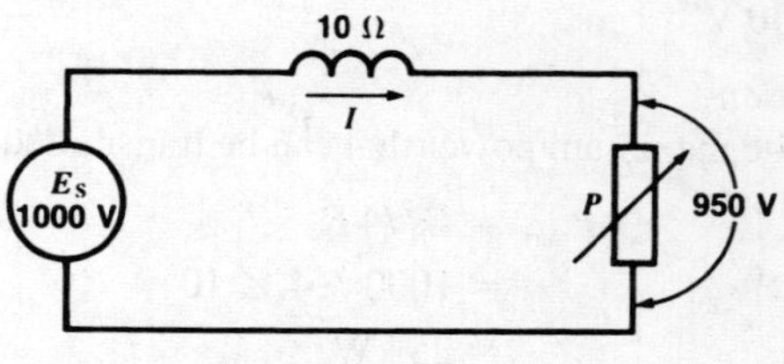

Figure 25.23
See Example 25-5.

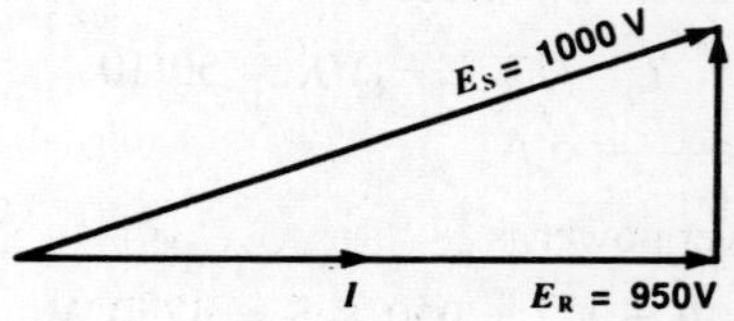

Figure 25.24
See Example 25-5.

25.22 Compensated inductive line

We can improve the regulation and power-handling capacity of an inductive line by adding a variable capacitive reactance X_C across the load (Fig. 25.25a). Indeed, we can get perfect regulation by adjusting the value of X_C so that the reactive power E_S^2/X_C supplied by the capacitor is at *all* times equal to *one-half* the reactive power I^2X absorbed by the line. For such a compensated line the value of the receiver voltage E_R will always be equal to the sender voltage E_S, irrespective of the active power P absorbed by the load.

However, there still is an upper limit to the power the line can transmit. A detailed analysis shows that we can maintain a constant load voltage ($E_R = E_S$) up to a maximum of

$$P_{max} = E_S^2/X \tag{25.3}$$

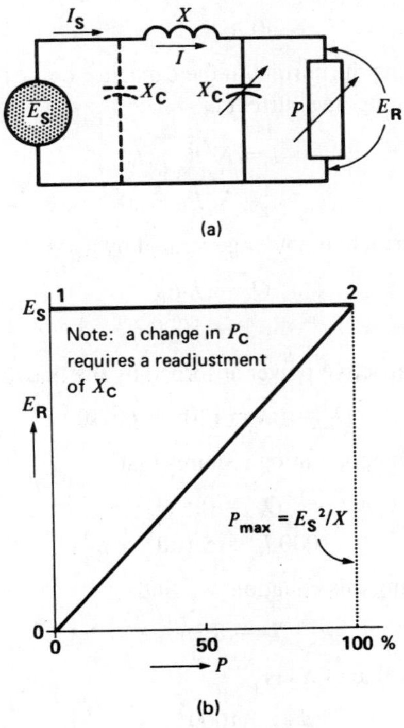

Figure 25.25
Characteristics of a compensated inductive line.

Beyond this limit, E_R gradually decreases to zero in a diagonal line, as shown by the graph of Fig. 25.25b. Note the following:

a. The voltage regulation is perfect until the load power reaches the limiting value $P_{max} = E_S^2/X$.
b. The compensated inductive line can deliver twice as much power (P_{max}) as an uncompensated line can. Moreover, it has the advantage of maintaining a constant load voltage.

Capacitor X_C supplies one-half the reactive power I^2X_L absorbed by the line; the remaining half is supplied by the sender E_S. If necessary, we can add a second capacitor X_C (dash line in Fig. 25.25a) at the input to the line. The source has then only to supply the active power P, while the reactive power is supplied by the capacitors at both ends.

Example 25-6

A single-phase line possesses an inductive reactance X of 10 Ω and is connected to a fixed sender voltage of 1000 V. If it is fully compensated, calculate the following:

a. The maximum active power that the line can deliver to a resistive load
b. The capacitive reactance that must be installed on the receiver side, in (a)
c. The capacitive reactance that must be installed on the receiver side when the active power is 40 kW

Solution

a. The maximum power that can be transmitted to the receiver is

$$P_{max} = E_S^2/X = 1000^2/10 = 100 \text{ kW}$$

b. Fig. 25.26 shows the compensated line with the capacitive reactance carrying a current I_C. The phasor diagram of Fig. 25.27 gives us the key to solving the value of X_C that is required. Using $E_R = 1000$ V as the reference phasor we reason as follows:

The current in the resistive load is

$$I_R = P_{max}/E_R = 100\,000/1000 = 100 \text{ A}$$

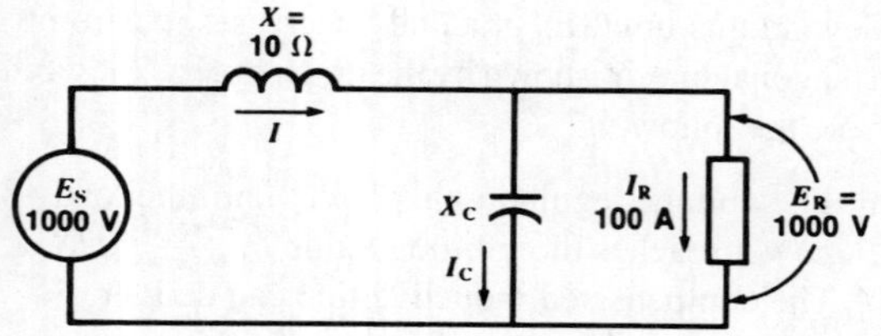

Figure 25.26
See Example 25-6.

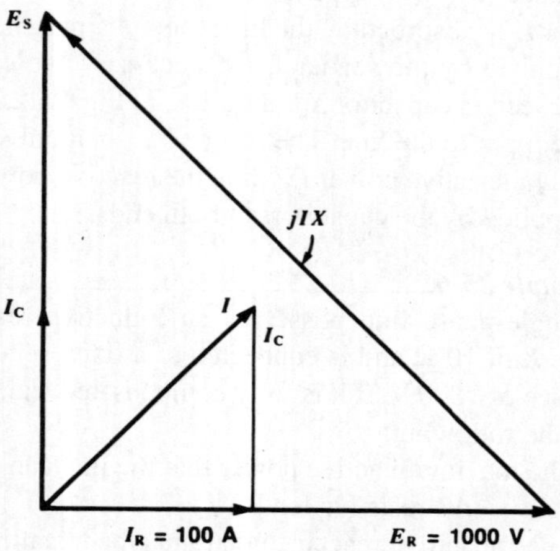

Figure 25.27
See Example 25-6.

The current I_C leads E_R by 90°.
The reactive power generated by X_C is

$$Q_C = E_R I_C$$
$$= 1000\ I_C$$

The current I in the line is

$$I = \sqrt{I_C^2 + I_R^2}$$
$$= \sqrt{I_C^2 + 100^2}$$

The reactive power absorbed by the line is

$$Q_L = I^2 X = (I_C{}^2 + 100^2)\ 10$$

In a fully compensated line we have

$$Q_C = 0.5\ Q_L$$

Consequently,

$$1000\ I_C = 5\ (IC^2 + 100^2)$$
$$5\ I_C{}^2 - 1000\ I_C + 5 \times 10^4 = 0$$

Solving this quadratic equation we find

$$I_C = 100\ \text{A}$$

The value of X_C is given by

$$X_C = E_R / I_C$$
$$= 1000/100$$
$$= 10\ \Omega$$

In Fig. 25.27, the fact that I_C = 100 A means that current I leads E_R by 45°. Consequently, E_S must be 90° ahead of E_R. Thus, the power transfer is maximum when the phase angle between E_S and E_R is 90°. This is compatible with Eq. 16.8 in Section 16.23.

c. When the load is 40 kW, the load current is

$$I_R = P/E_R = 40\,000/1000$$
$$= 40\ \text{A}$$

Letting the current in the capacitor be I_C, the resulting line current is

$$I = \sqrt{I_C^2 + I_R^2}$$
$$= \sqrt{I_C^2 + 40^2}$$

The reactive power generated by X_C is

$$Q_C = I_C E_R$$
$$= 1000\ I_C$$

The reactive power absorbed by the line is

$$Q_L = I^2 X = (40^2 + I_C{}^2)10$$

Full compensation requires that

$$Q_C = 0.5\ Q_L$$
$$1000\ I_C = 5\ (40^2 + I_C{}^2)$$

Solving this equation, we find

$$I_C = 8.35\ \text{A}$$

The value of X_C is

$$X_C = \frac{E_R}{I_C} = \frac{1000}{8.35} = 119.8\ \Omega$$

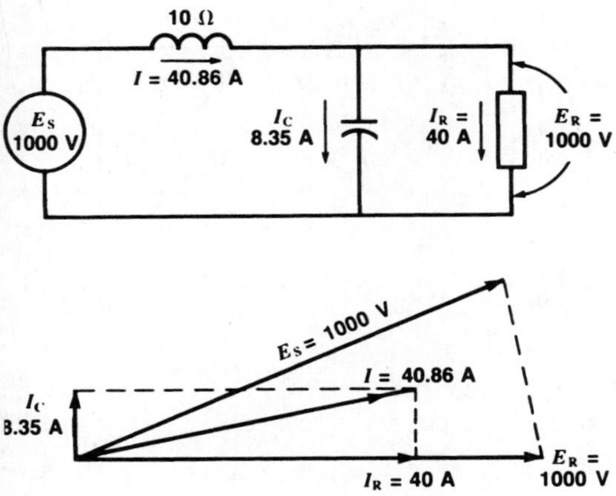

Figure 25.28
See Example 25-6.

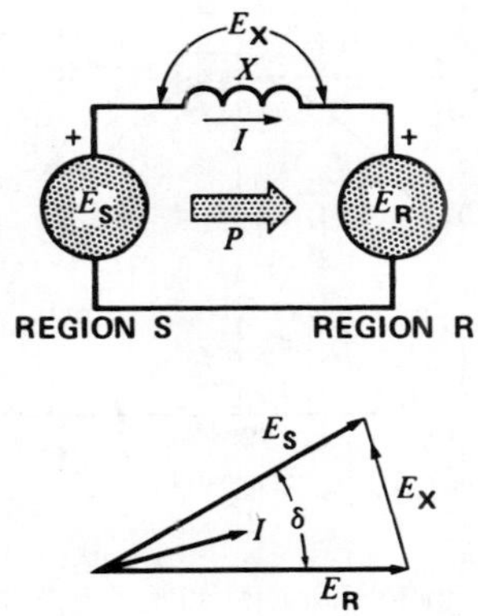

Figure 25.29
E_S leads E_R.

The circuit and phasor diagram for this compensated line is given in Fig. 25.28. We note that although the values of E_R and E_S are the same, E_R lags considerably behind E_S.

25.23 Inductive line connecting two systems

Large cities and other regional users of electrical energy are always interconnected by a network of transmission lines. Such a network improves the stability of the electric utility system and enables it to better endure momentary short-circuits and other disturbances. Interconnecting lines also enable energy exchanges between electrical utility companies. The 60 Hz frequency of such a network is everywhere the same.

The voltages of large regional users remain essentially independent of each other, both in value and in phase. In effect, because of their enormous power, the regional consumers appear as if they were independent, infinite buses. What happens when an additional transmission line is put in service between two such regions?

Fig. 25.29 shows the equivalent circuit of such an inductive line connecting two regional consumers S and R. We assume the terminal voltages E_S and E_R are fixed, each possessing the same magnitude E. Regarding the exchange of active power between the two regional consumers, we examine three distinct possibilities:

1. E_S and E_R in phase
2. E_S leading E_R by an angle δ
3. E_S lagging E_R by an angle δ

1. E_S and E_R in Phase. In this case, the line current is zero and no power is transmitted.

2. E_S Leads E_R by an Angle δ (Fig. 25.29). Region S supplies power to region R and, from the phasor diagram, we can prove (Section 16.23) that the active power transmitted is given by

$$P = \frac{E^2}{X} \sin \delta \tag{25.4}$$

where

P = active power transmitted per phase [MW]*
E = line-to-neutral voltage [kV]
X = inductive reactance of the line, per phase [Ω]
δ = phase angle between the voltages at each end of the line [°]

* In this equation, if E represents the line voltage, P is the *total* power transmitted by the three phases.

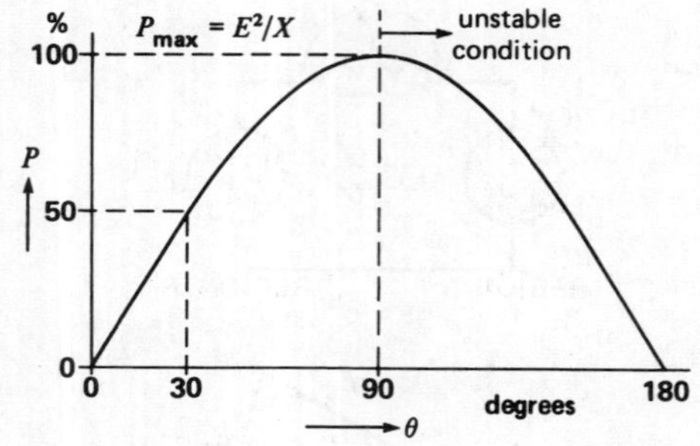

Figure 25.30a
Power versus angle characteristic.

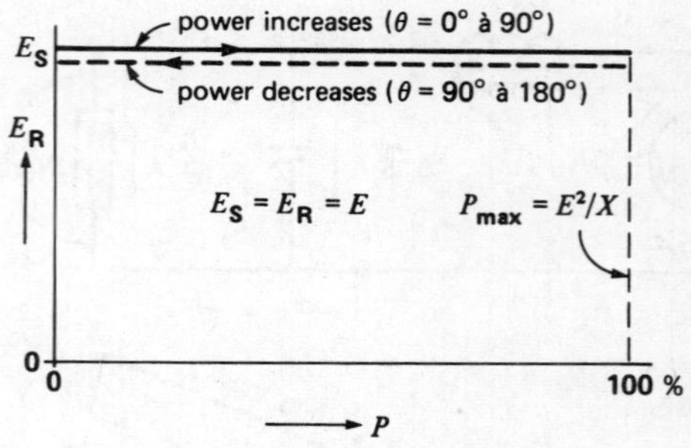

Figure 25.30b
Voltage versus power characteristic.

Fig. 25.30a shows the active power transmitted from region S to region R as a function of the phase angle between the two regions. Note that the power increases progressively and attains a maximum value of E^2/X when the phase angle is 90°. In effect, just as in the other transmission lines we have studied, a line connecting two power centers can transmit only so much power and no more. The power limit is the same as that of a compensated inductive line. Although we can still transmit power when the phase angle exceeds 90°, we avoid this condition because it corresponds to an unstable mode of operation. When δ approaches 90°, the two regions are at the point of pulling apart, and the line circuit breakers will trip.

Fig. 25.30b shows the load voltage E_R as a function of the active power transmitted. It is simply a horizontal line that stretches to a maximum value $P_{max} = E^2/X$ before falling back again to zero (dotted line). This voltage regulation curve should be compared with that of Fig. 25.25b for a compensated line.

Note that the line voltage drop E_x is quite large, even though the terminal voltages E_S and E_R are equal in magnitude (Fig. 25.29). Furthermore, it is clear that E_x increases as the phase angle between E_S and E_R increases.

3. E_S Lags Behind E_R by an Angle δ (Fig. 25.31). The active power has the same value as before, but it now flows in the opposite direction, from region R toward region S. The graph of active power versus phase angle is identical to that shown in Fig. 25.30a.

If we compare Figs. 25.29 and 25.31, we note that the direction of power flow does not depend upon the relative magnitudes of E_S and E_R (they are equal), but *only upon the phase angle between them.* On inductive lines, active power always flows from the leading to the lagging voltage side.

25.24 Review of power transmission

In summary, there is always a limit to the amount of power a line can transmit. The maximum power is proportional to the square of the sender voltage and

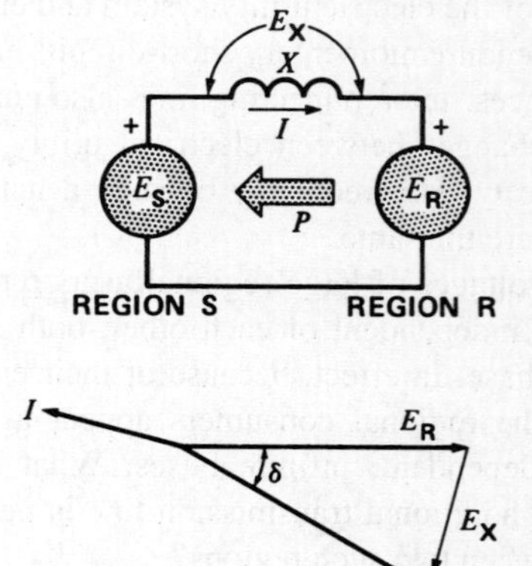

Figure 25.31
E_R leads E_S.

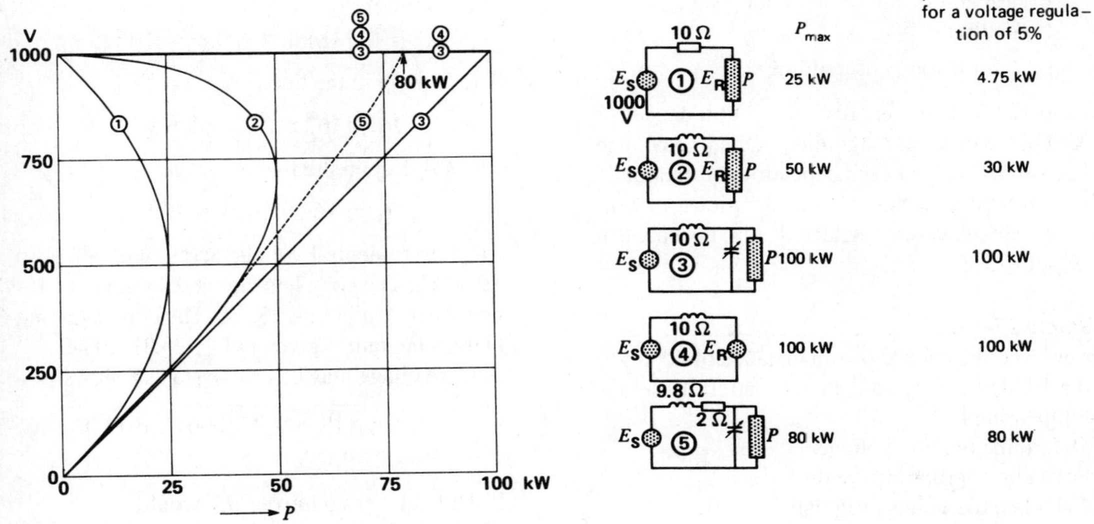

Figure 25.32
Comparison of the power-handling properties of various transmission lines.

inversely proportional to the impedance of the line. Fig. 25.32 enables us to compare actual values of power and voltage for the four transmission line models we have studied. Each model possesses an impedance of 10 Ω and the sender furnishes a voltage E_S of 1000 V. It is clear that the E_R versus P curves become flatter and flatter as we progress from a resistive to an inductive to a compensated line.

The table next to the graph shows the maximum power that can be transmitted assuming a regulation of 5 percent or better. Thus, the resistive line can transmit 4.75 kW, whereas the inductive line can transmit 30 kW.

Because all lines possess some resistance, we also show the voltage-power curve of a compensated line having a reactance of 9.8 Ω and a resistance of 2 Ω (curve 5). This fifth line also has an impedance of 10 Ω, but the maximum power it can transmit drops to 80 kW, compared to 100 kW for a line possessing no resistance.

In practice, the voltages and powers are much higher than those given in these examples. Nevertheless, the method of analysis is the same.

25.25 Choosing the line voltage

We have seen that for a given transmission line and for a given voltage regulation the maximum power P_{max} that can be transmitted is proportional to E^2/Z, where E is the voltage of the line and Z, its impedance. Thus,

$$P_{max} \propto \frac{E^2}{Z}$$

and so

$$E^2 \propto P_{max}Z$$

Because Z is proportional to the length of the line, we deduce that the line voltage can be expressed by

$$E = k\sqrt{Pl} \qquad (25.5)$$

where

E = 3-phase line voltage [kV]
P = power to be transmitted [kW]
l = length of the transmission line [km]
k = coefficient that depends on the type of line and the allowable voltage regulation. Typical values are

$k = 0.1$ for an uncompensated line having a regulation of 5%

$k = 0.06$ for a compensated line

Equation 25.5 is very approximate, but it does give an idea of the order of magnitude of the line voltage *E*. The value finally chosen depends upon economic factors as well as technical considerations; in general, the actual voltage selected will lie between 0.6 *E* and 1.5 *E*.

Example 25-7

Power has to be carried over a distance of 20 km to feed a 10 MW unity power factor load. If the line is uncompensated,

a. Determine the line voltage
b. Select an appropriate conductor size
c. Calculate the voltage regulation

Solution

a. Because the line is not compensated, we assume $k = 0.1$. A power of 10 MW is equal to 10 000 kW. Consequently,

$$E = k\sqrt{Pl} \qquad (25.5)$$
$$= 0.1\sqrt{10\,000 \times 20}$$
$$= 44.7 \text{ kV}$$

Any voltage between 0.6×44.7 kV (= 27 kV) and 1.5×44.7 kV (= 67 kV) is feasible. We shall use a standard line voltage of 34.5 kV. The line-to-neutral voltage is

$$E = 34.5/\sqrt{3} = 19.9 \text{ kV}$$

b. The conductor size depends mainly upon the current to be carried. The line current is

$$I = S/(\sqrt{3}\,E) \qquad (8.9)$$
$$= 10 \times 10^6/(1.73 \times 34\,500)$$
$$= 167 \text{ A}$$

According to Table 25D, we can use a No. 1 ACSR conductor:

$$\text{ampacity} = 200 \text{ A}$$
$$R = 0.9\ \Omega/\text{km} \times 20 \text{ km} = 18\ \Omega$$

From Table 25C we find

$$X_L = 0.5\ \Omega/\text{km} \times 20 \text{ km} = 10\ \Omega$$

c. The *IR* drop in the line is

$$IR = 167 \times 18 = 3006 \text{ V}$$

The IX_L drop in the line is

$$IX_L = 167 \times 10 = 1670 \text{ V}$$

The line-to-neutral voltage across the load is 19 900 V. The complete circuit diagram per phase is given in Fig. 25.33a. The corresponding phasor diagram is given in Fig. 25.33b. The sender voltage may be calculated as follows:

$$E_S = \sqrt{(19\,900 + 3006)^2 + 1670^2}$$
$$= 22\,967 \text{ V}$$

If the load were removed, E_R would rise to 22 967 V. The voltage regulation is, therefore,

$$\text{regulation} = (22\,967 - 19\,000)/19\,000$$
$$= 3967/19\,000$$
$$= 0.209 \text{ or } 20.9\%$$

Note that this medium-voltage line is more resistive than inductive.

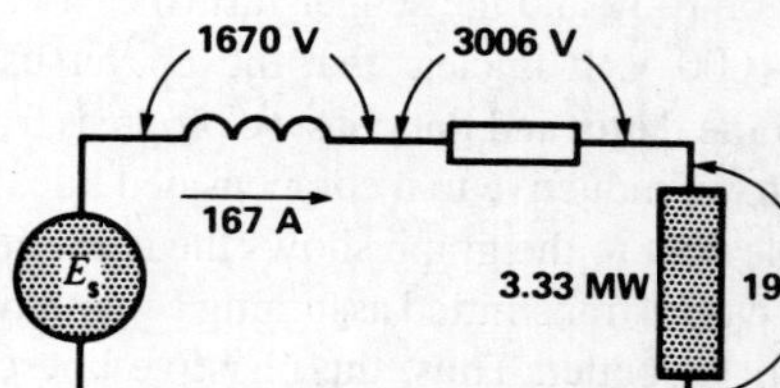

Figure 25.33a
Transmission line under load.

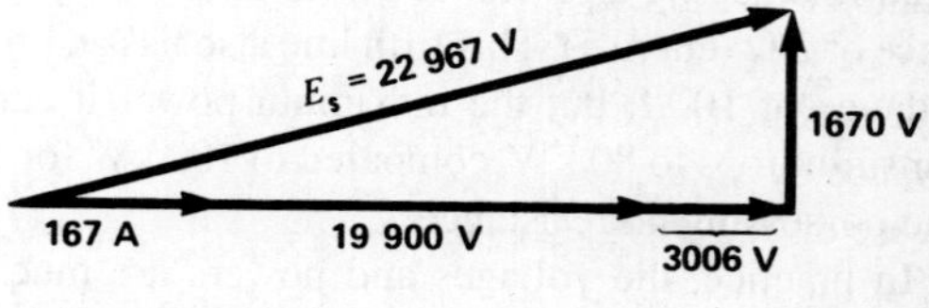

Figure 25.33b
Corresponding phasor diagram.

25.26 Methods of increasing the power capacity

High-voltage lines are mainly inductive, possessing a reactance of about 0.5 Ω/km. This creates problems when we have to transmit large blocks of power over great distances. Suppose, for example, that 4000 MW has to be transmitted over a distance of 400 km. The reactance of the line is 400 km × 0.5 Ω/km = 200 Ω, per phase. Since the highest practical line-to-line voltage is about 800 kV, the 3-phase line can transmit no more than

$$\begin{aligned} P_{max} &= E^2/X \\ &= 800^2/200 \\ &= 3200 \text{ MW} \end{aligned} \tag{25.3}$$

To transmit 4000 MW, the only solution is to use *two lines in parallel,* one beside the other. Note that doubling the size of the conductors would not help, because for such a line it is the *reactance* and not the resistance of the conductors that determines the maximum power that can be transmitted.

Additional lines are also useful to provide system security in the event that a parallel line trips out, due to a disturbance. Thus, if one line is lost, the scheduled power can still be carried by the remaining line.

To carry large blocks of power, we sometimes erect two, three, and even four transmission lines in parallel, which follow the same corridor across the countryside (Fig. 25.34). In addition to high cost, the use of parallel lines often creates serious problems of land expropriation. Consequently, special methods are sometimes used to increase the maximum power of a line. In effect, when we can no longer increase the line voltage, we try to reduce the line reactance X_L by greatly increasing the effective diameter of the conductors. This is done by using two or more conductors per phase, kept apart by spacers. Such *bundled conductors* can reduce the reactance by as much as 40 percent, permitting an increase of 67 percent in the power-handling capability of the line.

Another method uses capacitors in series with the three lines to artificially reduce the value of X_L.

Figure 25.34
Two 735 kV transmission lines in parallel carrying electrical energy to a large city. Each phase is composed of 4 bundled conductors (see Fig. 25.7). (*Courtesy of Hydro-Québec*)

With this arrangement, the maximum power is given by

$$P_{max} = E^2/(X_L - X_{cs}) \tag{25.6}$$

where X_{cs} is the reactance of the series capacitors per phase. Such series compensation is also used to regulate the voltage of medium-voltage lines when the load fluctuates rapidly.

25.27 Extra-high-voltage lines

When electrical energy is transmitted at extra-high voltages, special problems arise that require the installation of large compensating devices to regulate the voltage and to guarantee stability. Among these devices are synchronous capacitors, inductive reactors, static var compensators, and shunt and series capacitors.

To understand the need for such devices, and to appreciate the magnitude of the powers involved, consider a 3-phase, 735 kV, 60 Hz line, having a length of 600 km. The line operates at 727 kV and the inductive and capacitive reactances are respectively 0.5 Ω and 300 kΩ for each kilometer of length. We first determine the equivalent circuit of the transmission line per phase:

Sender voltage per phase (line-to-neutral) is

$$E_S = 727/\sqrt{3} = 420 \text{ kV}$$

Inductive reactance per phase is

$$X_L = 0.5 \times 600 = 300\ \Omega$$

Capacitive reactance per phase is

$$X_C = 300\ \text{k}\Omega/600 = 500\ \Omega$$

Equivalent capacitive reactance at each end of the line is

$$X_{C1} = X_{C2} = 2 \times 500\ \Omega$$
$$= 1000\ \Omega$$

The equivalent circuit, per phase, is shown in Fig. 25.35. Let us now study the behavior of the line under no-load and full-load conditions.

No-Load Operation. At no-load the circuit formed by X_L in series with X_{C2} produces a partial resonance and the terminal voltage E_R rises to 600 kV. In effect, we obtain

$$E_R = E_S \times \frac{X_{C2}}{X_{C2} - X_L}$$
$$= 420 \text{ kV} \times \frac{1000\ \Omega}{1000\ \Omega - 300\ \Omega} = 600 \text{ kV}$$

This represents an increase of 43 percent above the nominal voltage of 420 kV (Fig. 25.35). Such an abnormally high voltage is unacceptable. The only feasible way to reduce it is to connect an inductive reactance X_{L2} at the end of the line (Fig. 25.36). If we make X_{L2} equal to X_{C2}, the resulting parallel resonance brings voltage E_R back to 420 kV. In effect, the reactive power generated by X_{C2} ($420^2/1000 = 176$ Mvar) is entirely absorbed by X_{L2}. The latter must, therefore, have a capacity of 176 Mvar, *per phase.*

Despite this inductive compensation, we still have a reactive power of 176 Mvar, generated by X_{C1}, which has to be absorbed by the synchronous generator G. However, a capacitive load at the terminals of a generator creates overvoltages, unless we reduce the alternator exciting current (Section 16.13). But underexcitation is not recommended because it leads to instability. Consequently, we must install a second inductive reactance of 176 Mvar close to the generating station. In the case of very long transmission lines (500 km to 1500 km), several inductive reactances are installed along the line to distribute the inductive compensation evenly over its length.

Inductive reactors (fixed or variable) are composed of a large coil placed inside a tank and immersed in oil (Fig. 25.37). A laminated steel core split up into a series of short air gaps carries the magnetic flux. Intense magnetic forces are developed across the air gaps. On a 60 Hz system, these forces continuously oscillate between zero and several tons, at a mechanical frequency of 120 Hz. The core laminations and all metallic parts must, therefore, be firmly secured to reduce vibration and to limit noise to an acceptable level.

Operation Under Load, Characteristic Impedance. Returning again to the uncompensated line on open-circuit (Fig. 25.35), let us connect a variable unity power factor load across the receiver terminals. If we progressively increase the megawatt load, receiver voltage E_R will gradually decrease from its open-circuit value of 600 kV and for one particular load it will become exactly equal to the sender voltage E_S

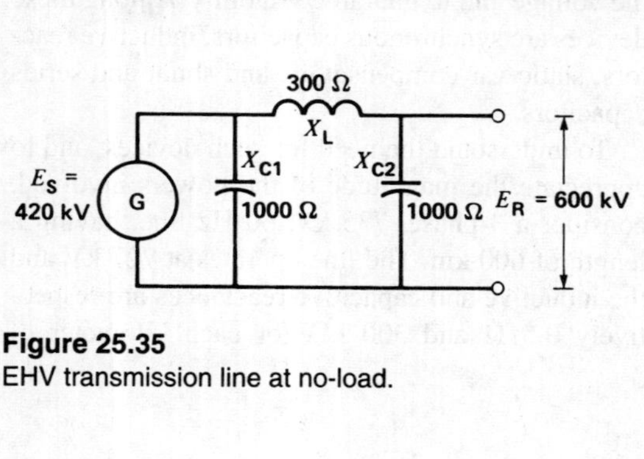

Figure 25.35
EHV transmission line at no-load.

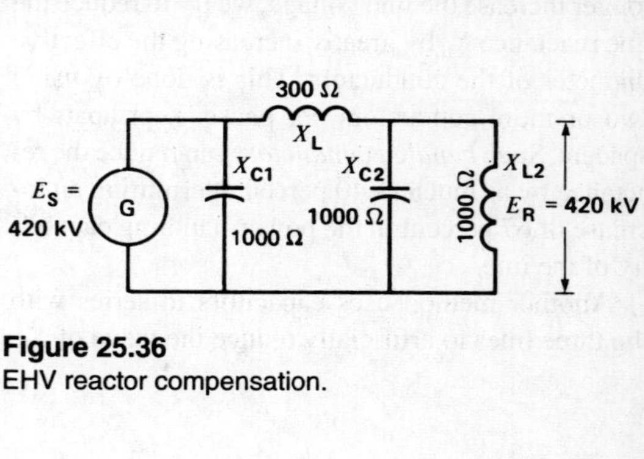

Figure 25.36
EHV reactor compensation.

Figure 25.37
Three large 110 Mvar, single-phase reactors installed in a substation to compensate the line capacitance of a very long 3-phase 735 kV transmission line.
(Courtesy of Hydro-Québec)

This particular load is called the *surge-impedance load* (Fig. 25.38). For most aerial lines the impedance of this load corresponds to a line-to-neutral load resistance of about 400 Ω per phase. This particular load resistance (called *surge impedance*) is independent of the system frequency or the length of the line. The surge impedance load (SIL) of a 3-phase transmission line is, therefore, given by the approximate equation:

$$\text{SIL} = E^2/400 \tag{25.7}$$

where

SIL = surge impedance load [MW]

E = 3-phase line voltage [kV]

In Fig. 25.38, the total surge-impedance load is approximately $727^2/400 = 1320$ MW.

When a transmission line delivers active power corresponding to its surge-impedance load, the reactive power generated by the capacitance of the line is equal to that absorbed by its inductance. The line, in effect, compensates itself. If the load exceeds the surge-impedance load, we can keep E_R at 420 kV by adding extra capacitors at the receiver end of the line. However, the maximum power is still limited to the value given by Eq. 25.3, namely

$$\begin{aligned} P_{max} &= 3 \times (E^2/X) \\ &= 3 \times (420^2/300) \\ &= 1764 \text{ MW} \end{aligned}$$

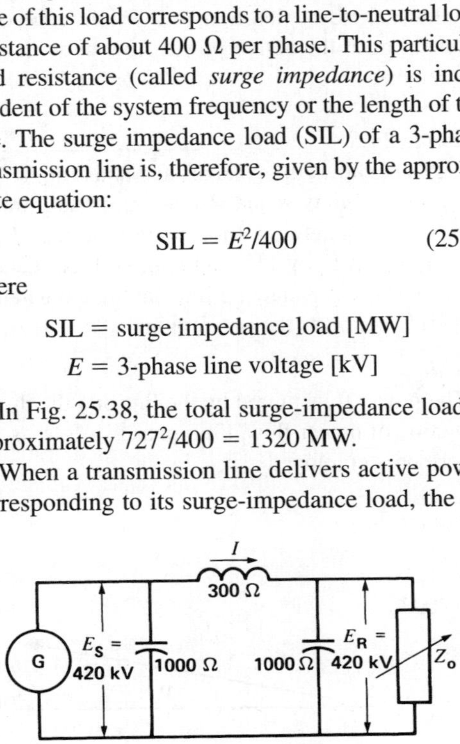

Figure 25.38
Surge impedance loading of a line.

Figure 25.39
Static var compensator for HV line.
(Courtesy of General Electric)

If the load is less than the surge-impedance load, we must add inductive reactance at the receiver end of the line to maintain a constant voltage. Conversely, if the load is greater than the surge-impedance load, a capacitive reactance must be added. Because the load continually changes throughout the day, the magnitude of the capacitive and inductive reactance must continually be varied to keep a steady voltage. This is done by means of static var compensators (Fig. 25.39), or rotating synchronous machines. The latter can deliver or absorb reactive power, according to whether they are over- or under-excited (Section 17.15).

25.28 Power exchange between power centers

We sometimes have to install an additional transmission line between regions that are already tightly interconnected. Such a line may be required to meet the energy needs of a rapidly growing area or to improve the overall stability of the network. In such cases, we use special methods so that the additional line will transmit the required power.

Consider, for example, two major power centers A and B that are already interconnected by a grid of transmission lines (not shown) (Fig. 25.40). The respective voltages E_a and E_b are equal, but E_a leads E_b by an angle δ. If we decide to connect the two centers by an extra transmission line having a reactance X, the active power P will automatically flow from A to B because E_a leads E_b (see Section 25.23). Furthermore, phase angle δ and reactance X will completely dictate the magnitude of the power transmitted because $P = (E^2/X) \sin \delta$.

However, the magnitude and direction of P may not correspond to what we want to achieve. For example, if we wish to transmit energy from region B to region A, the installation of a simple line will not do, because E_a leads E_b.

However, we can *force* a power exchange in one direction or the other by artificially modifying the phase angle between the two regions. All we have to do is to introduce a phase-shift autotransformer (Section 12.11) at one end of the line; by varying the phase angle of this transformer, we can completely control the active power flow between the two centers.

Example 25-8

Fig. 25.41a shows the voltages and phase angle between two regions A and B that are already interconnected by a network (not shown). Voltage E_b is known to lead E_a by 11°, and both voltages have a value of 100 kV. A new tie line having a reactance $X = 20\ \Omega$ connects the two regions.

Calculate

a. The power transmitted by the line and the direction of power flow, if no phase-shift transformer is employed

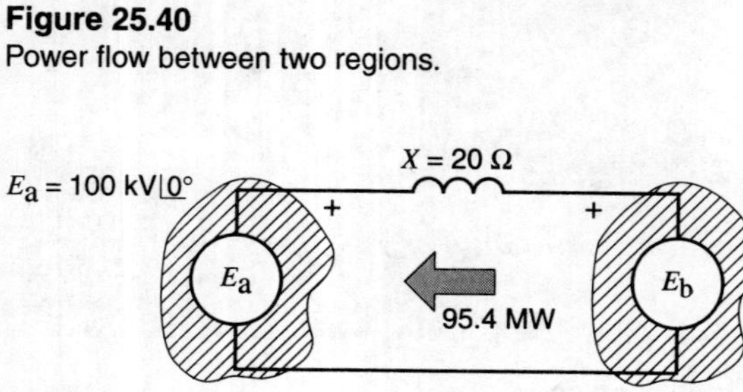

Figure 25.40
Power flow between two regions.

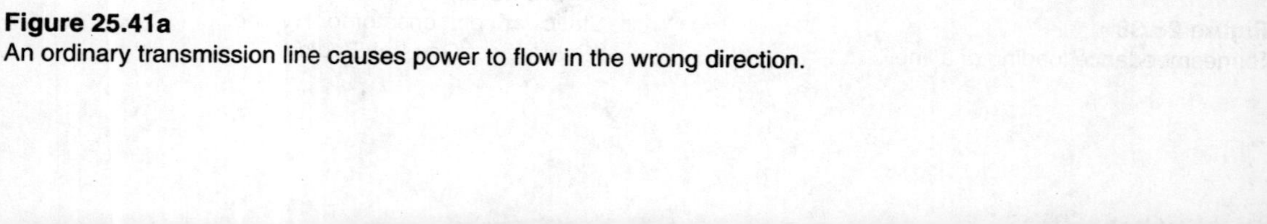

Figure 25.41a
An ordinary transmission line causes power to flow in the wrong direction.

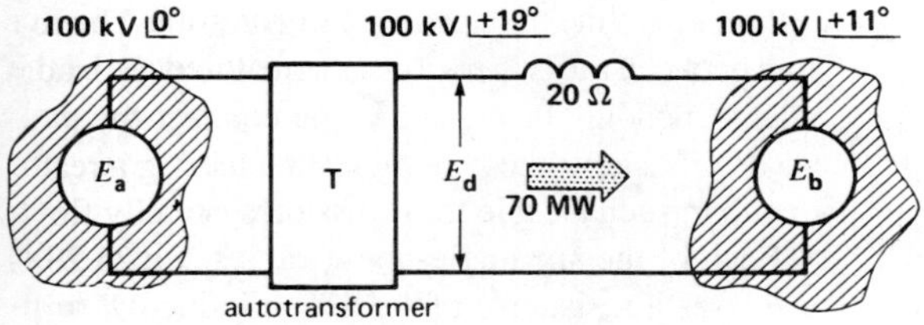

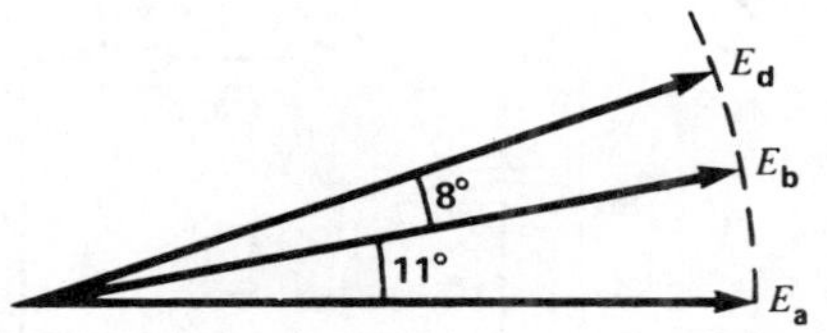

Figure 25.41b
A phase-shift autotransformer can force power to flow in the desired direction (Example 25-8).

b. The required phase-shift of the transformer so that the line will transmit 70 MW from A to B

Solution

a. The power transmitted in Fig. 25.41a is given by

$$P = (E^2/X) \sin \delta \qquad (25.4)$$
$$= (100^2/20) \sin 11° = 95.4 \text{ MW}$$

Because E_b leads E_a, the 95.4 MW will flow from B to A.

b. Referring to Fig. 25.41b, let us first calculate the phase angle δ_1 required between opposite ends of the transmission line, so that it will transmit 70 MW. We have

$$P = (E^2/X) \sin \delta_1 \qquad (25.4)$$
$$70 = (100^2/20) \sin \delta_1$$
$$\sin \delta_1 = 0.14$$

from which

$$\delta_1 = 8°$$

Consequently, voltage E_d produced by the phase-shift transformer must lead E_b by 8° in order that 70 MW may flow from A to B (Fig. 25.41b). Referring to the phasor diagram and noting that E_b already leads E_a by 11°, it follows that E_d must be 11° + 8° = 19° ahead of E_a. The autotransformer T must, therefore, produce a phase-shift of 19° between its primary and secondary windings, and the secondary voltage E_d must lead the primary voltage E_a. We can put the autotransformer at either end of the line or even in the middle.

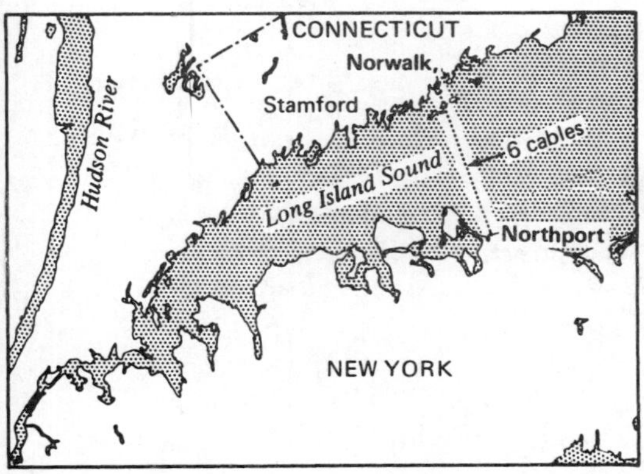

Figure 25.42
Six single-phase submarine cables join the state of Connecticut to Long Island.

25.29 Practical example of power exchange

We now consider a practical application of a phase-shift transformer. To facilitate power exchange between the state of Connecticut and Long Island, New York, six single-phase 138 kV submarine cables (two per phase) were installed between Norwalk and Northport, at the bottom of Long Island Sound (Fig. 25.42). Because the two regions were already interconnected by a grid of transmission lines above ground, it was decided to install a phase-shift autotransformer at Northport to control a maximum power flow of 300 MW. Variable taps enable a maximum phase shift of ±25 degrees. On the other side, at Norwalk, a 300 MVA variable-voltage autotransformer was installed to provide voltage control of up to 10 percent, without phase shift. By varying the phase shift and the voltage at either end

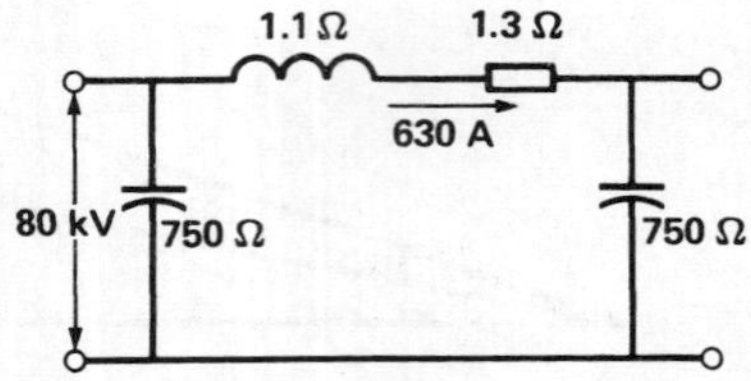

Figure 25.43
Equivalent circuit of each submarine cable.

of the 19 km line, it is possible to control the power flow between the two regions, in one direction or the other, depending on the need. The following technical details show the magnitude of the powers involved in such a cable transmission system.

Each of the six single-phase cables (Fig. 25.44) possesses a resistance of 1.3 Ω, an inductive reactance of 1.1 Ω, and a capacitive reactance of 375 Ω. The latter can be represented by two reactances of

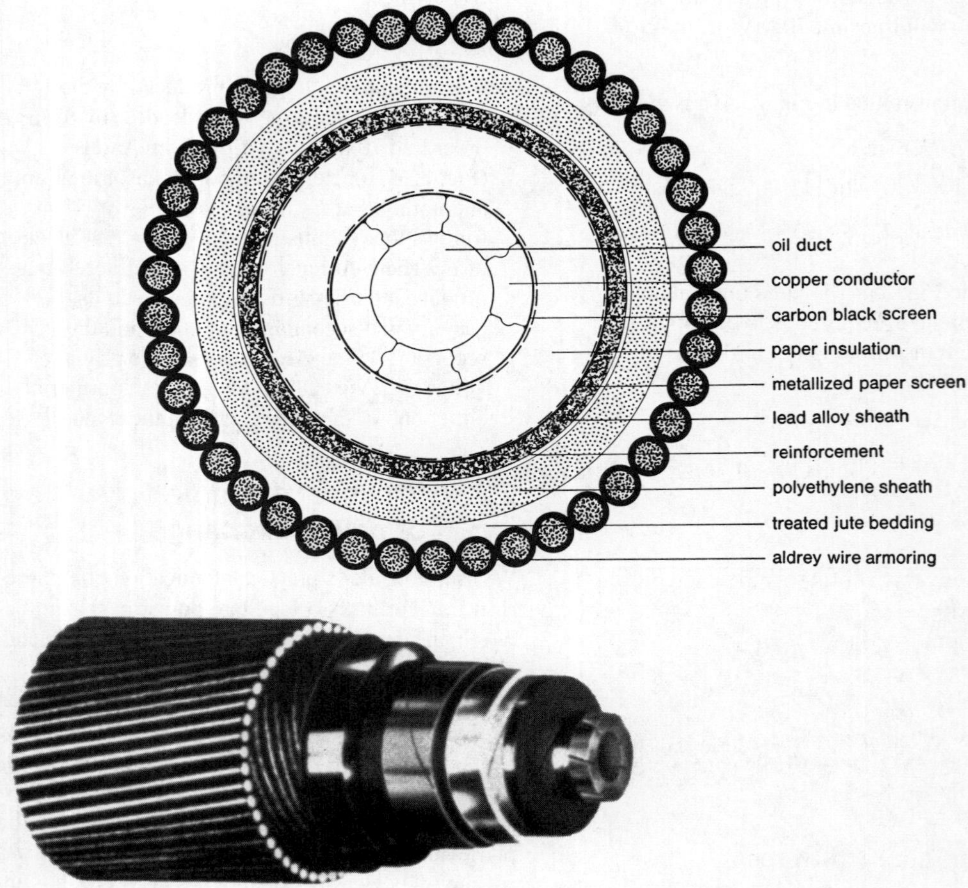

Figure 25.44
Cross-section view of submarine cable (138 kV, 630 A). This cable is one of seven cables submerged in Long Island Sound between Northport (Long Island) and Norwalk (Connecticut).
(Courtesy of Pirelli Cables Limited)

750 Ω at each end of the cable. The full-load current per cable is 630 A, and the line-to-neutral voltage is 80 kV. Referring to the equivalent circuit diagram for one cable (Fig. 25.43), we can readily calculate the value of the inductive, capacitive, and resistive powers associated with it. These powers Q_L, Q_C, P_J are listed in Table 25E.

TABLE 25E POWERS IN A SUBMARINE CABLE

Submarine cable installation	Power per cable	Total power
I^2R losses:		
$P_J = 630^2 \times 1.3$		
$= 0.516$ MW	0.516 MW	3.1 MW
Reactive power generated:		
$Q_C = (80\,000)^2/375$		
$= 17.06$ Mvar	17 Mvar	102 Mvar
Reactive power absorbed:		
$Q_L = 630^2 \times 1.1$		
$= 0.436$ Mvar	0.44 Mvar	2.6 Mvar
Active power transmitted:		
$P = 630 \times 80\,000$		
$= 50$ MW	50 MW	300 MW

In comparing them with the active power transmitted (300 MW), we can see that the capacitance of the cable is far more important than are its resistance or inductance. A cable behaves like an enormous capacitor, contrary to an aerial line which is mainly inductive. It is precisely the inherent large capacitance that prevents us from using cables to transmit energy over long distances. This restriction does not apply when direct current is used because capacitance then has no effect.

High-voltage dc transmission lines are covered in Chapter 28.

Questions and Problems

Practical level

25-1 Standard voltages are grouped into four main classes. Name them and state the approximate voltage range of each.

25-2 Explain what is meant by the following terms:
   a. Suspension-type insulator
   b. Ground wire
   c. Corona effect
   d. Sag of a transmission line
   e. Reactance of a line

25-3 Why must transmission line towers be solidly connected to ground?

25-4 A 735 kV transmission line, 745 miles long, transmits a power of 800 MW.
   a. Is there an appreciable voltage difference between the two ends of the line, measured line to neutral?
   b. Is there an appreciable phase angle between corresponding line-to-neutral voltages?

25-5 In some areas, two identical 3-phase lines are installed side by side, supported by separate towers. Could we replace these two lines by a single line, by simply doubling the size of the conductors? Explain.

25-6 Why do we seldom install underground cable (instead of aerial transmission lines) between generating stations and distant load centers?

25-7 In Problem 25-4 the average line span is 480 m. How many towers are needed between the source and the load?

25-8 A 20 km transmission line operating at 13.2 kV has just been disconnected from the source. A lineman could receive a fatal shock if he does not first connect the line to ground before touching it. Explain.

25-9 What is the ampacity of a 600 kcmil ACSR cable suspended in free air? Why can a copper conductor having the same cross-section carry a current that is considerably greater?

Intermediate level

25-10 Each phase of the two 735 kV lines shown in Fig. 25.34 is composed of 4 bundled subconductors. The current per phase is 2000 A and the resistance of each subconductor is 0.045 Ω/km.

Calculate

a. The total power transmitted by both lines at unity power factor load
b. The total I^2R loss, knowing the lines are 350 miles long
c. The I^2R loss as a percent of the total power transmitted

25-11 A single-phase transmission line possesses a resistance R of 15 Ω (Fig. 25.21a). The source E_S is 6000 V, and the impedance of the unity power factor load varies between 285 Ω and 5 Ω.
a. Calculate the terminal voltage E_R and the power P absorbed by the load when the impedance is successively 285 Ω, 45 Ω, 15 Ω, and 5 Ω.
b. Draw the graph of the terminal voltage E_R as a function of the power P.

25-12 In Problem 25-11, what is the phase angle between E_R and E_S when the load is 45 Ω?

25-13 The transmission line in Problem 25-11 is replaced by another having an inductive reactance of 15 Ω (Fig. 25.22a).
a. Calculate the voltage E_R at the terminals of the load and the power P it absorbs for the same impedance values.
b. Draw the graph of E_R as a function of P.

25-14 In Problem 25-13, what is the phase angle between E_R and E_S when the load impedance is 45 Ω? Does E_R lead or lag behind E_S?

25-15 A single-phase transmission line possesses an inductive reactance of 15 Ω. It is supplied by a source E_S of 6000 V.
a. Calculate the voltage E_R at the end of the line for the following capacitive loads: 285 Ω, 45 Ω.
b. Calculate the phase angle between E_R and E_S when the load is 45 Ω.

25-16 The line in Problem 25-15 possesses a resistance of 15 Ω (instead of a reactance of 15 Ω).
a. Calculate the voltage E_R at the end of the line for a capacitive load of 45 Ω.
b. If a line is purely resistive, can we raise the voltage at the end of the line by connecting a capacitor across it?

25-17 The following information is given for Fig. 25.25a:
a. Terminal voltage E_R: 6000 V
b. Equivalent load resistance: 45 Ω
c. Inductive reactance X_L of the line: 15 Ω
d. Capacitive reactance X_C in parallel with the load: 150 Ω

Neglecting the dotted reactance X_C in parallel with the source, calculate the following:
a. The reactive power supplied by the capacitor
b. The line current I
c. The reactive power absorbed by the line
d. The reactive power supplied by the sender
e. The apparent power supplied by the sender
f. The voltage E_S of the sender
g. The voltage E_R and the power P when E_S is 6 kV

25-18 In Problem 25-17, what is the phase angle between E_R and E_S?

25-19 Referring to Fig. 25.13, each section of the circuit represents a transmission line length of 1 km in which the impedances are

$$x_L = 0.5\ \Omega\ r = 0.25\ \Omega$$
$$x_c = 300\ \text{k}\Omega$$

Calculate the values of X_L, R, and X_C if the circuit is reduced to that shown in Fig. 25.14.

25-20 What is meant by the term *surge impedance load?*

Advanced level

25-21 A 3-phase, 230 kV transmission line having a reactance of 43 Ω, per phase, connects two regions that are 50 miles apart. The phase angle between the voltages at the two ends of the line is 20°.

Calculate

a. The active power transmitted by the line
b. The current in each conductor
c. The total reactive power absorbed by the line
d. The reactive power supplied to the line by each region

25-22 A 3-phase aerial line connected to a 115 kV, 3-phase source has a length of 200 km. It is composed of three 600 kcmil-type ACSR conductors. Referring to Fig. 25.17 and Tables 25C and 25D, if there is no load on the line, calculate the following:

a. The value of *R*, X_L, and X_C, per phase
b. The voltage between conductors at the load (open end)
c. The current drawn from the source, per phase
d. The total reactive power received by the source
e. The total I^2R loss in the line

25-23 **a.** In Problem 25-22, calculate the current drawn from the source if a 3-phase short occurs across the end of the line.
b. Compare this current with the ampacity of the conductors.

CHAPTER 26

Distribution of Electrical Energy

26.0 Introduction

In Chapter 25 we mentioned that an electrical power system is composed of high-voltage transmission lines that feed power to a medium-voltage (MV) network by means of substations. In North America these MV networks generally operate at voltages between 2.4 kV and 69 kV. In turn, they supply millions of independent low-voltage systems that function between 120 V and 600 V.

In this chapter, we cover the following main topics:

1. Substations
2. Protection of medium-voltage distribution systems
3. Low-voltage distribution
4. Electrical installation in buildings

SUBSTATIONS

Substations are used throughout an electrical system. Starting with the generating station, a substation raises the medium-voltage generated by the synchronous generators to the high voltage needed to transmit the energy economically.

The high transmission-line voltage is then reduced in those substations located close to the power-consuming centers. The electrical equipment in such distribution substations is similar to that found in substations associated with generating plants.

26.1 Substation equipment

A medium-voltage substation usually contains the following major components:

Transformers	Surge arresters
Circuit breakers	Current-limiting reactors
Horn-gap switches	Instrument transformers
Disconnect switches	Relays and protective devices
Grounding switches	

In the description that follows, we study the basic principles of this equipment. Furthermore, to understand how it all fits together, we conclude our study with a typical substation that provides power to a large suburb.

26.2 Circuit breakers

Circuit breakers are designed to interrupt either normal or short-circuit currents. They behave like big switches that may be opened or closed by local pushbuttons or by distant telecommunication signals emitted by the system of protection. Thus, circuit breakers will automatically open a circuit whenever the line current, line voltage, frequency, and so on, departs from a preset limit.

The most important types of circuit breakers are the following:

1. Oil circuit breakers (OCBs)
2. Air-blast circuit breakers
3. SF_6 circuit breakers
4. Vacuum circuit breakers

The nameplate on a circuit breaker usually indicates (1) the maximum steady-state current it can carry, (2) the maximum interrupting current, (3) the maximum line voltage, and (4) the interrupting time in cycles. The interrupting time may last from 3 to 8 cycles on a 60 Hz system. To interrupt large currents this quickly, we have to ensure rapid deionization of the arc, combined with rapid cooling. High-speed interruption limits the damage to transmission lines and equipment and, equally important, it helps to maintain the stability of the system whenever a contingency occurs.

The triggering action that causes a circuit breaker to open is usually produced by means of an overload relay that can detect abnormal line conditions. For example, the relay coil in Fig. 26.1 is connected to the secondary of a current transformer. The primary carries the line current of the phase that has to be protected. If the line current exceeds a preset limit, the secondary current will cause relay contacts C_1, C_2 to close. As soon as they close, the tripping coil is energized by an auxiliary dc source. This causes the three main line contacts to open, thus interrupting the circuit.

1. Oil Circuit Breakers. Oil circuit breakers are composed of a steel tank filled with insulating oil. In one version (Fig. 26.2), three porcelain bushings channel the 3-phase line currents to a set of fixed contacts. Three movable contacts, actuated simultaneously by an insulated rod, open and close the circuit. When the circuit breaker is closed, the line current for each phase penetrates the tank by way of a porcelain bushing, flows through the first fixed contact, the movable contact, the second fixed contact, and then on out by a second bushing.

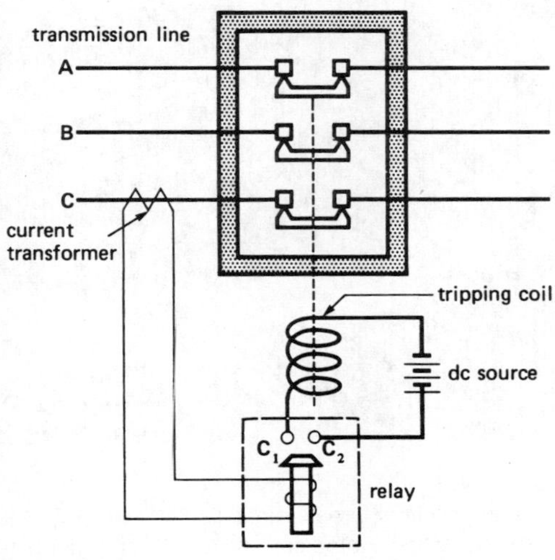

Figure 26.1
Elementary tripping circuit for a circuit breaker.

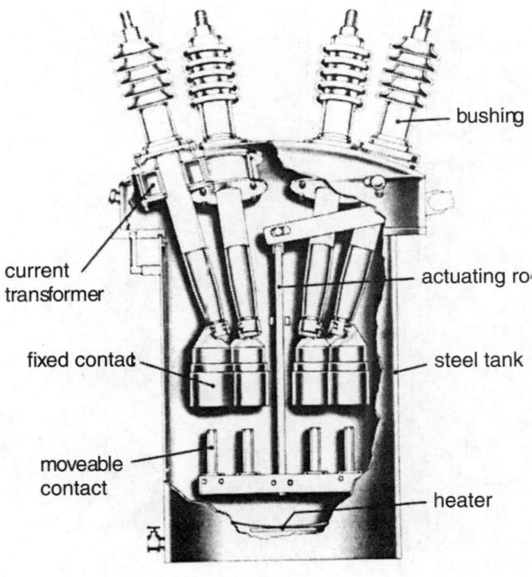

Figure 26.2
Cross section of an oil circuit breaker. The diagram shows four of the six bushings; the heater keeps the oil at a satisfactory temperature during cold weather. *(Courtesy of Canadian General Electric)*

If an overload occurs, the tripping coil releases a powerful spring that pulls on the insulated rod, causing the contacts to open. As soon as the contacts separate, a violent arc is created, which volatilizes the surrounding oil. The pressure of the hot gases creates turbulence around the contacts. This causes cool oil to swirl around the arc, thus extinguishing it.

In modern high-power breakers, the arc is confined to an explosion chamber so that the pressure of the hot gases produces a powerful jet of oil. The jet is made to flow across the path of the arc, to extinguish it. Other types of circuit breakers are designed so that the arc is deflected and lengthened by a self-created magnetic field. The arc is blown against a series of insulating plates that break up the arc and cool it down. Figs. 26.3 and 26.4 show the appearance of two typical OCBs.

*2. **Air-Blast Circuit Breakers.*** These circuit breakers interrupt the circuit by blowing compressed air at supersonic speed across the opening contacts. Compressed air is stored in reservoirs at a pressure of about 3 MPa (~435 psi) and is replenished by a compressor located in the substation. The most powerful circuit breakers can typically open short-circuit currents of 40 kA at a line voltage of 765 kV in a matter of 3 to 6 cycles on a 60 Hz line. The noise accompanying the air blast is so loud that noise-suppression methods must be used when the circuit breakers are installed near residential areas. Fig. 26.5 shows a typical 3-phase air-blast circuit breaker. Each phase is composed of three contact modules connected in series. Fig. 26.6 shows a cross section of the contact module.

Figure 26.3
Three-phase oil circuit breaker rated 1200 A and 115 kV. It can interrupt a current of 50 kA in 3 cycles on a 60 Hz system. Other characteristics: height: 3660 mm; diameter: 3050 mm; mass: 21 t; BIL: 550 kV.
(Courtesy of General Electric)

Figure 26.4
Minimum oil circuit breaker installed in a 420 kV, 50 Hz substation. Rated current: 2000 A; rupturing capacity: 25 kA; height (less support): 5400 mm; length: 6200 mm; 4 circuit-breaking modules in series per circuit breaker.
(Courtesy of ABB)

Figure 26.5
Air-blast circuit breaker rated 2000 A at 362 kV. It can interrupt a current of 40 kA in 3 cycles on a 60 Hz system. It consists of 3 identical modules connected in series, each rated for a nominal voltage of 121 kV. The compressed-air reservoir can be seen at the left. Other characteristics: height: 5640 mm; overall length: 9150 mm; BIL 1300 kV.
(Courtesy of General Electric)

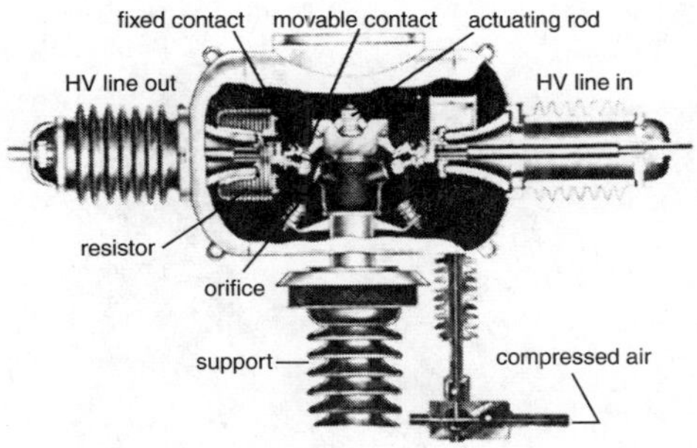

Figure 26.6
Cross section of one module of an air-blast circuit breaker. When the circuit breaker trips, the rod is driven upward, separating the fixed and movable contacts. The intense arc is immediately blown out by a jet of compressed air coming from the orifice. The resistor dampens the overvoltages that occur when the breaker opens.
(Courtesy of General Electric)

Figure 26.7
Group of 15 totally enclosed SF_6 circuit breakers installed in an underground substation of a large city. Rated current: 1600 A; rupturing current: 34 kA; normal operating pressure: 265 kPa (38 psi); pressure during arc extinction: 1250 kPa (180 psi). These SF_6 circuit breakers take up only 1/16 of the volume of conventional circuit breakers having the same interrupting capacity.
(Courtesy of ABB)

3. SF_6 Circuit Breakers. These totally enclosed circuit breakers, insulated with SF_6 gas*, are used whenever space is at a premium, such as in downtown substations (Fig. 26.7). These circuit breakers are much smaller than any other type of circuit breaker of equivalent power and are far less noisy than air circuit breakers.

4. Vacuum Circuit Breakers. These circuit breakers operate on a different principle from other breakers because there is no gas to ionize when the contacts open. They are hermetically sealed; consequently, they are silent and never become polluted (Fig. 26.8). Their interrupting capacity is limited to about 30 kV. For higher voltages, several circuit breakers are connected in series.

Vacuum circuit breakers are often used in underground distribution systems.

* Sulfur hexafluoride.

Figure 26.8
Three-phase vacuum circuit breaker having a rating of 1200 A at 25.8 kV. It can interrupt a current of 25 kA in 3 cycles on a 60 Hz system. Other characteristics: height: 2515 mm; mass: 645 kg; BIL: 125 kV.
(Courtesy of General Electric)

26.3 Air-break switches

Air-break switches can interrupt the exciting currents of transformers, or the moderate capacitive currents of unloaded transmission lines. They cannot interrupt normal load currents.

Air-break switches are composed of a movable blade that engages a fixed contact; both are mounted on insulating supports (Figs. 26.9, 26.10). Two arcing horns are attached to the fixed and movable contacts. When the main contact is broken, an arc is set up between the arcing horns. The arc moves upward due to the combined action of the hot air currents it produces and the magnetic field. As the arc rises, it becomes longer until it eventually blows out (Fig. 26.11). Although the arcing horns become pitted and gradually wear out, they can easily be replaced.

26.4 Disconnecting switches

Unlike air-break switches, disconnecting switches are unable to interrupt any current at all. They must only be opened and closed when the current is zero. They are basically isolating switches, enabling us to isolate oil circuit breakers, transformers, transmission lines, and so forth, from a live network. Disconnecting switches are essential to carry out maintenance work and to reroute power flow.

Fig. 26.12 shows a 2000 A, 15 kV disconnecting switch. It is equipped with a latch to prevent the switch from opening under the strong electromagnetic forces that accompany short-circuits. The latch is disengaged by inserting a hookstick into the ring and pulling the movable blade out of the fixed contact.

Fig. 26.13 shows another "disconnect" that carries a larger current, but at a much lower voltage. It, too, is opened by means of a manual hookstick. Fig. 26.14 shows another type of disconnecting switch and Fig. 26.15 shows how the fixed and movable contacts engage. Fig. 26.16 shows maintenance personnel working on a large disconnecting switch in a HV substation.

26.5 Grounding switches

Grounding switches are safety switches that ensure a transmission line is definitely grounded while repairs are being carried out. Fig. 26.17 shows such a 3-phase switch with the blades in the open (horizontal) position. To short-circuit the line to ground, all three grounding blades swing up to engage the stationary contact connected to each phase. Grounding switches are opened and closed only when the lines are de-energized.

26.6 Surge arresters

The purpose of a *surge arrester** is to limit the overvoltages that may occur across transformers and other electrical apparatus due either to lightning or switching surges. The upper end of the arrester is connected

* Also called lightning arrester, or surge diverter.

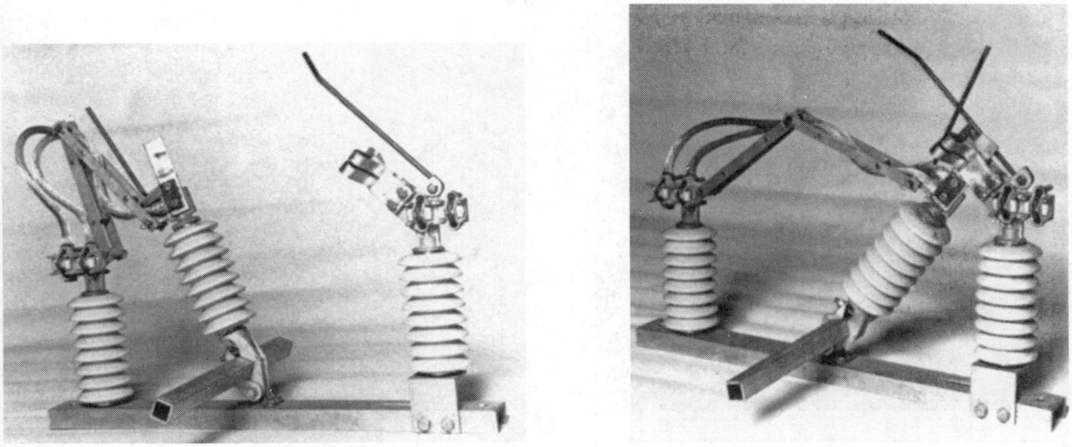

Figure 26.9
One pole of a horn-gap disconnecting switch rated 600 A, 27 kV, 60 Hz; (left) in the open position, (right) in the closed position.
(Courtesy of Dominion Cutout)

Figure 26.10
One pole of a 3-phase, 3000 A, 735 kV, 60 Hz horn-gap disconnecting switch in the open position (left); in the closed position (right). The switch can be operated manually by turning a hand wheel or remotely by means of a motorized drive located immediately below the hand wheel. Other characteristics: height when closed: 12 400 mm; length: 7560 mm; mass: 3 t; maximum current-carrying capacity for 10 cycles: 120 kA; BIL: 2200 kV.
(Courtesy of Kearney)

Figure 26.11
The arc produced between the horns of a disconnecting switch as it cuts the exciting current of a HV transformer provides the light to take this night picture.
(Courtesy of Hydro-Québec)

Figure 26.13
Disconnecting switch rated 10 kA, 1 kV for indoor use.
(Courtesy of Montell Sprecher and Schuh)

Figure 26.12
This hookstick-operated disconnecting switch is rated 2000 A, 15 kV and has a BIL of 95 kV.
(Courtesy of Dominion Cutout)

Figure 26.14
Disconnecting switch rated 600 A, 46 kV for sidewise operation.
(Courtesy of Kearney)

to the line or terminal that has to be protected, while the lower end is solidly connected to ground.

Ideally, a surge arrester clips any voltage in excess of a specified maximum, by permitting a large current, if need be, to be diverted to ground. In this way the arrester absorbs energy from the incoming surge. The *E-I* characteristic of an ideal surge arrester is, therefore, a horizontal line whose level corresponds to the maximum permissible surge voltage. In practice, the *E-I* characteristic slopes upward (Fig. 26.18) but is still considered to be reasonably flat.

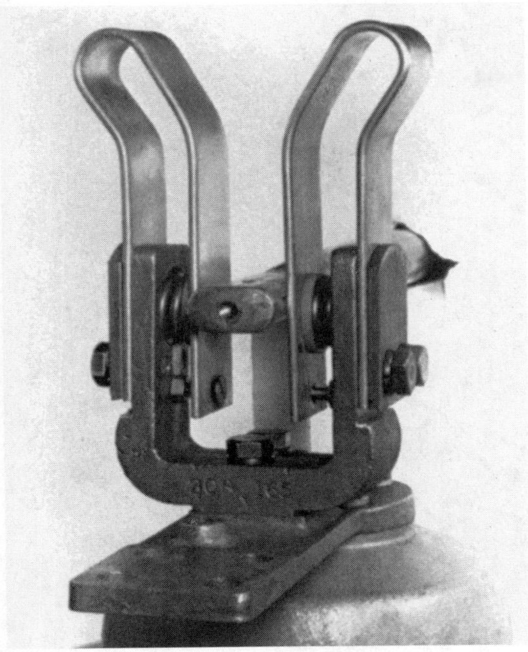

Figure 26.15
The blade of a vertical motion disconnecting switch is in tight contact with two fixed contacts, due to the pressure exerted by two powerful springs. When the switch opens, the blade twists on its axis as it moves upward. During switch closure the reverse rotary movement exerts a wiping action against the fixed contacts, thus ensuring excellent contact.
(Courtesy of Kearney)

Some arresters are composed of an external porcelain tube containing an ingenious arrangement of stacked discs, air gaps, ionizers, and coils. The discs (or valve blocks) are composed of a silicon carbide material. The resistance of this material decreases dramatically with increasing voltage.

Under normal voltage conditions, spark gaps prevent any current from flowing through the tubular column. Consequently, the resistance of the arrester is infinite. However, if a serious over-voltage occurs, the spark gaps break down and the surge discharges to ground. The 60 Hz follow-through current is limited by the resistance of the valve blocks and the arc is simultaneously stretched and cooled in a series of arc chambers. The arc is quickly snuffed out and the arrester is then ready to protect the line against the next voltage surge. The discharge period is very short, rarely lasting more than a fraction of a millisecond.

A more modern type of arrester has valve blocks made of stacked zinc-oxide discs without using any air gaps or other auxiliary devices. Its *E-I* characteristic is similar to that of a silicon carbide arrester, except that it is much flatter and therefore more effective in diverting surge currents. These metal-oxide varistor (MOV) arresters are largely used today.

Lightning arresters with very flat characteristics also enable us to reduce the BIL requirements of apparatus installed in substations (Section 25.12). On HV and EHV systems, the reduction in BIL significantly reduces the cost of the installed apparatus. Fig. 26.19 shows a lightning arrester installed in an EHV substation.

26.7 Current-limiting reactors

The MV bus in a substation usually energizes several feeders, which carry power to regional load centers surrounding the substation. It so happens that the output impedance of the MV bus is usually very low. Consequently, if a short-circuit should occur on one of the feeders, the resulting short-circuit current could be disastrous.

Consider, for example, a 3-phase, 69 MVA, 220 kV/24.9 kV transformer having an impedance of 8% and a nominal secondary current of 1600 A. It supplies power to eight 200 A feeders connected to the common MV bus (Fig. 26.20). Each feeder is protected by a 24.9 kV, 200 A circuit breaker having an interrupting capacity of 4000 A. Because the transformer impedance is 8%, it can deliver a secondary short-circuit current of

$$I = 1600 \times (1/0.08) = 20\,000 \text{ A}$$

Figure 26.16
Like all electric equipment, disconnecting switches have to be overhauled and inspected at regular intervals. During such operations the current has to be diverted by way of auxiliary tie lines within the substation. The picture shows one pole of a 3-phase disconnect rated 2000 A, 345 kV.
(Courtesy of Hydro-Québec)

This creates a problem because if a feeder becomes short-circuited, the resulting current flow could be as high as 20 000 A, which is five times greater than the interrupting capacity of the circuit breaker protecting the feeder. The circuit breaker could be destroyed in attempting to interrupt the circuit. Furthermore, the feeder might be damaged over its entire length, from the circuit-breaker to the fault. Finally, a violent explosion would take place at the fault itself, due to the tremendous amount of thermal energy released by the burning arc.

To prevent this from happening, a current-limiting reactor is connected in series with each phase of the feeder (Fig. 26.21). The reactance must be high enough to keep the current below the interrupting capacity of the circuit breaker but not so high as to produce a large voltage drop under normal full-load conditions. Fig. 26.22 shows another application wherein three current-limiting reactors are connected in series with a HV line.

26.8 Grounding transformer

We sometimes have to create a neutral on a 3-phase, 3-wire system to change it into a 3-phase, 4-wire system. This can be done by means of a *grounding*

Figure 26.17
Combined disconnecting switch and grounding switch rated at 115 kV. The grounding switch blades are shown in the open, horizontal position. These blades pivot upward to engage three fixed contacts at the same time the line is opened.
(Courtesy of Kearney)

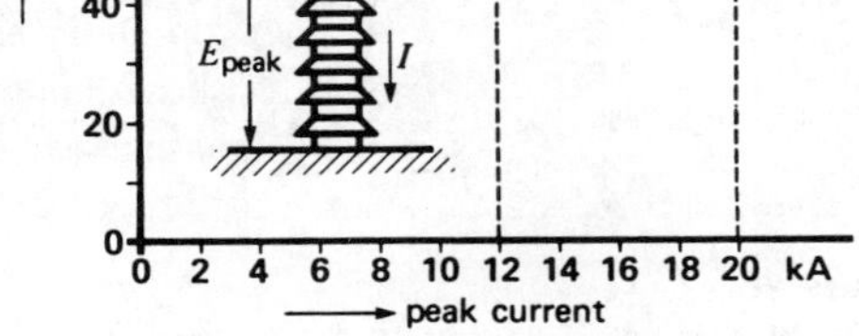

Figure 26.18
Voltage-current characteristic of a surge arrester having a nominal rating of 30 kV (42.4 kV peak), used on a 34.5 kV line (28.5 kV peak, line to neutral).

transformer. It is basically a 3-phase autotransformer in which identical primary and secondary windings are connected in series but in zigzag fashion on a 3-legged core (Fig. 26.23).

If we connect a single-phase load between one line and neutral, load current I divides into three equal currents $I/3$ in each winding. Because the currents are equal, the neutral point stays fixed and the line-to-neutral voltages remain balanced as they would be on a regular 4-wire system. In practice, the single-phase loads are distributed as evenly as possible between the respective three phases and neutral so that the unbalanced load current I remains relatively small.

26.9 Example of a substation

Fig. 26.24 shows the principal elements of a typical modern substation providing power to a large suburb. Power is fed into the substation at 220 kV and is distributed at 24.9 kV to various load centers within about a 5 km radius.

Figure 26.19
MOV surge arresters protect this EHV transformer.
(Courtesy of General Electric)

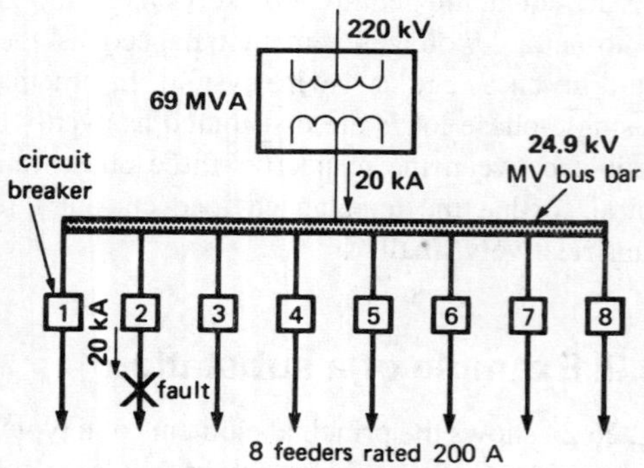

Figure 26.20
MV busbar feeding eight lines, each protected by a circuit breaker.

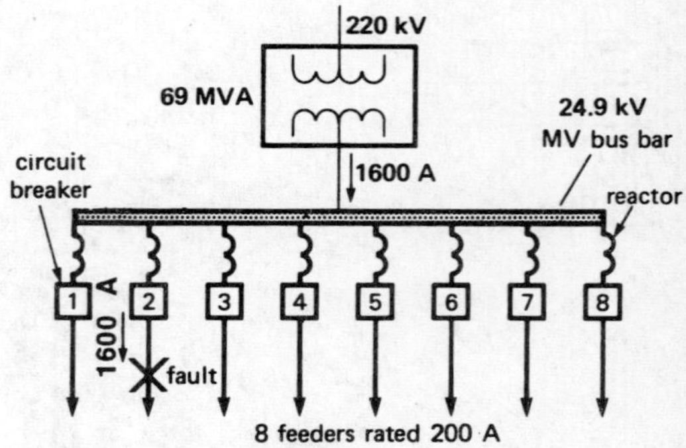

Figure 26.21
Current-limiting reactors reduce the short-circuit current.

Figure 26.22
Three 2.2 Ω reactors rated 500 A are connected in series with a 120 kV, 3-phase, 60 Hz line. They are insulated from ground by four insulating columns, and each is protected by a surge arrester.
(Courtesy of Hydro-Québec)

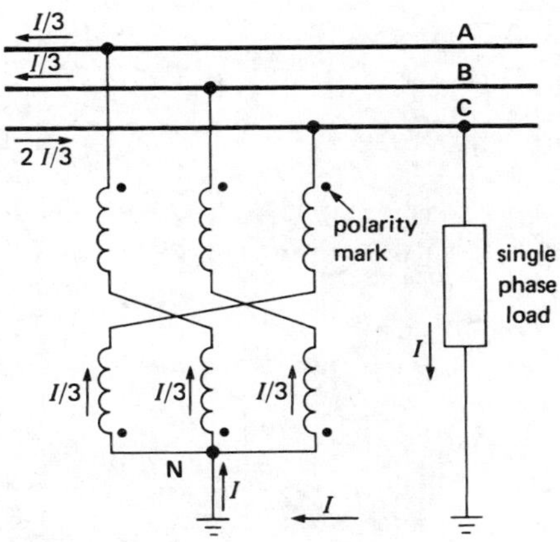

Figure 26.23
Grounding transformer to create a 3-phase neutral.

The substation is fed by three separate transmission lines, all operating at 220 kV. It contains six 3-phase transformers rated at 36/48/60 MVA, 220 kV/24.9 kV. The windings are connected in wye-delta and automatic tap-changers regulate the secondary voltage.

A neutral is established on the MV side by means of 3-phase grounding transformers. Consequently, single-phase power can be provided at $24.9\sqrt{3} = 14.4$ kV.

Minimum oil circuit breakers having an interrupting capacity of 32 kA protect the HV side. Conventional oil circuit breakers having an interrupting capacity of 25 kA are used on the MV side. Furthermore, all the outgoing feeders are protected by circuit breakers having an interrupting capacity of 12 kA.

This completely automatic and unattended substation covers an area of 235 m × 170 m. However, line switching and other operations can be carried out by telecommunications from a dispatching center.

The substation provides service to hundreds of single-family homes, dozens of apartment buildings, several business and shopping centers, a large university, and some industries. Figs. 26.25 and 26.26 show the basic layout and components of the substation. We now study the distribution system that branches out from the substation.

26.10 Medium-voltage distribution

Thirty-six 3-phase feeders (30 active and 6 spares), rated at 24.9 kV, 400 A lead outward from the substation. Each feeder is equipped with three current-limiting reactors that limit the line to ground short-circuit currents to a maximum of 12 kA. Some feeders are underground, others overhead, and still others are underground/overhead.

Underground feeders are composed of three single-phase stranded aluminum cables insulated with polyethylene. The insulation is in turn surrounded by a spiral wrapping of tinned copper conductors which act as the ground. The cable is pulled through underground concrete duct (Fig. 26.27) or simply buried in the ground. Spare cables are invariably buried along with active cables to provide alternate service in case of a fault.

The 24.9 kV aerial lines are supported on wooden poles. The latter also carry the LV circuits and telephone cable. The 24.9 kV lines are tapped off at various points to supply 3-phase and single-phase power to residences, commercial establishments, and recreation centers (Fig. 26.28).

For nearby areas the 24.9 kV line voltage is regulated within acceptable limits by the tap-changing transformers at the substation. In more remote districts, special measures have to be taken to keep the voltage reasonably stable with changing load. Thus, self-regulating autotransformers (Fig. 26.29) are often installed.

26.11 Low-voltage distribution

At the consumer end of the MV feeders that spread out from the substation, the voltage is stepped-down by transformers from 24.9 kV to the much lower voltages needed by the consumers. Two low-voltage systems are provided on this typical suburban network:

1. Single-phase, 120/240 V with grounded neutral
2. Three-phase, 600/347 V with grounded neutral

The first system is mainly used in individual dwellings and for single-phase power ranging up to

Figure 26.24
Aerial view of a substation serving a large suburb. The 220 kV lines (1) enter the substation and move through disconnecting switches (2) and circuit breakers (3) to energize the primaries of the transformers (4). The secondaries are connected to an MV bus (5) operating at 24.9 kV. Grounding transformers (6) and MV circuit breakers (7) feed power through current-limiting reactors (8). The power is carried away by 36 aerial and underground feeders to energize the suburb (9).

Figure 26.25
This sequence of 12 photos on the right shows how energy flows through the substation, starting from the 220 kV lines until it leaves by the 24.9 kV feeders.

1. 220 kV incoming line.
2. The line passes through three CTs (left) and the substation apparatus is protected by 3 lightning arresters (right).
3. Three HV disconnecting switches are placed ahead of the circuit breakers.
4. Minimum volume oil circuit breakers composed of three modules in series permit the line to be opened and closed under load.
5. Three-phase transformer bank steps down the voltage from 220 kV to 24.9 kV. Lightning arresters on the right protect the HV windings.
6. MV line from the transformer feeds the 24.9 kV bus.
7. Grounding transformer and its associated oil circuit breaker having an interrupting capacity of 25 kA.
8. Current-limiting reactors.
9. Three-phase circuit breaker having an interrupting capacity of 12 kA.

10, 11. MV underground feeder rated 400 A, 24.9 kV/14.4 kV leads into the ground toward a load center in the suburb.

12. All steel supports are solidly grounded by bare copper conductors to prevent overvoltages across equipment due to lightning strokes and other disturbances. Typical station ground resistance: 0.1 Ω.

1

2

3

4

5

6

7

8

9

10

11

12

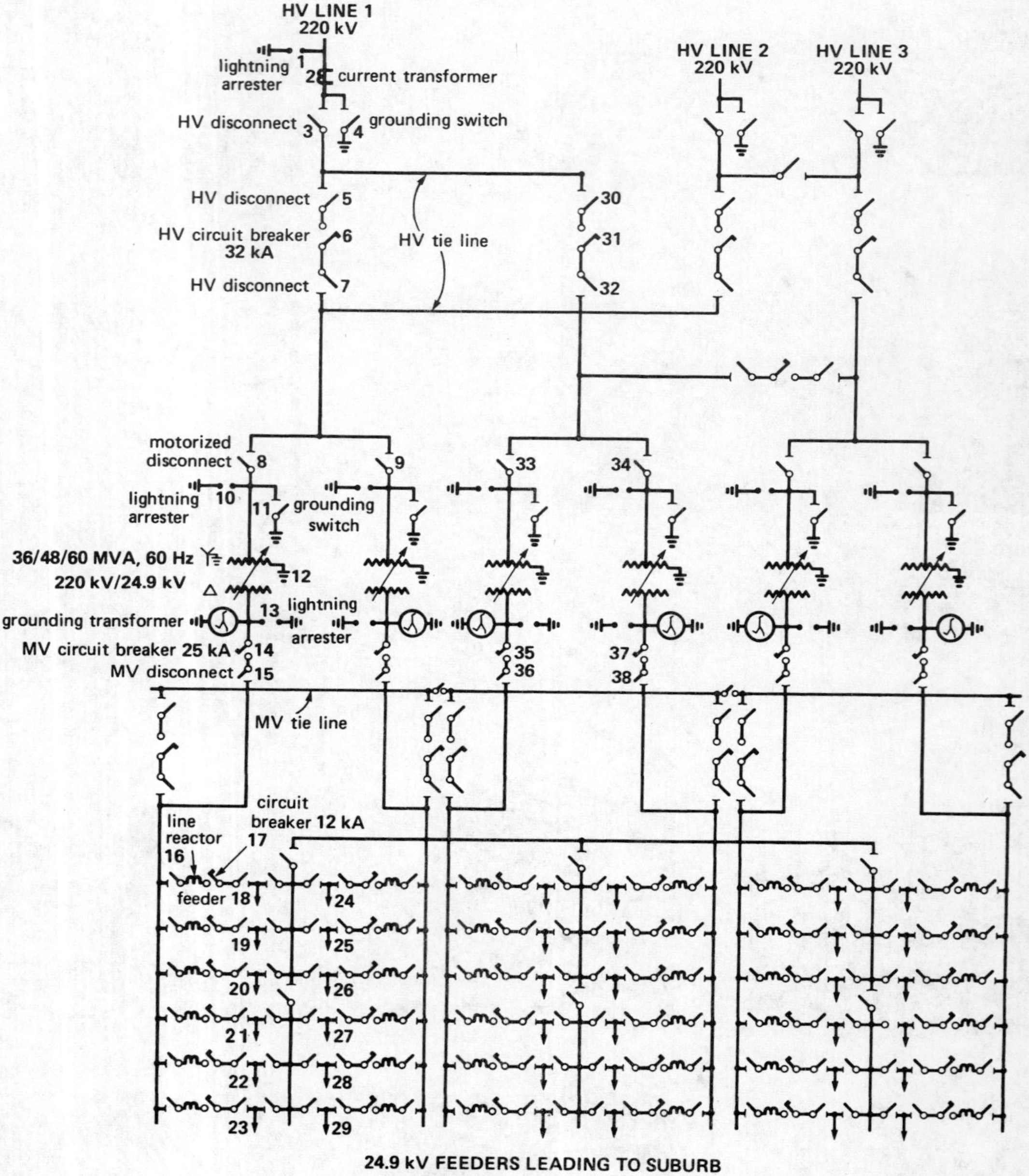

Figure 26.26
Schematic diagram of the substation in Fig. 26.24.

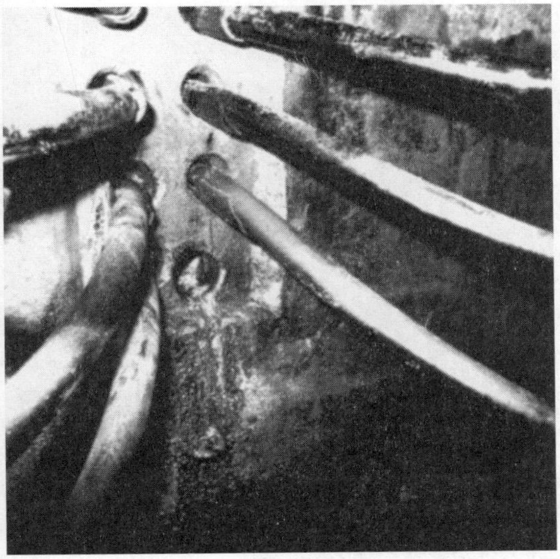

Figure 26.27
MV underground feeders in concrete duct.

Figure 26.28
MV aerial feeder serving a residential district.

Figure 26.29
Automatic tap-changing autotransformer maintains steady voltages on long rural lines.
(Courtesy of General Electric)

150 kVA. The second is used in industry, large buildings, and commercial centers where the power requirement is under 2000 kVA.

For single-phase service, the transformers are usually rated between 10 kVA and 167 kVA and they are pole-mounted. The voltage rating is typically 14 400 V/240–120 V. The transformers possess a single high-voltage bushing connected to one side of the HV winding. The other side of the winding is connected to the steel enclosure which, in turn, is connected to the neutral conductor and also to ground (Fig. 26.30).

In the case of 3-phase installations, 3 single-phase transformers rated at 14 400 V/347 V are used. The units are connected in wye-wye and the neutral on the primary side is solidly grounded.

The secondary side provides a line voltage of 600 V, and it may or may not be grounded. Such standard distribution transformers have no taps, and no circuit breakers or fuses are used on the

Figure 26.30
A fused cutout (top left) and lightning arrester (top right) protect a single-phase transformer rated 25 kVA, 14.4 kV/240 V–120 V, 60 Hz.

Figure 26.31
Expulsion-type fused cutout rated 7.5 kV, 300 A. *(Courtesy of Dominion Cutout)*

secondary side. The primary HV terminal is, however, protected by a cutout in order to prevent excessive damage to equipment in case of a fault (see Figs. 26.30 and 26.31).

PROTECTION OF MEDIUM-VOLTAGE DISTRIBUTION SYSTEMS

Medium-voltage lines must be adequately protected against short-circuits so as to limit damage to equipment and to restrict the outage to as small an area as possible. Such line faults can occur in various ways: falling branches, icing, defective equipment, lines that touch, and so forth. According to statistics, 85 percent of the short-circuits are temporary, lasting only a fraction of a second. The same studies reveal that 70 percent take place between one line and ground. Finally, short-circuits involving all three phases of a transmission line are rare. The methods of protection are based upon these statistics and on the necessity to provide continuity of service to the customers.

26.12 Coordination of the protective devices

When a fault occurs, the current increases sharply, not only on the faulted line, but on all lines that directly or indirectly lead to the short-circuit. To prevent the overload current from simultaneously tripping all the associated protective devices, we must design the system so that the devices trip selectively.

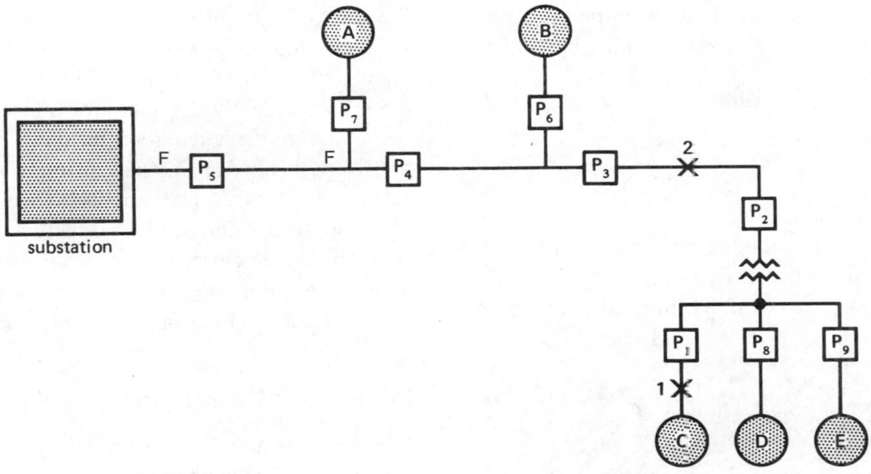

Figure 26.32
Protective devices must be coordinated.

A well-coordinated system will cause only those devices next to the short-circuit to open, leaving the others intact. To achieve this, the tripping current and tripping time of each device is set to protect the line and associated apparatus, while restricting the outage to the smallest number of customers.

Consider, for example, the simple distribution system of Fig. 26.32 composed of a main feeder F-F from a substation, supplying a group of subfeeders. The subfeeders deliver power to loads A, B, C, D, and E. A protective device is installed at the input to each subfeeder so that if a short-circuit occurs, it alone will be disconnected from the system. For instance, a short-circuit at point **1** will trip device P_1 but not P_2. Similarly, a fault at point **2** will open P_3 but not P_4, and so on. A short-circuit must be cleared in a matter of a few cycles. Consequently, the coordination between the protective devices involves delays that are measured in milliseconds. We must therefore know the tripping characteristics of the fuses and circuit breakers throughout the system. The most important protective devices used on MV lines are the following:

1. Fused cutouts
2. Reclosers
3. Sectionalizers

26.13 Fused cutouts

A *fused cutout* is essentially a fused disconnecting switch. The fuse constitutes the movable arm of the switch. It pivots about one end and the circuit can be opened by pulling on the other end of the fuse with a hookstick (Fig. 26.31). Cutouts are relatively inexpensive and are used to protect transformers and small single-phase feeders against overloads. They are designed so that when the fuse blows, it automatically swings down, indicating that a fault has occurred on the line.

Fused cutouts possess a fuse link that is kept taut by a spring. The fuse link assembly is placed inside a porcelain or glass tube filled with boracic acid, oil, or carbon tetrachloride. The fuse link must be replaced every time it blows, which often results in a relatively long outage. To ensure good coordination, the current/time characteristics are selected very carefully for each cutout. A burned-out fuse link must always be replaced by another having exactly the same rating.

26.14 Reclosers

A *recloser* is a circuit breaker that opens on short-circuit and automatically recloses after a brief time delay. The delay may range from a fraction of a second to several seconds. The open/close sequence may be repeated two or three times, depending on the internal control setting of the recloser. If the short-circuit does not clear itself after two or three attempts to reclose the line, the recloser opens the circuit permanently. A repair crew must then locate the fault, remove it, and reset the recloser.

Reclosers rated at 24.9 kV can interrupt fault currents up to 12 000 A. They are made for either single-phase or 3-phase lines, and are usually pole-mounted (Fig. 26.33). Reclosers are self-powered, drawing their energy from the line and storing it in powerful actuating springs by means of electromagnets.

Figure 26.33
Automatic recloser protecting a 3-phase feeder.

26.15 Sectionalizers

When a main feeder is protected by several fuses spotted over the length of the line, it is often difficult to obtain satisfactory coordination between them, based on fuse-blowing time alone. Under these circumstances, we resort to *sectionalizers.* A sectionalizer is a special circuit breaker that trips depending on the number of times a recloser has tripped further up the line. In other words, a sectionalizer works according to the "instructions" of a recloser.

For example, consider a recloser R and a sectionalizer S protecting an important main feeder (Fig. 26.34). If a fault occurs at the point shown, the recloser will automatically open and reclose the circuit, according to the predetermined program. A recorder inside the *sectionalizer* counts the number of times the recloser has tripped and, just before it trips for the last time, the sectionalizer itself trips—but permanently. In so doing, it deprives customers C and D of power but it also isolates the fault. Consequently, when the recloser closes for the last

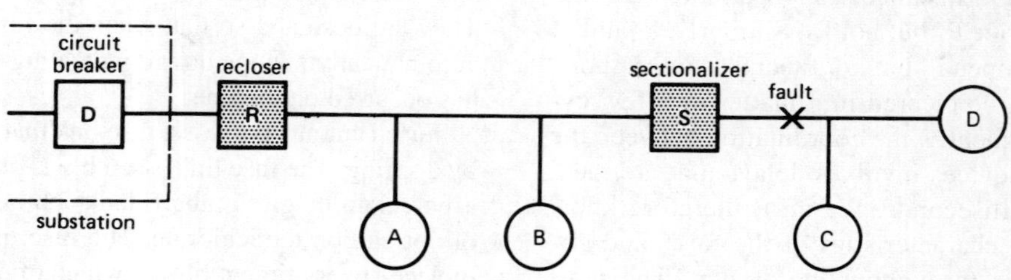

Figure 26.34
Recloser/sectionalizer protective system.

time, it will stay closed and customers A and B will continue to receive service. Unlike reclosers, sectionalizers are not designed to interrupt line currents. Consequently, they must trip during the interval when the line current is zero, which coincides with the time when the recloser itself is open.

Sectionalizers are available for single-phase and 3-phase transmission lines. They offer several advantages over fused cutouts. They can be reclosed on a dead short-circuit without fear of exploding, and there is no delay in searching for a fuse link having the correct caliber.

26.16 Review of MV protection

If we examine the single-line diagram of a typical distribution system, we find it contains dozens of automatic reclosers, sectionalizers, and hundreds of fused cutouts. The reclosing of circuit breakers at the substation may be coordinated with reclosers and sectionalizers elsewhere in the system. The variety of devices available makes it possible to provide adequate protection of MV lines by using combinations such as

1. Circuit breaker–fuse
2. Circuit breaker–fuse–fuse
3. Circuit breaker–recloser–fuse
4. Circuit breaker–recloser–sectionalizer
5. Circuit breaker–sectionalizer–recloser–sectionalizer–fuse, etc

In urban areas the lines are relatively short and the possibility of faults is rather small. Such lines are subdivided along their length into three or four sections, each protected by single-pole fused cutouts. Reclosers and sectionalizers are not required. On the other hand, in outlying districts, a 24.9 kV line may be quite long and consequently more exposed to faults. In such cases, the line is subdivided into sections and protected by reclosers and sectionalizers to provide satisfactory service.

LOW-VOLTAGE DISTRIBUTION

We have seen that electrical energy is delivered to the consumer via HV substations through MV networks and finally by LV circuits. In this section we briefly cover the organization of a low-voltage (LV) distribution system.

26.17 LV distribution system

The most common LV systems used in North America are

1. Single-phase, 2-wire, 120 V
2. Single-phase, 3-wire, 240/120 V
3. Three-phase, 4-wire, 208/120 V
4. Three-phase, 3-wire, 480 V
5. Three-phase, 4-wire, 480/277 V
6. Three-phase, 3-wire, 600 V
7. Three-phase, 4-wire, 600/347 V

In Europe and other parts of the world, 3-phase 380/220 V, 50 Hz systems are widely used. Despite the different voltages employed, the basic principles of LV distribution are everywhere the same.

Single-Phase, 2-Wire, 120 V System. This simple distribution system is only used for very small loads. When heavier loads have to be serviced, the 120 V system is not satisfactory because large conductors are required. Furthermore, the line voltage drop under load becomes significant even over short distances.

Single-Phase, 3-Wire, 240/120 V System. In order to reduce the current and hence conductor size, the voltage is raised to 240 V. However, because the 120 V level is still very useful, the 240 V/120 V 3-wire system was developed. This type of distribution system is widely used. Fig. 26.35 is a highly schematic diagram, showing the essential elements of such a system. The dual voltage is produced by a distribution transformer having a double secondary winding (Section 11.1). The common wire, called *neutral,* is solidly connected to ground. When the "live" lines A and B are equally loaded, the current in the neutral is zero. When the loading is unequal, the neutral current is equal to the difference between the line currents $I_A - I_B$ (Fig. 26.35). We try to distribute the 120 V loads as equally as possible between the two live wires and the neutral.

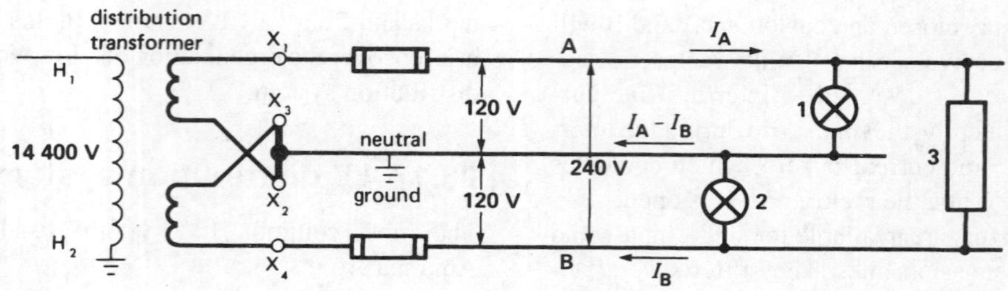

Figure 26.35
Single-phase, 240 V/120 V distribution system.

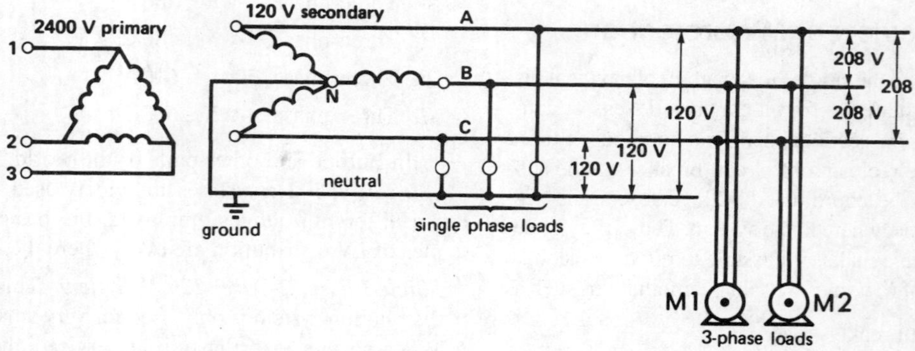

Figure 26.36
Three-phase, 4-wire, 208 V/120 V distribution system.

What are the advantages of such a 3-wire system?

1. The line-to-ground voltage is only 120 V, which is reasonably safe for use in a home.
2. Lighting and small motor loads can be energized at 120 V, while larger loads such as electric stoves and large motors can be fed from the 240 V line.

Both live lines are protected by fuses or circuit breakers. However, such protective devices must *never* be placed in series with the neutral conductor. The reason is that if the device trips, the line-to-neutral voltages become unbalanced. The voltage across the lightly loaded 120 V line goes up, while that across the more heavily loaded side goes down. This means that some lights are dimmer than others and, moreover, the intensity will vary as refrigerator motors, electric stove elements, and so forth, are switched on and off. Another reason is that when the neutral conductor is open, the line fuses are rendered useless.

Three-Phase, 4-Wire, 208/120 V System. We can create a 3-phase, 4-wire system by using three single-phase transformers connected in delta-wye. The neutral of the secondary is grounded, as shown in Fig. 26.36.

This distribution system is used in commercial buildings and small industries because the 208 V line voltage can be used for electric motors or other large loads, while the 120 V lines can be used for lighting circuits and convenience outlets. The single-phase loads between the three respective

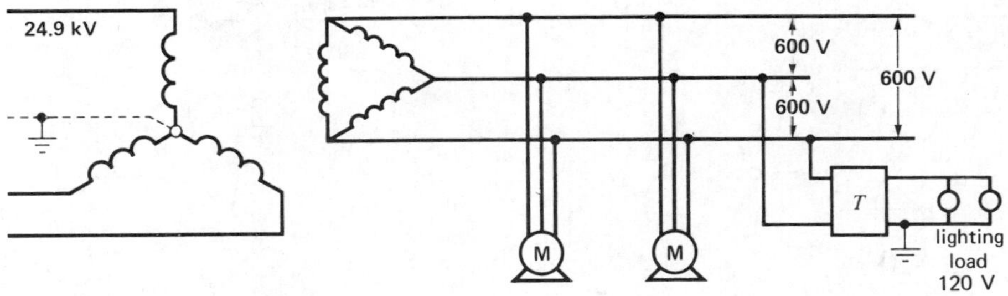

Figure 26.37
Three-phase, 3-wire, 600 V distribution system.

"live" lines and neutral are arranged to be about equal. When the loads are perfectly balanced, the current in the neutral wire is zero.

Three-Phase, 3-Wire, 600 V System. A 600 V, 3-phase, 3-wire system is used in factories where fairly large motors are installed, ranging up to 500 hp (Fig. 26.37). Separate 600 V/240-120 V step-down transformers, spotted throughout the premises, are used to service the lighting loads and convenience outlets.

Three-Phase, 4-Wire, 480/277 V System. In large buildings and commercial centers, a 480 V, 4-wire distribution system is used because it enables motors to run at 480 V while fluorescent lights operate at 277 V. For 120 V convenience outlets, separate transformers are required, usually fed from the 480 V line.

The same remarks apply to 600/347 V, 4-wire systems.

26.18 Grounding electrical installations

The grounding of electrical systems is probably one of the less well understood aspects of electricity. Nevertheless, it is a very important subject and an effective way of preventing accidents.

As we have seen, most electrical distribution systems in buildings are grounded, usually by connecting the neutral to a water pipe or the massive steel structure. On low-voltage systems, the purpose of grounding is mainly to reduce the danger of electric shock. In addition, for reasons of safety, the metal housing of electrical equipment is systematically grounded on HV, MV, and LV systems.

26.19 Electric shock

It is difficult to specify whether a voltage is dangerous or not because electric shock is actually caused by the *current* that flows through the human body. The current depends mainly upon the skin contact resistance because, by comparison, the resistance of the body itself is negligible. The contact resistance varies with the thickness, wetness, and resistivity of the skin.

It is generally claimed that currents below 5 mA are not dangerous. Between 10 mA and 20 mA the current is potentially dangerous because the victim loses muscular control and may not be able to let go; above 50 mA, the consequences can be fatal.

The resistance of the human body, taken between two hands, or between one hand and a leg, ranges from 500 Ω to 50 kΩ. If the resistance of a dry hand is, say, 50 kΩ, then momentary contact with a 600 V line may not be fatal (I = 600 V/50 kΩ = 12 mA). But the resistance of a clammy hand is much lower, so that an ac voltage as low as 25 V could be dangerous if the person is unable to let go.

When ac current flows through the body, the muscular contractions may prevent the victim from letting go. The current is particularly dangerous when it flows in the region of the heart. It induces temporary paralysis and, if it flows long enough, fibrillation may result. Fibrillation is a rapid and uncoordinated heart beat that is not synchronized with

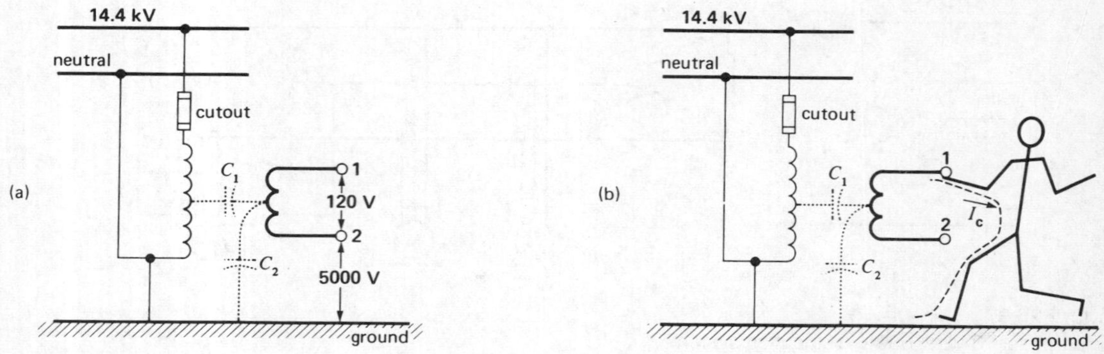

Figure 26.38
Transformer capacitance may produce high voltages on the LV side of a transformer.

the pulse beat. In such cases, the person can be revived by applying artificial respiration.

Statistical investigations* have shown that there is one chance in ten that a current may cause death if it satisfies the following equation:

$$I \geqslant 116/\sqrt{t} \quad (26.1)$$

where

I = current flow through the body [mA]
t = time of current flow [s]
116 = an empirical constant, expressing the probability of a fatal outcome

The time t is restricted to between 8 ms and 5 s. For example, a current of 58 mA flowing for 4 s could be fatal.

26.20 Grounding of 120 V and 240 V/120 V systems

Suppose the primary winding of a distribution transformer is connected between the line and neutral of a 14.4 kV line (Fig. 26.38a). If the secondary conductors are ungrounded, it would appear that a person could touch either one of them without harm because there is no ground return. However, this is not true.

First, the capacitive coupling C_1, C_2 between the primary, secondary, and ground can produce a high voltage between the secondary lines and ground. Depending upon the relative magnitude of C_1 and C_2, it may be as high as 20 to 40 percent of the primary voltage. If a person touches either one of the secondary wires, the resulting capacitive current I_c could be dangerous. For example, if I_c is only 20 mA, the person may no longer be able to let go (Fig. 26.38b).

Even more serious, suppose that a high-voltage wire accidentally touches a 120 V conductor. This could be caused by an internal fault in the transformer, or by a branch or tree falling across the MV and LV lines. Under these circumstances, the low-voltage system would be subjected to 14.4 kV. This high voltage between the secondary conductors and ground would immediately produce a massive flash-over. The flash-over could occur anywhere on the secondary network, possibly inside a home or factory. Consequently, an undergrounded secondary system is a potential fire hazard and may produce serious accidents under abnormal conditions.

On the other hand, if one of the secondary lines is firmly grounded, the accidental contact between a HV and a LV conductor produces a short-circuit. The short-circuit current follows the path shown in Fig. 26.39. The high current will blow the fuse on

* Daziel, C.F., 1968 "Reevaluation of Lethal Electric Currents," *IEEE, Transactions on Industry and General Application,* Vol. IGA-4, No. 5, pages 467–475.

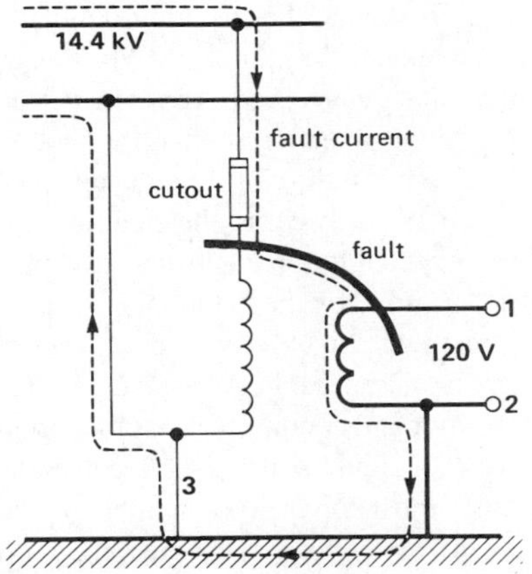

Figure 26.39
A HV to LV fault is not dangerous if the secondary is solidly grounded.

the MV side, thus effectively disconnecting the transformer and secondary distribution system from the MV line. In conclusion, if the neutral on the 120 V system is *solidly* grounded, the potential difference between the ground and live conductor 1 will only slightly exceed 120 V. However, if the ground electrode has a high resistance (say, 50 Ω), the voltage on conductor 1 produced by an MV-LV short-circuit current may still be large and potentially dangerous.

26.21 Equipment grounding

The consumer of electricity is constantly touching electrical equipment of all kinds, ranging from domestic appliances and hand-held tools to industrial motors, switchgear, and heating equipment. As we have seen, the voltages and currents associated with this equipment far exceeds those the human body can tolerate. Consequently, special precautions are taken to ensure that the equipment is safe to the touch.

In order to understand the safety features of modern distribution systems, let us begin with a simple single-phase circuit composed of a 120 V source connected to a motor M (Fig. 26.40). The neutral is solidly grounded at the service entrance.

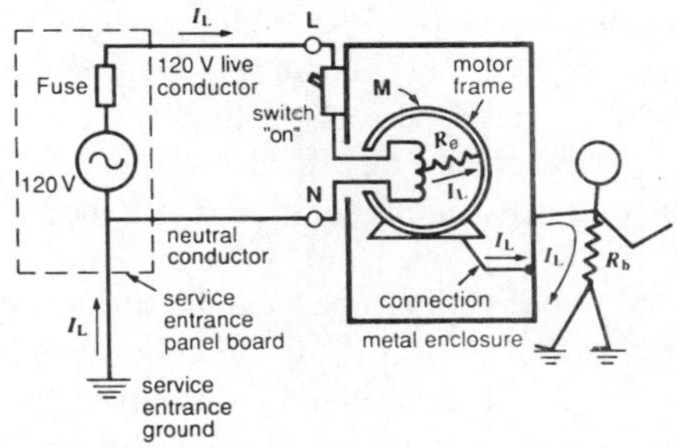

Figure 26.40
Undergrounded metallic enclosures are potentially dangerous.

Suppose the motor is part of an appliance, such as a refrigerator, and that the motor frame is connected to the ungrounded metal enclosure. If a person touches the enclosure, nothing will happen if the equipment is functioning properly. But should the motor winding insulation become faulty, resistance R_e between the windings and the motor frame may drop from several megohms to only a few hundred ohms or less. A person having a body resistance R_b would complete the current path to ground as shown in Fig. 26.40. If R_e is small, the leakage current I_L flowing through the person's body could be dangerously high. This system is unsafe.

As a first approach, we could remedy the situation by bonding the metal enclosure to the grounded neutral wire (Fig. 26.41). The leakage current now flows from the motor windings, through the motor

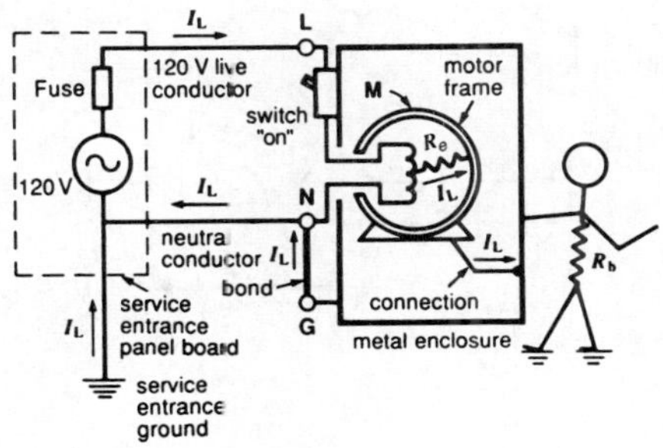

Figure 26.41
Bonding the enclosure to the neutral wire appears safe.

frame and the enclosure, and straight back to the neutral wire. Because the enclosure remains at ground potential a person touching the enclosure would not experience any shock.

The trouble with this solution is that the neutral wire may become open, either accidentally or due to a faulty installation. For example, if the switch controlling the motor is inadvertently connected in series with the neutral rather than the live wire, the motor can still be turned on and off. However, a person touching the enclosure while the motor is *off*, could receive a bad shock (Fig. 26.42). The reason is that when the motor with the defective windings is off, the potential of the motor frame and the enclosure rises to that of the live conductor.

To get around this problem, we install a third wire, called *ground* wire. It is bonded (connected) to the enclosure and is led to the system ground at the service entrance panel (Fig. 26.43). With this arrangement, the enclosure is forced to remain at ground potential. A faulty connection such as that in Fig. 26.42 would result in a short-circuit, causing the fuse to blow. In grounded systems the neutral wire must never be connected to the enclosure, except for special cases permitted by the National Electrical Code.

The ground wire may be bare, or, if insulated, it is colored green. In armored-cable and conduit installations, the armor and conduit serve as the ground conductor. The locknuts, squeeze-connectors, threads, and bushings must be screwed on tight so as to make a good electrical connection between the service entrance ground and the hundreds of outlets that sometimes make up a large installation.

Most electrical outlets are now provided with receptacles having three contacts—one live, one neutral, and one ground (Fig. 26.44). Consequently, electrical appliances and portable hand tools such as electric drills are equipped with a 3-conductor

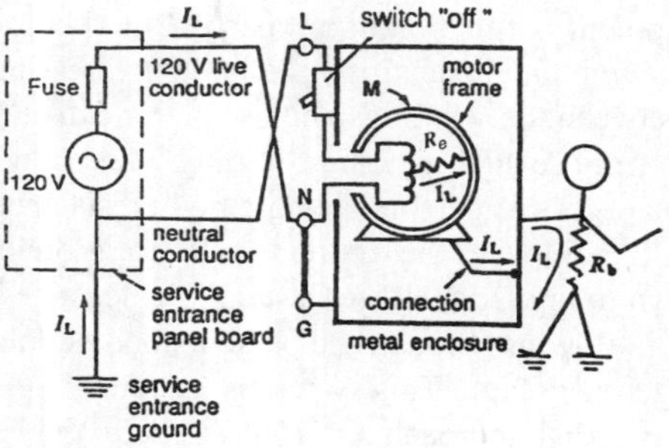

Figure 26.42
Enclosure-to-neutral bonding can still be dangerous.

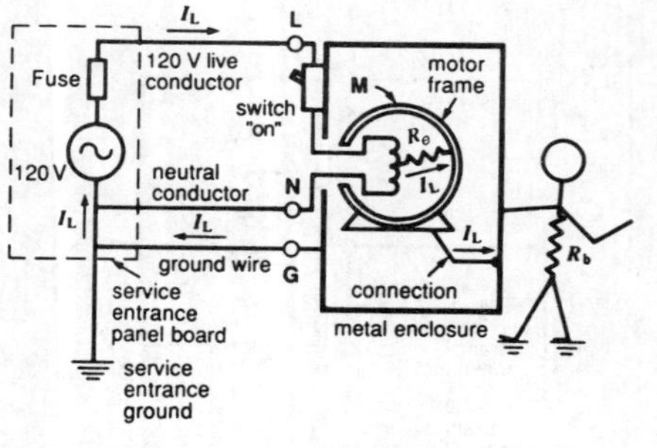

Figure 26.43
A separate ground conductor bonded to the enclosure is safe.

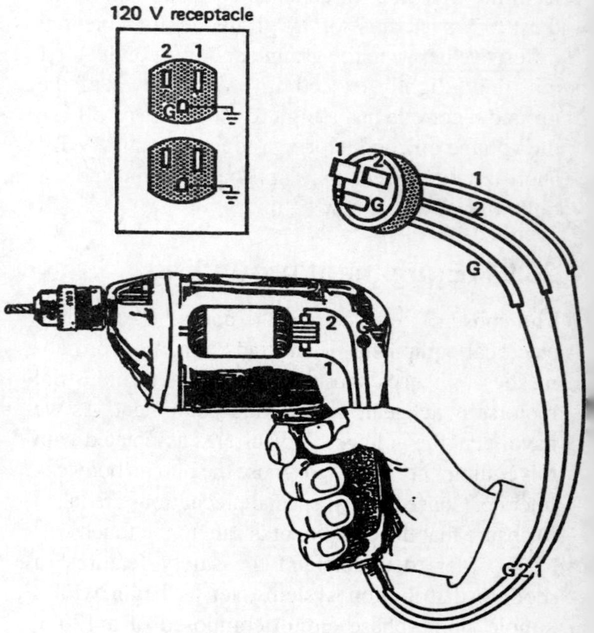

Figure 26.44
The metal housing of hand tools must be grounded.

cord and a 3-prong plug. One exception is the double-insulated devices that are completely enclosed in plastic enclosures. They are exempt from the ground wire requirement and so they are equipped with 2-prong plugs.

26.22 Ground-fault circuit breaker

The grounding methods we have covered so far are usually adequate, but further safety measures are needed in some cases. Suppose for example, that a person sticks his finger into a lamp socket (Fig. 26.45). Although the metal enclosure is securely grounded, the person will still receive a painful shock. Or suppose a 120 V electric toaster tumbles into a swimming pool. The heating elements and contacts will produce a hazardous leakage current throughout the pool, even if the frame of the toaster is securely grounded. Devices have been developed that will cut the source of power as soon as such accidents occur. These *ground-fault circuit breakers* will typically trip in 25 ms if the leakage current exceeds 5 mA. How do these protective devices operate?

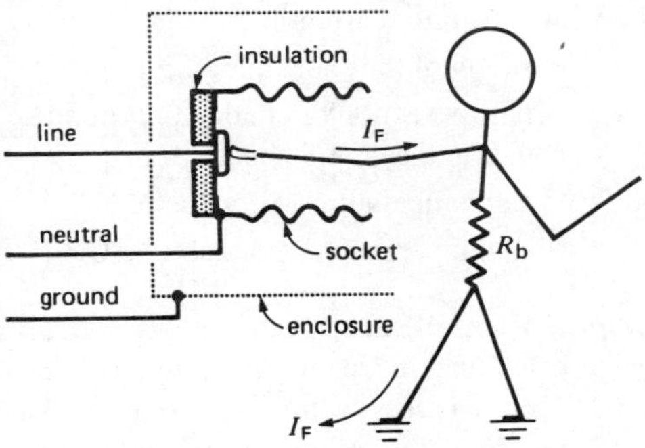

Figure 26.45
Special case where a grounding wire does not afford protection.

A small current transformer surrounds the live and neutral wires as shown in Fig. 26.46. The secondary winding is connected to a sensitive electronic detector that can trigger a circuit breaker CB that is in series with the 120 V line. Under normal conditions the current I_W in the line conductor is exactly equal to the current I_N in the neutral, and so the net current $(I_W - I_N)$ flowing through the hole in the toroidal core is zero. Consequently, no flux is produced in the core, the induced voltage E_F is zero, and breaker CB does not trip.

Suppose now that a fault current I_F leaks directly from the live wire to ground. This could happen if someone touched a live terminal (Fig. 26.45). A fault current I_L would also be produced if the insulation broke down between a motor and its grounded enclosure. Under any of these conditions, the net current flowing through the hole of the CT is no longer zero but equal to I_F or I_L. A flux is set up and a voltage E_F is induced, which trips CB. Because an imbalance of only 5 mA has to be detected, the core of the transformer must be very permeable at low flux densities. Supermalloy™ is often used for this purpose because

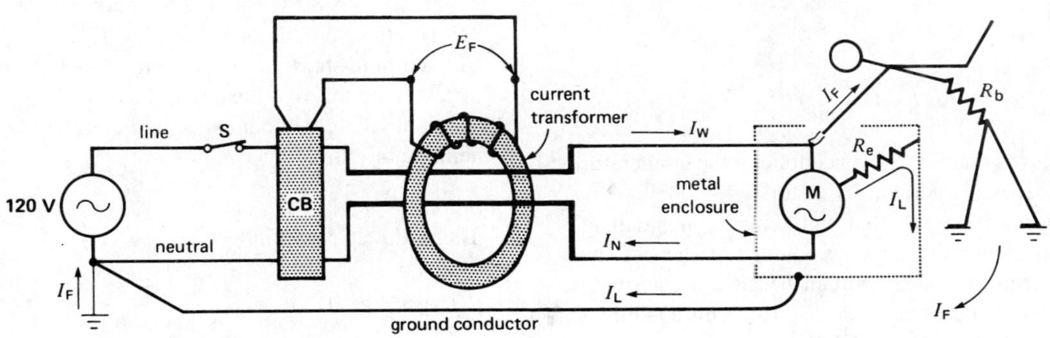

Figure 26.46
Ground fault circuit breaker trips when leakage currents I_L or I_F exceed about 5 mA.

it has a relative permeability of typically 70 000 at a flux density of only 4 mT.

26.23 Rapid conductor heating: The I^2t factor

It sometimes happens that a current far greater than normal flows for a brief period in a conductor. The I^2R losses are then very large and the temperature of the conductor can rise several hundred degrees in a fraction of a second. For example, during a severe short-circuit, intense currents can flow in conductors and cables before the circuit is opened by the fuse or circuit breaker.

Furthermore, the heat does not have time to be dissipated to the surroundings and so the temperature of the conductor increases very rapidly. What is the temperature rise under these conditions?

Suppose the conductor has a mass *m,* a resistance *R,* and a thermal heat capacity *c.* Moreover, suppose the current is *I* and that it flows for a period *t* that is typically less than 15 seconds. The heat generated in the conductor is given by

$$Q = I^2Rt \tag{26.2}$$

From Eq. 3.17, we can calculate the temperature rise Δt for a given value of *Q:*

$$Q = mc\Delta t$$

hence

$$I^2Rt = mc\Delta t$$

from which

$$\Delta t = \frac{R}{mc}(I^2t) \tag{26.3}$$

It follows that for a given conductor the temperature rise depends upon the I^2t factor.

It is well known that high temperatures damage the insulation that covers a conductor. The I^2t factor is, therefore, very important because it determines the temperature rise under short-circuit conditions. For example, a No. 2 AWG copper conductor, initially at a temperature of 90°C, cannot endure an I^2t factor in excess of 22×10^6 A^{2}s if its temperature is to be limited to 250°C during a short-circuit.

In general, the I^2t factor can be calculated knowing (a) the cross section of the conductor, (b) its composition (copper or aluminum), and (c) the maximum temperature it can tolerate. The I^2t factor for copper and aluminum conductors are given by the following equations:
for copper conductors,

$$I^2t = 11.5 \times 10^4 A^2 \log_{10}\left(\frac{234 + \theta_m}{234 + \theta_0}\right) \tag{26.4}$$

for aluminum conductors,

$$I^2t = 5.2 \times 10^4 A^2 \log_0\left(\frac{234 + \theta_m}{234 + \theta_0}\right) \tag{26.5}$$

where

I = short-circuit current [A]
t = duration of the short-circuit [s]
A = net cross section of conductor without counting the empty spaces [mm^2]
θ_0 = initial temperature of conductor [°C]
θ_m = final temperature of conductor [°C]

Example 26-1

An overhead line made of aluminum conductor No. 3 AWG has a cross section of 26.6 mm^2. Under normal conditions this conductor can continuously carry a current of 160 A.

a. Calculate the maximum permissible I^2t factor during a short-circuit, knowing that the initial temperature is 80°C and that the maximum temperature should not exceed 250°C.
b. A maximum short-circuit current of 2000 A is foreseen on this overhead line. For how long can it circulate without exceeding the 250°C temperature limit?

Solution

a. Using Eq. 26.5 we find

$$I^2t = 5.2 \times 10^4 A^2 \log_{10}\left(\frac{234 + \theta_m}{234 + \theta_0}\right)$$

$$= 5.2 \times 10^4 \times 26.6^2 \times \log_{10}\left(\frac{234 + 250}{234 + 80}\right)$$

$$= 7 \times 10^6 \text{ A}^2\text{s}$$

b. The 2000 A current can flow for a time t given by

$$I^2t = 7 \times 10^6$$
$$2000^2t = 7 \times 10^6$$
$$t = 1.75 \text{ s}$$

Example 26-2

It is proposed to use a No. 30 AWG copper wire as a temporary fuse. If its initial temperature is 50°C, calculate the following:

a. The I^2t needed to melt the wire (copper melts at 1083°C)
b. The time needed to melt the wire if the short circuit current is 30 A

Solution

a. From Eq. 26.4 we have

$$I^2t = 11.5 \times 10^4 \times 0.0507^2 \log_{10}\left(\frac{234 + 1083}{234 + 50}\right)$$
$$= 197 \text{ A}^2\text{s}$$

b. For a current of 30 A we obtain

$$I^2t = 197$$
$$30^2 t = 197$$
$$t = 0.22 \text{ s}$$

Thus, the fuse will blow in approximately 220 ms.

26.24 The role of fuses

In order to protect a conductor from excessive temperatures during a short-circuit, a fuse must be placed in series with the conductor. The fuse must be selected so that its I^2t rating is less than that which will produce an excessive temperature rise of the conductor. In effect, we want the fuse to blow before the conductor attains a dangerous temperature, usually taken to be 250°C. In practice, the I^2t rating of the fuse is such as to produce conductor temperatures far below this maximum limit. Nevertheless, the I^2t rating of the conductor is an important element in the choice of the fuse.

26.25 Electrical installation in buildings

The electrical distribution system in a building is the final link between the consumer and the original source of electrical energy. All such in-house distribution systems, be they large or small, must meet certain basic requirements:

1. Safety
   a. Protection against electric shock
   b. Protection of conductors against physical damage
   c. Protection against overloads
   d. Protection against hostile environments
2. Conductor voltage drop

   It should not exceed 1 or 2 percent.
3. Life expectancy

   The distribution system should last a minimum of 50 years.
4. Economy

   The cost of the installation should be minimized while observing the pertinent standards.

Standards are set by the National Electrical Code* and every electrical installation must be approved by an inspector before it can be put into service.

26.26 Principal components of an electrical installation

Many components are used in the makeup of an electrical installation. The block diagrams of Figs. 26.47 and 26.48, together with the following definitions†, will help the reader understand the purpose of some of the more important items.

1. Service Conductors. These are the conductors that extend from the street main feeder or from a

* In Canada, by the Canadian Electrical Code.
† Some taken from the National Electrical Code.

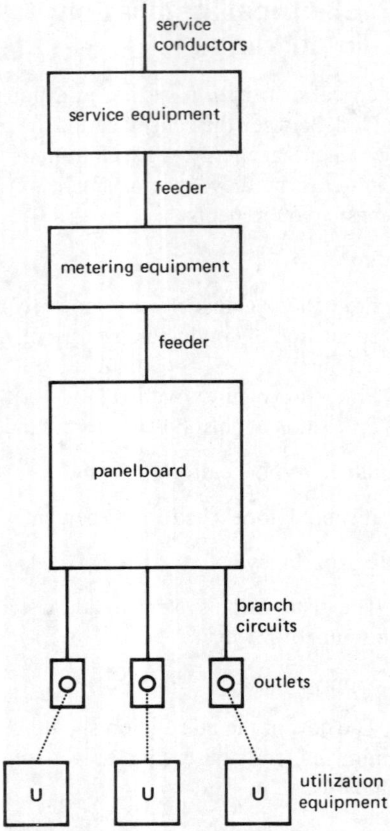

Figure 26.47
Block diagram of the electrical system in a residence. In many cases the meter is installed upstream from the service equipment.

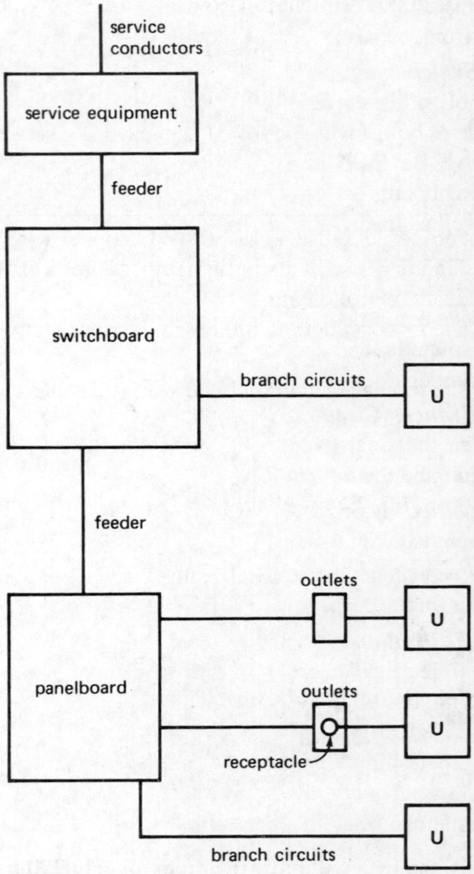

Figure 26.48
Block diagram of the electrical system in an industrial or commercial establishment.

transformer to the service equipment on the consumer premises.

2. Service Equipment. The necessary equipment, usually consisting of a circuit breaker or switch and fuses, and their accessories, located near the point of entrance of service conductors to a building or other structure, or an otherwise defined area, and intended to constitute the main control and means of cutoff of the supply.

3. Metering Equipment. Various meters and recorders to indicate the electrical energy consumed on the premises.

4. Panelboard. A single panel or group of panel units designed for assembly in the form of a single panel; including buses, automatic overcurrent devices, and with or without switches for the control of light, heat, or power circuits; designed to be placed in a cabinet or cutout box placed in or against a wall or partition and accessible only from the front.

5. Switchboard. A large single panel, frame, or assembly of panels on which are mounted on the face, back, or both, switches, over-current, and other protective devices buses, and usually instruments. Switchboards are generally accessible from the rear as well as from the front and are not intended to be installed in cabinets.

6. Feeder. All circuit conductors between the service equipment, or the generator switchboard of an isolated plant, and the final branch-circuit over-current device.

7. Branch Circuit. The circuit conductors between the final overcurrent device protecting the circuit and the outlet(s).

8. Outlet. A point on the wiring circuit at which current is taken to supply utilization equipment.

9. Receptacle. A contact device installed at the outlet for the connection of a single attachment plug.

10. Utilization Equipment. Equipment which utilizes electrical energy for mechanical, chemical, heating, lighting, or similar services.

The greatly simplified diagrams of Figs. 26.47 and 26.48 indicate the type of distribution systems used respectively in a home and in an industrial or commercial establishment.

Questions and Problems

Practical level

26-1 What is the difference between a circuit breaker and a disconnecting switch?

26-2 Name four types of circuit breakers.

26-3 The disconnecting switch shown in Fig. 26.13 can dissipate a rated maximum of 200 W. Calculate the maximum allowable value of the contact resistance.

26-4 What is the purpose of a grounding switch?

26-5 Name some of the main components of a substation.

26-6 The ground resistance of a substation is 0.35 Ω. Calculate the rise in potential of the steel structure if the station is hit by a 50 kA lightning stroke.

26-7 What is the purpose of the following equipment?

fuse cutout	receptacle
recloser	ground wire
current-limiting reactor	surge arrester

Intermediate level

26-8 A lightning arrester having the characteristics shown in Fig. 26.18 is connected to a line having a line-to-neutral voltage of 34.5 kV.

Calculate

a. The peak voltage between line and neutral

b. The current flowing in the arrester under these conditions

26-9 In Problem 26-8 an 80 kV surge appears between line and neutral.

Calculate

a. The peak current in the arrester

b. The peak power dissipated in the arrester

c. The energy dissipated in the arrester if the surge effectively lasts for 5 μs

26-10 Fig. 26.26 is a schematic diagram of a substation and Fig. 26.25 shows the actual equipment. Can you correlate the symbols of the schematic diagram with the equipment?

26-11 Repairs have to be carried out on HV circuit breaker No. 6 shown in Fig. 26.26. If the three 220 kV lines must be kept in service, which disconnecting switches must be kept open?

26-12 The current-limiting reactors (8) shown in Fig. 26.25 limit the short-circuit current to 12 kA on the 24.9 kV feeders. Calculate the reactance and inductance of each coil.

26-13 In Fig. 26.35 resistive loads, 1, 2, and 3, respectively, absorb 1200 W, 2400 W, and 3600 W. Calculate the current:

a. In lines A and B
b. In the neutral conductors
c. In the HV line

26-14 In Fig. 26.37 the lighting circuit is off and the two motors together draw 420 kVA from the 600 V line. Calculate the current in the MV lines.

26-15 Draw a graph (*I* versus *t*) of Eq. 26.1 for currents between 10 mA and 2 A.

Crosshatch the potentially mortal regions. State whether the following conditions are dangerous:
a. 300 mA for 10 ms
b. 30 mA for 2 min

26-16 Explain the operation of a ground fault circuit breaker.

Advanced level

26-17 The following loads are connected to the 240 V/120 V line shown in Fig. 26.35.

load 1: 6 kW, cos θ = 1.0

load 2: 4.8 kW, cos θ = 0.8 lagging

load 3: 18 kVA, cos θ = 0.7 lagging

a. Calculate the currents in lines A and B, and the neutral.
b. What is the current in the MV line?
c. What is the power factor on the MV side?

26-18 Referring to Fig. 26.36, the connected loads have the following ratings:

single phase loads: 30 kW each

motor M1: 50 kVA, cos θ = 0.5 lagging

motor M2: 160 kVA, cos θ = 0.80 lagging

a. Calculate the currents in the secondary windings.
b. Calculate the line currents and power factor on the 2400 V side.

26-19 In Fig. 26.37 a sensitive voltmeter reads 300 V between one 600 V line and ground, even though the 600 V system is not grounded. Can you explain this phenomenon?

26-20 The oil in the big power transformer shown on the extreme left-hand side of Fig. 26.26 has to be filtered and cleaned. Without interrupting the power flow from the three 220 kV incoming lines, state which circuit breakers and which disconnecting switches have to be opened, and in what order.

26-21 Referring to Fig. 26.25, items 10, 11, the three aluminum conductors that make up the 3-phase, 24.9 kV feeder (14.4 kV line to neutral) each have a cross section of 500 MCM. The cable possesses the following characteristics, per phase, and per kilometer of length:

resistance: 0.13 Ω

inductive reactance: 0.1 Ω

capacitive reactance: 3000 Ω

a. Draw the equivalent circuit of one phase if the line length is 5 km.
b. If no current-limiting line reactors are used, calculate the short-circuit current if a fault occurs at the end of the line.
c. Given the 12 kA rating of the circuit breakers, is a line reactor needed in this special case?

CHAPTER 27

The Cost of Electricity

27.0 Introduction

In 1999 the electric power utilities in the United States supplied approximately 3130 TW·h of electrical energy to their industrial, commercial, and residential customers (Table 27A). This enormous amount of energy represents 1.1 kW of power continually at the service of every man, woman, and child, 24 hours a day. The production, transmission, and distribution of this energy involves important costs that may be divided into two main categories—fixed costs and operating costs.

Fixed costs comprise the depreciation charges against buildings, dams, turbines, generators, circuit breakers, transformers, transmission lines, and other equipment used in the production, transmission, and distribution of electrical energy. These investments represent enormous sums measured in hundreds of billions of dollars.

Operating costs include salaries, fuel costs, administration, and any other daily or weekly expense.

Bearing in mind the relative importance of these two types of costs, utility companies have established rate structures that attempt to be as equitable as possible for their customers. The rates are based upon the following guidelines:

1. The amount of energy consumed [kW·h]
2. The *demand,* or rate at which energy is consumed [kW]
3. The power factor of the load

TABLE 27A CONSUMPTION OF ELECTRICAL ENERGY IN THE UNITED STATES (1999)*

Type of customer	Number of consumers	Total amount consumption [TW·h]	Monthly consumption per consumer [kW·h]
Industrial	527 000	1018	161 000
Commercial	13 964 000	971	5 792
Residential	109 817 000	1141	866

*These statistics for 1999 were drawn from information supplied by the Energy Information Administration (www.eia.doe.gov). It is expected that the yearly increase in energy consumption will be about 2 percent. Thus, in 2005 the total energy will amount to 3525 TW·h.

27.1 Tariff based upon energy

The cost of electricity depends, first, upon the amount of energy (kW·h) consumed. However, even if a customer uses no energy at all, he/she has to pay a minimum service charge, because it costs money to keep him/her connected to the line.

As consumption increases, the cost per kilowatt-hour drops, usually on a sliding scale. Thus, the domestic tariff may start at 20 cents per kilowatt-hour for the first one hundred kW·h, fall to 10 cents/kW·h for the next two hundred kW·h, and bottom out at 8 cents/kW·h for the rest of the energy consumed. The same general principle applies to medium-power and large-power users of electrical energy.

27.2 Tariff based upon demand

The monthly cost of electricity supplied to a large customer depends not only upon the energy consumed, but also upon the rate at which it is used. In other words, the cost also depends upon the active *power* (kW) drawn from the line. To understand the reason for this dual rate structure, consider the following example.

Two factories A and B are respectively connected to a high-voltage line by transformers T_A and T_B (Fig. 27.1). Factory A operates at full-load, night and day, including Saturdays and Sundays, constantly drawing 1000 kW of active power. At the end of the month (720 h), it has consumed a total of 1000 kW × 720 h = 720 000 kW·h of energy.

Factory B consumes the same amount of energy, but its load is continually changing. Thus, power fluctuates between 50 kW and 3000 kW, as shown in the figure. Obviously, the capacity of the transformer and the transmission line supplying factory B must be greater than that supplying factory A. The electric utility must, therefore, invest more capital to service factory B; consequently, it is reasonable that factory B should pay more for its energy.

It is advantageous, both to the customer and the utility company that energy be consumed at a constant rate. The steadier the power, the less the cost.

27.3 Demand meter

The graphs of Fig. 27.1 show a number of power spikes that last for a very short time. These spikes correspond to the high power drawn by motors when they are started up. However, the high start-up power does not last long enough to warrant the installation of correspondingly large equipment by the utility company. The question then arises: How long does the power surge have to last, in order to be considered significant? The answer depends upon sev-

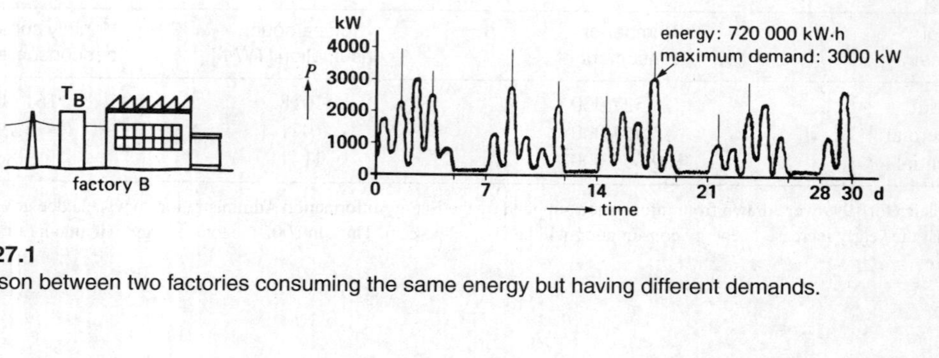

Figure 27.1
Comparison between two factories consuming the same energy but having different demands.

eral factors, but the period is usually taken to be 10, 15, or 30 minutes. For very large power users, such as municipalities, the averaging period may be as long as 60 minutes. It is called the *demand interval.*

To monitor the power drawn by a plant, a special meter is installed at the customer's service entrance. It automatically measures the average power during successive demand intervals (15 minutes, say). The average power measured during each interval is called the *demand.* As time goes by, the meter faithfully records the demand every 15 minutes and a pointer moves up and down a calibrated scale as the demand changes. In order to record the maximum demand, the meter carries a second pointer that is pushed upscale by the first. The second pointer simply sits at the highest position to which it is pushed. At the end of the month, a utility employee takes the maximum demand reading and resets the pointer to zero.

This special meter is called a *demand meter,* and it is installed at the service entrance of most industries and commercial establishments (Fig. 27.2). Fig. 27.3 shows a printing demand meter for metering large industrial loads. The printout constitutes a permanent record of the demand and is used for both diagnostic and billing purposes.

Figure 27.2
Combined energy and demand meter.
(Courtesy of Sangamo)

Example 27-1

The graph in Fig. 27.4 represents the active power drawn by a large factory between 7:00 and 9:00 in the morning. The demand meter has a 30 min demand interval. Let us assume that at 7:00 the first pointer reads 2 MW while the second (pushed)

Figure 27.3
Printing demand meter.
(Courtesy of General Electric)

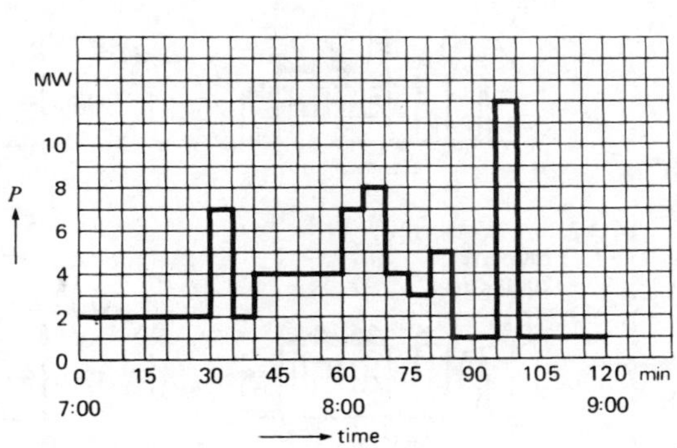

Figure 27.4
Instantaneous record of the active power absorbed by a plant.

pointer indicates 3 MW. What are the meter readings at the following times?
a. 7:30
b. 8:00
c. 8:30
d. 9:00

Solution

a. According to the graph, the average power (or demand) between 7:00 and 7:30 is 2 MW. Consequently, pointer 1 continues to indicate 2 MW at 7:30 and pointer 2 stays where it was at 3 MW.
b. The average power (or demand) between 7:30 and 8:00 is equal to the energy divided by time:

$$P_d = (7\text{ MW} \times 5\text{ min} + 2\text{MW} \times 5\text{ min} + 4\text{ MW} \times 20\text{ min})/30\text{ min}$$
$$= 4.17\text{ MW}$$

During this 30-minute interval, pointer 1 gradually moves from 2 MW (at 7:30) to 4.17 MW (at 8:00), pushing pointer 2 to 4.17 MW. Consequently, at 8:00 both pointers indicate 4.17 MW. Note that the demand reading is considerably less than the 7 MW peak which occurred during this interval.

c. The demand between 8:00 and 8:30 is

$$P_d = (7 \times 5 + 8 \times 5 + 4 \times 5 + 3 \times 5 + 5 \times 5 + 1 \times 5)/30$$
$$= 4.67\text{ MW}$$

Thus, at 8:30 both pointers have moved up to 4.67 MW.

d. The demand between 8:30 and 9:00 is

$$P_d = (1 \times 5 + 12 \times 5 + 1 \times 20)/30$$
$$= 2.83\text{ MW}$$

During this 30-minute interval, pointer 1 drops from 4.67 MW to 2.83 MW, but pointer 2 sits at 4.67 MW, the previous maximum demand.

27.4 Tariff based upon power factor

Many alternating-current machines, such as induction motors and transformers, absorb reactive power to produce their magnetic fields. The power factor of these machines is, therefore, less than unity and so, too, is the power factor of the factory where they are installed. A low power factor increases the cost of electrical energy, as the following example shows.

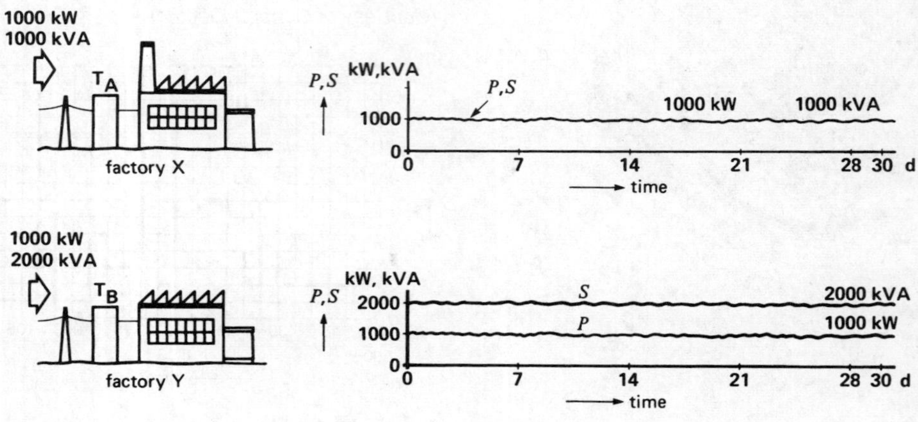

Figure 27.5
A low plant power factor requires larger utility company lines and equipment.

Consider two factories X and Y that consume the same amount of energy (kW·h) and, in addition, have the same maximum demand (kW). However, the power factor of X is unity while that of Y is 50 percent (Fig. 27.5).

The energy and demand being the same, the watthourmeters and demand meters will show the same reading at the end of the month. At first glance it would appear that both users should pay the same bill. However, we must not overlook the *apparent power* drawn by each plant.

Apparent power drawn by factory X:

$$S = P/\cos\theta \qquad (7.7)$$
$$= 1000/1.0$$
$$= 1000 \text{ kVA}$$

Apparent power drawn by factor Y:

$$S = P/\cos\theta = 1000/0.5$$
$$= 2000 \text{ kVA}$$

Because the line current is proportional to apparent power, factory Y draws twice as much current as factory X. The line conductors feeding Y must, therefore, be twice as big. Worse still, the transformers, circuit breakers, disconnect switches, and other devices supplying energy to Y must have twice the rating of those supplying X.

The utility company must, therefore, invest more capital to service factory Y; consequently, it is logical that it should pay more for its energy, even though it consumes the same amount. In practice, the rate structure is designed to automatically increase the billing whenever the power factor is low. Most electrical utilities require that the power factor of their industrial clients be 90 percent or more, in order to benefit from the minimum rate. When the power factor is too low, it is usually to the customer's advantage to improve it, rather than pay the higher monthly bill. This is usually done by installing capacitors at the service entrance to the plant, on the load side of the metering equipment. These capacitors may supply part, or all, of the reactive power required by the plant. Industrial capacitors for power factor correction are made in single-phase and 3-phase units rated from 5 kvar to 200 kvar.

27.5 Typical rate structures

Electrical power utility rates vary greatly from one area to another, and so we can only give a general overview of the subject. Most companies divide their customers into categories, according to their power demand. For example, one utility company distinguishes the following four power categories:

1. *Domestic power*—power corresponding to the needs of houses and rented apartments
2. *Small power*—power of less than 100 kilowatts
3. *Medium power*—power of 100 kilowatts and more, but less than 5000 kilowatts
4. *Large power*—power in excess of 5000 kilowatts

Table 27B shows, on a comparative basis, the type of rate structures that apply to each of these categories. In addition, a contract is usually drawn up between the electrical utility and the medium- or large-power customer. The contract may stipulate a minimum monthly demand, a minimum power factor, the voltage regulation, and various other clauses concerning firm power, growth rate, liability, off-peak energy, seasonal energy, price increases, and so forth. However, in the case of residences, the rate schedule is quite straightforward (see Table 27B).

27.6 Demand controllers

For industrial and commercial consumers the maximum demand plays an important role in compiling the electricity bill. Substantial savings can be made by keeping the maximum demand as low as possible. Thus, an alarm can be installed to sound a warning whenever the demand is about to exceed a pre-established maximum. Loads that are not absolutely essential can then be temporarily switched off until the peak has passed. This procedure can be carried out automatically by a demand controller that connects and disconnects individual loads so as to stay within the prescribed maximum demand (Fig. 27.6). Such a device can easily save thousands of dollars per year for a medium-power customer.

TABLE 27B TYPICAL RATE STRUCTURES

Residential rate structure

Typical clauses:
1. ". . . This rate shall apply to electric service in a single private dwelling . . .
2. . . . This rate applies to single-phase alternating current at 60 Hz . . ."

Rate schedule

Minimum monthly charge: $5.00 plus
first 100 kW·h per month at 5 cents/kW·h
next 200 kW·h per month at 3 cents/kW·h
excess over 200 kW·h per month at 2 cents/kW·h

General power rate structure (medium power)

Typical contract clauses:
1. ". . . The customer's maximum demand for the month, or its contract demand, is at least 50 kW but not more than 5000 kW . . .
2. . . . Utility Company shall make available to the customer 1000 kW of firm power during the term of this contract . . .
3. . . . The power shall be delivered at a nominal 3-phase line voltage of 480 V, 60 Hz . . .
4. . . . The power taken under this contract shall not be used to cause unusual disturbances on the Utility Company's system. In the event that unreasonable disturbances, including harmonic currents, produce interference with communication systems, the customer shall at his expense correct such disturbances . . .
5. . . . Voltage variations shall not exceed 7 percent up or down from the nominal line voltage . . .
6. . . . Utility Company shall make periodic tests of its metering equipment so as to maintain a high standard of accuracy . . .
7. . . . Customer shall use power so that current is reasonably balanced on the three phases. Customer agrees to take corrective measures if the current on the more heavily loaded phase exceeds the current in either of the two other phases by more than 20 percent. If said unbalance is not corrected, Utility Company may meter the load on individual phases and compute the billing demand as being equal to three times the maximum demand on any phase . . .
8. . . . The maximum demand for any month shall be the greatest of the demands measured in kilowatts during any 30-minute period of the month . . .
9. . . . If 90 percent of the highest average kVA measured during any 30-minute period is higher than the maximum demand, such amount will be used as the billing demand . . ."

Rate schedule

Demand charge: $3.00 per month per kW of billing demand
Energy charge: 4 cents/kW·h for the first 100 hours of billing demand
2 cents/kW·h for the next 50 000 kW·h per month
1.2 cents/kW·h for the remaining energy

General Power Rate Structure (large power)

Typical contract clauses:
1. ". . . Customer's maximum demand for the month or its contract demand is greater than 5000 kW . . .
2. Clauses similar to clauses 2 to 8 listed in the General Power (medium power) contract given above.
3. . . . Contract shall be for a duration of 10 years . . .
4. . . . The minimum bill for any one month shall equal 70 percent of the highest maximum demand charge during the previous 36 months . . .
5. . . . Utility Company shall not be obligated to furnish power in greater amounts than the customer's contract demand . . ."

TABLE 27B TYPICAL RATE STRUCTURES

	Rate schedule
Demand charge:	First 75 000 kW of demand per month at \$2.50 per kW
	Excess over 75 000 kW of demand per month at \$2.00 per kW
	Extra charge for any demand in excess of customer's contract demand at \$2.20 per month per kW
Energy charge:	First 20 million kW·h per month at 6.1 mills per kW·h*
	Next 30 million kW·h per month at 6.0 mills per kW·h
	Additional energy at 5.9 mills per kW·h

*1 mill = one thousandth of a dollar, or one tenth of a cent.

Example 27-2

Billing of a domestic customer

A homeowner consumes 900 kW·h during the month of August. Calculate the electricity bill using the residential rate schedule given in Table 27B.

Solution

Minimum charge	= \$5.00
First 100 kW·h @ 5 cents/kW·h	= 5.00
Next 200 kW·h @ 3 cents/kW·h	= 6.00
Remaining energy consumed	
(900 − 300) = 600 kW·h	
600 kW·h @ 2 cents/kW·h	= 12.00
TOTAL bill for the month	\$28.00

This represents an average cost of 2800/900 = 3.11 cent/kW·h.

Demand meters are not usually installed in homes because the maximum demand seldom exceeds 10 kW.

Table 27C shows the energy consumed by various electrical appliances found in a home. Fig. 27.7 is an example of an all-electric home heated by baseboard heaters.

Example 27-3

Billing for a medium-power customer

A small industry operating night and day, 7 days a week, consumes 260 000 kW·h per month. The maximum demand is 1200 kW, and the maximum kVA demand is 1700 kVA. Note that the demand in this factory is measured for both active power (kW) and apparent power (kVA). Calculate the electricity bill using the medium-power rate schedule (Table 27B).

Solution

Clause 9 is important here because 90% of the kVA demand is equal to 90% × 1700 = 1530 kVA, which is greater than the maximum demand of 1200 kW. Consequently, the demand for billing purposes is 1530 kW and not 1200 kW. The power factor of the

Figure 27.6
Automatic demand controller that sheds nonessential loads whenever the demand reaches a preset level or according to a set schedule. This model can control up to 96 loads.
(Courtesy of Gentec Inc.)

TABLE 27C AVERAGE MONTHLY CONSUMPTION OF HOUSEHOLD APPLIANCES

Average monthly consumption of a family of five people in a modern house equipped with an automatic washing machine and a dishwasher.

Appliance	kW·h consumed	Appliance	kW·h consumed
hot water heater (2000 gallons/month)	500	automatic washing machine	100
freezer	100	coffee maker	9
stove	100	stereo system	9
lighting	100	radio	7
dryer	70	lawn mower	7
dishwasher	30	vacuum cleaner	4
electric kettle	20	toaster	4
electric skillet	15	clock	2
electric iron	12		

plant is low; consequently, the *billing demand* (1530 kW) is higher than the *metered demand* (1200 kW).

Applying the rate schedule, the demand charge is

1530 kW @ \$3.00/kW = \$ 4590

The energy charge for the first 100 h is
1530 kW × 100 hours
= 153 000 kW·h @ 4 cents/kW·h
= 153 000 × 0.04 = 6120

The energy charge for the next 50 000 kW·h is
50 000 kW·h @ 2 cents/kW·h = 1000

The remainder of the energy is
(260 000 − 153 000 − 50 000) = 57 000 kW·h

The energy charge for the remainder of the energy is
57 000 kW·h @ 1.2 cents/kW·h = 684

TOTAL bill for the month \$12394

The average cost of energy is
unit cost = 12 394/260 000
= 4.77 cents/kW·h

Fig. 27.8 shows a plant equipped with both a demand controller and power-factor correcting capacitors.

Figure 27.7
All-electric home that consumes a maximum of 9400 kW·h in January, and a minimum of 2100 kW·h in July.

Example 27-4

Billing of a large-power customer

A paper mill consumes 28 million kilowatt-hours of energy per month. The demand meter registers a peak demand of 43 000 kW. Calculate the monthly bill using the large-power rate schedule given in Table 27B.

Solution

a. The demand charge is
43 000 kW @ \$2.50/kW = \$ 107 500

b. The energy charge for the first 20 million kW·h is
20 million kW·h @ 6.1 mill/kW·h
$20 \times 10^6 \times 6.1/1000$ = 122 000
The energy charge for the next

Figure 27.8
All-electric industry covering an area of 1300 m^2. It is heated by passing current through the reinforcing wire mesh embedded in the concrete floor. A load controller connects and disconnects the heating sections (nonpriority loads) depending on the level of production (priority loads). The demand is thereby kept below the desired preset level. Annual energy consumption: 375 000 kW·h; maximum demand in winter: 92 kW; maximum demand during the summer: 87 kW.
(Courtesy of Lab-Volt)

(28 − 20) = 8 million kW·h is	
8 million kW·h @ 6.0 mill/kW·h	
$8 \times 10^6 \times 6.0/1000$	= 48 000
TOTAL bill for the month	$ 277 500

Average cost per kW·h =
$277\,500/28 \times 10^6 = 9.9 \times 10^{-3} = 9.9$ mill

or about 1 cent/kW·h

A monthly bill of nearly $300 000 may appear high, but we must remember that it probably represents less than 5 percent of the selling price of the finished product.

Fig. 27.9 gives an idea of the power and energy consumed by a large city.

27.7 Power factor correction

Power factor correction (or improvement) is economically feasible whenever the decrease in the annual cost of electricity exceeds the amortized cost of installing the required capacitors. In some cases the customer has no choice but must comply with the minimum power factor specified by the utility company.

The power factor may be improved by installing capacitors at the service entrance to the factory or commercial enterprise. In other cases it may be desirable to correct the power factor of an individual device, or machine, if its power factor is particularly low.

Example 27-5

A factory draws an apparent power of 300 kVA at a power factor of 65% (lagging). Calculate the kvar capacity of the capacitor bank that must be installed at the service entrance to bring the overall power factor to

a. Unity
b. 85 percent lagging

Solution

a. Apparent power absorbed by the plant is

$$S = 300 \text{ kVA}$$

Active power absorbed by the plant is

$$P = S \cos \theta \tag{7.7}$$
$$= 300 \times 0.65 = 195 \text{ kW}$$

Reactive power absorbed by the factory is

$$Q = \sqrt{S^2 - P^2} \tag{7.4}$$
$$= \sqrt{300^2 - 195^2} = 228 \text{ kvar}$$

To raise the power factor to unity, we have to supply all the reactive power absorbed by the load (228 kvar). The 3-phase capacitors must, therefore, have a rating 228 kvar. Fig. 27.10a shows the active and reactive power flow.

b. The factory continues to draw the same amount of active power (195 kW) because the mechanical and thermal loads remain unchanged. Consequently, because the new overall power

Figure 27.9
In 1998, the City of Montreal with 908 343 customers consumed 26 335 GW·h of electric energy. Maximum demand during the winter, 6695 MW; during the summer, 3591 MW. Residential customers: 834 935; general and institutional customers: 67 234; industrial customers: 6174.
(Courtesy of Hydro-Québec and of Service de la C.I.D.E.M., Ville de Montréal)

factor is to be 0.85 lagging, the apparent power drawn from the line must be

$$S = P/\cos\theta$$
$$= 195/0.85 = 230 \text{ kVA}$$

The new reactive power supplied by the line is

$$Q = \sqrt{230^2 - 195^2} = 121 \text{ kvar}$$

Because the plant still draws 228 kvar and the line furnishes only 121 kvar, the difference must come from the capacitors. The rating of these units is

$$Q = (228 - 121) = 107 \text{ kvar}$$

Thus, if we can accept a power factor of 0.85 (instead of unity), we can install a smaller capacitor bank and, hence, reduce the cost. Fig. 27.10b shows the new power flow in the transmission line and the factory. Note that the factory draws the same active and reactive power, irrespective of the size of the capacitor installation.

The demand of commercial and industrial customers varies greatly throughout the day. As a result, it is common practice to install a variable capacitor unit at the service entrance. In the case of large customers, an automatic controller switches capacitor units in and out so that the power factor always lies slightly above 95 percent.

Example 27-6

A 600 kW induction furnace connected to an 800 V single-phase line operates at a power factor of 0.6 lagging. It is supplied by a 4 kV line and a step-down transformer (Fig. 27.11).

a. Calculate the current in the 4000 V line.
b. If a 500 kvar capacitor is installed on the HV side of the transformer, calculate the new power factor and the new line current.

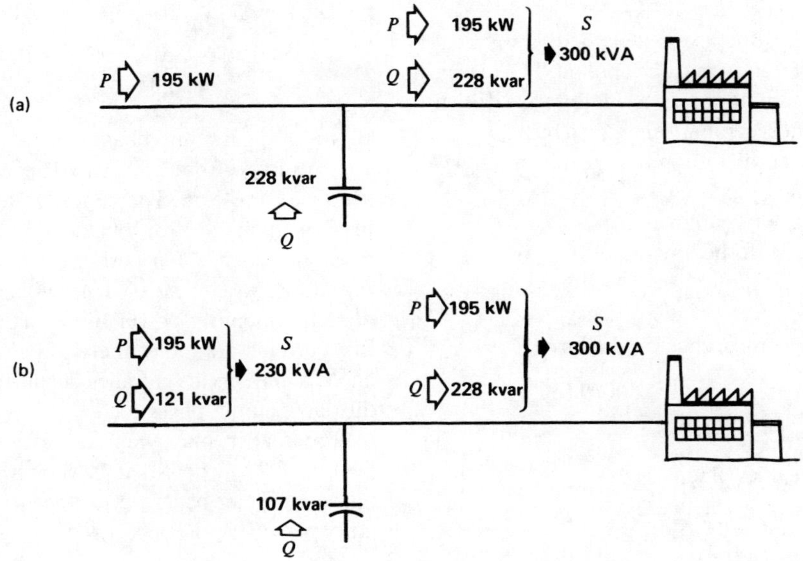

Figure 27.10
a. Overall power factor corrected to unity (Example 27-5).
b. Overall power factor corrected to 0.85.

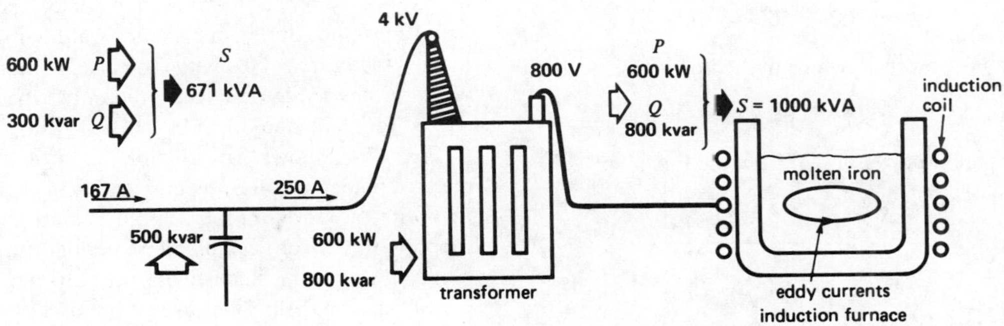

Figure 27.11
Individual load power factor correction (Example 27-6).

Solution

This is an interesting example where individual power factor correction must be applied. The reason is that the induction furnace is a single-phase device whereas the plant is certainly energized by a 3-phase line. We cannot correct the power factor of single-phase equipment by adding balanced 3-phase capacitors at the service entrance.

a. Active power absorbed by the furnace is

$$P = 600 \text{ kW}$$

Apparent power absorbed by the furnace is

$$S = P/\cos\theta = 600/0.6$$
$$= 1000 \text{ kVA}$$

Current in the 4 kV line is

$$I = S/E = 1000/4$$
$$= 250 \text{ A}$$

b. Reactive power absorbed by the furnace is

$$Q = \sqrt{S^2 - P^2}$$
$$= \sqrt{1000^2 - 600^2}$$
$$= 800 \text{ kvar}$$

Reactive power supplied by the capacitor is

$$Q_C = 500 \text{ kvar}$$

Reactive power that the line must supply is

$$Q_L = Q - Q_C$$
$$= 800 - 500 = 300 \text{ kvar}$$

Active power drawn from the line is

$$P_L = 600 \text{ kW}$$

Apparent power drawn from the line is

$$S_L = \sqrt{P_L^{\,2} + Q_L^{\,2}}$$
$$= \sqrt{600^2 + 300^2}$$
$$= 671 \text{ kVA}$$

New power factor is of the line

$$\cos\theta = P_L/S_L = 600/671 = 0.89$$

The new line current is

$$I = S_L/E = 671\,000/4000$$
$$= 168 \text{ A}$$

By installing a single-phase capacitor bank, the line current drops from 250 A to 168 A, which represents a decrease of 33 percent. It follows that the I^2R loss and voltage drop on the supply line will be greatly reduced. Furthermore, the power factor rises from 60% to 89% which will significantly reduce the monthly power bill. Finally, the 3-phase line currents are more likely to be reasonably balanced at the service entrance despite the presence of this large single-phase load.

The reader may want to refer to Chapter 8, Section 8.22, wherein it is shown how a single-phase load can be made to appear as a balanced, unity power-factor 3-phase load by using capacitors and inductors.

27.8 Measuring electrical energy, the watthourmeter

We have already seen that the SI unit of energy is the joule. However, for many years, power utilities have been using the kilowatt-hour to measure the energy supplied to industry and private homes. One kilowatt hour (kW·h) is exactly equal to 3.6 MJ.

Meters which measure industrial and residential energy are called *watthourmeters;* they are designed to multiply power by time. The electricity bill is usually based upon the number of kilowatt hours consumed during one month. Watthourmeters must, therefore, be very precise. *Induction* watthourmeters are practically the only types employed for residential metering.

Fig. 27.12 shows the principal parts of such a meter: a potential coil B_p wound with many turns of fine wire; a current coil B_c; an aluminum disc D supported by a vertical spindle; a permanent magnet A; and a gear mechanism that registers the number of turns made by the disc. When the meter is connected to a single-phase line, the disc is subjected to a torque which causes it to turn like a high-precision motor.

Figure 27.12a
Complete watthourmeter.
(Courtesy of General Electric)

27.9 Operation of the watthourmeter

The operation of a watthourmeter can be understood by referring to Fig. 27.13. Load current I produces an alternating flux Φ_c, which crosses the aluminum disc, inducing in it a voltage and, consequently, eddy currents I_f. On the other hand, potential coil B_p produces an alternating flux Φ_p, which intercepts current I_f. The disc is therefore subjected to a force (Section 2.22), and the resultant torque causes it to rotate. It can be shown that the torque is proportional to flux Φ_p and current I_f and the cosine of the angle between them. Because Φ_p and I_f are respectively proportional to voltage E and load current I, it follows that the motor torque is proportional to $EI \cos \theta$, which is the active power delivered to the load. This, however, is only part of the story.

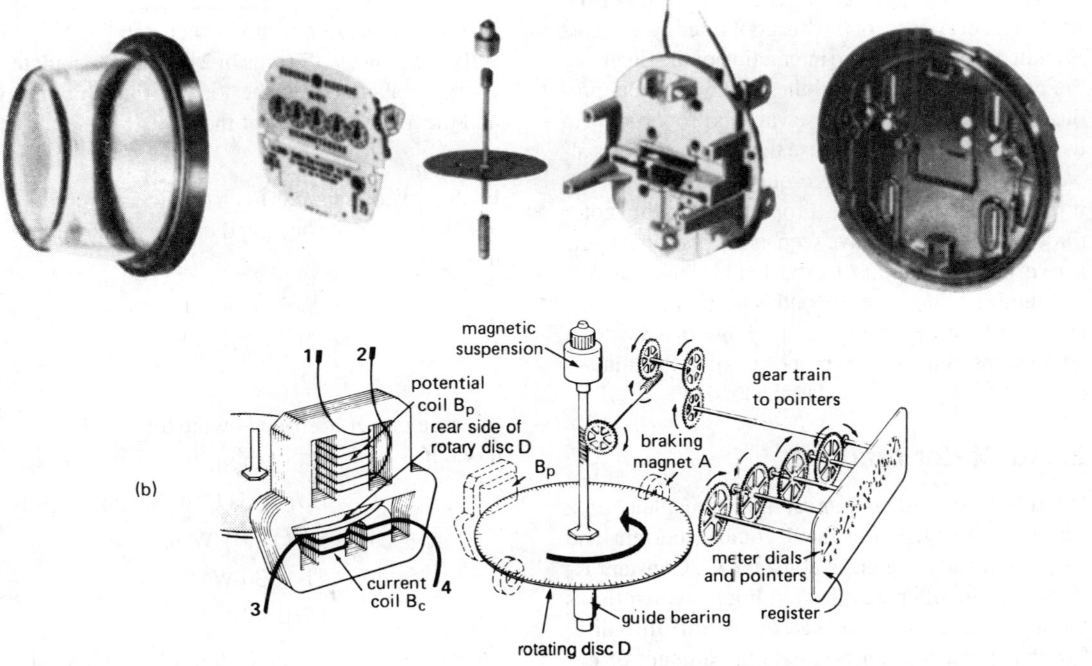

Figure 27.12b
Components making up the meter.
(Courtesy of General Electric)

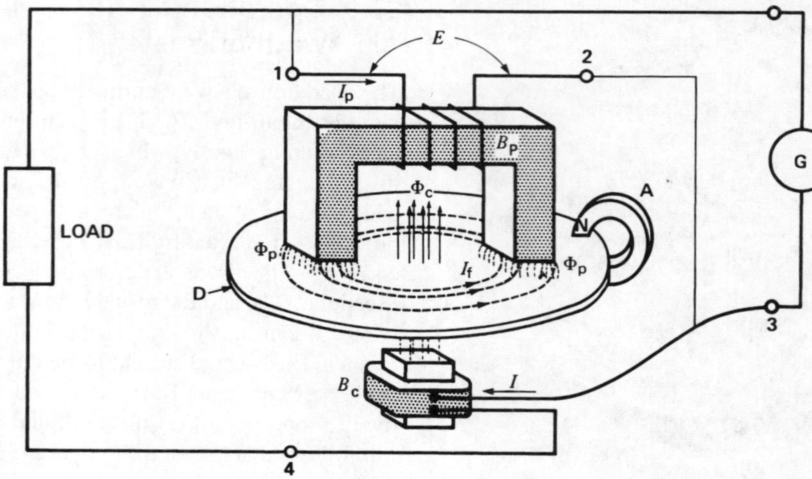

Figure 27.13
Principle of operation of watthourmeter.

As the disc moves between the poles of permanent magnet A, a second whirlpool of eddy-currents is induced in the disc. The interaction of the flux from the permanent magnet and these eddy currents produces a braking torque whose value is proportional to the *speed* of the disc. Because the motor torque is always equal to the braking torque (see Section 3.11), it follows that the speed is proportional to the motor torque. The latter, we have seen, is proportional to the active power supplied to the load. Consequently, the number of turns per second is proportional to the number of joules per second. It follows that the number of turns of the disc is proportional to the number of joules (energy) supplied to the load.

27.10 Meter readout

In addition to other details, the nameplate of a watthourmeter lists the rated voltage, current and frequency, and a metering constant K_h. Constant K_h is the amount of energy, in watt hours, which flows through the meter for each turn of the disc. Consequently, we can calculate the amount of energy that flows through a meter by counting the number of turns. Then, dividing energy by time, we can calculate the average value of the active power supplied to the load during the interval.

Example 27-7

The nameplate of a watthourmeter shows $K_h = 3.0$. If the disc makes 17 turns in 2 minutes, calculate the energy consumed by the load during this interval and the average power of the load.

Solution

Each turn corresponds to an energy consumption of 3.0 W·h. Energy consumed during the 2-minute interval is

$$\begin{aligned} E_h &= K_h \times \text{number of turns} \\ &= 3.0 \times 17 \\ &= 51 \text{ W·h} \end{aligned}$$

Average power absorbed by the load during this interval is

$$\begin{aligned} P &= E_h/t = 51/2 \text{ W·h/min} \\ &= 51/(1/30) \text{ W·h/h} \\ &= 51 \times 30 \text{ W} \\ &= 1530 \text{ W} \end{aligned}$$

Most watthourmeters have four dials to indicate the amount of energy consumed. The dials are read from left to right and the number so obtained is the number of kilowatthours consumed since the meter was first put in service. In reading the individual di-

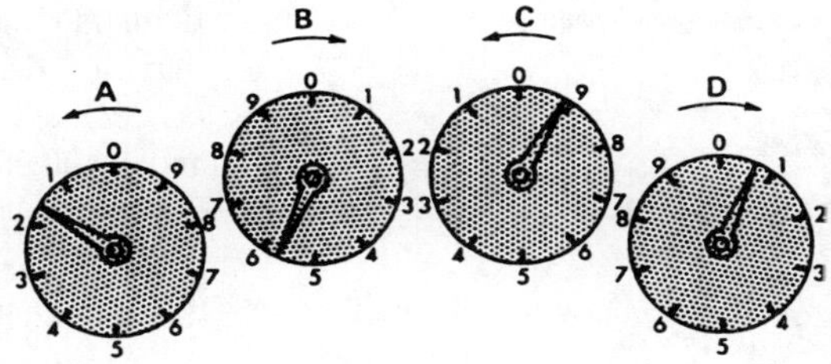

Figure 27.14
Reading the dials of a watthourmeter.

als, we always take the number which the pointer swept over last. For example, in Fig. 27.14, the reading is 1-5-9-0, or 1590 kW·h. To measure the energy consumed during one month, we simply subtract the readings at the beginning and end of the month. Some modern watthourmeters give a digital readout which, of course, is much easier to read.

27.11 Measuring 3-phase energy and power

The energy consumed by a 3-phase load (3-wire system) can be measured with two single-phase watthourmeters. The two meters are often combined into one by mounting the two discs on the same spindle and using a single register (Fig. 27.15). The current and potential coils are connected to the line in the same way as those of two wattmeters.

Fig. 27.16 is a 3-phase, solid-state watthourmeter having a precision exceeding that of induction-type watthourmeters. Electronic watthourmeters are now being developed that will monitor harmonic content and phase unbalance as part of the metering process to meet special contractual requirements.

Figure 27.15
Watthourmeter for a 3-phase, 3-wire circuit.
(Courtesy of General Electric)

Questions and Problems

Practical level

27-1 Explain what is meant by the following terms:

demand	billing demand
maximum demand	fixed cost
mill	demand interval

27-2 Using the rate schedule given in Table 27B, calculate the power bill for a homeowner who consumes 920 kW·h in one month.

27-3 Explain why a low power factor in a factory results in a higher power bill.

27-4 Explain the behavior of a demand meter.

27-5 Using the rate schedule given in Table 27B for a medium-power customer, calculate the monthly power bill under the following conditions:

demand meter reading	= 120 kW
billing demand	= 150 kW
energy consumed	= 36 000 kW·h

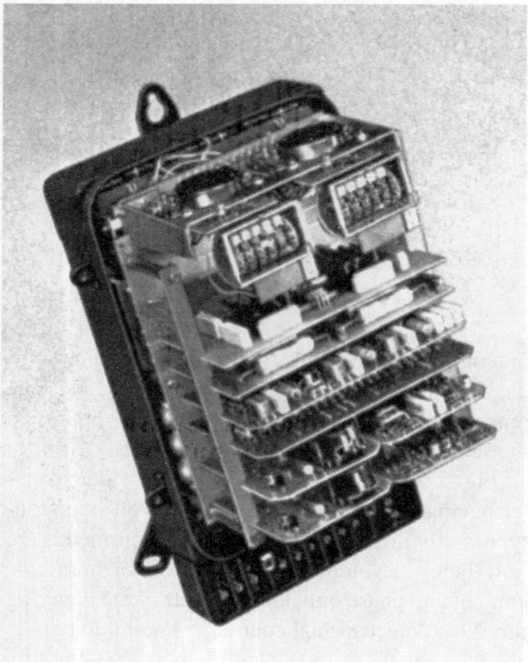

Figure 27.16
This high-precision electronic watthourmeter gives a numerical readout of the energy delivered by a 3-phase transmission line. It has an accuracy of 0.2 percent, which compares favorably with the 0.5 percent accuracy of some of the best induction-type watthourmeters. This meter is used on high-power lines where the monthly consumption exceeds 10 GW·h.
(Courtesy of Siemens)

Intermediate level

27-6 The demand meter in a factory registers a maximum demand of 4300 kW during the month of May. The power factor is known to be less than 70 percent.
- **a.** If capacitors had been installed so as to raise the power factor to 0.9, would the maximum demand have been affected?
- **b.** Would the billing demand have been affected?

27-7 According to Example 27-1, the maximum demand registered at 8:00 is 4.17 MW. If the demand meter were replaced by another one having a demand interval of 15 minutes, calculate the new value of the maximum demand at 8:00.

27-8
- **a.** Give an estimate of the energy consumed in one year by a modern city of 300 000 inhabitants in North America (refer to Fig. 27.9).
- **b.** If the average rate is 40 mill/kW·h, calculate the annual cost of servicing the city.

27-9 A motor draws 75 kW from a 3-phase line at a $\cos \theta = 0.72$ lagging.
- **a.** Calculate the value of Q and S absorbed by the motor.
- **b.** If a 20 kvar, 3-phase capacitor is connected in parallel with the motor, what is the new value of P and Q supplied by the line?
- **c.** Calculate the percent drop in line current after the capacitor is installed.

27-10 A plant draws 160 kW at a lagging power factor of 0.55.
- **a.** Calculate the capacitors [kvar] required to raise the power factor to unity.
- **b.** If the power factor is only raised to 0.9 lagging, how much less would the capacitor bank cost (in percent)?

27-11
- **a.** Assuming that power in a large industry can be purchased at 15 mill/kW·h, estimate the hourly cost of running a 4000 hp motor having an efficiency of 96 percent.
- **b.** If the motor runs night and day, 365 days per year, what would the annual saving be if the motor were redesigned to have an efficiency of 97%.

27-12
- **a.** Referring to the residential rate schedule given in Table 27B, calculate the cost per kW·h if only 20 kW·h are consumed during a given month.
- **b.** The heating element on an electric stove is rated at 1200 W. Using the same rate schedule, what is the least possible cost of running it for one hour?

27-13 A barrel of oil costing 32 dollars contains 42 gal (U.S.) having a heating value of 115 000 Btu/gal. When the fuel is burned in a thermal generating station to produce electricity, the overall efficiency is typically 35 percent. Calculate the minimum cost per kilowatt-hour, considering only the price of the fuel.

27-14 Describe the construction of a watthourmeter. Explain why the disc rotates.

27-15 The disc in Fig. 27.13 turns at 10 r/min for a load of 10 kW. If a 5 kvar capacitor is connected in parallel with the load, what is the new rate of rotation?

27-16 We want to determine the power of an electric heater installed in a home by means of a watthourmeter. All other loads are shut off and it is found that the disc makes 10 complete turns in 1 minute. If $K_h = 3.0$, calculate the power of the heater.

27-17 **a.** The flux created by the permanent magnet in Fig. 27.13 decreases by 0.5 percent in 10 years. What is the effect on the speed of rotation and the precision of the meter?

b. The resistance of coil B_c changes with temperature. Does this affect the speed of rotation if the active load remains fixed?

27-18 A domestic watthourmeter has a precision of 0.7 percent. Calculate the maximum possible error if the monthly consumption is 800 kW·h.

Industrial application

27-19 A 200 hp induction motor driving a centifugal pump delivers 10 000 gallons of water per minute when running at 1760 r/min with the valve fully open. When less water is needed, the valve is partly closed so as to throttle the flow.

It is proposed to use a variable speed inverter drive and leave the valve wide open at high- and low-water flows. The following information regarding the three modes of operation is given in Table 27D:

1. Valve fully open
2. Valve throttled
3. Inverter drive with valve fully open.

The cost of a variable speed inverter for the 200 hp motor is $32 000. The cost of energy is 6 cents/kWh and the throttled condition is on 17 hours per day, every day of the year. Referring to Table 27D, answer the following questions:

a. How much energy is saved per day by using an inverter instead of throttling the valve?

b. How much money is saved per year by installing the inverter?

TABLE 27D

	Motor input [kW]	Motor losses [kW]	Pump losses [kW]	Valve losses [kW]	Flow [gal/min]
(1)	135	10	25	0	10 000
(2)	133	10	27	32	8000
(3)	89	9	16	0	8000

CHAPTER 28
Direct-Current Transmission

28.0 Introduction

The development of high-power, high-voltage electronic converters has made it possible to transmit and control large blocks of power using direct current. Direct-current transmission offers unique features that complement the characteristics of existing ac networks. We cover here some of the various ways it is being adapted and used, both in North America and throughout the world. However, before undertaking this chapter, the reader should first review the principles of power electronics covered in Chapter 21.

28.1 Features of dc transmission

What are the advantages of transmitting power by dc rather than by ac? They may be listed as follows:

1. DC power can be controlled much more quickly. For example, power in the megawatt range can be reversed in a dc line in less than one second. This feature makes it useful to operate dc transmission lines in parallel with existing ac networks. When instability is about to occur (due to a disturbance on the ac system), the dc power can be changed in amplitude to counteract and dampen out the power oscillations. Quick power control also means that dc short-circuit currents can be limited to much lower values than those encountered on ac networks.
2. DC power can be transmitted in cables over great distances. We have seen that the capacitance of a cable limits ac power transmission to a few tens of kilometers (Section 25.29). Beyond this limit, the reactive power generated by cable capacitance exceeds the rating of the cable itself. Because capacitance does not come into play under steady-state dc conditions, there is theoretically no limit to the distance that power may be carried this way. As a result, power can be transmitted by cable under large bodies of water, where the use of ac cables is unthinkable. Furthermore, underground dc cable may be used to deliver power into large urban centers. Unlike overhead lines, underground cable is invisible, free from atmospheric pollution, and solves the problem of securing rights of way.
3. We have seen that ac power can only be transmitted between centers operating at the same frequency. Furthermore, the power transmitted

depends upon line reactance and the phase angle between the voltages at each end of the line (Section 25.23). But when power is transmitted by dc, frequencies and phase angles do not come into the picture, and line reactance does not limit the steady-state power flow. If anything, it is only the resistance of the line that limits the flow. This also means that power can be transmitted over greater distances by using dc. However, this is a marginal benefit because large blocks of ac power are already being carried over distances exceeding 1000 km.

4. Overhead dc transmission lines become economically competitive with ac lines when the length of the line exceeds several hundred kilometers. The width of the power corridor is less, and experience to date has shown that outages due to lightning are somewhat reduced. Consequently, dc transmission lines are being used to carry bulk power directly from a generating station located near a coal mine or waterfall, to the load center.
5. At the opposite extreme of great distance are back-to-back converters, which interconnect large adjacent ac systems with a dc transmission line that is only a few meters long. Back-to-back converters enable the two systems to operate at their respective frequencies and phase angles. As a result, disturbances on one system do not tend to destabilize the other system. Furthermore, the power flow between the systems can be modified and even reversed in a matter of milliseconds—much faster than could be achieved on an ac system.

Unlike ac transmission lines, it is not easy to tap power off at different points along a dc line. In effect, dc lines are usually point-to-point systems, tying one large generating station to one large power-consuming center. Electronic converters are installed at each end of the transmission line, but none in between. However, a multiterminal dc line originating at Radisson, near James Bay, has been built to supply power to New England and three other points in Quebec.

28.2 Basic dc transmission system

A dc transmission system consists basically of a dc transmission line connecting two ac systems. A converter at one end of the line converts ac power into dc power while a similar converter at the other end reconverts the dc power into ac power. One converter acts therefore as a rectifier, the other as an inverter.

Stripped of everything but the bare essentials, the transmission system may be represented by the circuit of Fig. 28.1. Converter 1 is a 3-phase, 6-pulse rectifier that converts the ac power of line 1 into dc power. The dc power is carried over a 2-conductor

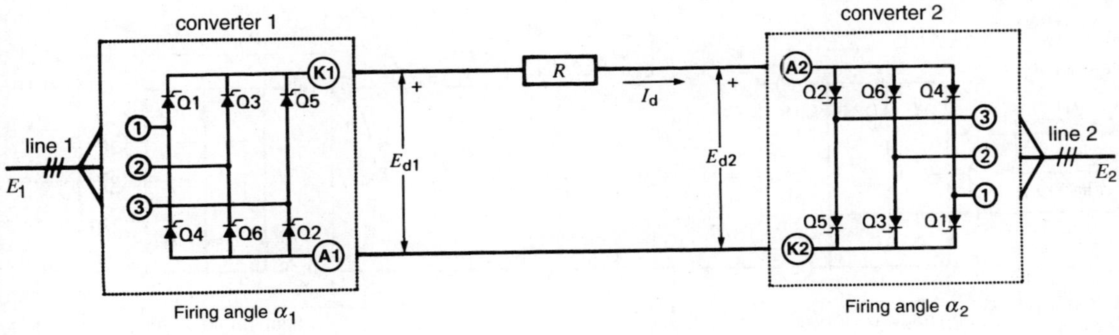

Figure 28.1
Elementary dc transmission system connecting 3-phase line 1 to 3-phase line 2.

transmission line and reconverted to ac power by means of converter 2, acting as an inverter. Both the rectifier and inverter are line-commutated by the respective line voltages to which they are connected (Sections 21.9, 21.20, 21.28, and 21.29). Consequently, the networks can function at entirely different frequencies without affecting the power transmission between them.

Power flow may be reversed by changing the firing angles α_1 and α_2, so that converter 1 becomes an inverter and converter 2 a rectifier. Changing the angles reverses the polarity of the conductors, but the direction of current flow remains the same. This mode of operation is required because thyristors can only conduct current in one direction.

The dc voltages E_{d1} and E_{d2} at each converter station are identical, except for the *IR* drop in the line. The drop is usually so small that we can neglect it, except insofar as it affects losses, efficiency, and conductor heating.

Due to the high voltages encountered in transmission lines, each thyristor shown in Fig. 28.1 is actually composed of several thyristors connected in series. Such a group of thyristors is often called a *valve.* Thus, a valve for a 50 kV, 1000 A converter would typically be composed of 50 thyristors connected in series. Each converter in Fig. 28.1 would, therefore, contain 300 thyristors. The 50 thyristors in each bridge arm are triggered simultaneously, so together they act like a super-thyristor.

28.3 Voltage, current, and power relationships

In a practical transmission line, smoothing inductors L_1 and L_2 (Fig. 28.2) must be used as a buffer between the ripple-free dc voltage E_d and the undulating output of the converters (Sections 21.10, 21.26, and 21.31). Thus, the potential difference between E_{1G} and E_d appears across inductor L_1. Similarly, the difference between E_{2G} and E_d appears across L_2. The inductors also reduce the ac harmonic currents flowing in the transmission line to an acceptable level.

If we neglect commutation overlap, the waveshape of E_{1G} on the dc side of the rectifier is as shown in Fig. 28.3a. Similarly, the waveshape of E_{2G} is as shown in Fig. 28.3b. We have assumed firing angles of $\alpha_1 = 15°$ and $\alpha_2 = 150°$, respectively, for the rectifier and inverter. Consequently, the dc line voltage is given by

$$E_d = 1.35\ E_1 \cos \alpha_1$$
$$= 1.35\ E_1 \cos 15° = 1.304\ E_1$$

Similarly,

$$E_d = 1.35\ E_2 \cos \alpha_2$$

In the case of dc transmission lines, the rectifier angle α_1 is simply designated α. Furthermore, the inverter firing angle is not considered as a delay (α_2) with respect to the rectifier zero firing point,

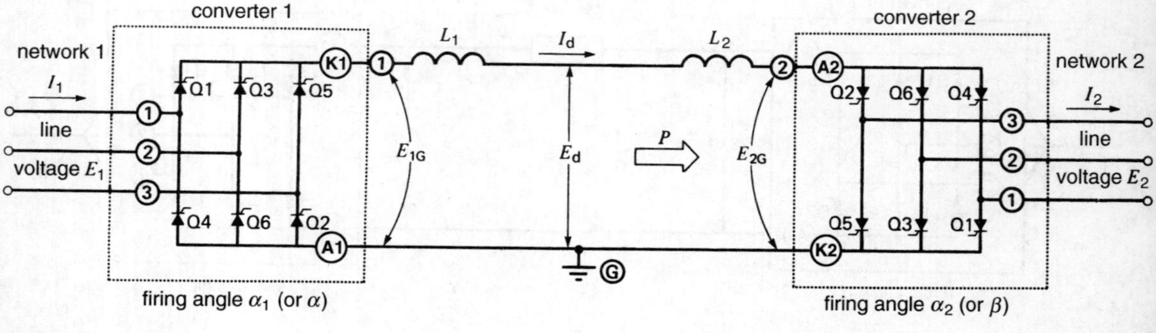

Figure 28.2
Smoothing inductors L_1 and L_2 are required between fluctuating dc voltages E_{1G}, E_{2G}, and ripple-free voltage E_d.

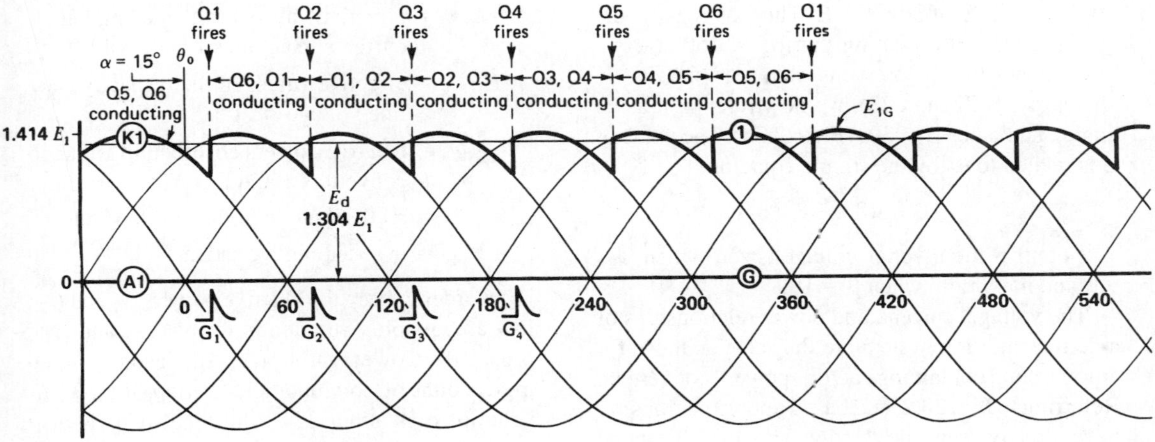

Figure 28.3a
Rectifier voltage waveshape E_{1G} for $\alpha = 15°$ (neglecting commutation overlap).

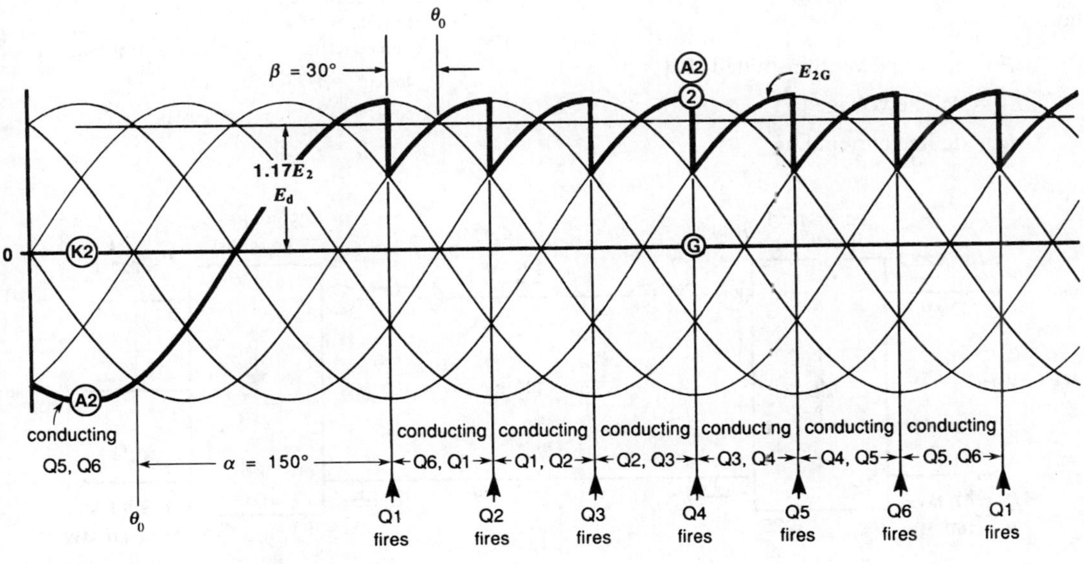

Figure 28.3b
Inverter voltage waveshape E_{2G} for $\beta = 30°$ (neglecting commutation overlap).

but as an angle of advance β. Thus, as regards the inverter, instead of stating that $\alpha_2 = 150°$ (as we have done in all previous inverter circuits in Chapters 21, 22, and 23), we now refer to it as an angle of advance $\beta = 30°$ (Fig. 28.3b). The value of β is related to α_2 by the simple equation

$$\beta = 180 - \alpha_2$$

Note that the inverter voltage is zero when β is 90° and maximum when $\beta = 0°$.

The voltage, current, and power relationships of a dc transmission system are the same as those for any circuit containing ac/dc power converters. Referring to Fig. 28.2, and based upon equations we have already seen, the relationships may be stated as follows:

$$P = E_d I_d \quad (21.17)$$

$$E_d = 1.35\, E_1 \cos\alpha$$

$$E_d = 1.35\, E_2 \cos\beta$$

$$I_1 = I_2 = 0.816\, I_d \quad (21.6)$$

$$Q_1 = P \tan\alpha \quad (21.18)$$

$$Q_2 = P \tan\beta$$

where

P = active power transmitted [W]
E_d = dc line voltage [V]
I_d = dc line current [A]
I_1, I_2 = effective values of the rectangular currents in ac lines 1 and 2 [A]
E_1, E_2 = effective values of the respective ac line voltages [V]
Q_1, Q_2 = reactive powers absorbed by converters 1 and 2 [var]
α = rectifier angle of delay [°]
β = inverter angle of advance [°]

In order to keep the reactive powers Q_1 and Q_2 as low as possible, we attempt to make α and β approach 0°. However, for practical reasons, and taking account of commutation overlap, the *effective* value of α is about 25°, while that of β is about 35°.* Using these values, we can calculate the relative magnitudes of the voltages and currents in a scale model of a transmission line. In this model, we assume the line delivers 1000 A at a potential of 100 kV (Fig. 28.4).

* The *effective* firing angles α^* and β^* depend upon the following:
1. The actual firing angles α and β
2. The commutation overlap angle μ
3. The extinction angle γ

The approximate relationship between these quantities is

$$\cos\alpha^* = 1/2\,(\cos\alpha + \cos(\alpha + \mu))$$

$$\cos\beta^* = 1/2\,(\cos\beta + \cos(\beta + \mu))$$

$$\beta = \gamma + \mu$$

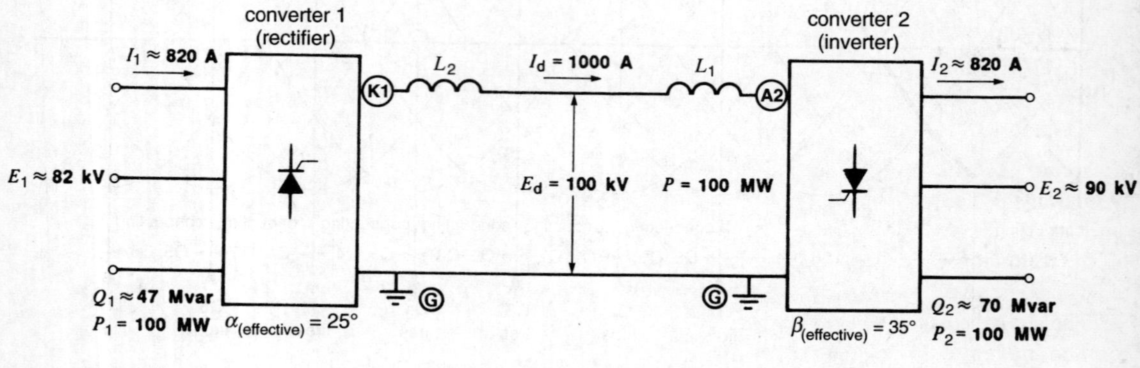

Figure 28.4
Scale model of a simple dc transmission system.

Thus, we have

$$E_d = 1.35\ E_1 \cos \alpha$$
$$100\text{ kV} = 1.35\ E_1 \cos 25°$$
$$E_1 = 82\text{ kV}$$

Furthermore,

$$E_d = 1.35\ E_2 \cos \beta$$
$$100\text{ kV} = 1.35\ E_2 \cos 35°$$
$$E_2 = 90\text{ kV}$$

also

$$I_1 = I_2 = 0.816\ I_d$$
$$= 0.816 \times 1000$$
$$= 820\text{ A}$$

$$P = E_d I_d$$
$$= 100\text{ kV} \times 1000\text{ A}$$
$$= 100\text{ MW}$$

$$Q_1 = P \tan \alpha$$
$$= 100 \tan 25°$$
$$= 47\text{ Mvar}$$

$$Q_2 = P \tan \beta$$
$$= 100 \tan 35°$$
$$= 70\text{ Mvar}$$

Figure 28.4 may thus be used as a scale model to determine the order of magnitude of the voltages, currents, and power in *any* dc transmission system.

Example 28-1

A dc transmission line operating at 150 kV carries a current of 400 A. Calculate the approximate value of the following:

a. The ac line voltage at each converter station
b. The ac line current
c. The active power absorbed by the rectifier
d. The reactive power absorbed by each converter

Solution

Using the scale model of Fig. 28.4 and multiplying by the appropriate ratios, we find the following:

a. The ac line voltages are

$$E_1 = (150\text{ kV}/100\text{ kV}) \times 82$$
$$= 123\text{ kV}$$

$$E_2 = (150\text{ kV}/100\text{ kV}) \times 90$$
$$= 135\text{ kV}$$

b. The effective value of the line current is

$$I_1 = I_2 = (400/1000) \times 820$$
$$= 328\text{ A}$$

c. The active power absorbed by the rectifier is

$$P_1 = 150\text{ kV} \times 400\text{ A}$$
$$= 60\,000\text{ kW}$$
$$= 60\text{ MW}$$

d. The reactive power absorbed by each converter is

$$Q_1 = (60/100) \times 47$$
$$= 28\text{ Mvar}$$

$$Q_2 = (60/100) \times 70$$
$$= 42\text{ Mvar}$$

28.4 Power fluctuations on a dc line

In order to ensure stability in transmitting dc power, the rectifier and inverter must have special voltage-current characteristics. These characteristics are shaped by computer-controlled gate-firing circuits. We can best understand the need for such controls by studying the behavior of the system when the controls are absent.

Fig. 28.5 shows a dc transmission line having a resistance R. The converters produce voltages E_{d1} and E_{d2}, and the resulting dc line current is given by

$$I_d = (E_{d1} - E_{d2})/R \qquad (28.1)$$

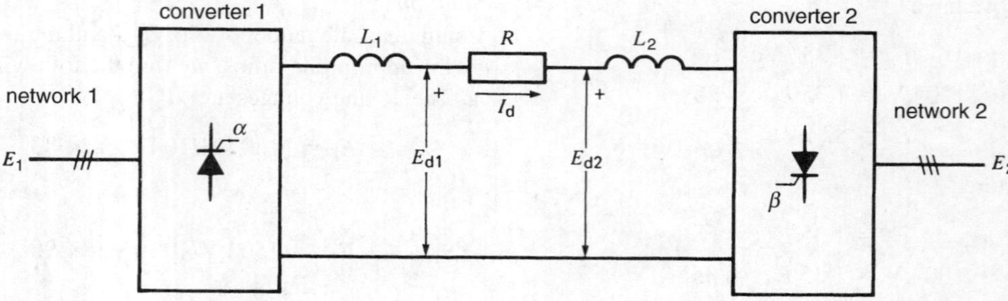

Figure 28.5
A small change in either E_{d1} or E_{d2} produces a very big change in I_d.

The line resistance is always small; consequently, a very small difference between E_{d1} and E_{d2} can produce full-load current in the line. Furthermore, a small variation in either E_{d1} or E_{d2} can produce a very big change in I_d. For example, if E_{d1} increases by only a few percent, the line current can easily double. Conversely, if E_{d2} increases by only a few percent, the line current can fall to zero.

Unfortunately, both E_{d1} and E_{d2} are subject to sudden changes because the associated ac line voltages E_1 and E_2 may fluctuate. The fluctuations may be due to sudden load changes on the ac networks or to any number of other system disturbances that can occur. Owing to the almost instantaneous response of the converters and transmission line, the dc current could swing wildly under these conditions, producing erratic power swings between the two networks. Such power surges are unacceptable because they tend to destabilize the ac networks at each end, and because they produce misfiring of the SCRs.

It is true that the firing angles α and β could be modulated to counteract the ac line voltage fluctuations. However, it is preferable to design the system so that large, unpredictable dc power surges are inherently impossible. We now show how this is done.

28.5 Typical rectifier and inverter characteristics

In a practical dc transmission system, the computer-controlled rectifier circuit is designed to yield the *E-I* curve shown in Fig. 28.6a. Assuming a fixed ac

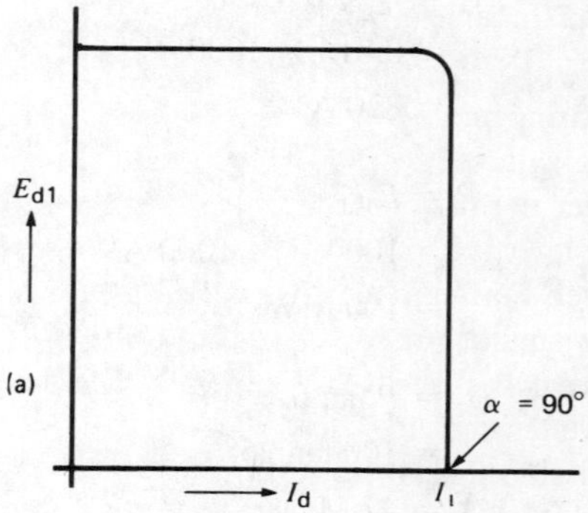

Figure 28.6a
Rectifier *E-I* characteristic.

line voltage E_1, the dc output voltage E_{d1} is kept constant until the line current I_d reaches a value I_1. Beyond this point, E_{d1} drops sharply, as can be seen on the curve. This *E-I* characteristic is obtained by keeping α constant until current I_d approaches the desired value I_1. The firing angle then increases (automatically) at a very rapid rate, so that I_d is equal to I_1, when $E_{d1} = 0$. In other words, if a short-circuit were to occur across the dc side of the rectifier, the resulting dc current would be equal to I_1.

As regards the inverter, it is designed to give the *E-I* curve shown in Fig. 28.6b. Assuming a fixed ac line voltage E_2, voltage E_{d2} is maintained at zero until the dc line current reaches a value I_2. This means that from zero to I_2, the firing angle β = 90°. As soon as the dc current approaches the desired value

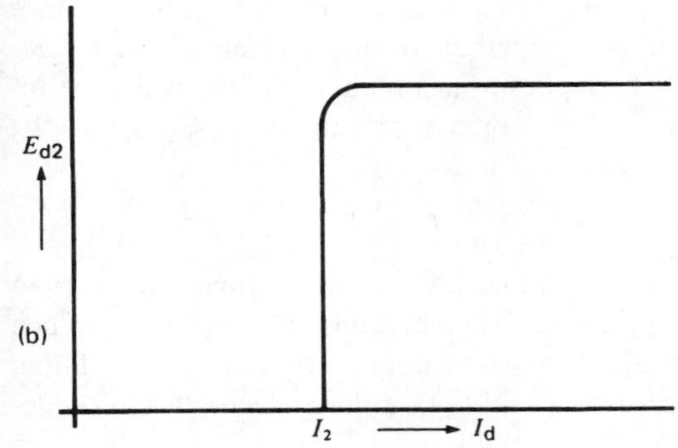

Figure 28.6b
Inverter E-I characteristic.

I_2, the firing angle β decreases (automatically) to a limiting value of about 30°.

Under normal operating conditions the inverter voltage level is kept slightly below the rectifier voltage level. Furthermore, limiting current I_2 is made slightly smaller than I_1. The effect of these constraints can best be seen by superposing the rectifier and inverter characteristics (Fig. 28.7a). The actual transmission-line voltage and the actual current correspond to the point of intersection of the two curves. It is obvious that the line current I_d is equal to I_1 (determined by the rectifier characteristic) while the line voltage E_d is equal to E_{d2} (determined by the inverter characteristic). The difference between I_1 and I_2 is called the *current margin* ΔI. It is held constant and equal to about 10 percent of the rated line current.

If the line has appreciable resistance, the *IR* drop modifies the effective rectifier characteristic so that it follows the dashed line in Fig. 28.7a. This, however, does not affect the operating point under normal conditions. The effective power input to the inverter is, therefore, given by the product $E_{d2}I_1$.

28.6 Power control

To vary the power flow over the dc line, the rectifier and inverter E-I characteristics are modified simultaneously. Voltages E_{d1} and E_{d2} are kept constant but I_1 and I_2 are varied simultaneously while keeping the current margin fixed. Thus, Fig. 28.7b shows the new E-I characteristics for a transmission line current I_d smaller than that in Fig. 28.7a. By thus shifting the E-I characteristics back and forth, we can cause the dc power to vary over a wide range. Note that the line voltage E_{d2} is constant, and that it is always determined by the inverter. On the other hand, the magnitude of the line current is determined by the rectifier.

At this point, the reader may wonder why the E-I characteristics have been given such odd shapes to attain such a simple result. The reason is that the

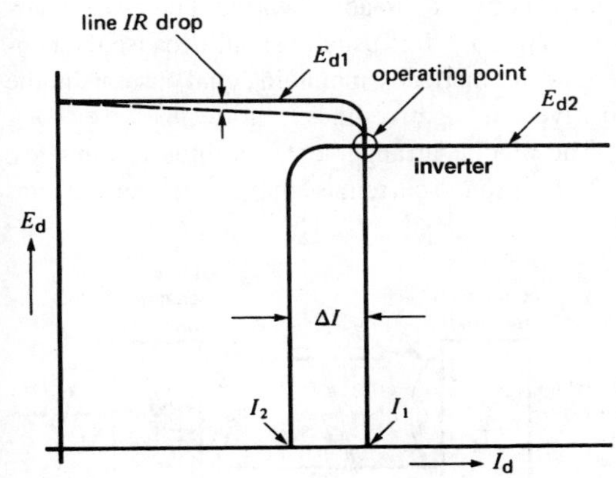

Figure 28.7a
Operating point when the transmission line delivers rated power.

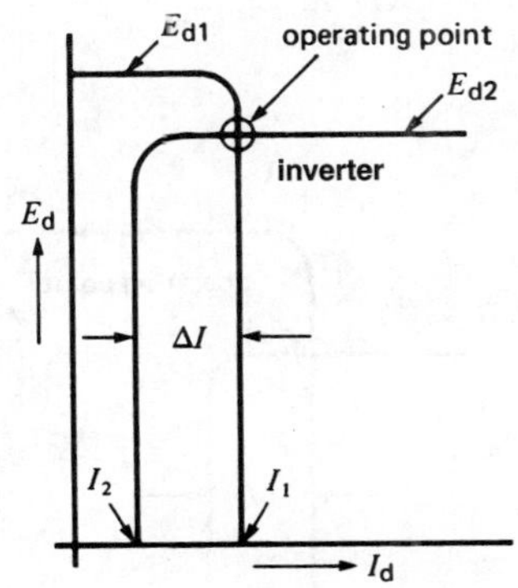

Figure 28.7b
Operating point when the line delivers 20 percent of rated power.

dc system must be able to accommodate serious ac voltage fluctuations at either end of the line without affecting the dc power flow too much. It must also limit the magnitude of the fault currents, should a short-circuit occur on the dc line. We will now explain how this is achieved.

28.7 Effect of voltage fluctuations

Referring to Fig. 28.7a, let us assume that the dc line carries full-load current I_1. If the ac voltage of line 1 increases suddenly, E_{d1} rises in proportion, but this has no effect on I_1 or E_{d2}. Consequently, the power flow over the line is unaffected.

On the other hand, if line voltage E_2 decreases, E_{d2} decreases in proportion. The dc line current is unaffected, but because E_{d2} is smaller than before, the dc power carried by the line is also less. However, the percent change in power cannot exceed the percent change in ac voltage E_2.

Next, if a large disturbance occurs on line 1, E_{d1} may fall drastically. This produces a new operating point, shown in Fig. 28.8. The dc line current decreases suddenly from I_1 to I_2, while the dc voltage decreases equally suddenly from E_{d2} to E_{d1}. With a current margin of 10 percent, the drop in current is not excessive. Consequently, the power flow is again not affected too much. As soon as the disturbance is cleared, the *E-I* characteristics return to the original curves given in Fig. 28.7a.

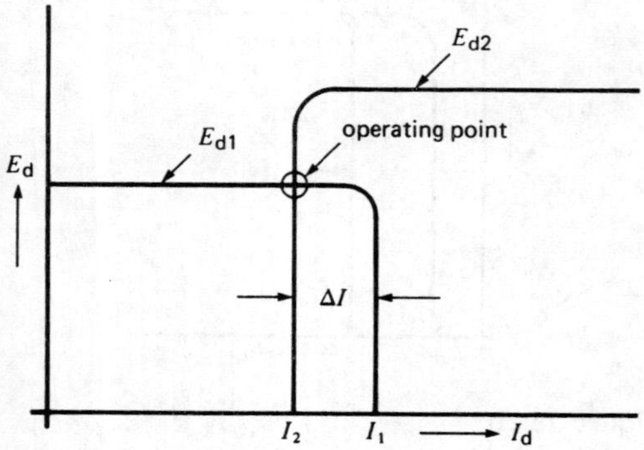

Figure 28.8
Change in operating point when E_1 falls drastically.

Finally, one of the worst conditions that can arise is a short-circuit on the dc line. Here again, the rectifier supplies a maximum current I_1 while the inverter draws a maximum current I_2. Consequently, the fault current

$$I_F = (I_1 - I_2)$$

is only 10 percent of the normal line current (Fig. 28.9). Fault currents are, therefore, much smaller than on ac transmission lines. In addition, because E_{d1} and E_{d2} are close to zero, the power delivered to the fault is small.

It is now clear that the special shape of the *E-I* characteristics prevents large power fluctuations on the line, and limits the short-circuit currents. In practice, the actual *E-I* characteristics differ slightly from those shown in Fig. 28.7. However, the basic principle remains the same.

28.8 Bipolar transmission line

Most dc transmission lines are *bipolar.* They possess a positive line and a negative line and a common ground return (Fig. 28.10a). A converter is installed at the end of each line, and the line currents I_{d1} and I_{d2} flow in the directions shown. Converters 1 and 3 act as rectifiers while converters 2 and 4 are inverters. Power obviously flows over both lines from ac network 1 to ac network 2. The ground current is $I_{d1} - I_{d2}$. It is usually small because the converters automatically maintain equal currents in the positive and negative lines.

The bipolar arrangement has three advantages. First, the ground current is small, under normal con-

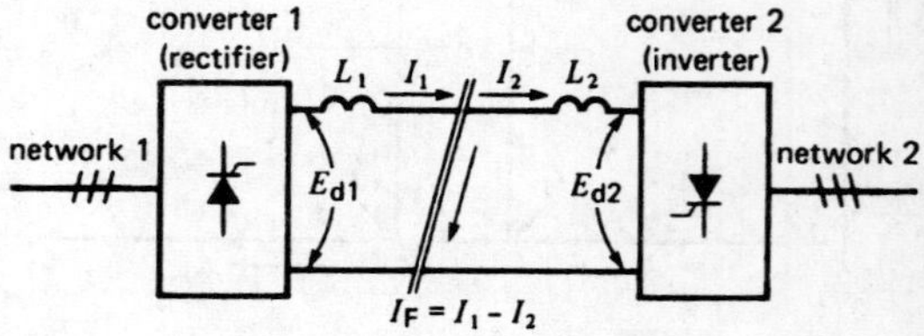

Figure 28.9
The short-circuit current at the fault cannot exceed 10 percent of the rated line current.

ditions. Consequently, corrosion of underground pipes, structures, and so forth, is minimized. Second, the same transmission-line towers can carry two lines, thus doubling the power, with a relatively small increase in capital investment. Third, if power flow on one line is interrupted, the other can continue to function, delivering half the normal power between the ac networks.

28.9 Power reversal

To reverse power flow in a bipolar line, we change the firing angles, so that all the rectifiers become inverters and vice versa. This reverses the polarity of the transmission lines, but the line currents I_{d1} and I_{d2} continue to flow in the same direction as before (Fig. 28.10b).

28.10 Components of a dc transmission line

In order to function properly, a dc transmission system must have auxiliary components, in addition to the basic converters. Referring to Fig. 28.11, the most important components are

1. DC line inductors (L)
2. Harmonic filters on the dc side (F_{dc})
3. Converter transformers (T_1, T_2)

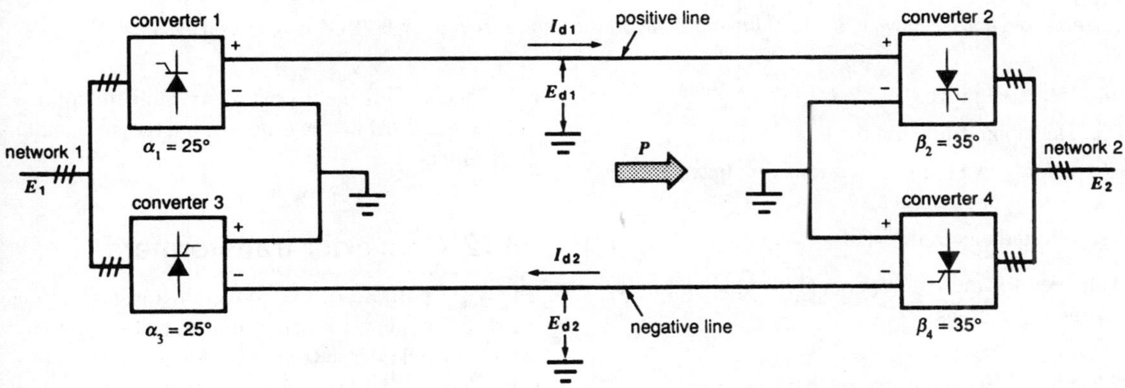

Figure 28.10a
Bipolar line transmitting power from network 1 to network 2.

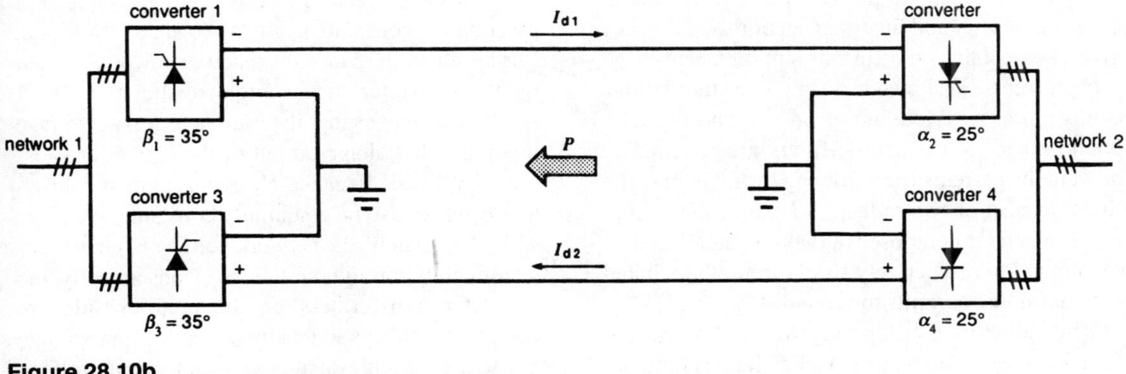

Figure 28.10b
Power reversal from network 2 to network 1 is obtained by reversing the line polarities.

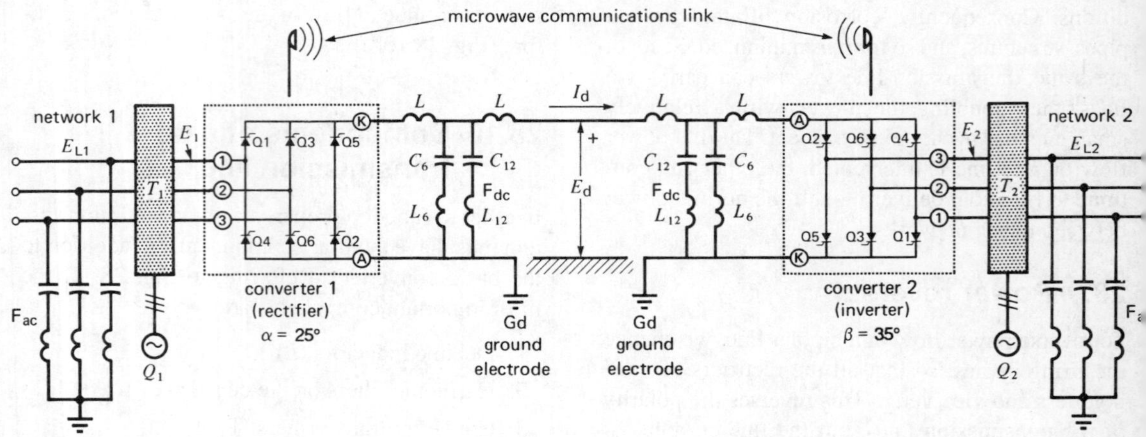

Figure 28.11
Schematic diagram showing some of the more important components of an HVDC transmission system.

4. Reactive power source (Q_1, Q_2)
5. Harmonic filters on the ac side (F_{ac})
6. Microwave communications link between the converter stations
7. Ground electrodes (Gd)

The need for these components is explained in the following sections.

28.11 Inductors and harmonic filters on the dc side (6-pulse converter)

Voltage harmonics are produced on the dc side of both the rectifier and inverter (Section 21.31). They give rise to 6th and 12th harmonic currents, and such currents, if allowed to flow over the dc line, could produce serious noise on neighboring telephone lines. Consequently, filters are required to prevent the currents from flowing over the line. The filters consist of two inductors L and a shunt filter F_{dc}. The latter is composed of two series LC circuits, each tuned to respectively short-circuit the 6th and 12th harmonic currents to ground (Fig. 28.11).

The inductors L also prevent the dc line current from increasing too rapidly if a line fault should occur. This enables the thyristors to establish control before the current becomes too large to handle electronically.

28.12 Converter transformers

The basic purpose of the converter transformer on the rectifier side is to transform the ac network voltage E_{L1} to yield the ac voltage E_1 required by the converter. Three-phase transformers, connected in either wye-wye or wye-delta, are used. A lower-voltage tertiary winding (Section 12.5) is sometimes added for direct connection to a source of reactive power (Q_1).

As we have seen, the dc line voltage E_d is kept essentially constant from no-load to full-load. Furthermore, to reduce the reactive power absorbed by the converter, firing angle α should be kept small. This means that the ratio between ac voltage input and dc voltage output of the converter is essentially fixed. Because E_d is constant, it follows that E_1 must also be essentially constant.

Unfortunately, the network voltage E_{L1} may vary significantly throughout the day. Consequently, the converter transformers on the rectifier side are equipped with taps so that the variable input voltage E_{L1} will give a reasonably constant output voltage

E_1. The taps are switched automatically by a motorized tap changer whenever the network voltage E_{L1} changes for a significant length of time. For the same reasons, taps are needed on the converter transformers on the inverter side.

28.13 Reactive power source

The reactive power Q absorbed by the converters must be supplied by the ac network or by a local reactive power source. Because the active power transmitted varies throughout the day, the reactive source must also be varied. Consequently, either variable static capacitors or a synchronous capacitor are required (Section 17.15).

28.14 Harmonic filters on the ac side

Three-phase, 6-pulse converters produce 5th, 7th, 11th, 13th (and higher) current harmonics on the ac side. These harmonics are a direct result of the choppy current waveforms (Section 21.11). Again, for reasons of telephone interference, these currents must not be allowed to flow over the ac lines. Consequently, the currents are bypassed through low-impedance filters F_{ac} connected between the 3-phase lines and ground. The filters for each frequency are connected in wye, and the neutral point is grounded. On a 60 Hz network, each 3-phase filter is composed of a set of series-resonant *LC* circuits respectively tuned to 300, 420, 660, and 780 Hz.

At 60 Hz these *LC* circuits are almost entirely capacitive. Consequently, they also furnish part of the reactive power Q absorbed by each converter.

28.15 Communications link

In order to control the converters at both ends of the line, a communications link between them is essential. For example, to maintain the current margin ΔI (Fig. 28.7), the inverter at one end of the line must "know" what the rectifier current setting I_1 is. This information is continually relayed by a high-speed communications link between the two converters.

28.16 Ground electrode

Particular attention is paid to the ground electrode at each end of the dc line. Direct currents in the ground have a corrosive effect on pipes, cables and metallic structures. Consequently, the actual ground electrode is usually located several kilometers from the converter station, to ensure that dc ground currents create no local problem around the station. The dc ground wire between the station and the actual grounding site is either pole-mounted or enclosed in a shielded cable. At the grounding site, special means are used to minimize electrode resistance. This is particularly important when a bipolar system operates temporarily in the monopolar mode. Under these circumstances, the ground current may exceed 1000 A, and the heat generated may eventually dry out the grounding bed, causing the ground resistance to increase.

The best grounds are obtained next to, or in, large bodies of water. But even in this case, elaborate grounding methods must be used.

28.17 Example of a monopolar converter station

Fig. 28.12 shows the elementary circuit diagram of a monopolar mercury-arc inverter station. The incoming dc line operates at 150 kV, and power is fed into a 230 kV, 3-phase, 60 Hz power line. Two smoothing inductors, each having an inductance of 0.5 H, are connected in series with the dc line. The two *LC* filters effectively short-circuit the 6th and 12th harmonic voltages generated on the dc side of the converter. The 9 Ω and 11 Ω resistors make the filters less sensitive to slight frequency changes on the outgoing ac line.

Three single-phase transformers connected wye-wye (with a tertiary winding) are connected to the ac side of the converter. A 160 Mvar synchronous capacitor, connected to the tertiary winding, provides the reactive power for the converter.

Filters for the 5th, 7th, 11th, and 13th harmonic currents are connected between the three ac lines and neutral of the 230 kV system. As previously explained, the filters shunt the ac harmonic currents so that they do not enter the 230 kV line.

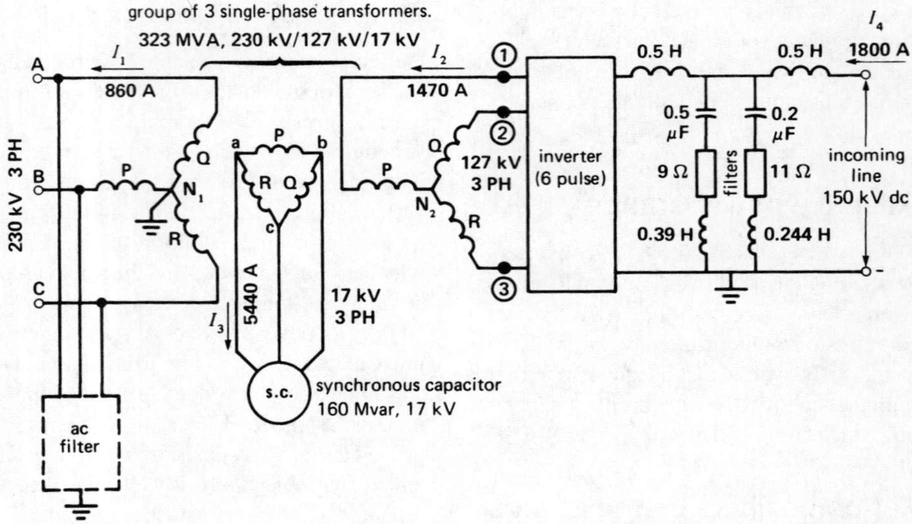

Figure 28.12
Simplified circuit of a 150 kV, 1800 A, 60 Hz mercury-arc inverter. See components illustrated in Figs. 28.13 to 28.17.

Figure 28.13
These 12 single-phase harmonic filters at an inverter station are tuned for 300 Hz, 420 Hz, 660 Hz, and 780 Hz. They are connected between the three lines and neutral of the outgoing 230 kV, 60 Hz transmission line. The filter in the foreground is tuned to 720 Hz. It is a series circuit composed of a 2 Ω resistor, a group of capacitors having a total capacitance of 0.938 μF, and an oil-filled inductor of 44.4 mH. The 720 Hz reactive power associated with the *LC* circuit amounts to 18.8 Mvar.
(Courtesy of GEC Power Engineering Limited, England)

Figs. 28.13 through 28.17 give us an idea of the size of these various components, and of the immense switchyard needed to accommodate them.

28.18 Thyristor converter station

Mercury-arc converters have been supplanted by thyristor converters and the design of the latter has become almost standardized. Thus, each pole is composed of two 6-pulse converters. Fig. 28.18a shows how two 200 kV converters are connected to produce a 400 kV dc output. The dc sides are connected in series, while the ac sides are essentially connected in parallel across the 230 kV, 3-phase line. This means that converter 2 (and the secondary winding of transformer T2) functions at a dc

Figure 28.14
Three-phase converter transformer bank rated 230 kV/127 kV/17 kV composed of 3 single-phase transformers each rated 323 MVA.
(Courtesy of Manitoba Hydro)

Figure 28.15
View of one 0.5 H smoothing inductor on the 450 kV dc side of the inverter station. The second inductor can be seen in the distance (lower right-hand corner). The space between the two units permits installing the filters on the dc side.
(Courtesy of Manitoba Hydro)

Figure 28.16
Portion of the 3-phase, 6-pulse mercury-arc inverter rated 270 MW, 150 kV.
(Courtesy of Manitoba Hydro)

Figure 28.17
Partial view of the refrigeration unit needed to cool the inverters.
(Courtesy of Manitoba Hydro)

potential of 200 kV. The windings must be especially well insulated to withstand these dc voltages, in addition to the 180 kV ac voltage.

The 180 kV windings of transformer T1 are connected in wye-delta, while those of transformer T2 are connected in wye-wye. This produces a 30° phase shift between the secondary voltages of T1 and T2. Consequently, the thyristors in converter 1 and converter 2 do not fire at the same time. In effect, the two converters act as a 12-pulse converter.

One important result of the 30° shift is that the 5th and 7th harmonic currents generated by the two converters tend to cancel each other on the primary side of T1 and T2 and do not, therefore, appear in the 230 kV line. Consequently, the filtering equipment for these frequencies is substantially reduced. Furthermore, the 30° phase shift eliminates the 6th harmonic on the dc side, which reduces the filtering equipment needed for F_{dc}.

Fig. 28.18b shows the three valves that make up a 12-pulse converter, together with the ac and dc connections. The valves are called *quadruple valves* because each is composed of four bridge arms. Fig. 28.21b illustrates the impressive size of these valves.

28.19 Typical installations

Power transmission by direct current is being used in many parts of the world. The following installations give the reader an idea of the various types of systems that have been built over the years, and the particular problem they were designed to solve.

1. Schenectady. Of historical interest is the 17 mile, 5.25 MW, 30 kV transmission line installed between Mechanicville and Schenectady, New York, in 1936. Using mercury-arc converters, it tied together a 40 Hz and 60 Hz system.

2. Gotland. The first important dc transmission line was installed in Sweden, in 1954. It connected the Island of Gotland (in the middle of the Baltic Sea) to the mainland by a 96 km submarine cable. The single-conductor cable operates at 100 kV and transmits 20 MW. The ground current returns by the sea.

3. English Channel. In 1961 a bipolar submarine link was laid in the English Channel between England and France. Two cables, one operating at +100 kV and the other at −100 kV, laid side-by-side, together carry 160 MW of power in one direction or the other. The power exchange between the two countries was found to be economical because the time zones are different and, consequently, the system peaks do not occur at the same time. Furthermore, France has excess hydro generating capacity during the spring, thus making the export of power attractive.

4. Pacific Intertie. In 1970 a bipolar link operating at ±400 kV was installed between The Dalles, Oregon, and Los Angeles, California. The overhead line transmits a total of 1440 MW over a distance of 1370 km. Power can be made to flow in either direction, depending upon the requirements of the respective NW and SW regions. The dc link also helps stabilize the 3-phase ac transmission system connecting the two regions.

5. Nelson River. The hydropower generated by the Nelson River, situated 890 km north of Winnipeg, Canada, is transmitted by means of two bipolar lines operating at ±450 kV. Each bipolar line carries 1620 MW, which is converted and fed into the ac system near Winnipeg. According to studies made, it was slightly more economical to transmit power by dc rather than by ac over this considerable distance.

6. Eel River. The back-to-back station at Eel River, Canada, provides an asynchronous intertie between the 230 kV electrical systems of Quebec and New Brunswick. Although both systems operate at a nominal frequency of 60 Hz, it was not feasible to connect them directly, due to stability considerations. In this application, the dc "transmission line" is only a few meters long, representing the length of the conductors to connect the rectifiers and inverters. Power may flow in either direction, up to a maximum of 320 MW (see Figs. 28.19 and 28.20).

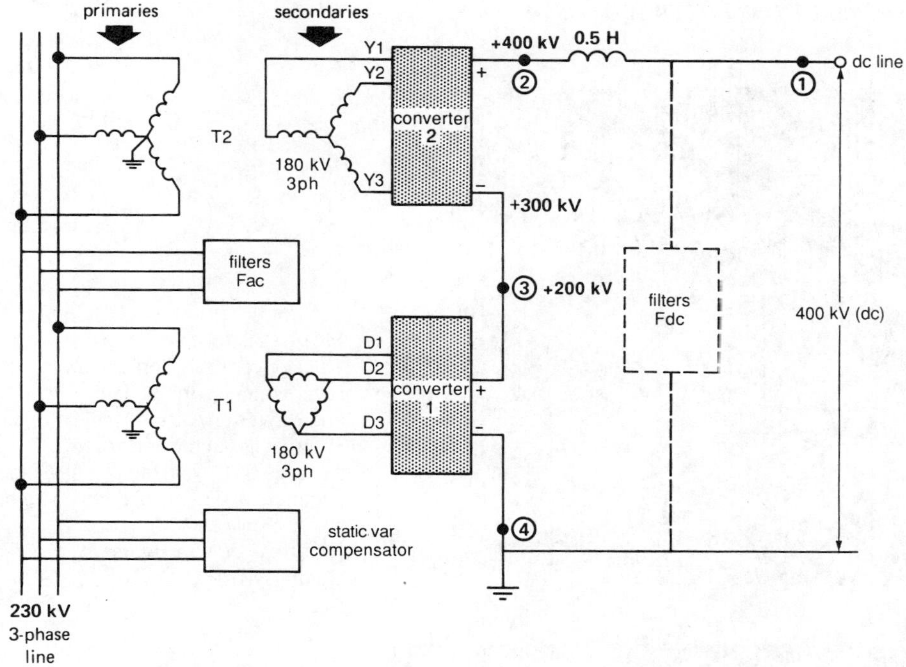

Figure 28.18a
Schematic diagram of one pole of a ±400 kV converter station. It consists of two 200 kV converters connected in series on the dc side. The converters are 6-pulse units, respectively connected to 3-phase voltages that are 30° out of phase. The dc filter is tuned to the 12th harmonic. The ac filters prevent the 11th, 13th, and higher harmonics from entering the 230 kV system. The static var compensator supplies the reactive power needed by the converter.

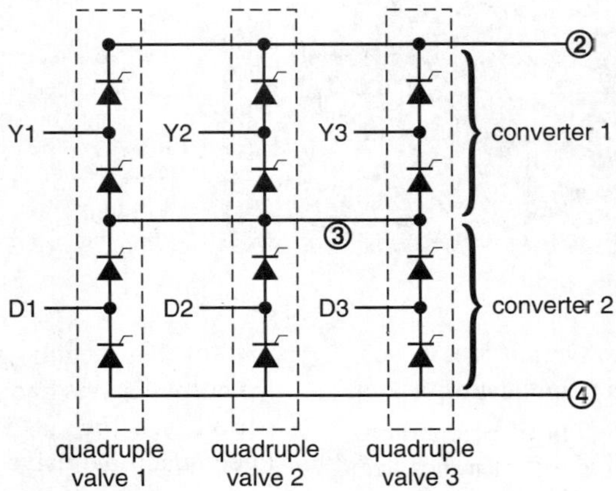

Figure 28.18b
Schematic diagram of the 12-pulse converter showing the two 6-pulse converters and line connections. Three quadruple valves constitute the main components in one pole of the valve hall.

Figure 28.19
This converter station and switchyard at Eel River connects the ac networks of Quebec and New Brunswick by means of a dc link. The rectifier and inverter are both housed in the large building in the center. It pioneered the commercial use of solid-state thyristors in HVDC applications.
(Courtesy of New Brunswick Electric Power Commission)

Figure 28.20
View of one 6-pulse thyristor valve housed in its rectangular cubicle. It is fed by a 3-phase converter transformer and yields an output of 2000 A at 40 kV. The hundreds of individual thyristors it contains are triggered by a reliable, interference-free fiber-optic control system.

Eight such cubicles, together with three synchronous capacitors and four converter transformers, make up the entire converter terminal.
(Courtesy of General Electric)

This pioneering station was the first to use thyristors in a large commercial application.

*7. **CU Project.*** The power output of a generating station situated next to the lignite coal mines near Underwood, North Dakota, is converted to dc and transmitted 436 miles eastward to a terminal near Minneapolis, Minnesota, where it is reconverted to ac. The bipolar line transmits 1000 MW at 1250 A, ± 400 kV. A metallic ground return is provided, in the event that one line should be out for a prolonged period (see Fig. 28.21a). Fig. 28.21b shows the three quadruple valves that make up one 12-pulse converter. Fig. 28.21c shows an aerial view of the terminal.

*8. **Châteauguay Substation.*** The Châteauguay substation, located near Montreal, is a back-to-back

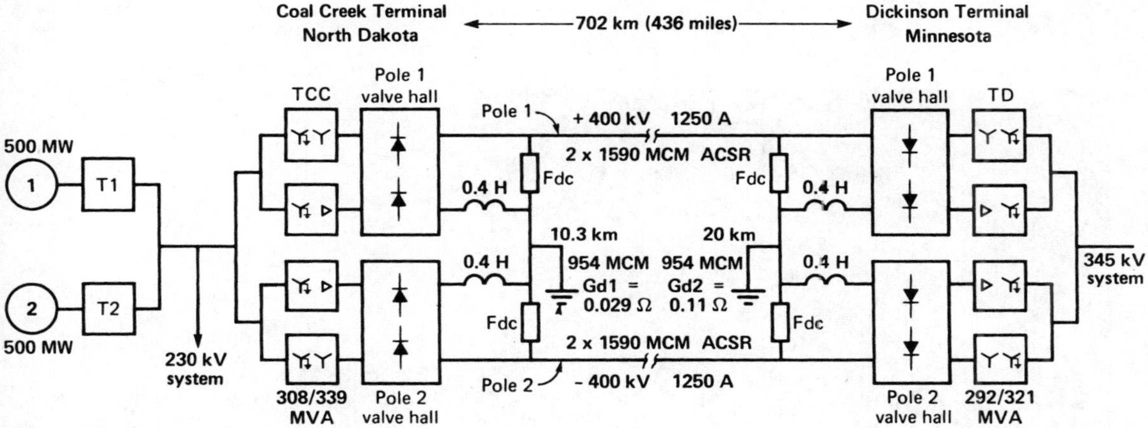

Figure 28.21a
Simplified schematic diagram of the bipolar HVDC transmission system that links the Coal Creek Terminal in North Dakota to the Dickinson Terminal in Minnesota. The ±400 kV line delivers 1000 MW over a distance of 702 km. The output from two 500 MW turboalternators is stepped up to 230 kV and transmitted to the Coal Creek Terminal where the ac power is converted to dc. The on-load tap-changing converter transformers TCC are connected wye-wye and wye-delta for 12-pulse converter operation.

The 0.4 H smoothing inductors are in series with the grounded lines, thus significantly reducing the insulation requirements. The dc filters Fdc, each composed of a 48.8 mH inductor in series with a 1 μF capacitor bank, prevent the 12th harmonic voltage from reaching the dc lines.

The positive and negative transmission lines consist of two bundled conductors (2 × 1590 MCM, ACSR). The dc grounds are situated at 10.3 km and 20 km from the respective terminals. Under normal conditions the line currents are controlled automatically so that the ground current is 20 A or less. However, if one pole is out of service for short periods, the ground current can be as high as 1375 A.

The 12-pulse inverter station (Dickinson Terminal) feeds into a 345 kV, 60 Hz system and tap-changing converter transformers TD are used to regulate the inverter voltage level.

The control system is arranged to operate each terminal unmanned from a telecommunications control center located in Minnesota.

Figure 28.21b
View of three quadruple valves being installed in one of the Coal Creek Terminal valve halls. Together they constitute one pole of the 400 kV system.
(Courtesy of United Power Association)

Figure 28.21c
Aerial view of the Coal Creek Terminal showing the two valve halls that respectively produce the +400 kV and −400 kV dc voltage. The switchyard contains circuit breakers, transformers, and filters.
(Courtesy of United Power Association)

Figure 28.22a
A quadruple valve, rated at 140 kV, 1200 A dc, being tested at IREQ, the Hydro-Québec research center. The valve is 12 m high, 6.9 m wide, and 2.7 m deep. It is designed for the Châteauguay substation and contains a total of 400 thyristors.
(Courtesy of Hydro-Québec)

Figure 28.22b
View of one 500 MW, 140 kV, 3600 A dc back-to-back converter at the Châteauguay substation. It is composed of 6 quadruple valves. The three valves on the right usually operate as rectifiers, and the three on the left usually function as inverters. The valve hall is 17.5 m wide and 18 m high.
(Courtesy of Hydro-Québec)

converter station rated at 1000 MW (Figs. 28.22a and 28.22b). In order to ensure high reliability, it is composed of two independent valve halls, each rated at 500 MW.

Power usually flows from the Hydro-Québec 735 kV ac system to the 765 kV ac system in the state of New York. Owing to the rectifier/inverter link, frequency changes on one system do not affect the other system. Furthermore, the direction of power flow can be reversed, depending upon the circumstances.

The thyristors are water-cooled, using deionized water and an elaborate water/glycol/air-heat exchanger.

HVDC LIGHT TRANSMISSION SYSTEM

So far in this chapter, we have seen that dc power is transported between two powerful ac networks that contain hundreds of large synchronous generators and motors. The respective grid voltages are therefore stable and undistorted. Consequently, the thyristor-controlled converters at both ends of the dc line can draw the reactive power they need from the respective grids to which they are connected. This enables the natural line commutation of the thyristors, as explained in Section 28.2.

28.20 Transporting electric power to remote locations

Many remote sites that need electric power are relatively small. They do not contain synchronous generators, and the synchronous motor load is often negligible. In such cases, we can supply power to the remote site by installing a simple overhead transmission line and connecting it to an existing grid of 3-phase power. If this solution is impossible or not feasible, a diesel-driven generator, located at the site, can supply the power needed. This is an expensive solution because it requires constant maintenance, and diesel fuel has to be carried to the site.

An overhead ac transmission line is often excluded because it is impossible to obtain the rights of way. An underground cable can then be considered. However, if the cable is more than a few kilometers in length, its capacitance will prevent efficient transmission of the electrical energy (see Section 25.29). However, an underground cable is well adapted to carry dc power because the undesirable aspects of large capacitive reactive power do not come into play.

Self-commutating converters using IGBTs and pulse width modulation offer an interesting solution when power has to be delivered to such a remote site. In effect, we saw in Section 21.50 that PWM converters operate essentially as solid-state ac generators. They can supply or absorb reactive power, and the voltage output can be controlled. Furthermore, active power can flow in both directions, from the ac side to the dc side and vice versa. As an additional feature, the magnitude, frequency, and phase angle of these static generators are all adjustable, and the short-circuit currents can be limited electronically.

To fully understand this novel way of transporting electric power, the reader should first review Sections 21.45 to 21.50 covering converters. Section 21.45 explains pulse width modulation and its application to single-phase converters. Section 21.49 explains the operation of a 3-phase PWM converter.

We will use this converter to introduce the so-called HVDC Light® way of transmitting electric power.

28.21 Components of a static generator

Figure 28.23 shows the main components of a static 3-phase generator. It comprises

- A self-commutated converter consisting of six IGBTs and six diodes. It is essentially a reproduction of the converter shown in Fig. 21.94
- Two capacitors C_1 connected in series
- Three inductances L_1
- Three carrier-frequency filters composed of resonant circuits L_2, C_2, and R_2

It is important to recall that this static generator converts dc power to 3-phase ac power, and vice versa. Depending upon the application, the "machine" can operate as a dc generator drawing its power from a 3-phase source connected to terminals d, e, and f. Alternatively, it can operate as a 3-phase generator powered by a dc source E_H connected to terminals **x** and **y.**

The two capacitors C_1 between the **x, y** terminals reduce the fluctuations of the dc voltage. They also establish a neutral point N midway between the (+) and (−) terminals of the dc supply.

We can consider that E_H is composed of two voltages E_d in series, where $E_d = E_H/2$. When E_H is

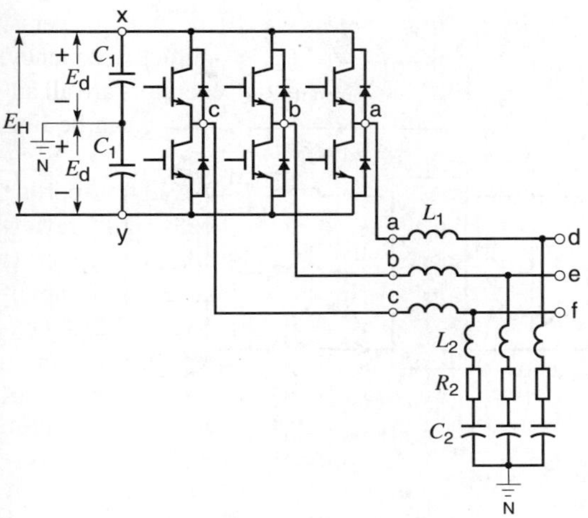

Figure 28.23
Components of a static 3-phase generator powered by a dc source E_H. Active power flows from left to right. Exactly the same setup is used to create a static dc generator powered by a 3-phase source. The latter is connected to terminals d, e, f and active power, then flows from right to left.

several tens of kilovolts, each of the six IGBT/diode groups shown in Fig. 28.23 represents several such groups connected in series. The reason is that high-voltage IGBTs and diodes can only withstand voltages of about 5 kV.

The 3-phase line-to-neutral PWM voltages appear between terminals **a, b, c** and the neutral **N.** For example, the voltage between terminals **a** and **N** is a PWM wave whose amplitude fluctuates rapidly between $+E_d$ and $-E_d$ at the carrier frequency f_c. The wave has two components:

a. A fundamental line-to-neutral voltage E_{aN} having a frequency f (usually 60 Hz or 50 Hz)
b. Carrier frequency harmonics

In practice, we are mainly interested in the line-to-line voltages E_{ab}, E_{bc}, and E_{ca}. When the ratio of the carrier frequency f_c to the fundamental frequency f is odd and a multiple of three, the two most important line-to-line harmonics have frequencies of $f_{H1} = f_c + 2f$ and $f_{H2} = f_c - 2f$.

Just like in a chopper, the three inductors L_1 absorb and deliver energy, which enables the transformation of dc power to ac power and vice versa. These inductors also reduce the harmonic currents that flow in the 3-phase lines. At the fundamental frequency, they possess a reactance given by $x = 2\pi f L_1$.

The filters L_2, C_2 short-circuit the harmonic voltages that would otherwise appear between lines **d, e, f** and the neutral N. The resistance R_2 establishes the bandwidth of the filter.

28.22 Overview of the HVDC Light transmission system

Figure 28.24a gives a global view of the novel HVDC Light transmission system. It consists of

- A very short line 1, 2, 3 that connects converter 1 to a 3-phase 60 Hz grid
- An ac to dc converter 1 that converts the ac power to dc
- A long dc cable that connects converter 1 to converter 2 at the remote site
- A dc to ac converter 2 that converts the dc power to ac
- The ac load at the remote site

Converter 1 is connected to the power grid by way of three reactors x that correspond to the inductances L_1 mentioned previously. Terminals 7 and 8 are connected to the dc cable. The other extremity of the cable is connected to terminals 9 and 10 of converter 2. The converter supplies power to the load by way of reactor x that is similar to those associated with converter 1. In order to simplify the circuit, the harmonic filters L_2, C_2, and R_2 are not shown. They are respectively connected between terminals **1, 2, 3** and the local neutral N, and between terminals **d, e, f** and the remote neutral N.

Converter 2 generates a fundamental 3-phase voltage (and harmonics) between terminals **a, b,** and **c.** The filtered output appears across terminals

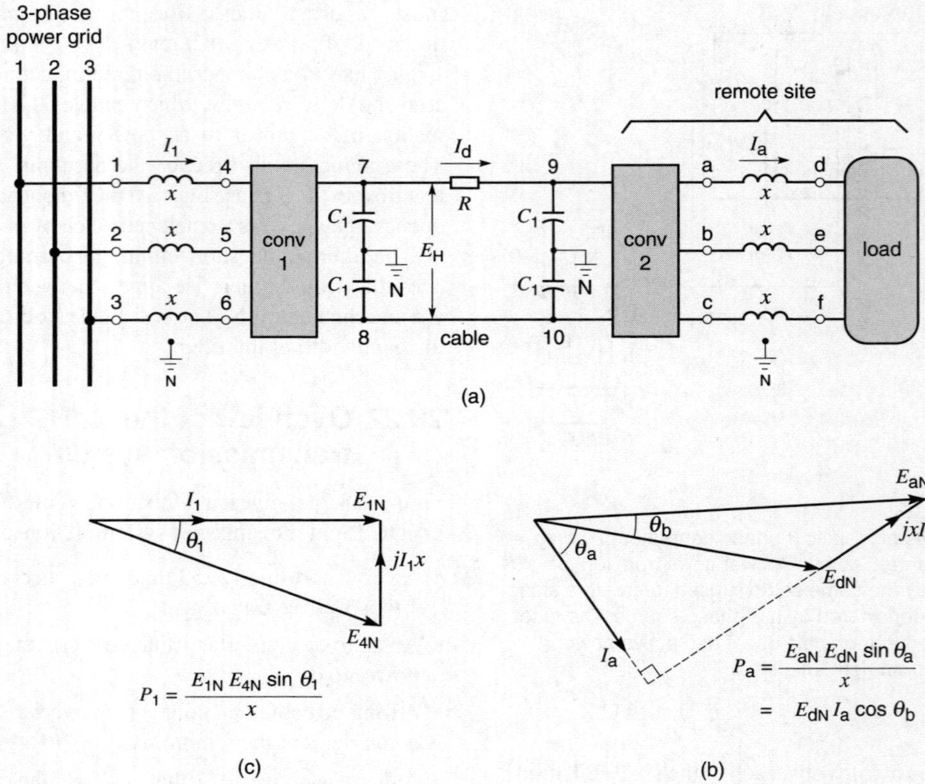

Figure 28.24
a. Global view of a HVDC Light transmission system using PWM converters. Converter 1 converts ac power to dc power. Converter 2 converts dc power to ac power. Converter 2 generates the desired 3-phase voltage and frequency required at the remote site. The line current and power factor at the site both depend upon the load.
b. Phasor diagram of the voltages and line current for phase **a** at the remote site.
c. Phasor diagram of the voltages and line current at the grid point **1** that furnishes the active power.

d, e, and **f.** However, it is easier to follow the behavior of the converter by observing the fundamental components of the voltage and current of only one phase. Let us select phase **a** and suppose that current I_a is θ_a degrees behind voltage E_{dN}. Since the voltage drop in the reactance is jxI_a, the voltage generated by the converter is given by $E_{aN} = E_{dN} + jxI_a$ (Fig. 28.24b). We note that E_{aN} leads E_{dN} by θ_b degrees. Consequently, the active power P flows from the converter to the load and its value is given by the well-known expression:

$$P = \frac{E_{aN}E_{dN}}{x}\sin \theta_b \qquad (16.8)$$

The active power per phase is also given by the expression:

$$P = E_{dN} I_a \cos \theta_a$$

The dc cable carries only the active component of the power absorbed by the load. The total power carried by the cable is therefore $3 \times P$. Since the dc voltage is E_H, the dc current in the cable is

$$I_d = 3P/E_H$$

What is the relationship between the ac line-to-line voltage E_{ab} and the dc voltage E_H? In order not to clip the peaks of the sinusoidal waveshape, the peak value of the line-to-neutral voltage must never exceed $E_H/2$. Suppose that the peak value of E_{aN} is 80% of $E_H/2$. Under these conditions, it can be shown that E_H is about twice the effective value of the line-to-line voltage of the converter. We can therefore write

$$E_H \approx 2\, E_{LL} \tag{28.2}$$

where

E_H = dc line-to-line voltage of the cable [kV]

E_{LL} = effective line-to-line ac voltage of the converter [kV]

Let us for a moment neglect the losses in the converters and the dc cable. Under steady-state conditions, the active power $3P$ drawn by converter 1 from the 3-phase grid is necessarily equal to the active power supplied to the load at the remote site. Let us choose phase 1 of the grid and suppose that voltage E_{1N} leads E_{4N} by θ_1 degrees (Fig. 28.24c). Power P is therefore given by the expression:

$$P = \frac{E_{1N}E_{4N}}{x}\sin \theta_1 \tag{16.8}$$

The magnitude and phase of E_{1N} are imposed by the grid. Furthermore, the value of x is fixed because the fundamental frequency (usually 60 Hz or 50 Hz) is constant. In order to generate the power P imposed by the remote load, the values of E_{4N} and the angle θ_1 must be adjusted accordingly. What values should they have? The best choice is to control the amplitude and phase of E_{4N} so that current I_1 is always in phase with voltage E_{1N} (Fig. 28.24c). Under these conditions, converter 1 does not draw any reactive power from the power grid. As a result, the rectifier (converter 1) operates at unity power factor. The control system that triggers the IGBTs of converter 1 must operate in such a way that angle θ_1 and voltage E_{4N} are continuously adjusted to maintain these objectives.

28.23 Control of active power

The total active power absorbed by converter 1 is controlled by the dc voltage E_H at the terminals of the cable. To show why this is so, let us again neglect the losses in the converters and the cable.

Under steady-state conditions, the active power of the remote load is constant. As a result, the power drawn from the cable between terminals 9 and 10 is equal to the power absorbed by the cable between terminals 7 and 8 (Figure 28.24a). Consequently, voltage E_H and current I_d are stable.

However, if the load connected to converter 2 diminishes, while angle θ_1 and voltage E_{4N} remain unchanged, the power input to the cable will be greater than its output. The difference between the two will charge up the capacitors C_1 which, in turn, will produce a rapid increase of the dc voltage E_H across the cable. This rapid increase is detected by the control system of converter 1. A correcting signal will immediately reduce both angle θ_1 and voltage E_{4N} (Fig. 28.24c). Consequently, the ac power absorbed by converter 1 will drop which, in turn, will reduce the power supplied to the cable. As soon as it is equal to the dc power absorbed by converter 2, the cable voltage will be restored close to its nominal value.

Contrary to the traditional way of controlling dc power flow by using thyristors, there is no need to continually telecommunicate the status of the two converters at each end of the line (see Section 28.15). Furthermore, large, costly filters are no longer needed. The reason is that the lowest harmonic frequencies are about 40 times the fundamental frequency of the system. Thus, on a 60 Hz basis, the lowest harmonic will be about 2400 Hz. High-frequency filters are small and cheap. We recall that on a conventional dc transmission system we needed large filters to absorb the relatively low-frequency 5th, 7th, 11th, and 13th harmonics (Fig. 28.13).

Clearly, the PWM converters offer several advantages over thyristor-driven converters that use natural line commutation. When we include the advantage of using underground cable, protected from inclement weather and freedom from securing rights of way, the PWM converters become even more attractive. However, IGBTs cannot yet handle powers as great as those of thyristors.

The first HVDC Light® transmission system was installed in 1999 on the island of Gotland, in Sweden. It carried 50 MW of dc power generated by a wind farm, over a distance of 70 km, to the town of Visby. Two cables operating respectively at +80 kV and −80 kV (E_H = 160 kV) were buried in the ground using a plow pulled by a tractor. The converters at each end of the line generate a 3-phase voltage of 80 kV, 50 Hz.

28.24 Example of a HVDC Light transmission system

As an example of a HVDC Light transmission system, Figure 28.25a shows a dc transmission system using two static IGBT converters. The system consists of a 3-phase grid that supplies power to a remote site that is 40 km away. The underground cable operates at 70 kV (+35 kV, −35 kV line-to-neutral) and it has a total dc resistance of 6.8 Ω. The ac line voltage at both ends is rated 34.5 kV, 60 Hz, 3 phase.

The load at the remote site draws a total power of 24 MVA at a lagging power factor of 75%. The total active power ($3P$) is therefore 0.75 × 24 MVA = 18 MW. The total reactive power absorbed by the load:

$$Q = \sqrt{(24^2 - 18^2)} = 15.9 \text{ Mvar}$$

The values of the various electrical components are shown in Fig. 28.25a. The voltages and currents are also shown when the site draws its rated power. These values are calculated as follows*:

1a. Line-to-line voltage at the terminals of the load

$$E_{de} = 34{,}500 \text{ V}$$

1b. Line-to-neutral voltage at the load

$$E_{dN} = 34{,}500/\sqrt{3} = 19{,}920 \text{ V}$$

2. Current I_a drawn by the load

$$I_a = \frac{S}{E\sqrt{3}} = \frac{24 \times 10^6}{34{,}500\sqrt{3}} = 401.6 \text{ A}$$

3. Phase angle between I_a and the line-to-neutral voltage E_{dN}

$$\theta_a = \arccos 0.75 = 41.4°$$

4. Reactance at 60 Hz of the 20 mH L_1

$$x = 2\pi f L_1 = 2\pi \times 60 \times 20 \times 10^{-3} = 7.54\ \Omega$$

5. Line-to-neutral voltage E_{aN} of converter 2

$$E_{aN} = 19{,}920 + j \times 7.54 \times 401.6\angle{-41.4°}$$
$$= 21{,}923 + j \times 2271 = 22{,}040\angle 5.9°$$

(see phasor diagram Fig. 28.25b)

6. Three-phase line-to-line voltage at the terminals of converter 2

$$E_{ab} = 22{,}040\sqrt{3} = 38{,}175 \text{ V}$$

7. DC power absorbed by converter 2

$$3P = 18 \times 10^6 \text{ W}$$

8a. DC voltage of cable between terminals 9 and 10 of converter 2

$$E_H = 70{,}000 \text{ V}$$

8b. Line-to-neutral dc voltage

$$E_d = E_{9N} = 70{,}000/2 = 35{,}000 \text{ V}$$

* Because the load is balanced, the value of the voltage or current selected for a particular phase is automatically the same as that for the other two phases.

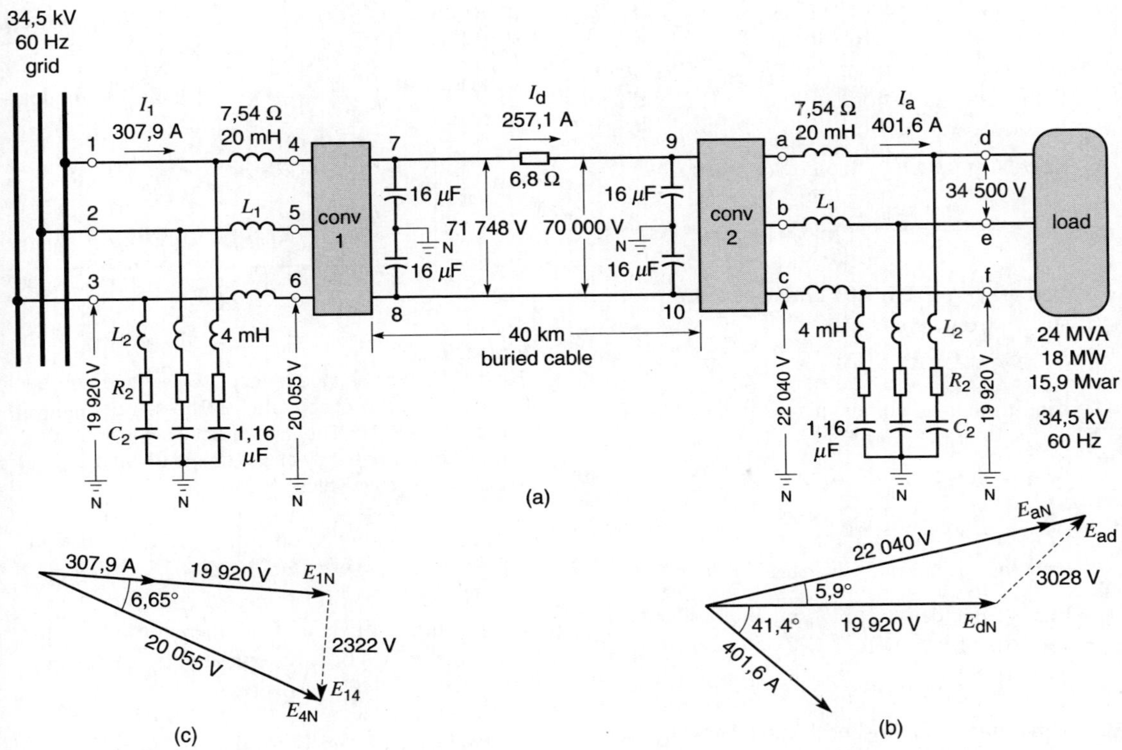

Figure 28.25
a. Numerical example of a HVDC Light transmission system that uses PWM converters.
b. Phasor diagram for phase **a** at the remote site.
c. Phasor diagram for phase **1** at the grid point that supplies the power.

9. DC current drawn by converter 2

$$I_d = 3P/E_H = 18 \times 10^6/70{,}000 = 257.1 \text{ A}$$

10. Cable resistance (both lines)

$$R = 6.8\ \Omega$$

11a. DC voltage between the terminals 7 and 8 of converter 1

$$E_{78} = 70{,}000 + 6.8 \times 257.1 = 71{,}748 \text{ V}$$

11b. DC line-to-neutral voltage at the terminals of converter 1

$$E_{7N} = 71{,}748/2 = 35{,}874 \text{ V}$$

12a. AC line-to-line voltage of the grid

$$E_{12} = 34{,}500 \text{ V}$$

12b. AC line-to-neutral voltage of the grid

$$E_{1N} = 34{,}500/\sqrt{3} = 19{,}920 \text{ V}$$

13. DC power delivered by converter 1

$$P = 257.1 \text{ A} \times 71{,}748 \text{ V} = 18.4 \text{ MW}$$

14. Total active power absorbed by converter 1 from the grid

$$P = 18.4 \text{ MW}$$

15. As mentioned previously, the phase angles and the voltages across terminals 4, 5, and 6 are automatically adjusted by the converter so that the power factor at terminals 1, 2, and 3 is 100%.

16. Current supplied by the grid

$$I_1 = \frac{S}{E\sqrt{3}} = \frac{18.4 \times 10^6}{34{,}500\sqrt{3}} = 307.9 \text{ A}$$

17. Voltage across the 7.54 Ω reactances upstream from converter 1

$$E_{14} = 7.54 \times 307.9 = 2322 \text{ V}$$

18. Line-to-neutral voltage across the terminals 4 and N of converter 1

$$E_{4\text{N}} = E_{1\text{N}} - E_{14} = 19{,}920 - j \times 2322$$

$$= 20{,}055 \text{ V}\angle -6.65°$$

(see phasor diagram Fig. 28.25c)

19. Phase angle between $E_{1\text{N}}$ and $E_{4\text{N}}$ produced by converter 1 is therefore

$$\theta_1 = 6.65°$$

20. Three-phase line-to-line voltage between terminals 4, 5, and 6 of converter 1

$$E_{\text{LL}} = 20{,}055\sqrt{3} = 34{,}735 \text{ V}$$

21. The series resonant circuit L_2, C_2 is tuned to the carrier frequency f_c. Let us choose a frequency ratio $m_f = f_c/f = 39$. The carrier frequency is therefore

$$f_c = 39 \times 60 \text{ Hz} = 2340 \text{ Hz}$$

The L_2, C_2 circuit will be tuned to this frequency. The major line-to-line harmonic frequencies will be

$$f_{\text{H1}} = (2340 + 2 \times 60) = 2460 \text{ Hz}$$

$$f_{\text{H2}} = (2340 - 2 \times 60) = 2220 \text{ Hz}$$

These harmonic frequencies are very close to the carrier frequency of 2340 Hz.

22. Figure 28.26 shows the rectangular waveshape of the PWM voltage between terminal **a** and the neutral **N** of converter 2. The fundamental sinusoidal component of this voltage has a peak value of $22\,040\sqrt{2}$ V = 31 169 V. The fundamental waveshapes between terminals **b, c** and the neutral have the same values but are separated by angles of 120° and 240°, respectively.

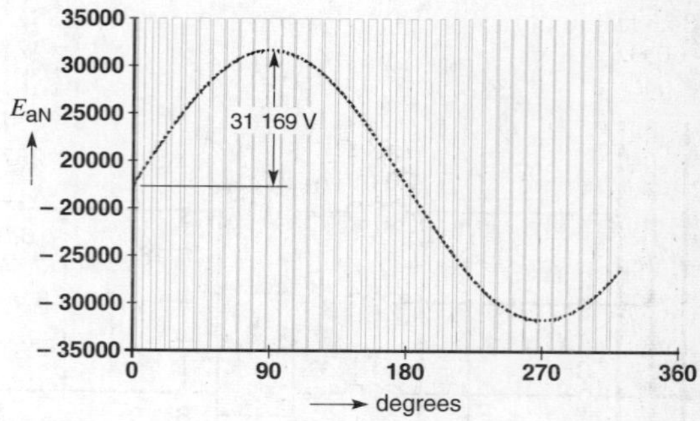

Figure 28.26
Rectangular waveshape of the PWM voltage between terminals **a** and **N** of converter 2. The carrier frequency is 2340 Hz. The fundamental sinusoidal component has a frequency of 60 Hz and an amplitude of 31 169 V (effective value 22 040 V).

Questions and Problems

Practical level

28-1 Give three examples where dc power transmission is particularly useful.

28-2 Name the principal components making up a dc transmission system.

28-3 Which harmonics occur on the ac side of a converter? On the dc side?

28-4 What is the purpose of the large dc line inductors?

28-5 A dc transmission line operating at 50 kV, carries a current of 600 A. The terminal contains a single 3-phase, 6-pulse converter.
   a. Calculate the approximate value of the secondary ac line voltage of the converter transformer.
   b. What is the effective value of the secondary line current?

28-6 The bipolar line shown in Fig. 28.10a operates at a potential of ±150 kV. If the dc line currents are respectively 600 A and 400 A, calculate the following:

a. The power transmitted between the two ac networks

b. The value of the ground current

28-7 The transmission line shown in Fig. 28.5 possesses a resistance of 10 Ω. The rectifier (converter 1) produces a dc voltage of 102 kV while the inverter generates 96 kV.

a. Calculate the dc line current and the power transmitted to network 2.

b. If the gates of the inverter are fired a little earlier in the cycle, will the dc line current increase or decrease? Explain.

c. If the inverter gates are fired so that the inverter generates 110 kV, will the power flow reverse? Explain.

28-8 When a short-circuit occurs on a dc line, the current in the fault itself is less than the full-load current. Explain.

28-9 Why is a communications link needed between the converter stations of a dc line?

Intermediate level

28-10 The converters shown in Fig. 28.2 are identical 3-phase, 6-pulse units, producing a voltage E_d of 50 kV and a current I_d of 1200 A.

a. Calculate the dc current per valve (bridge arm).

b. What is the approximate peak inverse voltage across each valve?

28-11 Referring to Section 28.19, calculate the line current per pole on the Pacific Intertie, and using the model of Fig. 28.4, estimate the total reactive power absorbed by each converter station.

28-12 The ground electrode of a bipolar converter station is located 15 km from the station, and possesses a ground resistance of 0.5 Ω. If the line currents in each pole are respectively 1700 A and 1400 A, calculate the power loss at the electrode.

28-13 Referring to Fig. 28.11, it is given that $E_d = 450$ kV, $I_d = 1800$ A, and the two dc smoothing inductors L each have an inductance of 0.5 H. If a short-circuit occurs between line and ground close to the rectifier station, calculate the magnitude of the rectifier current after 5 ms, assuming the gate triggering remains unaltered.

28-14 Each pole of the bipolar Nelson project (Fig. 28.18) is composed of two conductors (2-conductor bundle) of ACSR cable. Each conductor is composed of 72 strands of aluminum (diameter 0.16 in) and a central 7-strand (diameter 0.1067 in) steel core. Each 2-conductor bundle carries a nominal current of 1800 A over a distance of 550 miles. The voltage at the rectifier terminal is 450 kV.

Neglecting the presence of the steel core, calculate the following:

a. The effective cross section of the 2-conductor bundle [in^2]

b. The line resistance of the 2-conductor bundle at a temperature of 20°C

c. The corresponding I^2R loss

d. The dc voltage at the inverter terminal

e. The efficiency of the line (neglecting corona losses)

Advanced level

28-15 Referring to Fig. 28.12, calculate the following:

a. The resonant frequency of the two dc filters

b. The value of the respective series impedances

c. What is the dc voltage across the capacitors?

28-16 **a.** In Problem 28-15, if the 6th harmonic voltage generated on the dc side of the inverter is 20 kV, calculate the approximate value of the corresponding harmonic current.

b. Calculate the value of the 6th harmonic voltage across the 0.5 H inductor.

c. What is the value of the 360 Hz voltage at the input to the second 0.5 H line inductor?

CHAPTER 29

Transmission and Distribution Solid-State Controllers

29.0 Introduction

The successful development of thyristors, GTOs, and other electronic switches is promoting major changes in controlling power flow in the transmission and distribution sectors of electric power utilities.

With the exception of circuit breakers, tap-changing transformers, and static var compensators, transmission and distribution systems have comprised relatively passive elements. On the other hand, the multiplicity of transmission and distribution lines has made it ever more difficult to predict the amount and direction that power flows will take. Furthermore, the complexity of these transmission systems has made it necessary to allow wide margins of safety so that instabilities created by equipment failures, switching surges, and sudden load shedding do not create stability problems that might get out of hand.

The special problem of electric utilities is that the demand for electric power continues to grow, while it is becoming more difficult to obtain rights of way to erect more transmission and distribution circuits. For these and other reasons, electric utilities are looking for ways whereby they can increase the power-handling capacity of their existing lines without compromising reliability and stability. The idea is to load them up to their thermal limit and to utilize them all to carry the electrical load.

One of the important problems is that instabilities occur very quickly and can build up and spread out throughout an entire system in a matter of seconds. Thus, circuit breakers must be brought into play to disconnect devices and loads that might otherwise exacerbate the situation.

It is now possible to envisage power lines that are "active," in the sense that they can react almost instantaneously to any contingency and counteract a potentially dangerous situation. This rapid action is possible thanks to the existence of thyristors and GTOs that can now handle currents of several thousand amperes and several thousand volts. Indeed, we have seen in Chapter 28 that they are already being used in HVDC systems of several hundred kilovolts. These switching devices are now being incorporated into equipment such as series capacitors, var compensators, harmonic filters, and ultra-high-speed switches.

In this chapter we will cover some of the important solid-state controllers that have been developed recently and which have undergone tests in the field.

We begin with power flow controllers for transmission, which are classified under the acronym FACTS (Flexible AC Transmission System), followed by power electronic controllers for distribution. The FACTS program was pioneered by the Electric Power Research Institute (EPRI) of Palo Alto, California, in collaboration with equipment manufacturers and electric power utilities.

TRANSMISSION POWER FLOW CONTROLLERS

In the transmission sector we will look at the following equipment:

a. Thyristor-controlled series capacitor (TCSC)
b. Static synchronous compensator (STATCOM)
c. Unified power flow controller (UPFC)
d. Static frequency converter

29.1 Thyristor-controlled series capacitor (TCSC)

In Chapter 25, Section 25.26, we saw that the power-handling capability of a 3-phase transmission line can be increased by introducing a fixed capacitor in series with each phase. This reduces the effective series reactance and, therefore, the power of the transmission line can be raised. We recall that the power is given by

$$P = \frac{E^2}{X} \sin \delta \qquad (25.4)$$

wherein

P = active power transmitted [MW]
E = line-to-line voltage at each end of the line [kV]
X = inductive reactance per phase [Ω]
δ = phase angle between the voltages at each end of the line [°]

In the more general case, where the voltages E_S, E_R at each end of the line are not equal, the power equation becomes

$$P = \frac{E_S E_R}{X} \sin \delta \qquad (29.1)$$

The derivation of this equation was shown in Section 16.23.

The new TCSC approach is to vary the transmission line power capability in accordance with immediate requirements. This is accomplished by varying the capacitance in series with the line on an instantaneous as and when required basis.

Consider, for example, Fig. 29.1a in which two capacitors having a reactance x_c are connected in series with a transmission line having an inductive reactance X, per phase. Each capacitor can be connected to an inductive reactance x_a by means of

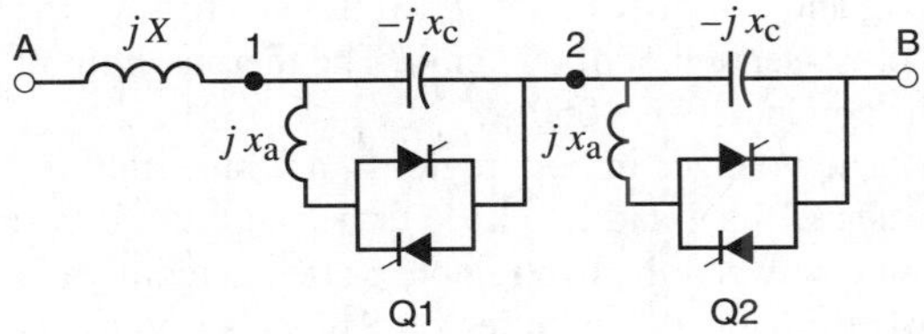

Figure 29.1a
One phase of a series-compensated line.

back-to-back thyristor valves labeled Q. The reactance x_a is considerably smaller than x_c.

When valves Q1, Q2 are blocked, only the capacitors are in the circuit and so the effective reactance of the line is $(X - 2x_c)$. On the other hand, if the Q1 valve is triggered "on" so that uninterrupted conduction takes place, x_a falls in parallel with x_c. The resulting impedance between points **1, 2** becomes inductive (Fig. 29.1b), with value equal to $jx_cx_a/(x_c - x_a)$. The effective reactance X_{eff} of the line is then the sum of the impedances seen in the figure, namely

$$X_{eff} = X + \frac{x_c x_a}{x_c - x_a} - x_c \qquad (29.2)$$

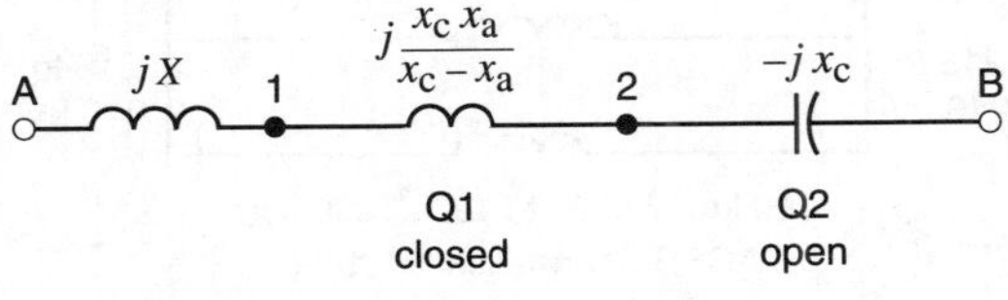

Figure 29.1b
Impedance when line is partially compensated.

The thyristor valves Q1, Q2 can be switched on and off independently; consequently, for a given phase angle between points **A** and **B,** the active power transported can be varied as required. The switching can be done within one cycle, which means that the power flow can be very quickly controlled.

The following example will illustrate the switching process, and the results that can be achieved.

Example 29-1

A 230 kV, 3-phase, 60 Hz transmission line connecting two strong regions S and R has an impedance of 54 Ω, per phase (Fig. 29.2). The line is 110 km long and comprises three ACSR conductors having a cross-section of 1000 kcmil. The thermal limit of the conductors is 1050 A.

The voltages in both regions vary randomly between 215 kV and 246 kV. Furthermore, the phase angle between the two regions varies randomly between 8° and 17°, with region S always leading region R. As we learned in Section 25.23, this means that region S will *always* deliver active power to region R.

In addition to its role as a stabilizing link between the two regions, the transmission line is a revenue-producing facility; consequently, every attempt is made to transport as much power as possible within the thermal limit of the conductors.

To meet these objectives, the transmission line is equipped with four capacitors in series, each having an impedance of 12 Ω. Each capacitor can be connected in parallel with an inductive reactance of 1.71 Ω by means of thyristor valves Q, as shown in Fig. 29.3. In practice, for over-voltage protection, metal oxide varistors (MOV) and a circuit breaker are also included in the circuit. They do not appear in the figure.

We wish to determine the following:

a. The effective impedance of a single capacitor/inductor unit when the thyristors conduct fully
b. The maximum nominal power that the transmission line can carry
c. The best configuration of the series compensation circuit (number of valves Q1, Q2, etc., in action) when the S region voltage is 218 kV, the R region voltage is 237 kV, and the phase angle between them is 15°

Solution

a. The inductive impedance x_p of the capacitor in parallel with the inductor is given by

$$x_p = \frac{x_c x_a}{x_c - x_a} \tag{29.3}$$

$$= \frac{12 \times 1.71}{12 - 1.71}$$

$$= 2\ \Omega$$

b. The maximum nominal power is determined by the nominal current and nominal voltage of the transmission line:

$$P_{\text{nominal}} = EI\sqrt{3}$$

$$= 230\,000 \times 1050 \times \sqrt{3}$$

$$= 418\ \text{MW}$$

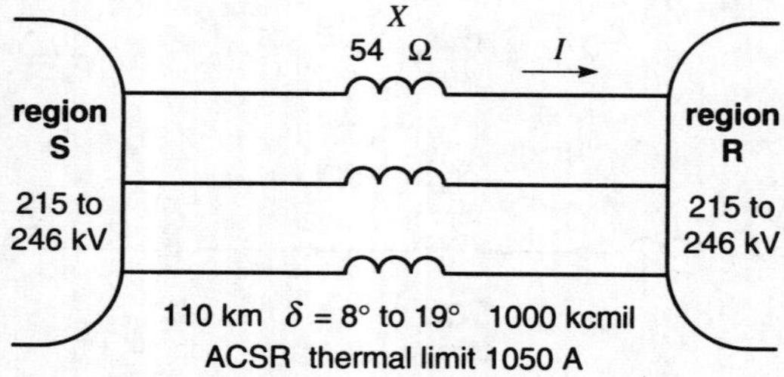

Figure 29.2
Transmission line connecting two regions S (sender) and R (receiver).

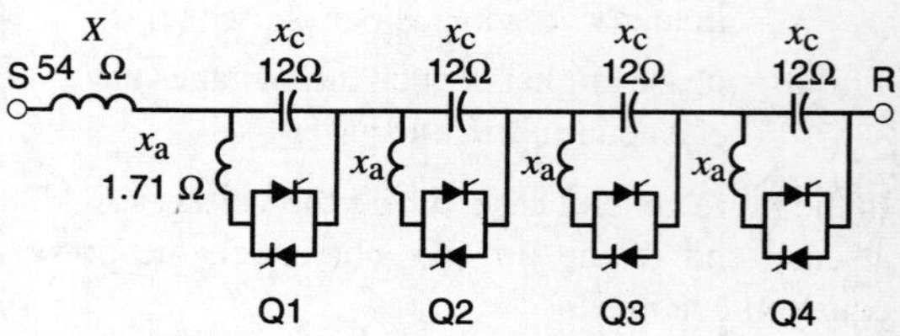

Figure 29.3
Transmission line with four thyristor-controlled series capacitors.

c. In order to carry the desired nominal power of 418 MW, given $E_S = 218$ kV, $E_R = 237$ kV, and $\delta = 15°$, the effective line impedance X_{eff} can be calculated using the expression

$$P = \frac{E_S E_R}{X_{eff}} \sin \delta \qquad (29.4)$$

$$418 = \frac{218 \times 237}{X_{eff}} \sin 15°$$

whence

$$X_{eff} = 32\ \Omega$$

By trial, the closest configuration approaching this result is given by Fig. 29.4a. It can be seen that two thyristor valves Q3, Q4 are conducting while the remaining two are not. The resulting net reactance of the transmission line is $54 - 24 + 4 = 34\ \Omega$. The actual power transmitted is, therefore,

$$P = \frac{E_S E_R}{X_{eff}} \sin \delta \qquad (29.4)$$

$$= \frac{218 \times 237}{34} \sin 15°$$

$$P = 393 \text{ MW}$$

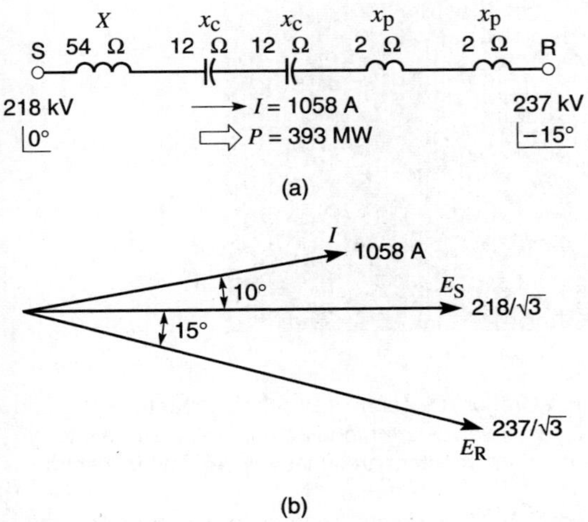

Figure 29.4
Circuit configuration for a given sender/receiver condition.

The 393 MW is quite close to the maximum rated power of 418 MW. The phasor diagram for this condition is shown in Fig. 29.4b.

This example shows that the thyristor-controlled series capacitors can be switched in and out to meet any power requirement within the thermal capability of the transmission line.

29.2 Vernier control

In some applications it is useful to reduce the conduction period of the thyristors so that the effective reactance x_a of the inductors is higher than its actual value. This vernier control enables the TCSC controller to vary the effective impedance of the transmission line over a much wider range.

Referring back to Example 29-1, suppose that the conduction period is shortened so that the effective reactance of the inductor is 4 Ω instead of 1.71 Ω. The combination of the 12 Ω capacitor in parallel with the 4 Ω reactor gives an inductive reactance of 6 Ω, as follows:

$$x_p = \frac{x_c x_a}{x_c - x_a} \qquad (29.3)$$

$$= \frac{12 \times 4}{12 - 4}$$

$$= -6\ \Omega \text{ (inductive)}$$

On the other hand, if the conduction period is shortened even more, the effective reactor impedance can be raised to 36 Ω. Under these conditions the resulting *LC* parallel combination yields a *capacitive* reactance of 18 Ω, as follows:

$$x_p = \frac{x_c x_a}{x_c - x_a} \qquad (29.3)$$

$$= \frac{12 \times 36}{12 - 36}$$

$$= -18\ \Omega \text{ (capacitive)}$$

Thus, the TCSC vernier technique is seen to offer an additional advantage as compared to a conventional series compensation arrangement.

However, care must be taken to prevent the shortened conduction period from creating a condition of parallel resonance wherein the reactance of the inductor approaches that of the capacitor. This means that a forbidden band must be skipped as the reactance of the inductor is progressively increased above its base value of 1.71 Ω.

Vernier control is particularly advantageous when stability problems arise between two regions. The low-frequency power oscillations that take place can be damped out by modulating the power flow over the transmission line in such a way as to counteract the oscillation. The almost instantaneous action of the thyristors, supported by feedback signals and computer algorithms, makes such a maneuver feasible.

Fig. 29.5 shows a large TCSC system installed in the C. J. Slatt Substation in Northern Oregon, on the Bonneville Power Administration's 500 kV, 3-phase, 60 Hz transmission system. It is composed of six identical TCSC modules that are individually protected by metal oxide varistors. The thyristor-controlled series capacitor unit has the following rating and components

1. Nominal system voltage (line-to-line): 500 kV
2. Nominal line current: 2900 A
3. Nominal 3-phase compensation: 202 Mvar
4. Nominal capacitive reactance, per phase (inductors not in circuit): 8 Ω
5. Maximum effective capacitive reactance, per phase (inductors in delayed conduction mode): 24 Ω
6. Effective inductive reactance, per phase (inductors in full conduction mode): 1.22 Ω
7. The TCSC is designed to withstand the following overload conditions:

   30-minute overload current: 4350 A

   10-second overload current: 5800 A

   maximum fault current through module: 20.3 kA

   maximum crest fault current in thyristor valve: 60 kA

Figure 29.5a
Overall view of the TCSC at the C. J. Slatt Substation in Northern Oregon. Disconnect switches are at the right, and bypass breakers are at the left. The capacitors, reactors, and thyristor valves are mounted on three platforms to isolate them from ground. On each platform, capacitors are at the right, reactors are in the middle, and thyristors are in the boxes at the left.

The TCSC is part of EPRI's Flexible AC Transmission System (FACTS) program. The project was developed by the Electric Power Research Institute in collaboration with the Bonneville Power Administration and General Electric Company.
(Courtesy of EPRI)

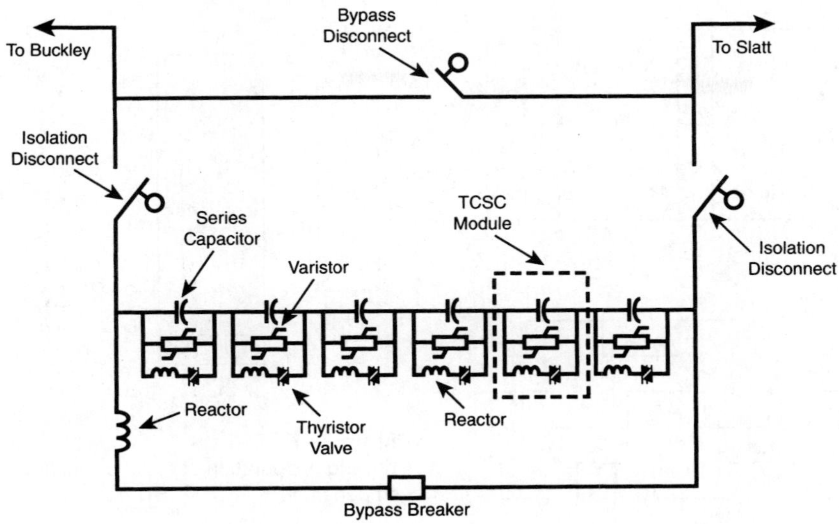

Figure 29.5b
Schematic circuit diagram of one phase of the TCSC system, installed in series with the 500 kV transmission line. *(Courtesy General Electric Company)*

It is worth noting that this installation is the first of its kind in the world.

29.3 Static synchronous compensator

In Sections 25.22 and 25.27 we saw that the voltage of a transmission line can be controlled by means of a compensator located at the receiver end of the line. The compensator delivers or draws reactive power in order to stabilize the voltage. Traditionally, these compensators have been rotating machines (Fig. 17.24) or static var compensators that require large capacitors and inductors (Fig. 25.39).

Today, it is possible to replace these machines and devices by a switching converter, a dc capacitor, and a group of transformers. This *static synchronous compensator,* or STATCOM, has numerous advantages over previous compensators. First, it acts much faster and can respond to voltage fluctuations in a matter of one cycle. Second, it can generate far more reactive power when the system voltage is low—which is just the moment when a lot of reactive power is needed to prevent further voltage collapse.

Switching converters were discussed in Section 21.44, and a 3-phase PWM version was described in Section 21.49. However, the converters we are interested in do not make use of high-frequency PWM techniques because the megawatt powers involved require the use of GTOs, and these switching devices can only operate at frequencies of a few hundred hertz. For this reason the converter operates in the rectangular wave mode in which the on/off switching is done at the 60 Hz line frequency.

The basic STATCOM converter is represented in Fig. 29.6 together with the rectangular waves it produces. It is essentially identical to the 6-step converter described in Section 23.10.

The rectangular line-to-line voltages contain a fundamental component whose peak value is equal to 1.10 E_H, where E_H is the dc voltage at the input to the converter. It follows that the effective line-to-line voltage is $1.10\ E_H/\sqrt{2} = 0.78\ E_H$ and the effective line-to-neutral voltage is $0.78\ E_H/\sqrt{3} = 0.45\ E_H$.

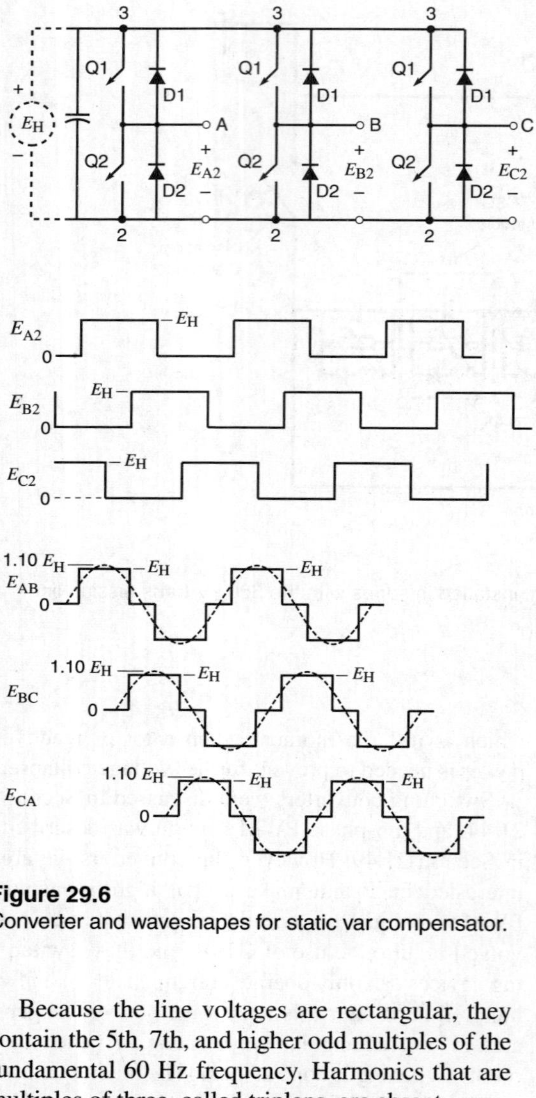

Figure 29.6
Converter and waveshapes for static var compensator.

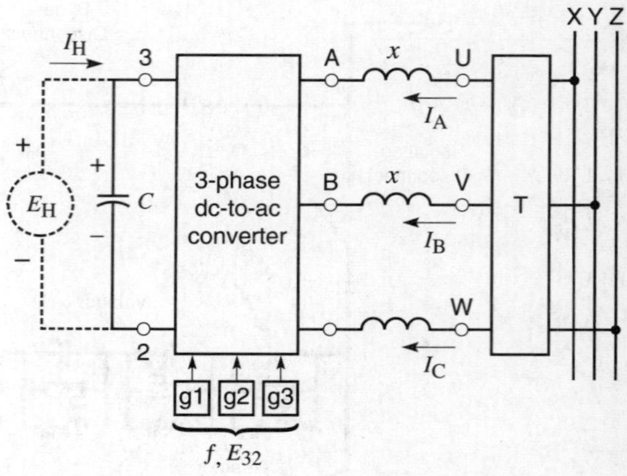

Figure 29.7
Principle of operation of a static synchronous compensator.

Because the line voltages are rectangular, they contain the 5th, 7th, and higher odd multiples of the fundamental 60 Hz frequency. Harmonics that are multiples of three, called triplens, are absent.

Fig. 29.7 is a schematic diagram of a converter installation. It comprises a 3-phase high-voltage transmission line X, Y, Z; an ideal 3-phase step-down transformer T; three reactances *x;* a 3-phase converter; a capacitor C; and a dc voltage source E_H.

The magnitude of the ac voltage between terminals A, B, C, is controlled by varying E_H, and the phase angle is controlled by appropriate timing of the GTO gate pulses g1, g2, g3. Thus, the phase angle of the converter voltage can be set to any value between zero and 360°, with respect to the transmission line voltages U, V, W on the secondary side of the transformer.

To understand what happens in the circuit, let us consider one phase of the 3-phase system. We select the line-to-neutral voltages for terminals A and U, namely E_{An} and E_{Un}. Because this is a var compensator, we are only interested in generating reactive power. Consequently, the line current I_A must lag or lead the line-to-neutral voltages by 90°. To obtain this result, the phase angle of converter voltage E_{An} is arranged so it is in phase with the corresponding transmission line voltage E_{Un}. We now examine three cases.

1. If $E_{An} = E_{Un}$ no current will flow in the reactance *x* and so the compensation is nil (Fig. 29.8a).
2. If E_{An} is less than E_{Un}, a current I_A will flow that lags 90° behind E_{Un} (Fig. 29.8b). Its magnitude is given by

$$I_A = \frac{E_{Un} - E_{An}}{x} \qquad (29.5)$$

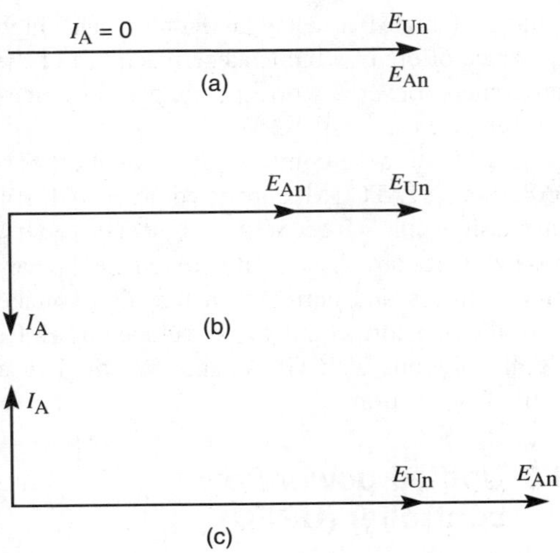

Figure 29.8
Phasor relationships of E_{Un} and I depend upon the value of E_{An}.

As a result, the compensator draws reactive power from the transmission line. The compensator behaves like a large inductance even though no coils are present and no magnetic field is produced.

3. If E_{An} is greater than E_{Un}, current I_A will lead E_{Un} by 90° (Fig. 29.8c). The magnitude of I_A is again given by Eq. 29.5, except that it is negative. As a result, the converter *delivers* reactive power to the transmission line. The converter then behaves as if it were a large capacitor even though no electrostatic plates and no electric field are present.

In practice, transformer T always has a certain leakage reactance. Therefore, under real-life conditions, it is the leakage reactance of the transformer that constitutes the reactance x in Fig. 29.7. It follows that the transformer fills a dual role: transforming the voltage, while providing the reactance needed to permit compensation to take place.

Next, let us look at the dc power supply E_H and the associated capacitor C. We have already learned that the converter can transfer power in both directions– from the dc side to the ac side and vice versa. This feature can be put to remarkably good use.

Suppose that the phase angle of the converter is delayed so that it lags slightly behind the transmission line voltage by, say, 1°. This will cause the converter to receive active power from the transmission line and this power will have to be absorbed by the dc power supply, minus the losses in the converter. On the other hand, if the phase angle of the converter voltage is arranged to lead the transmission line voltage by, say, 1°, active power will be delivered from the converter to the transmission line. This can only occur at the expense of the dc power supply which must now deliver dc power to the converter.

By adjusting the phase control, the current I_H drawn from the power supply can be set to zero. All that is required is to set the phase angles of converter voltages A, B, C so they lag slightly behind the corresponding transformer voltages U, V, W—just enough to provide the losses in the converter. The power supply E_H can therefore be dispensed with altogether, leaving only the capacitor C to maintain the required dc voltage. The voltage across the capacitor can be increased or reduced by simply advancing and retarding the small phase angle mentioned above.

In this way the capacitor is charged up to a dc voltage level E_H so that the resulting ac voltage across terminals A, B, C has precisely the value needed to produce the required var compensation.

Example 29-2

The converter in Fig. 29.7 is rated to generate a fundamental line voltage ranging from 4 kV to 6 kV at an effective current of 2000 A per phase.

The 230 kV transmission line voltage is stepped down to 4.8 kV by means of a transformer. The leakage reactance x of the transformer, referred to the secondary side, has a value of 0.2 Ω. The capacitor bank on the dc side of the converter has a capacitance of 500 μF.

a. Calculate the converter line voltage E_{AB} needed so as to deliver a total of 6.4 Mvar to the transmission line.

b. Calculate the dc voltage across the capacitor bank under these conditions.

Solution

a. The current needed to produce 6.4 Mvar is

$$I = \frac{Q}{E_{UV}\sqrt{3}} = \frac{6\,400\,000}{4800\,\sqrt{3}} = 770\,A$$

The voltage drop across the reactance is

$$E_x = Ix = 770 \times 0.2 = 154\ \text{V}$$

Line-to-neutral voltage induced on the secondary side of the transformer is

$$E_{Un} = 4800/\sqrt{3} = 2771\ \text{V}$$

The converter line-to-neutral voltage E_{An} must exceed E_{Un} by 154 V; hence

$$E_{An} = 2771 + 154 = 2925\ \text{V}$$

Converter line-to-line voltage

$$E_{AB} = 2925\,\sqrt{3} = 5066\ \text{V}$$

b. Capacitor dc voltage is

$$E_H = 2925/0.45^* = 6500\ \text{V}$$

29.4 Eliminating the harmonics

The rectangular waves generated by a single 3-phase converter, such as that shown in Fig. 29.7, would produce large current harmonics in the transmission line, a situation that could not be tolerated. For this reason, instead of only one converter, several converters are used.

Each converter produces a rectangular output voltage, but the respective voltages are shifted from each other by definite, specified angles. These phase-shifted voltages are isolated from each other and can, therefore, be applied individually to low-voltage transformer windings. The windings on the high-voltage side are connected in series in such a way as to cancel out most of the harmonics (5th, 7th, etc.), while successively adding up the fundamental 60 Hz components. The result is a composite sinusoidal voltage containing only the fundamental and high-frequency harmonics. The high impedance offered by the leakage reactance of the transformers ensures correspondingly low harmonic currents.

Fig. 29.9 shows a commercial installation of a ±100 Mvar STATCOM connected to a 161 kV transmission line. It contains eight converters, whose voltages are phase shifted to reduce the harmonic voltages and currents on the high-voltage side of the transformers. It was developed by EPRI in collaboration with TVA and Westinghouse Electric Corporation.

29.5 Unified power flow controller (UPFC)

Consider two electric utility regions A and B that are individually so strong that their voltages are essentially fixed in magnitude and in phase. Let us further assume that the line-to-neutral voltages E_A and E_B are equal and in phase (Fig. 29.10). Under these conditions, if the regions are linked by a transmission line having an impedance *X,* there can be no active or reactive power exchange between them, because the line current *I* would be zero. Adding capacitors in series with the line would not help because there would be no driving voltage between the two ends of the line.

This is unfortunate because one of the regions may have excess generating capacity that could be used in the neighboring region. Again, a sudden disturbance in one of the regions might require extra active and reactive power in order to maintain stability. It would be most useful if the other region could then help out to manage the contingency. Speed is of the essence during such emergencies, and so the flow of active and reactive power over the transmission line should be rapidly and selectively controlled.

To meet these objectives, suppose that an ac voltage source E_C, whose magnitude and phase can be varied, is somehow connected in series with the line. One solution is to use a dc/ac switching converter on the region A side of the line (Fig. 29.11a). The resulting voltage E_T ahead of the line reactance is now the phasor sum of E_A and E_C rather than its former value E_A. If the phase angle between E_T and

* 0.45 drawn from page 821.

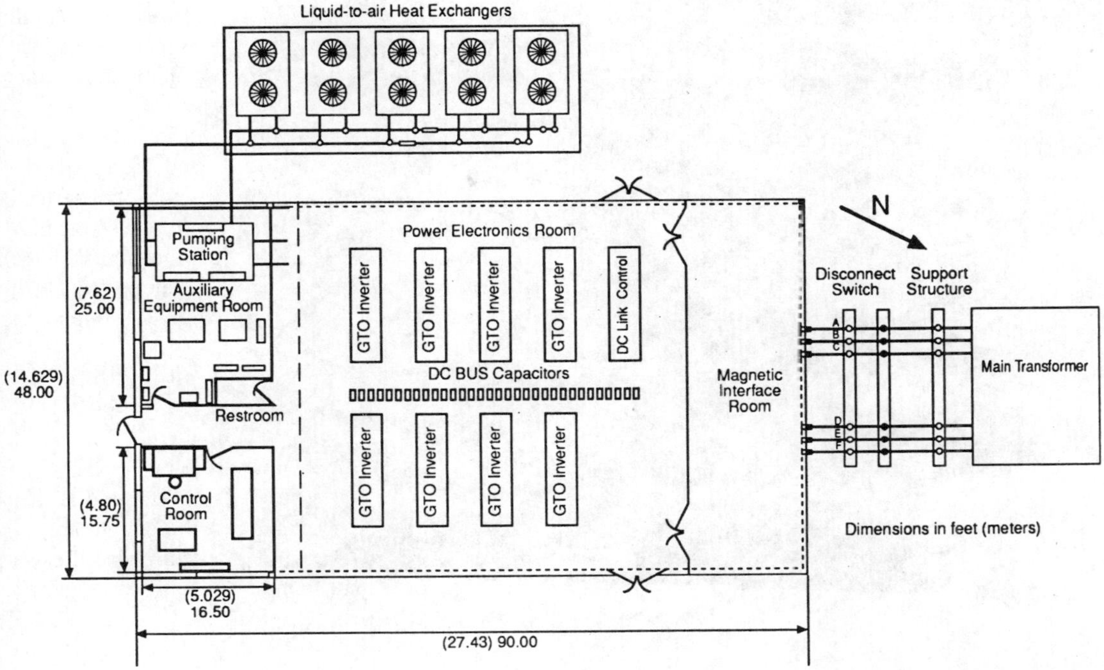

Figure 29.9a
Physical layout of the components of a ±100 Mvar static synchronous compensator (STATCOM) installed in the Tennessee Valley Authority (TVA) Sullivan Substation near Johnson City, Tennessee. This project represents a joint collaboration between the Electric Power Research Institute (EPRI), TVA, and the Westinghouse Science and Technology Center.
(Courtesy of Westinghouse Electric Corporation)

E_B is δ, it follows that active power will be transmitted over the line, given by

$$P = \frac{E_T E_R}{X} \sin \delta \qquad (29.6)$$

The phasor diagram (Fig. 29.11b) shows that if the phase angle ϕ of E_C is varied while keeping E_C constant, the tip of E_T will follow the dotted circle. As a result, angle δ will progressively change from a maximum positive to a maximum negative value, during which it will pass through zero. Thus, the active power transported over the line can be positive or negative, which means that power can flow in either direction. Moreover, its magnitude can be varied as needed by varying the magnitude and phase of E_C.

Note that when E_A and E_B are equal and in phase, phasor I is always at right angles to E_C. Consequently, no real power is delivered or absorbed by the converter. However, the converter delivers reactive power equal to $Q_C = E_C I$ vars. This is precisely the reactive power absorbed by the line reactance X. Note also that if the phase of E_C is set so that $\phi = 90°$, active power at unity power factor will be delivered by region A.

Suppose now that E_A and E_B are in phase but have different values, with E_A being smaller than E_B (Fig. 29.12). As before, the phase angle of E_C can be varied over a complete circle, pivoting around the end of phasor E_A. The voltage drop across the line impedance is $E_T - E_B$, and current I

Figure 29.9b
This is one of eight switching converters used in the TVA Sullivan Substation to control the reactive power of a 161 kV transmission line. The converter has a rating of 12.5 Mvar and operates from a nominal dc bus of 7600 V. The 3-phase, 60 Hz output voltage has a rating of 5.1 kV. Five GTOs rated at 4.5 KV and 4000 A turn-off current are connected in series for each switch arm. The entire converter station occupies an area 48 feet wide and 90 feet long. *(Courtesy of Westinghouse Electric Corporation)*

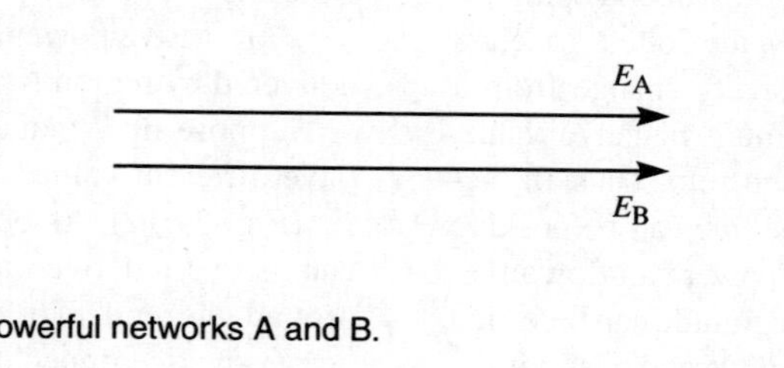

Figure 29.10
Transmission line linking two powerful networks A and B.

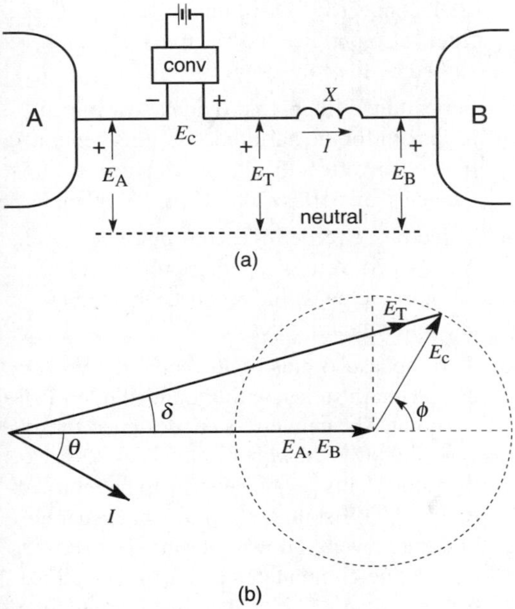

Figure 29.11

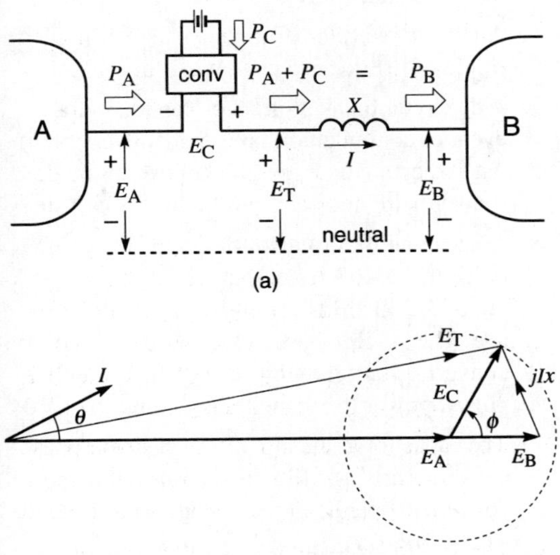

Figure 29.12
E_A and E_B in phase but unequal; phasor relationships.

must obviously lie 90° behind it. As a result, in Fig. 29.12b I will lead E_A and E_B by θ degrees. The following power equations can be written:
Active power P_A delivered by region A is

$$P_A = E_A I \cos \theta \tag{29.7}$$

Active power P_B received by region B is

$$P_B = E_B I \cos \theta \tag{29.8}$$

Active power P_C delivered by the converter is

$$P_C = E_C I \cos (\phi - \theta) \tag{29.9}$$

Thus, region A supplies active power P_A, the converter supplies active power P_C, and the sum of the two is equal to the active power P_B absorbed by region B. Because the converter delivers active power to the system, it must in turn draw real power from the battery, which will gradually discharge. However, instead of using a battery, power can be taken directly from the transmission line at the region A end.

This elegant solution requires two converters connected by a dc link, as shown in Fig. 29.13. Both converters are equipped with isolating transformers. They are included along with the converters on the ac side of the boxes labeled conv 1 and conv 2. Converter 1 rectifies the ac power at rated voltage E_A and delivers it to the dc link, whereupon converter 2 draws power from the dc link and injects it into the transmission line at voltage E_C.

The converters must be fully reversible as far as power flow is concerned. This requirement is

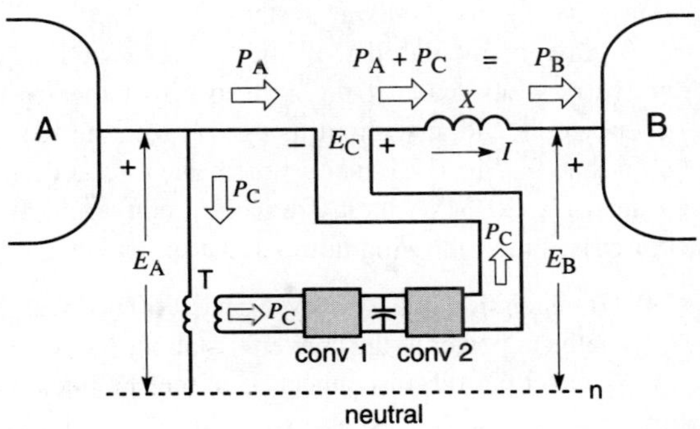

Figure 29.13
Unified power flow controller.

obtained automatically because it is one of the properties of all switching converters. Converter 2 is able to furnish any voltage E_C and phase angle that is required.

In addition to delivering real power to converter 2 (via the dc link), converter 1 can simultaneously absorb or deliver reactive power to region A, just like a static var compensator.

Thus, the two-converter arrangement of Fig. 29.13 constitutes a very versatile power controller and has indeed been named *unified power flow controller* (UPFC). It can replace phase-shifting transformers. Furthermore, on account of its extremely rapid operation, which depends only on the switching speed of the GTOs, the controller can be made to respond to any power flow contingency.

29.6 Static frequency changer

Frequency changers have been in service for many years, mainly to provide low-frequency power for railway transportation systems. The low frequencies were needed to reduce the reactance and, hence, the voltage drop, along the overhead power lines. A further reason was to permit satisfactory commutation of ac series motors that were the prime movers of electric locomotives at the time. These frequency converters always involved rotating machines, an example of which is given in Chapter 17, Fig. 17.2. It shows a rotary frequency converter that transforms the 50 Hz power of an electric utility to the 16 2/3 Hz power needed for a railway system.

Today, the availability of high-power switching converters has made it possible to effect the frequency conversion without using any rotating machines at all. Fig. 29.14 shows the basic circuit diagram of a 20 MW static frequency converter. It comprises the following numbered components:

1. Transmission line, 150 kV, 3 phase, 50 Hz, that delivers power to the converter station. A circuit breaker permits disconnection of the HV line.
2. Two 3-phase wye-delta-delta, and wye-delta-star transformer banks that reduce the 150 kV, 50 Hz line voltage to 1190 V for each converter bridge. The tertiary windings are in parallel, connected to harmonic filters (3). The filters also produce the reactive power absorbed by the converters.
3. Series-tuned filters to provide a low impedance path for the harmonic currents generated by the converters (5). Principal harmonic frequencies are 550 Hz, 650 Hz, and higher.
4. Three-phase feeder to each 6-pulse converter. The two converters together produce a 12-pulse output, which reduces the voltage and current harmonics.
5. Two 3-phase, 6-pulse ac/dc converter bridges, connected in series, with grounded intermediate point. The converters are designed for reversible power flow, hence the back-to-back thyristors. This permits energy to be returned to the 150 kV source when trains regenerate braking power on downhill runs. The converters are line-commutated and feed the dc link between points **1, 2.** The dc link operates at a nominal voltage of 2650 V. Thyristor rating: Repetitive peak off-state voltage: 4400 V; mean on-state current: 1650 A.
6. An inductive filter (6) reduces the harmonic ripple of the dc current flowing through it.
7. A dc circuit breaker offers protection in the event of commutation failure of converters (5) when they are operating in the inverter mode (power being fed back toward the 150 kV line).
8. A harmonic filter tuned to 33 1/3 Hz, which is twice the 16 2/3 Hz output frequency. It reduces the 33 1/3 Hz ripple of the dc link voltage. The single-phase power output of the converter station obliges the dc link to deliver pulsed power to the switching converters (10).
9. The capacitor at the input to each single-phase converter acts as a filter and ensures that the converters operate in the voltage-source mode.
10. The 16 2/3 Hz switching converter modules (Fig. 29.15) are single-phase water-cooled units. The GTOs in the converters operate at a carrier frequency of 150 Hz. Thus, the

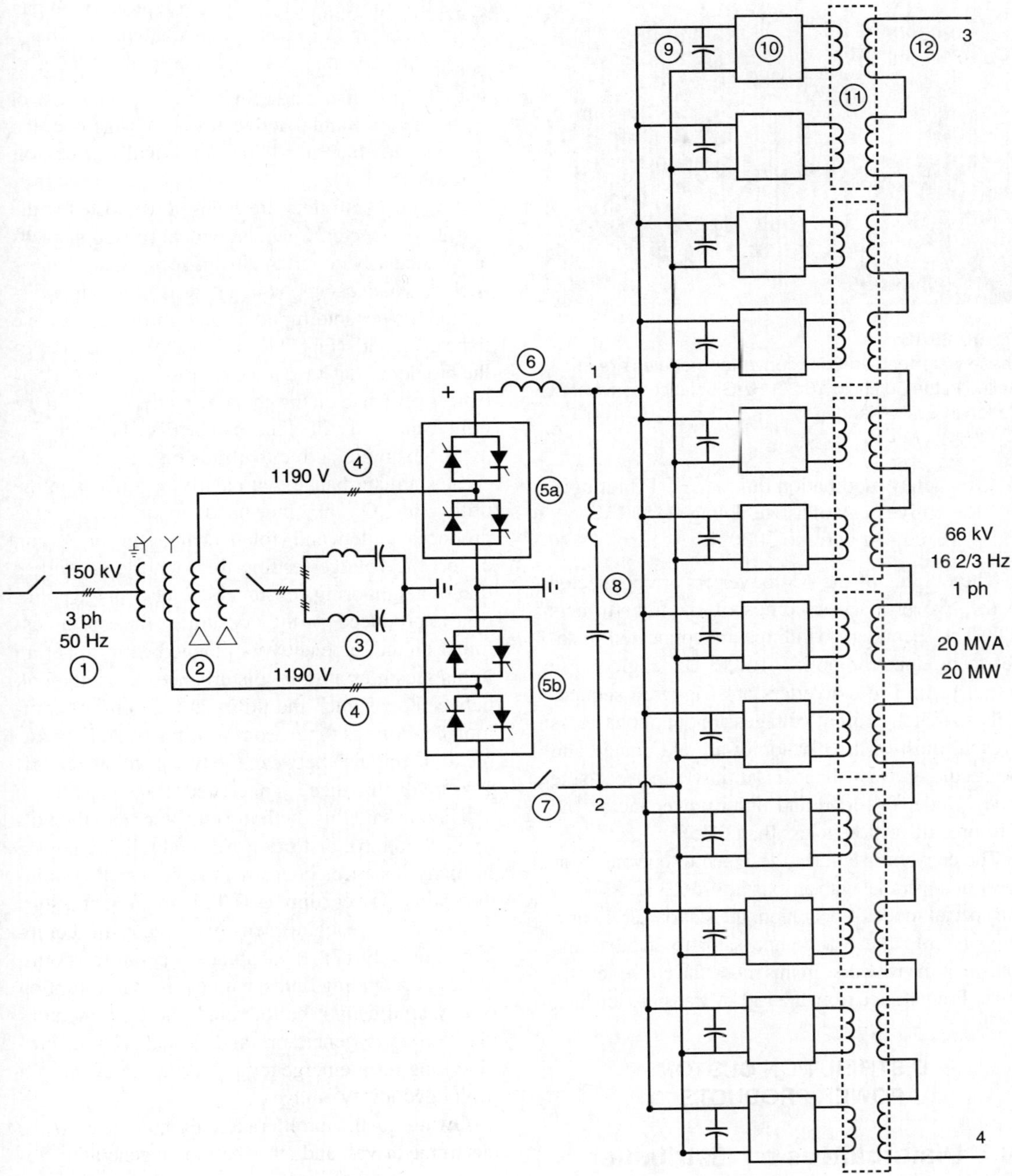

Figure 29.14
Schematic diagram of a 50 Hz to 16 2/3 Hz static frequency converter station. (*Diagram adapted from a circuit diagram in the ABB Review, 5/95 edition*)

Figure 29.15
These water-cooled GTO converter modules are installed in the 50 Hz to 16 2/3 Hz Giubiasco converter station in Switzerland.
(Courtesy of ABB)

frequency modulation ratio is 9. GTO rating: Repetitive peak off-state voltage: 4500 V; peak turn-off current: 3000 A.

The outputs of the 12 converters are connected to the two primary windings of six transformers (11). The secondary windings are connected in series to produce the 66 kV, 16 2/3 Hz single-phase output (12). The converters are triggered sequentially so that the output voltages are out of phase. As a result, most of the harmonics are eliminated and the resulting waveshape is almost a perfect sine wave. Under full-load and unity power factor, the harmonic distortion is less than 0.35%.

The converter station is designed to operate separately or in parallel with an existing 16 2/3 network. In one special mode of operation, the station serves as a *single-phase* static var compensator to stabilize the voltage of the network. In this mode the converter station is disconnected from the 150 kV transmission line.

DISTRIBUTION CUSTOM POWER PRODUCTS

29.7 Disturbances on distribution systems

We have seen that the voltage on high-voltage transmission lines can be regulated by using static synchronous compensators (STATCOMs). These units are connected in parallel with the line. The possibility also exists of injecting a voltage in series with the line, using a UPFC. The latter can control both the active and reactive power flowing over the transmission line, in addition to providing local var control.

Similar controllers are being developed for the distribution sector, where individual consumer needs are particularly important. In this sector, disturbances such as voltage sags, voltage swells, harmonic distortion, power interruptions, and power factor have to be dealt with (Fig. 29.16). Table 29A lists some of the problems that have to be addressed. Some disturbances originate on the consumer side, others on the utility side, and still others can be traced to both.

For example, a tree that falls on a 24 kV feeder creates a disturbance that clearly originates on the utility side. On the other hand, an arc furnace that produces random and violent changes in current can distort the voltage feeding the foundry, as well as that of neighboring consumers. Such voltage pollution is produced on the consumer side, but a customer on the same network plagued with flickering lights sees it as a utility disturbance. Thus, the link between consumer and utility at the point of common coupling is the reason why it is often impossible to distinguish between the two as far as the origin of a disturbance is concerned.

Having said this, both the customer and the utility want to have distortion-free and reliable power. In many instances consumers have installed uninterruptible power supplies (UPSs) to prevent disturbances from reaching sensitive electronic equipment (Fig. 29.17). In hospitals, operating rooms, and airport landing fields, where power interruption of any kind cannot be tolerated, the UPS includes diesel-electric generators and dc batteries to provide long-term emergency power in the event of a prolonged utility outage.

Owing to the proliferation of nonlinear loads, electronic drives, and other harmonic generating devices, some studies have shown that consumers would prefer to have the utility ensure the supply of quality power rather than doing so themselves. However, the reality of the situation is constantly

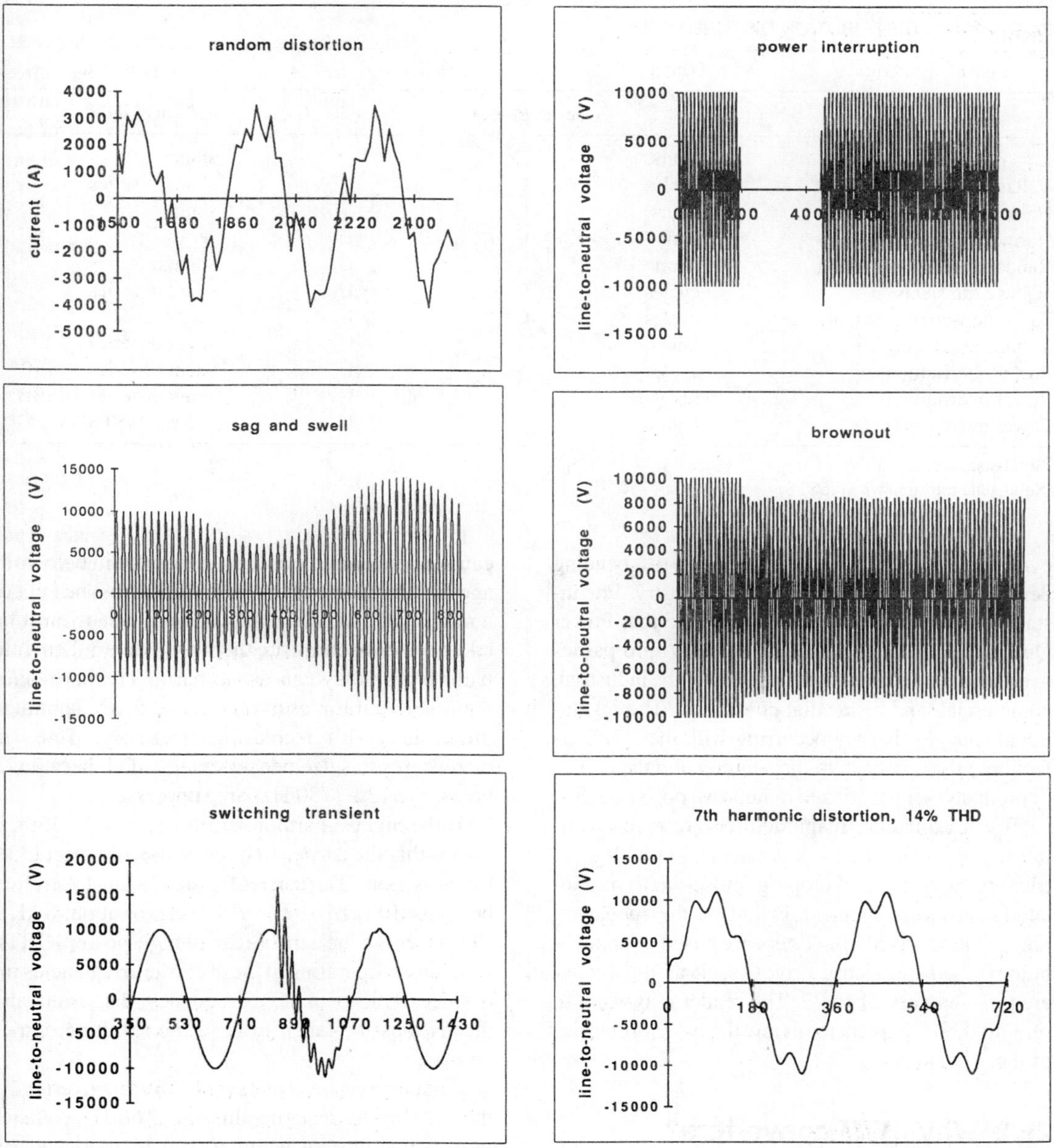

Figure 29.16
Typical disturbances that occur in distribution and transmission systems.

TABLE 29A DISTRIBUTION DISTURBANCES

Nature of disturbance	Duration	Origin		Compensation
		consumer side (C)	utility side (U)	(shunt or series)
Low power factor	hours	C		shunt
Voltage swells and sags	cycles	C	U	shunt or series
Harmonics (current)	hours	C		shunt
Harmonics (voltage)	hours	C	U	series
Random voltage distortion	hours	C	U	shunt or series
Voltage transients	cycles	C	U	shunt or series
High short-circuit current	cycles	C	U	series
Voltage regulation	hours		U	shunt or series
Power interruption	cycles		U	shunt or series + SSB[1]
Power interruption	seconds		U	shunt or series + SBB[1]
Power interruption	hours		U	shunt + SSTS[2]

[1]Solid-state breaker (SSB)
[2]Solid-state transfer switch (SSTS)

evolving, especially in the context of the pending deregulation of the electric utility industry. For instance, the lowest cost solution may be that Power Quality becomes a service provided by third parties to either the distributors of electricity or the industrial, commercial, and residential consumers. The institutional changes that are occurring will, therefore, affect both the approach to the solution *and* the choice of products that are utilized to improve power quality.

Toward this end, manufacturers, research institutes, and universities—in collaboration with electric utilities—are developing pulse-width modulated converters in the kilowatt to the megawatt range. These PWM converters are based upon technology used in electric drives, such as those covered in Chapters 21 to 23. The reader may want to refer to these chapters to review the basic properties of these converters.

29.8 Why PWM converters?

PWM converters are extremely versatile because they can generate a voltage of any shape, any frequency, and any phase by simply applying an appropriate gating signal to the IGBTs. This feature is particularly attractive in distribution systems because of the harmonics that are present in both voltages and currents. These harmonics must be kept to a minimum and, when they appear, means must be taken either to eliminate them or to divert them into paths where they can do no harm. The harmonics are usually multiples of 60 Hz, and their magnitude diminishes with increasing frequency. Thus, in many cases it is deemed acceptable if all harmonics below the 13th (780 Hz) are suppressed.

If the highest harmonic of interest is the 13th, it means that the carrier frequency should be about 10 times as great. The carrier frequency must therefore be about $10 \times 13 \times 60 = 7800$ Hz, or about 8 kHz. This is within the capabilities of high-power IGBTs. Converters operating at these carrier frequencies introduce their own high-frequency distortion and means must be taken to limit the resulting carrier current.

Another reason that favors PWM converters is their ability to generate sinusoidal 60 Hz voltages rather than the rectangular waves produced by GTOs. Consequently, PWM converters can be interfaced directly with the distribution network without having to filter or phase-shift the harmonics of the 60 Hz rectangular pulses. However, in the case of large power converters, where more than one

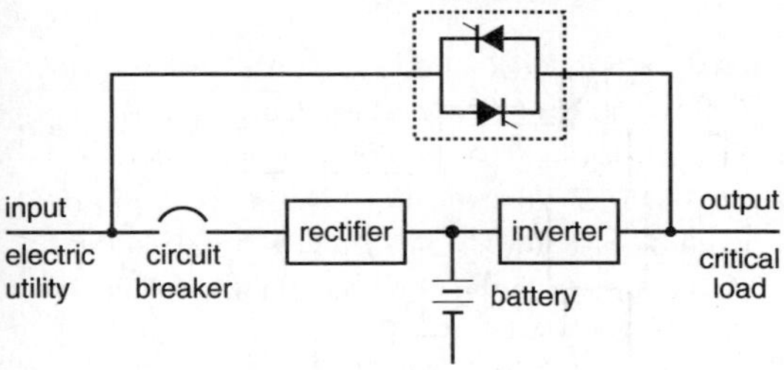

Figure 29.17a
This rudimentary single-line diagram shows the basic elements of an on-line UPS. Power from the electric utility is rectified and the output is connected to the terminals of a battery. The battery serves as a permanent standby source of energy and also ensures a ripple-free dc input to the inverter. The inverter generates the regulated, high-quality, 60 Hz voltage to power the critical load.

If a utility power interruption occurs, the inverter continues to operate, typically for several minutes, drawing its energy from the battery. The static bypass switch serves to automatically connect the electric utility to the load in the event of a failure in the conversion components.

Figure 29.17b
This 18 kVA, 120/208 V, 3-phase, 60 Hz on-line UPS generates an output of 120/208 V, 60 Hz at output power factors ranging from 0.7 lagging to 0.7 leading. The THD is less than 5 percent, even with nonlinear loads. The full-load efficiency is about 90 percent. The low noise level and small size are due to the high switching frequency (≈16 kHz) of the IGBT inverter. If power is interrupted, or exceeds the input tolerance window, the internal battery supplies power to the inverter for up to 10 minutes with no interruption to load. *(Courtesy Square D/Groupe Schneider)*

converter unit is required, phase-shift methods can be used to advantage.

A final reason for using PWM converters is that many distorted waveshapes produced by industrial processes contain voltage and current harmonics that bear no relationship to the 60 Hz line frequency. PWM switching converters are able to generate voltages and currents in opposition to these random distortions and thereby neutralize them.

The signals driving the IGBT gates are derived from feedback circuits wherein the actual voltage or current waveshape is compared with the wanted waveshape. The instantaneous difference between the two becomes the *correction* signal that triggers the gates (Fig. 29.18).

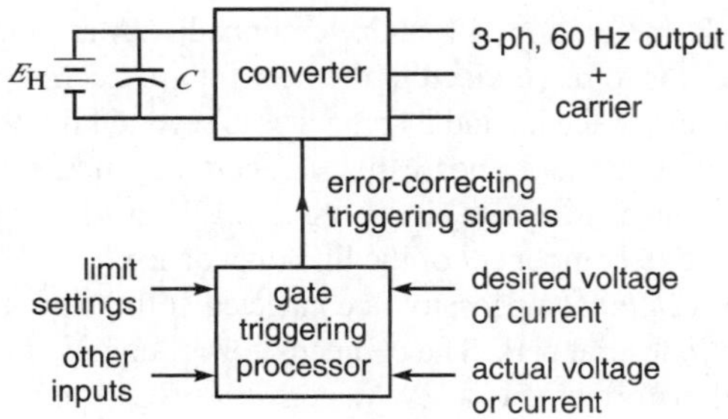

Figure 29.18
Generating a 3-phase voltage or current that is very close to the desired voltage or current.

29.9 Distribution system

In order to see the context in which shunt and series compensators operate, Fig. 29.19 shows a schematic diagram of one phase of a 13.2 kV, 3-phase distribution system composed of a radial feeder and its branches. The feeder emanates from a substation, where it is protected by a recloser, such as described in Section 26.14. The feeder and its branches furnish

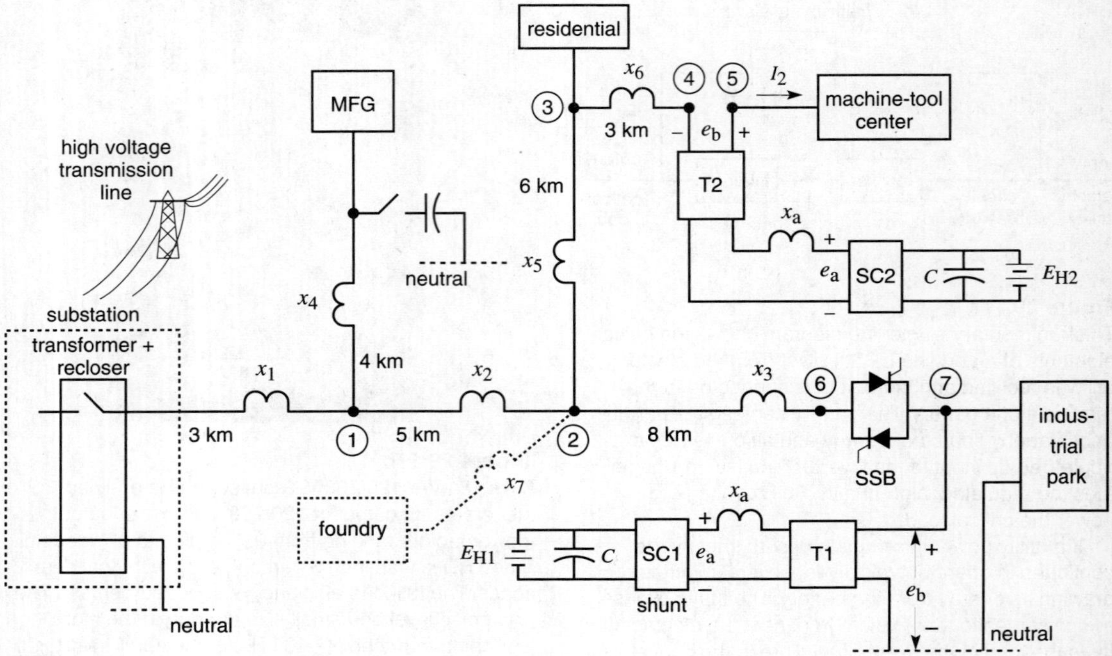

Figure 29.19
One-line diagram of a distribution system.

power to a manufacturing area, a residential area, a precision machine-tool center, and an industrial park. In addition, a foundry equipped with arc furnaces is to be serviced in the near future. Each section of the feeder and its branches is several kilometers long and possesses a certain inductive reactance, designated by $x_1, x_2, \ldots x_6$. We neglect the resistive component of the line impedance.

A *shunt* compensator is connected at the input to the industrial park. The compensator is composed of a transformer T1, a PWM converter SC1, and its battery/capacitor power supply. The transformer has a leakage reactance x_a referred to the secondary side. The converter generates a voltage which consists of a carrier modulated by the much lower frequency component e_a that we are interested in. We assume that the carrier frequency is adequately filtered so that its voltages and currents can be ignored. The voltage e_b at the entry to the industrial park consists of the fundamental 60 Hz component and any residual harmonics, switching surges, and other minor disturbances that the compensator has not been able to eliminate or suppress. The waveshape e_b is, therefore, excellent, thanks to the presence of the compensator.

A solid-state breaker SSB permits the immediate disconnection of the industrial park under certain critical conditions that will be described later.

Turning our attention to the machine-tool center, it is protected by a *series* compensator SC2, located at the service entrance. The compensator is composed of three individual converters connected in series with each line and isolated therefrom by three transformers T2. The diagram shows only one converter. The leakage reactance x_a of the transformer, the voltage e_b across the primary, and the voltage e_a generated by the converter bear the same symbols as in the case of the shunt compensator. However, it is understood that their values differ from those in the shunt compensator.

The proposed foundry is a particularly disturbing load because of the arc furnaces it contains. They produce random changes in current, which ordinarily produce corresponding fluctuations in the terminal voltage. As we will see, a shunt compensator is able to overcome this problem.

The electrical activity of such a distribution system is continually changing, and so the voltages and currents fluctuate. Among the many disturbances that occur, we cite the following:

- Power interruption when the recloser suddenly opens and recloses on a transient fault
- Sudden disconnection of an important load
- Across-the-line start of a large induction motor
- Switching surge when capacitors are turned on
- Transient line-to-ground fault on one phase
- Major disturbance on the high-voltage transmission line that supplies power to the substation

29.10 Compensators and circuit analysis

The PWM converter used in both shunt and series compensators is similar to the converter described in Sections 21.45 to 21.49. We assume a 3-phase unit operating at a carrier frequency of 6 kHz. However, to simplify the explanations we assume a single-phase converter applied to only one phase of the 3-phase system (Fig. 29.20a). The compensator is simplified even further in Fig. 29.20b, where it is shown as a simple voltage source e_a associated with an optional energy storage battery.

To understand the impact of a compensator on a distribution system, it is useful to make a circuit analysis. This is relatively easy, despite the many subcircuits and disturbances that occur in such a system.

In a circuit analysis involving transformers, it is best to use the per-unit approach, which reduces everything to a single voltage level. The transformers "disappear" and the resulting circuit is much easier to visualize and easier to solve. To achieve this result, we simply assume that in our circuit diagrams the transformers have a ratio of 1:1 and that

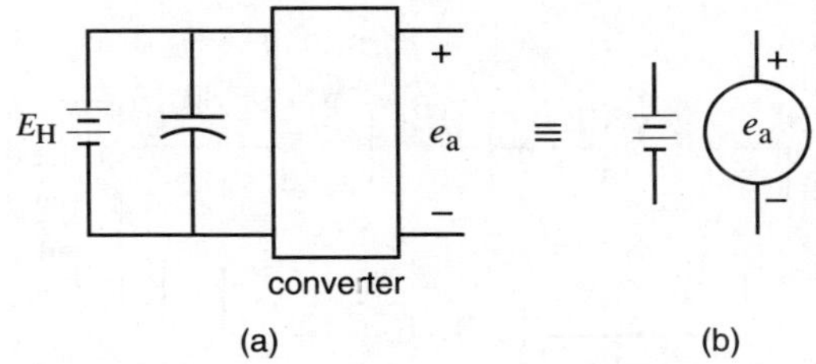

Figure 29.20
Equivalent circuit diagram and symbol of a switching converter. Optional energy storage is represented by battery.

the base per-unit voltage corresponds to the rated compensator voltage.

The choice of shunt or series compensation depends upon several factors, which will be discussed in the ensuing sections. We begin our study with the shunt-type PWM distribution compensator (DSTATCOM), sometimes referred to as *distribution static condenser*, or DSTATCON.

29.11 The shunt compensator: Principle of operation

The PWM shunt compensator has several applications. It can be used as a voltage regulator; short-term power source; harmonic distortion suppressor; power factor corrector and active filter. This section illustrates these applications.

Consider the circuit of Fig. 29.21a, which shows the shunt compensator for the industrial park and a portion of the distribution circuit around it. It is identical to the system of Fig. 29.19, except that the entire network to the left of point **6** has been replaced by an equivalent reactance X_{eq} and an equivalent voltage E_{eq}. This simplification is possible by virtue of Thevenin's theorem. The equivalent voltage E_{eq} comprises the fundamental 60 Hz component e_c and all the transient and harmonic distortions e_d that occur upstream from point **6.**

Fig. 29.21b is a replica of Fig. 29.21a in which the compensator has been replaced by its equivalent symbol and the industrial park is represented by an impedance Z. The SSB is closed. The equivalent

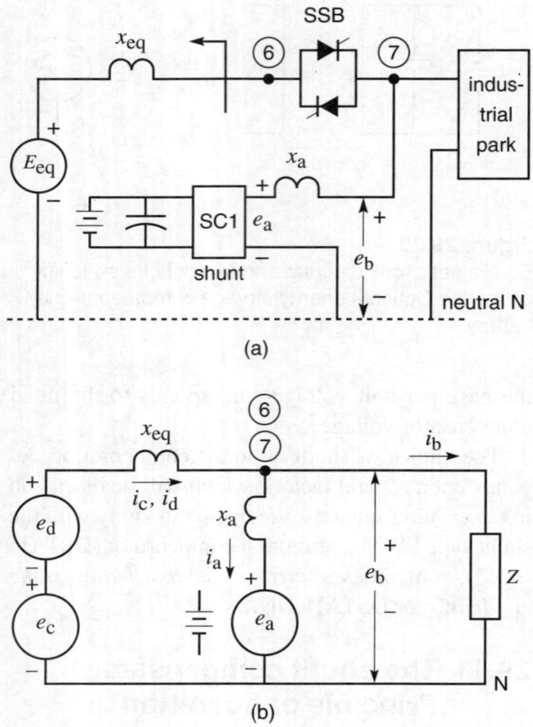

Figure 29.21
Deducing the equivalent circuit for the shunt compensator and the industrial park.

voltage E_{eq} has been replaced by a 60 Hz component e_c and a disturbance voltage e_d. We can now begin our study of voltage regulation, distortion, and other matters of interest.

Voltage Regulation. The purpose of the compensator is to maintain a constant 60 Hz voltage e_b at the service entrance of the industrial park in the face of a varying voltage e_c and a varying industrial load. For the moment we will neglect e_d. The compensator attempts to keep e_b constant by varying the voltage e_a (Fig. 29.22a). Varying e_a will change the compensator current i_a, which in turn will modify i_c, and hence e_b. In the following explanation we write the pertinent equations to determine what happens under these changing conditions. The phasor diagrams will be of particular help.

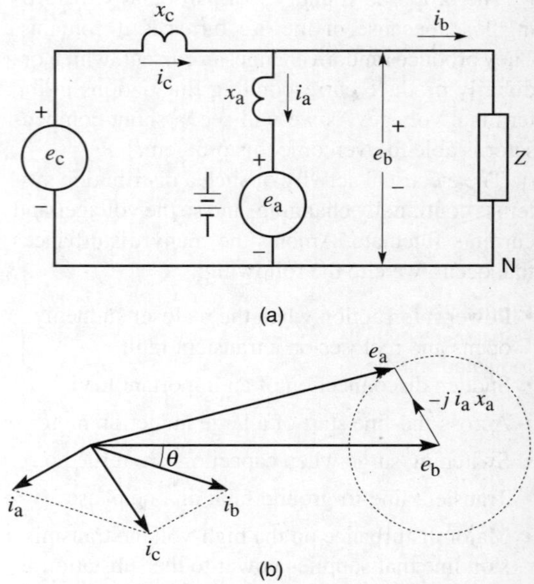

Figure 29.22
Voltage regulation by means of shunt compensator.

The first circuit equation is taken around the right-hand loop of Fig. 29.22a:

$$-e_a - ji_a x_a + e_b = 0$$

which can be cast in the form

$$ji_a x_a = e_b - e_a \tag{29.10}$$

Because e_b is regulated and hence constant, we take it as the reference phasor (Fig. 29.22b). The value of x_a is fixed and the magnitude of i_a can range from zero to $i_{a(max)}$, the maximum rated current of the converter. As the magnitude and phase angle of e_a are varied with respect to e_b, it is seen that the magnitude and phase angle of i_a will also change, subject to Eq. 29.10. In particular, if i_a is kept at its rated value $i_{a(max)}$ while varying e_a, the phasor $ji_{a(max)}x_a$ will trace out the locus of a circle. Thus, by making a relatively small change in the magnitude and phase of e_a, we can cause i_a to rotate through 360°. This observation leads us to a second circuit equation, this time taken around the left-hand loop of Fig. 29.22a:

$$-e_c + ji_c x_c + e_b = 0$$

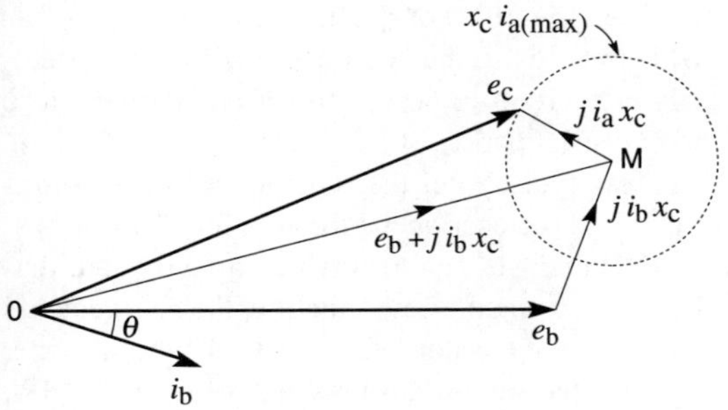

Figure 29.23a
Relationship between the source voltage e_c and the regulated voltage e_b.

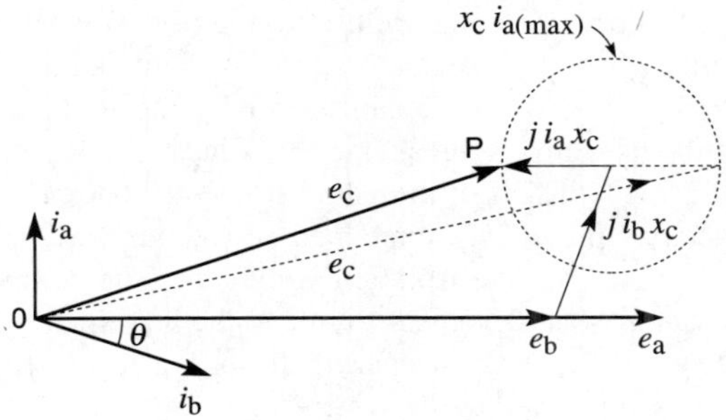

Figure 29.23b
Voltage regulation limits for a given load.

hence

$$e_c = e_b + ji_cx_c$$

however,

$$i_c = i_a + i_b$$

We can, therefore, write

$$e_c = (e_b + ji_bx_c) + ji_ax_c \qquad (29.11)$$

Referring now to Fig. 29.23a, the phase angle θ between e_b and i_b is determined by the power factor of the industrial park. Consequently, for a given load condition, the phasor OM ($= e_b + ji_bx_c$) is fixed. Phasor e_c is, therefore, the sum of phasor OM plus phasor ji_ax_c. But we have just seen that phasor i_a can swing through 360° and that it can have any value between zero and $i_{a(max)}$. It follows that the locus of $x_ci_{a(max)}$ is again a circle. At rated $i_{a(max)}$, the extremity of phasor e_c follows the outline of the circle, as shown in Fig. 29.23b. However, because i_a can be varied from zero to $i_{a(max)}$, it follows that the tip of e_c can lie anywhere within the bounding circle without in any way affecting the magnitude of e_b.

As far as the delivery of power to load Z is concerned, the phase angle between e_c and e_b is unimportant. We are only interested in knowing the maximum and minimum values of e_c that will still enable the compensator to produce the constant output voltage e_b. Furthermore, in order to eliminate the necessity for energy storage, the voltage regulation should be effected without demanding any real power from the compensator. Referring to Fig. 29.22a, this means that i_a must be at right angles to e_a. In turn, according to Eq. 29.10, this implies that e_a—the voltage generated by the compensator—must be in phase with the voltage e_b across the load.

Fig. 29.23b shows the resulting phasor relationships. It is seen that for the given load condition e_b, i_b, the minimum value of e_c corresponds to phasor OP and the maximum to phasor OQ. This is quite a broad range, but it depends upon the value of the line reactance x_c. If the line reactance is small, the diameter of the circle will be small, which reduces the regulatable range of e_c. Therefore, if a large sag or swell occurs in e_c, the compensator may be unable to keep the voltage e_b from changing. It is, therefore, difficult to regulate the variable voltage of a "stiff" feeder by means of a shunt compensator whose kVA rating is small compared to that of the feeder. As we will see, this problem can be resolved by using a series compensator.

Power Interruption. The industrial park represents a load of several megawatts, and the service contract stipulates that power shall not be interrupted by transients lasting 10 seconds or less. Power can be interrupted by either a sudden short-circuit or an open circuit on the feeder. In such cases the shunt compensator can be equipped with a battery to supply energy for the brief period that the feeder is disconnected. However, before supplying power the conductors feeding the park must be isolated from the main feeder by means of a solid-state circuit breaker SSB (Figs. 29.19 and 29.24). It consists of thyristors connected back-to-back, as previously explained in Section 21.23. The reason for the isolation is evident: The compensator was designed to meet the emergency needs of the industrial park and not that of other clients connected to the system.

What might cause a power interruption? Suppose that a snowstorm or hurricane has produced a momentary line-to-ground fault on the main feeder, 4 km from the substation (Fig. 29.19). This will cause the recloser to open after two or three cycles. However, before it can open, the short-circuit will cause the voltage across the affected lines to collapse, which will impact all consumers. To get around this problem, the solid-state breaker (SSB) opens the circuit so quickly (within one-half cycle) that the voltage at point **6** has not had time to collapse. Simultaneously, the battery begins furnishing energy to the compensator, which immediately converts it to 60 Hz power and delivers it to the industrial park.

A few cycles after the start of the intense short-circuit, the recloser opens for, say, 30 cycles (1/2 s) and then recloses again, at which time the fault has cleared. Sensing the new situation, the SSB recloses and the compensator returns to its normal state. Suppose that the park represents a load of 8 MW. During the power interruption, the converter must supply 8 MW × 0.5 s = 4 MW·s = 4 MJ of energy. This is quite within the capability of such energy storage systems, which can typically provide as much as 100 MJ.

The phasor relationships when only the compensator is supplying power to the park are illustrated in Fig. 29.24b. The compensator automatically keeps voltage e_b at its rated value, which means that it must generate a voltage e_a.

Voltage Distortion. Looking now at voltage distortion, consider Fig. 29.25, wherein a harmonic voltage e_d appears in the distribution system. We direct our attention to it alone, neglecting the 60 Hz voltage. The impedances are now higher than at 60 Hz and are therefore labeled x_{cd} and x_{ad}. The compensator will react to eliminate the harmonic voltage from appearing across the load, and so $e_{bd} = 0$. As a result, the distortion current i_{bd} circulating in the load is also zero. It follows that a harmonic current

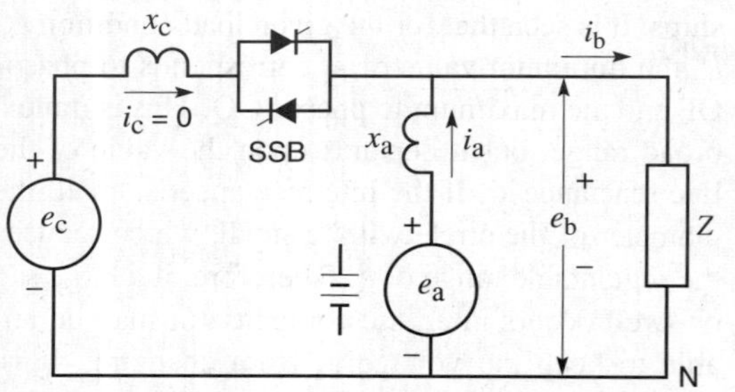

(a)

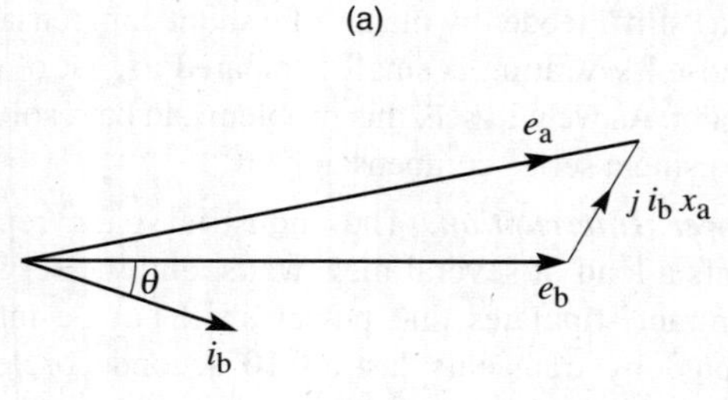

(b)

Figure 29.24
Behavior of compensator during a power interruption.

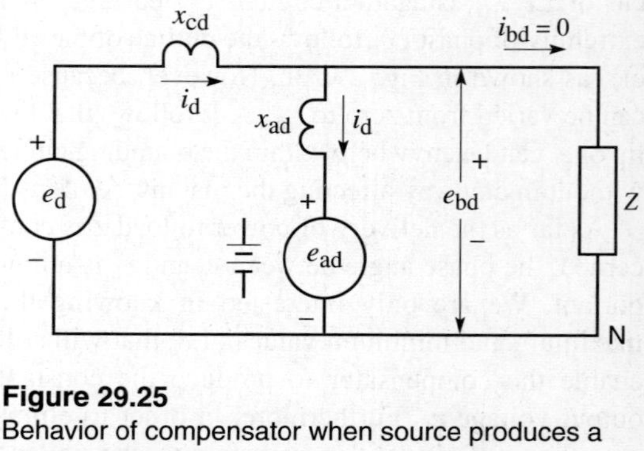

Figure 29.25
Behavior of compensator when source produces a voltage distortion e_d.

i_d will flow in both the source and the compensator. We can write the following equations:

$$-e_d + ji_d x_{cd} + e_{bd} = 0 \qquad (29.12)$$

$$-e_{ad} - ji_d x_{ad} + e_{bd} = 0 \qquad (29.13)$$

From these equations, and because e_{bd} is zero, we obtain

$$e_{ad} = -\frac{x_{ad}}{x_{cd}} \times e_d \qquad (29.14)$$

In most cases x_{ad} is considerably larger than x_{cd}; consequently, to prevent the harmonic voltage from appearing across the load, the compensator must generate a greater harmonic voltage e_{ad} than the originating harmonic voltage e_d.

It should be noted that a similar analysis applies to transient voltages, such as switching surges. For example, suppose that the manufacturing sector (Fig. 29.19) has a power-factor correction system that involves the on/off switching of capacitors. When the capacitors are switched on, it generates for a few cycles a surge of perhaps 5 kV, at approximately 900 Hz. This transient rides on top of the 60 Hz voltage (see Fig. 29.16). As it travels along the feeder, its amplitude will diminish rapidly but may still be substantial when it reaches the input of the industrial park. Again the compensator comes to the rescue, because its 6 kHz carrier frequency is considerably higher than 900 Hz and so the transient voltage can be suppressed.

Power-Factor Correction. The shunt compensator can be used to correct the power factor at the input to the industrial park. To do so, the compensator voltage e_a is arranged so that current i_a lags 90° behind voltage e_b (Fig. 29.26). Referring to the figure, suppose that the compensator has losses represented by resistance r_a. We can then write the following equation:

$$-e_a + i_a r_a + ji_a x_a + e_b = 0$$

hence

$$e_a = ji_a x_a + i_a r_a + e_b \qquad (29.15)$$

The corresponding phasor diagram is shown in Fig. 29.26b. Note that e_a is greater than e_b and lags

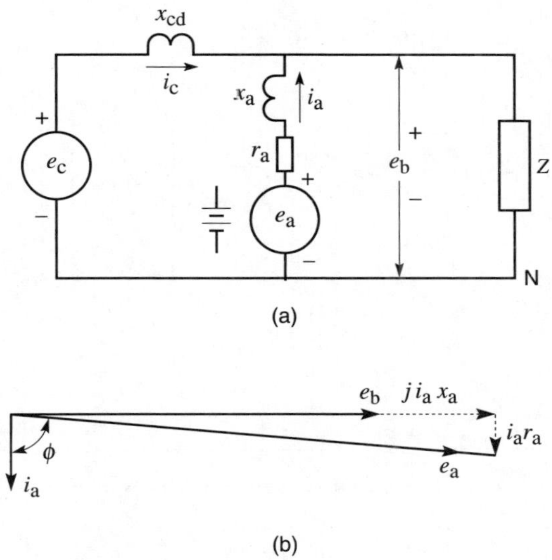

Figure 29.26
Power factor correction.

slightly behind it. Consequently, the distribution system receives reactive power $Q = e_b i_a$ and at the same time it furnishes the compensator with active power $P = e_a i_a \cos \phi$. Under these conditions, the battery supplying the dc input is not necessary. The capacitor is kept charged to the desired dc voltage level by controlling e_a so that it slightly lags or leads e_b, as was previously described for the STATCOM converter.

Nonlinear Load. We now examine the proposed foundry installation. It is fed by a line leading from point 2 on the main feeder (Fig. 29.19). A foundry is a nonlinear load Z (Fig. 29.27a) because the arc furnaces draw a highly fluctuating current i_c during certain phases of their operation. As a result, the voltage drop along the distribution feeder is nonlinear, which in turn produces a distorted voltage e_{bd} at the service entrance to the foundry. Indeed, the current changes so erratically that it is impossible to express the voltage in terms of harmonics and frequency-dependent reactances. However, the instantaneous voltage drop along the line is always equal to its inductance L times the rate of change of

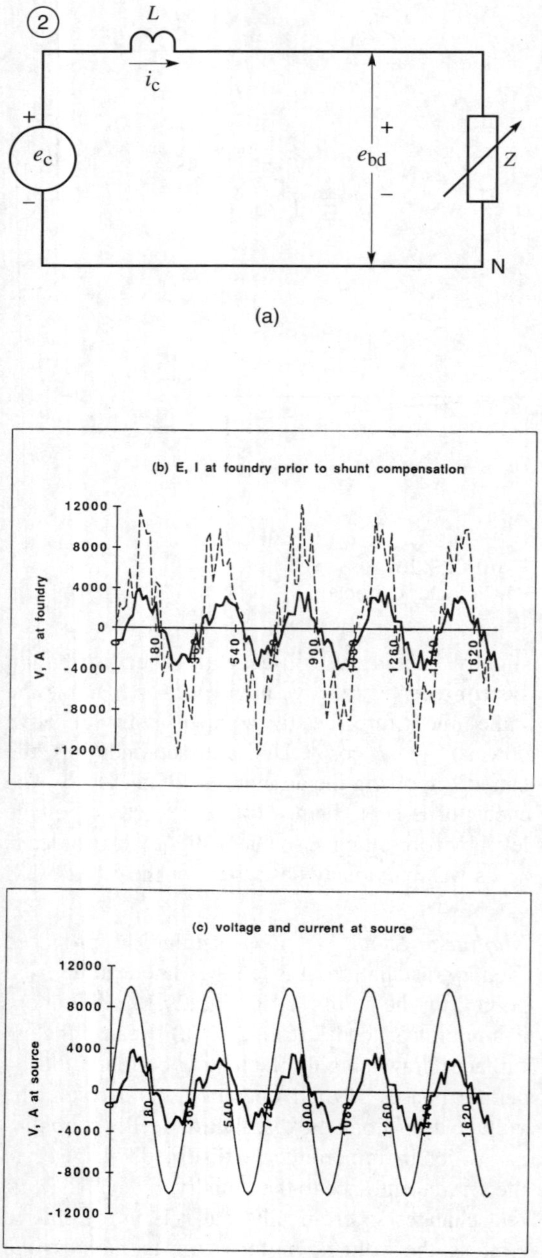

Figure 29.27
Equivalent circuit of foundry, voltages, and currents prior to installation of shunt compensator.

current. The instantaneous voltage e_{bd} at the foundry is, therefore, given by the equation

$$-e_c + L\frac{\Delta i_c}{\Delta t} + e_{bd} = 0$$

hence

$$e_{bd} = e_c - L\frac{\Delta i_c}{\Delta t} \tag{29.16}$$

For example, in this equation, if a feeder has a 60 Hz reactance x_7 (Fig. 29.19) of 11 Ω, its inductance L is given by

$$L = \frac{x_7}{2\pi f} = \frac{11}{2\pi \times 60} = 0.029\ \text{H}$$

Fig. 29.27b shows the current and voltage at the input to the foundry before any corrective measures are taken. The jagged current has an effective value of about 2300 A while the voltage reaches peaks of 12 kV.

Fig. 29.27c again shows the current i_c, together with the *fundamental* component of voltage e_c at point **2.** Although e_c is sinusoidal, the actual voltage at this point of common coupling will be polluted to a certain extent because of the distorted current. The amount of pollution will depend upon the impedance upstream from point **2.** If the impedance is substantial, the waveshape could be unacceptable as far as other consumers are concerned. It is therefore important to improve the waveshape of the current flowing in the feeder, in addition to improving the voltage waveshape at the input to the foundry itself.

Fig. 29.28 shows the foundry, the feeder, and the shunt compensator SC3, together with transformer T3. A current transformer CT monitors the instantaneous current i_c in the feeder, and this signal is fed into the gate-triggering processor. A second input provides the wanted instantaneous sinusoidal current. The processor compares the two signals and generates the triggering pulses to correct the waveshape of i_c.

As a result, the current in the feeder approaches a sine wave. Consequently, the voltage drop along the feeder is now sinusoidal and so, too, is the voltage at the entrance to the foundry. However, the current i_b delivered to the foundry is still distorted because the

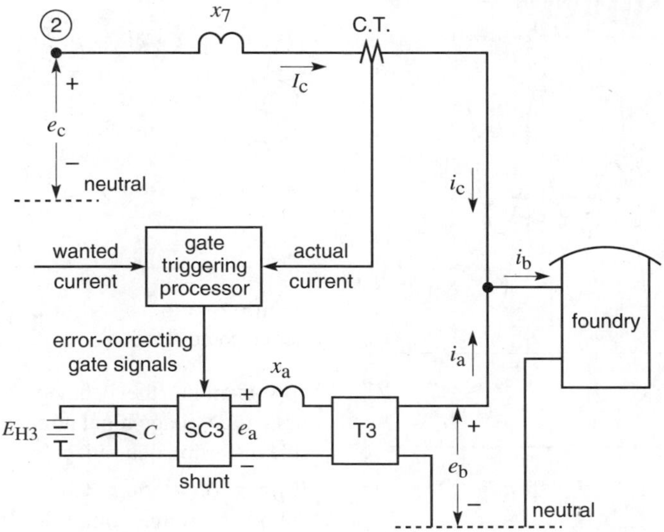

Figure 29.28
Shunt compensator at entrance to foundry.

load is inherently nonlinear. This means that the current i_a supplied by the shunt compensator is actually the distorted portion of the factory current. The compensator is now acting as an active filter.

Fig. 29.29a shows the voltage e_b at the factory entrance and the sinusoidal current flowing in the feeder. Fig. 29.29b shows the same voltage, along with the distorted current supplied to the foundry.

Fig. 29.29c shows the current i_a supplied by the compensator (about 800 A rms) and the corresponding instantaneous power that it delivers. Note that the power of the compensator fluctuates continuously between positive and negative values, reaching momentary peaks of 10 MW during the 80 ms interval covered by the graph. However, the net power, averaged over a few 60 Hz cycles, is zero because of the random nature of the alternating current i_a.

In conclusion, it is seen that the shunt compensator can respond to many different electrical disturbances and thereby ensure quality power to the consumer. However, correcting a power quality problem at one point on the distribution system of Fig. 29.19 does not benefit everyone to the same degree. Thus, a disturbance created by the manufacturing group will still be felt by the residential sector even though it has been eliminated at the entrance to the industrial park. A study of the related consequences of installing a compensator is always advisable.

29.12 The series compensator: principle of operation

The series compensator* (Fig. 29.32) is similar to a shunt compensator; the main difference is that it is connected in series with the feeder instead of in parallel. We recall that in Fig. 29.19 a series compensator is connected at the input to a machine-tool center. The equivalent circuit is derived the same way as was done for the shunt compensator. Thus, in Fig. 29.30, the machine-tool factory is represented by impedance Z, the compensator by voltage e_a, the effective line reactance by x_c, and the source by a 60 Hz sinusoidal voltage e_c and a distortion voltage e_d. We

* Sometimes called *dynamic voltage restorer* (DVR), or *static series voltage regulator* (SSVR).

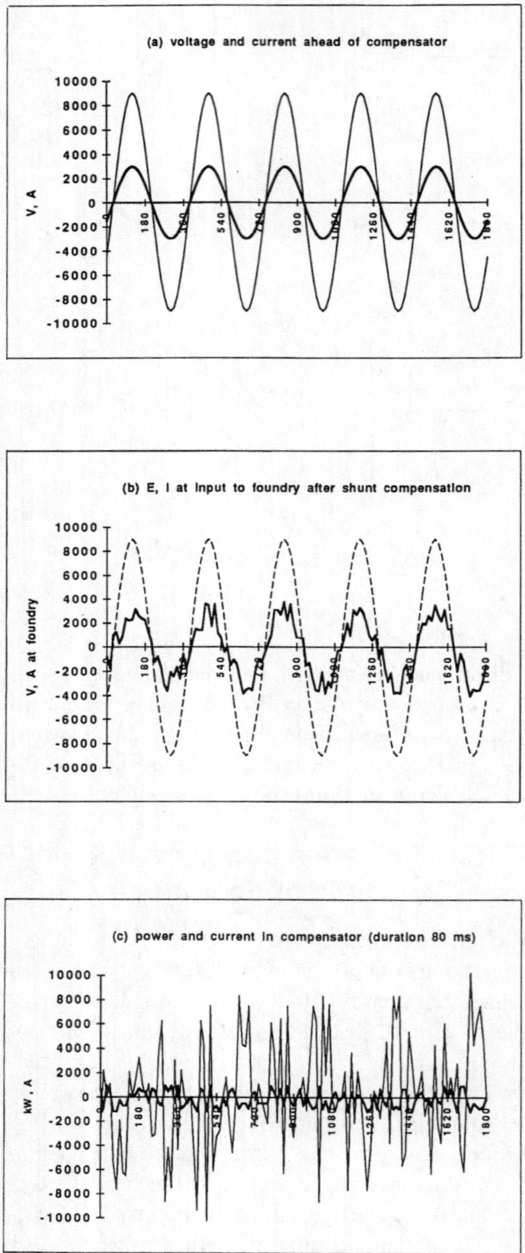

Figure 29.29
Voltages, currents, and converter power after the shunt compensator is installed.

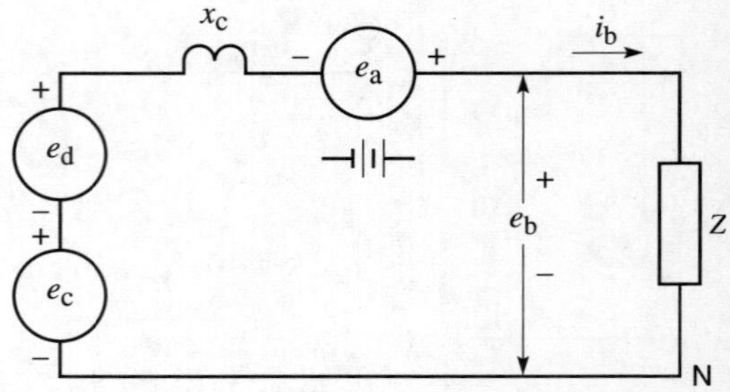

Figure 29.30
Series compensation.

now examine the behavior of the compensator—first, as a voltage regulator, and second, as a supply-side distortion neutralizer.

Voltage Regulation. Consider Fig. 29.31a in which the 60 Hz source voltage e_c acts alone in the circuit (no distortion), and the voltage e_b across the load is held constant by means of the series compensator. The load draws a current i_b. We can write the following equation:

$$-e_c + ji_b x_c + e_a + e_b = 0$$

hence

$$e_c = e_b + ji_b x_c + e_a \tag{29.17}$$

Suppose that i_b lags behind e_b and that the compensator generates a constant voltage $e_{a(max)}$, equal to its rated voltage. This yields the phasor diagram of Fig. 29.31b. The phase of $e_{a(max)}$ can be varied as desired, and so its locus describes a circle with center M.

Given that e_b is held constant, phasor e_c of the source can have any value and phase angle, provided that its extremity falls within the circle for $e_{a(max)}$. The phase angle between e_c and e_b is unimportant; the only objective is to keep the magnitude of e_b constant. In achieving this result, the maximum possible value of e_c is given by phasor OP and the minimum by phasor OQ (Fig. 29.28c). Thus, even if e_c sags and swells over this wide range, the series compensator can still hold the voltage constant across the load.

However, the phasor diagram reveals that the compensator must supply real power to the system when the magnitude of phasor e_c is equal to OQ.

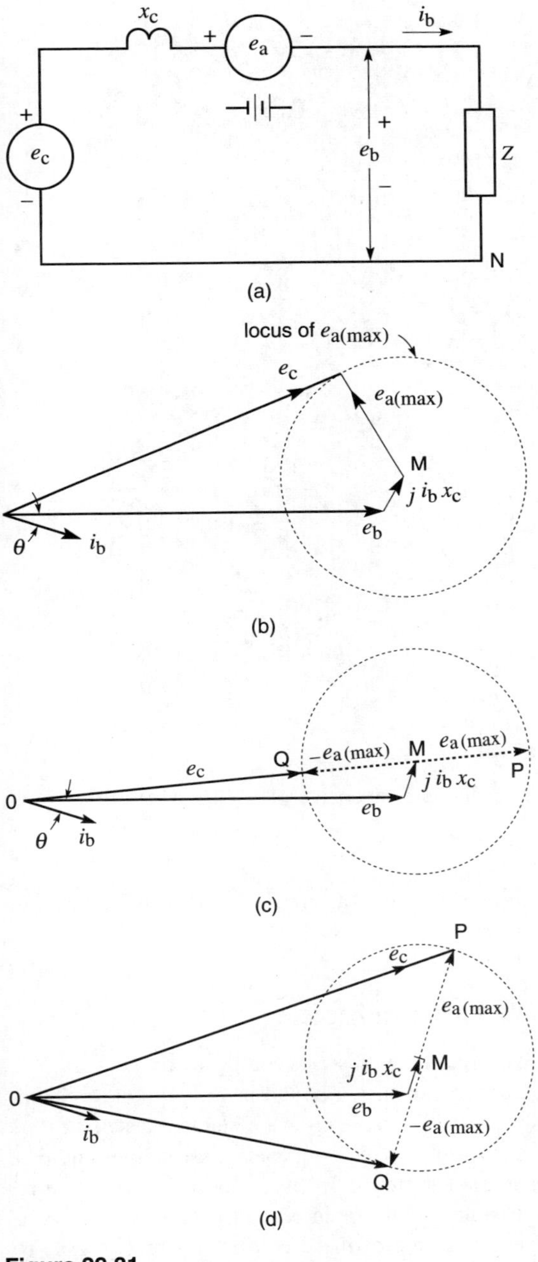

Figure 29.31
a. Voltage regulation with series compensator.
b. Voltage regulation with series compensator.
c. Sag and swell compensation.
d. Quadrature series compensator.

The reason is that phasor $-e_{a(max)}$ has a component that is 180° out of phase with current i_b. It is only when $-e_{a(max)}$ is in quadrature with i_b that the active power of the converter is zero. Similarly, the compensator must absorb real power when e_c is equal to OP. If this happens to be a short-term situation lasting, say, for 10 seconds, the battery will be able to supply or receive the required power. Thus, the full range of e_c from OQ to OP can be regulated. But it cannot be a long-term solution.

Voltage regulation is still possible on a long-term basis without the compensator drawing or delivering real power. This implies that phasor e_a must be kept at right angles to phasor i_b (Fig. 29.31a). The tip of phasor e_c must then follow the line PQ shown in Fig. 29.31d. The magnitude of e_c can, therefore, vary from length OP to length OQ, which is a narrower range than that in Fig. 29.28c. Note that the series compensator can regulate the voltage of even a very stiff (low impedance) feeder.

It should be noted that the voltage disturbances on the three phases may be quite different. For example, a single-phase line-to-ground fault on the network will generate unbalanced voltages on the three phases. Therefore, the three converters that make up the compensator must operate independently of each other in order to produce balanced line-to-line voltages at the entrance to the machine-tool center.

According to statistics, voltage sags account for about 90 percent of the disturbances affecting critical loads on a distribution system. The series compensator can be specifically designed to resolve this problem because it does not have to provide the entire power (or energy) during such a disturbance. Notably, the inverter power rating can be minimized by tailoring its output voltage to the expected depth of sag, while the energy storage is determined by its expected duration.

Consider, for example, a 480 V, 3-phase, 60 Hz feeder that delivers 600 kVA to a critical load. Suppose the expected worst-case voltage sag is 15 percent of the line-to-neutral voltage and that its expected duration is 20 cycles. The series compensator must, therefore, boost the voltage by 15 percent during the sag while still carrying the same line

Figure 29.32
This ±2 MVA converter assembly can be used in either a shunt or series compensator (DSTATCON or DVR). *(Courtesy of Westinghouse Electric Corporation)*

current. Consequently, its power rating need only be 15% × 600 kVA = 90 kVA, and the energy storage required is 90 kW × 20 cycles × (1/60) s = 30 kW·s = 30 kJ. Both the power rating and energy storage requirements are modest. In practice, the series compensator can typically provide boost voltages of 25, 50, 75, and 100 percent.

Thus, a series compensator is often a more cost-effective solution to the sag problem than using a solid-state breaker and a fully-rated shunt compensator plus energy storage.

Current Limiting. In some applications the series compensator can be preset to limit the short-circuit current in a stiff feeder. Its reaction time is so fast that it can immediately introduce a voltage in opposition to the feeder voltage and thereby limit the current flow to an arbitrary low value until the main circuit breaker trips.

29.13 Conclusion

We have seen that series compensators (Fig. 29.32), shunt compensators, and static circuit breakers (Fig. 29.33) enable almost instantaneous control of the power flowing over transmission lines and distribution systems. In every case this is rendered possible by the rapid response of switching converters. Some of these converters are also able to control the waveshape of voltages and currents, thereby filling the role of active harmonic filters.

The converters can also be used as high-power frequency converters in the megawatt range.

Figure 29.33
This 13.8 kV, 3-phase solid-state circuit breaker (SSB) comprises both GTOs and thyristors. The GTOs are rated 600 A and the thyristors are rated for 8000 A.
(Courtesy of Westinghouse Electric Corporation)

These new high-power devices will have a profound impact on the management of power in electric utility systems. As well, they enable dynamic control of system disturbances, thereby increasing the stability of the network. Finally, they enhance the control of electric power, improve power quality, and enable currently unused capacity to be mobilized.

Questions and Problems

Practical level

29-1 What is the main distinction between a GTO and a thyristor?

29-2 Explain why a GTO cannot be used in a high-frequency PWM converter.

29-3 A conductor carrying a 60 Hz current also bears a 23rd harmonic. What is the frequency of the harmonic?

29-4 The solid-state switches in Fig. 29.1a carry an effective ac current of 684 A. Calculate the peak current that flows through one of the thyristors.

29-5 What is meant by a *stiff* feeder?

29-6 A 3-phase switching converter operates from a dc bus of 2400 V. Calculate the approximate rms line-to-line voltage if the converter operates

a. In the rectangular wave mode

b. In the PWM mode with m = 1

29-7 In Problem 29-4 calculate the longest time needed to interrupt the 60 Hz current.

29-8 What is meant by *vernier control* of a TCSC?

29-9 Explain what is meant by
a. Switching surge
b. Brownout
c. Voltage swell
d. UPS

Intermediate level

29-10 A cable carries a 60 Hz current of 870 A and a 5th harmonic of 124 A. Calculate the effective value of the current.

29-11 In Problem 29-10 calculate the maximum possible value of the peak current.

29-12 Referring to Fig. 29.3, calculate the capacitance of the condensers and the inductance of the inductors.

29-13 In Fig. 29.6 calculate the peak 60 Hz line-to-neutral ac voltage if the voltage across the capacitor is 3400 V.

29-14 Referring to the series compensator of Fig. 29.12, it is known that $E_A = 6.9$ kV and $E_B = 7.4$ kV. The series compensator can develop a maximum voltage of 1.5 kV and its rated current is 800 A. Calculate the maximum active power that can be exchanged between regions A and B, knowing that E_A and E_B are in phase.

29-15 Explain the principle of operation of a UPFC.

29-16 Referring to Fig. 29.14, calculate the current flowing in the 150 kV transmission lines when the converter delivers rated single-phase power at 66 kV. The power factor of the 150 kV line is 0.96 lagging.

29-17 A 6700 kW load is backed up by a shunt compensator connected to a group of batteries operating at 240 V. The energy storage is designed to be 40 MJ. Calculate the ampere-hour capacity of the battery pack.

29-18 In Problem 29-17, for how many seconds can the battery deliver power to the load before its terminal voltage will suddenly begin to fall?

Advanced level

29-19 Referring to Fig. 29.31, we want to maintain a line-to-line voltage of 24 kV across the input of a conglomerate 3-phase load having a capacity of 6.8 MW at unity power factor. The feeder has a reactance of 5 Ω per phase. It is known that the source voltage may vary between 25 kV and 26.4 kV.

Calculate

a. The maximum voltage required, per phase, for the series compensator, on the understanding that it neither absorbs or delivers any long-term active power
b. The rated power of the compensator
c. If a brief sag occurs, what is the minimum voltage it can reach before the compensator is unable to keep the output voltage at 24 kV?
d. If a brief swell occurs, what is the maximum voltage it can reach before the compensator is unable to keep the output voltage at 24 kV?
e. If the compensator can deliver active and reactive power for a brief period, what is the minimum voltage in part (c) and the maximum voltage in part (d)?

CHAPTER 30

Harmonics

30.0 Introduction

Voltages and currents in industry are often distorted. The subject of distortion was first discussed in Chapter 2, Section 2.12 and we recommend the reader review it briefly. As was mentioned, the distortion may be caused by magnetic saturation in the core of a transformer, by the switching action of thyristors, or by any other nonlinear load. A distorted wave is made up of a fundamental and one or more harmonics. For example, Fig. 30.1, reproduced from Fig. 2.23, shows a distorted alternating current that contains a 5th and 7th harmonic and several other higher harmonics.

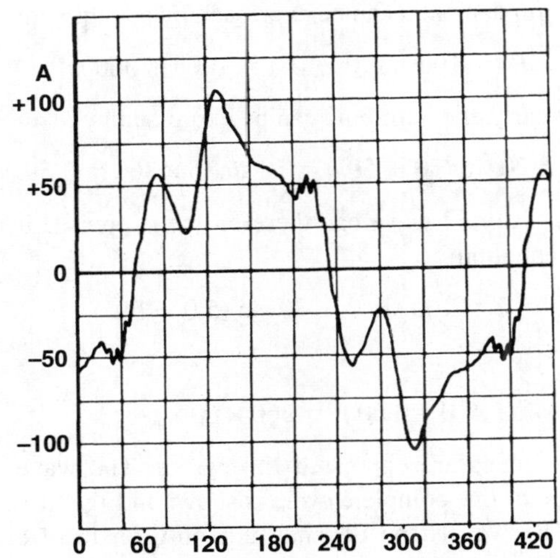

Figure 30.1
Waveshape of a distorted 60 Hz current having an effective value of 62.5 A. The current contains the following components: fundamental (60 Hz): 59 A; 5th harmonic: 15.6 A; 7th harmonic: 10.3 A. Higher harmonics are also present but their amplitudes are small.

30.1 Harmonics and phasor diagrams

We can represent a distorted wave by a composite phasor diagram. It indicates the frequency, amplitude, and initial value of each sinusoidal component. The amplitude is equal to the peak value of the voltage or current. For example, the phasor diagram

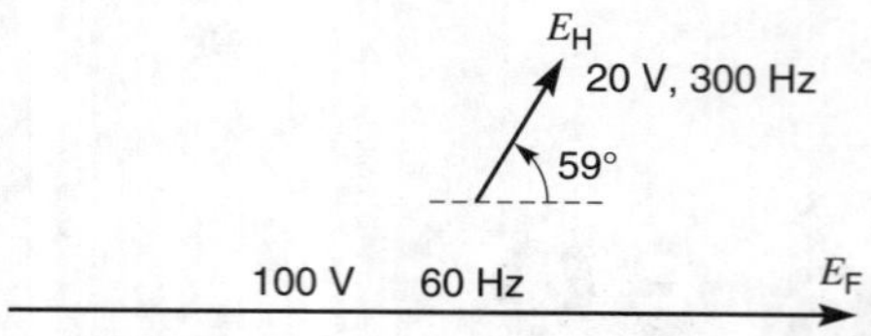

Figure 30.2
A distorted voltage can be represented by phasors revolving at different speeds. Their initial angular position also affects the waveshape.

of Fig. 30.2 represents a distorted voltage composed of two components:

1. A fundamental voltage E_F having an amplitude of 100 V, a frequency of 60 Hz and an initial angle of 0°. We can consider that the phasor rotates ccw at 60 revolutions per second.
2. A 5th harmonic E_H having an amplitude of 20 V, a frequency of 300 Hz, and an initial angle of 59°. This phasor also rotates ccw but 5 times faster than the fundamental.

The fundamental can be expressed by the equation:

$$E_F = 100 \sin(\theta + 0°) = 100 \sin 360\,ft$$

Similarly, the harmonic can be expressed by

$$E_H = 20 \sin(5\theta + 59°) = 20 \sin(5 \times 360\,ft + 59°)$$

The distorted wave can therefore be expressed by the equation:

$$E = 100 \sin\theta + 20 \sin(5\,\theta + 59°)$$

where

$$\theta = 360\,ft = 360 \times 60 \times t$$

The angles are expressed in degrees. The waveshape of one complete cycle is shown in Fig. 30.3.

The waveshape depends not only on the frequency and amplitude of the harmonics but also on their angular position with respect to the fundamental. For example, if the initial angle of the 5th harmonic in Fig. 30.2 is changed from 59° to 180°, the resulting voltage will have the flat-topped shape illustrated in Fig. 30.4.

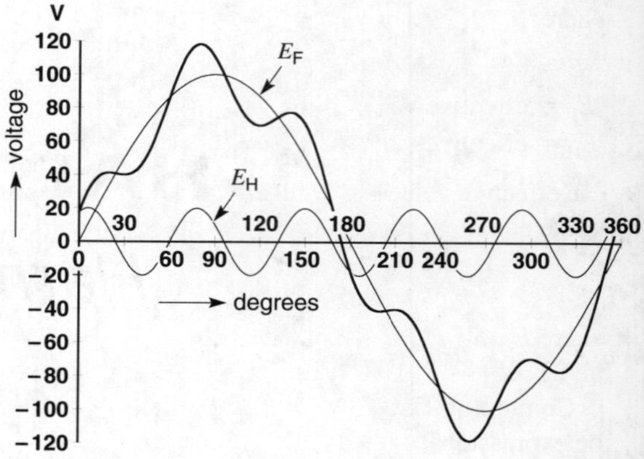

Figure 30.3
Waveshape of the voltage generated by the phasors in Fig. 30.2.

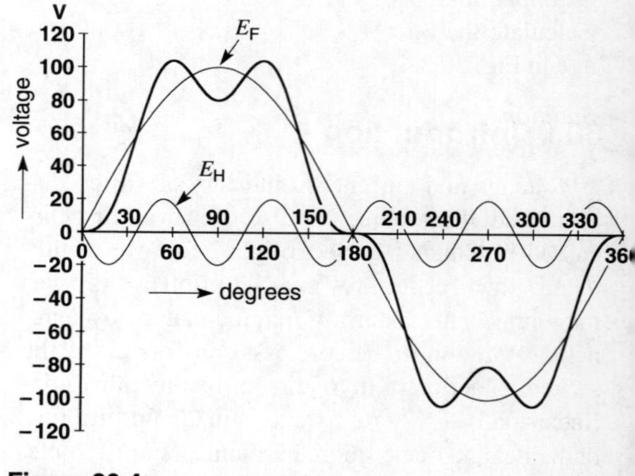

Figure 30.4
Waveshape of the voltage when the initial angle of the 5th harmonic is 180°.

30.2 Effective value of a distorted wave

The effective value of a distorted voltage is given by the equation:

$$E = \sqrt{E_F^2 + E_H^2} \tag{30.1}$$

where

E = effective value of the distorted voltage [V]
E_F = effective value of the fundamental [V]
E_H = effective value of all the harmonics [V]

The effective value E_H of all the harmonics is given by the equation:

$$E_H = \sqrt{E_2^2 + E_3^2 + \cdots + E_n^2} \quad (30.2)$$

where E_2, E_3, E_4, . . . E_n are the effective values of the 2nd, 3rd, 4th . . . nth harmonics.

Combining Equations 30.1 and 30.2, we obtain the expression:

$$E = \sqrt{E_F^2 + E_2^2 + E_3^2 + \cdots + E_n^2} \quad (30.3)$$

Similar equations apply in the case of distorted currents.

Example 30-1

Calculate the effective value of the distorted voltage in Fig. 30.3.

Solution

Effective value of the fundamental

$$E_F = 100/\sqrt{2} = 70.7 \text{ V}$$

Effective value of the 5th harmonic

$$E_3 = 20/\sqrt{2} = 14.1 \text{ V}$$

Effective value of the distorted voltage

$$E = \sqrt{E_F^2 + E_H^2} = \sqrt{70{,}7^2 + 14{,}1^2}$$
$$= \sqrt{5197} = 72{,}1 \text{ V}$$

Example 30-2

A square wave has an amplitude of 66 V. The amplitude of the fundamental is 84 V. Calculate

a. The effective value of the square wave
b. The effective value of the fundamental
c. The effective value of all the harmonics

Solution

a. Effective value of the square wave is clearly 66 V.
b. Effective value of the fundamental

$$E_F = E_{max}/\sqrt{2} = 84/\sqrt{2} = 59.4 \text{ V}$$

c. Using Eq. 30.1 we obtain

$$E = \sqrt{E_F^2 + E_H^2}$$
$$66 = \sqrt{59.4^2 + E_H^2}$$

from which $E_H = \sqrt{66^2 - 59.4^2} = 28.8 \text{ V}$

The effective value of all the harmonics is 28.8 V.

30.3 Crest factor and total harmonic distortion (THD)

There are several ways of describing the degree of distortion of a current or voltage. Two that are frequently used are *crest factor* and *total harmonic distortion* (THD).

By definition, the crest factor of a voltage is equal to the peak value divided by the effective (rms) value.

$$\text{crest factor} = \frac{\text{peak voltage}}{\text{effective voltage}} \quad (30.4)$$

In the case of a sinusoidal voltage (which evidently has no distortion) the crest factor is $\sqrt{2} = 1.41$. A wave having a crest factor less than 1.4 tends to be flat-topped. On the other hand, a crest factor greater than 1.4 indicates a voltage that tends to be pointy.

By definition, the total harmonic distortion (THD) of a current or voltage is equal to the effective value of all the harmonics divided by the effective value of the fundamental. In the case of a distorted current, the equation is

$$\text{Total harmonic distortion (THD)} = \frac{I_H}{I_F} \quad (30.5a)$$

In the case of a distorted voltage, the THD is given by

$$\text{Total harmonic distortion (THD)} = \frac{E_H}{E_F} \quad (30.5b)$$

From these expressions, it is seen that sinusoidal voltages and currents have a THD of zero.

Example 30-3

The distorted current shown in Fig. 30.1 has an effective value of 62.5 A. Knowing that the fundamental has an effective value of 59 A, calculate

a. The effective value I_H of all the harmonics
b. The total harmonic distortion, in percent
c. The effective value of all the harmonics above the 7th
d. The amplitude of the 7th harmonic

Solution

a. Effective (or rms) value of all the harmonics

$$I_H = \sqrt{I^2 - I_F^2} \qquad (30.1)$$

$$= \sqrt{62.5^2 - 59^2} = 20.6 \text{ A}$$

b. Total distortion factor

$$\text{THD} = \frac{I_H}{I_F} \qquad (30.5)$$

$$= \frac{20.6}{59} = 0.349 = 34.9\%$$

c. Noting the values of the 5th and 7th harmonics given in Fig. 30.1, the effective value of harmonics > 7th is

$$I_{>7H} = \sqrt{I_H^2 - I_5^2 - I_7^2}$$

$$= \sqrt{20.6^2 - 15.6^2 - 10.3^2}$$

$$= \sqrt{74.9} = 8.66 \text{ A}$$

d. Amplitude of the 7th harmonic = $10.3\sqrt{2}$ = 14.6 A.

30.4 Harmonics and circuits

It is important to know how a circuit responds to harmonics. In linear circuits composed of resistors, inductors, capacitors, and transformers, the various harmonics act independently of each other. The fundamental and each harmonic behaves as if the others were not there. In solving such a circuit for a particular harmonic, the voltage sources of the other harmonics, including that of the fundamental, are replaced by a short-circuit. Then, the total rms current in each branch is equal to the algebraic sum of the effective fundamental current and the effective values of the individual harmonic currents.

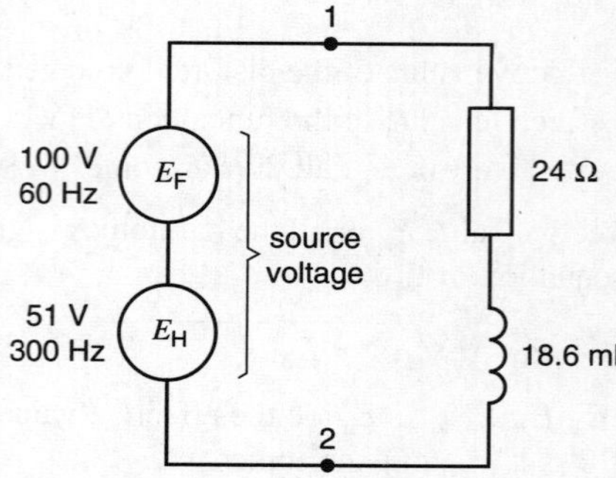

Figure 30.5
Distorted voltage applied to an *RL* circuit.

Example 30-4

Figure 30.5 shows a distorted voltage source composed of a fundamental of 100 V, 60 Hz, and a 5th harmonic of 51 V, 300 Hz.* The source is connected to a resistor of 24 Ω in series with an inductance of 18.6 mH. At 60 Hz the latter has a reactance

$$X_{60} = 2\pi fL = 2\pi \times 60 \times 0.0186 = 7\ \Omega$$

However, at 300 Hz the reactance is 5 times greater:

$$X_{300} = 5 \times 7\ \Omega = 35\ \Omega$$

Since the fundamental and 5th harmonic act independently of each other, we can draw separate circuits to calculate the respective currents and powers (Fig. 30.6 and 30.7). We recall that whenever a voltage source is ignored, it is replaced by a short-circuit. Referring to Fig. 30.6, the impedance of the 60 Hz circuit is

$$Z_{60} = \sqrt{24^2 + 7^2} = 25\ \Omega$$

The fundamental current is

$$I_{60} = \frac{E_{60}}{Z_{60}} = \frac{100}{25} = 4 \text{ A}$$

* In the absence of information to the contrary, the values of voltages and currents are rms values.

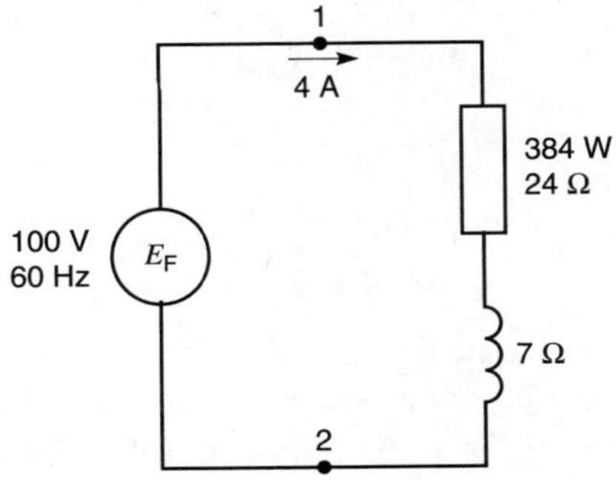

Figure 30.6
Impedances and resulting fundamental current component.

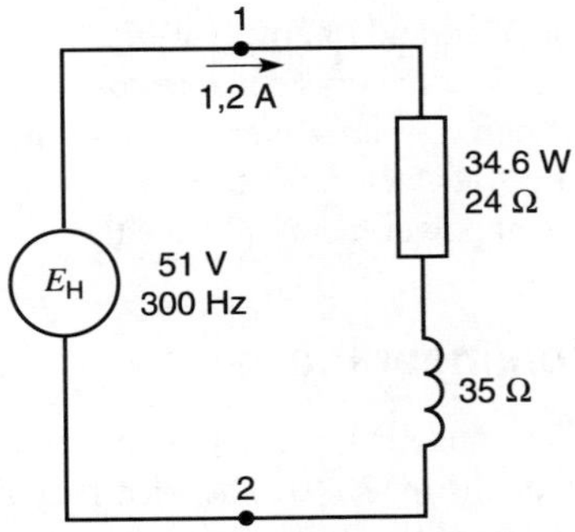

Figure 30.7
Impedances and resulting 5th harmonic current.

Active power dissipated in the resistor

$$P_{60} = I_{60}{}^2R = 4^2 \times 24 = 384 \text{ W}$$

Reactive power absorbed by the reactance

$$Q_{60} = I_{60}{}^2X_{60} = 4^2 \times 7 = 112 \text{ var}$$

Apparent power at 60 Hz

$$S_{60} = E_{60}I_{60} = 100 \times 4 = 400 \text{ VA}$$

Power factor at 60 Hz

$$PF_{60} = \frac{P_{60}}{S_{60}} = \frac{384}{400} = 0.96 \text{ or } 96\%$$

The fundamental current lags behind the fundamental voltage by an angle:

$$\theta_{60} = \arccos 0.96 = 16.3°$$

(In these calculations, the 300 Hz source was short-circuited.)

Let us now consider the circuit of Fig. 30.7 as regards the 5th harmonic. Proceeding the same as before but with the 60 Hz source in short-circuit, we obtain the following results:

Impedance of the circuit at 300 Hz

$$Z_{300} = \sqrt{24^2 + 35^2} = 42.4 \ \Omega$$

The 5th harmonic current

$$I_{300} = \frac{E_{300}}{Z_{300}} = \frac{51}{42.4} = 1.2 \text{ A}$$

Active harmonic power dissipated in the resistor

$$P_{300} = I_{300}{}^2R = 1.2^2 \times 24 = 34.6 \text{ W}$$

Reactive powers and apparent powers are not defined for harmonic voltages and currents. Consequently, we ignore them. Only active harmonic powers are considered.

The harmonic current lags behind the harmonic voltage by an angle:

$$\theta_{300} = \arctan\frac{X_{300}}{R} = \arctan\frac{35}{24} = 55.6°$$

We can now combine the fundamental and harmonic currents and voltages as follows:

Total effective current in the circuit

$$I = \sqrt{I_{60}^2 + I_{300}^2} = \sqrt{4^2 + 1.2^2} = 4.18 \text{ A}$$

The 60 Hz voltage across the resistor

$$E_{R60} = R\,I_{60} = 24 \times 4 = 96 \text{ V}$$

The 300 Hz voltage across the resistor

$$E_{R300} = R\,I_{300} = 24 \times 1.2 = 28.8 \text{ V}$$

Total effective voltage across the resistor

$$E_R = \sqrt{E_{R\,60}^{20} + E_{R\,300}^2} = \sqrt{96^2 + 28.8^2} = 100.2 \text{ V}$$

Total effective voltage of the source

$$E = \sqrt{E_{60}^2 + E_{300}^2} = \sqrt{100^2 + 51^2} = 112.2 \text{ V}$$

The current of 4.18 A and the voltage of 112.2 V (Fig. 30.8) are the values that would be measured by instruments designed to give rms readouts.

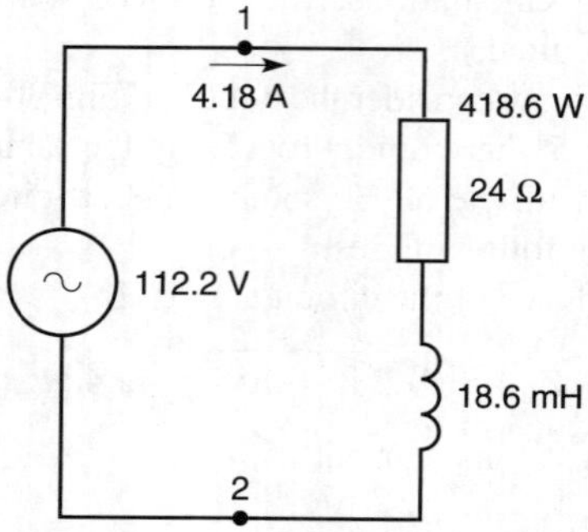

Figure 30.8
Effective voltages and currents due to the fundamental and harmonic components.

Total power dissipated in the resistor

$$P_{\text{total}} = P_{60} + P_{300} = 384 + 34.6 = 418.6 \text{ W}$$

This is also the total active power supplied by the source. It corresponds to the power that a wattmeter would indicate if it were connected in the circuit.

30.5 Displacement power factor and total power factor

The concept of power factor was first discussed in Section 7.9, Chapter 7. Its meaning must be enlarged when distorted voltages and currents are present. The terms *displacement power factor* and *total power factor* are then used.

In a single-phase circuit, the total apparent power is equal to the product of the effective voltage times the effective current. In Example 30.4 and referring to Fig. 30.8, we have

$$S_{\text{total}} = E_{\text{RMS of source}} \times I_{\text{RMS of source}}$$
$$= 112.2 \times 4.18 = 469 \text{ VA}$$

The *total power factor* is equal to the total active power divided by the total apparent power:

$$\boxed{PF_{\text{total}} = \frac{P_{\text{total}}}{S_{\text{total}}}} \qquad (30.6)$$

Since the total active power in our example is 418.6 W, we obtain:

$$PF_{\text{total}} = \frac{P_{\text{total}}}{S_{\text{total}}}$$
$$= \frac{418.6 \text{ W}}{469 \text{ VA}} = 0.893 \text{ or } 89.3\%$$

However, the traditional power factor is given by the cosine of the angle between the fundamental voltage and the fundamental current. When harmonics are present, this power factor is called *displacement power factor.*

$$\boxed{PF_{\text{displacement}} = \cos \phi} \qquad (30.7)$$

In Example 30.4, and referring to Fig. 30.6, the displacement power factor is equal to cos 16.3° = 0.96 or 96%. When no harmonics are present, the displacement power factor, the total power factor, and the traditional power factor all have the same value.

30.6 Nonlinear loads

Consider a sinusoidal voltage E connected to a nonlinear load (Fig. 30.9). The load may be a saturable reactance, a rectifier, or a set of mechanical switches that open and close periodically.

On account of the nonlinearity, the current will not be sinusoidal. It will contain a fundamental component I_F and harmonic components I_H. The fundamental component is produced by the sinusoidal voltage E, but the harmonic components are

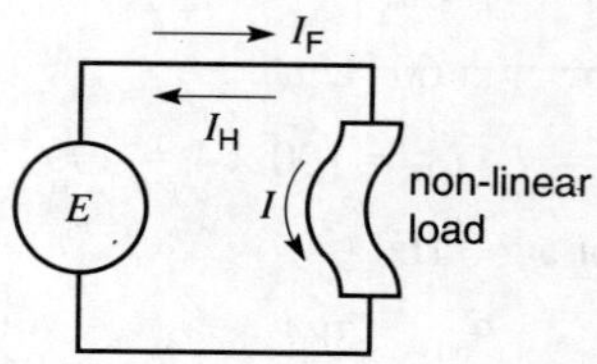

Figure 30.9
A sinusoidal source connected to a nonlinear load produces a fundamental current I_F and the load generates harmonic currents I_H.

generated by the load. Clearly, the harmonic currents flow in the sinusoidal source E as well as in the load.

As far as the fundamental component of current is concerned, it can lag, lead, or be in phase with voltage E. Thus, we can attribute traditional active and reactive powers to this nonlinear load. However, the product of the fundamental voltage and any one of the harmonic currents produces zero power.

30.7 Generating harmonics

The process whereby harmonics are created is quite remarkable. Consider, for example, the circuit of Fig. 30.10a in which a 1000 V, 60 Hz sinusoidal voltage is connected to a 10 Ω resistor in series with a switch. The switch opens and closes periodically in synchronism with the 60 Hz frequency. Figure 30.10b shows that the switch is closed during the last half of each half-cycle. We assume the switch is ideal, producing no sparks and having no losses.

If the switch were always closed, the voltage across the resistor would be sinusoidal, and the current would be 1000 V/10 Ω = 100 A. The power dissipated in the form of heat would be

$$P = I^2R = 100^2 \times 10 = 100 \text{ kW}$$

However, because the switch is open half the time, the power dissipated will be one-half of 100 kW, namely 50 kW. It follows that the chopped sinusoidal current has an effective value of 70.7 A, because $P = I^2R = (70.7 \text{ A})^2 \times 10\ \Omega = 50$ kW.

The synchronous switch does not heat up because the current is zero when the switch is open and the voltage across its terminals is zero whenever it is closed. Consequently, the switch doesn't absorb any net active power.

If we decompose the chopped current into its fundamental and harmonic components, we discover that it contains a fundamental 60 Hz component of 59.3 A that lags 32.5° behind the voltage (Fig. 30.11). Its peak value is 59.3 √2 = 84 A. The displacement power factor is cos 32.5° = 0.843

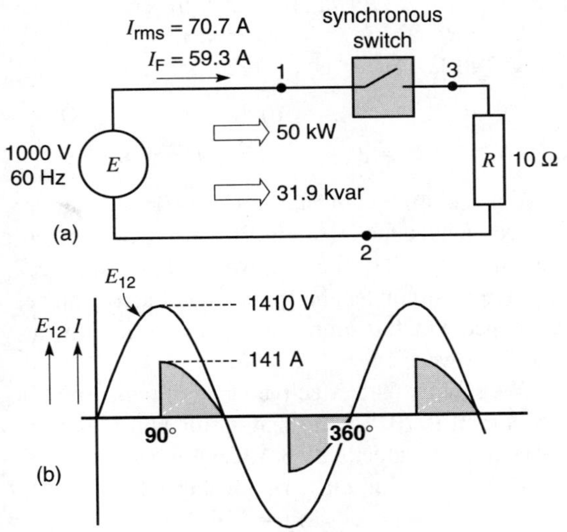

Figure 30.10
a. A synchronous switch in series with a resistor absorbs reactive power when current flow is delayed by the switching action.
b. Waveshape of the chopped current.

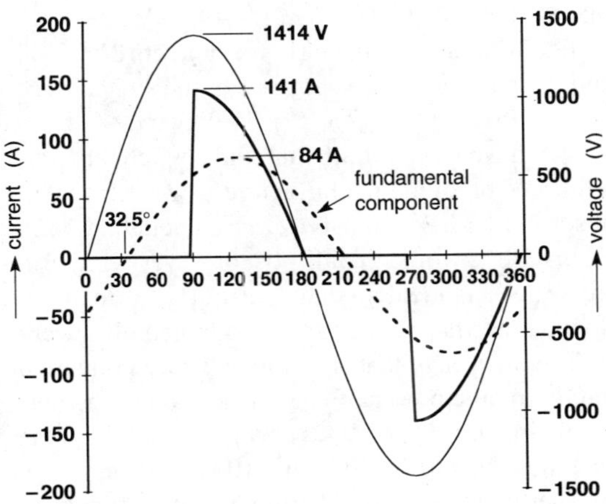

Figure 30.11
The chopped current contains a fundamental 60 Hz component whose amplitude is 84 A and that lags 32.5° behind the voltage of the source.

or 84.3%. Consequently, we obtain the following results:

Apparent fundamental power supplied by the source

$$S = EI = 1000 \text{ V} \times 59.3 \text{ A} = 59.3 \text{ kVA}$$

Active fundamental power supplied by the source

$$P = S \times PF = 59.3 \times 0.843 = 50 \text{ kW}$$

Reactive fundamental power supplied by the source

$$Q = \sqrt{S^2 - P^2} = \sqrt{59.3^2 - 50^2} = 31.9 \text{ kvar}$$

This indicates that the load consisting of the synchronous switch and resistor absorbs reactive power even though there is no magnetic field at all.

The resistor cannot absorb reactive power and so the synchronous switch must be absorbing it. That is a finding of great importance.

As far as the 10 Ω resistor is concerned, it absorbs a *fundamental* active power:

$$P = I^2R = 59.3^2 \times 10 \ \Omega = 35.2 \text{ kW}$$

Since the source delivers a fundamental active power of 50 kW and the resistor only absorbs 35.2 kW of it, the synchronous switch must be absorbing the remainder: $P_{\text{switch}} = (50 - 35.2) = 14.8$ kW.

Furthermore, since the source delivers 31.9 kvar and the resistor absorbs none of it, the switch must also be absorbing it: $Q_{\text{switch}} = 31.9$ kvar.

We have just found that the switch absorbs 14.8 kW of fundamental active power. But if it absorbs 14.8 kW it must *deliver* an equal amount, otherwise it would rapidly become very hot. But we know this ideal switch does not heat up at all. So what has happened to the fundamental power?

The answer is that it is immediately converted into harmonic power of equal magnitude. The harmonic power P_H of 14.8 kW generated by the switch is then absorbed by the 10 Ω resistor.

The fundamental and harmonic power flows are illustrated in Fig. 30.12. Note that the sum of the fundamental power of 35.2 kW plus the harmonic power of 14.8 kW does indeed equal the 50 kW dissipated by the resistor.

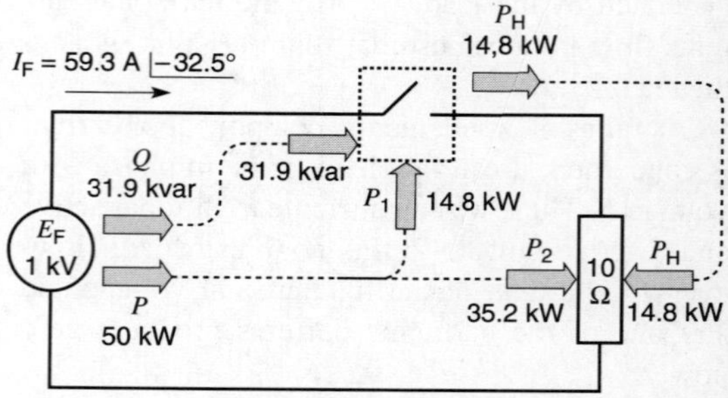

Figure 30.12
Circuit showing the flow of active and reactive fundamental power and the harmonic power P_H.

It is now evident that the switch behaves like a *frequency converter.* It converts the fundamental 60 Hz active power into a series of harmonic powers. It can be shown that the series is composed of all odd-numbered harmonics starting with the third harmonic $f_H = 3 \times 60$ Hz = 180 Hz.

Since we know the switch carries a fundamental current of 59.3 A and that it absorbs $P_{\text{switch}} = 14.8$ kW and $Q_{\text{switch}} = 31.9$ kvar, we can represent it by a resistance R_i in series with an inductive reactance X_i (Fig. 30.13a). Their values are respectively

$$R_i = P/I^2 = 14.8 \times 1000/59.3^2 = 4.21 \ \Omega$$
$$X_i = Q/I^2 = 31.9 \times 1000/59.3^2 = 9.07 \ \Omega$$

As far as the fundamental (60 Hz) components are concerned, the model of Fig. 30.13a is a perfect representation of the circuit. However, the "resistance" R_i merely simulates the fundamental active power absorbed which is immediately converted into harmonic power.

We saw that the effective value of the current in the circuit is 70.7 A and that its fundamental component has a value of 59.3 A. Consequently, the effective value of all the harmonic currents is

$$I_H = \sqrt{I^2 - I_F^2} = \sqrt{70.7^2 - 59.3^2} = 38.5 \text{ A}$$

The harmonic voltage across the 10 Ω resistor is therefore $E = IR = 38.5 \text{ A} \times 10 \ \Omega = 385$ V. Thus, as far as harmonics are concerned, the synchronous switch can be considered to be a distorted voltage

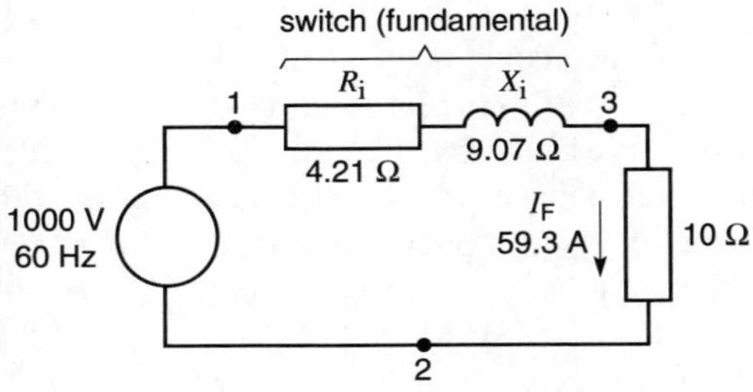

Figure 30.13a
Equivalent circuit for the fundamental components.

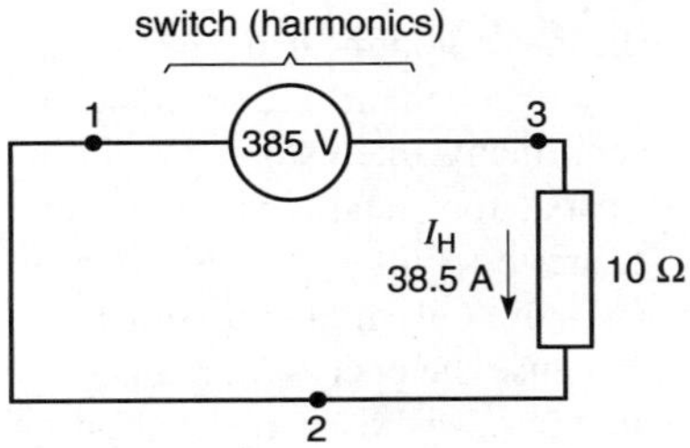

Figure 30.13b
Equivalent circuit for all the harmonic components.

source of 385 V (Fig. 30.13b). The harmonic power developed by this source is 385 V × 38.5 A = 14.8 kW and it comes from the fundamental 60 Hz power that was transformed by the switch.

30.8 Correcting the power factor

Given that the synchronous switch absorbs a reactive power of 31.9 kvar, it is reasonable to assume that a capacitor could supply this reactive power. Let us connect a capacitor of 31.9 kvar in parallel with the source (Fig. 30.14). The capacitor will draw a current of 31.9 kvar/1000 V = 31.9 A. The source will then only have to supply an active power of 50 kW, which means a fundamental current of 50 A in phase with the 1000 V source.

But the presence of the capacitor does not in any way affect the voltage between terminals 1 and 2. Consequently, the chopped current flowing in the switch and the 10 Ω resistor remains unchanged.

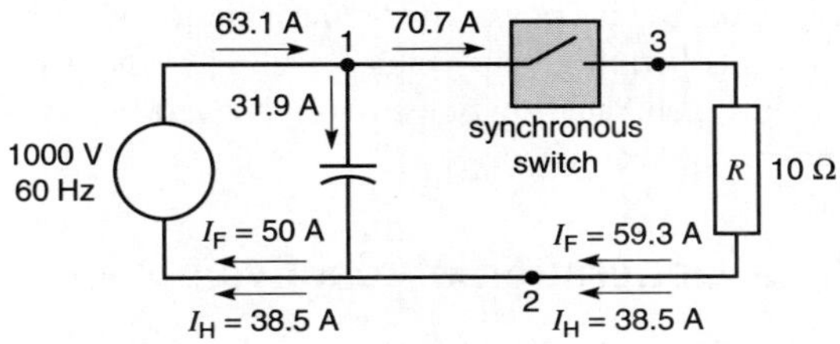

Figure 30.14
The capacitor can furnish the reactive power absorbed by the synchronous switch.

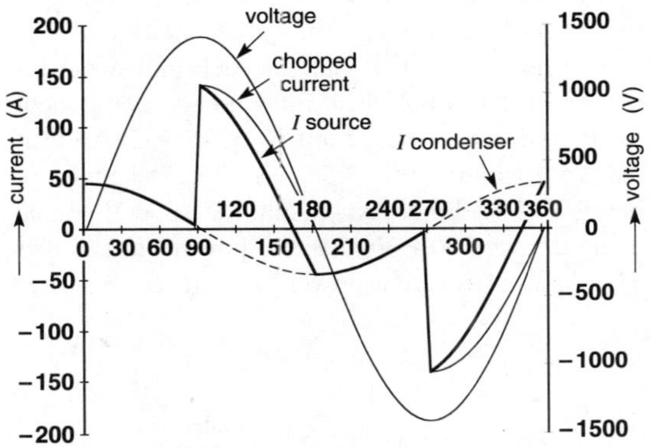

Figure 30.15
Waveshape of the current flowing in the 1000 V source when the capacitor (Fig. 30.14) is in the circuit.

However, the harmonic component of 38.5 A continues to flow in the 1000 V source because it appears as a short-circuit for all harmonics. As a result, with the capacitor installed, the new effective current flowing in the source is $I = \sqrt{(50^2 + 38.5^2)} = 63.1$ A.

Thus, the addition of the capacitor reduces the current in the 1000 V source from 70.7 A (Fig. 30.10) to 63.1 A (Fig. 30.14). The waveshape of the current in the source is equal to the sum of the chopped current flowing in the resistor and switch, plus the sinusoidal current drawn by the capacitor (Fig. 30.15). The peak value of the latter is $31.9\sqrt{2} = 45$ A.

The example we have studied demonstrates the nature and origin of harmonics. It also shows the origin of reactive power in nonlinear circuits. These concepts permit a better understanding of the harmonics generated by electronic converters and other nonlinear devices.

30.9 Generation of reactive power

In the previous section we saw that a non-linear load can absorb reactive power. Depending upon the relationship between the fundamental voltage and fundamental current, a nonlinear load can also *generate* reactive power.

Consider the circuit of Fig. 30.16. It is identical to Fig. 30.10 except that the synchronous switch is closed during the first half of each half-cycle instead of the last half. The fundamental component of the current in the circuit is again 59.3 A but it *leads* the voltage by 32.5° (Fig. 30.17) instead of being 32.5° behind. As a result, the 1000 V source again delivers 50 kW of active power but *absorbs* 31.9 kvar of reactive power. This reactive power can only come from the switch because the linear resistor can certainly not provide it.

As regards the fundamental components, they can be represented by the circuit of Fig. 30.18a. The switch behaves like a resistance in series with a capacitor, even though the "capacitor" does not produce any electrostatic field. As in the case of Fig. 30.13a, the resistance of 4.21 Ω represents the element that absorbs the fundamental power of 14.8 kW, which is immediately converted into harmonic power. As a matter of interest, we show the phasor diagram of the fundamental voltages and currents (Fig. 30.18b).

The fact that a nonlinear device such as a synchronous switch can absorb or deliver reactive power opens many interesting possibilities. Such artificial capacitors and inductors, created by switching, are less bulky than their real-life counterparts and store only minimal amounts of energy (joules). Because the energy stored is so small, the reactive powers can be changed almost instantaneously. The static synchronous compensator studied in Section 29.3, Chapter 29 is a practical example of how reactive power is generated and absorbed by using electronic switches.

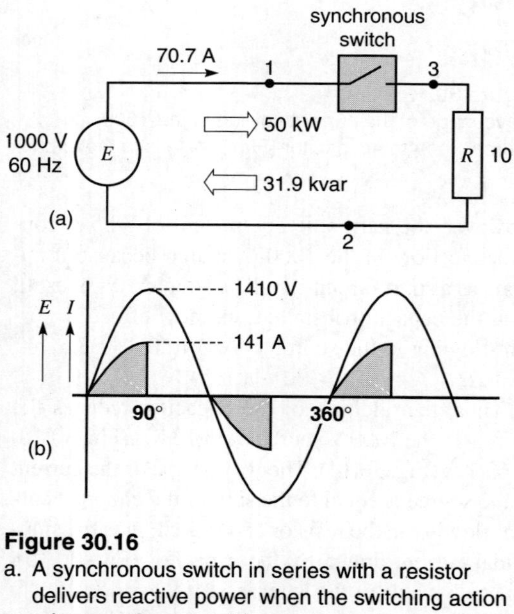

Figure 30.16
a. A synchronous switch in series with a resistor delivers reactive power when the switching action advances the current flow.
b. Waveshape of the current in the circuit.

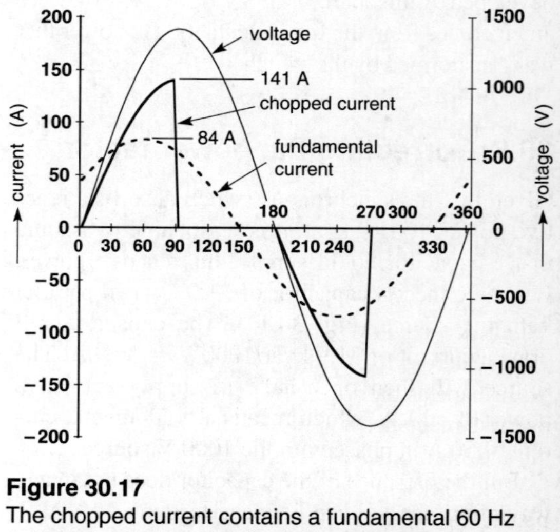

Figure 30.17
The chopped current contains a fundamental 60 Hz component having a peak value of 84 A. The current leads the applied voltage by 32.5°.

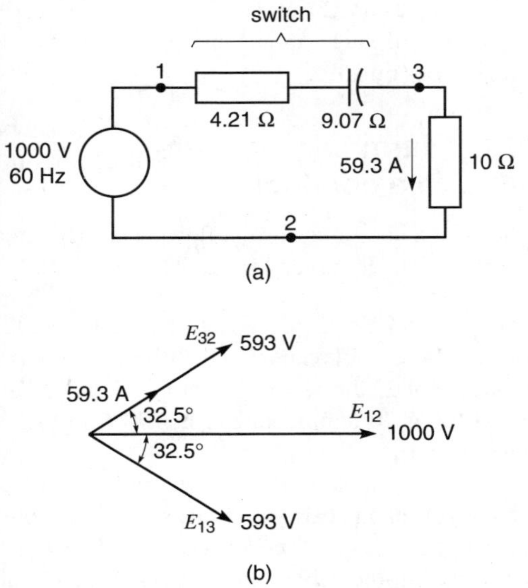

Figure 30.18
a. Equivalent circuit for the fundamental components of Fig. 30.16.
b. Phasor diagram of the fundamental voltages and currents.

EFFECT OF HARMONICS

Now that we know the nature of harmonics, what is their effect on electrical equipment? To illustrate, we will study a few practical examples.

30.10 Harmonic current in a capacitor

When a capacitor carries a distorted current, the voltage across its terminals does not have the same waveshape as the current. The reason is that the capacitive reactance is not the same at the fundamental and harmonic frequencies. Harmonics also affect the losses in the dielectric separating the metal plates. To a first approximation, the losses are proportional to the frequency and to the square of the corresponding voltage across the capacitor.

Example 30-5

A 442 μF, 600 V, 60 Hz capacitor has losses of 20 W when rated sinusoidal voltage is applied across its terminals. The capacitor is installed in a factory where it simultaneously carries a fundamental current of 100 A, 60 Hz and a harmonic current of 80 A, 300 Hz. The harmonic current is 25° ahead of the fundamental. Because the peak is √2 times the effective value, the distorted current can be described by the following equation:

$$I = 100\sqrt{2}\sin\theta + 80\sqrt{2}\sin(5\theta + 25°)$$

We wish to calculate

a. The effective value and THD of the current in the capacitor
b. The effective value and THD of the voltage across its terminals
c. The approximate value of the losses

Solution

a. The effective value of the distorted current is

$$I = \sqrt{(100^2 + 80^2)} = 128 \text{ A}$$
$$\text{THD} = I_H/I_F = 80 \text{ A}/100 \text{ A} = 80\%$$

b. Reactance of the capacitor at 60 Hz

$$X_{60} = 1/2\pi fC = 10^6/(2\pi \times 60 \times 442) = 6\ \Omega$$

Reactance at 300 Hz

$$X_{300} = (60 \text{ Hz}/300 \text{ Hz}) \times 6\ \Omega = 1.2\ \Omega$$

Fundamental voltage across the capacitor

$$E_F = I X_{60} = 100 \times 6 = 600 \text{ V}$$

Harmonic voltage across the capacitor

$$E_H = I X_{300} = 80 \times 1.2 = 96 \text{ V}$$

Total effective voltage across the capacitor

$$E = \sqrt{E_H^2 + E_F^2} = \sqrt{600^2 + 96^2} = 608 \text{ V}$$

THD of voltage

$$\text{THD} = E_H/E_F = 96/600 = 16\%$$

Note that the THD of voltage (16%) is much less than the THD of current (80%).

The equation of the terminal voltage E is deduced from current I, while recalling that the fundamental and harmonic voltages are respectively 90° behind the corresponding currents:

$$E = 600\sqrt{2} \sin (\theta - 90°) + 96\sqrt{2} \sin (5\theta + 25° - 90°)$$

from which

$$E = 600\sqrt{2} \sin (\theta - 90°) + 96\sqrt{2} \sin (5\theta - 65°)$$

Fig. 30.19 shows the waveshape of the capacitor current and voltage. It is seen that the voltage is less distorted than the current. This is to be expected because the reactance at 300 Hz is 5 times less than that at 60 Hz.

c. Knowing that the harmonic and fundamental voltages can be treated separately, we can estimate the losses associated with each. We recall that the losses at 600 V, 60 Hz = 20 W.

The losses due to the 5th harmonic will be calculated on the basis of the 60 Hz losses. We assume they are proportional to the frequency and the square of the voltage. Consequently, the losses at 96 V, 300 Hz are

$$P_{300\,\text{Hz}} = 20\ \text{W} \times \frac{300\ \text{Hz}}{60\ \text{Hz}} \times \left(\frac{96\ \text{V}}{600\ \text{V}}\right)^2$$

$$= 2.6\ \text{W}$$

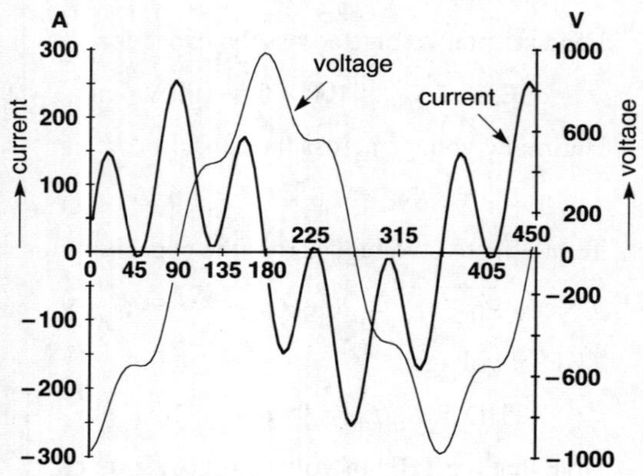

Figure 30.19
Distorted current in a capacitor and resulting voltage across its terminals. See Example 30–5.

Total losses are 20 W + 2.6 W = 22.6 W. The presence of the harmonic current has increased the losses by 13%.

30.11 Harmonic currents in a conductor

Whenever a harmonic current flows in a conductor, it increases the losses and raises its temperature.

Example 30-6

A No. 4 AWG cable having a length of 75 m has a resistance of 25.7 mΩ when it carries a 60 Hz current of 100 A. Its temperature is then 70°C in an ambient of 25°C.

After the installation of an electronic drive, the cable was found to carry an additional 7th harmonic current of 50 A, 420 Hz. We wish to calculate the new losses in the cable and the approximate temperature rise.

Solution

a. Original copper losses due to the current of 100 A

$$P_F = I_F^2 R = 100^2 \times 0.0257 = 257\ \text{W}$$

Assuming the resistance of the cable remains the same when it carries the additional harmonic current, the losses caused by the harmonic component are

$$P_H = I_H^2 R = 50^2 \times 0.0257 = 64\ \text{W}$$

The new losses are 257 + 64 = 321 W, which is an increase of 25% compared to 257 W. Consequently, the temperature rise will increase by 25%. Since the previous temperature rise was (70 − 25) = 45°C, the new temperature rise will be about 1.25 × 45°C = 56°C. It follows that thé temperature of the cable will increase to about (25°C + 56°C) = 81°C.

30.12 Distorted voltage and flux in a coil

In Section 9.2, Chapter 9 we saw that the peak flux ϕ in a coil is given by the equation:

$$\phi_{max} = \frac{E}{4.44\,fN} \qquad (9.2)$$

wherein E is the effective sinusoidal voltage, f is the frequency, and N is the number of turns on the coil. What happens if the applied voltage is distorted? To answer the question, we consider the following example.

Example 30-7

A distorted voltage is connected across the terminals of a coil having 1200 turns. The voltage has a fundamental component of 150 V, 60 Hz and a 3rd harmonic of 120 V, 180 Hz. The harmonic lags 135° behind the fundamental. The respective voltages can therefore be expressed by the equations:

$$E_F = 150\sqrt{2}\,\sin\theta = 212\sin\theta$$

$$E_H = 120\sqrt{2}\,\sin(3\theta - 135°) = 170\sin(3\theta - 135°)$$

We wish to determine

a. The waveshape and effective value of the distorted voltage
b. The waveshape of the flux and its peak value

Solution

a. The waveshape of the distorted voltage is shown in Fig. 30.20a. Its effective value is

$$E = \sqrt{(150^2 + 120^2)} = 192\text{ V}$$

As in previous examples, the respective fundamental and harmonic voltages act independently of each other. Consequently, we can determine the flux created by each, using Eq. 9.2. The fundamental flux has a peak value:

$$\phi_{60\,max} = \frac{E}{4.44\,fN}$$

$$= \frac{150}{4.44 \times 60 \times 1200} = 469\ \mu\text{Wb}$$

The flux is sinusoidal but it lags 90° behind the voltage (as seen in Fig. 9.1, Chapter 9). The equation of the fundamental flux, in microwebers, is therefore

$$\phi_F = 469\sin(\theta - 90°)$$

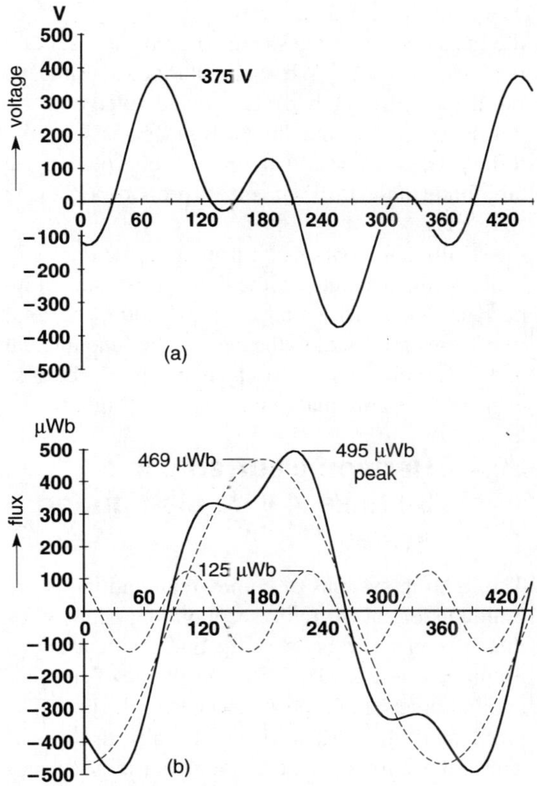

Figure 30.20
a. Distorted voltage applied to a coil.
b. Resulting magnetic flux and its components. See Example 30-7.

In the same way, the peak value of the 3rd harmonic flux is given by

$$\phi_{180\,max} = \frac{E}{4.44\,fN} \qquad (9.2)$$

$$= \frac{120}{4.44 \times 180 \times 1200} = 125\ \mu\text{Wb}$$

This flux also lags 90° behind the harmonic voltage and so its equation is

$$\phi_H = 125\sin(3\theta - 135° - 90°)$$

$$= 125\sin(3\theta - 225°)$$

The total flux inside the coil is equal to the sum of the instantaneous fluxes (Fig. 30.20b). It reaches a peak value of 495 μWb. Note that its waveshape is far different from that of the applied voltage.

Furthermore, the flux waveshape is less distorted. The reason is that for a given voltage, the amplitude of the flux is inversely proportional to the frequency.

If the coil contains an iron core, the core will heat up on account of the hysteresis and eddy-current losses. To a first approximation, the total iron losses are equal to the sum of the fundamental and harmonic losses. To calculate them, the loss curves of the core material must be consulted.

30.13 Harmonic currents in a 3-phase, 4-wire distribution system

The lighting systems of commercial and industrial buildings often use fluorescent and halogen lamps that are connected between the line and neutral of a 3-phase, 4-wire feeder. The same is true of computers and other single-phase electronic devices. The problem is that these devices usually draw non-sinusoidal currents that contain a strong 3rd harmonic. When the loads on the three phases are balanced, the fundamental components cancel out in the neutral conductor because their phasor sum is zero (see Section 8.8, Chapter 8). The same is true for all harmonics *except* those that are multiples of three. Unfortunately, instead of cancelling out, the 3rd, 9th, 15th, etc., harmonics add up in the neutral conductor. Consequently, these triplen components are 3 times greater in the neutral conductor than they are in the lines.

Figure 30.21 shows the waveshape of the current flowing in one phase of a 3-phase, 4-wire feeder that powers the lighting system in a hangar. The lights are connected between line and neutral of the 347 V/600 V system. The currents in the other two lines have the same waveshapes except they are displaced by 120°.

The rms line current is 113 A and the current in the neutral was found to be 45 A. After analyzing

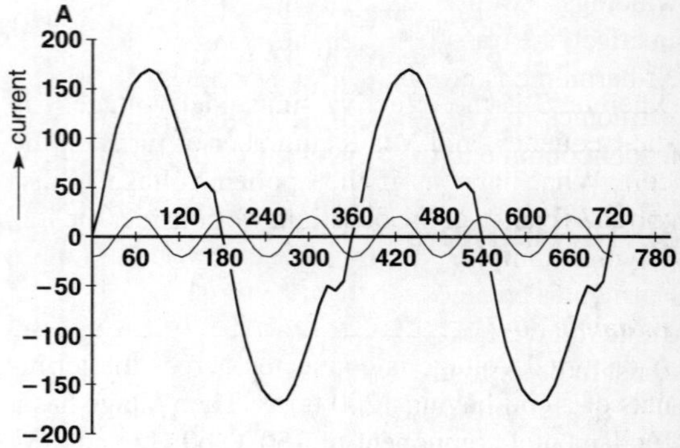

Figure 30.21
Distorted current of 113 A and 3rd harmonic component of 15 A flowing in each line of a 3-phase, 4-wire feeder.

the waveshape of the line current, it was found to have the following components:

fundamental (60 Hz):	112 A
3rd harmonic:	15 A
5th harmonic:	6.6 A
7th harmonic:	2.4 A

The test results confirm that the 3rd harmonic current in the neutral (45 A) is indeed 3 times that in the lines (15 A).

It is easy to understand why the 3rd harmonic line currents add up in the neutral. Figure 30.21 shows the waveshape of one of the line currents and its 3rd harmonic component. Comparing the harmonic with the distorted wave, we see that it repeats every 120°. Since the distorted line currents are themselves displaced by 120°, it follows that the 3rd harmonic currents in the three lines are all in phase. Consequently, they add up in the neutral.

In some cases the 3rd harmonic is so great that the neutral overheats and special measures must be taken to reduce the current. One way to block it is to interpose a transformer connected in delta-star between the source and the load. Under these conditions, the 3rd harmonic on the primary side (delta connection) cannot flow in the lines because the neutral return is absent. However, the 3rd harmonic current will continue to flow in the star-connected windings as well as in the delta-connected windings. In effect, the transformer acts as a filter as far as the 3rd harmonic is concerned. Unfortunately, the other harmonics (5th, 7th, etc.) flowing in the secondary feeder continue to flow in the primary feeder.

30.14 Harmonics and resonance

Harmonics created by nonlinear loads such as electronic converters can produce resonance conditions. In order to understand the problem, we begin with a brief introduction, followed by an industrial application.

Example 30-8

Figure 30.22 shows a factory that is supplied by a medium-voltage 60 Hz feeder that provides a voltage E_S. The feeder has an impedance X_S (see box).

The feeder is connected to a step-down transformer T having a turns ratio of a:1. Its total leakage reactance X_T is referred to the secondary side. The plant is equipped with a variable capacitor bank X_C to keep the power factor at an acceptable level. The value of X_C corresponds to the 60 Hz reactance. The plant also contains some nonlinear loads that generate a harmonic current I_H.

Transposing all elements on the primary side of the transformer to the secondary side, we obtain the equivalent circuit of Fig. 30.23. The procedure for shifting impedances was explained in Section 9.10. Combining X_T and X_S/a^2, we obtain the single 60 Hz inductive reactance X_L.

What is the nature of the circuit seen by the harmonic current I_H? First, the fundamental voltage E_S/a becomes a simple short-circuit (Fig. 30.24).

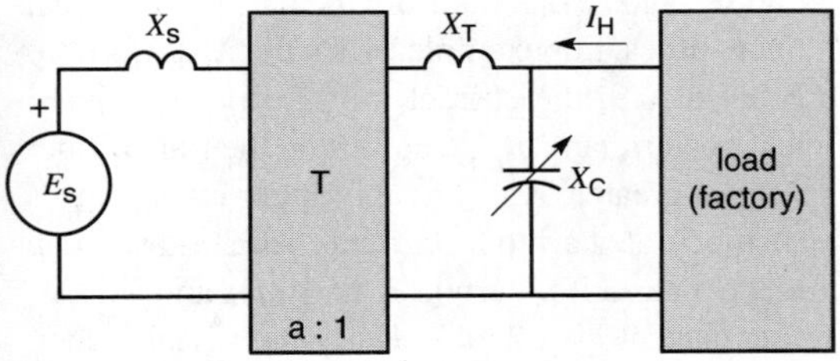

Figure 30.22
Medium-voltage source and transformer connected to a factory that contains some nonlinear loads.

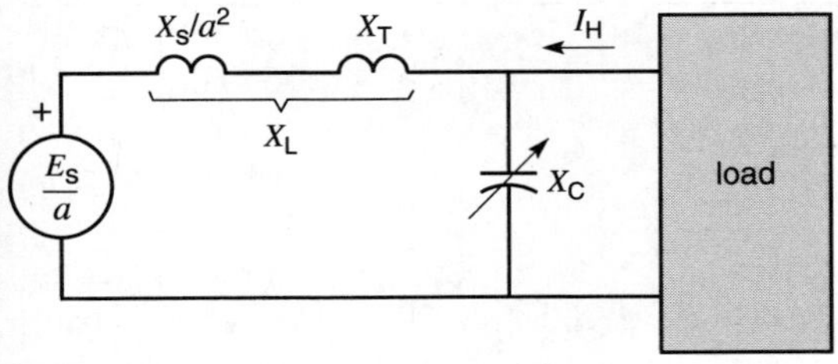

Figure 30.23
Circuit of Fig. 30.22 in which the reactances are transferred to the secondary side of the transformer.

IMPEDANCE OF A THREE-PHASE FEEDER

The impedance of a 3-phase feeder is usually inferred from its short-circuit capability (or short-circuit MVA). It is given by the formula:

$$S_{SC} = \frac{E_S^2}{X_S} \quad (30.8a)$$

or

$$X_S = \frac{E_S^2}{S_{SC}} \quad (30.8b)$$

where

S_{SC} = short-circuit capability of the feeder [MVA]
E_S = line-to-line voltage of the feeder [kV]
X_S = impedance of the feeder per phase [Ω]

The impedance is considered to be entirely reactive. For example, a 3-phase, 25 kV feeder having a short-circuit capability of 52 MVA has an impedance given by:

$$X_S = \frac{E_S^2}{S_{SC}} = \frac{25^2}{52} = 12\ \Omega$$

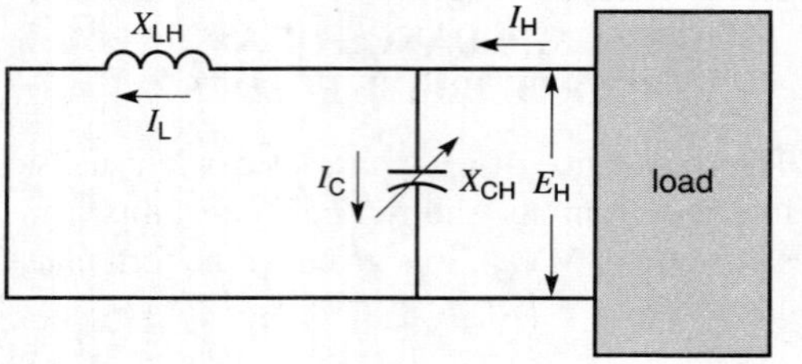

Figure 30.24
Circuit as seen by the harmonic currents.

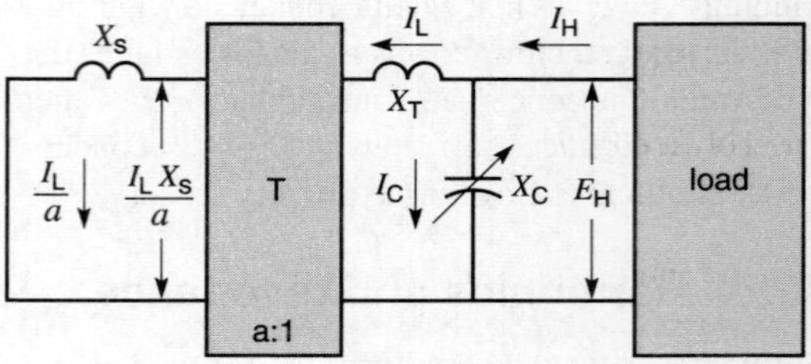

Figure 30.25
Harmonic voltages and currents on the primary and secondary side of the transformer.

The value of the harmonic inductive reactance X_{LH} increases in proportion to the harmonic order h of the harmonic, i.e., with the frequency. Consequently, we can write $X_{LH} = hX_L$.

On the other hand, the harmonic reactance X_{CH} of the capacitor bank decreases inversely with the frequency. Consequently, $X_{CH} = X_C/h$.

Note that X_{LH} is effectively in parallel with X_{CH}. Because the latter is variable, and because the harmonic frequency can have different values, it is clear that a parallel resonance condition is possible for at least one of the harmonics. Perfect resonance occurs when $X_{LH} = X_{CH}$, but even partial resonance (X_{LH} nearly equal to X_{CH}) can have important effects.

Under resonance conditions, current I_C in the capacitor as well as current I_L in the secondary of the transformer can become several times greater than the harmonic current I_H. Consequently, there is a risk of overheating the capacitor as well as the primary and secondary windings of the transformer.

Furthermore, it is well known that in a condition of resonance, the parallel impedance can be very high. Consequently, the harmonic voltage E_H (Fig. 30.24) can reach high values because it is equal to the harmonic current I_H times the parallel impedance. A high harmonic voltage will distort the voltage throughout the plant.

Finally, the harmonic current I_L flowing in the secondary of the transformer is reflected into the primary and from there into the feeder and the utility network (Fig. 30.25). This may be unacceptable to the electric utility. First, the harmonic will increase the losses in the feeder, thereby reducing its ability to carry useful power. Second, the harmonic may produce telephone interference; and third, it may upset sensitive electronic devices of other customers connected to the same feeder.

In order to appreciate the importance of the resonance effect, Table 30A shows several X_{CH}/X_{LH} ratios in the vicinity of resonance and the corresponding I_C/I_H and I_L/I_H multipliers. We see that even partial resonance can multiply the harmonic current I_H many times. For example, when the X_{CH}/X_{LH} ratio is equal to 0.9, the current in the capacitors is 10 times greater than I_H. The current in the transformer is 9 times greater. Thus, the multiplier effect means that a moderate harmonic current I_H of 30 A, say, can produce a capacitor current I_C of 300 A and a transformer current I_L of 270 A. That is no trivial matter.

TABLE 30A AMPLIFICATION OF CURRENT I_H

X_{CH}/X_{LH}	I_C/I_H	I_L/I_H
0.7	3.33	2.33
0.8	5	4
0.9	10	9
0.95	20	19
1	>20	>20
1.05	20	21
1.1	10	11
1.2	5	6
1.3	3.33	4.33

The following example will show the importance of resonance in an industrial context. It represents the potential situation of thousands of installations that contain electronic drives or other loads that generate harmonics.

Example 30-9

A factory, built in the 1980s, is powered by a 1000 kVA, 25 kV/600 V transformer that has an impedance of 6.5%. In order to keep the plant power factor above 95%, four 3-phase, 60 kvar capacitors, located at the service entrance, are automatically switched in and out.

In 1995, after several electronic drives had been installed, the fuses protecting the capacitors began to blow occasionally. Furthermore, it was found that the 3-phase voltage was sometimes distorted. The distortion was particularly noticeable whenever the load drew 600 kVA at a power factor of 80%. All 4 capacitors were then in service, raising the power factor of the plant to above 95%. It was also found that the capacitor currents were sometimes considerably higher than normal.

An analysis of the situation yielded the following information (Fig. 30.26):

1. Number of capacitors in service: 4
2. Nominal 3-phase rating of each capacitor: 60 kvar
3. Line-to-neutral capacitance of each capacitor: 442 μF
4. Line-to-neutral voltage (measured): 360 V
5. Total apparent power of the load: 600 kVA
6. Total active power of the load: 480 kW
7. Total reactive power of the load: 360 kvar
8. Harmonic currents I_H generated by the load:

3rd harmonic:	negligible
5th harmonic:	90 A
7th harmonic:	60 A
11th harmonic:	25 A

9. Short-circuit capability of the 25 kV, 3-phase feeder that supplies power to the factory: 140 MVA

Analysis of the 60 Hz circuit

Before considering the harmonics, let us make a few calculations regarding the 60 Hz aspects in the plant. Fig. 30.27 shows the load conditions for one phase (line to neutral).

10. Apparent power of the load: 600/3 = 200 kVA
11. Active power of the load: 480/3 = 160 kW
12. Reactive power of the load: 360/3 = 120 kvar
13. Capacitive reactance of one capacitor:

$$X_C = \frac{1}{2\pi fC} = \frac{10^6}{2\pi \times 60 \times 442} = 6\ \Omega \quad (2.11)$$

14. Capacitive reactance of all four capacitors: $6\ \Omega/4 = 1.5\ \Omega$
15. Reactive power generated by the four capacitors:

$$Q_C = \frac{E^2}{X_C} = \frac{360^2}{1.5} = 86.4\text{ kvar}$$

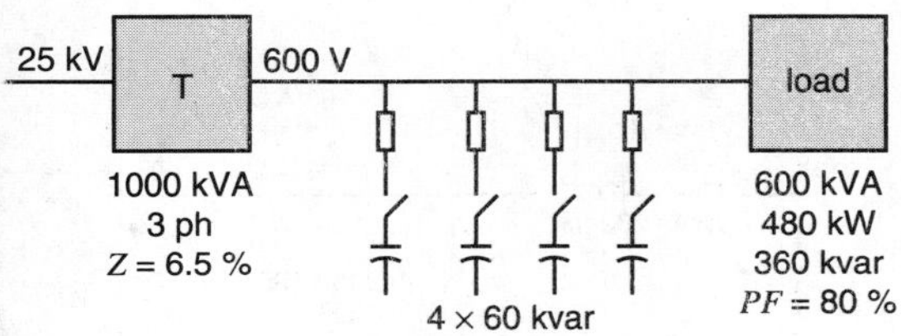

Figure 30.26
Single-line diagram of a factory with its power factor correcting capacitors. See Example 30-9.

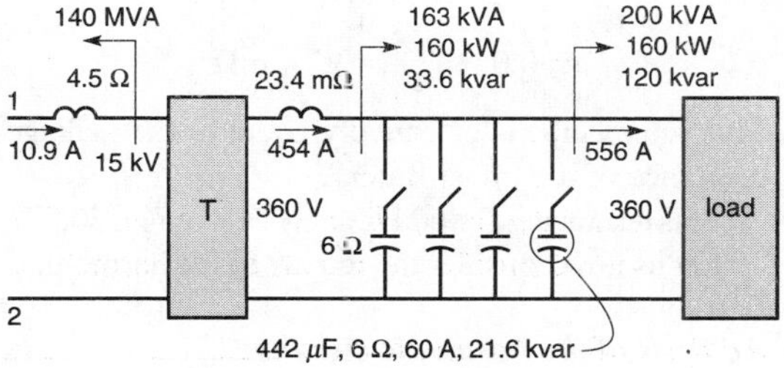

Figure 30.27
Equivalent circuit of the fundamental components.

16. Reactive power supplied by the transformer:

$$Q_T = 120 \text{ kvar} - 86.4 \text{ kvar} = 33.6 \text{ kvar}$$

17. Active power supplied by the transformer:

$$P_T = 160 \text{ kW}$$

18. Apparent power supplied by the transformer:

$$S_T = \sqrt{(160^2 + 33.6^2)} = 163 \text{ kVA}$$

19. Fundamental current on the secondary side of the transformer:

$$I_T = S_T/E = 163\,000/360 = 454 \text{ A}$$

20. Line-to-neutral voltage on the primary side of the transformer:

$$E_{TP} = 360 \text{ V} \times (25 \text{ kV}/600 \text{ V}) = 15 \text{ kV}$$

21. Fundamental current in the primary of the transformer:

$$I_{LF} = 454 \text{ A } (600 \text{ V}/25\,000 \text{ V}) = 10.9 \text{ A}$$

22. Impedance of the 25 kV feeder:

$$X_S = \frac{E_S^2}{S_{SC}} = \frac{25^2}{140} = 4.5\ \Omega \qquad (30.8b)$$

23. Impedance of the feeder referred to the secondary side of the transformer:

$$X_S/a^2 = 4.5\ \Omega\ (600/25\,000)^2 = 2.6 \text{ m}\Omega$$

24. Impedance of the transformer referred to the secondary side (see Sections 10.12 to 10.14):

$$X_T = 6.5\% \times Z_n = 6.5\% \times \frac{E_n^2}{S_n} \qquad (10.9)$$

$$= 6.5\% \times \frac{600^2}{1\,000\,000}$$

$$= 0.0234\ \Omega = 23.4 \text{ m}\Omega$$

This impedance is effectively equal to the leakage reactance of the transformer.

This terminates the 60 Hz analysis (see Fig. 30.27). Let us now consider the impact of the harmonics.

Analysis of the harmonic circuits

25. Leakage inductance of the transformer:

$$L_T = \frac{X_T}{2\pi f} = \frac{0.0234}{2\pi \times 60} = 62\ \mu\text{H}$$

26. Inductance of the feeder referred to the secondary side of the transformer:

$$L_L = \frac{X_S/a^2}{2\pi f} = \frac{0.0026}{2\pi \times 60} = 7\ \mu\text{H}$$

27. Total of the feeder inductance and leakage inductance:

$$L_{total} = 62 + 7 = 69\ \mu\text{H}$$

Fig. 30.28 shows that the 69 μH is effectively in parallel with the capacitors. Their capacitance can vary from zero to 1768 μF in 4 steps of 442 μF. Let us calculate the resonant frequency for each step, using the formula:

$$\boxed{f_{resonance} = \frac{1}{2\pi\sqrt{LC}}} \qquad (30.9)$$

where

L = inductance of the LC circuit [H]
C = capacitance of the LC circuit [F]

When L = 69 μH and C = 442 μF, the resonant frequency is

$$f_{resonance} = \frac{1}{2\pi\sqrt{LC}} \qquad (30.9)$$

$$= \frac{1}{2\pi\sqrt{69 \times 10^{-6} \times 442 \times 10^{-6}}}$$

$$= 912 \text{ Hz}$$

Then, as C successively switches from 884 μF to 1326 μF to 1768 μF, we obtain the corresponding resonant frequencies of 644 Hz, 526 Hz, and 456 Hz.

The resonant frequency of 456 Hz is very close to the 7th harmonic frequency (420 Hz). Similarly,

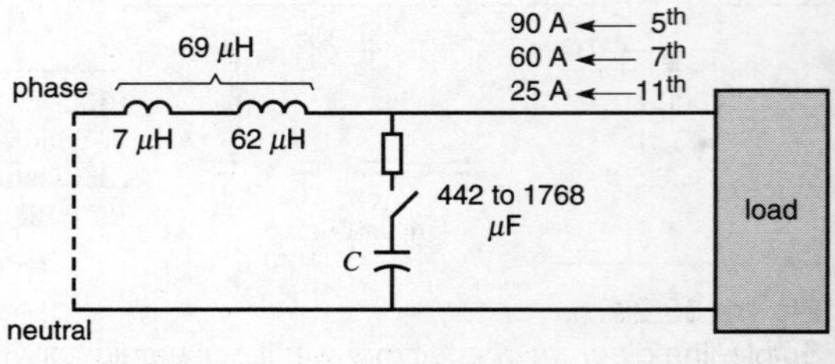

Figure 30.28
Equivalent circuit of the harmonic components.

644 Hz is very close to the 11th harmonic frequency (660 Hz). Thus, the 7th and 11th harmonics are potentially dangerous.

Suppose the four capacitors are in service as shown in Fig. 30.29. As expected, the 7th harmonic then creates a problem. At 420 Hz, the transformer and feeder inductances have a reactance of $2\pi \times 420 \times 69\ \mu H = 182\ m\Omega$. At this frequency, the capacitive reactance of the capacitors is $1/(2\pi \times 420 \times 1768\ \mu F) = 214\ m\Omega$.

The impedance of the two reactances in parallel is

$$Z_{parallel} = \frac{182 \times 214}{214 - 182} \tag{2.17}$$

$$= 1217\ m\Omega = 1.22\ \Omega$$

The 7th harmonic has a value of 60 A and so it will produce a voltage of 60 A × 1.22 Ω = 73 V across the capacitors as well as across the two inductances in series. The harmonic current flowing in the four capacitors is therefore 73 V/214 mΩ = 341 A. Also, the harmonic current flowing in the secondary of the transformer is 73 V/182 mΩ = 401 A. The 60 A harmonic is therefore amplified in both the capacitor bank and the transformer on account of parallel resonance (Fig. 30.29).

The secondary winding of the transformer carries a total rms current:

$$I^2 = \sqrt{I_F^2 + I_H^2}$$

$$= \sqrt{454^2 + 401^2} = 605\ A$$

This is much higher than the load current of 454 A. The primary winding also carries a current that is proportionally greater. Thus, the 401 A harmonic current

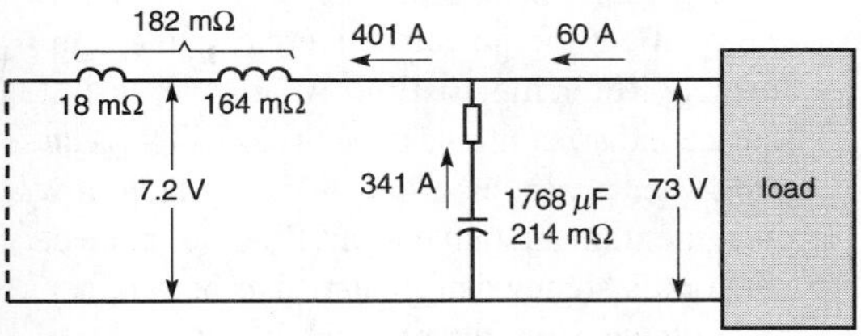

Figure 30.29
Equivalent circuit for the 7th harmonic. Note the large currents flowing in the transformer and the capacitors.

in the secondary is reflected into the primary in the ratio of transformation. The primary harmonic current is 401 × (600 V/25 000 V) = 9.6 A. This unwanted harmonic current is almost as large as the load current of 10.9 A that was calculated previously (Fig. 30.27).

The effective current in the primary winding (and in the 25 kV feeder) is $I = \sqrt{(10.9^2 + 9.6^2)} = 14.5$ A. The transformer will be hotter and the losses greater than if the harmonic were absent.

As far as the four capacitors are concerned, they each carry a harmonic current of 341/4 = 85 A. This current is even greater than the nominal fundamental current of 60 A. Thus, the total rms current carried by each capacitor is $\sqrt{(85^2 + 60^2)} = 104$ A. The capacitors will overheat. If they are protected by 75 A fuses, the fuses will blow after a certain time. This is a worrisome situation, particularly when the harmonic problem is not immediately apparent.

Next, the 73 V, 420 Hz harmonic voltage across the capacitors will be superimposed on the 360 V, 60 Hz line-to-neutral voltage in the factory. The resulting line-to-neutral voltage will be $\sqrt{(360^2 + 73^2)} = 367$ V. Compared to the usual 360 V, this is not a significant increase and would not be noticed by reading an ordinary voltmeter. However, an instrument that can measure harmonic content would indicate that the voltage THD is 73 V/360 V = 20.3%. The distortion will be present throughout the plant and could affect sensitive devices such as computers and electronic drives.

We saw that the 25 kV feeder carries a 420 Hz harmonic current of 9.8 A and a useful 60 Hz current of 10.9 A. This is an undesirable situation as far as the electric utility is concerned because the presence of the harmonic diminishes the loading capacity of the feeder. Furthermore, the distortion could affect the quality of the voltage supplied to other customers.

Note that the 73 V distortion across the secondary is not reflected into the primary according to the ratio of turns. To calculate the harmonic voltage across the primary we note that the voltage across the feeder impedance of 18 mΩ is 401 A × 18 mΩ = 7.2 V (Fig. 30.29). On the primary side, the harmonic voltage is therefore 7.2 V × (25 000 V/600 V) = 300 V. The resulting distortion is 2% of the line-to-neutral voltage of 25 kV/$\sqrt{3}$ = 14.4 kV, which may be just barely acceptable.

We have only examined the effect of the 7th harmonic. A fuller study would require analyzing the impact of all the harmonics. For example, a resonant situation can occur when two capacitors are in service. In this case, the 11th harmonic creates a resonance problem.

In more complex situations a computer program is mandatory to identify the problems that can arise. For example, induction motors appear as inductive reactances between the line and neutral. As the number of motors in service changes throughout the day, random resonances may occur which complicate the matter even further. For this reason, *harmonic filters* are often used to provide a specific low-impedance path for the harmonic currents.

In effect, when it is impossible to suppress the harmonics, they can be channeled through paths where they can do no harm. We briefly examine the nature of these filters in the following section.

30.15 Harmonic filters

We have seen that power-factor correcting capacitors can create a resonance problem when harmonics are present. In three-phase circuits the 5th harmonic is usually the lowest harmonic of interest. Consequently, it is the lowest harmonic that could produce a resonance condition.

One way to eliminate the problem is to add an inductance L in series with each capacitor C so that the combined LC circuit is tuned to the 5th harmonic. Under these conditions the series circuit provides a low-impedance path for the 5th harmonic current. As a result, the 5th harmonic will flow by way of the LC circuit rather than in other parts of the network.

As regards harmonics higher than the 5th, the LC circuit will always be inductive. Consequently, it is impossible to produce a resonance condition. The following example, based upon Example 30-9, shows how this "blocking filter" eliminates the resonance problem.

Example 30-10

Fig. 30.30 shows the inductances (coils) that are added in series with each of the 442 μF capacitors. Their values are calculated as follows:

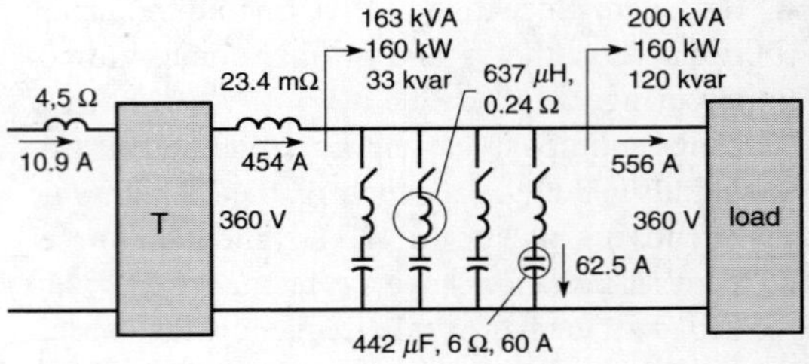

Figure 30.30
Equivalent circuit of the fundamental components when tuned coils are installed in series with the capacitors.

1. Reactance of each capacitor at 60 Hz is 6 Ω; consequently, the reactance at the 300 Hz 5th harmonic = 6 Ω/5 = 1.2 Ω.
2. Desired reactance of the coils at 300 Hz = 1.2 Ω
3. Inductance needed:

$$L = X_L/2\pi f = 1.2/(2\pi \times 300) = 637\ \mu\text{H}$$

Having installed these coils, let us determine the behavior of the system as regards the 60 Hz voltages and currents.

4. Reactance of the coils at 60 Hz:

$$X_{60} = 2\ \pi f L = 2\pi \times 60 \times 637 \times 10^{-6} = 0.24\ \Omega$$

5. Impedance of the series LC circuit at 60 Hz is 6 Ω − 0.24 Ω = 5.76 Ω. The fundamental current flowing in each capacitor is therefore I = 360 V/5.76 Ω = 62.5 A. The 60 Hz line-to-line voltage across the capacitor terminals is

$$E_{60} = 62.5\ \text{A} \times 6\ \Omega \times \sqrt{3} = 650\ \text{V}$$

This is about 10% higher than rated voltage of 600 V.

The addition of the coils does not significantly affect the power delivered by the transformer. Referring to Fig. 30.30, we assume the secondary continues to deliver 163 kVA and 454 A per phase, as it did in Fig. 30.27. However, the fundamental current flowing in the capacitors is somewhat greater than before, as is the voltage across their terminals.

With the LC blocking filters now in place, let us examine the new flow of the harmonics generated by the load.

6. As regards the 5th harmonic with the four capacitors in service, we obtain the equivalent circuit shown in Fig. 30.31. The 90 A current flows entirely in the resonant *LC* branch because its impedance at that 300 Hz is effectively nil. As a result, the 5th harmonic current in the transformer drops to zero. Each capacitor carries a 5th harmonic current of 90/4 = 22.5 A. The harmonic voltage across the terminals of the capacitors is

   $$E_{300} = 90\text{ A} \times 0.3\ \Omega \times \sqrt{3} = 46.8\text{ V}$$

7. As regards the 7th harmonic, and based upon the circuit of Fig. 30.31, the impedance of the coils is 0.3 Ω × (420 Hz/300 Hz) = 0.42 Ω while that of the capacitors becomes 0.3 Ω × (300 Hz/420 Hz) = 0.214 Ω. The impedance of the *LC* circuit to the 7th harmonic is therefore inductive:

   $X_L = 0.42 - 0.214 = 0.206\ \Omega = 206\text{ m}\Omega$ (Fig. 30.32).

8. The 7th harmonic current of 60 A divides between the 182 mΩ and 206 mΩ impedances.

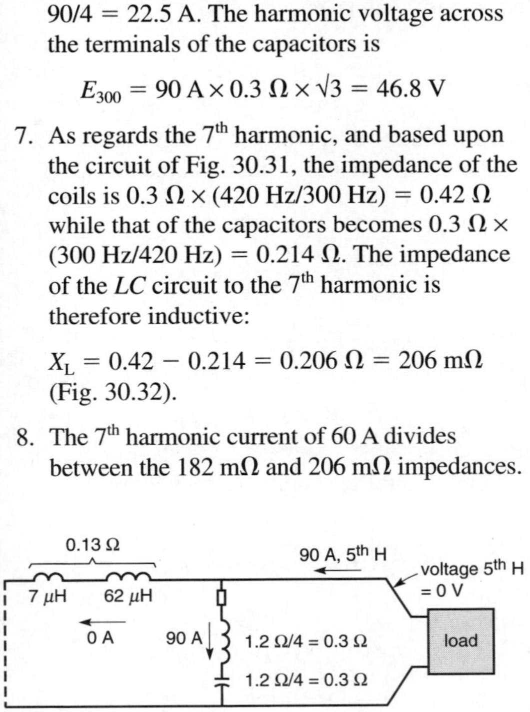

Figure 30.31
Equivalent circuit of the 5th harmonic components when the coils are installed in series with the capacitors.

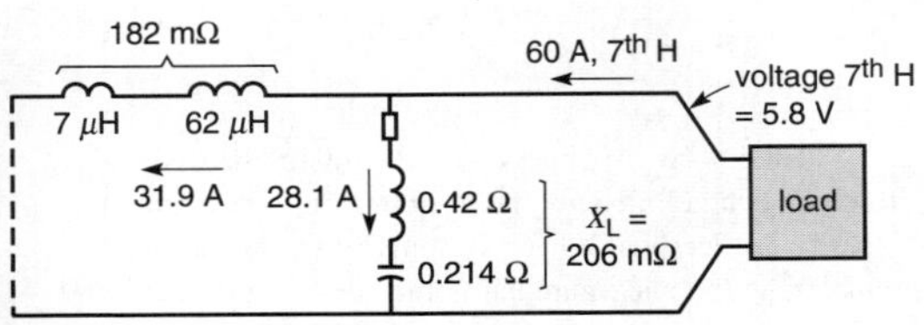

Figure 30.32
Equivalent circuit of the 7th harmonic components when the coils are installed in series with the capacitors.

Consequently, the current in the capacitor bank is now 60 A × 182/(182 + 206) = 28.1 A. This is a huge drop from the previous value of 341 A. The current in the transformer has likewise fallen to 31.9 A from the previous value of 401 A (see Fig. 30.29).

In large capacitor banks of several thousand kvars, some of the capacitor groups are tuned to the 5th harmonic while others are tuned to higher harmonics such as the 7th, 11th, and 13th. The objective is to channel the harmonic flows to specific paths and to minimize them everywhere else in the network, including that of the electric utility.

30.16 Harmonics in the supply network

Harmonics that are generated in a manufacturing plant may find their way into the electric utility network. This produces a voltage distortion that affects the quality of service for all customers connected to the same feeder. To understand the problem, consider the one-line diagram of Fig. 30.33a. It shows the voltage source E_S of an electric utility that provides power to a number of customers A1, A2, A3, A4 by way of a main feeder having a 60 Hz reactance X_S. The feeder terminates at a *point of common coupling* (PCC)*. Fig. 30.33b shows one phase of the 3-phase circuit. Among the customers on the line is a large manufacturing plant A1. It draws a fundamental current I_1 but, on account of some nonlinear loads, it also injects a harmonic current I_H into the distribution system. The other customers respectively draw fundamental currents I_2, I_3, I_4, but their harmonic contributions are negligible. The feeder therefore carries a total fundamental current I_F where $I_F = I_1 + I_2 + I_3 + I_4$, and a harmonic current I_H.

The fundamental current I_F produces a voltage drop I_FX_S along the length of the feeder. Similarly,

* By definition, a PCC is the point of the public supply network, electrically nearest to a particular consumer's installation, and at which other consumers' installations are, or may be, connected.

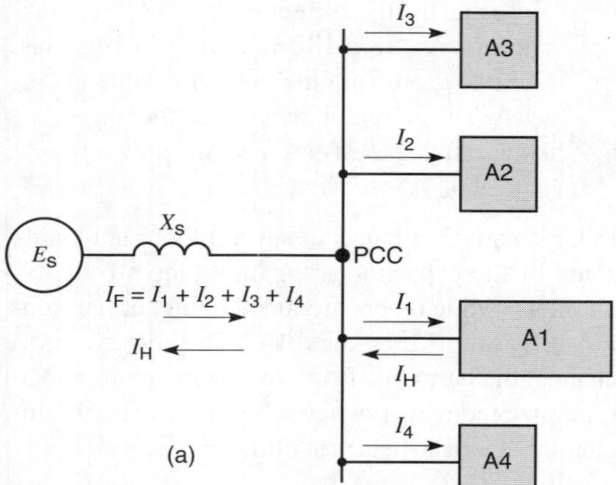

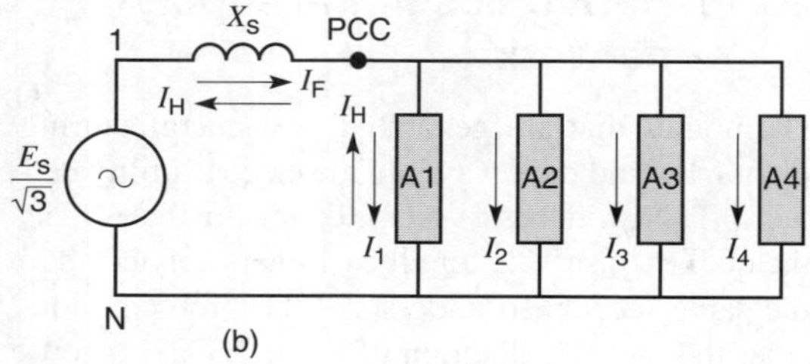

Figure 30.33
a. Point of common coupling PCC.
b. Harmonic voltages created at the PCC on account of the harmonic currents generated by load A1.

current I_H produces a harmonic voltage drop E_H given by

$$E_H = I_H h X_S$$

where h is the order of the harmonic. For example, if I_H is a 7th harmonic, $h = 7$.

For a high value of h the voltage drop E_H could be quite large. Because the supply voltage E_S contains no harmonics, it follows that E_H must appear at the PCC. Thus, the harmonic *current* I_H generated by factory A1 affects the quality of the *voltage* supplied to all customers connected to the same PCC.

It is therefore important to limit the magnitude of the harmonic currents that flow into the electric utility network. In general, the THD of the voltage at the PCC should not exceed 3%.*

Example 30-11

Factory A1 in Fig. 30.33a absorbs an apparent power of 4600 kVA from a 25 kV, 60 Hz network. Non-linear loads in the plant produce a 5th and 29th harmonic current. Compared to the fundamental current, the 5th harmonic has a value of 0.12 pu (12%) and the 29th harmonic has a value of 0.024 pu (2.4%). The feeder at the point of common coupling has a short-circuit capacity of 97 MVA.

Calculate

a. The reactance X_S of the feeder
b. The value of the 5th and 29th harmonics
c. The value of the harmonic voltages at the PCC
d. The relative values, with respect to the 25 kV feeder voltage, of the harmonic voltages at the PCC
e. The THD at the PCC

Solution

a. Referring to Fig. 30.33, the 60 Hz reactance of the feeder is:

$$X_S = \frac{E_S^2}{S_{SC}} = \frac{25^2}{97} = 6.44\ \Omega \qquad (30.8b)$$

b. Fundamental current drawn by factory A1:

$$I_1 = \frac{S}{E_S\sqrt{3}} = \frac{4600 \times 10^3}{25\,000\sqrt{3}} = 106\ \text{A}$$

The 5th harmonic current:

$$I_5 = 0.12 \times 106 = 12.7\ \text{A}$$

The 29th harmonic current:

$$I_{29} = 0.024 \times 106 = 2.5\ \text{A}$$

c. The 5th harmonic voltage, line-to-line:

$$E_5 = I_5 h X_S \sqrt{3}$$
$$= 12.7 \times 5 \times 6.44 \times \sqrt{3} = 708\ \text{V}$$

* ANSI/EEE Standard No. 519-1992 entitled "IEEE Recommended Practices and Requirements for Harmonic Control in Electrical Power Systems" gives guidelines concerning the maximum harmonic currents that a customer may inject into a power system. This 100-page document also gives a general overview of harmonic-related problems in a distribution system.

The 29th harmonic voltage, line to line

$$E_{29} = I_{29}hX_S\sqrt{3}$$
$$= 2.5 \times 29 \times 6.44 \times \sqrt{3} = 809 \text{ V}$$

d. Relative value of E_5

$$E_5 \text{ (pu)} = 708/25\,000 = 0.028 = 2.8\%$$

Relative value of E_{29}

$$E_{29} \text{ (pu)} = 809/25\,000 = 0.032 = 3.2\%$$

Note that the voltage distortion due to the 29th harmonic is greater than that due to the 5th harmonic even though the 29th harmonic current is 5 times smaller than the 5th.

e. Total voltage distortion at the PCC

$$\text{THD} = \sqrt{(0.028^2 + 0.032^2)} = 0.043 = 4.3\%$$

This THD is considered to be high.

30.17 Transformers and the K factor

In a transformer, some of the leakage flux lines surrounding the windings intercept the turns of the primary and secondary windings. As a result, these flux lines induce feeble voltages inside the copper (or aluminum) conductors which, in turn, produce eddy currents.

These eddy currents produce additional losses in the windings over and above the usual Joule effect I^2R losses. These additional losses are called *stray losses.* Stray losses are particularly important when the windings carry distorted currents.

Distorted currents produce harmonic leakage fluxes in addition to the fundamental leakage flux. When these harmonic fluxes pierce the copper conductors, they induce harmonic voltages and therefore harmonic eddy currents. Unfortunately, for a given flux density, harmonic leakage fluxes of order h induce voltages that are h times greater than those induced by the fundamental leakage flux. The corresponding harmonic eddy currents are also h times greater. Consequently, because losses increase as the square of the current, it follows that stray losses increase as the *square* of the harmonic order of the leakage flux density.

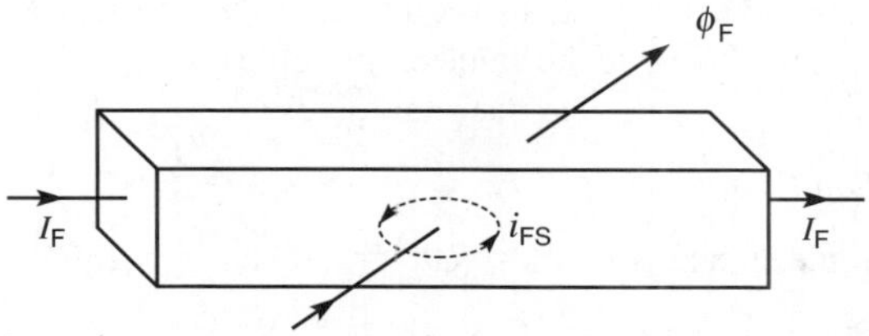

Figure 30.34
The leakage flux at fundamental frequency induces eddy currents i_{FS} in the copper windings.

Suppose, for example, that a fundamental current of 40 A flowing in the primary winding produces stray losses of 4 W. A 7th harmonic current of the same value would produce stray losses of $7^2 \times$ 4 W = 196 W. Clearly, a distorted current can produce serious stray losses in the windings, which, in turn, affects their temperature rise.

Fig. 30.34 displays a short portion of one turn in a transformer winding. It carries a 60 Hz undistorted current I_F. A portion ϕ_F of the leakage flux produced by I_F pierces the turn, inducing in it an eddy current i_{FS}. The sum of these eddy currents along the length of the winding produces the fundamental frequency stray losses.

Suppose that the dc resistance of the winding is R_0 ohms. The *Joule effect* losses due to this resistance are equal to $R_0I_F^2$. Let the stray losses represent a fraction g of these $R_0I_F^2$ losses. Depending upon the size of the transformer, the value of g can vary from 2% to 15%.

The total losses P_T at the fundamental frequency can therefore be expressed by the equation:

total losses = Joule effect losses + stray losses

$$P_T = P_J + P_K$$
$$= R_0I_F^2 + gR_0I_F^2$$

thus

$$P_T = I_F^2(R_0 + gR_0) \tag{30.10}$$

Example 30-12

The primary of a transformer carries an undistorted current I_F of 85 A. The dc resistance of the winding is 0.04 Ω. The stray losses amount to 9% of the I^2R losses. Calculate the value of the Joule effect losses, the stray losses, and the total losses.

Solution

Joule effect losses: $P_J = R_0 I_F^2 = 0.04 \times 85^2 = 289$ W

Stray losses: $P_K = 9\% \times 289 = 26$ W

Total losses: $P_T = 289 + 26 = 315$ W

Fig. 30.35 shows the same winding section when the winding carries a distorted current composed of a fundamental component I_F and several harmonics $I_2, I_3, I_4, \ldots I_h$. The distorted current has an effective value I_T. Thus,

$$I_T = \sqrt{I_F^2 + I_2^2 + I_3^2 + \cdots + I_h^2}$$

Note that the leakage flux comprises fundamental flux lines ϕ_F and harmonic flux lines ϕ_H. They respectively induce eddy currents i_{FS} and i_{HS}.

The total stray losses are equal to the sum of the individual stray losses contributed by the components of I_T. As mentioned above, the individual losses are proportional to the square of the respective currents and the square of their harmonic orders (frequencies). We can therefore write

$$\begin{aligned} P_T &= P_J + P_K \\ &= R_0 I_T^2 + gR_0(I_F^2 + 2^2 I_2^2 + 3^2 I_3^2 + \cdots + h^2 I_h^2) \\ &= I_T^2 \left\{ R_0 + gR_0 \frac{(I_F^2 + 2^2 I_2^2 + 3^2 I_3^2 + \cdots + h^2 I_h^2)}{I_T^2} \right\} \end{aligned}$$

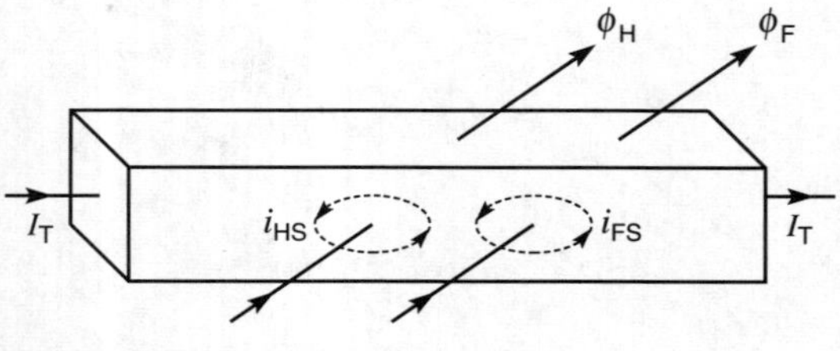

Figure 30.35
The harmonic leakage fluxes induce eddy currents i_{HS} in the copper windings.

thus,

$$P_T = I_T^2(R_0 + gKR_0) \tag{30.11}$$

Comparing Eq. 30.11 with Eq. 30.10, we see that the factor K represents the multiplier effect on stray losses due to the presence of harmonics. The value of K is given by the equation:

$$K = \frac{I_F^2 + 2^2 I_2^2 + 3^2 I_3^2 + \cdots + h^2 I_h^2}{I_F^2 + I_2^2 + I_3^2 + I_4^2 + \cdots + I_h^2}$$

that is

$$K = \frac{I_F^2 + 2^2 I_2^2 + 3^2 I_3^2 + \cdots + h^2 I_h^2}{I_T^2} \tag{30.12}$$

This equation is sometimes expressed in abbreviated form:

$$\boxed{K = \Sigma h^2 I_{h(pu)}^2} \tag{30.13}$$

where

K = stray loss factor due to harmonics
h = order of the harmonic
$I_{h(pu)}$ = relative value of the harmonic with respect to the total effective current I_T

It is seen that the K factor is a property of the distorted current and not of the transformer. Nevertheless, it indicates the potential heating effect when the distorted current flows in a transformer. For this reason, some transformers are designed with a specific K factor to indicate the level of distortion they can tolerate without overheating.

When the current carried by the windings is undistorted, $K = 1$. On a 60 Hz system, harmonics higher than the 31st are usually ignored. For example, the K factor of a 60 Hz square wave (Table 2A) is about 13. Figure 30.45 shows an instrument that can measure the K factor of a current.

Example 30-13

The primary winding of a transformer carries a distorted current having the following components:

fundamental current:	520 A
3rd harmonic:	270 A
23rd harmonic:	47 A

The winding has a dc resistance of 3 mΩ and the stray losses are equal to 4% of the Joule effect losses.

Calculate

a. The effective value I_T of the current
b. The K factor
c. The Joule effect losses in the primary winding
d. The stray losses and the total losses in the primary winding
e. The component in I_T that produces the largest Joule effect loss
f. The component in I_T that produces the largest stray loss

Solution

a. Effective value of I_T

$$I_T = \sqrt{520^2 + 270^2 + 47^2}$$
$$= 588 \text{ A}$$

b. The K factor

$$K = \frac{I_F^2 + 3^2 I_3^2 + 23^2 I_{23}^2}{I_T^2} \quad (30.12)$$
$$= \frac{520^2 + 3^2 \times 270^2 + 23^2 \times 47^2}{588^2}$$
$$= 0.782 + 1.898 + 3.380 = 6.06$$

c. The Joule effect losses

$$P_J = I_T^2 R_0 = 588^2 \times 0.003 = 1037 \text{ W}$$

d. The stray losses

$$P_K = gP_J K = 4\% \times 1037 \times 6.06 = 251 \text{ W}$$

The total losses

$$P_T = P_J + P_K = 1037 \text{ W} + 251 \text{ W} = 1288 \text{ W}$$

e. The largest Joule effect losses are produced by the 520 A fundamental current:

$$P_{J\,(\text{fundamental})} = R_0 I_F^2$$
$$= 0.003 \times 520^2$$
$$= 811 \text{ W}$$

f. The largest stray losses are produced by the 23rd harmonic:

$$P_{K(h=23)} = P_K \times \frac{K_{23}}{K}$$
$$= 251 \times \frac{3.380}{6.06} = 140 \text{ W}$$

In this example, the stray losses are 251 W/1037 W = 0.24 or 24% of the Joule effect losses, commonly called the I^2R losses. This illustrates that one must be prudent when calculating the losses in a transformer that carries a distorted current. The situation is particularly serious because stray losses are not uniformly distributed over the surface of the windings. Rather they are concentrated in certain regions, often near the top and bottom of the windings. Thus, some regions may become considerably hotter than others. These overheated regions can significantly reduce the service life of the transformer. Special transformers are built in which the K factor they can tolerate is specified.*

HARMONIC ANALYSIS

30.18 Procedure for analyzing a periodic wave

We have seen that harmonics play an important role in electrical installations. Although special instruments (Figs. 30.44, 30.45) are available to measure them in the field, we now describe a method whereby any distorted wave can be decomposed into its harmonic components using a simple hand calculator. The procedure is based on Fourier series analysis.

1. Given a distorted wave you want to analyze, decide which harmonic H you are interested in. For example, if it is the 7th harmonic, H = 7; if it is the fundamental, H = 1.
2. Multiply the harmonic order H by 10. The number 10 H is the minimum number of readings required per cycle to ensure that the accuracy will be of the order of ±5%. For

---

* See ANSI/IEEE C57.110-1986 Standard entitled "IEEE Recommended Practice For Establishing Transformer Capability When Supplying Nonsinusoidal Load Currents."

example, in the case of the 7th harmonic, 10 H $= 10 \times 7 = 70$ readings.

3. Since one cycle comprises 360°, the approximate interval D between readings is $D = 360°/10\ H$. In the case of a 7th harmonic, $D = 360°/70 = 5.14°$. This number can be rounded to 5°, which simplifies the listing in degrees.
4. Prepare a 4-column table similar to that shown in Table 30B. The crosses indicate the numbers you will be filling in.

   In column [1] headed by the symbol θ, write down the angles from zero to 360°, spaced by intervals of D degrees. If $D = 5°$ the column will list the numbers 0, 5, 10, 15, . . . up to 360. They represent the angles, in degrees, of the distorted wave during one cycle.
5. Select a starting point on the distorted wave. It is usual (although not necessary) to choose the moment when the wave passes through zero. However, no matter where the starting point is, it is always designated as the 0° angle.
6. In column [2] headed by symbol A, write down the values of the distorted wave corresponding to the angles listed in column [1].
7. In column [3] headed by symbol A sin (Hθ), calculate for each row, the product $A \times \sin(H\theta)$.

TABLE 30B HARMONIC ANALYSIS

harmonic H = ___ D = ___

[1] θ	[2] A	[3] A sin Hθ	[4] A cos Hθ
0	x	x	x
x	x	x	x
.	.	.	.
.	.	.	.
.	.	.	.
x	x	x	x
	sum S_0	sum S_1	sum S_2
	$A_0 = S_0D/360$	$X = S_1D/180$	$Y = S_2D/180$

For example, if $\theta = 235°$, $A = 49$, and $H = 7$, we obtain for this row:

$$A \sin(H\theta) = 49 \times \sin(7 \times 235°) = 49 \sin 1645° = -20.7$$

8. In column [4] headed by symbol A cos (Hθ), calculate for each row the product of $A \times \cos(H\theta)$.

   For example, if $\theta = 235°$, $A = 49$, and $H = 7$, we obtain $A\cos(H\theta) = 49 \times \cos(7 \times 235°) = 49 \times \cos 1645° = -44.4$.
9. Calculate the sum S_1 of the values in column [3], excluding the value corresponding to $\theta = 360°$. Then calculate the value of X according to the equation:

$$\boxed{X = S_1D/180} \qquad (30.14)$$

10. Calculate the sum S_2 of the values in column [4], excluding the value corresponding to $\theta = 360°$. Then calculate the value of Y according to the equation:

$$\boxed{Y = S_2D/180} \qquad (30.15)$$

11. The amplitude A_H of the desired harmonic component is then given by:

$$\boxed{A_H = \sqrt{X^2 + Y^2}} \qquad (30.16)$$

12. The angular position α of the harmonic with respect to the starting point ($\theta = 0°$) is given by:

$$\boxed{\alpha = \arctan Y/X} \qquad (30.17)$$

The following rule applies to Eq. 30.17:

If the value of X is negative, 180° must be added to the angle.

13. The harmonic component you are seeking is given by the expression:

$$\text{harmonic } H = A_H \sin(H\theta + \alpha) \qquad (30.18)$$

   The effective or rms value of the component is equal to $A_H/\sqrt{2}$.
14. In some cases, the wave may contain a dc component A_0, in addition to the ac compo-

nents. To determine its value, calculate the sum S_0 of the values in column [2], excluding the value for $\theta = 360°$. The value of A_0 is given by

$$\boxed{A_0 = S_0D/360} \quad (30.19)$$

The above calculations can be done by hand, but the task is much easier using a computer or spreadsheet.

Example 30-14

Figure 30.36 displays an unusual waveshape. The positive half of the wave is triangular and the negative half is rectangular. We wish to determine:

a. The amplitude and position of the fundamental
b. The amplitude and position of the 4th harmonic

Solution

a. We want to analyze the fundamental; consequently, H = 1 and 10 H = 10 × 1 = 10. Thus, at least 10 readings must be taken during one cycle of the distorted wave. The interval D is therefore 360°/10 = 36°. Let us make D = 30°, which will improve the accuracy slightly. We must therefore take 360°/30° = 12 readings during one cycle.

Note that the value of the wave changes abruptly at 160°, 240°, and 320°. In such cases, we take the average of the maximum and minimum values. Thus, at 160° the average value is (40 + 0)/2 = +20. The average value at 240° (and at 320°) is −20.

Table 30C is the four-column table mentioned previously. Column [1] shows the angles from 0° to 360° in intervals D of 30°. By tracking the waveshape, the value A corresponding to each angle is determined and listed in column [2]. The necessary calculations are then made to complete columns [3] and [4].

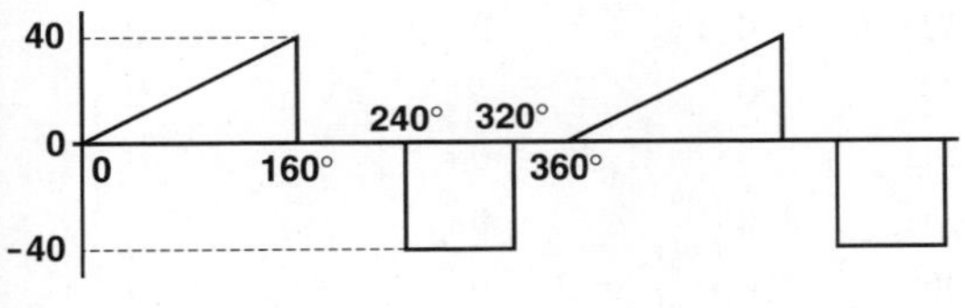

Figure 30.36
Analysis of a distorted wave.

TABLE 30C HARMONIC ANALYSIS

harmonic H = 1		D = 30°	
[1] θ	[2] A	[3] A sin Hθ	[4] A cos Hθ
0	0	0	0
30	7.5	3.75	6.5
60	15	13	7.5
90	22.5	22.5	0
120	30	26	−15
150	37.5	18.75	−32.5
180	0	0	0
210	0	0	0
240	−20	17.3	10
270	−40	40	0
300	−40	34.6	−20
330	0	0	0
360	0	0	0
		$S_1 = 175.9$	$S_2 = -43.5$
$X = S_1D/180 = 29.3$		$Y = S_2D/180 = -7.3$	

The sum S_1 in column [3] gives 175.9. Consequently, we obtain

$$X = S_1D/180 = 175.9 \times 30/180 = 29.3$$

Similarly, the sum of the values in column [4] yields $S_2 = -43.5$. Consequently, we obtain

$$Y = S_2D/180 = -43.5 \times 30/180 = -7.3$$

Applying Eqs. 30.16 and 30.17, we obtain the amplitude A_1 and phase angle α of the fundamental

$$A_1 = \sqrt{X^2 + Y^2} = \sqrt{29.3^2 + (-7.3)^2} = 30.2$$

$$\alpha = \arctan\left(\frac{Y}{X}\right) = \arctan\left(\frac{-7.3}{29.3}\right)$$

$$= \arctan(-0.249) = -14°$$

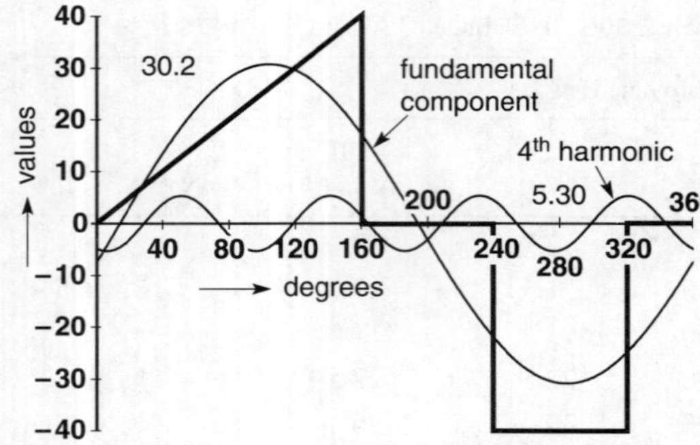

Figure 30.37
Fundamental and 4th harmonic components of the wave illustrated in Fig. 30.36.

The fundamental can therefore be expressed by the equation:

$$H_1 = A_1 \sin (H\theta + \alpha) = 30.2 \sin (\theta - 14°)$$

The effective value of the fundamental is $30.2/\sqrt{2} = 21.3$.

Figure 30.37 shows the fundamental superposed on the original wave.

b. Let us now consider the 4th harmonic. In this case, we must select at least 10 H = 10 × 4 = 40 readings on the distorted wave. The interval D must therefore be no greater than 360°/40 = 9°

TABLE 30D HARMONIC ANALYSIS

harmonic H = 4 D = 9°

[1] θ	[2] A	[3] A sin Hθ	[4] A cos Hθ
0	0	0	0
9	2.25	1.32	1.82
18	4.5	4.28	1.39
27	6.75	6.42	−2.09
36	9.0	5.29	−7.28

(continued)

[1] θ	[2] A	[3] A sin Hθ	[4] A cos Hθ
45	11.25	0	−11.25
54	13.5	−7.94	−10.92
63	15.75	−14.98	−4.87
72	18.0	−17.12	5.56
81	20.25	−11.9	16.38
90	22.5	0	22.50
99	24.75	14.55	20.02
108	27.0	25.68	8.34
117	29.25	27.82	−9.04
126	31.5	18.52	−25.48
135	33.75	0	−33.75
144	36.0	−21.16	−29.12
153	38.25	−36.38	−11.82
162	0	0	0
171	0	0	0
180	0	0	0
189	0	0	0
198	0	0	0
207	0	0	0
216	0	0	0
225	0	0	0
234	0	0	0
243	−40	38.04	12.36
252	−40	38.04	−12.36
261	−40	23.51	−32.36
270	−40	0	−40.0
279	−40	−23.51	−32.36
288	−40	−38.04	−12.36
297	−40	−38.04	12.36
306	−40	−23.51	32.36
315	−40	0	40.0
324	0	0	0
333	0	0	0
342	0	0	0
351	0	0	0
360	0	0	0
		$S_1 = -29.11$	$S_2 = -101.96$

Table 30D again lists the 4 columns. In this case, the sum S_1 of column [3] gives -29.11 and that of column [4] gives $S_2 = -101.96$. It follows that

$$X = S_1D/180 = -29.11 \times (9°)/180 = -1.46$$

$$Y = S_2D/180 = -101.96 \times (9°)/180 = -5.10$$

The amplitude of the 4th harmonic is therefore

$$A_4 = \sqrt{X^2 + Y^2} = \sqrt{(-1.46)^2 + (-5.1)^2} = 5.30$$

and the phase angle is

$$\alpha = \arctan\left(\frac{Y}{X}\right) = \arctan\left(\frac{-5.10}{-1.46}\right)$$

$$= \arctan 3.49 = 74°$$

However, since X is negative, we must add 180° to the calculated value of 74°. The true angle is therefore $\alpha = 74° + 180° = 254°$.

The 4th harmonic can be expressed by the equation:

$$H_4 = 5.3 \sin (4\theta + 254°)$$

Figure 30.37 shows the 4th harmonic superposed on both the original waveshape and the fundamental wave.

By repeating the same exercise, we can find expressions for harmonics from the 2nd to the 12th

TABLE 30E HARMONIC COMPONENTS

Fundamental	30.2 sin (θ − 14°)
2nd H	7.7 sin (2θ + 100°)
3th H	7.4 sin (3θ + 119°)
4th H	5.3 sin (4θ + 254°)
5th H	4.1 sin (5θ + 110°)
6th H	4.6 sin (6θ + 239°)
7th H	2.1 sin (7θ + 269°)
8th H	3.3 sin (8θ − 8°)
9th H	1.4 sin (9θ + 184°)
10th H	3.0 sin (10θ + 1°)
11th H	1.5 sin (11θ + 97°)
12th H	1.9 sin (12θ + 117°)

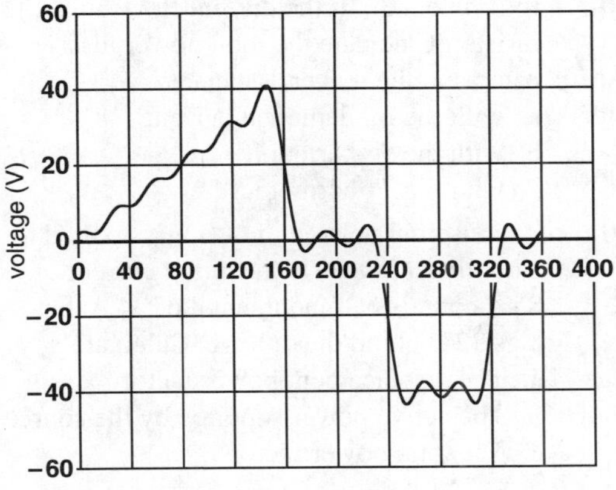

Figure 30.38
Waveshape obtained by summing the fundamental and the first 12 harmonics of Fig. 30.36.

(see Table 30E). The sum of the fundamental and the first twelve harmonics is shown graphically in Fig. 30.38. The resulting waveshape is quite close to the original waveshape even though the number of harmonics is quite limited.

Questions and Problems

Practical level

30-1 A 60 Hz distorted current contains a 5th harmonic of 20 A and a fundamental of 30 A (rms values). Calculate
a. The effective value of the distorted current
b. The frequency of the fundamental
c. The frequency of the harmonic

30-2 A 60 Hz voltage having an effective value of 485 V contains several harmonics. The fundamental has an effective value of 481 V. Calculate the effective value of all the harmonics.

30-3 In Problem 30-2, calculate the THD in percent.

30-4 A current has the following components: fundamental: 960 A; 5th harmonic: 156 A; 7th harmonic: 235 A. Calculate
a. The effective value of the current
b. The distortion factor, in percent

30-5 In Problem 30-4, the current flows in a 2 Ω resistor. Calculate the total power dissipated and the power associated
   a. with the fundamental current
   b. with the 5th harmonic
   c. with the 7th harmonic

30-6 A sinusoidal voltage of 480 V is applied to a nonlinear load. The resulting current of 85 A contains a fundamental of 74 A that lags 32° behind the voltage. Calculate
   a. The displacement power factor
   b. The active power supplied by the source
   c. The total power factor

30-7 A 3-phase, 4-wire cable feeds a group of halogen lamps that are connected between line and neutral. The current in the lines has an effective value of 320 A of which 47 A is due to a 3rd harmonic. Calculate the value of the current flowing in the neutral.

Intermediate level

30-8 A voltage of 4300 V has a THD of 26%. Calculate the rms values of
   a. The fundamental
   b. All the harmonics

30-9 A 60 Hz source contains a fundamental of 730 V and a 5th harmonic of 108 V. The source is connected to an inductance of 5 mH in series with a resistance of 10 Ω. Calculate the effective values of the following currents and voltages:
   a. Fundamental current
   b. 5th harmonic current
   c. Current in the circuit
   d. Voltage across the resistor
   e. Voltage across the inductor

30-10 A 3-phase cable carries a distorted current of 830 A that contains a 7th harmonic of 60 A. The resistance of the cable is 2 mΩ. If the harmonic is suppressed, by how much will the losses in the cable decrease?

30-11 A square wave has an amplitude of 100 V. Using the method described in Section 30.18, determine the peak value of the fundamental component. Take intervals of 30°. Compare your value with the exact value given in Table 2A, Chapter 2.

30-12 The triangular wave of Fig. 30.39 has a peak value of 100 V. Determine the approximate rms value of the fundamental.

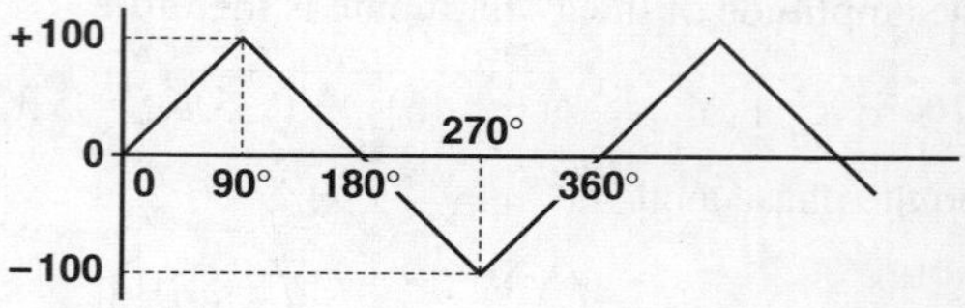

Figure 30.39
See Problem 30-12.

Advanced level

30-13 In Fig. 30.40, using the method of Section 30.18, determine the peak values of
   a. the fundamental
   b. the 3rd harmonic
   c. the 5th harmonic

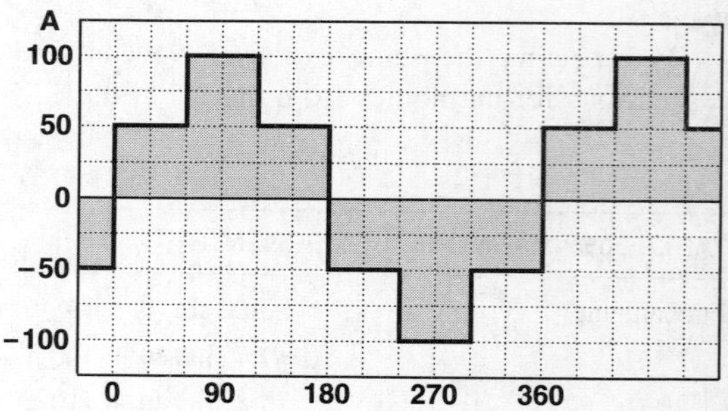

Figure 30.40
See Problem 30-13.

30-14 In Fig. 30.41, determine the peak values of
   a. the fundamental
   b. the 3rd harmonic
   c. the 5th harmonic

30-15 In Problem 30-13, determine
   a. The effective value of the current
   b. The effective value of the fundamental

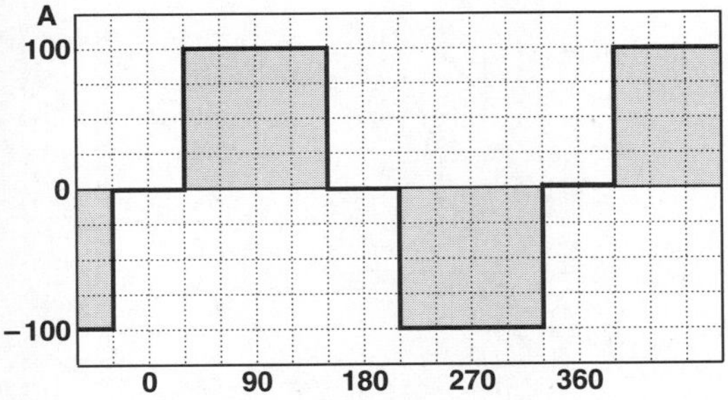

Figure 30.41
See Problem 30-14.

- **c.** The effective value of all the harmonics
- **d.** The THD

30-16 A three-phase 24 kV feeder that supplies power to a commercial building has a short-circuit capacity of 60 MVA.

Calculate

- **a.** The reactance of the feeder, per phase
- **b.** The current per phase if a short-circuit occurred at the service entrance to the building upstream from the step-down transformer

30-17 In Fig. 30.42 the rectangular current has a peak value of 100 A. Its amplitude is zero during successive intervals of 36°, as shown.

- **a.** Calculate the effective value of the fundamental
- **b.** Show that the 5th harmonic is essentially zero

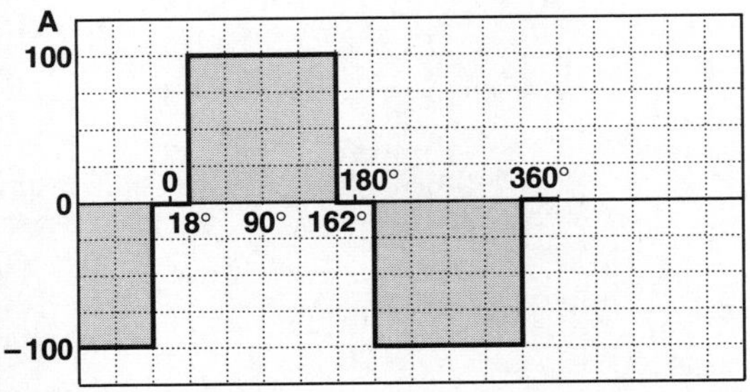

Figure 30.42
See Problem 30-17.

30-18 A distorted voltage is represented by the following equation (angles expressed in degrees, t in seconds):

$$E = 850 \sin 18\,000\, t + 340 \sin (126\,000\, t - 30°)$$

Calculate

- **a.** The frequency of the fundamental and the harmonic
- **b.** The effective value of the fundamental and the harmonic
- **c.** The effective value of the distorted voltage
- **d.** The instantaneous voltage when $t = 1$ ms
- **e.** Draw a phasor diagram that represents the distorted voltage and sketch its waveshape.

30-19 A nonlinear load generates the following harmonics when it is connected to a 50 Hz source:

5th: 20 A   7th: 4 A   11th: 9 A   13th: 8 A

The currents flow in a circuit that contains an inductance of 1300 μH in parallel with a capacitor of 40 μF.

Calculate

- **a.** The value of the respective harmonic voltages across the terminals of the inductance
- **b.** The effective value of all the harmonic voltages across the inductance
- **c.** The effective value of the current flowing in the capacitor

30-20 In Fig. 30.11, determine the amplitude and phase angle of the fundamental component of the chopped current. Use intervals of 6°.

30-21 Figure 30.43 shows a periodic voltage consisting of a succession of sinusoidal pulses having an amplitude of 100 V. Using intervals D of 6 °, determine

- **a.** The amplitude and phase angle of the fundamental
- **b.** The dc component
- **c.** The effective value of the voltage
- **d.** The effective value of all the harmonics.

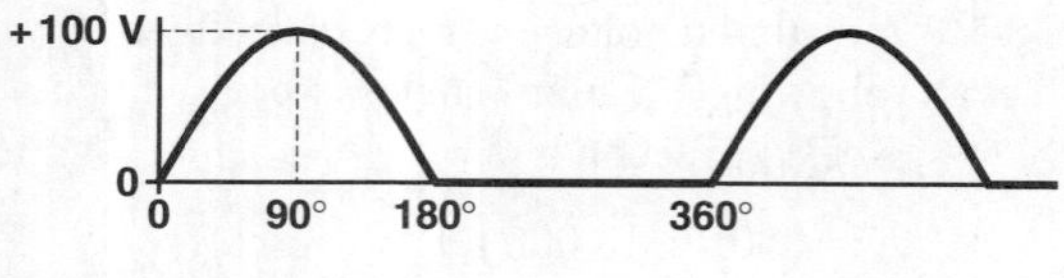

Figure 30.43
See Problem 30-21.

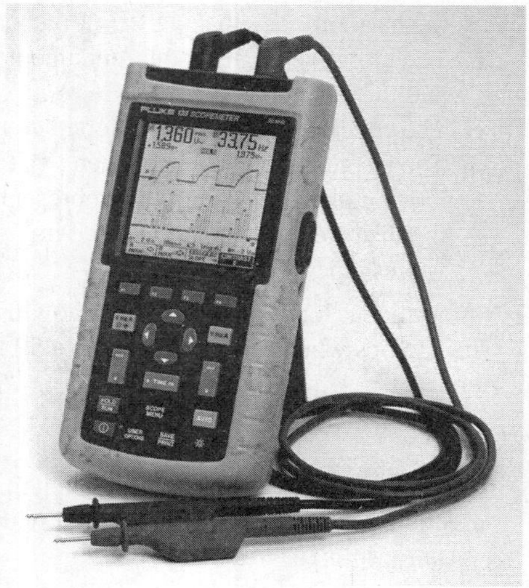

Figure 30.44
This portable instrument, the "Scopemeter" incorporates an oscilloscope, a multimeter, and a recorder. It is used to verify control systems including variable-speed electronic drives.
(Courtesy of Fluke Electronics Canada Inc.)

Figure 30.45
This portable instrument, the "Power Harmonics Analyzer" can measure the total harmonic distortion (THD) of a voltage or current up to the 31st harmonic. It can also measure the active, reactive and apparent power in a 3-phase circuit, and its power factor. It also gives a readout of the K factor of a current.
(Courtesy of Fluke Electronics Canada Inc.)

CHAPTER 31

Programmable Logic Controllers

31.0 Introduction

Of all the devices that are used to control manufacturing operations, the *programmable logic controller* (PLC) is one of the most important. The first PLCs were introduced in the early 1960s, mainly by the automobile industry. Up until then, the automatic control of manufacturing equipment was achieved by using hundreds, and even thousands, of relays enclosed in metal cabinets.

The annual automobile-model changes required frequent modifications to the production lines and their associated relay-control systems. Because the control systems were complex, the modifications took a lot of time, and errors often occurred when making connections. For these reasons, control engineers developed a computerized programmable system to replace the relay racks.

This presented a big challenge for many companies. In effect, computers that had previously been used to do accounting jobs were modified to respond to the needs of industry. Little by little, the techniques were improved and more users of the new technology were found. However, a full decade went by before the new concept was systematically adopted by manufacturers.

Today, the programmable logic controller (sometimes called *programmable controller*) is the main control device used in industry. More than 50 manufacturers offer hundreds of different models.

31.1 Capacity of industrial PLCs

In the beginning, PLCs were mainly used to replace hard-wired physical relays. This offered many advantages because the PLCs took up less space than conventional relay cabinets and consumed much less energy. Furthermore, they were programmable and equipped with LED (light-emitting diode) indicators that made it easy to check the operation of the control system and to diagnose problems.

Today, thanks to the evolution in electronics and computer technology, the performance of PLCs is impressive. While they are still used to replace relays, PLCs can now perform mathematical operations and control and regulate industrial processes. For instance, they can regulate temperature, pressure, flow rates, motor drives, and so forth. In addition, PLCs can now communicate with each other as well as with a central computer. The latter can collect data, change the operating parameters, and even modify the PLC programming.

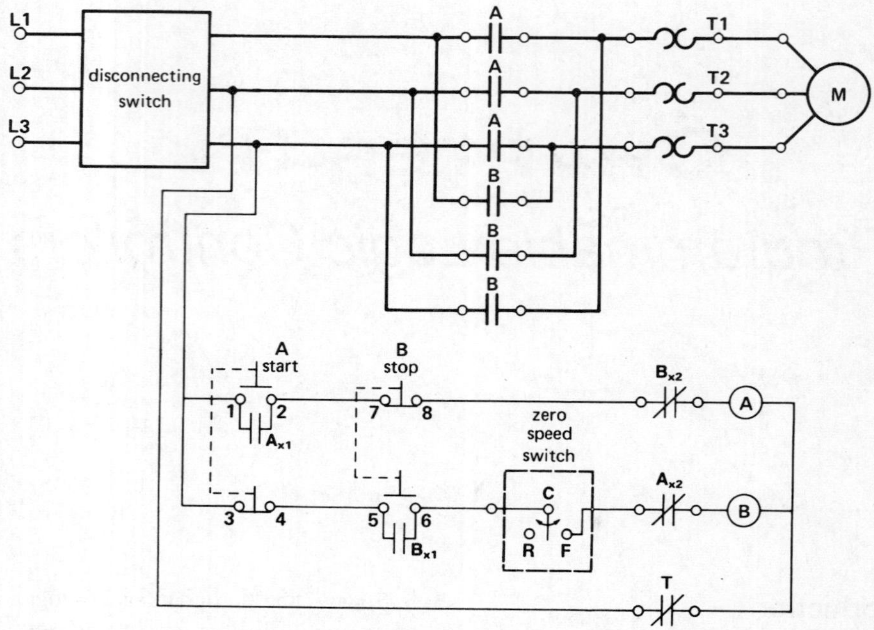

Figure 20.24a (reproduction)
Simplified schematic diagram of a starter with plugging control.

Some programmable controllers can accommodate more than 3000 inputs and outputs. These PLCs can easily replace more than 10 000 conventional relays. Consequently, it is possible to control a complete factory with a single PLC. However, in the case of larger factories, it is always preferable to install several PLCs throughout the plant and link them by a communications network. By using individual PLCs to handle specific production processes, the PLCs can be made smaller, faster, and easier to program.

In the following sections we will explain the basic principle of the programmable logic controller using a very simple model. This is then followed by a closer look at the actual physical construction of a PLC. Finally, we will examine how PLCs are applied in industry and how the transition from hard-wired relays to PLCs is made.

31.2 Elements of a control system

During our study of control systems in Chapter 20, we saw that a few pushbuttons, relays, and low-power auxiliary contacts were able to control big contactors to start and stop electric motors. Furthermore, in examining the schematic diagrams of Figs. 20.16b, 20.24a, and 20.25 in Chapter 20, we perceive that they are very similar. If we ignore the number of control devices that are used in each case, we see that the fundamental difference between the three diagrams lies in the way the control devices are interconnected.

Suppose that we have a "black box" inside which various connections can be made between the *control* devices (pushbuttons, auxiliary contacts) and the *controlled* devices (holding coils of contactors, pilot lights). In the case of Fig. 20.24a

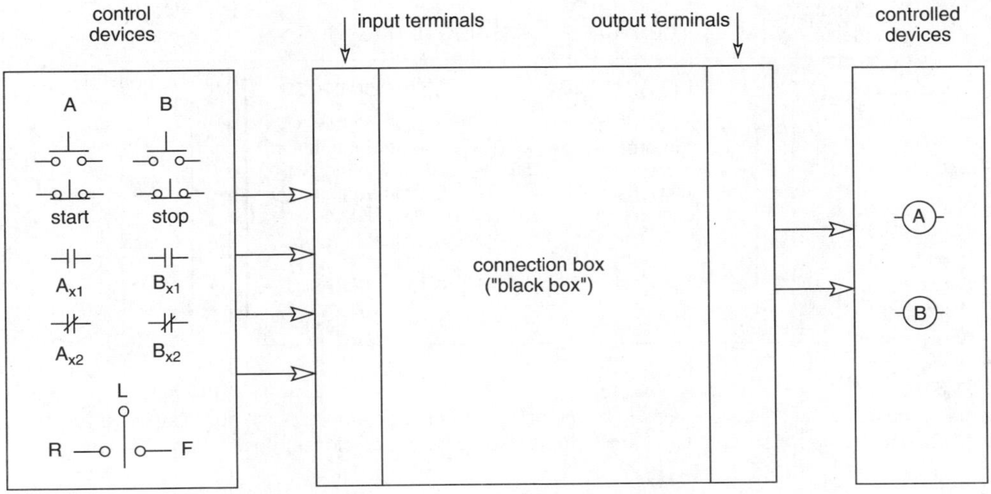

Figure 31.1
An automated system is composed of *control* devices and *controlled* devices. These on/off devices are all of the same nature, irrespective of the type of automated system. The systems differ only as to the number of devices and the connections between them.

(reproduced here for convenience), this approach results in the set-up shown in Fig. 31.1. The control devices (start and stop pushbuttons, auxiliary contacts, and zero-speed switch) are connected to the *input terminals* of the black box. In the same way, the devices that are controlled (holding coils A and B) are connected to the *output terminals* on the right-hand side of the black box.

Suppose the black box is a computer. The computer is designed to *simulate* the relays, relay coils, relay contacts, as well as the connections between them. This approach opens up enormous possibilities because the computer can simulate hundreds of relays having thousands of contacts. The number is only limited by the computer's memory capacity. The control system can therefore take the general form shown in Fig. 31.2. A programmable logic controller consists of five basic parts.

1. A *central processing unit* (CPU), which is a computer that can simulate the required relay contacts and relay coils, as well as the connections between them.

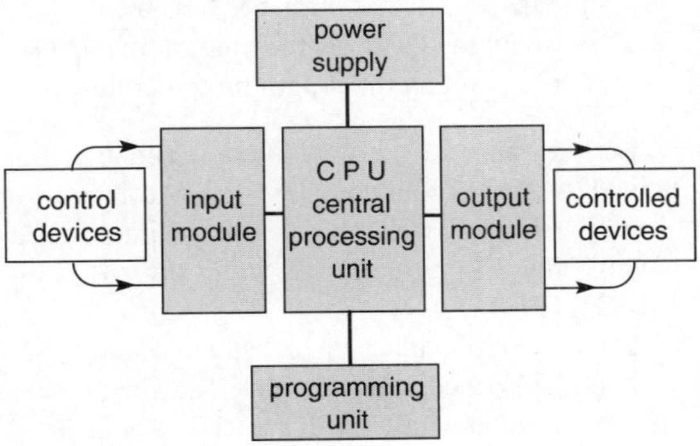

Figure 31.2
The five parts of a PLC.

2. An *input module,* which serves as an interface between the actual control devices and the CPU.
3. An *output module,* which serves as an interface between the CPU and the actual devices that are being controlled.

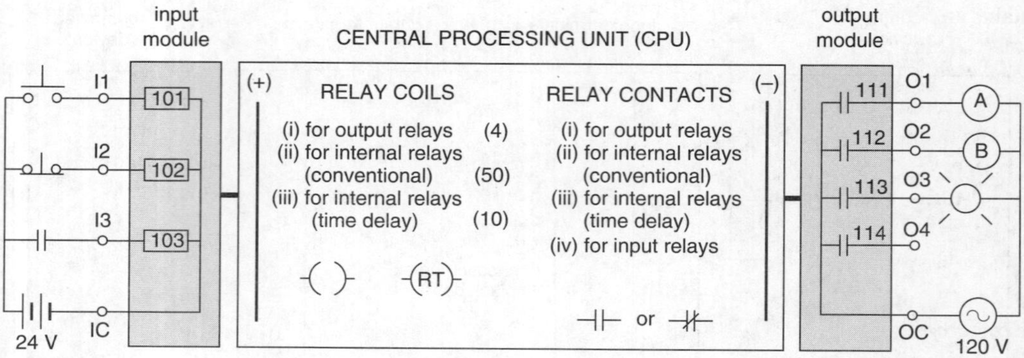

Figure 31.3
The central processing unit (CPU) contains in its memory a "stock" of elements such as "relay coils," "contacts," "counters," etc. The "relay coils" in the CPU are represented by truncated circles.

4. A *programming unit* consisting of a keyboard and monitor to program the CPU. It enables us to select different types of "relays" and "contacts" that the computer can simulate, as well as the way they are to be connected.
5. A *power supply* that furnishes the power needed by the CPU, by the input/output (I/O) modules, and by the programming unit.

Let us examine the construction and the role played by the first four components listed above. To simplify matters, we choose a very simple PLC having only 3 input terminals and 4 output terminals (Fig. 31.3).

The *input module* has three terminals labeled I1, I2, and I3, and a common terminal IC. The real external control devices are respectively connected between the I1, I2, and I3 terminals and one side of a 24 V source. The other side of the source is connected to terminal IC, as shown in the figure. A small rectangle bearing a reference number (address) is associated with each terminal. For example, the address 102 is associated with terminal I2.

To understand the operation of the input module, it is useful to imagine that each rectangle corresponds to a "relay coil" that is "excited" by the associated external control device. For example, "coil" 102 is normally "excited" because the pushbutton with which it is associated is normally closed (NC). On the other hand, "coil" 101 is normally "not excited" because the pushbutton associated with it is normally open (NO). In the same way, "coil" 103 is normally "not excited" because the auxiliary contact associated with it is NO. The "contacts" associated with "coils" 101, 102, and 103 are in the CPU, where they form part of the virtual (i.e., simulated) control circuit. The simulated control circuit is not shown in Fig. 31.3.

The *output module* (Fig. 31.3) has four terminals O1, O2, O3, and O4, as well as a common terminal OC. The four terminals are associated with four normally open contacts that bear reference numbers 111, 112, 113, and 114. These NO contacts are sometimes the mechanical contacts of relays. In other cases, they are electronic switches (such as triacs) that will open or close depending on the signal received from a "relay coil" in the CPU.

Figure 31.3 shows two external contactor coils A and B and a pilot lamp, respectively connected between three of these output module terminals and one side of a 120 V ac source. The other side of the ac source is connected to terminal OC. Terminal O4 is not connected to anything. The reference numbers on the input and output modules are "addresses" established by the manufacturer of the PLC.

The *central processing unit* has a memory function and an operating function. We can imagine that it contains an enormous stock of "contacts" and "relay coils." This inventory of parts is stored in the memory of the CPU. The simple model of Fig. 31.3 contains the following virtual (simulated) components in its memory:

1. The "contacts" that correspond to the relay "coils" (rectangles) in the input module. The number of "contacts" per "coil" and their NO or NC condition is set by means of the programming unit. These particular contacts (not explicitly shown in Fig. 31.3) would bear the same reference numbers as the "relay coils," namely 101, 102, and 103.
2. The "coils" of the "relays" associated with the four NO contacts of the output module. These particular "coils" (not explicitly shown) would carry the same reference numbers 111, 112, 113, and 114 as the contacts they activate. Because there are four output terminals, the number of "output coils" is also four.
3. The "relay coils" and "contacts" of the "internal relays." The "coils" and "contacts" of these "internal relays" operate entirely inside the CPU; they do not appear in the input or output modules.

The memory contains an almost unlimited number of "contacts" that can be associated with any one of the internal "relay coils." The "contacts" bear the same reference numbers as the "relay coil" that activates them. Depending upon the requirements of the control system, we can program as many "contacts" per "relay" as needed. In order to "excite" the various "relay coils," the CPU simulates a power supply represented by two vertical "bus bars" (+) and (−). Let us assume that the CPU inventory contains the following internal items:

1. 50 "coils" of conventional "relays" bearing reference numbers 701 to 750; and
2. 10 "coils" of "time-delay relays" bearing reference numbers 901 to 910. The time delays associated with these "relays" can be set during the programming period.

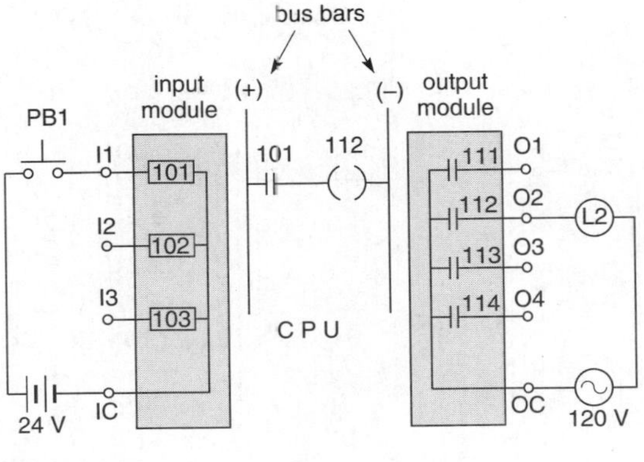

Figure 31.4
"Contact" 101, "coil" 112, and the connections between them and the "bus bars" are all programmed from the keyboard. Rectangle 101 simulates the "coil" of relay 101.

We will now use five examples to illustrate the behavior of this simple PLC.

31.3 Examples of the use of a PLC

Example 31-1

In Fig. 31.4, we want lamp L2 to light up when pushbutton PB1 is depressed.

Solution

1. Because PB1 is connected to terminal I1, "coil" 101 is excited when the pushbutton is depressed.
2. Because lamp L2 is connected to terminal O2, contact 112 (relay contact or triac) is closed when L2 lights up.
3. By virtue of (1), the operator must select a normally open "contact" carrying reference number 101 from the stock of components in the CPU memory. In the same way, by virtue of (2), he must select the output "relay coil" numbered 112. (The simulated relay coils are shown as truncated circles.)

The selections are made by using the keyboard. Finally, using the monitor and the keyboard, the operator programs the connections between "contact"

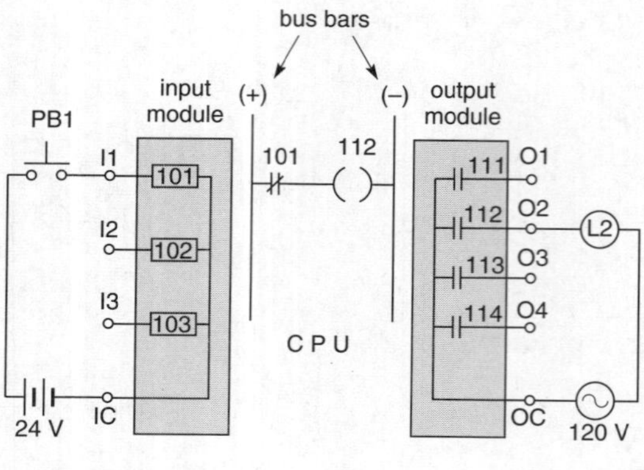

Figure 31.5
This diagram is similar to the one in Fig. 31.4 except that a normally closed "contact" 101 has been programmed in the CPU instead of a normally open (NO) contact.

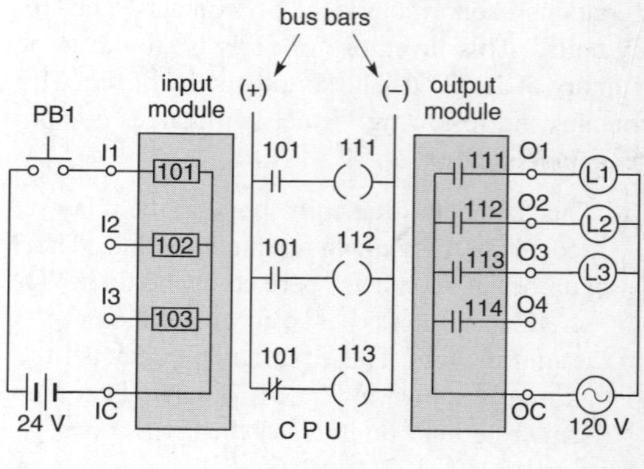

Figure 31.6
By programming additional "contacts" and "relay coils" into the ladder circuit, a more complex control system can be developed.

101, "coil" 112, and the (+) and (−) "bus bars" as shown in Fig 31.4.

As a result of this program, when pushbutton PB1 is depressed, "coil" 101 is activated by the external 24 V dc source. This causes "contact" 101 to close, which in turn excites "coil" 112. When "coil" 112 is excited, contact 112 closes and L2 lights up.

Note that "contact" 101 and "coil" 112 do not really exist. They are merely virtual elements simulated by the computer. When "coil" 112 is "excited" it causes contact 112 to close. As a result, the real lamp L2 is powered by the real 120 V source. (As mentioned previously, the normally open contacts 111 to 114 in the output module are usually triacs or mechanical contacts.)

Example 31-2

Referring to Fig. 31.5, pushbutton PB1 must again activate pilot lamp L2, but this time the lamp must go out when PB1 is depressed.

Solution

1. The setup is identical to the one in Example 31-1 except that the operator must select from the memory a "contact" 101 that is normally closed. As a result, "coil" 112 is normally excited and so *real* contact 112 is normally closed. By pressing a few keys on the keyboard the operator can make this change in less than a minute.

Example 31-3

In Fig. 31.6, pushbutton PB1 must control three lamps (L1, L2, and L3) so that when PB1 is depressed, L1 and L2 light up and L3 goes out.

Solution

1. The three lamps are connected to terminals O1, O2, and O3 and are therefore controlled by contacts 111, 112, and 113. Consequently, the PLC operator must select the three corresponding "coils" 111, 112, and 113.
2. The input "coil" 101 must now be equipped with three "contacts" (all labeled 101), two of which are normally open and one normally closed. The operator must program the connections as shown by the "ladder circuit" between the (+) and (−) "bus bars."

Note that we can add "contacts," increase the number of "relays," and change the "connections" by simply pushing a few keys on the keyboard. We never have to strip wires or mount a relay on a rack. As before, contacts 111, 112, and 113 are real components (usually triacs). The 120 V source and the three lamps are, of course, also real.

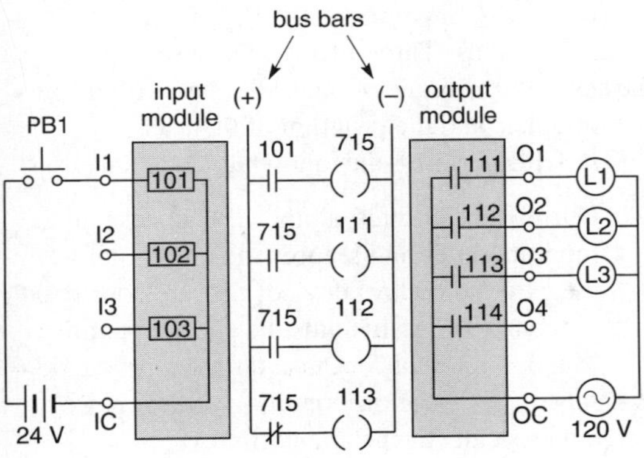

Figure 31.7
The external devices connected to the input and output modules perform the same way as in Fig. 31.6, but the CPU circuit is programmed in a different way. In this case, an internal auxiliary "relay" 715 has been added.

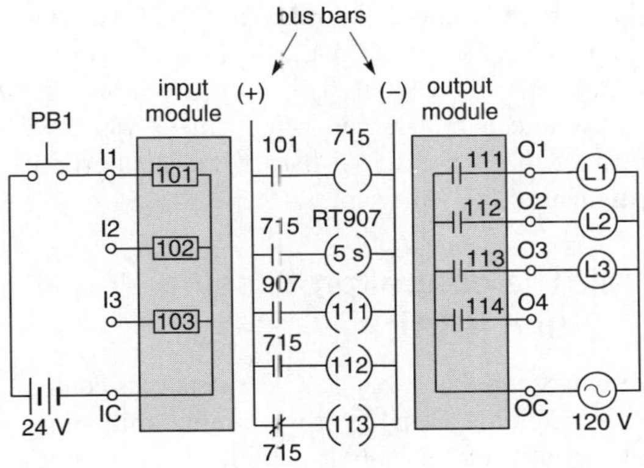

Figure 31.8
This CPU ladder circuit uses an internal "time-delay relay" labeled RT907. The time delay is programmed, as are all the other elements between the (+) and (–) "bus bars."

Example 31-4

In Fig. 31.7, the operation of pushbutton PB1 and of the lamps is the same as in Example 31-3, but the PLC will now make use of an "internal relay."

Solution

1. Among the 50 internal "relays" labeled 701 to 750 that the operator can select from the CPU memory bank, he decides to choose "relay" 715. In addition, he selects three associated "contacts," all bearing the number 715. Two of these contacts are normally open and one is normally closed.
2. The operator then programs the CPU "connections" as shown in Fig. 31.7.

When PB1 is depressed, "coil" 101 is excited, which closes "contact" 101. This excites "coil" 715, causing "coils" 111 and 112 to become "excited." As a result, contacts 111 and 112 close, thus lighting lamps L1 and L2. At the same time, "coil" 113 is "deactivated," causing contact 113 to open, which thereby extinguishes L3.

We again note that this new circuit involves only the computer. The external connections to the input module and output module in Figs. 31.6 and 31.7 are the same.

Example 31-5

In Fig. 31.8, the same control is required as in Example 31-4, but lamp L1 must light up 5 seconds after the pushbutton is depressed.

Solution

1. In this case the operator must add an internal "time-delay relay" to activate lamp L1. The remainder of the circuit stays the same.
2. The operator selects "time-delay relay" RT 907 from the CPU memory bank. He then adds normally open "contact" 907 and makes the CPU "connections" as shown in Fig. 31.8. Finally, he programs the time delay of RT 907 at 5 seconds.

When PB1 is depressed, "contact" 101 closes, which excites the "coil" of relay 715. The two normally open "contacts" 715 immediately close and normally closed "contact" 715 opens. Consequently, lamp L2 lights up at once and lamp L3 goes out. The virtual "coil" RT907 is excited but its "contact" 907 only closes 5 seconds later. Thus, lamp L1 comes on after a delay of 5 seconds.

These changes can all be made in a minute. Indeed, it is clear that we could make the lamps blink on and off in any way we please by simply adding more "time-delay relays," "contacts," and so forth. In other words, we can change the on/off performance of the lamps by simply punching a few keys. Quite a remarkable achievement when we consider that the external hard-wired connections remain absolutely the same.

31.4 The central processing unit (CPU)

We have seen that every PLC consists of a central processing unit (CPU), a programming unit, an input module, and an output module (Fig. 31.2). In the five preceding examples we have shown the role played by these components. We will now describe the construction and mode of operation of these components, starting with the CPU.

The central processing unit is the brain of the PLC. It is a complex circuit composed of one or more microprocessors. Without going into details, we will briefly describe the CPU memory and how it is used.

There are two types of memory. The first is *non-volatile,* which means that its contents cannot be erased or modified. The second is *volatile,* which means its memorized contents can be changed readily. The *non-volatile* memory contains all the instructions needed for the management of the PLC. These instructions are used to check the input modules and to determine the status of the control devices. It also transmits orders to the output modules. Finally, it interprets and executes instructions that are furnished by the keyboard, then carries out the user program.

In the memory section the PLC manufacturer installs the range of functions that can be executed by the PLC. In addition to relay-type functions—such as the coil function, the contact function, etc.—the PLC offers hundreds of other functions. These may be arithmetic functions, drum-switch functions, timer functions, counters, and registers. In effect, the non-volatile memory establishes all the operating parameters of the PLC. The contents of the non-volatile memory are defined by the manufacturer and cannot be erased or modified by the user.

The *volatile* memory of the PLC is divided into several sections. Three of them are used to record the status of the input modules, the status of the output modules, and the program of the user.

The CPU performs the following sequential tasks:

1. During a brief interval, the CPU checks all the input modules and records the on/off status of the external control devices that are connected to them. (The status must be checked at millisecond intervals because during a production schedule, the on/off condition of the control devices can change at any time.)
2. The CPU runs the program of the user. During this period, and depending on the program and the status of the inputs that have been recorded, the CPU decides which outputs should be activated. While the CPU program is being carried out, these decisions are stored in a memory section reserved for this purpose.
3. The CPU transmits the memorized decisions to the output modules. During this interval, the output modules activate or deactivate the external devices that are connected to the output terminals.

   The operating cycle consists of (a) taking successive readings of the status of the inputs, (b) carrying out the user program, and (c) transmitting the results to the output modules. The operating cycle is named *scanning.*

   The sequential scanning process goes on continually when the PLC is in operation. The time to make a complete scan depends upon the speed of the PLC and the size of the user program. As a general rule, it takes from 2 ms to 10 ms to make a complete scan.
4. During the scanning process, the CPU systematically checks the correct functioning of the hardware by diagnostic analysis.

31.5 Programming unit

The programming unit, composed of a keyboard and monitor, is used to program the PLC. But its usefulness does not end there. It also enables the user to observe the status of the input and output modules and to make changes to certain parameters. The programming unit is also used as a tool to check and diagnose the PLC. Finally, it is used to save the programs on tape or disc, and to retrieve these programs from the same supports. However, although the programming unit plays several roles, it is not needed when the PLC is operating. Consequently, the programming unit can be disconnected once the industrial process is in operation.

The programming unit can take the form of a small hand-held unit composed of a keyboard and a tiny monitor (Figs. 31.9 and 31.10). It can also be a computer with a large screen and keyboard having special keys. Because it is designed for industrial use, the programming unit must be portable and robust. Using the proper software, a personal computer is often used as a PLC programming unit.

31.6 The I/O modules

As mentioned previously, the input and output modules (designated by the abbreviation I/O) are the interfaces between the external control and controlled devices, and the central processing unit (CPU). The interface function is crucial. In effect, the CPU accepts and emits only low-voltage and low-power dc signals (0 to 5 V). The CPU is very sensitive and could be damaged if exposed to signals exceeding this voltage range. Thus, all communication links between the CPU and the external devices must be done via the I/O modules.

Each input module and each output module can be connected to several devices. We then speak of the number of "points" of entry and exit. Individual I/O modules possess 4, 8, 16, or 32 points; some have as many as 96 points. The 16-point modules are the most common. In the case of a large automated production process, several I/O modules may be required.

31.7 Structure of the input modules

The parts shown in Fig. 31.11 comprise the input module. It consists of a terminal board, a filter and conversion section, a status indicator, an isolation

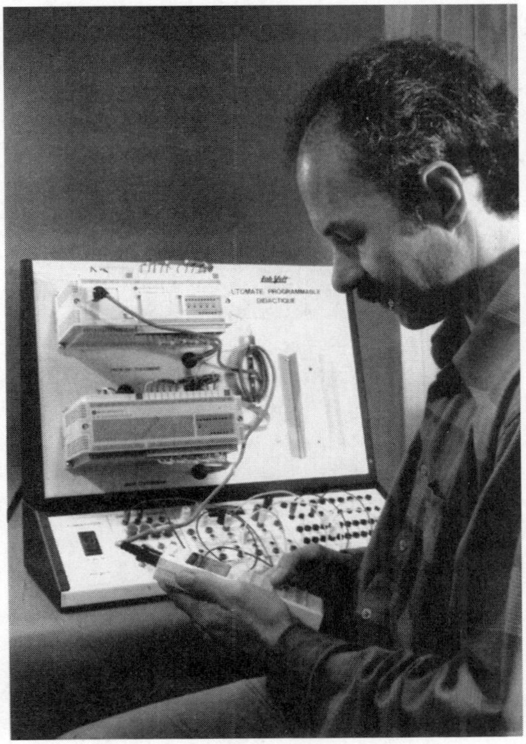

Figure 31.9
This industrial PLC has been adapted for educational purposes. The operator punches the keys of the hand-held programming unit and tracks the effect on the small screen. The programming unit interacts with the two parts of the PLC that are mounted on the upright panel. The upper part contains the central processing unit (CPU), the power supply, and the input and output (I/O) modules. The lower part is simply an extension of the upper part, offering additional I/O modules. This PLC has 10 input points and 6 output points.
(Courtesy of Lab-Volt)

section, and a communication board. Apart from the communication board, this configuration is repeated for each entry point.

In order to prevent spurious signals from activating the PLC, the filter and conversion section suppresses electrical noise such as may be caused by induced voltages or contact bounce. The conversion portion reduces the input voltage that appears

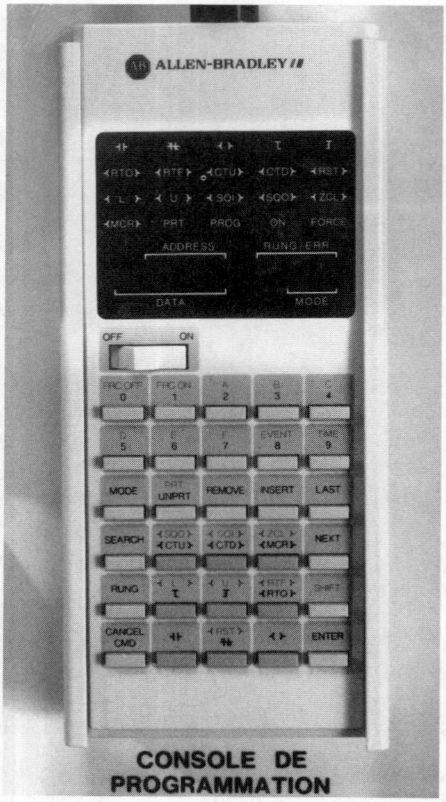

Figure 31.10
This portable programming unit shows the keyboard used for programming. The small screen above the keyboard enables the operator to see the "contacts," "relay coils," "time delays," etc. as they are programmed. These elements all bear a reference number or address. The programming unit can also be used to check the status of the external input and output devices. Consequently, it is a useful tool for both programming and diagnosing the control system. *(Courtesy of Lab-Volt)*

across the input terminals and, if necessary, rectifies ac signals.

The status indicator is a light emitting diode (LED) that is on or off depending on the signal received at each external terminal. It facilitates checking the operation of the control devices connected to the terminal board.

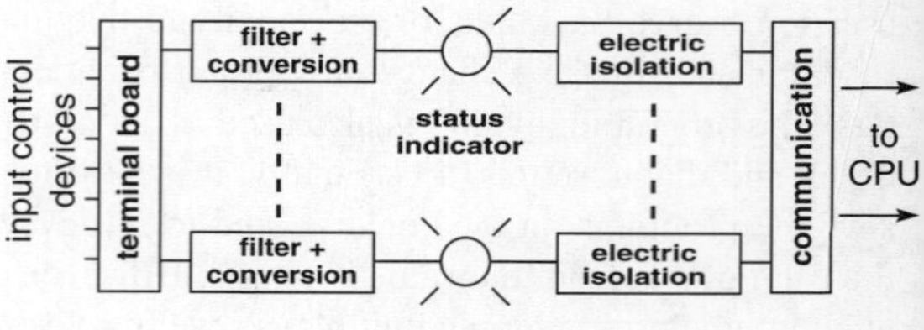

Figure 31.11
Structure of the input module.

The electric isolation section protects the CPU from electric noise and random voltage spikes. The isolation is achieved by means of an optical coupler which converts the incoming electric signal into a light signal. The light signal, in turn, is converted back into an electrical signal by means of a phototransistor.

On the input side, the optical coupler can withstand peaks of up to 1500 V. Thus, while it permits the transmission of signals, the optical coupler completely isolates the sensitive CPU circuits from those connected to the input terminals.

As regards the communication section, it registers all the status conditions of the input circuits and transmits them to the CPU.

The impedance of the input module is one of its important properties. Depending upon the voltage for which the module was designed, the input impedance of each point will range from 5 kΩ to 12 kΩ. The current required to activate a circuit is about 10 mA. This low current permits a reduction in the size of the external control devices, as well as the size of the cables linking them to the PLC.

Note that the user must furnish the power supply for the external control devices. Several voltages may be used: 24 V to 120 V ac or 10 V to 100 V dc. The filter and conversion section of the input module drops these voltages to a level that is compatible with the optical coupler.

31.8 Structure of the output modules

The output modules are built using the architecture displayed in Fig. 31.12. Moving outward from the CPU, the constituent parts are the (a) communica-

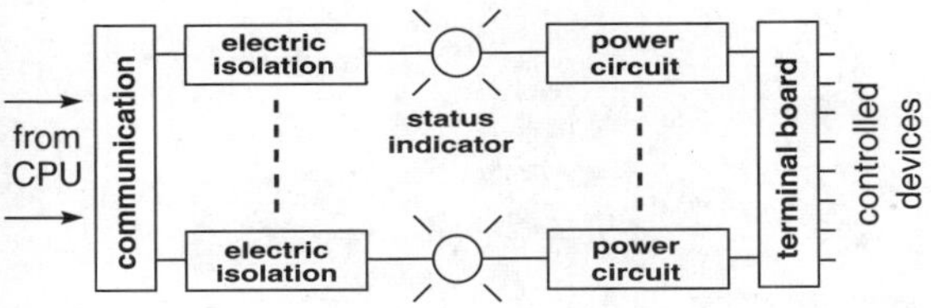

Figure 31.12
Structure of the output module.

tion section, (b) electric isolation, (c) status indicator, and (d) power circuit. Except for the communication section, the construction is the same for each output terminal.

The communication section receives the commands transmitted by the CPU and memorizes them until it receives new commands. In effect, the CPU is not constantly in touch with the output module. The CPU communicates with the output module in sequential fashion, according to the previously mentioned scanning process. The time between two successive scans varies from 10 ms to 2 ms (100 to 500 communications per second).

The isolation sections and the status indicators play the same roles as in the input modules. By optical coupling, they protect the sensitive CPU circuits from voltage surges. The LED indicators help check the status of the controlled devices.

The *power circuit* amplifies the signal from the CPU so as to operate the devices connected to the output terminals. As we have seen, each output point acts like a switch or contact (see Fig. 31.3). It closes or opens the circuit that is connected to the external device. A triac is often used to open and close the circuit. The user furnishes the power supply to drive the external devices.

Although the output modules are intended to control industrial devices, their current-carrying capacity is limited. Most of them can carry a maximum current ranging from 0.5 A to 2 A per output terminal. If an external device requires a larger current, an auxiliary relay must be used. For example, in Fig. 31.14, auxiliary relay B is employed to activate the holding coil A of a large contactor.

Fuses are also recommended to protect the equipment controlled by the PLC. Their main purpose is to protect the wiring and components in the event of a catastrophic short circuit.

Voltage spikes can damage the output modules. To eliminate the problem, it is recommended that voltage-limiting devices be installed whenever an external device tends to create transitory overvoltages across the output module.

31.9 Modular construction of PLCs

One of the important features of a PLC is its modular construction. Thus, the CPU and the I/O modules are all mounted in individual slots (Fig. 31.13a). Modularity offers a big advantage because if a module is presumed to be defective, it can immediately be replaced by another one. Thus, in a matter of minutes, the PLC can be up and running again. The only module that requires special attention when replaced is the one that contains the memory of the PLC. The original program (previously saved) has to be retrieved using the programming unit. This operation, which takes only a few minutes, is equivalent to replacing an entire relay rack.

Another advantage of modularity is the ability to expand the capacity of the PLC to meet the growing needs of the user. Thus, I/O modules can be added as and when required. The memory capacity of the PLC is the only thing that limits the number of I/O modules that can be accommodated. Figure 31.13b shows the construction of a 16-point output module in which each point is controlled on/off by a small relay.

31.10 Remote inputs and outputs

We have just seen that users can tailor the PLC to meet their needs. The modular nature of the PLC also enables the installation of I/O modules at remote locations, far removed from the CPU itself. We then speak of remote I/O modules. Such modules are placed close to the particular automated process or production line that has to be controlled.

These modules can be located as near as 3 meters to as far as 3 km from the CPU. Each I/O module is equipped with a power supply and a communications

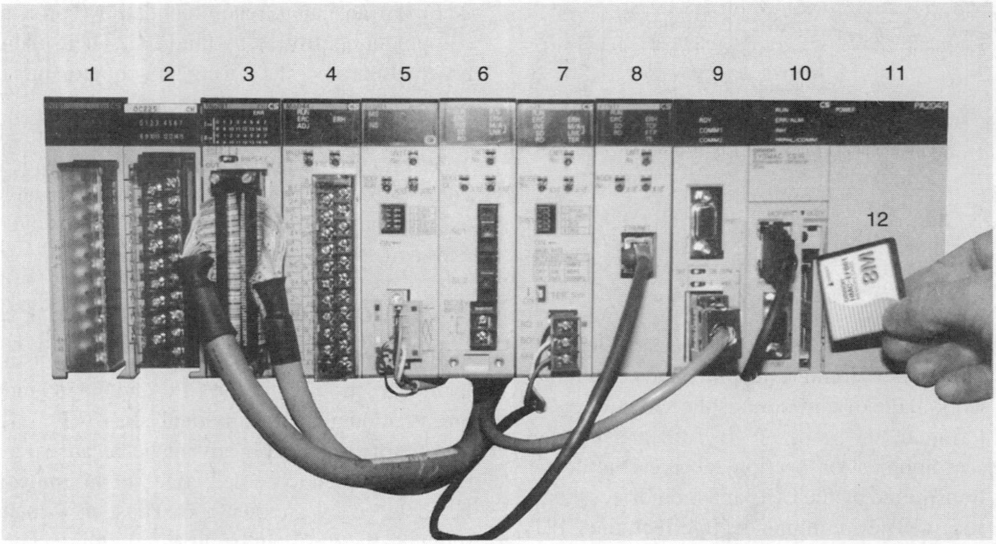

Figure 31.13a
Modular PLC for the distributed control of I/O devices of any type, including position control and the control of industrial processes. The PLC rack shown contains ten modules of various kinds. Racks having capacities to hold from two to ten modules are available. Seven such racks connected locally have a potential capacity of more than 5000 local I/O points (modules 1–4 above). However, most I/O modules are now installed close to the transducers and actuators and tied to the PLC by communication networks whose protocols are either proprietary or standardized by industrial manufacturers' associations (module 5).

The remote modules can themselves be micro-PLCs. In general, rather than using a single PLC, several PLCs are installed in a factory, each controlling a machine or a section. The PLCs are often interconnected by means of a factory communication network (modules 6–7). Finally, the factory network can also be connected to the information network of the business enterprise, making use of the embedded gateway capability of the PLC (module 8).
Description of modules:

1. 16-point input module with screw terminals
2. 16-point output module with screw terminals (see internal construction in Figure 31.13b)
3. 96-point I/O module including pre-wired cable for external input terminal blocks and output modules
4. 8-point configurable analogue input module
5. DeviceNet® network module (mainly for the control of remote I/O modules, contactors, variable speed drives, etc.)
6. Controller Link® network module using fiber optics (mainly for supervision and exchange of data at high speed)
7. Controller Link® network module using twisted-pair cable
8. Network module for communication by Ethernet® protocol (mainly for supervision, data acquisition, and management of information)
9. Optional CPU inner board with two programmable serial communication ports
10. Central processing unit (CPU) of the PLC (two configurable serial ports can be seen on the front)
11. Power supply for the PLC
12. Optional memory card to save local files concerning the project. This may be the project development file itself, electrical wiring diagrams, or to hold rapid and intensive local data acquisition by the PLC.

(Courtesy of OMRON Canada Inc.)

Figure 31.13b
This picture shows the interior of a 16-point relay-type output module. The relays are mounted on plug-in bases and can readily be replaced by means of an extractor that is included in the module. On account of their robustness, versatility, and low cost, output modules with relays are often used instead of semiconductor devices. However, a relay is an electromechanical device whose useful life is limited by the electrical load and the number of operations. Typical load capacity is 2 amperes. Note that the terminal board can be lifted easily, so the wiring does not have to be undone when the module is removed from the PLC rack.
(Courtesy of OMRON Canada Inc.)

Figure 31.13c
This "remote" I/O module can be used locally by connecting it to a PLC, such as shown in module 3 of Fig. 31.13a. The connection is made by means of pre-wired cables of different lengths (up to a maximum of ten meters). The relay module can also be connected further away by adding a communication module of the desired choice. External output modules allow for a wider choice of output types. Also, modules having greater capacities can be installed, thus facilitating direct interfacing of the controlled devices connected to the output.
(Courtesy of OMRON Canada Inc.)

module. A twisted or coaxial cable, or a fiber-optic link, connects the remote station to the CPU. Fig. 31.13c shows a remote output module.

31.11 Conventional control circuits and PLC circuits

It is now evident that we can use a PLC in place of a conventional relay control circuit. The following examples show how the change is made.

Example 31-6

Consider the conventional control circuit of Fig. 20.16b (reproduced here for convenience) which controls the start/run/stop operation of a motor. Fig. 31.14 uses a PLC to perform the same operations. We recall that each input to the input module behaves like the coil of a relay. The "coil" has one or more "contacts," located in the CPU, whose respective NO or NC conditions are programmed by the user.

Note that "contact" 102 associated with the stop pushbutton is programmed to be normally open (NO). In effect, since this NC pushbutton is connected to terminal 102, "coil" 102 is "excited," which causes the NO "contact" 102 in the CPU to be closed. This is true as long as the stop pushbutton is not depressed.

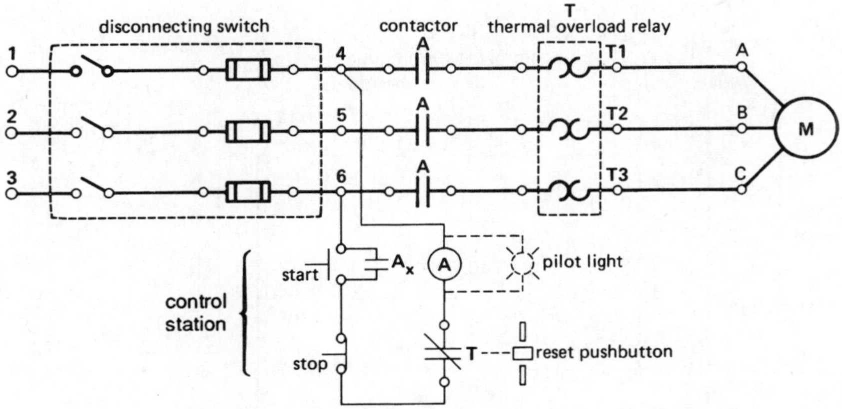

Figure 20.16b (reproduction)
Schematic diagram of a 3-phase across-the-line magnetic starter.

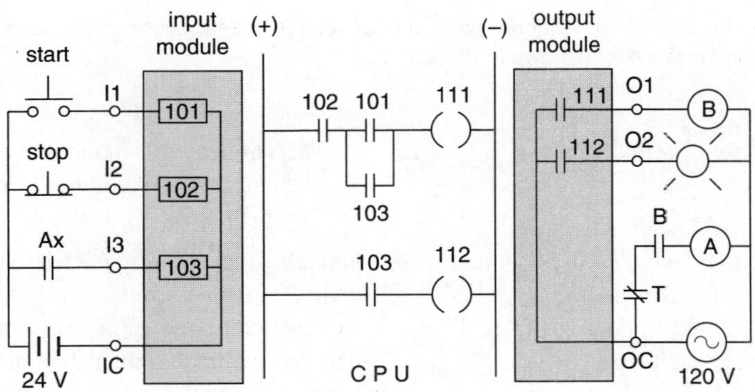

Figure 31.14
This PLC virtual control system produces the same machine performance as the hardware control system shown in Fig. 20.16b.

We also note that an auxiliary relay B had to be added to the output module. The reason is that terminal O1 cannot furnish the relatively large current needed to excite to the holding coil of big contactor A. By using the small relay B, whose contacts are robust enough to carry the exciting current of coil A, we get around the problem.

Let us now examine the behavior of the virtual contacts and coils of the PLC. Prior to pushing the start pushbutton, "coil" 102 is excited which means that "contact" 102 is closed. The "contacts" 101 and 103 are open because "coils" 101 and 103 are not excited. As a result, "coils" 111 and 112 are not "excited." It follows that contacts 111 and 112 in the output module are open. Thus, auxiliary coil B is not excited and the pilot lamp connected to O2 is off. As a result, contact B is open, which means that holding coil A is not excited and so the motor will not start.

Let us push the start pushbutton momentarily and see what happens.

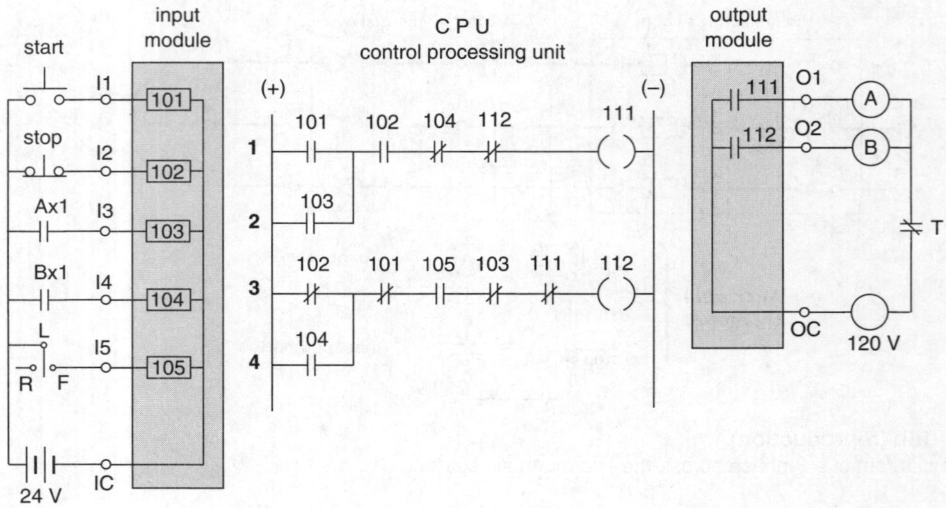

Figure 31.15
This PLC control system for starting and plugging a motor possesses the same security features and produces the same effect as the all-hardware system shown in Fig. 20.24a.

1. "Coil" 101 is "excited," which closes "contact" 101.
2. Because "contact" 102 is already closed, "coil" 111 is "excited," which closes contact 111, thus exciting relay coil B.
3. The NO contact B closes, which excites contactor coil A, thus starting the motor.
4. As soon as contactor A closes, the NO auxiliary contact A_X closes, which excites "coil" 103, thus causing both "contacts" 103 to close. These contacts remain closed as long as contactor A is energized. As a result, contact 112 closes, causing the pilot lamp to light up.
5. When the pressure on the start pushbutton is released, it causes "contact" 101 to open, but since "contact" 103 is closed, the motor continues to run.
6. When the stop pushbutton is depressed, "coil" 102 is no longer excited, thus causing "contact" 102 to open. As a result, "coil" 111 is deenergized, which opens contact 111, which deenergizes coil B, thus deenergizing coil A, which stops the motor. It is readily seen that the opening of A_X will extinguish the pilot light.

Note that the wires connected to terminals I1, I2, I3, and IC carry a current of only a few milliamperes. Consequently, the cable connected to these terminals can be much lighter than in conventional relay control circuits. Also, the 24 V power supply has only to deliver a few watts at the most.

The simple control circuit of Fig. 20.16b would not justify using a PLC. However, it illustrates the principles that are involved.

Example 31-7

We want to use a PLC to replace the conventional control system shown in Fig. 20.24a, displayed at the beginning of this chapter. The resulting PLC circuit and "ladder diagram" are shown in Fig. 31.15. It is called a ladder diagram because the (+) and (−) "bus bars" look like the sidepieces of a ladder while the horizontal circuits **1, 2, 3, 4,** containing the "contacts" and "coils" look like rungs.

The NO contacts of the **start** pushbutton and the NC contacts of the **stop** pushbutton are connected to terminals I1 and I2 of the PLC. The cumbersome mechanical interlock (for security purposes) of the two pushbuttons of Fig. 20.24a is now replaced by the NC "contact" 102 of rung 3 and the NC "contact" 101, also of rung 3. The NO auxiliary contacts (A_{X1} and B_{X1}) of contactors A and B are respectively connected to terminals I3 and I4 of the input module. The former NC auxiliary contacts (A_{X2} and B_{X2}) are no longer required. The NO "contacts" 103 and 104 of rungs **2** and **4** are the holding contacts. The NC "contacts" 104 and 103 of rungs **1** and **3** constitute a security interlock.

As a further measure of security, NC "contacts" 112 and 111 of rungs **1** and **3** were programmed into the CPU memory. This eliminates the potential danger of a break in the connection of contacts A_{X1} and B_{X1}. It is obvious that considerable economies have been realized in the number of external devices connected to the I/O modules. The **start** and **stop** pushbuttons now have only one contact and the main contactors A and B have each only one auxiliary contact, namely A_{X1} and B_{X1}.

The programming of ladder diagrams such as that of Fig. 31.15 takes considerable knowledge of logic circuits. We leave the analysis of the behavior of this circuit to the reader.

31.12 Security rule

By using a PLC, it is possible to invert the status of the external contacts connected to the input module. Thus, a real NO contact connected to the input module can be programmed by the user as an NC "contact" in the PLC's CPU (see Examples 31-1 and 31-2, Section 31.3). This freedom to reverse the state of a contact must be used with discretion, particularly as regards the selection of the type of contact (NO or NC) of the devices connected to the input module. The following rule must *always* be observed:

Any "contact" associated with a device that serves to initiate an action of some kind must be of the NO type. Conversely, any "contact" associated with a device that serves to stop an action must be of the NC type.

If this rule is not observed, a break in a cable connecting an input device to the PLC could produce unexpected start-ups or make it impossible to stop an automated process.

31.13 Programming the PLC

In order to program a PLC, we must "write" the operations it has to perform. These instructions are typed on the programming unit keyboard, observed on the monitor, and stored in the CPU memory. From the very beginning, particular attention was devoted to the method of programming. The technical criteria stipulated that the system should be quickly and easily programmable and reprogrammable by the user. The PLC was therefore carefully designed to make it simple to use. However, it is useful to have some computer knowledge to program a PLC.

31.14 Programming languages

The term *programming language* refers to the list of symbols that are used and the way they have to be configured to program the PLC. The three principal languages are: (1) the ladder diagram, (2) Boolean logic, and (3) the Sequential Flow Chart (SFC). The European equivalent of the SFC language is called *Grafcet.* Other languages have been developed in recent years, so that a total of about six options are available, at the discretion of the user.

The ladder diagram

Among the several programming languages that are used, the ladder diagram is the simplest. Without saying so explicitly, we used ladder diagrams in Figs. 31.6, 31.7, 31.8, and 31.14. Figure 31.15 shows yet another ladder diagram.

In programming a ladder diagram from the keyboard, the desired circuit is progressively displayed on the monitor. During this process, the cursor is moved to the desired place on the screen and the desired function is selected by pushing the appropriate key to create a NO or NC "contact," an "internal relay coil," an "output relay coil," and so forth. When the function is chosen, it is given a reference number. The same procedure is followed for the remainder of the control circuit.

During the programming phase, only a portion of the control circuit can be displayed on the screen. However, most PLCs that use the ladder programming language can be connected to a printer. Consequently, the entire control circuit can be displayed, which enables the programmer to verify the diagram and the behavior of the system. Figure 31.16 shows a portion of the menu and ladder diagram displayed on the monitor of a PLC.

Boolean language

The Boolean programming language is based on Boolean algebra. This algebra is used to solve problems of logic. It was invented in the middle of the 19th century by the British mathematician George Boole.

One of the drawbacks of this language is the difficulty one has in reading it. Thus, starting from a ladder diagram, it is easy to write a program using the Boolean language. However, the reverse procedure is difficult; it is hard to read a program in Boolean language and then translate it into the corresponding ladder diagram.

The SFC language

The *sequential flow chart* (SFC) language is a very effective tool in diagnosing PLCs and automated systems in general. It is a PLC programming method that enables the user to organize the individual machine operations of a process into a series of steps and transitions. Ladder logic can then be used to implement the program.

31.15 Advantages of PLCs over relay cabinets

There are many reasons for the universal popularity of PLCs. We list them as follows.

- The PLC is flexible. Because it is programmable, it is easy to modify as the need arises. In the case of control systems using physical relays, any change means replacing relays and reconnecting them. This is risky because connection errors can easily be made.
- The flexibility of PLCs is extraordinary. Thus, whenever a given control system is no longer required, it can readily be reprogrammed for a completely different system. With relay racks, such a changeover is not feasible and the racks would simply be scrapped, replaced, and rewired.
- The PLC is much less bulky than a conventional relay control system. For example, a CPU having a volume of 0.1 m^3 replaces hundreds of control relays, as well as the hard wiring needed to connect the contacts and holding coils. Furthermore, the PLC consumes far less energy.
- A PLC is more reliable than a relay cabinet. One important reason is the absence of moving parts. Relays have moving parts that deteriorate as the equipment gets older. Relay contacts wear out and have to be replaced, all of which requires a sustained maintenance program. "Relay coils" and "contacts" in CPUs never wear out.
- In addition, the opening and closing of relay contacts, while rapid, takes a certain time. The time interval is not the same for all relays and, moreover, it may change with time. In some applications where the opening and closing sequence is important, the time variations may introduce control errors. Such errors are very difficult to diagnose because of their random nature. In the case of PLCs, the "contact" opening and closing times are fixed. Consequently, sequence operations are never a problem.
- The relay cabinet has to be assembled by hand. Hundreds and even thousands of wires must be connected between the contacts and relay coils, which implies a big chance of making errors. These errors are difficult to locate. By contrast, with a PLC, all that is needed is to draw a ladder diagram according to a plan. Here again, if an error is made, the hand-held programming unit (or the more sophisticated computer) contains utility functions that make it easy to correct a mistake.

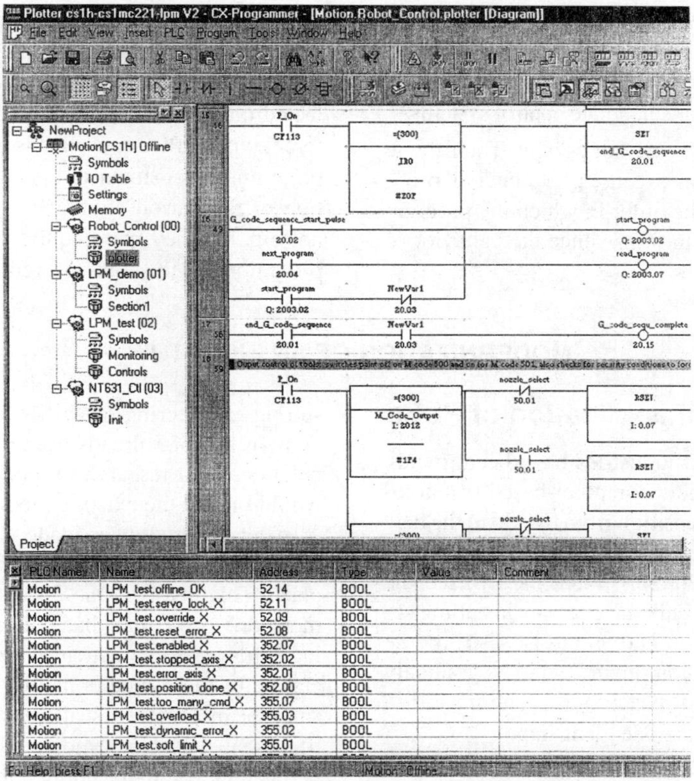

Figure 31.16
Software programs for PLCs are evolving rapidly. Small, dedicated programming consoles that permit only a very limited interface with the user are now almost only employed because of their portability and their ability to make quick, minor modifications in the field.

But the most frequently used tool is the portable computer whose software is based upon Microsoft Windows®. Evidently, these software programs permit the development and configuration of the PLC, but they also enable the adequate documentation of the programs.

Portable computers also enable an operator to communicate with more than one PLC at a time. Furthermore, changes to the program can be made without having to stop a machine or interrupt a process controlled by the PLC. They also constitute a powerful tool to diagnose or debug a problem. The reason is that the operator can visualize the situation in the form of chronograms and other graphic displays. Ladder diagrams can be "frozen" when specific conditions have been identified and registered in real-time by the PLC.

The most practical and frequently used programming language is still the ladder logic as displayed in this figure. However, more and more PLCs offer complementary programming tools such as sequential flow charts, functional block diagrams, literal (Boolean) language, and high-level languages such as Basic or C. In addition, specialized software using dedicated languages can be tied in with the main development software. They are used for more specific tasks like positioning applications, process-manufacturing controls, or other tasks by integrated co-processors on the PLC. Finally, other auxiliary software programs are used to perform simulations, supervision, data acquisition, control, and management.
(Courtesy of OMRON Canada Inc.)

- As regards cost, a PLC is cheaper than a conventional relay rack as soon as the number of relays exceeds about ten or fifteen. The economy is obviously greater for more elaborate control systems.

Having said this, PLCs are not perfect. Their mode of operation sometimes causes sequencing problems. For example, the order in which the program is written can sometimes influence the behavior of the controlled system.

Finally, the effect of a program may not be the same from one PLC to another. This anomaly stems from the fact that manufacturers have not yet established common standards. Thus, every time a different type of PLC is used, it is important to read the programming manual to ensure the proper operation of the various functions. The differences are not big, but they may require slight changes when programming the control circuit.

MODERNIZATION OF AN INDUSTRY

31.16 Industrial application of PLCs

We are all aware that industries have been greatly transformed by the new computer-based technologies. How does the transition from the old to the new take place? To answer this question, let us consider a large stevedoring enterprise that modernized the handling of one of its bulk materials by installing sophisticated equipment and controls. During the changeover, the new equipment had to be gradually integrated with the old because it was unthinkable to make the changeover in one giant step.

The stevedoring operation consists of unloading freighters carrying bulk products such as rock salt, cement, pig iron, powdered nickel, bauxite, and alumina. The modernization involved the handling of alumina, a powder used to make aluminum. Its chemical composition is given by the formula Al_2O_3. During a typical stevedoring operation, some 700 tons per hour of alumina are sucked out of the ship's hold, moved by conveyor belts (Fig. 31.17) to a waiting train, and blown through ports into cylindrical-shaped wagons. A typical wagon is loaded in a matter of 10 minutes.

31.17 Planning the change

When management decided to modernize the alumina stevedoring procedure, a small team of experts was given the task of determining what methods should be used and how the entire process could be automated. This in-depth study took more than a year to complete. It required the input from consulting engineering firms, visits to stevedoring operations that had already been modernized, cost calculations, and research on how the modernization would impact the existing labor force.

After the study was made, the *gradual* transformation of the stevedoring operation began to take place. This involved the installation of new equipment, driven by more than one hundred motors ranging in power from fractional size to 1500 hp. The operation of these motors had to be coordinated. But since the motors were scattered over a wide area, and because they had to be monitored from a central control station, communication of their status was of the essence. Thus, the current, speed, phase unbalance, temperature of the windings, temperature of the bearings, vibration, etc., had to be monitored on a continuous basis. Furthermore, if anything ran out of line, an alarm had to be sounded to have the problem fixed. For example, if one of the 500 hp blower motors (Fig. 31.18) began to vibrate, the situation had to be corrected quickly because damage to the bearings or to the driven equipment could result.

Motorized valves demanded special position controls. Thus, as the alumina was rushing through 500 mm pipes, the flow had to be kept at the desired level to ensure that it was neither too high nor too low.

Clearly, such a complete control over the industrial process could only be achieved by computers. But during the transition, much of the older equipment, together with its relays, hard wiring, limit switches, pushbuttons, and so forth, had to function as before. Consequently, the stevedoring operation involved a progressive marriage of the new with the

Figure 31.17
One of the many intersections of two conveyor belts that are more than 1 km long. The conveyors are used to store bulk products, and to load and unload freighters in the Port of Québec.
(Courtesy of St. Lawrence Stevedoring)

old, wherein computers controlled one section while human operators continued to control another. Furthermore, the older hard wiring had to be integrated (temporarily) with new coaxial cable and fiber-optic links. This required the installation of appropriate interfacing devices.

All these alterations had to be made, not in a laboratory, but in the field, where huge gantry cranes and powerful motors could easily wreck equipment if something went wrong. Thus, another important aspect of the transition was the proper operation of the apparatus and the safety of personnel.

Another vital consideration was the impact of this new technology on the working habits and continued employment of the workers. In effect, the modernization and automation of the stevedoring operation meant that many manual jobs would no longer be required. Because labor relations are always important, it became necessary to ensure that jobs that were lost would be replaced by tasks that were more satisfying, less routine, and more interesting.

31.18 Getting to know PLCs

How was the new equipment installed and who was to look after it? It is interesting to note that technicians that had been doing their regular jobs for years were quickly able to absorb the new technology. The verbal exchange between company representatives that were supplying the PLCs and fiber-optic devices enabled the older technicians to understand the new language of ladder logic diagrams, Ethernet®,

Figure 31.18
Blower motors to siphon alumina powder from freighter to special train wagons. The 3-phase motors have a rating of 500 hp, 4160 V, 3600 r/min. The picture shows (1) a position-controlled pneumatic valve, (2) a thermal detector to sense the temperature of the motor windings, and (3) a vibration detector.
(Courtesy of St. Lawrence Stevedoring)

Internet, megabits per second, etc. And so it became evident that not only were the equipment and controls gradually being changed, but that the same process was going on at the human level. Valuable knowledge acquired over many years was gradually being enhanced by new information.

Some individuals welcomed the challenge of learning something new, but others were more apprehensive about their ability to cope with these new-fangled concepts. But time and daily contact with new equipment inevitably transform a person's way of thinking. As the transition took place, the lingo became familiar, the tasks became routine, the computers became less intimidating, and before long the gray-haired veteran realized he had become part of the high-tech team. He now knows how to handle a keyboard, he understands what the computer screen reveals, he knows what to do if an alarm sounds, and he can quickly communicate his findings to others (Fig. 31.19).

The newly-hired technician also had the advantage of working closely with these experienced vet-

Figure 31.19
Strategic control and surveillance center of all bulk products handled in the Port of Québec. All the communication networks, cameras, and status of PLCs are centralized at this point.
(Courtesy of St. Lawrence Stevedoring)

erans. As a result, the technical-human link between the old and the new is considerably reinforced.

31.19 Linking the PLCs

The entire stevedoring facility is controlled by about fifteen PLCs, two of which are assigned to the alumina-handling operation. Some are linked by a communications network in order to coordinate specific operations. Other PLCs perform isolated tasks that do not have to be integrated with the system. However, plans are under way to centralize all the PLCs. One reason is to control the peak power that is drawn by the stevedoring facility. For example, the cost of electric power can be reduced by staggering the use of large motors so they do not run at the same time. Such peak-load control can save thousands of dollars per month.

31.20 Programming the PLCs

Naturally, the entire industrial process had to be programmed on computers. Towards this end, programming specialists were hired to implement the new control techniques and to incorporate them in the PLC memory blocks. This became the task of new graduates from technical institutes working in conjunction with manufacturers' representatives. They programmed the PLCs using languages such as SFC and, more recently, block diagrams. For the

Figure 31.20
This 600-V, 3-phase motor control center is equipped with PowerLogic® devices that provide sophisticated monitoring capabilities such as active and reactive power, voltage, current, and waveform analysis. It includes Internet transmission capabilities and possesses embedded Web pages.
(Courtesy of Schneider Electric)

Figure 31.21
This motor starter with its on/off/jog pilot lights has a 3-phase contactor and disconnect switch. In addition, it includes a multifunction protection relay that protects the motor against mechanical overloads, overheating, voltage and current unbalance, and phase failure. In addition, it monitors the power factor, starting time, ground faults, and starting current. It transmits all this information to a PLC using a Modbus® protocol. Copper or fiber-optic cable may be used to make the connection.
(Courtesy of Schneider Electric)

experienced programmer, the latter are often more convenient to use than ladder diagrams.

In setting up a new control sequence to handle, say, the movement of a crane, the programmer must incorporate fail-safe features by simulating the operation of the crane to see if any bugs arise. The preliminary simulation phase is very important because it enables the programmer to verify the safety and integrity of the system. Finally, when a program is put into actual operation for the first time, the technical group watches closely to see that everything is behaving as planned. Towards this end, emergency pushbuttons are spotted at strategic points to interrupt a wrongly programmed activity.

As regards the motor control centers (Fig. 31.20), they contain the usual contactors to start and stop electric motors. However, they also include monitoring devices that continually check the condition of the motor (Fig. 31.21). This information is re-

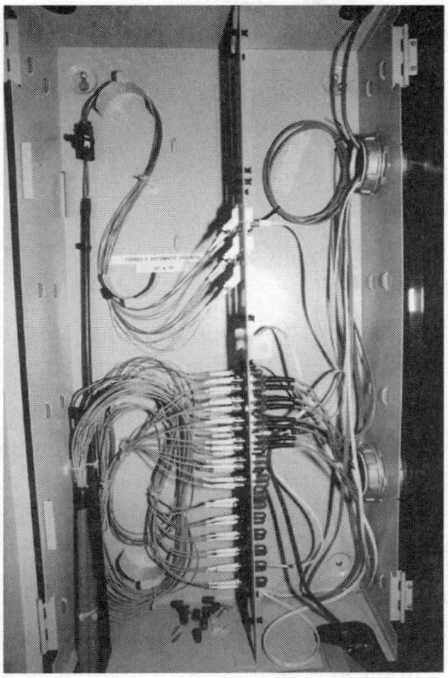

Figure 31.22
This fiber-optic junction box facilitates connections between cables.
(Courtesy of St. Lawrence Stevedoring)

layed to the relevant PLC by fiber optics consisting of a single strand of flexible cable (Fig. 31.22).

In conclusion, the installation of this modern control system has significantly reduced the cost of the alumina stevedoring operation. At the same time it has stimulated the operating personnel, and has offered interesting job opportunities.

Figures 31.23, 31.24, and 31.25 convey the flavor of this modernization process. It is typical of all renovations and computer-modernizing procedures that are carried out by industry today.

31.21 The transparent enterprise

As an extension of the automation process we have just described, the tendency today is to integrate it with commercial transactions. In effect, the Internet is making it possible to communicate with everyone involved in the manufacturing, marketing, purchasing, and end-use of products. In order to simplify these links, great efforts are being made to standardize the communication systems that are used in these diverse activities. The end result is a "transparent" e-business atmosphere that not only facilitates commercial transactions, but also is integrated with the actual manufacturing and service activities of an enterprise.

Thus, the PLC is no longer just an ingenious relay-operating device; it has become part of a sophisticated control system that reaches into every echelon of business.

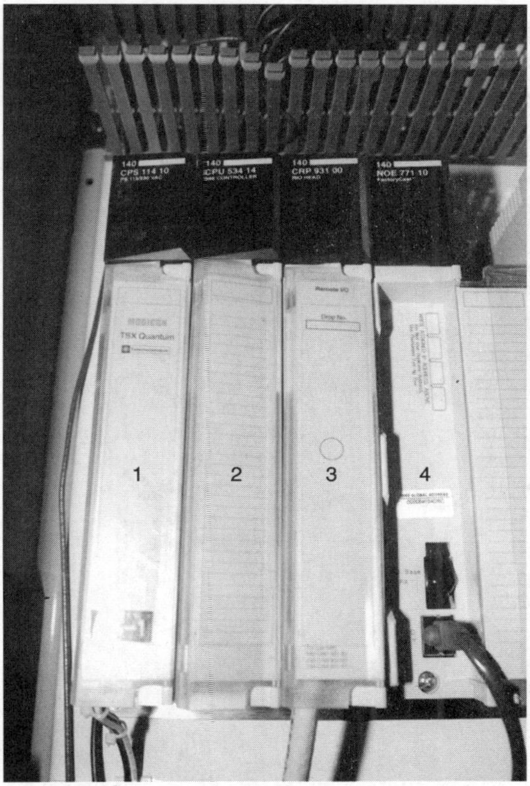

Figure 31.23
This Quantum® PLC has three parts. From left to right: (1) I/O module, (2) CPU, and (3) power supply. At the far right is (4) a Web server which establishes the 100 Mb/s Internet connection using either fiber-optic or wired cable.
(Courtesy of Schneider Electric)

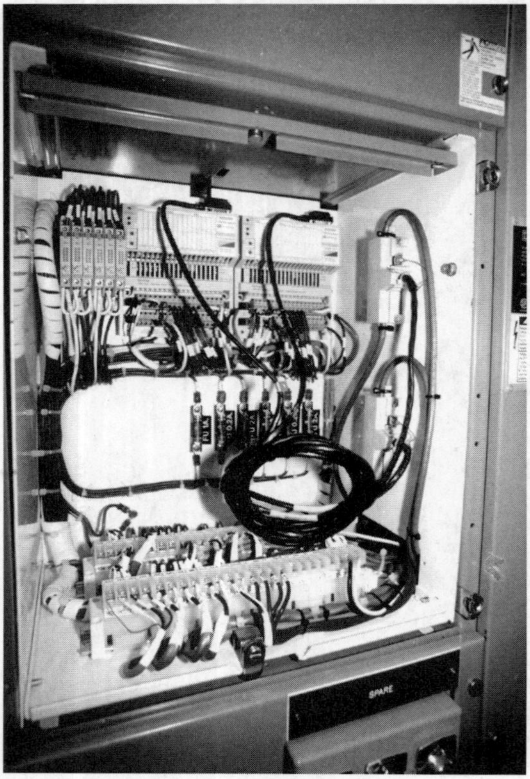

Figure 31.24
This programmable logic controller belongs to the Momentum® family. It has the usual I/O modules but it includes embedded Web pages and possesses communication facilities that enable it to receive and send data by Internet protocol.
(Courtesy of Schneider Electric)

Questions and Problems

31-1 Name the principal parts of a programmable logic controller.

31-2 In a PLC, what is the purpose of the input module?

31-3 In a PLC, what is the purpose of the output module?

31-4 In a control system, name four advantages of using a PLC instead of relay racks.

31-5 A PLC is able to simulate relay coils, contacts, and the connections between them. Explain how this simulation makes it easy to set up and modify an industrial control system.

31-6 In a PLC, describe the purpose of the central processing unit (CPU).

31-7 Name three languages that are used in programming a PLC.

31-8 The PLCs in a large organization are often interconnected and tied to a main computer. Explain how this enables communication between the manufacturing process and the business and marketing activities of an enterprise.

Figure 31.25
The four devices shown act as bridges between the Ethernet® and Modbus® protocols. The bridges enable older communication technologies to be transmitted over the Internet. Bridges are high-performance gateways. *(Courtesy of Schneider Electric)*

REFERENCES

BOOKS

The following books provide information on a variety of topics. Some books predating the 1980s are listed on account of their historical significance.

1. ANSI, 1997. AC High-voltage circuit breaker rated on a symmetrical current basis—preferred ratings and related required capabilities (C37.06). Piscataway, N.J.: Inst. Electrical and Electronics Eng.
2. Arillaga, J. 1983. *High voltage direct current transmission.* London: Peregrinus Ltd.
3. ASTM, 1996. *Annual book of ASTM standards: Copper and copper alloys.* Philadelphia: American Society for Testing and Materials.
4. Bartnikas, R. 1987. *Engineering dielectrics.* Baltimore: ASTM.
5. Beeman, D. 1995. *Industrial power systems handbook.* New York: McGraw.
6. Bennet, W. R. Jr. 1994. *Health and low-frequency electromagnetic fields.* New Haven: Yale University Press.
7. Biddle, 1997. *Getting down to earth.* Dallas: Avo International Training Institute.
8. Bonneville Power Administration, 1976. *Transmission line reference book HVDC to ± 600 kV.* Palo Alto: Electric Power Research Institute.
9. Bose, B. K. 1981. *Adjustable speed ac drive systems.* Piscataway, N.J.: Inst. of Electrical and Electronic Eng.
10. Boylestad, R. D. 1996. *Introductory circuit analysis.* Upper Saddle River, N.J.: Prentice Hall.
11. Canadian Standards Association, 2000. *Metric Practice Guide Z 234.1-00.* Toronto: CSA.
12. Chapman, S. J. 1999. *Electric machinery fundamentals.* New York: McGraw.
13. Cogdell, J. R. 1996. *Foundations of electrical engineering.* Upper Saddle River, N.J.: Prentice Hall.
14. Crompton, T. R. 1995. *Battery reference book.* Boston: Butterworth-Heinemann.
15. Dorf, R. C. 1993. *The electrical engineering handbook.* Boca Raton, Florida, 33431: CRC Press.
16. Edison Electric Institute, 1998. *Statistical yearbook of the electric utility industry/1998.* Washington: Edison Electric Institute.
17. Elgerd, O. 1982. *Electric energy system theory: An introduction.* New York: McGraw.
18. Fink, D. G. 1993. *Standard handbook for electrical engineers.* New York: McGraw.
19. Finney, D. 1998. *Variable frequency ac motor drive systems.* London: Peregrinus Ltd.
20. Ford, R. A. 1996. *Homemade lightning.* New York: McGraw.
21. General Electric, 1975. *Transmission line reference book 345 kV and above.* New York: Fred Weidner and Son Printers Inc.
22. Gieras, J. F. and Wing, M. 1997. *Permanent magnet motor technology.* New York: Dekker.
23. Greenwood, A. 1991. *Electrical transients in power systems.* New York: Wiley.
24. Gyugyi, L. and Pelly, B. R. 1976. *Static frequency changers.* New York: Wiley.

25. Hamdi, E. S. 1994. *Design of small electrical machines.* New York: Wiley.

26. Harter, J. H. 1995. *Electomechanics.* Upper Saddle River, N.J.: Prentice Hall.

27. Hingorani, N. G. and Gyugyi, L., 2000. *Understanding Facts.* Piscataway, N.J.: IEEE Press.

28. Holden, A. 1992. *The nature of solids.* Mineola, N.Y.: Dover.

29. IEEE, 1998. *IEEE recommended practices for establishing transformer capability when supplying nonsinusoidal load currents* (C57.110). Piscataway, N.J.: Inst. Electrical and Electronic Eng.

30. _____, ASTM 1997. *Standard for the use of the international system of units: The modern metric system.* Piscataway, N.J.: Inst. Electrical and Electronic Eng.

31. _____, 1994. *Power electronics and motion control proceedings of the IEEE.* Piscataway, N.J.: Inst. of Electrical and Electronic Eng.

32. _____, 1993. *Graphic symbols for electrical and electronics diagrams* (315). Piscataway, N.J.: Inst. Electrical and Electronic Eng.

33. _____, 1993. *IEEE guide for transformer impulse tests* (C57.98). Piscataway, N.J.: Inst. Electrical and Electronic Eng.

34. _____, 1993. *IEEE standard general requirements for liquid-immersed distribution, power, and regulation transformers* (C57.12.00). Piscataway, N.J.: Inst. Electrical and Electronic Eng.

35. _____, 1993. *1993 Industry applications meeting Parts I, II, III Catalog No 93CH3366-2.* Piscataway, N.J.: Inst. of Electrical and Electronic Eng.

36. _____, 1992. *IEEE recommended practices and requirements for harmonic control in electric power systems* (519). Piscataway, N.J.: Inst. Electrical and Electronic Eng.

37. _____, 1992. *IEEE standard practices and requirements for thyristor converters for motor drives* (444R1992). Piscataway, N.J.: Inst. Electrical and Electronic Eng.

38. _____, 1992. *The new IEEE standard dictionary of electrical and electronics terms.* New York: Wiley.

39. _____, 1991. *IEEE recommended practice for grounding of industrial and commercial power systems* (141). New York: Inst. Electrical and Electronic Eng.

40. Jackson, H. W. and White, P. A. 1988. *Introduction to electric circuits.* Upper Saddle River, N.J.: Prentice Hall.

41. Kazimierczuk, M. K. and Czarkowski, D., 1995. *Resonant power converters.* New York: Wiley.

42. Kenjo, T. 1994. *Stepping motors and their microprocessor controls.* New York: Oxford.

43. _____, and Nagamori, S. 1985. *Permanent magnet and brushless dc motors.* New York: Oxford.

44. Kimbark, E. W. 1995. *Power system stability.* Piscataway, N.J.: Inst. Electrical and Electronic Eng.

45. _____, 1971. *Direct current transmission.* Melbourne, FL: Krieger.

46. Kloss, A. 1984. *A basic guide to power electronics.* New York: Wiley.

47. Leonhard, W. 1995. *Control of electrical drives.* New York: Springer-Verlag.

48. Matsch, L. W. 1986. *Electromagnetic and electromechanical machines.* New York: Wiley.

49. Maxwell, J. C. 1891. *A treatise on electricity and magnetism, volumes 1 and 2.* Mineola, N.Y.: Dover.

50. McPartland, J. F. and McPartland, B. 1993. *McGraw-Hill's national electrical code handbook.* New York: McGraw.

51. Miller, T. J. E. 1989. *Brushless permanent-magnet and reluctance motor drives.* New York: Oxford.

52. Moczala, H. 1998. *Small electric motors* ISBN 0 852 96 921 X. U.K.: The Institution of Electrical Engineers.

53. Moohan, N., Undeland, T. M., Robbins, W. P. 1995. *Power electronics.* New York: Wiley.

54. Moskowitz, L. R. 1995. *Permanent magnet and application handbook.* Melbourne, FL: Krieger.

55. Nailen, R. L., 1996. *Managing Motors.* Chicago: Barks Publications.

56. National Fire Protection Association. 1993. *National electrical code 1993.* Quincy, MA: Delmar.

57. NEMA, 1993. *Motors and generators* (ANSI-NEMA No. MG1.-1993). Washington: National Electrical Manufacturers Association.

58. _____, 1970. *Electrical insulation terms and definitions.* Washington: Insulating materials division, National Electrical Manufacturers Association.

59. Ogorkiewicz, R. M. 1970. *Engineering properties of thermal plastics.* Ann Arbor, MI: Bks Demand.

60. Paice, D. A. 1996. *Power electronic converter harmonics.* Piscataway, N.J.: Inst. of Electrical and Electronic Eng.

61. Pelly, B. R. 1971. *Thyristor phase-controlled converters and cycloconverters.* New York: Wiley.

62. Piron, D. L. 1994. *The electrochemistry of corrosion.* Houston: Nace International.

63. Rajashekara, K. and Kawamura, A. 1996. *Sensorless control of ac motor drives.* Piscataway, N.J.: Inst. Electrical and Electronics Eng.

64. Ramshaw, R. S. 1993. *Power electronics semiconductor switches.* London: Chapman and Hall/Halsted P. R.

65. Rashid, M. H. 1993. *Power electronics.* Upper Saddle River, N.J.: Prentice Hall.

66. Richardson, D. V. and Caisse, A. J. 1997. *Rotating electric machinery and transformer technology.* Reston: Reston Publ. Co.

67. Sandford, R. L. and Cooter, I. L. 1962. *Basic magnetic quantities and measurement of the magnetic properties of materials.* Washington: Nat. Bur. Stds., U.S. Dept. Comm.

68. Shugg, W. T. 1995. *Handbook of electrical and electronic insulating materials.* Piscataway, N.J.: Inst. of Electrical and Electronic Eng.

69. Steinmetz, C. P. 1915 *Lectures on electrical engineering, volumes 1, 2, 3.* Mineola, N.Y.: Dover.

70. Stevenson, W. D. Jr. 1981. *Elements of power system analysis.* New York: McGraw.

71. Tarnawicky, M. Z. 1971. *Manitoba power conference EHV-DC.* Winnipeg: University of Manitoba.

72. TVA, 1975. *Annual report of the Tennessee Valley Authority, Volume II-appendices.* Knoxville: Tennessee Valley Authority.

73. Uhlmann, E. 1975. *Power transmission by direct current.* New York: Springer-Verlag.

74. Uman, M. A. 1969. *Lightning.* Mineola, N.Y.: Dover.

75. Underwriters Laboratories, 1997. *Ground-fault circuit interrupters* (UL943). Northbrook, IL: Underwriters Laboratories Inc.

76. _____, 1978. *Systems of insulating materials* (UL1446). Northbrook, IL: Underwriters Laboratories Inc.

77. Vas, P. 1990. *Vector control of ac machines.* New York: Oxford.

78. Veinott, C. G. 1972. *Computer-aided design of electrical machinery.* Cambridge: MIT Pr.

79. Vielstich, W. 1970. *Fuel cells.* Ann Arbor, MI: Bks Demand.

80. Viollette, J. L. N. and White, D. R. S. 1987. *Electromagnetic compatibility handbook.* New York: Van Nostrand Reinhold.

81. Vinal, G. W. 1955. *Storage batteries.* New York: Wiley.

82. Vithayathil, J. 1995. *Power electronics.* New York: McGraw.

83. Webb, J. W. and Reis, R. A. 1995. *Programmable logic controllers.* Upper Saddle River, N.J.: Prentice Hall.

84. Westinghouse, 1965. *Electric utility engineering reference book.* Pittsburgh: Westinghouse Electric Corp.

85. _____, 1964. *Electrical transmission and distribution reference book.* Pittsburgh: Westinghouse Electric Corp.

86. Wildi, T. 1995. *Metric units and conversion charts.* New York: Wiley.

87. Wright, A. and Newbery, P. G. 1982. *Electrical fuses.* London: Peregrinus.

ARTICLES AND TECHNICAL REPORTS

1. Allan, J. A. et al 1975. Electrical aspects of the 8750 hp gearless ball-mill drive at St. Lawrence Cement Company. *IEEE Trans. Ind. Gen. Appl.* 1A-11, No. 6: 681–687.

2. Allan, R. (ed). 1975. Power semiconductors. *Spectrum.* Nov.: 37–44.

3. American National Standard, 1979. Standard nominal diameters and cross sectional areas of AWG sizes of solid round wires used as electrical conductors. *ANSI/ASTM B* 258–65 (Part 6): 536–542.

4. Apprill, M. R. 1978. Capacitors reduce voltage flicker. *Electrical World* 189, No. 4: 55–56.

5. Bachmann, K. 1972. Permanent magnets. *Brown Boveri Rev.* 9: 464–468.

6. Balzhiser, R. E. 1977. Capturing a star: Controlled fusion power. *EPRI Journal* Dec.: 6–13.

7. Beaty, H. W. 1978. Charts determine substation grounds. *Electrical World* 189, No. 2: 56–58.

8. Beaty, H. W. (ed). 1978. Underground distribution. *Electrical World* 189, No. 9: 51–66.

9. Beutler, A. J. and Staats, G. 1969. A 100 000-Joule system for charging permanent magnets. *IEEE Trans. Ind. and Gen. Appl.* 1GA-5, No. 1: 95–100.

10. Brown Boveri Review. *Electric Drives.* May/June 1967, Vol 54, No. 5/6 215–337. Baden, Switzerland.

11. Brown Boveri Review. *Frequency Conversion.* August/September, 1964, Vol 51, No. 8/9 519–554. Baden, Switzerland.

12. Creek, F. R. L. 1976. Large 1200 MW four-pole generators for nuclear power stations in the USA. *GEC J. Sc. and Tech.* 43, No. 2: 68–76.

13. Dalziel, C. F. 1968. Reevaluation of lethal electric currents. *IEEE Trans. Ind. and Gen. Appl.* 1GA-4, No. 5: 467–475.

14. Drake, W. D. and Sarris, A. E. 1968. Lightning protection for cement plants. *IEEE Trans. Ind. Gen. Appl.* 1GA-4, No. 1: 57–67.

15. Duff, D. L. and Ludbrook, A. 1968. Semiconverter rectifier go high power. *IEEE Trans. Ind. Gen. Appl.* 1GA-4, No. 2: 185–192.

16. DuPont, 1972. "Tefzel" ETFE fluoropolymer: An exciting new resin. *Journal of "Teflon"* 13: No. 1.

17. Electrical World 1978. Statistical Report. *Electrical World* 189, No. 6: 75–106.

18. Elliott, T. C. (ed). 1976. Demand control of industry power cuts utility bills, points to energy savings. *Power* 120, No. 6: 19–26.

19. Engstrom, L., Mutanda, N. M., Adams, N. G. and Flisberg, G. 1975. Refining copper with HVDC. *Spectrum* 12, No. 12: 40–45.

20. Fagenbaum, J. 1980. Cogeneration: An energy saver. *Spectrum* 17, No. 8: 30–34.

21. Fickett, A. 1976. Fuel cells—versatile power generators. *EPRI Journal,* April: 14–19.
22. Finley, W. R. 1994. *Troubleshooting Motor Problems.* IEEE Transactions on Industry Applications, Vol. 30, No. 5 September/October. New York. Inst. Electrical and Electronic Eng.
23. Friedlander, G. D. 1977. UHV: Onward and upward. *Spectrum* 14, No. 2: 57–65.
24. Gaupp, O., Linhofer, G., Lockner, G. and Zanini, P., 1995. Powerful Static Frequency Converters for Transalpine Routes., *ABB Review,* 5/95 4–10.
25. Gazzana-Priaroggia, P., Piscioneri, J. H. and Margolin, S. W. 1971. The Long Island Sound submarine cable interconnection. *Spectrum* 8, No. 10: 63–71.
26. Goodbrand, W. and Ross, C. A. 1972. Load-rejection testing of steam turbine generators. *Ontario Hydro Rsrch Qtly.* 24, No. 2: 1–7.
27. Graf, K. 1973. AC pump drives with static-converter slip-power recovery system for the Lake Constance water supply scheme. *Siemens Rev.* XL: 539–542.
28. Gyugyi, L., Schauder, C. D., Williams, S. L., Reitman, T. R., Togerson, D. R. and Edris A. 1995. The Unified Power Controller: A New Approach to Power Transmission Control. *IEEE Transactions on Power Delivery,* Vol. 10, No. 2: 1085–1097, April 1995.
29. Hand, C. (ed). 1977. Batteries. *Canadian Electronics Engineering,* May: 19–28.
30. Harris, S. W. 1960. Compensation dc motors for fast response. *Control Engineering* Oct. 1960: 115–118.
31. Herbst, W., Käuferle, F. P. and Reichert, K. 1974. Controllable static reactive power compensation. *Brown Boveri Rev.* 61: 433–439.
32. Hoffmann, A. H. 1969. Brushless synchronous motors for large industrial drives. *IEEE Trans. Ind. and Gen. Appl.* 1GA-5, No. 2: 158–162.
33. Holburn, W. W. 1970. Brushless excitation of 660 MW generators. *Journal of Science and Technology,* 37, No. 2: 85–90.
34. Hossli, W. (ed). 1976. Large steam turbines. *Brown Boveri Rev.* 63: 84–147.
35. IEEE, 1994. *Power Electronics and Motion Control.* Proceedings of the IEEE, New York: Inst. Electrical and Electronic Eng.
36. Iwanusiw, O. W. 1970. Remanent flux in current transformers. *Ont. Hydro Rsrch Qtly.* 3rd Qtr: 18–21.
37. Jacobs, A. P. and Walsh, G. W. 1968. Application considerations for SCR dc drives and associated power system. *IEEE Trans Ind. Gen. Appl.* 1GA-4, No. 4: 396–404.
38. Javetski, J. 1978. Cogeneration. *Power.* 122, No. 4: 35–40.
39. Joos, G. and Barton, H. B. 1975. Four quadrant DC variable-speed drives-design considerations, *Proc. IEEE,* 63, No. 12: 1660–1668.
40. Joyce, J. S. 1974. Factors influencing reliability of large generators for nuclear power plants. *IEEE Trans. Pwr App. Syst.,* PAS-93, No. 1: 210–219.
41. Kolm, H. H. and Thornton, R. D. 1972. Electromagnetic flight. *Scientific American,* 229, No. 4: 17–25.
42. Krick, N. and Noser, R. 1976. The growth of turbogenerators. *Brown Boveri Rev.* 63: 148–155.
43. Kronenberg, K. J. and Bohlmann, M. A. 1968. Stability of permanent magnets. *Applied Magnetics; Indiana Current Corp.* 15, No. 1.
44. Lee, R. H. 1975. The effect of color on temperature of electrical enclosures subject to solar radiation. *IEEE Trans. Ind. Appl.* 1A-11, No. 6: 646–653.
45. Lengyel, G. 1962. Arrhenius theorem aids interpretation of accelerated life test results. *Can. Electronics Engineering.* Nov.: 35–39.
46. Lyman, J. (ed). 1975. Battery technology. *Electronics.* April: 75–82.
47. Machine Design, 1979. Electrical and electronics reference issue. *Machine Design Magazine* 51, No. 11: entire issue.
48. Manian, V. S. 1971. Electric water heaters for high-usage residences. *Ontario Hydro Rsrch Quarterly,* 3rd quarter: 7–13.
49. McCormick, L. S. and Hedding, R. A. 1974. Phase-angle regulators optimize transmission line power flows. *Westinghouse Engineer.* July: 87–91.
50. McLaughlin, M. H. and Vonzastrow, E. E. 1975. Power semiconductor equipment cooling methods and application criteria. *IEEE Trans. Ind. Appl.* 1A-11, No. 5: 546–555.
51. Matta, U. (ed). 1975. Industrial electro-heat. *Brown Boveri Rev.* 62: 4–67.
52. Methé, M. 1971. The distribution of electrical power in large cities. *Canadian Engineering Journal,* October: 15–18.
53. Minnick, L. and Murphy, M. 1976. The breeder—when and why. *EPRI Journal* March 6–11.
54. Moor, J. C. 1977. Electric drives for large compressors. *IEEE Trans. Ind. Gen. Appl.* 1A-13, No. 5: 441–449.
55. Patterson, W. A. 19977. The Eel River HVDC scheme. *Can. Elec. Eng. J.* 2, No. 1: 9–16.
56. Quinn, G. C. 1977. Plant primary substation trends. *Power* 121, No. 3: 29–35.
57. Rieder, W. 1971. Circuit breakers. *Scientific American* 224, No. 1: 76–84.
58. Robichaud, G. G. and Tulenko, J. S. 1978. Core design: Fuel management as a balance between in-core efficiency and economics. *Power* 122, No. 5: 52–57.

59. Robinson, E. R. 1968. Redesign of dc motors for applications with thyristors power supplies. *IEEE Trans. Ind. Gen. Appl.* 1GA-4, No. 5: 508–514.

60. Schauder, C. D., Gernhardt, M., Stacy, E., Cease, T. W. and Edris, A. 1995. *Development of ±100 Mvar Static Condenser for Voltage Control of Transmission Systems. IEEE Transactions on Power Delivery,* Vol. 10, No. 3: 1468–1496, July 1995.

61. Schonung, A. and Stemmler, H. Static frequency changers with "subharmonic" control in conjunction with reversible variable speed drives. Brown Boveri Rev. September, 1964, 555–577.

62. Schwieger, R. (ed). 1978. Industrial Boilers—what's happening today. *Power* 122, No. 2: 1–24.

63. Sebesta, D. 1978. Responsive ties avert system breakup. *Electrical World* 180, No. 7: 54–55.

64. Selzer, A. 1971. Switching in vacuum: A review. *Spectrum* 8, No. 6: 26–37.

65. Sullivan, R. P. 1978. Uranium: Key to the nuclear fuel cycle. *Power* 122, No. 4: 58–63.

66. Summers, C. M. 1971. The conversion of energy. *Scientific American* 224, No. 3: 148–160.

67. Urbanek, J., Piwko, R. J., Larsen, E. V., Damsky, B. L., Furumasu, B. C., Mittlelstadt, W. and Eden, J. D. 1993. *Thyristor Controlled Series Compensation-Prototype Installation at Slatt 500 kV Substation. IEEE Transactions on Power Delivery,* 1460–1469, July 1993.

68. Vendryes, G. A. 1977. Superphénix: A full-scale breeder reactor. *Scientific American* 236, No. 3: 26–35.

69. Waldinger, H. 1971. Converter-fed drives. *Siemens Rev.* 38: 387–390.

70. Woll, R. F. 1977. Electric motor drives for oil well walking beam pumps. *IEEE Trans. Ind. Gen. Appl.* 1A-13, No. 5: 437–441.

71. Woll, R. F. 1975. Effect of unbalanced voltage on operation of polyphase induction motors. *IEEE Trans. Ind. Appl.* 1A-11, No. 1: 38–42.

72. Woll, R. F. 1964. High temperature insulation in ac motors. *Westinghouse Engineer* Mar. 1964: 1–5.

73. Woodson, R. D. 1971. Cooling towers. *Scientific American* 224, No. 5: 70–78.

74. Zimmermann, J. A. 1969. Starting requirements and effects of large synchronous motors. *IEEE Trans. Ind. and Gen. Appl.* 1GA-5, No. 2: 169–175.

WEBSITES

Topics and Websites

The following websites provide useful information on a variety of topics covered in this book. The websites usually open the door to other topics, in addition to the ones listed here.

Batteries

http://www.saftbatteries.com
http://www.exideworld.com

Cables

http://www.pirelli.com
http://www.usawire-cable.com

Educational and General

http://www.asee.org
http://www.ieee.org
http://www.abet.org
http://www.asme.org
http://www.astm.org
http://standards.ieee.org/catalog/sol
http://www.abb.com/abbreview
http://www.electricityforum.com
http://www.labvolt.com
http://www.epri.com
http://www.prenhall.com

Electric Vehicles

http://www.eaaev.org
http://www.aerovironment.com

Fuel cells

http://www.nfcrc.uci.edu
http://www.ballard.com

Magnets

http://www.magnetweb.com
http://www.stanfordmagnets.com
http://www.magnetsales.com

Motor Control (fuses)

http://www.littlefuse.com
http://www.bussmann.com

Motor Control (starters, PLCs)

http://www.ab.com
http://www.omron.com

Motors, Single-Phase

http://www.baldor.com

Motors, Three-Phase

http://www.usmotors.com
http://www.baldor.com
http://www.reliance.com

Motors and Generators
http://www.usmotors.com
http://www.baldor.com
http://www.micromo.com
http://www.jenkins.com

Patents and Trademarks
http://patents.uspto.gov/
http://patents1.ic.gc.ca

Power Electronics
http://www.irf.com
http://www.ixys.com
http://www.siliconix.com
http://www.pwrx.com

Power Systems
http://www.tva.com
http://www.eei.org
http://www.ieee.org/power
http://www.hydroquebec.com
http://www.alstom.com
http://www.edf.com
www.eia.doe.gov

Resistors
http://www.ohmite.com
http://www.bourns.com
http://www.vishay.com

Transformers
http://www.ustransformer.com
http://www.advancedcomponents.com
http://www.ge.com

Variable-Speed Drives
http://www.tbwoods.com
http://www.rockwell.com
http://www.abb.com

Special information on using the Internet
http://bobalden.com

Bob Alden used the Internet for teaching four university-level courses for several years. He wrote a monthly column "Travelling the Information Highway with Bob Alden" which appeared in print and on-line for IEEE's newspaper *The Institute* between 1992 and 2002–all articles are linked from his web site. Retired from McMaster University, he is a web consultant and remains very active in IEEE at the local, national and international level.

For further information on *Electrical Machines, Drives, and Power Systems* and other books by Theodore Wildi please contact:

http://www.wildi-theo.com
e-mail wildi@wildi-theo.com

We welcome your questions and comments.

APPENDIX

AX0 CONVERSION CHARTS

The conversion charts listed in this Appendix make it very easy to convert from one unit to any other. Their use is explained in Chapter 1, Section 10.

Quantities such as AREA, MASS, VOLUME, and so forth, are listed in alphabetical order for quick reference. Multipliers between units are either exact, or accurate to ±0.1 percent.

Examples at the bottom of each page are intended to assist the reader in applying the conversion rule which basically states:

WITH THE ARROW—MULTIPLY

AGAINST THE ARROW—DIVIDE

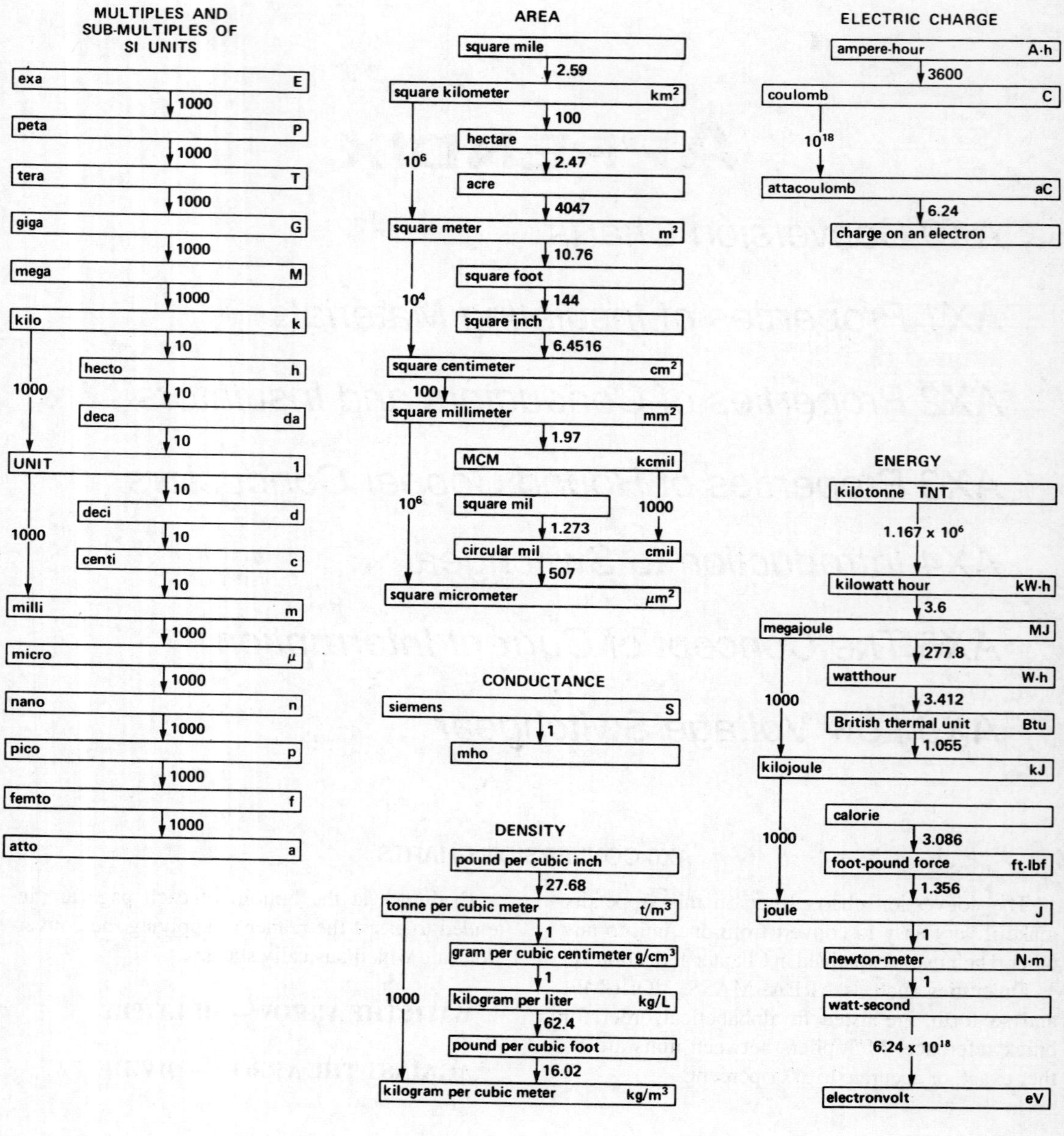

Example: **Convert 1590 MCM to square inches.**

Solution: **1590 MCM = 1590(÷ 1.97) (÷ 100) (÷ 6.4516) in² = 1.25 in².**

FORCE

- kip
  - ↓ 4.448
- kilogram force — kgf
  - ↓ 9.806 (kgf to newton)
- pound force — lbf
  - ↓ 4.448
- newton — N

MAGNETIC FIELD INTENSITY

- oersted — Oe
  - ↓ 2.02
- ampere-turn per inch
  - ↓ 39.37
- ampere per meter — A/m
  - (oersted to ampere per meter: 79.6)

MASS

- megagram — Mg
  - ↓ 1
- tonne — t
  - ↓ 1.102
- ton (2000 lb)
  - ↓ 907
- kilogram — kg
  - ↓ 2.205
- pound — lb
  - (megagram to kilogram: 1000)

MAGNETIC FLUX

- weber — Wb
  - ↓ 10^6
- microweber — μWb
  - ↓ 100
- maxwell
  - ↓ 1
- line of force

FLOW

- cubic meter per second — m^3/s
  - ↓ 35.3
- cubic foot per second
  - ↓ 6.23
- gallon (Canadian) per second
  - ↓ 1.201
- gallon (U.S.) per second
  - ↓ 3.785
- cubic decimeter per second — dm^3/s
  - ↓ 1
- liter per second
  - (cubic meter per second to cubic decimeter per second: 1000; gallon (Canadian) per second to cubic decimeter per second: 4.55)

MOMENT OF INERTIA

- kilogram meter² — $kg{\cdot}m^2$
  - ↓ 23.73
- pound mass foot² — $lb{\cdot}ft^2$
  - ↓ 5.97
- ounce force inch second² — $oz{\cdot}in{\cdot}s^2$
  - ↓ 386.1
- ounce mass inch² — $oz{\cdot}in^2$

MAGNETIC FLUX DENSITY

- tesla — T
  - ↓ 10
- kilogauss
  - ↓ 1000
- gauss
  - ↓ 6.45
- line per square inch
  - ↓ 15.5
- microtesla — μT
  - (tesla to microtesla: 10^6)

LENGTH

- mile
  - ↓ 1.609
- kilometer — km
  - ↓ 1000
- meter — m
  - ↓ 3.28
- foot
  - ↓ 12
- inch
  - ↓ 2.54
- centimeter — cm
  - ↓ 10
- millimeter — mm
  - ↓ 39.37
- mil (0.001 inch)
- nanometer — nm
  - ↓ 10
- angstrom
  - (meter to centimeter: 100; millimeter to nanometer: 10^6)

PRESSURE AND STRESS

- kgf/mm^2
  - ↓ 9.81
- megapascal — MPa
  - ↓ 10
- bar
  - ↓ 1.02
- kgf/cm^2
- pound per square inch (psi)
  - ↓ 6.89
- kilopascal — kPa
  - ↓ 7.5
- millimeter of mercury (0°C)
- pascal — Pa
  - ↓ 1
- newton per square meter
  - (megapascal to kilopascal: 1000; kilopascal to pascal: 1000)

MAGNETOMOTIVE FORCE

- ampere — A
  - ↓ 1
- ampere-turn
  - ↓ 1.257
- gilbert

Example: **Convert 580 psi to megapascals.**
Solution: **580 psi = 580 (× 6.89) (÷ 1000) MPa = 4 MPa.**

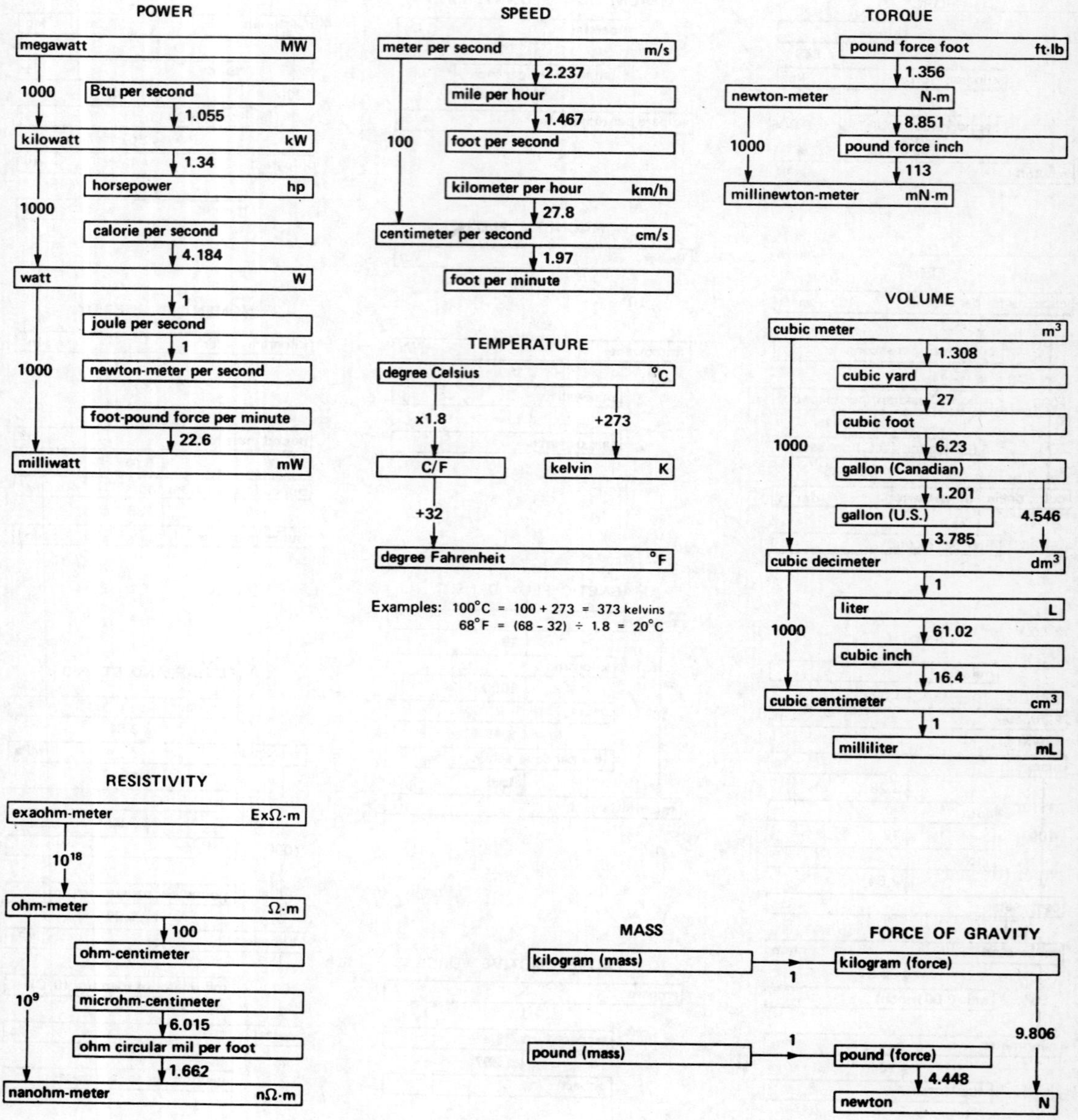

Example: **Calculate the force of gravity (in newtons) that acts on a mass of 9 lb.**

Solution: 9 lb. $\rightarrow$ 9 ($\times$ 1) ($\times$ 4.448) N = 40 N.

TABLE AX1 PROPERTIES OF INSULATING MATERIALS

Insulator	Electrical Properties		Thermal Properties		Mechanical Properties	Notes
	dielectric strength	dielectric constant	max operating temperature	thermal conductivity	density	
	MV/m or kV/mm	ϵ_r	°C	W/(m·°C)	kg/m^3	
dry air	3	1	2000	0.024	1.29	gas density is at 0°C 101 kPa
hydrogen	2.7	1	-	0.17	0.09	
nitrogen	3.5	1	-	0.024	1.25	
oxygen	3	1	-	0.025	1.43	
sulfur hexafluoride (SF_6)	30 MV/m at 400 kPa	1	-	0.014	6.6	
solid asbestos	1	-	1600	0.4	2000	
asbestos wool	1	-	1600	0.1	400	
askarel	12	4.5	120	-	1560	synthetic liquid (restricted)
epoxy	20	3.3	130	0.3	1600 to 2000	
glass	100	5 to 7	600	1.0	2500	
magnesium oxide	3	4	1400	2.4	-	(powder)
mica	40 to 240	7	500 to 1000	0.36	2800	
mineral oil	10	2.2	110	0.16	860	
mylar®	400	3	150	-	1380	a polyester
nylon	16	4.1	150	0.3	1140	a polyamide
paper (treated)	14	4 to 7	120	0.17	1100	
polyamide	40	3.7	100 to 180	0.3	1100	
polycarbonate	25	3.0	130	0.2	1200	
polyethylene	40	2.3	90	0.4	930	
polyimide	200	3.8	180 to 400	0.3	1100	
polyurethane	35	3.6	90	0.35	1210	
polyvinylchloride (PVC)	50	3.7	70	0.18	1390	
porcelain	4	6	1300	1.0	2400	
rubber	12 to 20	4	65	0.14	950	
silicon	10	-	250	0.3	1800 to 2800	
teflon	20	2	260	0.24	2200	

TABLE AX2 ELECTRICAL, MECHANICAL AND THERMAL PROPERTIES OF SOME COMMON CONDUCTORS (AND INSULATORS)

Material	Chemical symbol or composition	Electrical properties: resistivity ρ 0°C nΩ·m	resistivity ρ 20°C nΩ·m	temp coeff at 0°C ($\times 10^{-3}$)	Mechanical properties: density kg/m³ or g/dm³	yield strength MPa	ultimate strength MPa	Thermal properties: specific heat J/kg·°C	thermal conductivity W/m·°C	melting point °C
aluminum	Al	26.0	28.3	4.39	2703	21	62	960	218	660
brass	≈ 70% Cu, Zn	60.2	62.0	1.55	≈ 8300	124	370	370	143	960
carbon/ graphite	C	8000 to 30 000	-	≈ −0.3	≈ 2500	-	-	710	5.0	3600
constantan	54% Cu, 45% Ni, 1% Mn	500	500	−0.03	8900	-	-	410	22.6	1190
copper	Cu	15.88	17.24	4.27	8890	35	220	380	394	1083
gold	Au	22.7	24.4	3.65	19 300	-	69	130	296	1063
iron	Fe	88.1	101	7.34	7900	131	290	420	79.4	1535
lead	Pb	203	220	4.19	11 300	-	15	130	35	327
manganin	84% Cu, 4% Ni, 12% Mn	482	482	±0.015	8410	-	-	-	20	1020
mercury	Hg	951	968	0.91	13 600	-	-	140	8.4	−39
molybdenum	Mo	49.6	52.9	3.3	10 200	-	690	246	138	2620
monel	30% Cu, 69% Ni, 1% Fe	418	434	1.97	8800	530	690	530	25	1360
nichrome	80% Ni, 20% Cr	1080	1082	0.11	8400	-	690	430	11.2	1400
nickel	Ni	78.4	85.4	4.47	8900	200	500	460	90	1455
platinum	Pt	9.7	10.4	3.4	21 400	-	-	131	71	1773
silver	Ag	15.0	16.2	4.11	10 500	-	-	230	408	960
tungsten	W	49.6	55.1	5.5	19 300	-	3376	140	20	3410
zinc	Zn	55.3	59.7	4.0	7100	-	70	380	110	420
air	78% N_2, 21% O_2	-	-	-	1.29	-	-	994	0.024	-
hydrogen	H_2	-	-	-	0.090	-	-	14 200	0.17	-
pure water	H_2O	-	2.5×10^{14}	-	1000	-	-	4180	0.58	0.0

TABLE AX3 PROPERTIES OF ROUND COPPER CONDUCTORS

Gauge number AWG/ B & S	Diameter of bare conductor		Cross section		Resistance mΩ/m or Ω/km		Weight g/m or kg/km	Typical diameter of insulated magnet wire used in relays, magnets, motors, trans-formers, etc.
	mm	mils	mm²	cmils	25°C	105°C		mm
250 MCM	12.7	500	126.6	250 000	0.138	0.181	1126	
4/0	11.7	460	107.4	212 000	0.164	0.214	953	
2/0	9.27	365	67.4	133 000	0.261	0.341	600	
1/0	8.26	325	53.5	105 600	0.328	0.429	475	
1	7.35	289	42.4	87 700	0.415	0.542	377	
2	6.54	258	33.6	66 400	0.522	0.683	300	
3	5.83	229	26.6	52 600	0.659	0.862	237	
4	5.18	204	21.1	41 600	0.833	1.09	187	
5	4.62	182	16.8	33 120	1.05	1.37	149	
6	4.11	162	13.30	26 240	1.32	1.73	118	
7	3.66	144	10.5	20 740	1.67	2.19	93.4	
8	3.25	128	8.30	16 380	2.12	2.90	73.8	
9	2.89	114	6.59	13 000	2.67	3.48	58.6	3.00
10	2.59	102	5.27	10 400	3.35	4.36	46.9	2.68
11	2.30	90.7	4.17	8 230	4.23	5.54	37.1	2.39
12	2.05	80.8	3.31	6 530	5.31	6.95	29.5	2.14
13	1.83	72.0	2.63	5 180	6.69	8.76	25.4	1.91
14	1.63	64.1	2.08	4 110	8.43	11.0	18.5	1.71
15	1.45	57.1	1.65	3 260	10.6	13.9	14.7	1.53
16	1.29	50.8	1.31	2 580	13.4	17.6	11.6	1.37
17	1.15	45.3	1.04	2 060	16.9	22.1	9.24	1.22
18	1.02	40.3	0.821	1 620	21.4	27.9	7.31	1.10
19	0.91	35.9	0.654	1 290	26.9	35.1	5.80	0.98
20	0.81	32.0	0.517	1 020	33.8	44.3	4.61	0.88
21	0.72	28.5	0.411	812	42.6	55.8	3.66	0.79
22	0.64	25.3	0.324	640	54.1	70.9	2.89	0.70
23	0.57	22.6	0.259	511	67.9	88.9	2.31	0.63
24	0.51	20.1	0.205	404	86.0	112	1.81	0.57
25	0.45	17.9	0.162	320	108	142	1.44	0.51
26	0.40	15.9	0.128	253	137	179	1.14	0.46
27	0.36	14.2	0.102	202	172	225	0.908	0.41
28	0.32	12.6	0.080	159	218	286	0.716	0.37
29	0.29	11.3	0.065	128	272	354	0.576	0.33
30	0.25	10.0	0.0507	100	348	456	0.451	0.29
31	0.23	8.9	0.0401	79.2	440	574	0.357	0.27
32	0.20	8.0	0.0324	64.0	541	709	0.289	0.24
33	0.18	7.1	0.0255	50.4	689	902	0.228	0.21
34	0.16	6.3	0.0201	39.7	873	1140	0.179	0.19
35	0.14	5.6	0.0159	31.4	1110	1450	0.141	0.17
36	0.13	5.0	0.0127	25.0	1390	1810	0.113	0.15
37	0.11	4.5	0.0103	20.3	1710	2230	0.091	0.14
38	0.10	4.0	0.0081	16.0	2170	2840	0.072	0.12
39	0.09	3.5	0.0062	12.3	2820	3690	0.055	0.11
40	0.08	3.1	0.0049	9.6	3610	4720	0.043	0.1

AX4

Introduction to Switchgear

Arun Ingole, Ex-General Manager, Siemens Ltd.

Z01.1 What is Switchgear

As we are aware, faults on power systems can damage any equipment or its part. To avoid this, we must protect the power system and this must be achieved without switching-off the entire power system. Hence, it is necessary to identify the faulty circuit or portion, switch it off & then isolate it so that the balance system continues to function. This activity is carried out by the 'switchgear' (equipment and devices) which are capable of switching, monitoring, measuring, controlling & signaling. Thus, switchgear includes all equipments & accessories which perform, directly or indirectly, one or many of the following functions.

a. Switching the circuit 'ON' to supply power to the 'loads' as & when required or desired.
b. Switching the circuit 'OFF' to stop the power supply as & when required or desired.
c. Monitoring the 'healthiness' of the power system continuously.
d. Identifying the 'faulty' circuit or portion in case of a fault.
e. Generating 'alarm' & 'trip' signals & send them to the switching devices.
f. Switching off the faulty circuit or portion at the earliest possible.
g. Isolating the faulty circuit from the rest of the power system so that the former can be repaired/ maintained with full safety of the personnel.
h. Measuring the various system parameters.

Accordingly, the switchgear includes (i) circuit breakers (CB), switches, isolators; (ii) contactors, fuses, motor starters, actuators; (iii) current, potential & special purpose transformers, lightning arresters; (iv) control, alarm, signalling devises, etc. of various ratings & types and any combination of two or more of the above.

Thus the 'switchgear' is an extremely important part of any T&D system.

Z01.2 Essential Features

The human life is & will always remain dependent on the electric power. Hence, it is important that 'quality' power is always available at all locations. This demands the following essential features from all switchgear equipments.

Z01.2.1 Adequacy

It means that the switchgear must have suitable 'ratings' (i.e. capabilities) to be able to perform correctly under the most severe conditions of the network thereat.

Z01.2.2 Sensitivity

The monitoring section must possess a high 'sensitivity' to be able to detect the fault at the instance of occurrence or in its initial stage itself.

Z01.2.3 Reliability or Availability

This requires that each section must be 'ever-eady' to perform 'round-the-clock' & complete the full 'mandatory' operating cycle after the fault occurs. Also, the switchgear must return to its 'normal state' after removal of the fault & be ready for next operating cycle (in case of next fault) after it is 'reset' manually or automatically (i.e. self-initiated).

Z01.2.4 Discrimination

This means that the switchgear must be able to identify the faulty circuit or network portion & disconnect only that portion leaving the rest operating in normal manner. The designers must build this discrimination in the equipment/ system. Let us understand this further for a simple power system of Fig. 1.1. When a fault occurs at point *P*, fault current flows through circuit CBs *A*, *B* & *C*. Discrimination requires that only *A* trips, (i.e. *B* & *C* remain closed) so that the faulty circuit is disconnected, leaving rest of the network in normal operation. This is achieved by proper co-ordination of the current & time 'settings' of associated protection equipment so that tripping of CBs *B* & *C* is delayed by certain time during which CB *A* trips.

These four features decide the quality of the switchgear as well as its suitability for a particular application. To ensure that the switchgear of different Manufacturers have same quality, 'Standards' have been formulated and all concerned, i.e. Manufacturers, Users, Consultants, etc., follow them.

Z01.3 Terminology

It is not possible to learn about the switchgear without understanding the following frequently used terms & phrases.

Z01.3.1 Main or Power Circuit

It comprises of all conducting parts of the switchgear which carry power to the connected 'load'. The current in this circuit is called the 'main' or 'power' current.

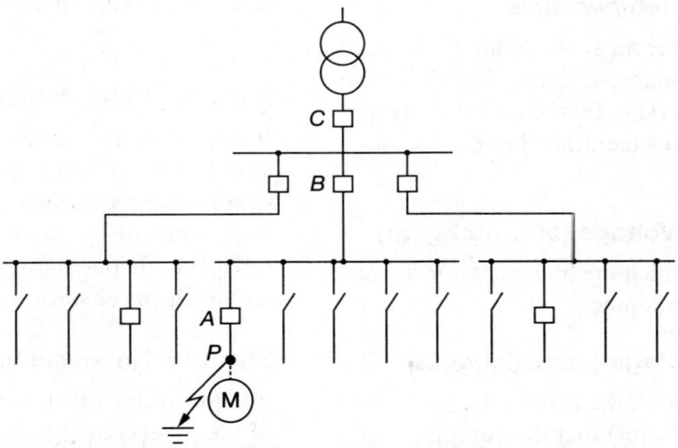

Figure 1.1 'Discrimination' in a simple power system

Z01.3.2 Control Circuit

It comprises of all conducting parts of the switchgear (other than the main circuit) which are used to 'control' the closing & opening operations of the latter.

Z01.3.3 Auxiliary Circuit

It comprises of all conducting parts of the switchgear which form electrical circuit other than the main & control circuits. Circuits pertaining to alarm, indication, signaling, etc fall under this category.

Z01.3.4 Normal Condition

It is defined as the 'condition' when the system voltages & currents are within the specified & accepted limits & there is no fault of any nature.

Z01.3.5 Abnormal Condition

It is a condition other than the 'normal condition'.

Z01.3.6 Ambient Conditions

The weather conditions such as air temperatures and pressures, rain, humidity, pollution, etc. at the location of the switchgear installation are called the 'ambient conditions' thereat. Since their values vary with time, they are presented in different ways such as, average, highest, lowest, 'range', etc.

Z01.3.7 Ambient Temperature

The temperature of the air surrounding the switchgear is called the 'ambient temperature' for the switchgear. Obviously, this may be different from the temperatures mentioned under 'ambient conditions'.

Z01.3.8 Nominal Voltage (of switchgear)

It is the voltage to which the manufacturer 'identifies' the concerned equipment.

Z01.3.9 Rated Voltage (of switchgear)

It is the highest value of the RMS voltage (recommended by manufacturer) that the equipment can operate at continuously without any damage.

Z01.3.10 Rated Current

It is the highest value of the RMS current (recommended by manufacturer) that the equipment can carry continuously without any deterioration &/ or excessive temperature rise under the specified ambient conditions.

Z01.3.11 Prospective Current

It is the current that would flow at a given point in the network if the latter were 'short-circuited' at that point.

Z01.3.12 Rated Breaking Current

It is the highest value of the prospective current that the switchgear can interrupt at a particular voltage & under pre-determined fault conditions.

Z01.3.13 Rated Making Current

It is the 'peak' value of the highest current that the switchgear is capable of making (i.e. closing on) at a particular voltage & under pre-determined fault conditions.

Z01.3.14 Short Time Withstand Current or Short Time (Current) Rating

It is the highest RMS value of the current that the switchgear can carry in its 'closed' status for a particular duration without any permanent damage to itself. These current values are evaluated for 1 & 3 seconds.

Z01.3.15 Peak Withstand Current

It is peak value of the highest current that the switchgear can withstand momentarily in its closed position under pre-determined conditions. Since large currents generate enormous mechanical forces in all conducting parts, this parameter represents the mechanical strength of the switchgear.

Z01.3.16 Recovery Voltage

It is the voltage that appears across the terminals of the pole(s) of the switchgear after the current interruption.

Z01.3.17 Transient Recovery Voltage (TRV) or Restriking Voltage

It is the recovery voltage moments after current interruption. It contains 'high frequency' components of large magnitude.

Z01.3.18 Power Frequency Recovery Voltage

It is the 'post-TRV' recovery voltage i.e. after the high frequency components have subsided to negligible values.

Z01.3.19 Power Frequency Withstand Voltage

It is the highest RMS value of the sinusoidal voltage waveform of power frequency that the switchgear insulation can withstand under pre-determined conditions without any damage.

Z01.3.20 Impulse Withstand Voltage

It is the peak value of the standard 'impulse voltage waveform' that the switchgear insulation can withstand under pre-determined conditions without any damage. This is popularly called as the 'basic insulation level' (BIL) & is a measure of the switchgear's ability to withstand voltage surges due to 'lightning' or 'switching of circuits'.

Z01.3.21 Opening Time

It is the duration from the instant the 'switching element' receives the opening command upto the instant the arcing contacts separate in all poles of the switchgear. In practice, this parameter is most relevant to circuit breakers.

Z01.3.22 Arcing Time

It is the duration between the instant of the first initiation of the arc & the instant of arc extinction in all three poles of the switchgear.

Z01.3.23 Break Time

It is the duration between the instants of the 'beginning' of the 'opening time' & the 'end' of the 'arcing time'.

Z01.3.24 Closing Time

It is the duration between the instants when the closing operation is initiated & when the contacts touch in all poles of the switchgear.

Z01.3.25 Make Time

It is the duration between the instants of initiation of closing operation & beginning of current flow in the main circuits of all poles of the switchgear.

Z01.3.26 Operating Characteristic

It is the graphical representation of the relation between the current flowing through the switchgear & its operating time (duration). Generally, the time & current are plotted on the 'Y'& 'X' axes respectively.

Z01.3.27 Insulation Level or Basic Insulation Level (BIL)

'BIL' of the switchgear describes its capability or capacity of (a) Power frequency voltage withstand, (b) Lightning impulse voltage withstand & (c) Switching impulse voltage withstand.

Z01.3.28 Closing Operation

It is an operation whereby the switchgear is brought from the 'open/OFF' condition to the 'closed/ ON' condition.

Z01.3.29 Opening Operation

It is an operation whereby the switchgear is brought from the 'closed/ ON' condition to the 'open/ OFF' condition.'

Z01.3.30 Making Operation

It is a special closing operation wherein the concerned main circuit is 'live' (i. e. at non-zero potential) & the current starts flowing immediately after closing.

Z01.3.31 Breaking Operation

It is a special opening operation wherein current is flowing in the main circuit at that instant & the switchgear interrupts the current.

Z01.3.32 Tripping Operation

It is an opening operation that is caused by the fault on associated circuit for the purpose of disconnecting the faulted portion. It is initiated by the 'protection equipment' which detects the fault.

Z01.3.33 Operating Mechanism (OM)

It is that integral portion of the switchgear (outside the main circuit) which provides motion to the 'contacts' in the main circuit for the closing & opening of switchgear (including storing & release of the energy). It may be manual, electrical, pneumatic, hydraulic type or combination thereof. Many different types of operations are possible.

Z01.3.34 Fixed Trip Mechanism

It is a mechanism that can be activated to open the switchgear only when the latter is in 'closed' position.

Z01.3.35 Trip Free Mechanism

It is so designed that the opening command must 'ride/ prevail over' the closing command. This means this mechanism brings the switchgear to open position if opening command is given after closing command.

Z01.3.36 Dependent Manual Operation

This operation is carried out by 'directly applied manual' energy whereby the speed of operation depends on the operator's action. Therefore, the completion of the operation can't be guaranteed. Hence, this operation is not recommended for equipments like CBs which operate in 'on-load' conditions because of potential hazards. It is quite suitable for 'off-load' switches & isolators.

Z01.3.37 Dependent Power Operation

It employs non-manual energy (from electric motors, solenoids, etc.) & its completion is dependent on the continuity of power supply. It is very common for LT switchgear.

Z01.3.38 Stored Energy Operation

It employs energy that is 'stored in itself' prior to the initiation of or during the operation & is sufficient to complete it even if electricity supply is not available. For such operations, (a) the origin of energy may be manual or electricity; (b) the method for storing energy may be mechanical (in springs/ weights) or pneumatic or hydraulic & (c) the energy may be released manually or electrically.

Z01.3.39 Independent Manual Operation

It is a stored energy operation wherein the energy is sourced from manual power, stored and released in a controlled & uninterrupted manner to ensure completion of operation independent of the operator's actions.

Z01.3.40 Terminal

It is a conducting part of any electrical equipment (including switchgear) that is used for connecting the latter to the external circuit.

Z01.3.41 Contact

It is a set or assembly of conducing parts that is employed to make or break a circuit by means of its motion with relation to another set or assembly of conducting parts.

Z01.3.42 Main Contact

It is a contact in the main circuit of the switchgear. It carries and, in many cases, both makes & breaks the main current.

Z01.3.43 Arcing Contact

It is a contact in the main circuit which 'bears' the arc during the entire arcing period while both opening & closing of the switchgear.

Z01.3.44 Control Contact

It is a contact in the control circuit of the switchgear that is mechanically attached to the main contact for simultaneous change of state.

Z01.3.45 Auxiliary Contact

It is a contact in the auxiliary circuit of the switchgear that is mechanically attached to the main contact for simultaneous change of state.

Z01.3.46 Normally Open (NO) or Make Contact

It is a control or auxiliary contact which is open when the main contact is open & closed when the latter is closed.

Z01.3.47 Normally Closed (NC) or Break Contact

It is a control or auxiliary contact which is closed when the main contact is open & open when the latter is closed.

Z01.3.48 Changeover (c/o) Contact

It is a 'three-terminal' auxiliary contact which is a combination of one NC (say A) & one NO (say B) contacts. When the status of switchgear changes, contact A opens & contact B closes.

Z01.3.49 Release

It is a device, mechanically attached to the switchgear, that (when activated) disengages the 'means of holding' of the operating mechanism (i. e. it de-latches the OM) thus allowing the opening operation. It gets activated or 'operates' by the 'open/ trip' command from the control circuitry.

Z01.3.50 Instantaneous Release

It is a release that operates immediately on receiving the opening command without any 'intentional' delay.

Z01.3.51 Overcurrent (OC) Release

It is a release that is connected in the main circuit, directly or through the (conversion or isolating) device(s) of the switchgear. It operates when the main current exceeds the pre-determined value or the 'threshold'.

Z01.3.52 Direct OC Release

It is an OC release that is connected directly in the main circuit & is energized by the main current.

Z01.3.53 Indirect OC Release

It is an OC release that is energized by a current which is proportional to the main current. It is connected in the secondary circuit of the 'current transformer' or a 'shunt' mounted in the main circuit.

Z01.3.54 Definite Time OC Release

It is an OC release that operates after a definite time delay. This delay may be adjustable but is independent of the extent of OC.

Z01.3.55 Inverse Time OC Release

It is an OC release that operates after a time delay which is inversely proportional to the extent of OC.

Z01.3.56 Undervoltage Release

It is a release which initiates & causes opening of the switchgear when the voltage across its terminals falls below a pre-determined value.

Z01.3.57 Open Circuit Shunt Release

It is a release that is energized by an auxiliary supply. It can be used to 'trip' the switchgear.

Z01.4 Classification

It is always helpful to classify the large range of switchgear for purpose of designing, manufacturing & operating them as well as learning about them. There are several criteria for this classification.

Z01.4.1 Nature of Installation

Essentially, there are two classes as per this consideration.

Z01.4.1.1 Indoor Switchgear

It is installed inside a building or under shade so that it is 'effectively' protected from rain, dripping or splashing water, snow, direct sunrays, etc. At present, switchgear rated upto 11 kV is generally indoor type. Herein, the switchgear is assembled inside sheet steel or cast-iron or plastic enclosures.

Z01.4.1.2 Outdoor Switchgear

The switchgear which does not qualify as indoor type is called as outdoor one. Switchgear rated at 66 kV & above is always outdoor type, except the SF6 gas filled one which may be in indoor execution. 22 & 33 kV rated switchgear is available in both of these types. If any LT switchgear must be installed outdoor, it is placed inside weather-proof enclosures with canopies.

Z01.4.2 Voltage Level

Depending on the nominal or rated voltage assigned to the switchgear, we have:

a. Low Voltage (LV or LT) switchgear rated upto 1000 V;

b. Medium Voltage (MV) switchgear rated at 1.1, 2.2, 3.3, 6.6, 11, 22 & 33 kV;

c. High Voltage (HV) switchgear rated at 66, 110, 132, 220, 245 kV &

d. Extra High Voltage (EHV) switchgear rated at 400, 500, 575, 750 kV & above.

Z01.4.3 Operational Speed

Among the various aspects of switchgear operations, the duration of current interruption or the breaking time is the most critical one. Thus, the breaking time defines the switchgear speed. Accordingly, we have following types of switchgear; mainly circuit breakers.

Z01.4.3.1 Fast acting Switchgear

CBs having breaking time of less than 100 milliseconds fall in this category. HRC fuses with 'current limiting' feature are also termed as fast acting.

Z01.4.3.2 Slow Acting Switchgear

The switchgear having breaking time in excess of 100 milliseconds is classified as slow acting type.

Z01.4.4 Type of Supply

As per this criterion, we have the (a) alternating current (AC) & (b) direct current (DC) types.

Z01.4.4.1 AC Switchgear

It is employed for most of the applications & forms 99% of the total switchgear manufactured every year. It has a very wide range of voltage & current ratings.

Z01.4.4.2 DC Switchgear

It has very limited applications like rectifies, storage batteries, DC power packs, DC auxiliary supplies, etc. The interruption & making of direct current is more difficult or severe than that of alternating current.

Z01.5 Important Switchgear (Equipments)

They (a) circuit breakers, (b) switches, disconnectors & isolators, (c) fuses, (d) switch-fuse combinations, (e) contactors, releases & relays, (f) motor starters, (g) switchboards, (h) instrument transformers, (i) protection relays, etc.

Z01.5.1 Circuit Breakers

They are the most critical equipment in the switchgear range. They perform complex operations of switching circuits to enable safe transfer of Gigawatts of power at potentials upto 1000 kV with extreme precision, speed & reliability. A CB of any type & size has following important parts. (a) Conducting path; comprising of fixed & moving contacts, terminals, connections, arc control & extinction devices. (b) Body or enclosure & supporting structure. (c) Insulation medium. (d) Operating mechanism. (e) Accessories & auxiliaries.

Z01.5.1.1 Capabilities

A CB normally performs following operations. (a) Closing of a circuit in 'on-load' or 'off-load' conditions. (b) Opening of a circuit 'on load' or 'off load'. (c) Carrying the load current continuously.

(d) Interrupting the fault currents repeatedly without any damage to self. (e) Closing the circuits 'on faults' (i.e. while the fault exists) safely, if so desired.

Further, based on its design, it may or may not be able to perform the following. (f) Closing & opening of charged & uncharged transmission lines. (g) Switching of capacitive & inductive circuits. (h) Closing & opening of unloaded transformer circuits. (i) Synchronization of two or more power sources.

Z01.5.2 Disconnectors & Isolators

Their function is to 'close' & 'open' the electrical circuits in 'off load' condition and to maintain a safe 'isolating distance' in their open status. They are designed to carry the 'rated' load /circuit currents continuously without overheating or deterioration. They are not expected to 'break' any current except may be 'transformer magnetizing' or 'cable charging' currents. However, they are designed to 'make on load' &, at times, 'make under fault' conditions.

Z01.5.3 Switches

It performs all functions of a disconnector or a isolator & has additional capability to break 'full load' or at times,'higher' currents.

Z01.5.4 Fuses

The fuse is the 'first' switchgear device. In essence, it is a small 'metallic element' inserted in the circuit at convenient location. It is designed to carry the 'rated circuit current' continuously without any deterioration. However, under overcurrent conditions it melts & interrupts the current before any damage to the circuit equipment.

Z01.5.5 Switch-fuse Combinations

It is a 'series, combination of a (load break type) switch & a set of fuses so connected in circuit that the switch is on 'line side'.

Z01.5.6 Contactors and Overload Releases or Relays

They are specially designed for Motor Control duty. The contactor is an 'automatic' (i.e. electromagnet controlled) device developed for the 'switching' function whereas the overload release or relay is employed to 'monitor' the circuit current for purpose of protecting the motor against overcurrent faults.

Z01.5.7 Motor Starters

The 'starter' is the combination of contactor(s), overload release/ relay & fuses to switch, control & protect the Motor.

Z01.5.8 Instrument Transformers (IT)

They are of two different types; Current & Voltage or Potential transformers (CT & VT/ PT). The ITs are very different from the normal (power) transformers in both application & design. They are used to monitor the voltages & currents for (a) measurement of powers, currents & voltages and (b) generation of signals for the switching of the circuit breakers.

Z01.5.9 Switchboards

No switchgear is used in open execution; it is always mounted inside an enclosure which provides protection to (a) the switchgear equipment from external objects and (b) the operating personnel & general public (against contact with the switchgear inside). A Switchboard comprises of many 'incoming' & 'outgoing' feeders of different ratings, neatly arranged in one or more 'panels' (enclosures) to form a 'power distribution sub-system'. The switchboards are manufactured to operate at 'upto 33 kV'.

Z01.6 Construction – Components & Materials

The switchgear equipments are manufactured using various components/ parts. The materials required for a particular category of components, say 'contacts' are same/ similar irrespective of the final equipment.

Z01.6.1 Body & Supporting Structure

The 'body' holds the various components together. It may be made of steel, other metals, porcelain or moulded thermo-setting type plastics. It must be robust & designed to withstand the mechanical forces generated inside the switchgear during the normal & abnormal conditions, but it should not be bulky or voluminous. For the 'outdoor' switchgear, the body must be climate-proof & corrosion-resistant. The supporting structure is required for the outdoor switchgear only. It is always made of steel & is either painted or galvanized.

Z01.6.2 Insulation

They are the components & materials that provide electrical insulation between the 'current-carrying' parts which are 'live' in energized status, & the 'others' which are always at earth potential; as under.

Z01.6.2.1 Insulation Medium

It provides the insulation between the (i) moving & fixed contacts of the same pole when the switchgear is open; (ii) various poles or phases of the switchgear; (iii) poles & the body of switchgear and (iv) poles & the operating mechanism. It also helps to extinguish the arc & interrupt the current. It is, basically, a 'dielectric' material with properties like: (a) high dielectric strength; (b) chemically inert, non-inflammable & non-corrosive; (c) low dielectric loss; (d) harmless to people, animals & environment; (e) light in weight & thermally stable; (f) the products of its decomposition (at high temperatures) recombine to form 'itself'; (g) high tracking resistance (if it is solid) & high flash points (if fluid); (h) homogeneity at normal temperature & pressure so that there is no sedimentation, etc.

Z01.6.2.2 Other Insulations

Additionally, there are many other insulating components in the switchgear, like, insulation between the moving contacts & the shaft of operating mechanism, supports for fixed contacts, etc. They are solids & can be classified as below.

Z01.6.2.3 Synthetic Thermosetting Resins

They are 'polymerized' plastics with excellent dielectric & mechanical properties, are flame-retardant & resistant to climatic severities; like epoxy, phenol formaldehyde (PF), melamine formaldehyde (MF), etc. PF & MF are used in busbar supports, contact bridges, arc chambers, outer casings, etc. in LV switchgears. Epoxy mouldings find use in CTs, PTs, bushings, etc. upto 33 kV.

Z01.6.2.4 Resin-impregnated Woods

Herein, veneers of selected timber or teak wood are bonded together by impregnating them in resin under vacuum & then densified under heat & pressure. This wood, called 'permali' has excellent dielectric & mechanical properties & resistance to climatic severities. It is used in busbar supports, contact carriers, other moving insulating parts in all switchgears of all voltage ratings.

Z01.6.2.5 Ceramics

These natural minerals, such as Porcelain & Steatite, are good insulating materials due to their high dielectric strength but are heavy & brittle. Hence, they are used in 'static' insulating components, like bushing insulators, supports for stationery conducting parts, etc.

Z01.6.2.6 Mica

It is a natural mineral with excellent dielectric properties & the unique ability to withstand very high temperatures without slightest deterioration. Mica flakes are bonded by resin & pressed into sheets & blocks. They are used as stationary insulating parts, e. g. supports in arc-quenching devices. Thin mica sheets are used as inter-layer insulation in EHV CTs, PTs, etc.

Z01.6.2.7 Other Insulating Materials

They are fiber-glass, synthetic resin bonded paper (SRBP), etc. which have specific applications. SRBP is used in bushing insulators. The fiber-glass-mounted parts are used as link between moving contacts & drive shaft in breakers.

Z01.6.3 Conducting Circuit

The fixed & moving contacts and other 'current carrying' parts are important portions of any switchgear. Every part of the conducting circuit should be designed to carry the required currents & withstand the consequential electrodynamic forces. It comprises of all or some of the following components/parts.

Z01.6.3.1 Main Contacts

They carry the load currents & 'let-through' overcurrents. They are bulky & made of pure copper with thick silver coating. Their mating surfaces are slightly 'roughened' to ensure 'least contact resistance'.

Z01.6.3.2 Arcing Contacts

The switchgear may or may not have arcing contacts in addition to the main contacts. However, when provided, they exist on both fixed & moving contact sets. They are 'open' when the switchgear is in 'closed' status & they do not carry any currents. They function as follows. (a) During closing operation, the fixed & moving arcing contacts touch each-other first, then the main contacts touch & arcing contacts separate. (b) During opening operation, the arcing contacts first touch each-other, then the main contacts separate & arcing contacts separate thereafter. With this arrangement, the arc is always struck between the arcing contacts only. Fig. 1.2 shows typical shapes & relative 'positioning' of main & arcing contacts.

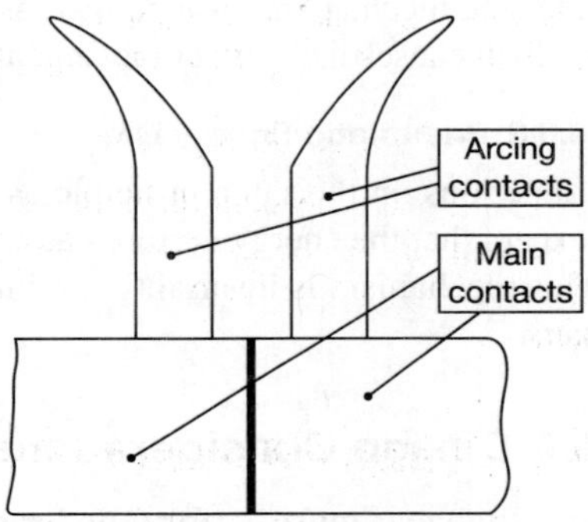

Figure 1.2 Main and arcing contacts

Z01.6.3.3 Terminals

They are used to connect any switchgear equipment in the 'external' circuit & are always 'stationary'. They are made of electrolytic grade copper or aluminium.

Z01.6.3.4 Flexibles

They are used as 'links' between the terminals & (corresponding) moving contact. They are made of thin copper strips brazed together or copper braids.

Z01.6.4 Contact Materials

The contacts are made of pure copper &/or high conductivity copper alloys like, cadmium copper, silver copper, chromium copper, etc. They have following properties.

Z01.6.4.1 High Electrical Conductivity

It should be in excess of 99.99 % (with reference to pure copper having 100%) so that both heat losses & voltage drops in the conducting paths are minimal.

Z01.6.4.2 Thermal Conductivity

This should be high as it helps in efficient dissipation of heat generated so that the 'temperature rise' in contact is within safety limit. This criterion becomes important during the 'let-through short circuit current' conditions when the switchgear must carry high currents without 'softening' of contact material or 'welding of contacts'.

Z01.6.4.3 Machinability

Since the contacts generally have complicated shapes their materials should have good machinability.

Z01.6.4.4 Mechanical Properties

They are as under.

a. High shear strength: During short-circuits, large electrodynamic forces act on the conductors in direction perpendicular to that of current flow. These forces try to 'shear' or break the conductors which must be stopped.

b. High elasticity: In closed conditions, the contacts press against each-other. If the materials yield under this force, the contacts will be unusable.

c. Resistance to wear & tear: The contacts must perform thousands of 'open-close' operations without getting 'worn-out'.

Z01.6.4.5 Corrosion Resistance

Since the contacts of outdoor switchgear equipments are exposed to the atmosphere they must be made of corrosion & oxidation-resistant materials. The 'mating-faces' of such fixed & moving contacts are 'silver-coated'.

Z01.6.4.6 Resistance to Arc Erosion

The intense heat generated during arcing vaporizes some material from the surfaces of both fixed & moving contacts. This causes 'pits' formation on the contact surfaces if they are not made of 'arc erosion resistant' materials. Cadmium-copper has higher erosion resistance than pure copper but higher electrical resistance also. Therefore, the main contacts are made of pure copper & the arcing contacts of cadmium-copper.

Z01.6.5 Arc Control Devices (ACD)

They are employed in circuit breakers to quickly extinguish the arc & interrupt the current. The development of breaker technology has taken four directions; (a) larger continuous currents, (b) higher operating voltages, (c) higher short-circuit current breaking capacities & (d) faster operation. To achieve this, very sophisticated & effective ACDs were developed. They perform functions like: (i) confining the arc to a small portion of the pole ,(ii) lengthening the arc & making it zigzag, (iii) forcing the cold insulating medium onto the arc to cool it rapidly, (iv) 'churning' the insulating medium between the fixed & moving contacts to enable 'quick build-up' of the dielectric strength of the gap. The ACDs are so mounted in the breaker poles that the contacts separate 'within the former'.

Z01.6.5.1. Advantages of ACD

They are: (a) successful current interruption, (b) compact & lighter CBs, (c) much less deterioration of the insulation medium, (d) shorter arc durations & (e) reduced amount of energy generated during arcing (which mitigates all associated difficulties).

Z01.6.6 Operating Mechanisms (OM)

Based on the means of storing energy, there are the following three basic types of the OMs.

Z01.6.6.1 Mechanical Energy OM

Herein, the energy is stored in the 'charged', i.e. compressed or tensioned, springs. This tensioning or compression is done by hand or motor. During operation, the OM is 'delatched' whereby the charged springs release their stored energy & return to their normal state. This energy is converted into the desired force with help of interconnected links, chains & levers which cause movement of contacts. Separate springs are used for closing & opening operations.

Z01.6.6.2 Hydraulic Energy OM

Herein the operative energy is stored in compressed fluid or oil at high pressures. For switching operation, a set of valves are opened & closed so that compressed oil from the 'oil (reservoir) tank' activates the mechanism through pistons, shafts & links which causes the contact movement.

Z01.6.6.3 Pneumatic Energy OM

This functions on the same principle as hydraulic OM except that the energy is stored as compressed air. This mechanism is invariably used in air-blast breakers.

Z01.7 Design Considerations

Since switchgear must perform under both 'normal' & 'abnormal' conditions, every part of it must be designed to meet the worst operating situations. The following factors are applicable to every switchgear equipment (particularly CBs); fully or partly.

Z01.7.1. Temperature Rise

Since every current carrying part has some resistance, it generates heat. This results in temperature rise of all parts, including insulating parts. This 'temperature rise' must be limited to avoid the occurrence of (a) breakdown of insulators or insulating supports & insulating medium and (b) softening, melting or burning of metal parts.

Z01.7.2 Short Circuit Current Forces

Two conductors placed side by side & carrying currents exert electromagnetic forces on each other. The magnitude of this force is, $F = I_1 * I_2/d^2$, where I_1 & I_2 are currents and d is the distance between conductors. The conductors attract each other if their currents are in same direction & repel if currents are in opposite directions. The conductors & the supporting arrangement should be strong to withstand these forces.

Z01.7.3 Thermal Effects of Short Circuit Currents

Under specific conditions, switchgears located in the 'upstream' portion of the power system must carry the full fault current, equivalent to their 'short time current rating' (ref. Article Z01.3.14) for a certain time which causes intense heating inside them. All parts & their assembly should, therefore, be designed to 'sustain' this heat without any permanent distortion.

Z01.7.4 Contact Erosion due to Arcing

Whenever a switchgear interrupts current, an arc is established between the parting contacts. During arcing, some portion of contact (surface) material vaporizes. This is called 'contact erosion' which must be minimized.

Z01.7.5 Clearances

For reliable operation of any switchgear equipment, safe 'clearances' i.e. 'clear (straight-line) distances', must be maintained between (i) phases, (ii) phase & neutral, (iii) between any live part & adjoining earthed parts. Their values depend on the rated voltage & basic insulation level of the system and the environment around the equipment.

Z01.7. 6 Insulation Levels

Any switchgear must be provided with 'appropriate' insulation. This is characterized by two ratings, namely, (i) 'power frequency withstand voltage' & (ii) 'impulse withstand voltage'; also called 'basic insulation level'.

Z01.7.7 Electrical & Mechanical Life

The life/ lifespan of the switchgear is defined by the number of switching operations it is capable of performing without any damage, under specific conditions. The electrical life is given as number of ON-OFF (i.e. ON followed by OFF) operations under normal load conditions, whereas the mechanical life is given as number of ON-OFF operations without any current through the contacts.

Z01.7.8 Earthing

The 'body' of every switchgear must be 'effectively' connected to the EARTH, i.e. 'it must be earthed' for the safety of equipments & personnel. For this purpose, one or more 'earthing terminals' must be provided on each switchgear. If switchgear has 'multiple' bodies (as for EHV breakers), each body must be separately earthed.

AX5

The Concept of Current Interruption

Arun Ingole, Ex-General Manager, Siemens Ltd.

Z02.1 Introduction

The interruption of current in both normal & abnormal conditions of the electrical circuit is the most important function of all switching devices. In this chapter, we will concentrate on the interruption of alternating current (AC) only. Furthermore, we will generally discuss about the 'short circuit currents', since their interruption is more severe than the others (i.e., load & overload) and with reference to circuit breakers (CB) as they are the most important switchgear for current interruption. However, same theory will be valid for all other switchgears.

The basic steps in current interruption by a CB are as below.

a. The measuring & monitoring system identifies an abnormality in the network & gives a 'tripping' signal to the operating mechanism.
b. The mechanism gets 'activated' & the contacts of the CB start separating. An electric 'arc' is struck between these 'parting' contacts.
c. This arc is 'permanently' extinguished or quenched. Thus, the current is reduced to zero & the circuit is 'opened'.

This chapter will deal with the various aspects of the last step only, namely the 'quenching/ extinction of the arc' in Switchgears.

Z02.2 Electrical Discharge or Arc

When a potential or voltage difference is maintained between two electrodes physically separated from each other i.e. having a 'gap' between them, an 'electrical discharge' occurs between the electrodes or across the gap & continues till the potential difference is maintained. This is due to 'ionization' of the 'substance' or the 'matter' that exists between the electrodes. The voltage sets up an electrical field between the electrodes, as shown (by arrows) in Fig. 2.1. Thus, the substance between the contacts is subjected to 'electrical stress' & it may 'break down' if it can not

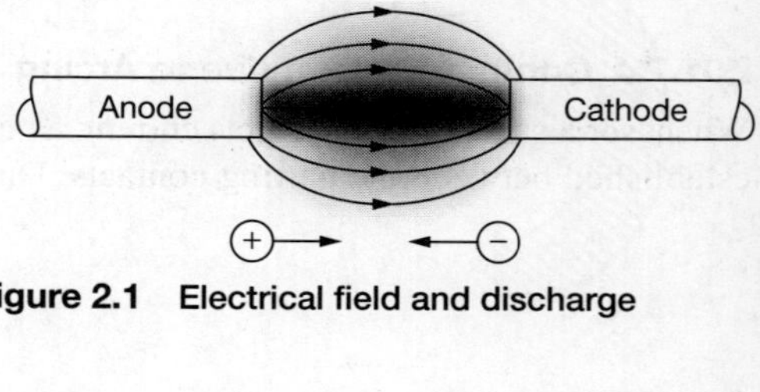

Figure 2.1 Electrical field and discharge

'withstand' the stress. In such case, the negatively charged 'electrons' of the molecules or atoms of the substance get 'free', thus generating an equal number of positively charged 'ions'. While the electrons travel towards the 'anode' the ions travel to the 'cathode' & create an 'electrical discharge' in the gap as shown by dark area in the diagram. This discharge 'completes the circuit' & 'sets up' a current therein. The discharge appears to the human eye as a 'glowing zone' in the gap which varies from a 'bright streak of light' to a 'dull glowing blob'. The discharges encountered in switchgears like circuit breakers, switches, contactors, etc are quite different from those in the luminaries or vacuum tubes. Herein, the electrodes are termed as the 'contacts' (one as fixed & the other as moving); the substance (between the contacts) as 'insulating medium' & the discharge as 'switchgear arc' or simply 'arc'. Herein, the insulating mediums are air or compressed air or water (which is no more used in practice) or transformer oil or SF6 gas, except for the vacuum breakers wherein there is no substance. For this reason, the arcs in vacuum breakers are little different.

The switchgear arcs have, in general, a cross-section as shown in Fig. 2.2(a). The central core (shown by dark area) comprises of 'plasma' like matter at temperatures upto 25000° C. The middle ring (dotted area) contains highly ionized matter in gaseous form at temperatures ranging from 3000 to 6000° C. The outer ring (hashed area) comprises of very hot mixture of gases & liquid or only gases/ air (depending on the insulating medium) at temperatures upto 1000° C.

As expected, the current density is highest in the core; nearing few thousands of amperes per sq. cm. This reduces gradually towards the outer edges. Similarly, the arc voltage reduces as the current increase with the gap length remaining the same. A very approximate relation between them is given by

$$V_{arc} = A + C / I_{arc} \qquad \text{(Eq. 2.1)}$$

where A & C are constants. This is shown in Fig. 2.2(b).

The matter in the arc zone is in unstable or volatile condition. There is a continuous decomposition of molecules into smaller molecules & atoms, i.e. ionization, as well as the 'recombination' of these smaller molecules, atoms & ions to form the original molecule of the insulating medium.

In the switchgear, connected in 'energized' network & in 'closed' condition, the fixed & moving 'main' contacts are fully 'engaged' with each other. In 'ideal' condition current density is uniform over the entire area of the contacts as shown in Fig 2.3(a). However, in practice, the mating surfaces of the contacts are undulating at 'micro-level' resulting in some 'pressure points' with high current densities, popularly called 'hotspots' and some 'voids' with negligible current densities. This results in non-uniform current

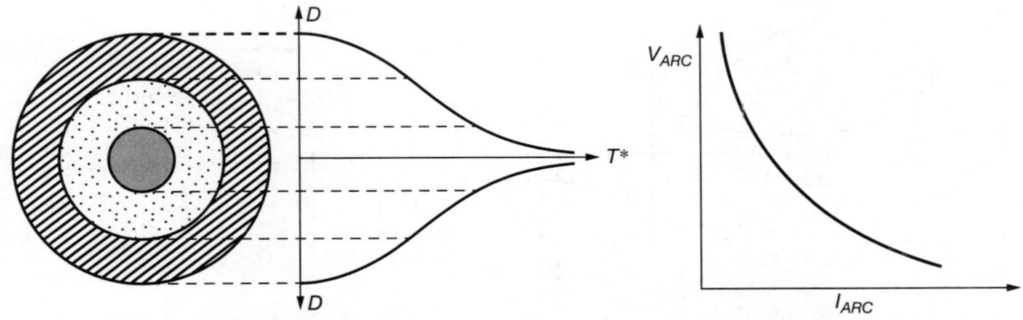

(a) Temperature zones in an arc (b) V-I curve of an arc

Figure 2.2 The switchgear arc properties

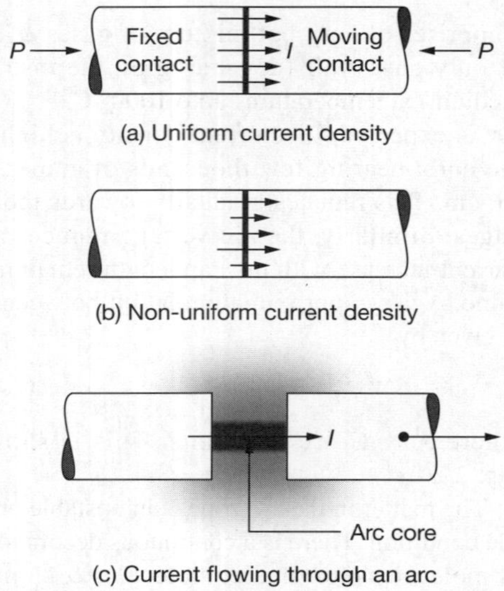

Figure 2.3 Arc striking process

densities as shown in Fig. 2.3(b). These hotspots vaporize (miniscule quantities of) the contact material to generate 'free' electrons & (molecular) ions between the contact faces. Similarly, the miniscule volumes of insulating material, which get trapped in the voids, vaporize or decompose due to heat. As the contacts separate (on receiving the opening command), these ionization products, supported by the electrons & ions already present in the immediate vicinity of the contacts constitute a current between the contacts, thus 'striking an arc' across the gap as shown in Fig. 2.3(c).

Z02.3 Arc Voltage and Current Waveforms

As we discussed, every arc requires a definite voltage across itself. Detailed study of AC arcs has shown that their resistances are inversely proportional to the current during any half cycle. Accordingly, the power factor (i.e. R/L) of the circuit being opened by the breaker, continuously varies during the total arcing duration whereby the circuit current is not sinusoidal. For example, the resistance of an arc of 10 kA RMS in oil may be less than 1 ohm over most part of the half cycle. However, as the current approaches zero, the arc resistance increases very rapidly & may reach few hundreds of kilo-ohms. Fig. 2.4 shows waveforms for the (a) average arc voltage, (b) actual current, (c) system voltage & (d) 'normal' sinusoidal current. The difference between the actual & normal currents is the 'adverse' effect of the arc. This effect is less at higher current when arc resistance is low and it is more when the current is small but arc resistance is high. Also, the instant of 'zero current' (ZC) is shifted from its 'natural' position in

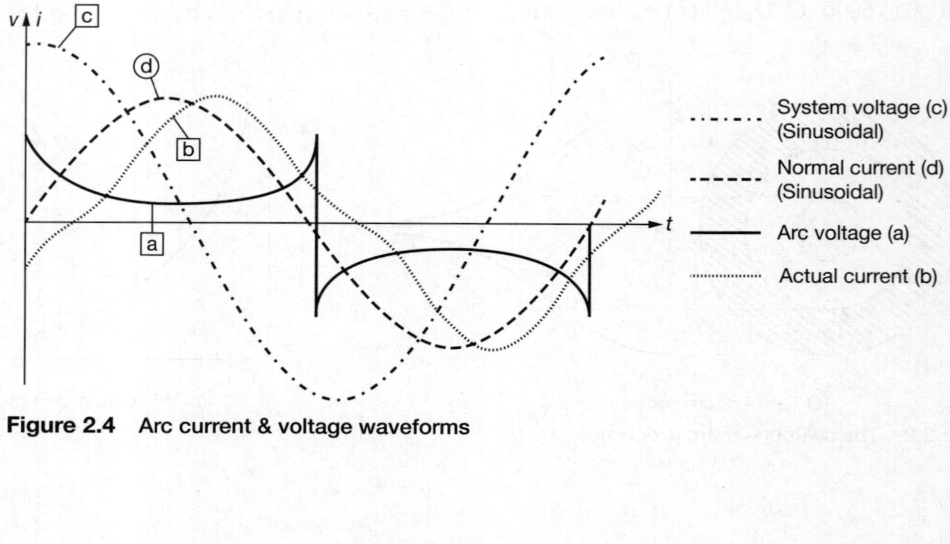

Figure 2.4 Arc current & voltage waveforms

time & it occurs at a system voltage value that is less than the peak.

Z02.4 Alternating Current Interruption

Since every insulating 'medium' has a certain 'insulation or dielectric strength', the 'gap' between the contacts has a dielectric strength which is expressed in kV. This depends on the (i) length of the gap & (ii) extent of 'ionization' of the medium in the gap. This gap's dielectric strength opposes the striking of an arc due to the electrical stress of the system voltage. The restriking of arc after the ZC can be avoided only if the gap's dielectric strength is higher than the system voltage; both at that instant.

In AC network, the ZC occurs twice in every cycle. These instances are called 'current zero' (CZ). Permanent current interruption is achieved by allowing the current to reach zero but not rise again after the CZ by increasing the gap's dielectric strength very rapidly, i.e. not allowing 'restriking of the arc'. It is not desirable to 'cut off' (i.e. abruptly reduce to zero) the current since that results into 'overvoltages'. Ideally, permanent current interruption should happen at the very first CZ after contact opening for all the values of currents upto the 'rated current breaking capacity' of the CB.

At micro-level the current interruption process is as follows. As the contacts part, an arc is set-up across the gap. This creates heat that generates more electrons & ions in the gap which help to stabilize & maintain the arc with a certain voltage across it. As contacts move further away, the arc requires higher voltage on account of (i) its increasing length & (ii) simultaneous de-ionization of the 'gap'. During this period, either of the following two can happen.

a. If the 'required arc voltage' across the gap at any instant exceeds the system voltage at that instant, the arc gets extinguished. This means that dielectric strength or 'build-up' across gap (which equals the arc voltage) exceeds the system voltage or the dielectric stress thereof; represented by curve [A] of Fig. 2.5.

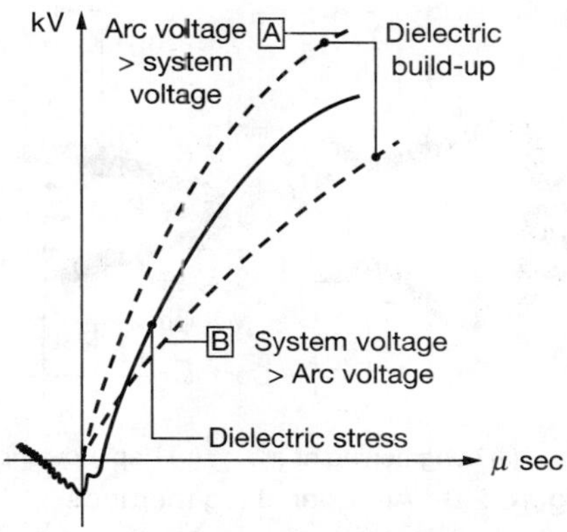

Figure 2.5 Dielectric build-up and stress curves

b. If the system voltage exceeds the required arc voltage, the arc will persist. Herein, the rate of 'build-up' of dielectric strength is less than the dielectric stress due to system voltage; represented by curve [B]. This establishes that, for current interruption, the basic problem pertains to 'building-up' of the dielectric strength between the contacts or across the gap before the CZ instant, so that immediately after the CZ, the dielectric strength of gap exceeds the dielectric stress due to system voltage. The various alternative ways of achieving the above are as under.

Z02.4.1 Arc Lengthening

A longer arc requires higher voltage to maintain the former. This can be achieved by increasing the distance between the contacts. However, there is a limit to this as the equipment becomes very voluminous. Alternately, arc can be lengthened by forcing it to take a 'zigzag' shape as shown in Fig 2.6(a) so that arc voltage is higher than peak system voltage.

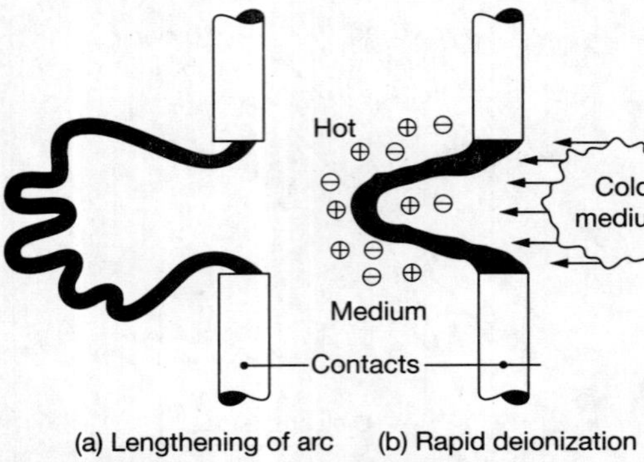

Figure 2.6 Arc quenching methods

Z02.4.2 Deionizing of Gap

During arcing, the insulating medium in gap is in gaseous or liquid-cum-gas form with plasma in the central core. It is very hot and full of electrons & ions. If sufficient quantity of cold medium is added in gap, that zone gets cooled & 'deionized' (as electrons recombine with ions at lower temperatures) whereby the dielectric strength increases rapidly; as shown in Fig. 2.6(b). Since this is a very effective & practical way, CB manufacturers have developed many 'arc quenching devices' based on same. If the current is not interrupted at the first CZ 'A', the same forces come into action again & interrupt the current permanently at subsequent CZs, i.e. B or C, as shown in Fig. 2.7.

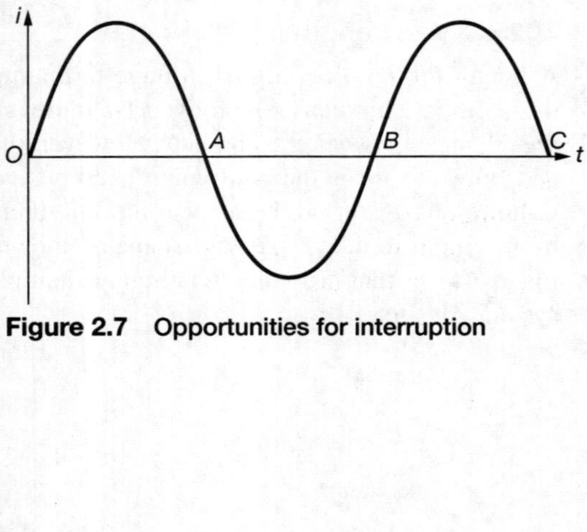

Figure 2.7 Opportunities for interruption

Z02.5 Effect of Power Factor (PF) or Series Inductance

Since the current is zero at any CZ, the entire system voltage appears across gap & it has to withstand the same. Hence, the instantaneous value of system voltage affects the chance of current interruption. This instantaneous value depends on the PF of the concerned circuit. If the PF is high, represented by voltage wave 'V_1' in Fig. 2.8, the system voltage across the gap at CZ is low & so is the chance of arc restriking; thus improving the prospect of current interruption. The opposite is true if the PF is low, i.e. the chance of current interruption is low in case of the wave 'V_2' of Fig. 2.8. In many cases of faults, the PF is very close to zero due to low R/L ratio, especially near generators or at ends of long transmission lines. Hence the highest system voltage appears across the gap at the instant of CZ or within 0.005 second thereafter. Generators, transformers, transmission lines, etc., introduce inductances in a power system.

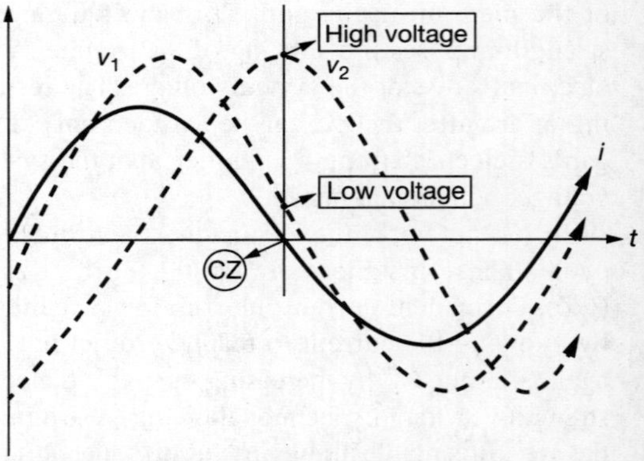

Figure 2.8 *v* and *i* waves for different PF

Z02.6 Effect of Parallel Capacitance

For accurate study of fault current interruption, it is necessary to consider, in addition to above mentioned inductive impedances, several capacitances in parallel with switchgear. These are (a) capacitance to earth of line & all connections on generator side of CB and (b) capacitance between each contact & body of CB i.e. its 'self-capacitance' as shown in Fig. 2.9. Thus, when CB

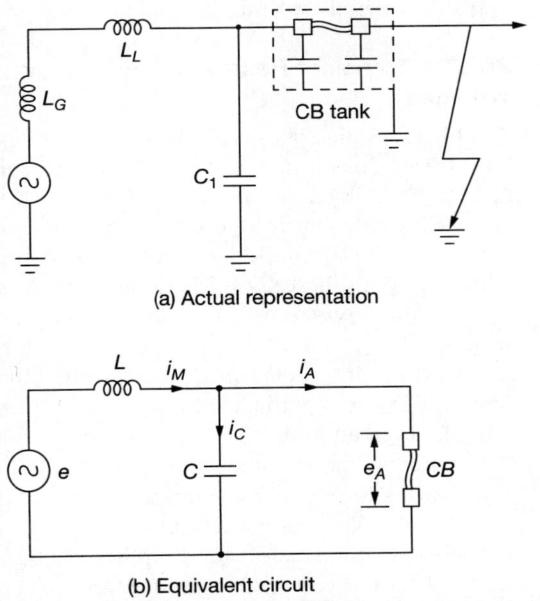

Figure 2.9 Simple power system under earth fault

opens on a phase to earth fault, capacitance '*C*' & a part of self-capacitance come in parallel with arc. This affects (a) arc current just before CZ & (b) voltage across gap just after CZ. For the circuit in Fig. 2.9(b), we have

$$i_A = i_M - i_C \ \& \qquad \text{[Eq. 2.2(a)]}$$

$$e = L\,\frac{di_M}{dt} + e_A \text{ or } \frac{di_M}{dt}$$

$$= (e - e_A)/L \qquad \text{[Eq. 2.2(b)]}$$

where, e = system EMF or voltage, e_A = arc voltage, i_A = arc current, i_M = main current and i_C = capacitor current.

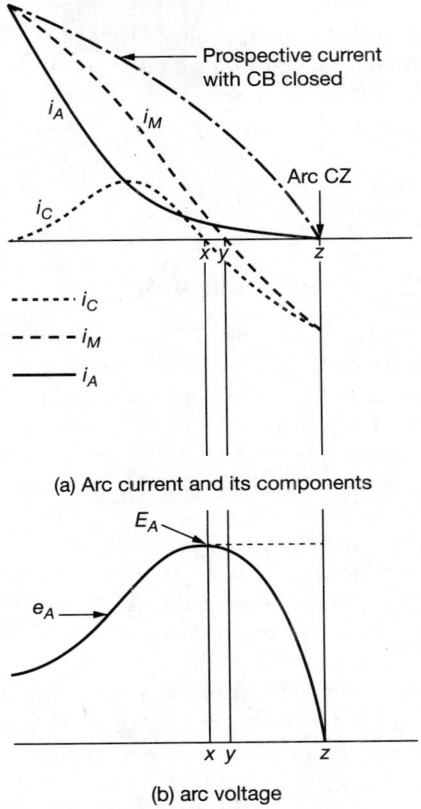

Figure 2.10 Events around the CZ

The events near the CZ are of real interest. Fig. 2.10 shows the relevant current & voltage waveforms around instant of CZ. As i_A approaches zero, e_A increases substantially. The higher arc voltage causes decrease in main current more rapidly as shown in Fig. 2.10(a). The rapidly increasing arc voltage causes current to flow through capacitance C which is given by $i_C = 1/C$ (de_A / d_t). This current is positive. Since i_C is part of i_M, it becomes smaller & falls more rapidly than i_M. At instant '*x*' of Fig 2.10(b), arc voltage reaches its peak, meaning $d_C/d_t = 0$ & $i_A = i_M$ & $i_C = 0$. By this time, capacitance C gets charged to its peak value E_A. Thereafter, it starts discharging with current in opposite direction. At instant

'y', the main current is zero & arc is supported by capacitance current only. During interval 'y-z', both main & capacitance currents are negative. Still, i_A is positive because i_C is larger than i_M in magnitude, till instant 'z' when $i_C = i_M$ & $i_A = 0$. Accordingly, net effect of parallel capacitance is to considerably slow down the falling of arc current near CZ.

Z02.7 Restriking Voltage

As we have seen, post-CZ events are of immense importance for successful interruption of current. Essentially, pre-CZ events amount to the 'preparation' for current interruption whereas the results are apparent only in post- CZ period. When arc disappears at CZ, the instantaneous voltage across gap is very low. However, very next moment, the entire system voltage (less voltage across series capacitance which is negligible) appears across the gap & tries to 're-strike' it. Hence, this voltage is called 'restriking voltage'. Parallelly, after the arc disappears, the insulating medium in gap starts 'getting deionized' & the dielectric strength of gap starts 'rising'. These two potentials, namely, restriking & dielectric strength are in opposition to each other for all time after CZ. The post-CZ instantaneous voltage depends on power factor (PF) of the circuit & has a definite value. The way 'gap voltage' reaches the 'aforesaid' value, starting from zero, is of critical importance for determining post-CZ scenario. For example, in a 'capacitanceless' circuit, voltage variation would be instantaneous. Thus, gap will not get any time for 'build-up' of dielectric strength &, therefore, arc will almost definitely restrike.

Z02.7.1 Transient Restriking and Recovery Voltages

The Fig. 2.11 illustrates typical current & voltage waveforms during interruption period. As contacts start parting at instant t_0, arc is struck which gets extinguished & re-ignited at instants t_1 & t_2 because dielectric build-up is less than system voltage at both these CZs. The gradual increase in arc voltage value in each subsequent cycle, which is due to increasing gap length, must be noted. At instant t_3, current is successfully interrupted. The very next instant, a 'high frequency' (HF) & 'high amplitude' voltage appears across the contacts, represented by V_{TR} in Fig. 2.11. This causes high electrical stress in the gap & tries to 'restrike' arc, but it does not succeed as the build-up of the dielectric strength exceeds the stress. This HF voltage is called 'restriking' or 'transient restriking' voltage (TRV). The TRV is

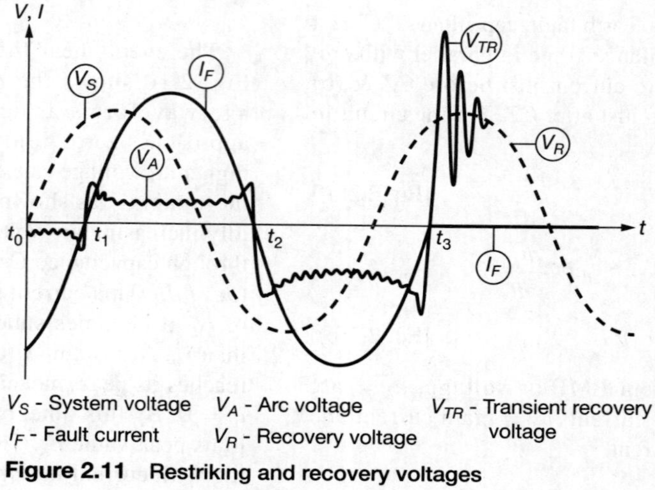

Figure 2.11 Restriking and recovery voltages

a superimposition of a HF component on the sinusoidal system voltage. The HF component 'dies out' in a few milliseconds leaving only system voltage across the gap which is termed as 'recovery voltage'. The HF voltage is generated because of the exchange of energy (trapped in capacitance at instant t_3) between inductance & capacitance of power system (i.e. the 'oscillation' of a L-C-R circuit). The oscillations stop as this energy gets consumed by resistance & gets converted into heat in each cycle. It has been established that role of the 'rate of rise of the restriking voltage' (RRRV) is very critical in the post-CZ period. Higher the RRRV, greater is the possibility of arc restriking & vice-versa.

Z02.7.2 Expressions for TRV and RRRV

Both the system & product designers must calculate the maximum values of TRV & RRRV in the concerned power system. Fig. 2.12 shows a typical system under fault & its equivalent electrical circuit. So long as the CB is closed; the fault current flows through *R* & *L* which represent line resistance & inductance respectively. However, after complete opening of CB, the current is diverted through *C*, the line capacitance. This circuit, shown in Fig. 2.12(b) oscillates at the 'natural' frequency 'f_N' wherein

$$f_N = \frac{\omega}{2\pi} = \frac{1}{2\pi * \sqrt{L*C}} \quad \text{(Eq. 2.3)}$$

In a typical AC system, *R* is very small compared to *L*. Hence the former is neglected (in practical calculations). Thereafter, referring to Fig 2.12(b), we have,

$$e = v_L + v_C = \left(L * \frac{di}{dt}\right) + v_C \quad \text{(Eq. 2.4)}$$

where, $e = E_M * \sin(\omega * t)$ is the system's steady state voltage & is the voltage across *C* as well as the CB contacts. Since $i = dq/dt = d(C * v_C)/d_t$ we have

$$\frac{di}{dt} = \frac{d^2(C * v_C)}{dt^2} = C * \left(\frac{d^2 v_C}{dt^2}\right) \quad \text{(Eq. 2.5)}$$

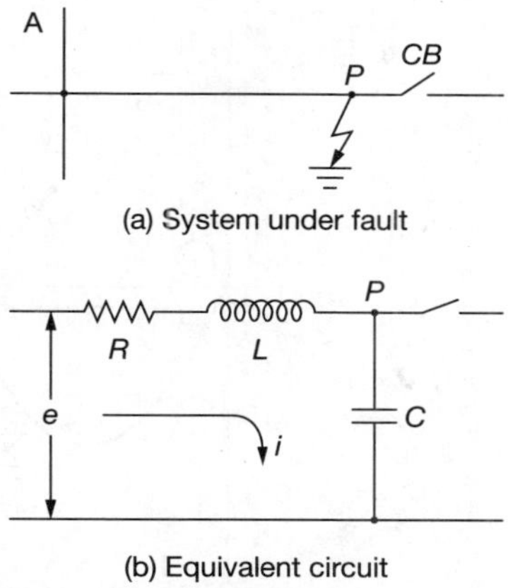

Figure 2.12 System under fault

Hence, we have

$$e = E_M * \sin(\omega_N * t) = L * C * \left(\frac{d^2 v_C}{dt^2}\right) \quad \text{(Eq. 2.6)}$$

Solving this equation and after simplification, we get

$$v_C = E_M * (1 - \cos\omega_N * t)$$
$$= \text{Restriking voltage (TRV)} \quad \text{(Eq. 2.7)}$$

Furthermore,

$$\text{RRRV} = \frac{dv_C}{dt} = d\frac{\{E_M * (1 - \cos\omega_N * t)\}}{dt}$$
$$= \omega_N * E_M * \sin(\omega_N * t) \quad \text{(Eq. 2.8)}$$

Solving the equations 2.7 & 2.8, we have the maximum values of TRV & RRRV as

$$\text{TRV}_M = 2E_M \quad \text{(Eq. 2.9)}$$
$$\text{RRRV}_M = \omega_N * E_M \quad \text{(Eq. 2.10)}$$

Z02.8 Current Zero Pause

Since knowledge of the actual situation around CZ is essential for proper designing of CB, we will examine situation at 'micro-level'. Fig. 2.13(a) shows the current & voltage waveforms occurring when a CB opens against a large fault current of

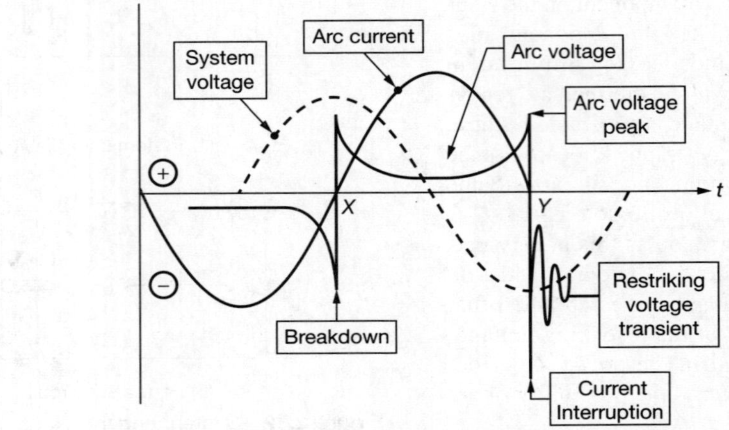

(a) Current and voltage waveforms during interruption

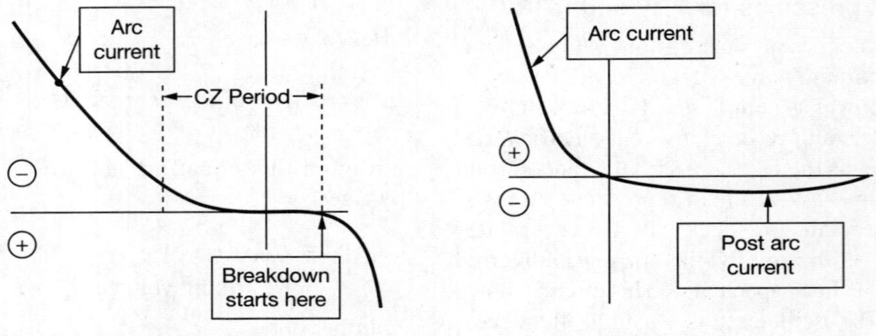

(b) CZ-X period: 1st breakdown (c) CZ-Y period: interruption

Figure 2.13 Interrupting large fully inductive current-CZ pause situations

zero PF. At CZ-X, gap break- down happens (i.e. arc restrikes) inspite of an attempt of current interruption & the arc current reaches its maximum value. At CZ-Y, the current is successfully interrupted & full TRV appears across contacts followed by power frequency recovery voltage. As mentioned earlier, the current during arcing period is not sinusoidal around CZs. This distortion increases at every subsequent CZ whereat the current falls rapidly in initial period but it 'flattens' just before CZ thereby slightly delaying the instant of CZ as shown in Fig. 2.13(b) and 2.13(c). This is due to the presence of parallel capacitance. After CZ, the current rise is 'slower' compared to the normal sinusoidal wave. This is because the gap tries to build-up its dielectric strength (although unsuccessfully after CZ '*X*') through more intense 'deionization' of arc zone or by lengthening of arc. This phenomenon of relatively small current flowing over a little longer period is called 'current zero pause'. The extent of current distortion & length of current zero pause are determined by factors like magnitude of fault current, PF of the circuit, gap-length, nature of insulating medium, deionization technique employed, etc. Importantly, this 'pause' is helpful for the current interruption.

Z02.9 Current Chopping

The CBs are designed to interrupt current at natural CZ. However, if CB, for whatever reason, forces a large current to zero much before instant of natural CZ, the phenomenon is called 'current chopping'. This happens with a CB which creates a 'constant' or 'same' deionization force for all values of currents, i.e. from lowest to its 'rated current breaking capacity'. Since the deionization force is large enough to interrupt rated breaking current, the former is too 'huge' when CB opens on normal load currents (which may be few % of the rated breaking capacity) & current gets 'chopped' with consequential very high 'overvoltages'. Fig. 2.14(a) shows

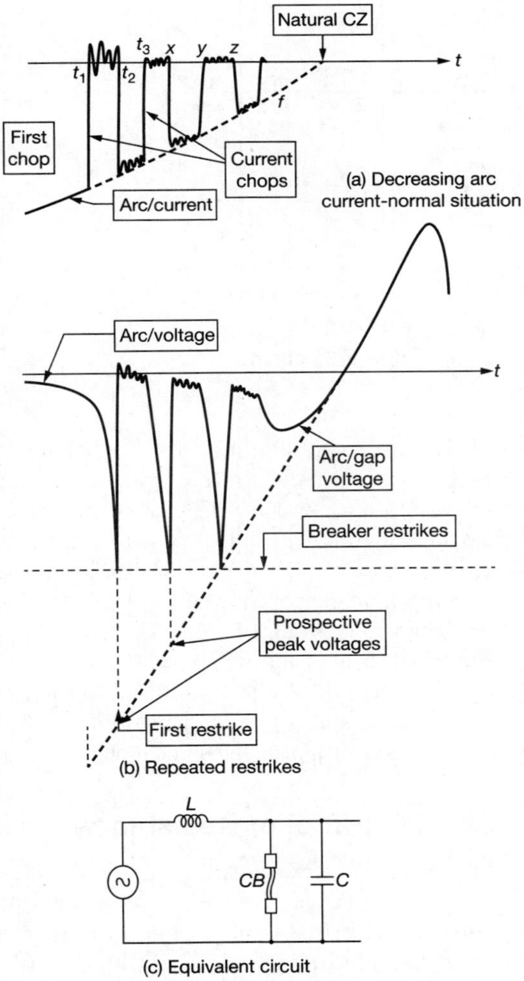

Figure 2.14 Current chopping – *V* and *I* curves

that the arc current is falling in normal manner with a small arc voltage. Suddenly, arc gets destabilised due to extremely high deionizing force & extinguished, thus forcing current to zero at instant t_1; this being the first chop. This entire current gets diverted to capacitance C (as current in inductance L can not change instantaneously), whose voltage starts rising at rate of $dv/dt = i_A / C$ as shown in Fig. 2.14(b). The charging stops only after entire energy in L is stored in C, whereby capacitance reaches peak voltage v_P. Thus, we have,

$$(1/2) * L * i_A^2 = (1/2) * C * v_P^2$$

or
$$v_P = i_A * \sqrt{\frac{L}{C}} \qquad \text{(Eq. 2.11)}$$

This voltage appears across the gap & is generally very high compared to system voltage. However, this 'prospective' peak voltage is not reached as the gap breaks down at some instant t_2 on the rising voltage curve as shown in Fig. 2.14(b) & the arc is established. The value of this voltage, where restrike happens, depends on the rate of rise of voltage (RRV) across gap, the rate of deionization, etc. At lower RRV, deionization is more & 'restriking' voltage is higher. The arc may still not be stable as deionization force is large & a second chop takes place at instant t_3. Since this chop current is smaller than earlier one, prospective peak voltage is also less. Further current chops can also occur as shown in figure until restriking becomes no more feasible due to very high dielectric build-up of the gap & the current is finally interrupted. To find typical values of prospective overvoltages, we consider a system having rated continuous current of 2000 A & a dead three phase to ground fault current of 25 kA. If CB, while opening at 1000 A (which is 50% of its rated continuous current & only 4% of is rated current breaking capacity) chops current, the prospective peak voltage can be upto 1425 kV.

Z02.10 Capacitive Current Interruption

This task, which is encountered in operations like opening of long, unloaded overhead transmission

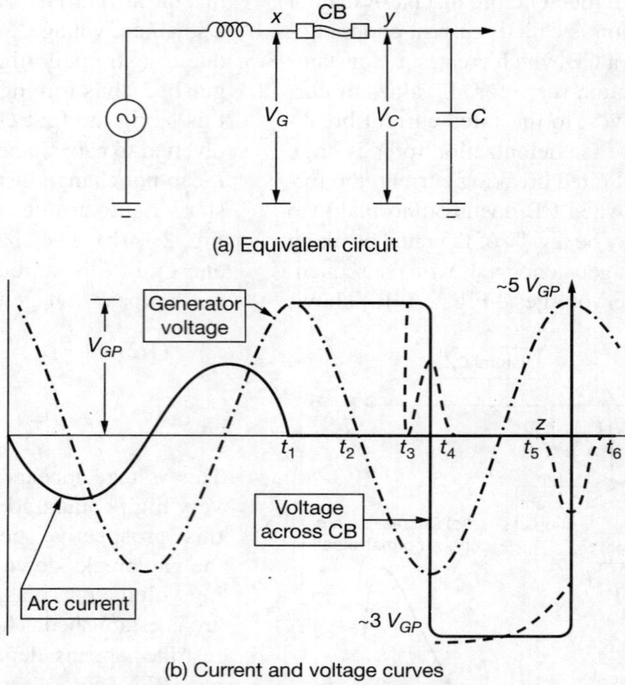

Figure 2.15 Capacitive current breaking – *V* & *I* curves

lines, pose special problems. These are feeders which are connected to power sources at one end but 'open' at the other. As we very well know, there is a capacitance between each phase conductor & the Earth which is distributed through the length of line. Since these conductors are at system voltage while the Earth is at zero potential, there is a small capacitive current in each phase although there is no 'load' current. Fig. 2.15(a) shows a simple equivalent circuit of this situation while Fig. 2.15(b) shows voltage & current waveforms applicable during opening of source side CB. At instant t_1, when arc current gets interrupted, source/generator voltage is at its peak 'V_{GP}' & so is the line voltage. As time passes, source voltage falls towards zero, while that of line remains (almost) constant at V_{GP}. Herein, one the contact of CB is at source voltage, while the other is at line voltage. After t_1, source voltage becomes negative, thus increasing potential difference between two contacts beyond V_{GP}. At t_4, this would become $2V_{GP}$. However, at some instant t_3, just before t_4, gap may break- down due to large 'gap voltage' (close to $2V_{GP}$) & arcing starts. This creates an 'oscillatory circuit' with transient voltage peak of $4V_{GP}$, thereby charging line capacitance to $-3V_{GP}$. This process may repeat in next cycle whereby line capacitance gets charged close to $+5V_{GP}$, $-7V_{GP}$, $+9V_{GP}$, etc. But this does not happen in practice since line voltage falls due to 'leakage to Earth' & 'corona loss'. As dielectric strength of the gap builds up, breakdown does not happen after some time.

Z02.11 Effect of Resistance

In practical power transmission or distribution feeders, 'series' resistance is always very small whereby its effect is negligible in most cases. However, a resistance in parallel with the CB contacts, as shown in Fig. 2.16, can play a significant role as follows.

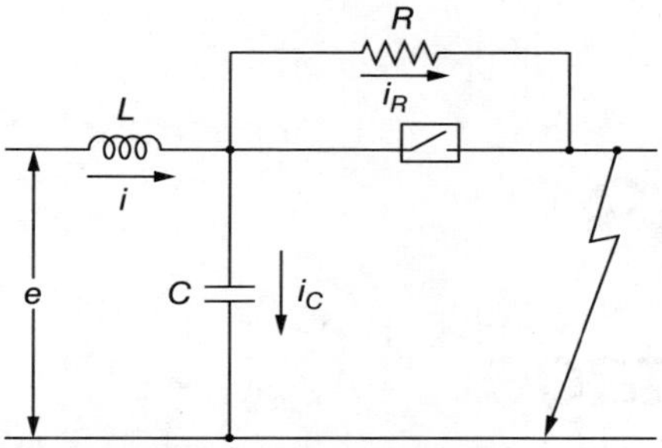

Figure 2.16 Resistance in parallel

a. The parallel resistance decreases the current in arc, thereby reducing extent of ionization & helping in build-up of dielectric strength of the gap column. This increases arc resistance thus further decreasing the arc current.

b. It assists in reducing both the maximum restriking voltage & RRRV. For the circuit under consideration, we have

$$e = L * \frac{di}{dt} + \frac{1}{C} * \int i_C * dt \qquad \text{[Eq. 2.12]}$$

and $$i = i_C + i_R \qquad \text{(Eq. 2.13)}$$

On simplification we get

$$e = L * C * \frac{d^2V_C}{dt^2} + \frac{L}{R} * \frac{dV_C}{dt} + V_C \qquad \text{(Eq. 2.14)}$$

It is quite difficult to arrive at the theoretical solution to this equation. However, we can find 3 practical solutions for three different values of resistance R relative to L & C as follows.

- *Case A*: Assuming R as infinite & no other resistance in circuit, we get, for the voltage across CB, $v = e * (1 - \cos\sqrt{L * C} * t)$. This voltage rises from zero to $2E_M$ [ref. eq. 2.10], then falls to zero & continues to oscillate about value E (which is the value of e at CZ). The 'damped' frequency of this oscillation is given by

$$f_D = \frac{1}{2\pi} * \sqrt{\frac{1}{L * C} - \frac{1}{4R^2 * C^2}} \qquad \text{(Eq. 2.15)}$$

which is much higher than 50 Hz.

- *Case B*: If R if finite but greater than $\sqrt{L * C/2}$, then the HF oscillations get 'damped' out gradually as shown in Fig. 2.17(a), wherein the system PF is presumed to be zero. The value of voltage peak reached is slightly less than $2E_M$, which is due to the 'damping' effect of the resistance
- *Case C*: If R is equal to $\sqrt{L * C/2}$, the restriking voltage does not oscillate at all. It rises to E_M &, thereafter, follows normal system voltage waveform (of 50 Hzs) as shown in Fig. 2.17(b).
- *Case D*: If R is less than $\sqrt{L * C/2}$, the restriking voltage does not oscillate at all as shown in Fig. 2.17(c). It rises 'exponentially to a value 'E' which is less than E_M &, thereafter, follows normal system voltage waveform (of 50 Hz).

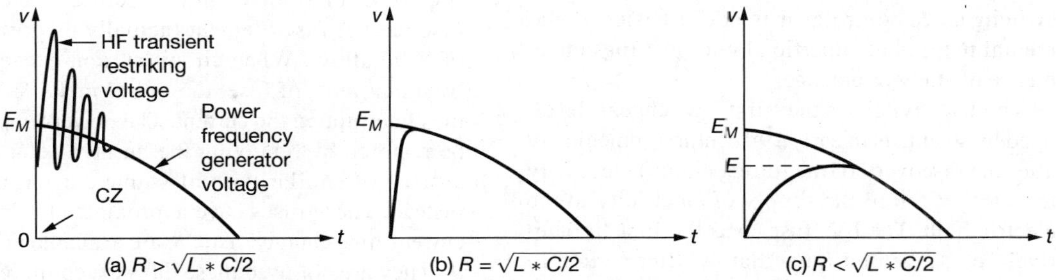

Figure 2.17 Waveforms of restriking voltage

AX6

Low Voltage Switchgear

Arun Ingole, Ex-General Manager, Siemens Ltd.

Z03.1 Introduction

Most (i.e. about 90 %) of the total actual power consumption is at low voltage (LV), i.e. below 1100 V. Accordingly, the total requirement of the LV switchgear is tremendous. The important LV switchgears are Switches/ Isolators, Fuses, Circuit Breakers, Contactors, Overcurrent Relays & Combinations thereof as well as accessories, such as Releases, Protection Relays, etc. The switchgear which is used in the 'control & auxiliary circuits', i.e. for control, measurement, protection, alarm & indication, etc. of the 'power' equipments is called 'controlgear'. This is simply to facilitate 'distinguishing' between switchgear which is connected in the 'primary' (i.e. power) circuit & the 'secondary' circuit. Thus, the differentiation between switchgear & controlgear is not of basic/ fundamental nature but superficial one; just for convenience of study & practice.

The LV 'switch' is the 'first' switchgear developed by scientists in early 19th century immediately after the discovery of the (direct circuit) electricity to 'start' & 'stop' the supply of electricity to the electric bulb. The LV 'fuse' was the first 'protective' gear, invented immediately after switch to 'protect' the bulbs from adverse effects of 'electrical faults'.

Z03.2 Fuses

A fuse is a small metallic element inserted in the main or primary circuit at a convenient location so that it carries the full circuit current. It is designed to carry the rated current (I_R) of the circuit continuously without any deterioration. However, under overcurrent (OC) conditions, it melts & interrupts the current before any damage to the 'protected' (i.e. connected downstream) equipment. They are used very extensively in LV networks, i.e. in 'utilization' segment & sparingly in distribution segment, upto 33 kV. Basically, they are of two types, namely, 'rewirable' & 'non-rewirable'.

Z03.2.1 Rewirable Fuse

It consists of a porcelain or bakelite fuse carrier, fuse base & fuse-element (actually a wire) made of 'lead alloy'. When circuit current exceeds the 'rated current' of fuse, the 'wire' melts & breaks thus interrupting the current. The power supply can be restored by removing the burnt wire & fitting a piece of similar wire of 'same current rating' instead. These fuses have approximately 'inverse' current-time characteristic & are available upto 100 A. They are not used these days except in residential premises. Their merits are; (i) very inexpensive

& (ii) very simple for replacement. Their disadvantages are; (a) anybody can tamper with them which is dangerous, (b) any wire can be used to replace the burnt element leading to unreliability, (c) element deteriorates due to climate & (d) low current breaking capacity.

Z03.2.2 Non-rewirable Fuse

Herein, the fuse element is completely enclosed inside a strong 'body' of insulating material & is permanently connected to the terminals. If the element burns due to OC, entire 'fuse link' must be replaced with a new one of exactly same type & rating. Hence incorrect replacement is not possible or can be avoided.

Z03.2.3 HRC Fuse

HRC stands for 'high rupturing capacity'. Basically, it consists of a fuse element enclosed inside a strong porcelain body & the space in-between is filled with finely granulated quartz powder of special quality. When 'element' melts due to OC, its material vapourises. This vapour reacts chemically with the surrounding quartz powder thereby producing a solid substance having high dielectric strength. Thus, as metal vapour is rapidly removed from inside of fuse body, the arc is quickly quenched & does not restrike. Fig. 3.1

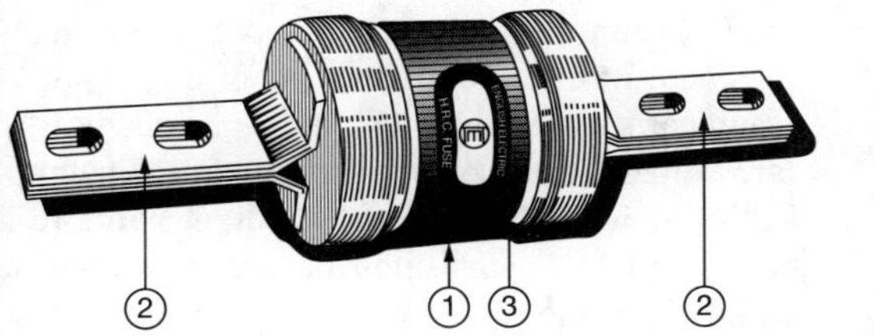

① Porcelain body ② Terminal ③ 'Blown' indicator

Figure 3.1 Link type HRC fuse

shows a typical 'link' type HRC fuse manufactured for ratings upto 63 A- continuous current & 50 kA-breaking current.

It has 'inverse' time-current operating characteristic. It possesses 'current limiting' feature. Herein, as current reaches the 'cut-off' value which is much smaller than the 'peak prospective' current, the (fuse) element breaks, arc is struck & it is quickly extinguished whereby both the breaking time & the arc energy are minimum.

Z03.3 Switches

Switch was the first device used for controlling the electrical circuits. A switch can 'close' & 'open' circuits under 'load' conditions & isolate the downstream equipment for maintenance.

Z03.3.1 Normal Duty or Load Break Switches (LBS)

They can make & break its rated or full current at rated voltage and PF of 0.8 or higher. They are used in resistive circuits like lighting, heating, etc.

Z03.3.2 Heavy Duty Switches

They are designed to make & break its rated current at rated voltage & PF as low as 0.5. They are used for motor control & for switching of transformers, reactors, blowers, capacitors, etc.

Z03.3.3 Motor Duty or 'HP Rated' Switches

They are designed to make & break currents upto 6 times of their rated value at rated voltage and PF of 0.35 or higher. Therefore, they can be used for direct switching of motors without the contactors.

Z03.3.4 Rotary Switches

Cam operated rotary switches are very popular. Fig. 3.2 shows typical power & control switches. It comprises of many 'grooved' plastic cams mounted on the main shaft. A set of contacts are positioned around these cams. As shaft rotates, cams also rotate &, depending on shapes of the cams, contacts change their status (i.e. OPEN to CLOSE & CLOSE to OPEN) or remain in same status. Apart from ON/OFF switching function, the rotary switches can perform many 'programmed' functions.

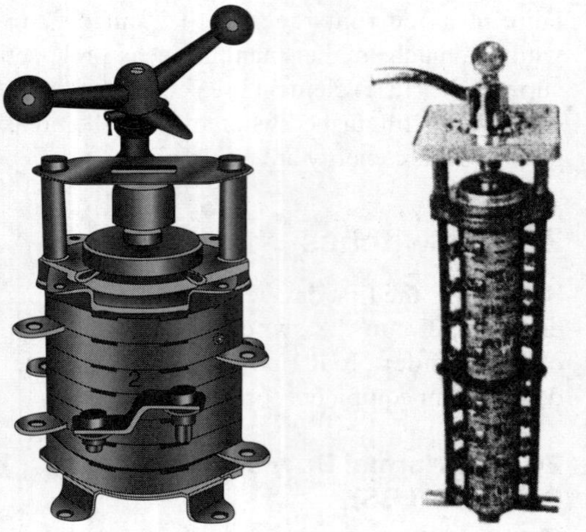

(a) 600 A power switch (b) Control switch

Figure 3.2 Rotary type switches

Z03.3.5 Knife Blade Switches

They are used for still higher current ratings. Herein the moving contact is 'knife-blade' while the fixed contact is 'U-shaped' & spring-loaded, called 'lyra' contact. Many times, two sets of 'fixed & moving' contacts are used in series, i.e. 'double-break', to increase the current breaking capacity.

Z03.4 Circuit Breakers (CB)

The CB (or simply a breaker) is the most important switchgear. It was invented in later parts of 19th century to give 'permanent/ long-term' 'fault-clearing' capacity to switch. This enabled 'dispensing-off' with the fuses (which need replacement after every fault clearing). From the beginning till date, oil, air, air-blast, SF6 (sulphur hexafluoride) gas & vacuum have been used as insulating & arc quenching medium in the CBs (of various voltage ratings) although LV breakers always employ air as medium. Herein, we have three types, namely; (i) air circuit breakers (ACB), (ii) moulded case circuit breakers (MCCB) & (iii) miniature circuit breakers (MCB).

Z03.4.1 Air Circuit Breakers

They are assembled in a sheet steel frame, are available in continuous current (CC) ratings upto 6000 A & are useful for switching & protection of important feeders. Every major manufacturer has several models of ACBs. Fig. 3.3 shows a section through model CN-CS of M/S L&T. It has 'quick-make & quick-break' operating mechanism. Its important components are: Pole Assembly, Arc Chutes, Operating Mechanism & OC Release.

Z03.4.1.1 Pole Assembly

It comprises of moving contact arm, fixed contact (4), two terminals (5) & the arc chute (12). The moving contact arm consists of a number of fingers (1) on which main & arcing contacts (2) & (3) are fitted. The fingers are individually spring-loaded. This contact includes a compensating fulcrum (11) & latch (9). Three pole assemblies are held inside metal frame with insulating partitions between them. The current carrying parts are made of copper with silver plating. The contacts are faced with 'anti-weld' material like silver-tungsten.

Z03.4.1.2 Arc Chutes

They enclose arcing contacts and serve to cool & quench the arc. They are fixed to main assembly with clips. They comprise of several 'de-ion' plates (21) located perpendicular to the 'arc-axis' inside a housing (19) of light insulating material. The arc between the parting contacts gets pushed in the chute wherein it (arc) gets confined & split in many parts by the de-ion plates. This increases the 'arc voltage' & makes it unsustainable. The upper half of de-ion plate is coated with special arc-resistant material which ensures that arc is extinguished within the chute.

Z03.4.1.3 Operating Mechanism

Its important parts are shown in Fig. 2 by numbers (7) to (18). Immediately after completion of closing operation, motor starts again, recharges the spring (13), which is maim energy source, thus keeping ACB ready for closing operation. This spring can be charged manually also. The control

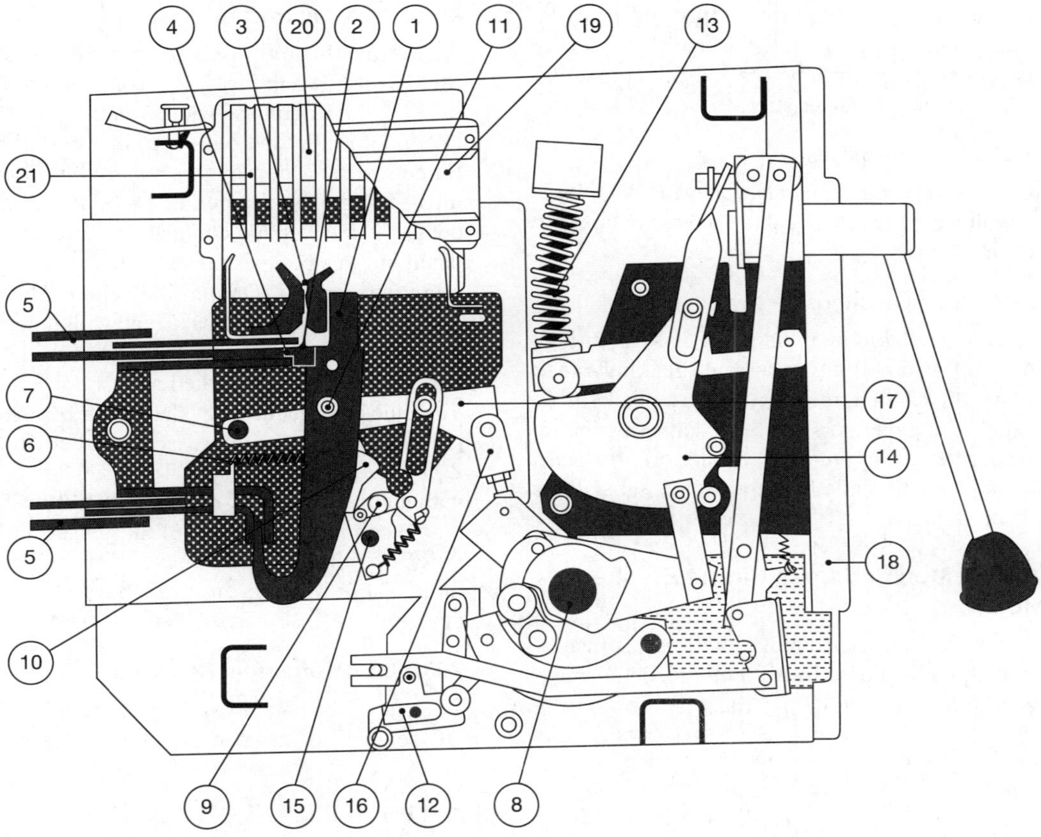

(1) Moving contact arm
(2) Main contact
(3) Arcing contact
(4) Fixed contact
(5) Terminal
(6) Moving contact spring
(7) Fixing point
(8) Main shaft
(9) Latch for rapid closing
(10) Cam for rapid closing
(11) Fulcrum of moving contact
(12) Holding clip
(13) Rapid closing spring
(14) Interlocking cam
(15) Fixing point
(16) Mechanism latch
(17) Insulating connector
(18) Control box
(19) Arc chute housing
(20) Arc chutes
(21) De-ion plates

Figure 3.3 Section of a typical ACB

box (18) contains manual operating handle, 'close' & 'trip' push buttons, ON & OFF indications, etc.

Z03.4.1.4 Overcurrent (OC) Release

It is a 'thermo-magnetic' release for OC protection. On activation, it directly 'unlatches' the mechanism to trip the ACB. It has one set each of bimetallic (i.e. thermal) & electromagnetic elements for overload (OL) & short circuit (SC) protections respectively. Both these elements are provided separately for each phase but all act on the common 'trip bar'. All elements are fed by CTs which are mounted on ACB terminals. The operating currents or 'thresholds' of these elements can be selected & changed with help of 'taps & setting-adjusters' provided thereon. The OL release has 'inverse' & SC release has 'constant minimum' (called instantaneous) 'time- current' characteristics.

Z03.4.1.5 Accessories

Normal accessories are undervoltage (UV) release, overvoltage (OV) release, shunt release & auxiliary switch.

Z03.4.1.6 Applications

They are available in a wide range of CC ratings; from 400 A to 6000 A & current breaking capacity of 100 kA. Therefore, they are used for (a) switching of generators, power & large distribution transformers, large motors, capacitors, furnaces, etc. and (b) automatic load transfer in substations, industrial plants, etc.

Z03.4.2 Moulded Case Circuit Breakers (MCCB)

It is a very 'compact' breaker with air as insulating medium; enclosed inside a moulded housing & cover both of insulating material.

Z03.4.2.1 Construction

A section through a Crompton Greaves make MCCB is shown in Fig. 3.4. It comprises of a housing (1) with interphase insulation barriers & cover (1A), both moulded out of high strength, heat & flame resistant, non-hygroscopic, non-toxic, thermos-setting plastic material. Three sets of moving contacts (11) & fixed contacts (10) are accommodated in three compartments with a common operating mechanism (OM) at the center. The OM is 'quick-make & quick-break' type with independent manual trip-free feature. The operating knob (2) has three positions, marked as ON, OFF & TRIP. The quick arc quenching is achieved by arc chutes (5) with 'de-ion' plates, as described in article Z03.4.1.2, within 20 msecs. The MCCB is provided with a three sets of OC releases (7) & (8) which act on the common 'trip bar' (6) thus ensuring 'three-pole' opening of MCCB even for single-phase fault. These MCCBs are available for CC ratings upto 1600 A & SC capacities upto 50 kA.

Z03.4.2.2 Overcurrent Releases

This MCCB employs thermo-magnetic type OC release. It has two elements - thermal (i.e.

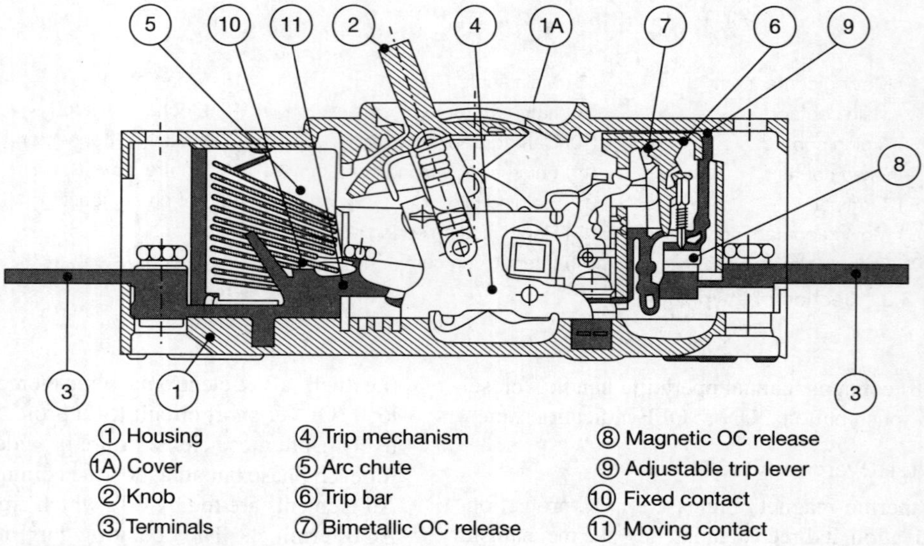

Figure 3.4 MCCB - section

bimetallic) for OL & electromagnetic for SC protections respectively- connected in series. The thermal element has 'inverse I-T' characteristics while the electromagnetic one is 'instantaneous' type.

Z03.4.2.3 Internal Accessories

MCCBs can be fitted with UV release, shunt release, auxiliary switch & alarm switch.

Z03.4.2.4 Applications

MCCBs have been successfully used to replace (less sophisticated) 'switch-fuse' or 'fused switch' combinations & (more expensive) ACBs. MCCBs are generally used at the final distribution & utilization points for protection of Transformers upto 1000 kVA, Feeder Cables, Motors, Lights, VAC, DC Equipments, etc.

Z03.4.3 Miniature Circuit Breakers (MCB)

They are manufactured as 'single-pole' (SP) units with insulation level of 415 V so that the three-pole assembly can be used upto 415 V AC. They are really tiny in size.

Z03.4.3.1 Construction

The Fig. 3.5 shows a section through a MCB manufactured by Siemens Ltd., India. It comprises of a moulded housing made from polypropylene or polystyrene having high dielectric & mechanical strengths. The current carrying parts are made

(1) Power contacts (main and arcing)
(2) Arc runner
(3) Arc chute
(4) Electromagnetic SC release
(5) Thermal OL release
(6) Latching mechanism
(7) Toggle (handle)
(8) Terminal (top, bottom)
(9) Snap-on fixing arrangement

Figure 3.5 MCB - section

out of copper & are silver-plated. The contacts are faced with anti-weld material like silver tungsten. The OM is spring-assisted 'quick-make & quick-break' type with trip-free feature. It has arc control device having 13 'arc-splitters' (de-ion plates) which imparts 'current limiting' feature. The operating knob acts directly on moving contacts. It has bimetallic & electromagnetic releases, both with fixed settings, for OL & SC protections, respectively. Multi-pole MCBs are produced by assembling the correct number of SP units together. A 'bridge' is fixed onto knobs of all SP MCBs to achieve the 'gang' operation.

Z03.4.3.2 Performance

They have inverse I-T characteristics in OL range & instantaneous response in SC range. When it trips due to over- current, the knob jumps to OFF position. It has SC interruption time of 15-20 m-secs. Due to current limiting, the 'let- through' energy is small. This simplifies the co-ordination with the upstream MCCBs & fuses which provide 'back-up' protection.

Z03.4.3.3 Ratings

Herein, the standard current ratings are 6 A, 10 A, 16 A, 20 A, 25 A, 32 A, 40 A, 50 A, & 63 A. The normal current breaking capacity is 5 kA.

Z03.4.3.4 Advantages and Applications

They were developed to replace fuses in household usage. They have advantages such as: (a) completely tamper-proof, (b) offer definite protection, (c) compact with snap-on fixing feature that reducs panel space & assembly time. They are most suitable for protection of lighting, fans, domestic air-conditioners, etc.

Z03.5 Contactors

The 'contactor' was developed to give 'automatic' feature to switch which is very essential for control of motor that needs to be switched ON & OFF very frequently. It is simple, both in design & construction, and inexpensive compared to CB (which is another automatic switch) of same voltage & current ratings. Fig. 3.6 shows a typical power

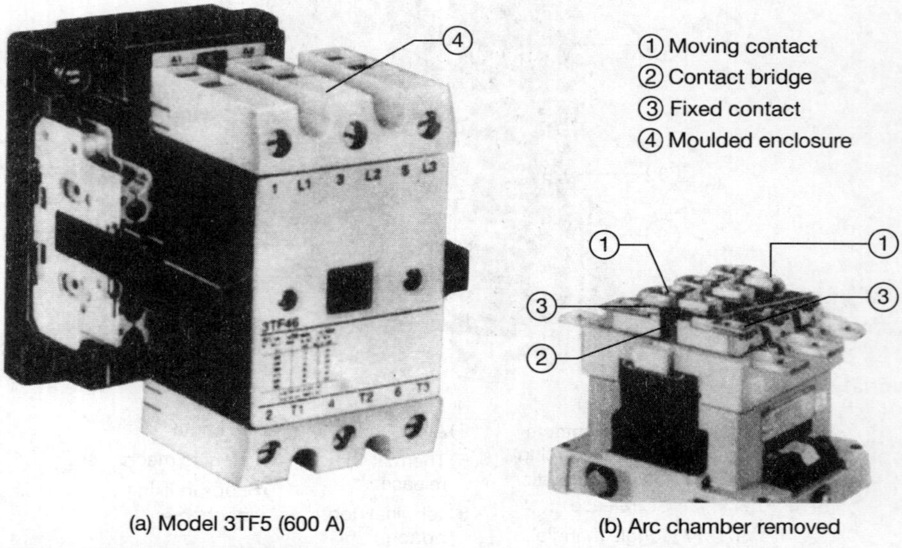

(a) Model 3TF5 (600 A)

(b) Arc chamber removed

Figure 3.6 Power contactor

contactor made by M/S Siemens Ltd, India. It consists of a set of three moving contacts (1) mounted on 'contact bridge' (2) of insulating material. This bridge is fixed on the 'moving armature' (not visible) of an electromagnet; popularly called 'coil'. The whole assembly is housed inside a moulded enclosure (4) alongwith a set of six fixed contacts (3). When the electromagnet is energized, the armature is attracted whereby the moving contacts engage with the fixed ones thereby closing the circuit. The contact pressure is maintained by leaf springs. On de-energizing the electromagnet, the contact bridge returns to its original position. The contacts separate, arcs are drawn- two in each phase & subsequently quenched; thus, interrupting the current. The contactors are of two types; (i) power & (ii) auxiliary.

Z03.5.1 Power Contactors

They are used for switching power circuits & are available upto CC rating of 500 A. They have 'double break' type main contacts. They are used for: (a) Motor Control like starting, stopping, reversing, plugging, inching, etc., (b) Switching of Resistors, Reactors & Capacitors, (c) Control of Battery Chargers, (d) Automatic Power Transfer from the 'main' to 'standby' supply & vice-versa. They are provided with a set of NO & NC auxiliary contacts to be used for indication, sequential control & interlocking functions.

Z03.5.2 Auxiliary Contactors

They have several normal NO, NC & C/O contacts having current ratings of 5 or 10 A. They are widely used in the 'control' & 'auxiliary' circuits. By combining several contactors, any type of sequential operation or electrical interlock can be achieved. These are often required for motors associated with compressors, large blowers, fuel injectors, dam-valves, machine tools, cranes & hoists, lifts & elevators, conveyers, etc.

Z03.5.3 Mechanical & Electrical Endurance

Normally, motors are switched ON & OFF very often. Some motor applications like, cranes, machine tools, etc. require very frequent starting & stopping. Therefore, complete contactor & particularly the contacts are designed for millions of operations.

Z03.5.4 Bounce-free Contacts

When the moving contacts touch the fixed contacts, the former may bounce due to spring force. This must be avoided because bouncing causes 'contact burning' & reduces 'contact life'.

Z03.5.5 Chatter-free Magnet

Herein, magnet design is very critical. It should be light & compact but also powerful so that it can 'hold' fixed & moving contacts together against spring-forces. There should be no 'chattering' of magnet, as it causes contact bouncing, contact burning & a disturbing noise.

Z03.5.6 Arc Quenching

The arc should be quenched in shortest duration to avoid contact-metal vapourization which reduces contact life. The arc splitters & de-ionization chambers, etc. are used to achieve this.

Z03.6 Overload Relays/ Releases

The OL relays were developed to protect the connected motors from the potential damages due to OC. They are used exclusively with the contactors for the protection of LV motors. They are different from the 'protection relays', which are used for the protection of all sorts of transmission lines, generators, transformers, large motors, etc. To differentiate, these OL relays are very often called 'releases' which are simple & cheap. They are either 'current operated' or 'voltage operated'. They are so connected in network that they monitor the currents & voltages in power circuit, detect the existence of fault (if any), identify the faulty circuit & generate signals to isolate the same. They are of three types; (a) eutectic alloy, (b) bimetallic & (c) electromagnetic. While eutectic alloy releases are obsolete, electromagnetic ones are rarely used as they have 'instantaneous' I-T response. Thus, bimetallic release is the most commonly used one.

Z03.6.1 Bimetallic Release

Herein, the current is monitored by a 'bimetal strip' comprising of two strips of dissimilar metals, having different 'co-efficient of thermal expansion', fused together. As the temperature of the bimetal increases, one strip expands (in length) more than the other which results into bending of the bimetal. Fig. 3.7 shows internal arrangement of a typical 3-phase bimetal release. It comprises of three bimetallic 'elements' (1) mounted in three compartments of a plastic housing (2). Each element is made of a bimetal strip (3) & a heating coil or heater (4) wound around strip. The heater carries either fullcircuit current or proportionately reduced current. Each bimetal is attached to a firm support (5) at one end, the other end having freedom of transverse movement due to bending of strip. Till the circuit current is less than the set value, bimetal's 'free-end' remains away from the 'trip-lever' (6). When the circuit current exceeds the 'set' value, excessive bending of the bimetal causes its free end to push the trip or lever. This 'operates' the auxiliary switch (7) whose NC contact opens circuit of contactor coil & trip or open the latter. As any of three bimetals can push the trip-lever, release operates due to OL in any phase. It exhibits 'inverse' I-T characteristic.

Z03.7 Motor Starters

The combination of contactor & OL release is called "motor starter". It is used for switching motors due to special requirements of 'motor duty', which are, (a) frequent starting & stopping', (b) remote & multiple point control, (c) sequential operation and (d) switching under (motor) 'stalled' conditions.

Z03.7.1 Types of Starters

Most industrial machines & all water-pumps have squirrel cage rotors wherein 'starting' current is several times of full load current when subjected to rated voltage. This causes considerable drop in the supply voltage, especially when large motors start, which affects all other loads. To avoid this, big motors are started on 'reduced voltage'. Thus, we have the following types of motor starters.

Z03.7.2 Direct-on-line (DOL) Starter

Herein, full voltage 'V_T' is applied to the motor. It is quite safe for all small motors & several medium

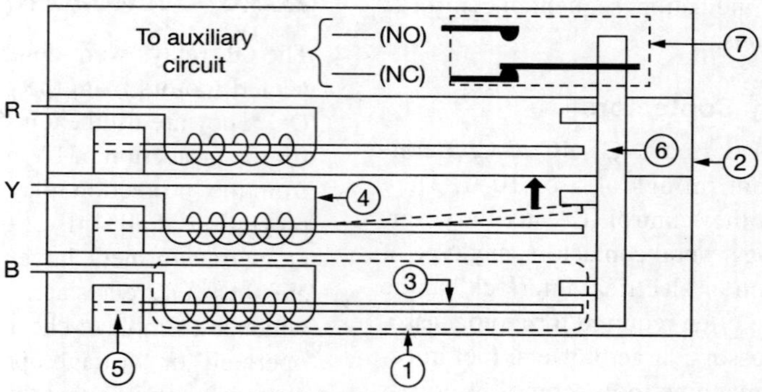

(1) Bimetal element (2) Housing (plastic) (3) Bimetallic strip (4) Heating coil
(5) Support (6) Trip lever (7) Auxiliary switch

Figure 3.7 Bimetallic overload release

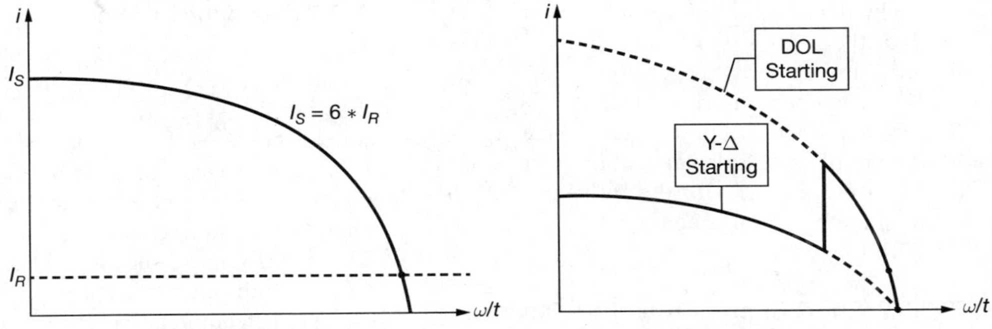

(a) Direct-on-line starting (b) Star-delta starting

Figure 3.8 Current – Speed characteristics for induction motors

size ones which do not start on full 'shaft load' or have short starting periods. The 'current - speed' (I-ω) characteristic for a standard squirrel cage, delta connected motor is shown in Fig. 3.8 (a). The normal starting time is 1-2 seconds.

Z03.7.3 Star-delta (Y-Δ) Starter

This employs 'reduced voltage' starting. It has two-step starting namely, 'star' & 'delta' and the relevant 'I-ω' characteristic is shown in Fig. 8(b). As the motor is started its windings get connected in 'star' configuration wherein the phase voltage 'V_P' is $1/\sqrt{3}$ times 'V_T' & the starting current is reduced to 1/3, i.e. reduction by 66%. After the motor has acquired some speed the windings connection is changed to delta configuration. The current increases to some extent but it does not exceed three times rated current. The change-over from 'star' to 'delta' is 'manual' as in Manual Y-Δ Starter or 'automatic' as in Automatic Y-Δ Starter.

Z03.8 Motor Protection

Since 75 % of total power is consumed by LV motors, their control & protection is a very important matter. Any abnormality in the motor is reflected as change in value & phase angle of the circuit current (vector), i.e. OC. The OC may be a fraction or several times of 'I_R'. As the motors need very 'close' protection to avoid damage, the associated switchgear must have maximum discrimination, optimum operation time, high repeat accuracy, etc. For proper analysis, the OC is divided in two ranges, namely (i) OL range covering 1.1 to 8 times 'I_R' & (ii) SC range beyond OL.

The starter is designed to protect motor against faults within the OL range, i.e. it incorporates 'OL protection device' (OLPD). For protection against higher fault currents, additional 'SC protection device' (SCPD) is employed which is a HRC fuse or CB, i.e. MCCB or MCB. Also, these OLPD & SCPD must be co-ordinated properly as per the following universally accepted guidelines.

(a) Neither of the OLPD & SCPD should operate during the normal motor starting.

(b) For OC between 1.05 – 8 times 'I_R' only the OLPD should operate.

(c) For OC in excess of 8 times 'I_R', the SCPD should operate at earliest.

(d) If the OLPD fails to operate within the OL range, the SCPD should operate within such time that the equipment is not seriously damaged, i.e. the SCPD should provide the 'back-up protection'.

Z03.8.1 Overload Protection & Devices

OL causes excessive temperature rise in the motor windings beyond tolerable limits. Some important factors causing temperature rise are; (a) undervoltage or overvoltage, (b) single phasing, (c) variation in supply frequency, (d) locking of rotor, (e) excess load (at the shaft), (f) higher ambient & cooling-medium temperatures, etc. They must detect the motor temperature rise directly or indirectly & give an alarm or tripping signal. There are two basic types of OLPDs namely, (a) those influenced by motor current, i.e. Current Influenced OLPD & (b) (motor winding) Temperature Influenced OLPD.

Z03.8.2 Short Circuit Protection Devices

Two equipments are available for SC protection, namely, (i) HRC fuses & (ii) CBs. The SCPD is connected between power switch & starter (which acts as OLPD as well). Since starter is delicate compared to motor, it gets damaged first. Hence it is customary to link the damage to starter with the co-ordination between the OLPD & SCPD. The three options in practice for SC protection are:(a) co-ordination between OLPD & HRC fuse as SCPD which is the most common one, (b) co-ordination between OLPD & CB as SCPD and (c) co-ordination between Motor Protection Circuit Breaker & HRC fuse.

Z03.9 Enclosed Switchgear and Switchboards

None of the switchgear mentioned above is used in 'open' execution but is always mounted inside an enclosure or housing. The enclosure is meant to provide protection to (a) the switchgear from external objects & effects and (b) the operating personnel against direct or indirect contact with the switchgear. Their design depends on (c) environmental conditions (d) electrical parameters like system voltage, fault levels, rated currents and (e) special requirements, if any. They are made of sheet steel (SS), cast iron (CI), cast aluminium, aluminium sheet & plastics.

Z03.9.1 Enclosures

These are basically of (a) indoor, (b) outdoor & (c) flame-proof or explosion-proof type.

Z03.9.1.1 Indoor Enclosures

They are suitable for installation in a room which is completely closed on all sides & at top so that they are not subjected to dripping or splashed water. They do not offer any resistance to 'water penetration'. They are made of SS and/or plastics with sleek & elegant look. They are useful in residential & commercial buildings, (normal) industrial plants & workshops, offices, etc. However, CI enclosures are preferred in envirounment with moisture, steam, non-hazardous fumes etc., as in the textile industries, compressor rooms, etc.

Z03.9.1.2 Outdoor or Weatherproof Enclosures

They are suitable for installation in open air, direct sun, rain, wind, dust & fumes and are designed to prevent ingress of dust & water inside. However, they are not safe against hazardous gases & inflammable liquids & solids. They are normally made of CI & the 'mating' surfaces are properly machined. Gaskets are provided on all hinged doors, bolted covers, end-plates & at every joint between enclosures. However, due to limitation on their sizes, CI enclosures are used only for small switchgears. Bigger enclosures are made of SS; hot-dip-galvanized or painted by epoxy & provided with a 'canopy' at top. Split gaskets of neoprene rubber are used around every cut or open edge of the enclosures. The flange type openings are provided at places where doors or covers mate with the housings. They are used for irrigation motor starters, distribution boards for street lights, etc.

Z03.9.1.3 Flame- or Explosion-proof Enclosures

They are used at hazardous locations. Their basic requirements are; (a) they should be air-tight, (b) any electric arc or fire inside the enclosures should not propagate out of them, (c) they should be strong enough so that no part of enclosures or any equipment inside 'flies out' even if there is an explosion inside.

Z03.9.2 Enclosed Combination Switchgear

The switchgears or combinations thereof which are available as standard products fitted inside enclosures are (a) Rotary or Knife type Switches upto 600 V & 100 A, (b) Switch-fuse units & Fused Switches rated upto 630 A at 600 V, (c) DOL Starters rated upto 100 HP at 415 V & (d) Star-Delta Starters rated upto 200 HP at 415 V. All these units are complete with internal wiring, power & control terminals, cable glands, cut-outs, mounting accessories, etc.

Z03.9.3 Switchboards

A switchboard is an enclosed switchgear wherein several incoming & outgoing feeders of different ratings are arranged in a neat layout inside one or more panels (i.e. enclosures or housings) which are mechanically & electrically coupled together, forming a power distribution network.

Z03.9.3.1 Classification or Types

There are many types of switchboards based on several criteria as under.

a. Based on method of mounting we have; (i) floor mounting- free standing, (ii) pedestal mounting & (iii) wall mounting.
b. Based on application we have; (i) 'power control centers' (PCC), (ii) motor control centers (MCC) and (iii) distribution & sub-distribution boards (DB/ SDB).
c. Based on arrangement of switchgear & feeders we have; (i) 'compartmentalized', (ii) 'open'/ non-compartmentalized, (iii) 'withdrawable', (iv) 'fixed', etc.

Z03.9.3.2 Main Structural Elements

They are (a) enclosure (including doors, covers), (b) busbars (with support insulators), (c) power circuit chamber/ compartment, (d) control circuit chamber & (e) termination chamber (for connection to cables or busducts).

Z03.9.3.3 Enclosure

It is fabricated out of sheet steel or assembled from many cast iron housings. It must be designed to withstand the severest thermal & mechanical stresses & the worst weather conditions at point of installation. The SS enclosure is 'welded' or 'bolted' type. The enclosure size must be enough to 'accommodate' all equipment with sufficient clearances as warranted. The enclosures must have suitable ventilation. The indoor enclosures are 'painted' while outdoor ones are 'galvanized'.

Z03.9.3.4 Busbars

They are a set of conductors to which the incoming & outgoing feeders are connected. They are made of 'electrolytic' grade copper or 'high-conductivity' aluminium & arranged in three-phase (TP) or three-phase with neutral (TPN) or single-phase & neutral (SPN) configuration as per application. Their (current) ratings depend on those of incoming & outgoing feeders & their 'layout'. They are mounted either at 'top' or 'bottom' of switchboard depending on the 'cable entry' being from bottom or top respectively. Rectangular flats, channels & angular sections of copper & aluminium are preferred. Their shapes & sizes depend on the parameters like the CC rating, SC capacity, short-time thermal rating, permissible temperature rise, etc. They are mounted on 'busbar supports' made of high-quality insulating materials like, permali wood, phenol formaldehyde, melamine formaldehyde, etc.; permali being the best.

Z03.9.3.5 Power Circuit Chamber

Herein, the 'main or power circuit' switchgear of feeders like CB, power switch, fuses, contactor, release, etc. are mounted.

Z03.9.3.6 Control Circuit Chamber

Herein, all equipments of control & auxiliary circuits are mounted. This includes protection & signaling relays, indication, metering, process monitoring & supervisory devices.

Z03.9.3.7 Termination Chamber

Herein, the feeder is connected to outside network via cables or busduct. There should be ample space for cable connections as the same is done at the site.

Z03.9.4 Power Control Center (PCC)

They are used for the 'main' distribution of power in large plants, industries, buildings, etc. The feeders comprise of breakers &/or fused-switches. The Single Line Diagram & possible feeder arrangement of a typical PCC are shown in Fig. 3.9. The salient features of a modern PCC are; (a) CBs with high current ratings are mounted in 'single-tier' (i.e. one per panel) whereas the lower rated CBs are in 'multi-tier' arrangement & (b) it is fully 'compartmentalized', i.e. all equipments of a feeder is placed in one 'self-contained' compartment. Thus, every feeder is isolated & separated from others which helps in quick repair & maintenance of that feeder.

Z03.9.5 Motor Control Centers (MCC)

They are used to distribute power to various motors inside an industrial plant/ installation. Using a MCC to supply power to a group of motors located in a particular area or motors associated with a particular process is the best way of power utilization. Thus, a MCC contains many feeders of various ratings. They are made in many executions, like (a) Non-compartmentalized MCC, (b) Compartmentalized MCC, (c) Sheet steel clad box type MCC, (d) Cast iron clad box type MCC, (e) Sheet steel clad panel type MCC, (f) Panel Type Compartmentalized MCC, (g) Non-drawout MCC,

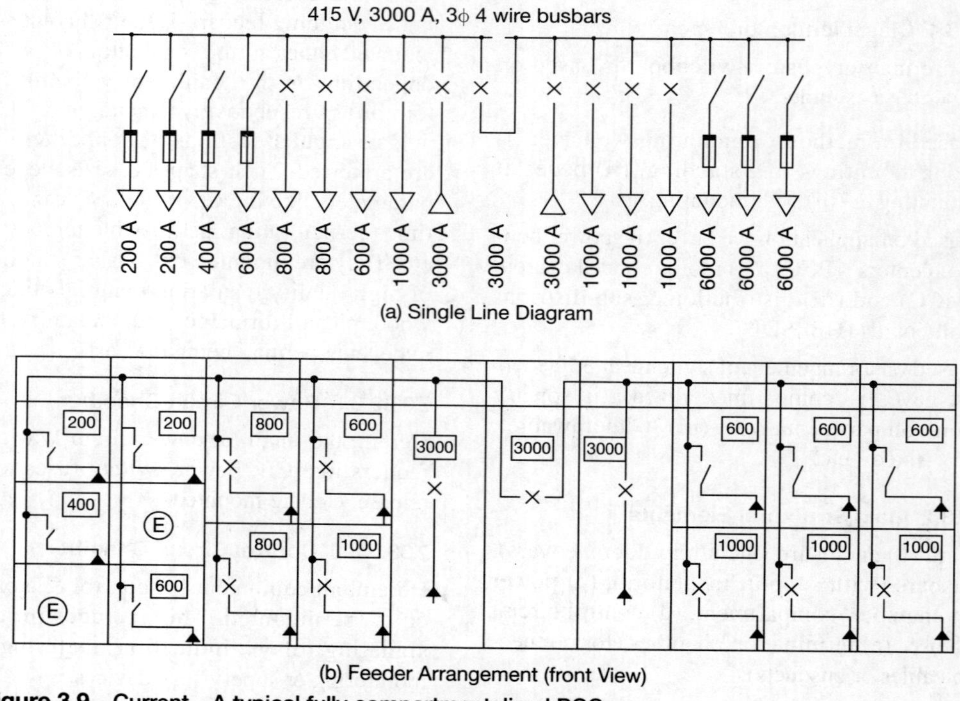

Figure 3.9 Current – A typical fully compartmentalized PCC

(h) Single Drawout MCC, (i) Double-drawout MCC, (j) Fully-drawout MCC, (k) Double Front (DF) MCC, etc.

Z03.9.6 Distribution Boards (DBs)

In any establishment, small or big, DBs are required to supply power to loads like lighting, air-conditioning, ventilation, fans, lifts, heaters, kitchen, office equipments, etc. The designs of DBs vary widely, from the sleek-looking 'cabinet' type (for lights & fan switching) to the bigger 'panel' type ones for heating & air-onditioning. They are designed to suit the switchgear components to be used in the DB. Fig. 3.10 shows a typical 'lighting DB' widely used in offices. It comprises of a sleek SS 'cabinet' (housing)which is normally installed in a slot or recess on a wall, so that it is 'flush' with the wall surface. It can be 'projection' mounted also. It has 'double-door' arrangement; outer door is 'hinged' while inner door or cover is 'screwed' type. All equipments are mounted behind this cover so that operating knobs of the CBs or switches 'project' out through 'cut-outs' provided on the cover. Hence, switching of feeders is possible without opening cover, thus giving complete safety to the Operator. These DBs incorporate MCCB as incomers & MCBs as outgoing feeders. All feeders are wired upto a 'terminal block' at the bottom of the housing so that the cable termination is very simple. Since available MCBs are 'clip-on' type, they are simply pushed onto the special 'rail' (without need to 'bolt' individual MCB). This reduces the assembly-time considerably.

Figure 3.10 Standard lighting DB

ANSWERS TO PROBLEMS

Note: The following numerical answers are usually rounded off to an accuracy of ±1%. Answers that are preceded by the symbol ~ are accurate to ±5%.

Chapter 1

7. MW **8.** TJ **9.** mPa **10.** kHz **11.** GJ **12.** mA **13.** μWb **14.** cm **15.** L **16.** mg **17.** μs **18.** mK **19.** mrad **21.** mT **22.** mm **23.** r **24.** MΩ **33.** mL **34.** L/s or m^3/s **35.** Hz **36.** rad **37.** Wb **38.** kg/m^3 **39.** W **40.** K or °C **41.** kg **62.** 11.95 yd^2 **63.** 126.9 mm^2 **64.** 2.549 in^2 **65.** 6.591 mm^2 **66.** 2.59 km^2 **67.** 76.77 Btu/s **68.** 0.746 kW **69.** 7.079 m^3 **70.** 13.56×10^6 μJ **71.** 4.536 kgf **72.** 0.93 T **73.** 12 kilogauss **74.** 1.417 kg **75.** 6049.6 A/m **76.** 3.107 miles **77.** 288 000 C **78.** 111.2 N **79.** 11.34 kg **80.** 6615 lb **81.** 0.001 Wb **82.** 8304 kg/m^3 **83.** 67.7 mbar **84.** 1.378×10^6 Pa **85.** 482.3×10^3 N/m^2 **86.** 1.57 rad/s **87.** 393 K **88.** 366.3 K **89.** 120 K **90.** 1.67, 50, 0.33 **91.** 10.4 A, 231 Ω **92.** 3.3 kΩ **93a.** 402 **93b.** 0.076 **93c.** 16m^2 **93d.** 64m^3 **93e.** 93.75 **93f.** 3.24×10^5

Chapter 2

2a. $E_{16} = -80$ V **2b.** $E_{25} = +80$ V **2c.** $E_{52} = 0$ **3.** +20 V, 0 V, − 30 V, +30 V **4.** 20 V **5.** 1.8 V **7.** 320, 160, 112 **8.** 3840 A **9a.** 960 N **9b.** 960 N **9c.** no **10b.** 31.3 V, 141 V, −200 V **11.** 70.7 A **12a.** 12 A **12b.** 169.7 V **12c.** 1440 W **12d.** 2880 W **13.** 23 Hz **14.** 1.67 ms **15a.** I_1 lags I_3 by 60° **15b.** I_3 lags I_2 by 90° **15c.** E lags I_1 by 150° **16c.** 2400 W, −800 W **17b.** 120V **18.** box A **19.** no **20.** −17.3 V, 8.13 V

Chapter 3

1. 392 N **2.** 2940 J **4.** 60 N·m **5.** 251 kW, 336 hp **6.** 10.8 kW, 14.5 hp **7a.** 100 kW, 134 hp **7b.** 83.3% **7c.** 68 256 Btu/h **8.** 415.7 J **9a.** 1096 J **9b.** 3288 J **9c.** 242 kJ **11b.** 50 N·m **13.** zero **14.** 209 W **15.** 209 W **16.** 1.89 kW, 2.53 hp **17a.** 13.1 N·m **17b.** 88.8 kJ **17c.** 2195 W **17d.** 2400 W **18a.** 1222 N·m **18b.** 1332 N·m **19a.** 475 N·m **19b.** 4455 N **20.** 3.04 MJ **21.** 7.68 MJ **22.** 1568 N·m, 239 r/min **23.** 1568 N·m, 47.8 r/min

Chapter 4

9a. 103 V **9b.** 288 W **9c.** 10.4 N·m **10a.** $E_{NL} = 138$ V **10b.** polarity reverses **10c.** voltage increases by less than 10% **11a.** 5000 A **11b.** 7800 A **12.** 2 A **13.** A = 18 V, B = 18 V, C = 18 V **14.** at 90° $E_A = 20$ V, at 120° $E_A = 18$ V **16.** 276.5 V **17a.** 12 brush sets **17b.** 150 A **19.** E_{XY} is (+) **20a.** E_{34} is (−) **21a.** 292 V **21b.** 0.436 T **21c.** 530 μs **23a.** 333 A **23b.** 83.25 A

Chapter 5

9a. 221 V **9b.** 13 800 W **9c.** 13.26 kW, 17.8 hp **10a.** 1533 A **10b.** 1.85 Ω **11a.** 2975 A **11b.** 2400 A **12.** 144 V, 9.6 V **13a.** 11.7 kW, 94% **13b.** 10 A **13c.** 8 mΩ, 223 V **13d.** less than 4 A **14a.** 0.48 Ω **14b.** 30 kW, 1.9 kW, 0 kW **15a.** 0.96 Ω **15b.** 45 kW, 8.43 kW, 0 kW **16a.** 17.8 kg/m^2 **16b.** 140 kJ **16c.** 70 kJ

Chapter 6

8. 180°C **9.** 131.4 kW, 547 A **10.** 22.8 hp **11.** 882 A **12a.** 28°C **12b.** 88°C too hot **14.** 47.2% **15.** 10.4 kW, 14 hp **16.** <155°C, <145°C, <129°C **17a.** 139°C **17b.** 108°C **18.** 1 year **19a.** 2.28 A/mm^2 **19b.** 13.4 W/kg **20a.** 58.7 W/kg **20b.** 985 cmil/A **21.** 26.2 kW, 35 hp **22.** 64 years **23.** ~768 h

Chapter 7

2. 100 kVA **6.** 64.3% **7.** 667 kVA, 291 kvar **8.** 4.34 kvar **9a.** 1440 W **9b.** 1440 VA **9c.** 2880 W **9d.** 1/120 s **10a.** 1440 var **10b.** 1440 VA **10c.** 1440 W **10d.** 1440 W **10e.** 1/240 s **11a.** A is the active source **11b.** C is the active source **11c.** F is the reactive source **11d.** J is the reactive source **11e.** L is the active source **11f.** M is the reactive source **12.** 7.2 A, 9.6 A **13.** 0.72, 2665 var **14a.** 2765 W **14b.** 745 var **14c.** 2864 VA **14d.** 11.9 A **14e.** 96.5% **15a.** 3.71 Ω **15b.** 6.32 Ω **15c.** 12.16 Ω **16a.** 320 kW **16b.** 240 kvar **17a.** 1200 W **17b.** 500 var **17c.** 1300 VA **17d.** 0.923 **18a.** 2 kW **18b.** zero **19.** 900 var **20a.** 2765 W **20b.** 3512 VA **20c.** 0.787 **21a.** 3845 var **21b.** −4000 var **21c.** 769 W **21d.** 784.5 VA **22a.** 102 V **22b.** 20.4 Ω **23a.** 519.6 W and 300 var, both flowing from B to A **23b.** 519.6 W from D to C, 300 var from C to D

Chapter 8

1. 4157 V **2a.** −100, 0, 50, 50, −86.6 V **2b.** +, 0,−, −, +, **2c.** 50, −86.6, −100, 50, 86.6 V **3.** yes **4a.** 358 V **4b.** 23.87 A **4c.** 25.6 kW **5a.** 694 A **5b.** 13.2 kV **5c.** 9.16 MW **5d.** 27.5 MW **5e.** 19 Ω **6a.** a − b − c **6b.** yes **7.** 26 kVA **8.** 120 V **9a.** 13 kW **9b.** 6.5 kW **10.** single phase **11a.** 41.6 A **11b.** 41.6 A **11c.** 2.89 Ω **12a.** 160 Ω **12b.** 480 Ω **13.** 0.9 Ω **14.** 8 Ω **15a.** 89.5% **15b.** 62.3 kVA **15c.** 37.2 kvar **15d.** 80.2% **16a.** 14.6 kW, 7.78 kvar, 16.5 kVA **16b.** 270 V **17a.** XZY **18a.** 5 A **18b.** 19.9 kvar **19.** lamp connected to Z **20.** 20 kW **21a.** 18 A **21b.** 130 A **21c.** 72.1 A **22.** 18.3 A **23a.** 4.63 Ω, 3.44 Ω **23b.** 36.7° **24a.** 9.6 Ω **24b.** 7.72 Ω, 5.79 Ω **25a.** 6.1 kVA **25b.** 82% **26a.** 21.3 kW **26b.** 18.1 kW **26c.** 63.9 kW·h **27a.** 15.5% **27b.** 88.4 A

Chapter 9

1a. 2 A **1b.** 2.83 A **1c.** 1415 A **1d.** 0.9 mWb **2.** 472 A, 0.3 mWb **4a.** 360 V **4b.** 30 A **4c.** 18 A **4d.** 10 800 W **4e.** 10 800 W **5.** 33.3 Ω **6.** 400 V, 0.02 A

Chapter 10

11. 120 V **12.** 60 kV **13a.** 110.4 V **13b.** 0.353 A, 22.08 A **14.** 2.42 kW, 11 A, 22 A **15.** 50 A, 1250 A **16.** 1.88 mWb **18a.** 144 V **18b.** 2.25 mWb **18c.** 0.9 mWb **19a.** zero **19b.** 520 V **19c.** additive **20a.** short-circuit **23a.** 72 Ω **23b.** 0.115 Ω **24a.** 126.4 V **24b.** 5.22 A, 95 A **25a.** 466.9 kW **25b.** 466.9 kW, 99.1% **27.** 9 mWb **29a.** 84.1 Ω **29b.** 3.04% **29c.** 23.36 mΩ **29d.** 3.04% **29e.** 976 W **29f.** 1.3%, 2.75% **30a.** 1.9 Ω, 36.6 Ω **30b.** 453.6 Ω **30c.** 8.4% **31.** 99.08% **32a.** 28.9 W/kg **32b.** 156 W/kg

Chapter 11

5. 300 turns **6.** 0.2 V **7.** 1300 kVA **8.** H1-X2 or H2-X1 together **9.** 92 kVA **10.** 13 mA **11a.** 0.45 V **11b.** 2.25 mV **11c.** 250 A/5 A

Chapter 12

2a. 20.8 A, 433 A **2b.** 20.8 A, 250 A **3.** 1506 A, 65 kA **4.** 17.7 kA, 2175 A **5a.** 1278 A **5b.** yes **6a.** delta-delta **6b.** 577 A, 48.1 A **6c.** 333 A, 27.8 A **7a.** 236 kVA **7b.** 1.89 kV **8a.** no **8b.** 433 kVA **9a.** 347, 600, 347 V

Chapter 13

7. no **10a.** 360 r/min **10b.** no **10c.** 20 **12.** 936 A, 156 A, 55 A **15a.** 600 r/min **15b.** 564 r/min **16a.** 3 V, 45 Hz **16b.** 0.67 V, 10 Hz **16c.** 1 V, 15 Hz **17a.** 15 A, 90 A, 5.25 A **17b.** 882 r/min, 812 N·m **18.** 97.2 A **19a.** 120 V, 30 Hz **19b.** 60 V, 15 Hz **19c.** 960 V, 240 Hz **20a.** −8.66 A, 8.66 A, 0 **20b.** 86.6 A **21.** 3, slot 1 to slot 8 **22a.** 23.56 m/s **22b.** 3.3 V **22c.** 196.35 mm **23a.** 87.9% **23b.** 2298 kW **23c.** 34.5 kW **23d.** 2251 kW, 30.3 kN·m, 96% **26.** 1500 A, 75 N **27.** 20 N **28.** 38 kW **29a.** 4.49 mΩ, 68.9 mΩ **29b.** 1067 V, 40 Hz; 16 V, 0.6 Hz **29c.** 1035 kvar **29d.** 2.07 kW **29e.** 50 kW **30a.** 18.6 Mvar **30b.** 670 kW **30c.** 1498 kW **30d.** zero **30e.** 23.8 kN·m **31a.** 400 V **31b.** 508 mΩ, 314 kW **31c.** 455 A **32.** 264.5 mm **34.** 100 mm, 120 kW

Chapter 14

10. 78% **12a.** 3 hp **12b.** 54 or 56 **13.** 438, 280, 315 ft·lb; zero, 675, 765 r/min **14a.** 3.8 kW **14b.** 586 r/min **14c.** 222.4 kW **14d.** 5.3 kW **15a.** 140 Hz **15b.** 54 kW **15c.** 23.8 kvar **15d.** 65.6 A **15e.** 100 hp **16a.** 1109 A **16b.** 434 kW **16c.** 90.2 kW **16d.** 5212 A, 83.5 kN·m **16e.** 43.3 kN·m **17.** 4.7°C **18a.** 39.4 s **18b.** 105 000 Btu **19a.** 456 V, 1740 r/min **19b.** ~16 hp **20a.** design D **20b.** same **21a.** 54.5 mΩ **21b.** 2.23 Ω **22a.** ~1100 N·m **22b.** 11.4 kg·m^2 **23.** 270 kJ **24a.** 795 kg, 1509 lb·ft^2 **24b.** 810 r/min, 260 ft·lb **24c.** 702 ft·lb **25a.** 916 N·m **25b.** 1.3 s **25c.** 11.3 kJ **25d.** 6.7 s **26a.** 134 r/min **26b.** 11:1 **26c.** 358 A **26d.** 50 t **26e.** 728 MJ **26f.** 39 min **26g.** 91 kW·h

Chapter 15

2a. 5.05 Ω, 82° **2b.** 811 r/min **2c.** 45.4 A **2d.** 332 N·m **3a.** yes, 366 N·m **3b.** no, as a brake, 35 N·m **4.** 26.7 Ω, 202 Ω **5.** 0.4 Ω, 0.5 Ω, 1.48 Ω, 268 N·m **6.** 37.9 kN·m, 2.4 kN·m **7.** 13.9 N·m, 35.5 N·m **8.** 10.5 N·m, 42.6 N·m

Chapter 16

3a. 20 poles **3b.** 360 r/min **4.** increased **6.** 12 poles **7.** 4 **8a.** decrease **8b.** decrease **8c.** increase **9a.** 7500 V, 50 Hz **9b.** 37.5 V, 0.25 Hz **12a.** 150 A **12b.** 50 A **13.** 2400 V **14b.** 0, 353, 600, 750, 600, 0 kW **15.** 807 mm **16a.** 145 Ω **16b.** 192 Ω **16c.** 144 Ω **16d.** 10 A **16e.** 1750 V **16f.** 3.031 V **16g.** 57.6 kW **16h.** 36.9° **17.** 16 kV **18a.** 44.56° **18b.** 2.475° **18c.** 7.87 in **19a.** 0.45 Ω **19b.** 0.412 Ω **19c.** .916 **19d.** 1.09 **20a.** 8130 kW **20b.** 720 kW **20c.** 24.23 MN·m **20d.** 22.7°C **21.** 0.409 T **22a.** 126 MW **22c.** 85.7% leading **23a.** 228.5 MW **23b.** 7230 A **24.** 0 W, delivers 63.3 Mvar to the bus **25a.** 236 r/min **25b.** 108°, 1944° **26a.** 40 **26b.** 180 **26c.** 1.5 **26d.** 1.73 in **26e.** 3.7 Ω, 3565 W

Chapter 17

7. 2300 hp **9a.** 2217 kVA **9b.** 90.2% **9c.** 956 kvar **9d.** 32 poles **11a.** 333 A **11b.** 3 Ω **12.** 500 r/min **14a.** 36.9° **14b.** 2.16 MW **14c.** 100% **14d.** zero **15a.** 300 A, 0° **15b.** 720 kvar delivered **17a.** 3457 kVA **17b.** 289 A **17c.** 5889 V **17d.** 1.44° **17e.** 1569 kvar **17f.** 9150 hp **18a.** 4741 V **18b.** 32.8° **19a.** 14.6 Ω, 1594 V **19b.** 6807 ft·lb **19c.** 142 A **20a.** 4269 kW, 45.3 kN·m **20b.** 1704 kW, 36.2 kN·m **20c.** 40.7 kN·m **20d.** ~83 s

Chapter 18

9a. 14 A, 14 A **9b.** 33.8° **9c.** 26.8 A **9d.** 70.7% **10a.** no **10b.** probably not **12a.** 50 Hz **12c.** 4.26 J **13a.** 8 mhp **13b.** 55% **13c.** 0.28 **13d.** 0.79 pu, 1.06 pu **14a.** 4.42 ft·lb **14b.** 4.44 pu **14c.** zero **14d.** 2.5 pu **15a.** 157.5 V **15b.** 93.2° **16a.** 0.577 A **16b.** 86.6% lagging **16c.** 30 W **16d.** 37% **17a.** 1.94 Ω **17b.** 21.2 A, 84 V **17c.** 3.2 N·m

Chapter 19

4. 1152 **6.** 30° **8.** true **9.** 240 ms **10.** 0.00175 in **11a.** 144 W **11b.** 78.5 W **12a.** 30 mN·m **12b.** 0.79 mhp **12c.** 1.77 J **14.** 437.5 r/min **15a.** 1.5 ms **15b.** 4.5 ms **15c.** 0.23 A **16a.** 7.2° **16b.** 3.6° **16c.** 1.8° **18a.** 3000 r/min, 0.93 hp **18b.** 13 ms **18c.** 0.16 ms

Chapter 20

10a. quadrant 1 **10b.** quadrant 4 **11.** 6.3 hp **12.** 26 V, 7.5 Hz **13a.** 40 A **13b.** 120 A **13c.** 40 A or 113 A **14a.** 2 or 4 **14b.** 1 or 3 respectively **14c.** 4 or 2 respectively **15.** clockwise **16a.** 2 min **16b.** 5 s **18.** 208 days **22.** 28 s **23a.** 18.85 kW **23b.** 11.3 kW **23c.** 30.15 kW **24.** 1.57, 16, 12.57 kW **25a.** 345 V, 45 Hz **25b.** 633 V, 82.5 Hz **26.** 38 V, 5 Hz **28a.** 30 A **28b.** 4.29 hp **28c.** 63.7 N·m **28d.** 56.4 ft·lb **29b.** 10 Hz **30a.** 834 ft·lb, 358 ft·lb **30b.** 149 ft·lb **31a.** 307 V, 40 Hz **31b.** 67.3 kJ **31c.** 29.9 kJ **32b.** 29.5 ft·lb **33.** 282 V

Chapter 21

6a. 1620 V **6b.** 200 A **6c.** 600 A **7a.** 3240 V **7b.** 200 A **8a.** 540 V **8b.** 540 V **8c.** 18 A **8d.** 9 A **8e.** 9720 W **9a.** 150 V **9b.** 3.75 A **10.** 45 kW **11a.** 0.72 kW **11b.** 99.96% **12a.** negative **12b.** increasing **13a.** 36 A **13b.** 170 V **13c.** > 65 J **13d.** 0.1 H **13e.** 170 V **14a.** 324 V **14b.** 243 kW **14c.** 750 A **14d.** 5.55 ms **14e.** 612 A **14f.** zero **14g.** 45.4 V **15a.** 24 kW **15b.** 24 kW **15c.** 12a **15d.** 400 A **15e.** 300 Hz **15f.** 167 Ω **16a.** zero **16b.** 77.7° **16c.** 102.3° **17a.** 14 kV **17b.** 6.3 MW **17c.** 367 A **17d.** 23.5 Mvar **18a.** 40 kV **18b.** −14.64 kV **18c.** 54.64 kV **19a.** 40 A **19b.** 24 kW **19c.** zero **19d.** 100% **19e.** zero **20a.** 12.66 A **20b.** 4.7 kW **20c.** 70% **20d.** 10.6 kVA **20e.** 44% **20f.** 63.5% **20g.** 5.72 kvar **21.** 6.25 mH **22a.** 340 V **22b.** 147° **22c.** 30.4 A **23.** 1/24 s **24a.** 3.29 V·s **24b.** 0.47 H **25a.** 120 A **25b.** 48 kJ **25c.** 4 kW **26a.** 120 A **26b.** 80 A **26c.** 200 A **26d.** 160 A **27a.** 135.2° **27b.** 57.5 kW **27c.** 57 kvar

Chapter 22

3. 91 Hz **4a.** 626 V **4b.** 169 kW **4c.** 90 A **4d.** 220 hp **8a.** 200 V **8b.** 283 V **8e.** 2 A **9a.** 31.3° **9b.** 5.1 kvar **9c.** 28.6 A **9d.** 113 V **10a.** 85.1° **10b.** 16.8 kvar **11a.** 343 A **11b.** 146° **12a.** 300 V **12b.** 315 V **13a.** 150 A **13b.** 75 V **13c.** 60 V **14a.** zero **14b.** 150 A **14c.** 15 V **15a.** 100.7° **15b.** 87.3° **16a.** 232 A, 240 A **16b.** 700 V **17a.** 192 V **17b.** 250 A **19a.** 0.02976 **19b.** 164 A **19c.** 0.04576, 249 A **19d.** The current ripple would be much greater. The current would oscillate between +2047 A and −807 A. **20a.** 44V **20b.** 44 V **20c.** 14 Hz **20d.** 14 Hz **20e.** 220 W **20f.** 2.5 N·m **21b.** 2880 μF **22a.** 24 V **22b.** 97.8° **22c.** 7340 var

Chapter 23

3. 230 V, 30 Hz **4a.** 1620 r/min **4b.** 8.78 N·m **5.** 600 r/min **10a.** 8 Hz **10b.** 42 V **11a.** 50 ms **11b.** 13 ms **12a.** 8 N·m, 1080 r/min, 1.2 hp **12b.** 3.5 N·m, 720 r/min, 0.35 hp **13a.** 16.5 hp **13b.** 39.5° **13c.** 12.4 kvar **15a.** 141 A **15b.** 422 A **15c.** 566 V **15d.** 46.7 Hz **17a.** 20.7 W **17b.** 36.3 W **18.** 194 V **19a.** 3600 r/min **19b.** 15 kW **19c.** 337 V **19d.** 7.6 Ω, 15 kW **20.** 325 μs **21a.** 115 V, 15 Hz **21b.** 85 A **22.** 31.8 A **23.** 50 V, 15 Hz

Chapter 24

7. 1176 MW **11a.** 41.2×10^3 m^3/s **11b.** 40 400 MW **11c.** 312 mi^3 **12.** 15.6 h **13a.** 60 MW, 50 MW **13b.** 80 MW, 30 MW **14a.** 5400 MW **14b.** 2615 Mvar **14c.** 9364 yd^3/s **16a.** 5715 tons **16b.** ~57 000 tons **16c.** 21.6 m^3/s **17.** 0.43 m^3/s **18a.** 1.86×10^{13} J, 1.76×10^{10} Btu **18b.** 0.207 g **19a.** 90.6 TW·h **19b.** 10.34 GW **20.** 1580 MW

Chapter 25

7. ~2500 **9.** 750 A **10a.** 5092 MW **10b.** 151.8 MW **10c.** ~3% **11a.** 5700 V, 114 kW; 4500 V, 450 kW; 3000 V, 600 kW; 1500 V, 450 kW **12.** 0° **13a.** 5992 V, 126 kW; 5692 V, 720 kW; 4243 V, 1200 kW; 1897 V, 720 kW **14.** E_R is 18.4° lagging α **15a.** 6577 V, 9000 V **15b.** 0° **16a.** 5692 V **16b.** no **17a.** −240 kvar **17b.** 139.2 A **17c.** 290.6 kvar **17d.** 50.6 kvar **17e.** 802 kVA **17f.** 5759 V **17g.** 6251 V, 868 kW **18.** 20.3° **19.** 4 Ω, 2 Ω, 37.5 kΩ **21a.** 421 MW **21b.** 1074 A **21c.** 148.8 Mvar **21d.** 74.3 Mvar **22a.** 22 Ω, 100 Ω, 1500 Ω **22b.** 119 kV **22c.** 45 A **22d.** 9 Mvar **22e.** 34.6 kW **23a.** 648.5 A

Chapter 26

3. 2 μΩ **6.** 17.5 kV **8a.** 48.8 kV **8b.** zero **9a.** 12 000 A **9b.** 960 MW **9c.** 4800 J **11.** 5 and 7 **12.** 1.2 Ω, 3.18 mH **13a.** 25 A, 35 A **13b.** 10 A **13c.** 0.5 A **14.** 9.74 A **15a.** not dangerous **15b.** hazardous **17a.** 115.6 A, 124.7 A, 31.6 A **17b.** 2A **17c.** 81.8% lagging **18a.** 777 A **18b.** 67.3 A, 86.8% **21b.** 17.5 kA **21c.** yes

Chapter 27

2. $28.40 **5.** $1470 **7.** 4.33 MW **8a.** 3975 GW·h **8b.** 159 million dollars **9a.** 72 kvar, 104 kVA **9b.** 75 kW, 52 kvar **9c.** 12.5% **10a.** 243 kvar **10b.** 32% **11a.** 46.64 $/h **11b.** $4205 **12a.** 30 cent/kW·h **12b.** 2.4 cents **13.** 6.45 cent/kW·h **15.** 10 r/min **16.** 1800 W **17a.** meter reads 1 percent high **17b.** no **18.** ±5.6 kW·h

Chapter 28

5a. ~45 kV **5b.** ~492 A **6a.** 150 MW **6b.** 200 A **7a.** 600 A, 57.6 MW **10a.** 400 A **10b.** 64 kV **11.** 1800 A, 1000 Mvar **12.** 45 kW **13.** 4050 A **14a.** 2.9 in^2 **14b.** 13.38 Ω **14c.** 43.4 MW **14d.** 426 kV **14e.** 94.7% **15a.** 360 Hz, 720 Hz **15b.** 9 Ω, 11 Ω **15c.** 150 kV **16a.** 17.7 A **16b.** 20 kV **16c.** 159 V

Chapter 29

2. The maximum frequency of a high-speed GTO is limited to about 2 kHz. **3.** 1380 Hz **4.** 967 A **6a.** 1870 V **6b.** 1470 V **7.** 8.33 ms **10.** 879 A **11.** 1406 A **12.** 4.5 mH, 221 μf **13.** 2159 V **14.** 5.52 MW **16.** 80.2 A **17.** 46.3 A·h **18.** 6 s **19a.** 5.57 kV **19b.** 2.7 MVA **19c.** 24 kV **19d.** 26.4 kV **19e.** 14.4 kV, 33.7 kV

Chapter 30

1a. 36.0 A **1b.** 60 Hz **1c.** 300 Hz **2.** 62.2 V **3.** 12.9% **4a.** 1000 A **4b.** 29.4% **5a.** 1843 kW **5b.** 48.7 kW **5c.** 110 kW **6a.** 84.8% **6b.** 30.1 kW **6c.** 73.8% **7.** 141 A **8a.** 4163 V **8b.** 1082 V **9a.** 71.7 A **9b.** 7.86 A **9c.** 72.1 A **9d.** 721 V **9e.** 154 V **10.** 21.6 W **11.** 124.4 V **12.** 58.6 A **13a.** 95.4 A **13b.** ≈ 0 A **13c.** 18.7 A **14a.** 110 A **14b.** 0 A **14c.** 21.6 A **15a.** 70.7 A **15b.** 67.5 A **15c.** 21.1 A **15d.** 31.4% **16a.** 9.6 Ω **16b.** 1443 A **17a.** 85.6 A **17b.** $I_5 = 0$; $I_3 = 24.7$ A **18a.** 50 Hz; 350 Hz **18b.** 601 V; 240 V **18c.** 647 V **18d.** 601 V **19a.** $E_5 = 46.8$ V; $E_7 = 15.3$ V; $E_{11} = 107$ V; $E_{13} = 323$ V **19b.** 344 V **19c.** 55.1 A **20.** 83.5 A peak; −32.4° **21a.** 35.36 V; 0° **21b.** 31.8 V **21c.** 50 V **21d.** 15.4 V

Chapter 31

1. see Section 31.2 **2.** see Section 31.2 **3.** see Section 31.2 **4.** see Section 31.15 **5.** see end of Sections 31.3 and 31.9 **6.** see Section 31.4 **7.** see Section 31.14 **8.** see Sections 31.19 and 31.21

ANSWERS TO INDUSTRIAL APPLICATION PROBLEMS

Chapter 1

94. 0.926 pu **95.** 0.208 pu 1.416 pu **97.** 6.0 pu 0.39 pu

Chapter 2

21a. $-E_1 + IR = 0$ **21b.** $-E_1 - IR = 0$ **21c.** $E_1 + IR = 0$ **21d.** $-E_2 + E_1 - IR = 0$ **22a.** $I = -3$ A **22b.** $I = -13$ A **22c.** $I = 9$ A **23a.** $-10 - 5I_1 = 0; 5I_1 + 2I_2 = 0; I_1 + I_3 = I_2$ **23b.** $-98 - 7I_3 + 42I_1 = 0; -42I_1 + 15I_2 = 0; I_1 + I_2 + I_3 = 0$ **23c.** $-48 + 6I_3 - 4I_2 = 0; 4I_2 + (7 + 12)I_1 = 0; I_3 + I_2 - I_1 = 0$ **23d.** $-40 - 12I_4 + 4I_3 + 60 = 0; -6I_2 + 2I_1 = 0; I_1 + I_2 + I_3 + I_4 = 0$ **24a.** 0.25 Hz **24b.** 1000 W **24c.** 2000 J **24d.** 500 W **24e.** 70.7 V **24f.** 70.7 V **24g.** 50 V **25a.** 0.125 Hz **25b.** 1000 W **25c.** 4000 J **25d.** 500 W **25e.** 70.7 V **25f.** 70.7 V **25g.** 0 V **26a.** $E_{21} + 20I_1 = 0; I_3 = I_1 + I_2; E_{21} + I_2(50j) = 0$ **26b.** $E_A + 20I_1 = 0; E_A + I_2(-30j) = 0; I_3 = I_1 + I_2$ **26c.** $E_{21} + 20I_1 = 0; E_{21} - I_2(-30j) = 0; I_1 = I_3 + I_2$ **26d.** $E_{ba} - 20I_1 = 0; E_{ba} + 60jI_2 = 0; E_{ba} - E_A - I_3(-30j) = 0; I_4 + I_1 + I_3 = I_2$ **26e.** $E_{ab} + (7 - 24j)I = 0; E_{ac} + (-24j)I = 0; E_{bc} - 7I = 0$ **26f.** $E_{21} + E_B - I(40j - 45j) = 0; E_{13} + 40jI - E_B = 0; E_{23} - I(-45j) = 0$ **26g.** $-E_3 + 40jI_3 + E_{32} = 0; -E_3 + E_{12} = 0; E_{23} - 30I_2 = 0; E_{23} + 40jI_1 = 0; I_2 + I_3 = I_1$

Chapter 3

24. 52 070 Btu, 7.63 h **25.** Transformer temperature will rise with aluminum paint **26.** 52.9 kW **27.** ~ 47 °C

Chapter 4

24a. 480 A **24b.** 15 319 W **24c.** 5520 W **25.** 203.5 W/kg **26.** 1385 N.m **27.** 261.6 W

Chapter 5

19. 2514 r/min **20a.** 400 conductors **20b.** 85.1 V **20c.** 4.4 mWb **21.** 674 ft^3/min **22.** 21 Ω 425 W **23.** 0.0273 pu 0.00346 pu

Chapter 6

24. 310 kg **25.** 52.8 mΩ **26.** 4.78 kg **27.** 915 W 224 V **28.** No. 2 AWG **29.** 0.81 V 223 W/m **30.** $t_2 = R_2/R_1(228 + t_1) - 228$ **31.** 1948 ft/min 22 mi/h **32a.** 0.00614 Ω **32b.** 0.092 V **32c.** 1.29 V **32d.** 38.7 W **32e.** 1.33 N **32f.** 0.528 J **32g.** 26.4 W **32h.** 5.8%

Chapter 7

24. 345 microfarad **25a.** 650 V **25b.** 72.9 J **26.** 68 000 Ω 3.4 W **27a.** 288 A **27b.** 0.2 MW 1.0 Mvar **27c.** 2.8 MW, 1.0 Mvar, 3 MVA **27d.** 10 300 V **28a.** 1976 W, 1796 var **28b.** 9.63 A **28c.** no **29a.** 20.83 A **29b.** 16.7 A

Chapter 8

28. 24 A $I_c = 0$ **29.** 16 A, 16 A, 27.7 A **30.** 156.6 kW **31.** 55.4 A, 48 A **32.** 100 kW **33.** 1359 lb/h **34a.** 31.88 kW **34b.** 38.41 kVA **34c.** 48.2 A **35a.** 332 A **35b.** 602 kvar **35c.** 25.8°

Chapter 9

7. 245 turns, 980 turns **8a.** 33.87 Ω **8b.** 30.5 Ω, 80.9 mH **8c.** 64.3° **9.** $\Phi = 0.657$ mWb, $\Phi_{m1} = 0.516$ mWb, $\Phi_{f1} = 0.141$ mWb **10.** The 330 V/120 V transformer is the most appropriate.The 40 microfarad capacitor must be connected to the 330 V winding.

Chapter 10

34. 0.023 Ω **35.** 217 mm^2 **36.** 85 W/kg, 225 W/kg **37.** 72 V, 16.7 A

Chapter 11

12. 13.88 V **13.** The LV winding is wound on top of the 120 V winding **14a.** 15.15 V **14b.** 5.31 V **14c.** ~2300 V

Chapter 12

10. 1.3 A **11.** $177 **13b.** 465 V **13c.** 12.9° **14.** 121 A 125.8 kVA **15.** transformer 41.9 kVA, motor 33.8 kVA

Chapter 13

35a. the speed will drop **35b.** the starting torque will increase **35c.** the temperature will rise slightly **36a.** 90 coils **36b.** 30 **36c.** 5 **36d.** 266 mm **36e.** 108 100 mm^2 **36f.** 58.4 mWb **37.** 1196 r/min **38.** 14.9 N **39.** 2340 r/min, 3660 r/min **40.** rotor delivers active power **41a.** 18.9 Hz **41b.** 605 kW

Chapter 14

27. 4 times per year every 4.5 years **28.** $17 900 **29.** $670 **30.** 9 Ω **31a.** R = 0.0547 Ω X = 0.162 Ω **31b.** 1493 A **31c.** 1118 ft·lbf **31d.** 93% **32.** 0.39 pu 8.47 pu 2.88 pu 1.36 pu

Chapter 15

9a. 15.9 mH, 292 mH **9b.** 5 Ω, 91.7 Ω **9c.** 212 V **10a.** 8 Ω, 147 Ω **10b.** 19.2 N.m, 6.3 hp

Chapter 16

27a. 43.5 hp **27b.** max is 120°C **28a.** 220 MW at unity PF, 198 MW at 90% PF **28b.** 96 Mvar **28c.** 0.787 **28d.** 1.1 Ω, **28e.** 2785 kW **29a.** 194 370 hp **29b.** 719 MJ **29c.** 2279 MJ **29d.** 5.67s **30.** 28.6°C, 2000 Ω·m

Chapter 17

21. 96.8 A **22a.** 17.57 t **22b.** 123 gal/min **22c.** 32 500 lb·ft^2 **22d.** 260 kW **22e.** 97.1% **22f.** 4358 kvar **22g.** 0.0713 Ω **22h.** 0.413 Ω

Chapter 18

18a. 3.33 pu, 6 pu, 2.22 pu **18b.** 12.2 N.m **18c.** 11.7 microfarad **19a.** 10.3 N·m **19b.** 24.8 microfarad

Chapter 19

19. 0.5227 N·m, 0.07769 N·m **20.** 56.5 Ω **21.** 1.02 ms **22a.** 200 pulses per second **22b.** 22 mN·m **22c.** 10.5 mN·m **22d.** 11.5 mN·m **23.** suggest a gear box having a ratio of 18:25

Chapter 20

34. slightly less than 60 s **35a.** 4.39 pu, 1.32 pu, **35b.** 14 s **36a.** 348 W **36b.** 838 W, yes **37.** 1747 Ω, 151 Ω

Chapter 21

28a. 41 V, 7 V **28b.** 26.8 V **28c.** 72 W **29.** 748.7 A, 137.6 A **30.** 147.1 V **31.** All thyristors will be destroyed **32a.** 78 kW **32b.** 1344 W **32c.** 52 kW **32d.** 1344 W **32e.** 104 J **32f.** 336 J **32g.** 231 J **32h.** 1065 W **32i.** 0.395 **33a.** 10.5 μs, 49.5 μs **33b.** 16.67 kHz **34a.** 210 V, yes **34b.** 390 V, yes **34c.** 180 V, negative **35a.** 14 μs, 26 μs **35b.** 26 μs, 14 μs **36a.** 99 A **36b.** 77.4 A **36c.** 2450 V

Chapter 22

23. A is negative with respect to C **24.** 98 A, 24 V **25.** 13 A, 1857 V/s **26.** I_a is decreasing 550 A/s

Chapter 23

24a. 500 Hz **24b.** −563 V **24c.** 43.5° **24d.** 73.7 A **24e.** 360 Hz **24f.** 3000 Hz **24g.** 72.5% **24h.** 60 A **25a.** 25.8 N·m, 6.4 N·m, **25b.** 21.7 W **26a.** 28.8 N **26b.** 57.6 N **27a.** 300 r/min **27b.** 16.1 N·m **28.** 57.2 V **29a.** 8258 A **29b.** 4129 A **29c.** 5839 A **30a.** 5.83 Hz to 16.33 Hz **30b.** 7695 kW, 6786 kvar **30d.** 22.3 h **31a.** 430.8 V, angle 28° **31b.** converter absorbs 138 kW and delivers 33.9 kvar **32a.** 200 A **32b.** 402.5 A angle + 62° **32c.** 513.5 V, angle + 23.2° **32d.** 0.902 **33a.** 2.892 ms, 0.441 ms, D = 0.868 **33b.** 1.593 ms, 1.740 ms, D = 0.478 **34a.** 7.2 Ω **34b.** 6.26 A, angle − 19° **34c.** 1.65 A **34d.** 5.95 A **34e.** 10.1 N·m **35.** 8.41 A, 1.03 A, 8.83 N·m

Chapter 24

21a. 59.985 Hz **21b.** 26 993 cycles **21c.** 27 000 cycles **21d.** 116 ms **22.** 15 hp **23.** ~20 hp **24.** 552 W/m^2 **25.** 520 W **26a.** 1780 kN·m **26b.** 4021 hp **27a.** 872 kVA **27b.** 730 A **27c.** 445 kvar **28a.** 387 kW **28b.** 92.1% **29.** 38.4 r/min **30.** 24.6 **31.** 7.5 kW **32.** 2.5 MW **33a.** 317 km/h **33b.** 5.0 **34.** 1650 **35.** 350 400 MWh, 25.4% **36.** 35% **37a.** 1500 r/min **37b.** 1800 r/min **37c.** 300 r/min **37d.** 0.2 **37e.** 2.5 MW **37f.** 0.5 MW **37g.** 0.5 MW **37h.** 16.7% **37i.** 10 Hz

Chapter 27

19a. 748 kWh **19b.** $16 380

INDEX